Index of Applications

Business and Economics

General Interest

Life Sciences

Social Sciences

Applied Calculus with supplemental material prepared by Frank A. Farris

Santa Clara University, Department of Mathematics and Computer Science

4th Edition

Stefan Waner | Steven R. Costenoble

CENGAGE Learning™

Australia • Brazil • Japan • Korea • Mexico • Singapore • Spain • United Kingdom • United States

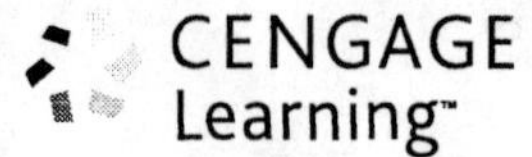

Applied Calculus with supplemental material prepared by Frank A. Farris: Santa Clara University, Department of Mathematics and Computer Science, 4th Edition

Stefan Waner | Steven R. Costenoble

Executive Editors:
Michele Baird
Maureen Staudt
Michael Stranz

Project Development Manager:
Linda deStefano

Senior Marketing Coordinators:
Sara Mercurio
Lindsay Shapiro

Senior Production / Manufacturing Manager:
Donna M. Brown

PreMedia Services Supervisor:
Rebecca A. Walker

Rights & Permissions Specialist:
Kalina Hintz

Cover Image:
Getty Images*

* Unless otherwise noted, all cover images used by Custom Solutions, a part of Cengage Learning, have been supplied courtesy of Getty Images with the exception of the Earthview cover image, which has been supplied by the National Aeronautics and Space Administration (NASA).

ISBN-13: 978-0-495-84000-8

ISBN-10: 0-495-84000-9

Cengage Learning
5191 Natorp Boulevard
Mason, Ohio 45040
USA

Cengage Learning is a leading provider of customized learning solutions with office locations around the globe, including Singapore, the United Kingdom, Australia, Mexico, Brazil, and Japan. Locate your local office at: **international.cengage.com/region**

Cengage Learning products are represented in Canada by Nelson Education, Ltd.

For your lifelong learning solutions, visit **custom.cengage.com**

Visit our corporate website at **cengage.com**

Printed in the United States of America

Brief Contents

Preface

Applied Calculus, Fourth Edition, is intended for a one- or two-term course for students majoring in business, the social sciences, or the liberal arts. Like the earlier editions, the Fourth Edition of *Applied Calculus* is designed to address the challenge of generating enthusiasm and mathematical sophistication in an audience that is often under-prepared and lacks motivation for traditional mathematics courses. We meet this challenge by focusing on real-life applications that students can relate to, by presenting mathematical concepts intuitively and thoroughly, and by employing a writing style that is informal, engaging, and occasionally even humorous.

The Fourth edition goes further than earlier editions in implementing support for a wide range of instructional paradigms: from settings incorporating little or no technology to courses taught in computerized classrooms, and from classes in which a single form of technology is used exclusively to those incorporating several technologies. We fully support three forms of technology in this text: TI-83/84 graphing calculators, Excel spreadsheets, and the use of online utilities we have created for the book. In particular, our comprehensive support for Excel, both in the text and online, is highly relevant for students who are studying business and economics, where skill with spreadsheets may be vital to their future careers.

Our Approach to Pedagogy

Real World Orientation We are particularly proud of the diversity, breadth and abundance of examples and exercises included in this edition. A large number of these are based on real, referenced data from business, economics, the life sciences and the social sciences. Examples and exercises based on dated information have generally been replaced by more current versions; applications based on unique or historically interesting data have been kept.

Adapting real data for pedagogical use can be tricky; available data can be numerically complex, intimidating for students, or incomplete. We have modified and streamlined many of the real world applications, rendering them as tractable as any "made-up" application. At the same time, we have been careful to strike a pedagogically sound balance between applications based on real data and more traditional "generic" applications. Thus, the density and selection of real data-based applications has been tailored to the pedagogical goals and appropriate difficulty level for each section.

Readability We would like students to read this book. We would like students to *enjoy* reading this book. Thus, we have written the book in a conversational and student-oriented style, and have made frequent use of question-and-answer dialogues to encourage the development of the student's mathematical curiosity and intuition. We hope that this text will give the student insight into how a mathematician develops and thinks about mathematical ideas and their applications.

Five Elements of Mathematical Pedagogy to Address Different Learning Styles The "Rule of Four" is a common theme in many texts. Implementing this approach, we discuss many of the central concepts **numerically, graphically** and **algebraically,** and clearly delineate these distinctions. The fourth element, **verbal communication** of mathematical concepts, is emphasized through our discussions on translating English sentences into mathematical statements, and our Communication and Reasoning exercises at the end of each section. A fifth element, **interactivity,** is implemented through expanded use of question-and-answer dialogs, but is seen most dramatically within the student website. Using this resource, students can interact with the material in several ways: through interactive tutorials specific to concepts and examples covered in sections, and on-line utilities that automate a variety of tasks, from graphing to regression and matrix algebra.

Exercise Sets The substantial collection of exercises provides a wealth of material that can be used to challenge students at almost every level of preparation, and includes everything from straightforward drill exercises to interesting and rather challenging applications. The exercise sets have been carefully graded to move from straightforward "basic skills" exercises that mimic examples in the text to more interesting and challenging ones. With this edition, basic skills exercises and the most difficult exercises are marked for easy reference. We have also included, in virtually every section of every chapter, interesting applications based on real data, Communication and Reasoning exercises that help students articulate mathematical concepts, and exercises ideal for the use of technology.

Many of the scenarios used in application examples and exercises are revisited several times throughout the book. Thus, for instance, students will find themselves using a variety of techniques, from graphing through the use of derivatives and elasticity, to analyze the same application. Reusing scenarios and important functions provides unifying threads and shows students the complex texture of real-life problems.

New To This Edition

Content:

- Chapter 3 (page 183): We now discuss limits and continuity in their traditional place before derivatives, but they may still be treated as optional if so desired.
- Chapter 6 (page 417): To help students better understand the definite integral and the Fundamental Theorem of Calculus, we have completely rewritten the chapter on the integral with greater emphasis on the computation of Riemann sums from graphs.
- Chapter 2 (page 113): We have placed more emphasis on half-life and doubling time in the chapter on exponential and logarithmic functions
- Complete sections on Taylor Polynomials, the Chain Rule for Multivariate Calculus, and Calculus Applied to Probability are available as optional topics for custom published versions of this text.
- Throughout, we have improved the presentation of proofs and derivations of important results for clarity and accuracy.

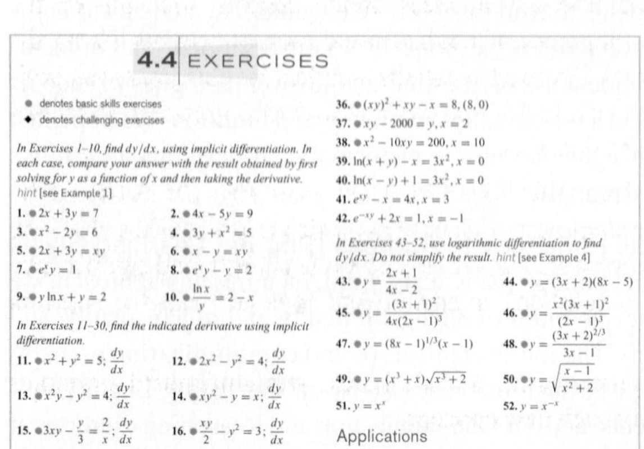

4.4 EXERCISES

● denotes basic skills exercises
◆ denotes challenging exercises

In Exercises 1–10, find dy/dx, using implicit differentiation. In each case, compare your answer with the result obtained by first solving for y as a function of x and then taking the derivative. hint [see Example 1]

1. ● $2x + 3y = 7$
2. ● $4x - 5y = 9$
3. ● $x^2 - 2y = 6$
4. ● $3y + x^2 = 5$
5. ● $2x + 3y = xy$
6. ● $x - y = xy$
7. ● $e^x y = 1$
8. ● $e^x y - y = 2$
9. ● $y \ln x + y = 2$
10. ● $\frac{\ln x}{y} = 2 - x$

In Exercises 11–30, find the indicated derivative using implicit differentiation.

11. ● $x^2 + y^2 = 5; \frac{dy}{dx}$
12. ● $2x^2 - y^2 = 4; \frac{dy}{dx}$
13. ● $x^2 y - y^2 = 4; \frac{dy}{dx}$
14. ● $xy^2 - y = x; \frac{dy}{dx}$
15. ● $3xy - \frac{y}{3} = \frac{2}{x}; \frac{dy}{dx}$
16. ● $\frac{xy}{2} - y^2 = 3; \frac{dy}{dx}$

36. ● $(xy)^2 + xy - x = 8, (8, 0)$
37. ● $xy - 2000 = y, x = 2$
38. ● $x^2 - 10xy = 200, x = 10$
39. $\ln(x + y) - x = 3x^2, x = 0$
40. $\ln(x - y) + 1 = 3x^2, x = 0$
41. $e^{xy} - x = 4x, x = 3$
42. $e^{-xy} + 2x = 1, x = -1$

In Exercises 43–52, use logarithmic differentiation to find dy/dx. Do not simplify the result. hint [see Example 4]

43. ● $y = \frac{2x + 1}{4x - 2}$
44. ● $y = (3x + 2)(8x - 5)$
45. ● $y = \frac{(3x + 1)^2}{4x(2x - 1)^3}$
46. ● $y = \frac{x^2(3x + 1)^2}{(2x - 1)^3}$
47. ● $y = (8x - 1)^{1/3}(x - 1)$
48. ● $y = \frac{(3x + 2)^{2/3}}{3x - 1}$
49. ● $y = (x^3 + x)\sqrt{x^3 + 2}$
50. ● $y = \sqrt{\frac{x - 1}{x^2 + 2}}$
51. $y = x^x$
52. $y = x^{-x}$

Applications

Exercises:

- ← Basic skills exercises at the beginning of each exercise set and challenging exercises near the end of some exercise sets are now highlighted to guide students and instructors.
- We have expanded the exercise sets themselves and carefully reorganized them to gradually increase in level and to include more basic skills exercises that carefully follow the examples.
- We have annotated representative exercises with references to specific examples in the text where similar problems are solved.

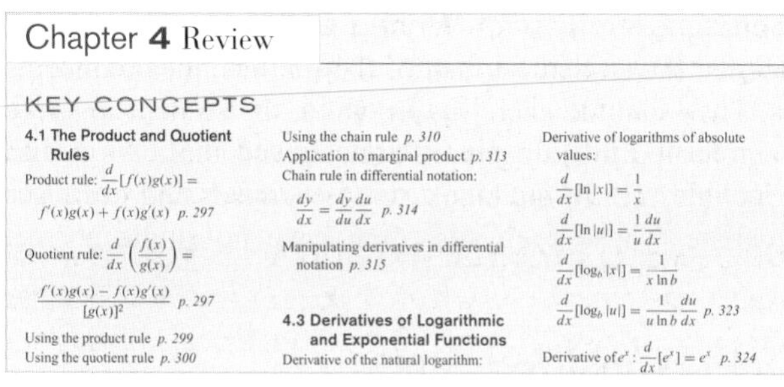
Chapter 4 Review

KEY CONCEPTS

4.1 The Product and Quotient Rules

Product rule: $\frac{d}{dx}[f(x)g(x)] = f'(x)g(x) + f(x)g'(x)$ *p. 297*

Quotient rule: $\frac{d}{dx}\left(\frac{f(x)}{g(x)}\right) = \frac{f'(x)g(x) - f(x)g'(x)}{[g(x)]^2}$ *p. 297*

Using the product rule *p. 299*

Using the quotient rule *p. 300*

Using the chain rule *p. 310*

Application to marginal product *p. 313*

Chain rule in differential notation: $\frac{dy}{dx} = \frac{dy}{du}\frac{du}{dx}$ *p. 314*

Manipulating derivatives in differential notation *p. 315*

4.3 Derivatives of Logarithmic and Exponential Functions

Derivative of the natural logarithm:

Derivative of logarithms of absolute values:

$\frac{d}{dx}[\ln|x|] = \frac{1}{x}$

$\frac{d}{dx}[\ln|u|] = \frac{1}{u}\frac{du}{dx}$

$\frac{d}{dx}[\log_b|x|] = \frac{1}{x \ln b}$

$\frac{d}{dx}[\log_b|u|] = \frac{1}{u \ln b}\frac{du}{dx}$ *p. 323*

Derivative of e^x: $\frac{d}{dx}[e^x] = e^x$ *p. 324*

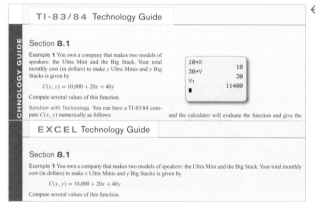

- We have greatly expanded the chapter review exercise sections.
- A list of key concepts for review now appears at the end of each chapter.

Pedagogy:

- New Portfolios are designed to convey to the student real-world experiences of professionals who have a background in mathematics and use it in their daily business interactions.

mathematics At Work

Deb Farace

TITLE Sr. National Accounts Manager
INSTITUTION PepsiCo Beverages & Foods

Working for the national accounts division for PepsiCo Beverages & Foods, I need to understand applied mathematics in order to control the variables associated with making profit, manufacturing, production, and most importantly selling our products to mass club channels. Examples of these large, "quality product at great value" outlets are Wal*Mart, Costco and Target. The types of products I handle include Gatorade, Tropicana, and Quaker foods.

A number of factors must be taken into consideration in order to meet my company's financial forecasts. Precision using mathematical models is key here, since so many variables can impact last-minute decision-making. Extended variables of supply-and-demand include time of year, competitive landscape, special coupon distribution and other promotions, selling cycles and holidays, size of the outlets, and yes—even the weather.

For example, it's natural to assume that when it's hot outside people will buy more thirst-quenching products like Gatorade. But since our business is so precise, we need to understand mathematically how the weather affects sales. A

- End-of-Chapter Technology Guides We have placed detailed TI-83/84 and Microsoft® Excel Guides at the end of each chapter. This has allowed us to expand these instructions while not interrupting the flow of pedagogy in the text. These Guides are referenced liberally at appropriate points in the chapter, so instructors and students can easily use this material or not, as they prefer. Groups of exercises for which the use of technology is suggested or required appear throughout the exercise sets.

TI-83/84 Technology Guide

TECHNOLOGY GUIDE

Section 8.1

Example 1 You own a company that makes two models of speakers: the Ultra Mini and the Big Stack. Your total monthly cost (in dollars) to make x Ultra Minis and y Big Stacks is given by

$C(x, y) = 10{,}000 + 20x + 40y$

Compute several values of this function.

Solution with Technology You can have a TI-83/84 compute $C(x, y)$ numerically as follows:

```
10→X
                 10
30→Y
                 30
Y1
              11400
```

and the calculator will evaluate the function and give the

EXCEL Technology Guide

Section 8.1

Example 1 You own a company that makes two models of speakers: the Ultra Mini and the Big Stack. Your total monthly cost (in dollars) to make x Ultra Minis and y Big Stacks is given by

$C(x, y) = 10{,}000 + 20x + 40y$

Compute several values of this function.

- Question and Answer Dialogue We frequently use informal question-and-answer dialogues that anticipate the kind of questions that may occur to the student and also guide the student through the development of new concepts. This feature has been streamlined, as has the "Frequently Asked Questions" feature at the end of each section.

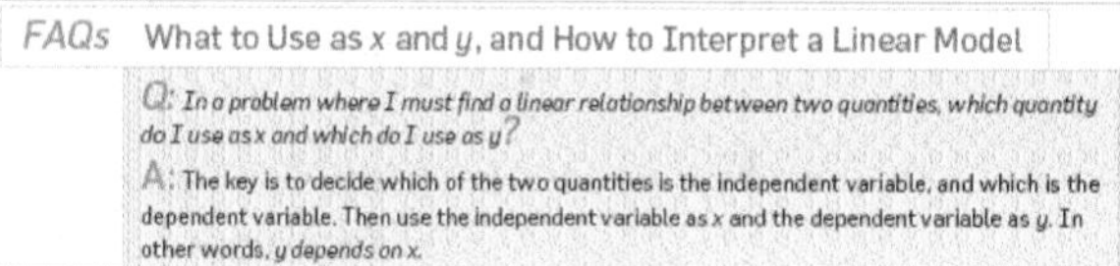
FAQs What to Use as x and y, and How to Interpret a Linear Model

Q: *In a problem where I must find a linear relationship between two quantities, which quantity do I use as x and which do I use as y?*

A: The key is to decide which of the two quantities is the independent variable, and which is the dependent variable. Then use the independent variable as x and the dependent variable as y. In other words, *y depends on x*.

Continuing Features

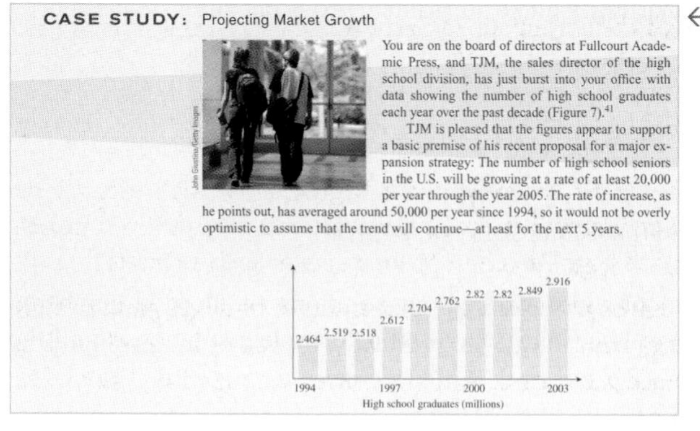
CASE STUDY: Projecting Market Growth

You are on the board of directors at Fullcourt Academic Press, and TJM, the sales director of the high school division, has just burst into your office with data showing the number of high school graduates each year over the past decade (Figure 7).[41]

TJM is pleased that the figures appear to support a basic premise of his recent proposal for a major expansion strategy: The number of high school seniors in the U.S. will be growing at a rate of at least 20,000 per year through the year 2005. The rate of increase, as he points out, has averaged around 50,000 per year since 1994, so it would not be overly optimistic to assume that the trend will continue—at least for the next 5 years.

- Case Studies Each chapter ends with a section titled "Case Study," an extended application that uses and illustrates the central ideas of the chapter, focusing on the development of mathematical models appropriate to the topics. These applications are ideal for assignment as projects, and to this end we have included groups of exercises at the end of each.
- Before We Go On Most examples are followed by supplementary discussions, which may include a check on the answer, a discussion of the feasibility and significance of a solution, or an in-depth look at what the solution means.
- Quick Examples Most definition boxes include quick, straightforward examples that a student can use to solidify each new concept.

- Communication and Reasoning Exercises for Writing and Discussion These are exercises designed to broaden the student's grasp of the mathematical concepts and develop modeling skills. They include exercises in which the student is asked to provide his or her own examples to illustrate a point or design an application with a given solution. They also include "fill in the blank" type exercises and exercises that invite discussion and debate. These exercises often have no single correct answer.

ThomsonNOW™ with Personalized Study

Help your students maximize study time, minimize stress, and get a better grade by finding out how they will do on a test before they take it! ThomsonNOW™ with Personalized Study is a customized learning tool for students that diagnoses their problem areas through a pre-test and then tailors individual solutions to fit their unique needs. Based on content from the author's widely recognized website, ThomsonNOW with Personalized Study is fully integrated with the text and features the following valuable assets:

- Interactive Tutorials Highly interactive tutorials are included on major topics, with guided exercises that parallel the text.
- Detailed Chapter Summaries Comprehensive summaries with interactive elements review all the basic definitions and problem solving techniques discussed in each chapter. These are a terrific pre-test study tool for students.
- Downloadable Excel Tutorials Detailed Excel tutorials are available for almost every section of the book. These interactive tutorials expand on the examples given in the text.
- Online Utilities Our collection of easy-to-use online utilities, written in Java™ and Javascript, allow students to solve many of the technology-based application exercises directly on the web page. The utilities available include function graphers and evaluators, regression tools, powerful matrix utilities and linear programming solvers. These utilities require nothing more than a standard, Java-capable web browser.
- Downloadable Software In addition to the web-based utilities the site offers a suite of free and intuitive stand-alone Macintosh® programs, including one for function graphing.
- Supplemental Topics We include complete interactive text and exercise sets for a selection of topics not ordinarily included in printed texts, but often requested by instructors.

Supplemental Material

For Students

Student Solutions Manual *by Waner and Costenoble*
ISBN: **0495016993**
The student solutions manual provides worked-out solutions to the odd-numbered exercises in the text (excluding Case Studies) as well as complete solutions to all the chapter review exercises.

Microsoft Excel Computer Laboratory Manual *by Anne D. Henriksen*
ISBN: **0495115010**
This laboratory manual uses Microsoft Excel to solve real-world problems in a variety of scientific, technical, and business disciplines. It provides hands-on experience to

demonstrate for students that calculus is a valuable tool for solving practical, real-world problems, while helping students increase their knowledge of Microsoft Excel. The manual is a set of self-contained computer exercises that are meant to be used over the course of a 15-week semester in a separate, 75-minute computer laboratory period. The weekly labs parallel the material in the text.

vMentor™ When students get stuck on a particular problem or concept, they need only log on to **vMentor**. Accessed through ThomsonNOW, vMentor allows students to talk (using their own computer microphones) to tutors who will skillfully guide them through the problem using an interactive whiteboard for illustration. Students who purchase access to vMentor have access to up to 40 hours of live tutoring a week!

For Instructors

Instructor's Solution Manual *by Waner and Costenoble*
ISBN: **0495016950**
The instructor's solutions manual provides worked-out solutions to all of the exercises in the text including Case Studies.

Test Bank *by James Ball*
ISBN: **0495016950**
This test bank contains numerous multiple choice and free response questions.

Instructor's Suite CD-ROM
ISBN: **0495016977**
The Instructor's Suite CD-ROM contains the instructor's solutions manual and test bank both in MS Word and as PDF files. There is also a multimedia library containing all of the art from the book in MS PowerPoint as well as individual jpeg files.

JoinIn on Turning Point Thomson Brooks/Cole is pleased to offer you book-specific JoinIn content for electronic response systems tailored to *Applied Calculus, 4th edition*. You can transform your classroom and assess your students' progress with instant in-class quizzes and polls. Turning Point software lets you pose book-specific questions and display students' answers seamlessly within Microsoft PowerPoint slides of your own lecture, in conjunction with the "clicker" hardware of your choice. Enhance how your students interact with you, your lecture, and each other.

Acknowledgments

This project would not have been possible without the contributions and suggestions of numerous colleagues, students and friends. We are particularly grateful to our colleagues at Hofstra and elsewhere who used and gave us useful feedback on previous editions. We are also grateful to everyone at Brooks/Cole for their encouragement and guidance throughout the project. Specifically, we would like to thank Curt Hinrichs for his unflagging enthusiasm, Danielle Derbenti for whipping the book into shape, Joe Rogove for telling the world about it, and Carolyn Crockett for stepping in at the last minute. In addition, we would like to thank Ann Day for coordinating our many ancillaries, Beth Gershman for her administrative support, and Cheryll Linthicum for shepherding the project through production.

We would also like to thank the numerous reviewers and accuracy checkers who provided many helpful suggestions that have shaped the development of this book.

Stefan Waner
Steven R. Costenoble

Applied Calculus

Fourth Edition

0 Algebra Review

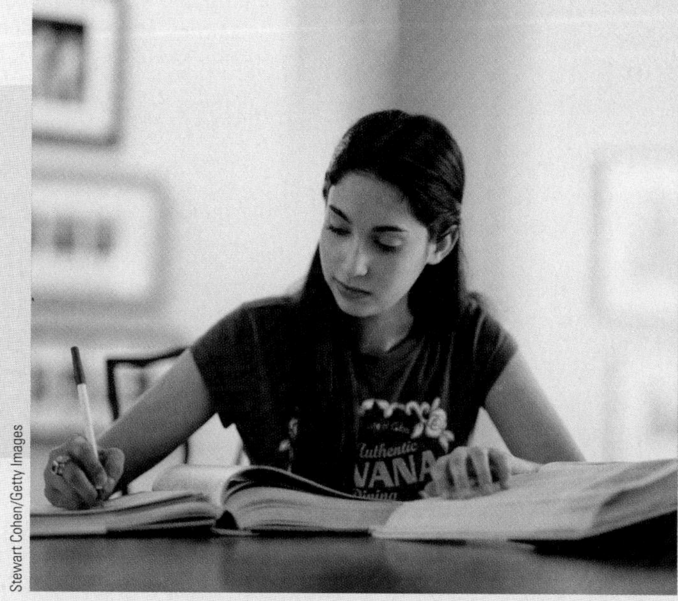

Stewart Cohen/Getty Images

Introduction

In this chapter we review some topics from algebra that you need to know to get the most out of this book. This chapter can be used either as a refresher course or as a reference.

There is one crucial fact you must always keep in mind: The letters used in algebraic expressions stand for numbers. All the rules of algebra are just facts about the arithmetic of numbers. If you are not sure whether some algebraic manipulation you are about to do is legitimate, try it first with numbers. If it doesn't work with numbers, it doesn't work.

0.1 Real Numbers

The **real numbers** are the numbers that can be written in decimal notation, including those that require an infinite decimal expansion. The set of real numbers includes all integers, positive and negative; all fractions; and the irrational numbers, those with decimal expansions that never repeat. Examples of irrational numbers are

$$\sqrt{2} = 1.414213562373\ldots$$

and

$$\pi = 3.141592653589\ldots$$

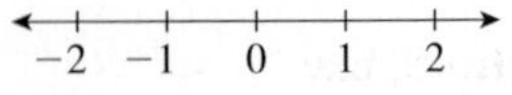

Figure **1**

It is very useful to picture the real numbers as points on a line. As shown in Figure 1, larger numbers appear to the right, in the sense that if $a < b$ then the point corresponding to b is to the right of the one corresponding to a.

Intervals

Some subsets of the set of real numbers, called **intervals,** show up quite often and so we have a compact notation for them.

Interval Notation

Here is a list of types of intervals along with examples.

	Interval	*Description*	*Picture*	*Example*
Closed	$[a, b]$	Set of numbers x with $a \le x \le b$	 a ● ——— ● b (includes end points)	$[0, 10]$
Open	(a, b)	Set of numbers x with $a < x < b$	 a ○ ——— ○ b (excludes end points)	$(-1, 5)$
Half-Open	$(a, b]$	Set of numbers x with $a < x \le b$	 a ○ ——— ● b	$(-3, 1]$
	$[a, b)$	Set of numbers x with $a \le x < b$	 a ● ——— ○ b	$[0, 5)$

Infinite	$[a, +\infty)$	Set of numbers x with $a \le x$		$[10, +\infty)$
	$(a, +\infty)$	Set of numbers x with $a < x$		$(-3, +\infty)$
	$(-\infty, b]$	Set of numbers x with $x \le b$		$(-\infty, -3]$
	$(-\infty, b)$	Set of numbers x with $x < b$		$(-\infty, 10)$
	$(-\infty, +\infty)$	Set of all real numbers		$(-\infty, +\infty)$

Operations

There are five important operations on real numbers: addition, subtraction, multiplication, division, and exponentiation. "Exponentiation" means raising a real number to a power; for instance, $3^2 = 3 \cdot 3 = 9$; $2^3 = 2 \cdot 2 \cdot 2 = 8$.

A note on technology: Most graphing calculators and spreadsheets use an asterisk * for multiplication and a caret sign ^ for exponentiation. Thus, for instance, 3×5 is entered as `3*5`, $3x$ as `3*x`, and 3^2 as `3^2`.

When we write an expression involving two or more operations, like

$$2 \cdot 3 + 4$$

or

$$\frac{2 \cdot 3^2 - 5}{4 - (-1)}$$

we need to agree on the order in which to do the operations. Does $2 \cdot 3 + 4$ mean $(2 \cdot 3) + 4 = 10$ or $2 \cdot (3 + 4) = 14$? We all agree to use the following rules for the order in which we do the operations.

Standard Order of Operations

Parentheses and Fraction Bars

First, calculate the values of all expressions inside parentheses or brackets, working from the innermost parentheses out, before using them in other operations. In a fraction, calculate the numerator and denominator separately before doing the division.

quick Examples

1. $6(2 + [3 - 5] - 4) = 6(2 + (-2) - 4) = 6(-4) = -24$.

2. $\dfrac{(4-2)}{3(-2+1)} = \dfrac{2}{3(-1)} = \dfrac{2}{-3} = -\dfrac{2}{3}$

3. $3/(2+4) = \dfrac{3}{2+4} = \dfrac{3}{6} = \dfrac{1}{2}$

4. $(x + 4x)/(y + 3y) = 5x/(4y)$

Exponents
Next, perform exponentiation.

quick Examples

1. $2 + 4^2 = 2 + 16 = 18$
2. $(2 + 4)^2 = 6^2 = 36$

Note the difference.

3. $2\left(\frac{3}{4-5}\right)^2 = 2\left(\frac{3}{-1}\right)^2 = 2(-3)^2 = 2 \times 9 = 18$
4. $2(1 + 1/10)^2 = 2(1.1)^2 = 2 \times 1.21 = 2.42$

Multiplication and Division
Next, do all multiplications and divisions, from left to right.

quick Examples

1. $2(3 - 5)/4 \cdot 2 = 2(-2)/4 \cdot 2$ Parentheses first
   $= -4/4 \cdot 2$ Left-most product
   $= -1 \cdot 2 = -2$ Multiplications and divisions, left to right
2. $2(1 + 1/10)^2 \times 2/10 = 2(1.1)^2 \times 2/10$ Parentheses first
   $= 2 \times 1.21 \times 2/10$ Exponent
   $= 4.84/10 = 0.484$ Multiplications and divisions, left to right
3. $4\frac{2(4-2)}{3(-2 \cdot 5)} = 4\frac{2(2)}{3(-10)} = 4\frac{4}{-30} = \frac{16}{-30} = -\frac{8}{15}$

Addition and Subtraction
Last, do all additions and subtractions, from left to right.

quick Examples

1. $2(3 - 5)^2 + 6 - 1 = 2(-2)^2 + 6 - 1 = 2(4) + 6 - 1 = 8 + 6 - 1 = 13$
2. $\left(\frac{1}{2}\right)^2 - (-1)^2 + 4 = \frac{1}{4} - 1 + 4 = -\frac{3}{4} + 4 = \frac{13}{4}$
3. $3/2 + 4 = 1.5 + 4 = 5.5$
4. $3/(2 + 4) = 3/6 = 1/2 = 0.5$

Note the difference.

5. $4/2^2 + (4/2)^2 = 4/2^2 + 2^2 = 4/4 + 4 = 1 + 4 = 5$

tech Ex

Entering Formulas

Any good calculator or spreadsheet will respect the standard order of operations. However, we must be careful with division and exponentiation and use parentheses as necessary. The following table gives some examples of simple mathematical expressions and their equivalents in the functional format used in most graphing calculators, spreadsheets, and computer programs.

Mathematical Expression	*Formula*	*Comments*
$\frac{2}{3-x}$	`2/(3-x)`	Note the use of parentheses instead of the fraction bar. If we omit the parentheses, we get the expression shown next.
$\frac{2}{3}-x$	`2/3-x`	The calculator follows the usual order of operations.
$\frac{2}{3\times 5}$	`2/(3*5)`	Putting the denominator in parentheses ensures that the multiplication is carried out first. The asterisk is usually used for multiplication in graphing calculators and computers.
$\frac{2}{x}\times 5$	`(2/x)*5`	Putting the fraction in parentheses ensures that it is calculated first. Some calculators will interpret `2/3*5` as $\frac{2}{3\times 5}$, but `2/3(5)` as $\frac{2}{3}\times 5$.
$\frac{2-3}{4+5}$	`(2-3)/(4+5)`	Note once again the use of parentheses in place of the fraction bar.
2^3	`2^3`	The caret ^ is commonly used to denote exponentiation.
2^{3-x}	`2^(3-x)`	Be careful to use parentheses to tell the calculator where the exponent ends. Enclose the *entire exponent* in parentheses.
2^3-x	`2^3-x`	Without parentheses, the calculator will follow the usual order of operations: exponentiation and then subtraction.
3×2^{-4}	`3*2^(-4)`	On some calculators, the negation key is separate from the minus key.
$2^{-4\times 3}\times 5$	`2^(-4*3)*5`	Note once again how parentheses enclose the entire exponent.
$100\left(1+\frac{0.05}{12}\right)^{60}$	`100*(1+0.05/12)^60`	This is a typical calculation for compound interest.
$PV\left(1+\frac{r}{m}\right)^{mt}$	`PV*(1+r/m)^(m*t)`	This is the compound interest formula. PV is understood to be a single number (present value) and not the product of P and V (or else we would have used `P*V`).
$\frac{2^{3-2}\times 5}{y-x}$	`2^(3-2)*5/(y-x)` or `(2^(3-2)*5)/(y-x)`	Notice again the use of parentheses to hold the denominator together. We could also have enclosed the numerator in parentheses, although this is optional. (Why?)
$\frac{2^y+1}{2-4^{3x}}$	`(2^y+1)/(2-4^(3*x))`	Here, it is necessary to enclose both the numerator and the denominator in parentheses.
$2^y+\frac{1}{2}-4^{3x}$	`2^y+1/2-4^(3*x)`	This is the effect of leaving out the parentheses around the numerator and denominator in the previous expression.

Accuracy and Rounding

When we use a calculator or computer, the results of our calculations are often given to far more decimal places than are useful. For example, suppose we are told that a square has an area of 2.0 square feet and we are asked how long its sides are. Each side is the square root of the area, which the calculator tells us is

$$\sqrt{2} \approx 1.414213562$$

However, the measurement of 2.0 square feet is probably accurate to only two digits, so our estimate of the lengths of the sides can be no more accurate than that. Therefore, we round the answer to two digits:

$$\text{Length of one side} \approx 1.4 \text{ feet}$$

The digits that follow 1.4 are meaningless. The following guide makes these ideas more precise.

Significant Digits, Decimal Places, and Rounding

The number of **significant digits** in a decimal representation of a number is the number of digits that are not leading zeros after the decimal point (as in .0005) or trailing zeros before the decimal point (as in 5,400,000). We say that a value is **accurate to *n* significant digits** if only the first n significant digits are meaningful.

When to Round

After doing a computation in which all the quantities are accurate to no more than n significant digits, round the final result to n significant digits.

quick Examples

1. 0.00067 has two significant digits. — The 000 before 67 are leading zeros.
2. 0.000670 has three significant digits. — The 0 after 67 is significant.
3. 5,400,000 has two or more significant digits. — We can't say how many of the zeros are trailing.*
4. 5,400,001 has 7 significant digits. — The string of zeros is not trailing.
5. Rounding 63,918 to three significant digits gives 63,900.
6. Rounding 63,958 to three significant digits gives 64,000.
7. $\pi = 3.141592653...$ $\frac{22}{7} = 3.142857142...$ Therefore, $\frac{22}{7}$ is an approximation of π that is accurate to only three significant digits (3.14).
8. $4.02(1 + 0.02)^{1.4} \approx 4.13$ — We rounded to three significant digits.

*If we obtained 5,400,000 by rounding 5,401,011, then it has three significant digits because the zero after the 4 is significant. On the other hand, if we obtained it by rounding 5,411,234, then it has only two significant digits. The use of scientific notation avoids this ambiguity: 5.40×10^6 (or 5.40 E6 on a calculator or computer) is accurate to three digits and 5.4×10^6 is accurate to two.

One more point, though: If, in a long calculation, you round the intermediate results, your final answer may be even less accurate than you think. As a general rule,

When calculating, don't round intermediate results. Rather, use the most accurate results obtainable or have your calculator or computer store them for you.

When you are done with the calculation, *then* round your answer to the appropriate number of digits of accuracy.

0.1 EXERCISES

Calculate each expression in Exercises 1–24, giving the answer as a whole number or a fraction in lowest terms.

1. $2(4+(-1))(2\cdot -4)$

2. $3+([4-2]\cdot 9)$

3. `20/(3*4)-1`

4. `2-(3*4)/10`

5. $\dfrac{3+([3+(-5)])}{3-2\times 2}$

6. $\dfrac{12-(1-4)}{2(5-1)\cdot 2-1}$

7. `(2-5*(-1))/1-2*(-1)`

8. `2-5*(-1)/(1-2*(-1))`

9. $2\cdot(-1)^2/2$

10. $2+4\cdot 3^2$

11. $2\cdot 4^2+1$

12. $1-3\cdot(-2)^2\times 2$

13. `3^2+2^2+1`

14. `2^(2^2-2)`

15. $\dfrac{3-2(-3)^2}{-6(4-1)^2}$

16. $\dfrac{1-2(1-4)^2}{2(5-1)^2\cdot 2}$

17. `10*(1+1/10)^3`

18. `121/(1+1/10)^2`

19. $3\left(\dfrac{-2\cdot 3^2}{-(4-1)^2}\right)$

20. $-\left(\dfrac{8(1-4)^2}{-9(5-1)^2}\right)$

21. $3\left(1-\left(-\frac{1}{2}\right)^2\right)^2+1$

22. $3\left(\frac{1}{9}-\left(\frac{2}{3}\right)^2\right)^2+1$

23. `(1/2)^2-1/2^2`

24. `2/(1^2)-(2/1)^2`

Convert each expression in Exercises 25–50 into its technology formula equivalent as in the table in the text.

25. $3\times(2-5)$

26. $4+\dfrac{5}{9}$

27. $\dfrac{3}{2-5}$

28. $\dfrac{4-1}{3}$

29. $\dfrac{3-1}{8+6}$

30. $3+\dfrac{3}{2-9}$

31. $3-\dfrac{4+7}{8}$

32. $\dfrac{4\times 2}{\left(\frac{2}{3}\right)}$

33. $\dfrac{2}{3+x}-xy^2$

34. $3+\dfrac{3+x}{xy}$

35. $3.1x^3-4x^{-2}-\dfrac{60}{x^2-1}$

36. $2.1x^{-3}-x^{-1}+\dfrac{x^2-3}{2}$

37. $\dfrac{\left(\frac{2}{3}\right)}{5}$

38. $\dfrac{2}{\left(\frac{3}{5}\right)}$

39. $3^{4-5}\times 6$

40. $\dfrac{2}{3+5^{7-9}}$

41. $3\left(1+\dfrac{4}{100}\right)^{-3}$

42. $3\left(\dfrac{1+4}{100}\right)^{-3}$

43. $3^{2x-1}+4^x-1$

44. $2^{x^2}-(2^{2x})^2$

45. 2^{2x^2-x+1}

46. $2^{2x^2-x}+1$

47. $\dfrac{4e^{-2x}}{2-3e^{-2x}}$

48. $\dfrac{e^{2x}+e^{-2x}}{e^{2x}-e^{-2x}}$

49. $3\left(1-\left(-\frac{1}{2}\right)^2\right)^2+1$

50. $3\left(\frac{1}{9}-\left(\frac{2}{3}\right)^2\right)^2+1$

0.2 Exponents and Radicals

In Section 1 we discussed exponentiation, or "raising to a power"; for example, $2^3 = 2 \cdot 2 \cdot 2$. In this section we discuss the algebra of exponentials more fully. First, we look at *integer* exponents: cases in which the powers are positive or negative whole numbers.

Integer Exponents

Positive Integer Exponents

If a is any real number and n is any positive integer, then by a^n we mean the quantity $a \cdot a \cdot \cdots \cdot a$ (n times); thus, $a^1 = a$, $a^2 = a \cdot a$, $a^5 = a \cdot a \cdot a \cdot a \cdot a$. In the expression a^n the number n is called the **exponent,** and the number a is called the **base.**

quick Examples

$3^2 = 9$ $\qquad 2^3 = 8$

$0^{34} = 0$ $\qquad (-1)^5 = -1$

$10^3 = 1000$ $\qquad 10^5 = 100{,}000$

Negative Integer Exponents

If a is any real number *other than zero* and n is any positive integer, then we define

$$a^{-n} = \frac{1}{a^n} = \frac{1}{a \cdot a \cdot \cdots \cdot a} \quad (n\ a\text{'s in the denominator})$$

quick Examples

$2^{-3} = \frac{1}{2^3} = \frac{1}{8}$ $\qquad 1^{-27} = \frac{1}{1^{27}} = 1$

$x^{-1} = \frac{1}{x^1} = \frac{1}{x}$ $\qquad (-3)^{-2} = \frac{1}{(-3)^2} = \frac{1}{9}$

$y^7 y^{-2} = y^7 \frac{1}{y^2} = y^5$ $\qquad 0^{-2}$ is not defined

Zero Exponent

If a is any real number other than zero, then we define

$a^0 = 1$

quick Examples

$3^0 = 1$ $\qquad 1{,}000{,}000^0 = 1$

0^0 is not defined

When combining exponential expressions, we use the following identities.

Exponent Identity	*quick* Examples
1. $a^m a^n = a^{m+n}$	$2^3 2^2 = 2^{3+2} = 2^5 = 32$ $x^3 x^{-4} = x^{3-4} = x^{-1} = \frac{1}{x}$ $\frac{x^3}{x^{-2}} = x^3 \frac{1}{x^{-2}} = x^3 x^2 = x^5$
2. $\frac{a^m}{a^n} = a^{m-n}$ if $a \neq 0$	$\frac{4^3}{4^2} = 4^{3-2} = 4^1 = 4$ $\frac{x^3}{x^{-2}} = x^{3-(-2)} = x^5$ $\frac{3^2}{3^4} = 3^{2-4} = 3^{-2} = \frac{1}{9}$
3. $(a^n)^m = a^{nm}$	$(3^2)^2 = 3^4 = 81$ $(2^x)^2 = 2^{2x}$
4. $(ab)^n = a^n b^n$	$(4 \cdot 2)^2 = 4^2 2^2 = 64$ $(-2y)^4 = (-2)^4 y^4 = 16y^4$
5. $\left(\frac{a}{b}\right)^n = \frac{a^n}{b^n}$ if $b \neq 0$	$\left(\frac{4}{3}\right)^2 = \frac{4^2}{3^2} = \frac{16}{9}$ $\left(\frac{x}{-y}\right)^3 = \frac{x^3}{(-y)^3} = -\frac{x^3}{y^3}$

Caution

- In the first two identities, the bases of the expressions must be the same. For example, the first gives $3^2 3^4 = 3^6$, but does *not* apply to $3^2 4^2$.
- People sometimes invent their own identities, such as $a^m + a^n = a^{m+n}$, which is wrong! (Try it with $a = m = n = 1$.) If you wind up with something like $2^3 + 2^4$, you are stuck with it; there are no identities around to simplify it further. (You can factor out 2^3, but whether that is a simplification depends on what you are going to do with the expression next.)

Example 1 Combining the Identities

$$\frac{(x^2)^3}{x^3} = \frac{x^6}{x^3} \qquad \text{By (3)}$$
$$= x^{6-3} \qquad \text{By (2)}$$
$$= x^3$$

$$\frac{(x^4y)^3}{y} = \frac{(x^4)^3y^3}{y} \qquad \text{By (4)}$$

$$= \frac{x^{12}y^3}{y} \qquad \text{By (3)}$$

$$= x^{12}y^{3-1} \qquad \text{By (2)}$$

$$= x^{12}y^2$$

Example 2 Eliminating Negative Exponents

Simplify the following and express the answer using no negative exponents.

a. $\dfrac{x^4y^{-3}}{x^5y^2}$ **b.** $\left(\dfrac{x^{-1}}{x^2y}\right)^5$

Solution

a. $\dfrac{x^4y^{-3}}{x^5y^2} = x^{4-5}y^{-3-2} = x^{-1}y^{-5} = \dfrac{1}{xy^5}$

b. $\left(\dfrac{x^{-1}}{x^2y}\right)^5 = \dfrac{(x^{-1})^5}{(x^2y)^5} = \dfrac{x^{-5}}{x^{10}y^5} = \dfrac{1}{x^{15}y^5}$

Radicals

If a is any nonnegative real number, then its **square root** is the nonnegative number whose square is a. For example, the square root of 16 is 4, because $4^2 = 16$. We write the square root of n as $\sqrt{n}$. (Roots are also referred to as **radicals.**) It is important to remember that $\sqrt{n}$ is never negative. Thus, for instance, $\sqrt{9}$ is 3, and not -3, even though $(-3)^2 = 9$. If we want to speak of the "negative square root" of 9, we write it as $-\sqrt{9} = -3$. If we want to write both square roots at once, we write $\pm\sqrt{9} = \pm 3$.

The **cube root** of a real number a is the number whose cube is a. The cube root of a is written as $\sqrt[3]{a}$ so that, for example, $\sqrt[3]{8} = 2$ (because $2^3 = 8$). Note that we can take the cube root of any number, positive, negative, or zero. For instance, the cube root of -8 is $\sqrt[3]{-8} = -2$ because $(-2)^3 = -8$. Unlike square roots, the cube root of a number may be negative. In fact, the cube root of a always has the same sign as a.

Higher roots are defined similarly. The **fourth root** of the *nonnegative* number a is defined as the nonnegative number whose fourth power is a, and written $\sqrt[4]{a}$. The **fifth root** of any number a is the number whose fifth power is a, and so on.

Note We cannot take an even-numbered root of a negative number, but we can take an odd-numbered root of any number. Even roots are always positive, whereas odd roots have the same sign as the number we start with. ■

Example 3 *n*th Roots

$\sqrt{4} = 2$	Because $2^2 = 4$
$\sqrt{16} = 4$	Because $4^2 = 16$
$\sqrt{1} = 1$	Because $1^2 = 1$
If $x \geq 0$, then $\sqrt{x^2} = x$	Because $x^2 = x^2$
$\sqrt{2} \approx 1.414213562$	$\sqrt{2}$ is not a whole number.
$\sqrt{1+1} = \sqrt{2} \approx 1.414213562$	First add, then take the square root.*
$\sqrt{9+16} = \sqrt{25} = 5$	Contrast with $\sqrt{9} + \sqrt{16} = 3 + 4 = 7$.
$\sqrt[3]{27} = 3$	Because $3^3 = 27$
$\sqrt[3]{-64} = -4$	Because $(-4)^3 = -64$
$\sqrt[4]{16} = 2$	Because $2^4 = 16$
$\sqrt[4]{-16}$ is not defined	Even-numbered root of a negative number
$\sqrt[5]{-1} = -1$, since $(-1)^5 = -1$	Odd-numbered root of a negative number
$\sqrt[n]{-1} = -1$ if n is any odd number	

* In general, $\sqrt{a+b}$ means the square root of the *quantity* $(a + b)$. The radical sign acts like a pair of parentheses or a fraction bar, telling us to evaluate what is inside before taking the root. (See the *Caution* on the next page.)

Q: *In the example we saw that $\sqrt{x^2} = x$ if x is nonnegative. What happens if x is negative?*

A: If x is negative, then x^2 is positive, and so $\sqrt{x^2}$ is still defined as the nonnegative number whose square is x^2. This number must be $|x|$, the **absolute value of *x*,** which is the nonnegative number with the same size as x. For instance, $|-3| = 3$, while $|3| = 3$, and $|0| = 0$. It follows that

$$\sqrt{x^2} = |x|$$

for every real number x, positive or negative. For instance,

$$\sqrt{(-3)^2} = \sqrt{9} = 3 = |-3|$$

and $$\sqrt{3^2} = \sqrt{9} = 3 = |3|$$

In general, we find that

$$\sqrt[n]{x^n} = x \text{ if } n \text{ is odd, and } \sqrt[n]{x^n} = |x| \text{ if } n \text{ is even}$$ ■

We use the following identities to evaluate radicals of products and quotients.

Radicals of Products and Quotients

If a and b are any real numbers (nonnegative in the case of even-numbered roots), then

$$\sqrt[n]{ab} = \sqrt[n]{a}\sqrt[n]{b}$$ Radical of a product = Product of radicals

$$\sqrt[n]{\frac{a}{b}} = \frac{\sqrt[n]{a}}{\sqrt[n]{b}} \quad \text{if } b \neq 0$$ Radical of a quotient = Quotient of radicals

Notes

- The first rule is similar to the rule $(a \cdot b)^2 = a^2b^2$ for the square of a product, and the second rule is similar to the rule $\left(\frac{a}{b}\right)^2 = \frac{a^2}{b^2}$ for the square of a quotient.
- ***Caution*** There is no corresponding identity for addition:

$$\sqrt{a+b} \text{ is } \textit{not} \text{ equal to } \sqrt{a} + \sqrt{b}$$

(consider $a = b = 1$, for example). Equating these expressions is a common error, so be careful!

quick Examples

1. $\sqrt{9 \cdot 4} = \sqrt{9}\sqrt{4} = 3 \times 2 = 6$ Alternatively, $\sqrt{9 \cdot 4} = \sqrt{36} = 6$

2. $\sqrt{\frac{9}{4}} = \frac{\sqrt{9}}{\sqrt{4}} = \frac{3}{2}$

3. $\sqrt{4(3+13)} = \sqrt{4(16)} = \sqrt{4}\sqrt{16} = 2 \times 4 = 8$

4. $\sqrt[3]{-216} = \sqrt[3]{(-27)8} = \sqrt[3]{-27}\sqrt[3]{8} = (-3)2 = -6$

5. $\sqrt{x^3} = \sqrt{x^2 \cdot x} = \sqrt{x^2}\sqrt{x} = x\sqrt{x} \quad \text{if } x \geq 0$

6. $\sqrt{\frac{x^2+y^2}{z^2}} = \frac{\sqrt{x^2+y^2}}{\sqrt{z^2}} = \frac{\sqrt{x^2+y^2}}{|z|}$ We can't simplify the numerator any further.

Rational Exponents

We already know what we mean by expressions such as x^4 and a^{-6}. The next step is to make sense of *rational* exponents: exponents of the form p/q with p and q integers as in $a^{1/2}$ and $3^{-2/3}$.

Q: *What should we mean by $a^{1/2}$?*

A: The overriding concern here is that all the exponent identities should remain true. In this case the identity to look at is the one that says that $(a^m)^n = a^{mn}$. This identity tells us that

$$(a^{1/2})^2 = a^1 = a$$

That is, $a^{1/2}$, when squared, gives us a. But that must mean that $a^{1/2}$ is the *square root* of a, or

$$a^{1/2} = \sqrt{a}$$

A similar argument tells us that, if q is any positive whole number, then

$$a^{1/q} = \sqrt[q]{a} \quad \text{the } q\text{th root of } a$$

Notice that if a is negative, this makes sense only for q odd. To avoid this problem, we usually stick to positive a. ■

Q: *If p and q are integers (q positive), what should we mean by $a^{p/q}$?*

A: By the exponent identities, $a^{p/q}$ should equal both $(a^p)^{1/q}$ and $(a^{1/q})^p$. The first is the qth root of a^p, and the second is the pth power of $a^{1/q}$, which gives us the following.

Conversion Between Rational Exponents and Radicals

If a is any nonnegative number, then

$$a^{p/q} = \sqrt[q]{a^p} = \left(\sqrt[q]{a}\right)^p$$

↑ Exponential form ↑ ↑ Radical form

In particular,

$$a^{1/q} = \sqrt[q]{a} \quad \text{the } q\text{th root of } a$$

Notes

- If a is negative, all of this makes sense only if q is odd.
- All of the exponent identities continue to work when we allow rational exponents p/q. In other words, we are free to use all the exponent identities even though the exponents are not integers.

quick Examples

1. $4^{3/2} = (\sqrt{4})^3 = 2^3 = 8$

2. $8^{2/3} = (\sqrt[3]{8})^2 = 2^2 = 4$

3. $9^{-3/2} = \dfrac{1}{9^{3/2}} = \dfrac{1}{(\sqrt{9})^3} = \dfrac{1}{3^3} = \dfrac{1}{27}$

4. $\dfrac{\sqrt{3}}{\sqrt[3]{3}} = \dfrac{3^{1/2}}{3^{1/3}} = 3^{1/2-1/3} = 3^{1/6} = \sqrt[6]{3}$

5. $2^2 2^{7/2} = 2^2 2^{3+1/2} = 2^2 2^3 2^{1/2} = 2^5 2^{1/2} = 2^5\sqrt{2}$

■

Example 4 Simplifying Algebraic Expressions

Simplify the following.

a. $\dfrac{(x^3)^{5/3}}{x^3}$ **b.** $\sqrt[4]{a^6}$ **c.** $\dfrac{(xy)^{-3}y^{-3/2}}{x^{-2}\sqrt{y}}$

Solution

a. $\dfrac{(x^3)^{5/3}}{x^3} = \dfrac{x^5}{x^3} = x^2$

b. $\sqrt[4]{a^6} = a^{6/4} = a^{3/2} = a \cdot a^{1/2} = a\sqrt{a}$

c. $\dfrac{(xy)^{-3}y^{-3/2}}{x^{-2}\sqrt{y}} = \dfrac{x^{-3}y^{-3}y^{-3/2}}{x^{-2}y^{1/2}} = \dfrac{1}{x^{-2+3}y^{1/2+3+3/2}} = \dfrac{1}{xy^5}$

Converting Between Rational, Radical, and Exponential Form

In calculus we must often convert algebraic expressions involving powers of x, such as $\dfrac{3}{2x^2}$, into expressions in which x does not appear in the denominator, such as $\dfrac{3}{2}x^{-2}$. Also, we must often convert expressions with radicals, such as $\dfrac{1}{\sqrt{1+x^2}}$, into expressions with no radicals and all powers in the numerator, such as $(1+x^2)^{-1/2}$. In these cases, we are converting from **rational form** or **radical form** to **exponential form.**

Rational Form

An expression is in **rational form** if it is written with positive exponents only.

quick Examples

1. $\dfrac{2}{3x^2}$ is in rational form.
2. $\dfrac{2x^{-1}}{3}$ is not in rational form because the exponent of x is negative.
3. $\dfrac{x}{6}+\dfrac{6}{x}$ is in rational form.

Radical Form

An expression is in **radical form** if it is written with integer powers and roots only.

quick Examples

1. $\dfrac{2}{5\sqrt[3]{x}}+\dfrac{2}{x}$ is in radical form.
2. $\dfrac{2x^{-1/3}}{5}+2x^{-1}$ is not in radical form because $x^{-1/3}$ appears.
3. $\dfrac{1}{\sqrt{1+x^2}}$ is in radical form, but $(1+x^2)^{-1/2}$ is not.

Exponential Form

An expression is in **exponential form** if there are no radicals and all powers of unknowns occur in the numerator. We usually write such expressions as sums or differences of terms of the form

$$\text{Constant} \times (\text{Expression with } x)^p \qquad \text{As in } \frac{1}{3}x^{-3/2}$$

quick Examples

1. $\dfrac{2}{3}x^4-3x^{-1/3}$ is in exponential form.
2. $\dfrac{x}{6}+\dfrac{6}{x}$ is not in exponential form because the second expression has x in the denominator.
3. $\sqrt[3]{x}$ is not in exponential form because it has a radical.
4. $(1+x^2)^{-1/2}$ is in exponential form, but $\dfrac{1}{\sqrt{1+x^2}}$ is not.

Example 5 Converting From One Form to Another

Convert the following to rational form:

a. $\dfrac{1}{2}x^{-2}+\dfrac{4}{3}x^{-5}$ **b.** $\dfrac{2}{\sqrt{x}}-\dfrac{2}{x^{-4}}$

Convert the following to radical form:

c. $\dfrac{1}{2}x^{-1/2}+\dfrac{4}{3}x^{-5/4}$ **d.** $\dfrac{(3+x)^{-1/3}}{5}$

Convert the following to exponential form:

e. $\dfrac{3}{4x^2} - \dfrac{x}{6} + \dfrac{6}{x}$ **f.** $\dfrac{2}{(x+1)^2} - \dfrac{3}{4\sqrt[5]{2x-1}}$

Solution

For (a) and (b), we eliminate negative exponents as we did in Example 2:

a. $\dfrac{1}{2}x^{-2} + \dfrac{4}{3}x^{-5} = \dfrac{1}{2} \cdot \dfrac{1}{x^2} + \dfrac{4}{3} \cdot \dfrac{1}{x^5} = \dfrac{1}{2x^2} + \dfrac{4}{3x^5}$

b. $\dfrac{2}{\sqrt{x}} - \dfrac{2}{x^{-4}} = \dfrac{2}{\sqrt{x}} - 2x^4$

For (c) and (d), we rewrite all terms with fractional exponents as radicals:

c.
$$\frac{1}{2}x^{-1/2} + \frac{4}{3}x^{-5/4} = \frac{1}{2} \cdot \frac{1}{x^{1/2}} + \frac{4}{3} \cdot \frac{1}{x^{5/4}}$$
$$= \frac{1}{2} \cdot \frac{1}{\sqrt{x}} + \frac{4}{3} \cdot \frac{1}{\sqrt[4]{x^5}} = \frac{1}{2\sqrt{x}} + \frac{4}{3\sqrt[4]{x^5}}$$

d. $\dfrac{(3+x)^{-1/3}}{5} = \dfrac{1}{5(3+x)^{1/3}} = \dfrac{1}{5\sqrt[3]{3+x}}$

For (e) and (f), we eliminate any radicals and move all expressions involving x to the numerator:

e. $\dfrac{3}{4x^2} - \dfrac{x}{6} + \dfrac{6}{x} = \dfrac{3}{4}x^{-2} - \dfrac{1}{6}x + 6x^{-1}$

f.
$$\frac{2}{(x+1)^2} - \frac{3}{4\sqrt[5]{2x-1}} = 2(x+1)^{-2} - \frac{3}{4(2x-1)^{1/5}}$$
$$= 2(x+1)^{-2} - \frac{3}{4}(2x-1)^{-1/5}$$

Solving Equations with Exponents

Example 6 Solving Equations

Solve the following equations:

a. $x^3 + 8 = 0$ **b.** $x^2 - \dfrac{1}{2} = 0$ **c.** $x^{3/2} - 64 = 0$

Solution

a. Subtracting 8 from both sides gives $x^3 = -8$. Taking the cube root of both sides gives $x = -2$.

b. Adding $\frac{1}{2}$ to both sides gives $x^2 = \frac{1}{2}$. Thus, $x = \pm\sqrt{\frac{1}{2}} = \pm\frac{1}{\sqrt{2}}$.

c. Adding 64 to both sides gives $x^{3/2} = 64$. Taking the reciprocal (2/3) power of both sides gives

$$(x^{3/2})^{2/3} = 64^{2/3}$$
$$x^1 = \left(\sqrt[3]{64}\right)^2 = 4^2 = 16$$

so $$x = 16$$

0.2 EXERCISES

Evaluate the expressions in Exercises 1–16.

1. 3^3 **2.** $(-2)^3$ **3.** $-(2\cdot 3)^2$ **4.** $(4\cdot 2)^2$

5. $\left(\frac{-2}{3}\right)^2$ **6.** $\left(\frac{3}{2}\right)^3$ **7.** $(-2)^{-3}$ **8.** -2^{-3}

9. $\left(\frac{1}{4}\right)^{-2}$ **10.** $\left(\frac{-2}{3}\right)^{-2}$ **11.** $2\cdot 3^0$ **12.** $3\cdot(-2)^0$

13. $2^3\,2^2$ **14.** $3^2 3$ **15.** $2^2 2^{-1} 2^4 2^{-4}$ **16.** $5^2 5^{-3} 5^2 5^{-2}$

Simplify each expression in Exercises 17–30, expressing your answer in rational form.

17. x^3x^2 **18.** x^4x^{-1} **19.** $-x^2x^{-3}y$

20. $-xy^{-1}x^{-1}$ **21.** $\frac{x^3}{x^4}$ **22.** $\frac{y^5}{y^3}$

23. $\frac{x^2y^2}{x^{-1}y}$ **24.** $\frac{x^{-1}y}{x^2y^2}$ **25.** $\frac{(xy^{-1}z^3)^2}{x^2yz^2}$

26. $\frac{x^2yz^2}{(xyz^{-1})^{-1}}$ **27.** $\left(\frac{xy^{-2}z}{x^{-1}z}\right)^3$ **28.** $\left(\frac{x^2y^{-1}z^0}{xyz}\right)^2$

29. $\left(\frac{x^{-1}y^{-2}z^2}{xy}\right)^{-2}$ **30.** $\left(\frac{xy^{-2}}{x^2y^{-1}z}\right)^{-3}$

Convert the expressions in Exercises 31–36 to rational form.

31. $3x^{-4}$ **32.** $\frac{1}{2}x^{-4}$ **33.** $\frac{3}{4}x^{-2/3}$

34. $\frac{4}{5}y^{-3/4}$ **35.** $1-\frac{0.3}{x^{-2}}-\frac{6}{5}x^{-1}$

36. $\frac{1}{3x^{-4}}+\frac{0.1x^{-2}}{3}$

Evaluate the expressions in Exercises 37–56, rounding your answer to four significant digits where necessary.

37. $\sqrt{4}$ **38.** $\sqrt{5}$ **39.** $\sqrt{\frac{1}{4}}$

40. $\sqrt{\frac{1}{9}}$ **41.** $\sqrt{\frac{16}{9}}$ **42.** $\sqrt{\frac{9}{4}}$

43. $\frac{\sqrt{4}}{5}$ **44.** $\frac{6}{\sqrt{25}}$ **45.** $\sqrt{9}+\sqrt{16}$

46. $\sqrt{25}-\sqrt{16}$ **47.** $\sqrt{9+16}$ **48.** $\sqrt{25-16}$

49. $\sqrt[3]{8-27}$ **50.** $\sqrt[4]{81-16}$ **51.** $\sqrt[3]{27/8}$

52. $\sqrt[3]{8\times 64}$ **53.** $\sqrt{(-2)^2}$ **54.** $\sqrt{(-1)^2}$

55. $\sqrt{\frac{1}{4}(1+15)}$ **56.** $\sqrt{\frac{1}{9}(3+33)}$

Simplify the expressions in Exercises 57–64, given that x, y, a, b, and c are positive real numbers.

57. $\sqrt{a^2b^2}$ **58.** $\sqrt{\frac{a^2}{b^2}}$ **59.** $\sqrt{(x+9)^2}$

60. $(\sqrt{x+9})^2$ **61.** $\sqrt[3]{x^3(a^3+b^3)}$ **62.** $\sqrt[4]{\frac{x^4}{a^4b^4}}$

63. $\sqrt{\frac{4xy^3}{x^2y}}$ **64.** $\sqrt{\frac{4(x^2+y^2)}{c^2}}$

Convert the expressions in Exercises 65–80 to exponential form.

65. $\sqrt{3}$ **66.** $\sqrt{8}$ **67.** $\sqrt{x^3}$

68. $\sqrt[3]{x^2}$ **69.** $\sqrt[3]{xy^2}$ **70.** $\sqrt{x^2y}$

71. $\frac{x^2}{\sqrt{x}}$ **72.** $\frac{x}{\sqrt{x}}$ **73.** $\frac{3}{5x^2}$

74. $\frac{2}{5x^{-3}}$ **75.** $\frac{3x^{-1.2}}{2}-\frac{1}{3x^{2.1}}$

76. $\frac{2}{3x^{-1.2}}-\frac{x^{2.1}}{3}$ **77.** $\frac{2x}{3}-\frac{x^{0.1}}{2}+\frac{4}{3x^{1.1}}$

78. $\frac{4x^2}{3}+\frac{x^{3/2}}{6}-\frac{2}{3x^2}$ **79.** $\frac{1}{(x^2+1)^3}-\frac{3}{4\sqrt[3]{(x^2+1)}}$

80. $\frac{2}{3(x^2+1)^{-3}}-\frac{3\sqrt[3]{(x^2+1)^7}}{4}$

Convert the expressions in Exercises 81–92 to radical form.

81. $2^{2/3}$ **82.** $3^{4/5}$ **83.** $x^{4/3}$

84. $y^{7/4}$ **85.** $(x^{1/2}y^{1/3})^{1/5}$

86. $x^{-1/3}y^{3/2}$ **87.** $-\frac{3}{2}x^{-1/4}$

88. $\frac{4}{5}x^{3/2}$ **89.** $0.2x^{-2/3}+\frac{3}{7x^{-1/2}}$

90. $\frac{3.1}{x^{-4/3}}-\frac{11}{7}x^{-1/7}$ **91.** $\frac{3}{4(1-x)^{5/2}}$ **92.** $\frac{9}{4(1-x)^{-7/3}}$

Simplify the expressions in Exercises 93–102.

93. $4^{-1/2}4^{7/2}$ **94.** $2^{1/a}/2^{2/a}$ **95.** $3^{2/3}3^{-1/6}$

96. $2^{1/3}2^{-1}2^{2/3}2^{-1/3}$ **97.** $\frac{x^{3/2}}{x^{5/2}}$ **98.** $\frac{y^{5/4}}{y^{3/4}}$

99. $\frac{x^{1/2}y^2}{x^{-1/2}y}$ **100.** $\frac{x^{-1/2}y}{x^2y^{3/2}}$

101. $\left(\frac{x}{y}\right)^{1/3}\left(\frac{y}{x}\right)^{2/3}$ **102.** $\left(\frac{x}{y}\right)^{-1/3}\left(\frac{y}{x}\right)^{1/3}$

Solve each equation in Exercises 103–116 for x, rounding your answer to four significant digits where necessary.

103. $x^2 - 16 = 0$ **104.** $x^2 - 1 = 0$ **105.** $x^2 - \frac{4}{9} = 0$

106. $x^2 - \frac{1}{10} = 0$ **107.** $x^2 - (1 + 2x)^2 = 0$

108. $x^2 - (2 - 3x)^2 = 0$ **109.** $x^5 + 32 = 0$

110. $x^4 - 81 = 0$ **111.** $x^{1/2} - 4 = 0$

112. $x^{1/3} - 2 = 0$ **113.** $1 - \frac{1}{x^2} = 0$ **114.** $\frac{2}{x^3} - \frac{6}{x^4} = 0$

115. $(x - 4)^{-1/3} = 2$ **116.** $(x - 4)^{2/3} + 1 = 5$

0.3 Multiplying and Factoring Algebraic Expressions

Multiplying Algebraic Expressions

Distributive Law

The **distributive law** for real numbers states that

$$a(b \pm c) = ab \pm ac$$
$$(a \pm b)c = ac \pm bc$$

for any real numbers a, b, and c.

quick Examples

1. $2(x - 3)$ is *not* equal to $2x - 3$ but is equal to $2x - 2(3) = 2x - 6$.
2. $x(x + 1) = x^2 + x$
3. $2x(3x - 4) = 6x^2 - 8x$
4. $(x - 4)x^2 = x^3 - 4x^2$
5. $(x + 2)(x + 3) = (x + 2)x + (x + 2)3 = (x^2 + 2x) + (3x + 6) = x^2 + 5x + 6$
6. $(x + 2)(x - 3) = (x + 2)x - (x + 2)3 = (x^2 + 2x) - (3x + 6) = x^2 - x - 6$

There is a quicker way of expanding expressions like the last two, called the "FOIL" method (First, Outer, Inner, Last). Consider, for instance, the expression $(x + 1)(x - 2)$. The FOIL method says: Take the product of the first terms: $x \cdot x = x^2$, the product of the outer terms: $x \cdot (-2) = -2x$, the product of the inner terms: $1 \cdot x = x$, and the product of the last terms: $1 \cdot (-2) = -2$, and then add them all up, getting $x^2 - 2x + x - 2 = x^2 - x - 2$.

Example 1 FOIL

a. $(x - 2)(2x + 5) = 2x^2 + 5x - 4x - 10 = 2x^2 + x - 10$

↑ First ↑ Outer ↑ Inner ↑ Last

b. $(x^2 + 1)(x - 4) = x^3 - 4x^2 + x - 4$

c. $(a - b)(a + b) = a^2 + ab - ab - b^2 = a^2 - b^2$

d $(a + b)^2 = (a + b)(a + b) = a^2 + ab + ab + b^2 = a^2 + 2ab + b^2$

e. $(a - b)^2 = (a - b)(a - b) = a^2 - ab - ab + b^2 = a^2 - 2ab + b^2$

The last three are particularly important and are worth memorizing.

Special Formulas

$(a-b)(a+b) = a^2 - b^2$	Difference of two squares
$(a+b)^2 = a^2 + 2ab + b^2$	Square of a sum
$(a-b)^2 = a^2 - 2ab + b^2$	Square of a difference

quick **Examples**

1. $(2-x)(2+x) = 4 - x^2$
2. $(1+a)(1-a) = 1 - a^2$
3. $(x+3)^2 = x^2 + 6x + 9$
4. $(4-x)^2 = 16 - 8x + x^2$

Here are some longer examples that require the distributive law.

Example 2 Multiplying Algebraic Expressions

a. $(x+1)(x^2+3x-4) = (x+1)x^2 + (x+1)3x - (x+1)4$
$= (x^3+x^2) + (3x^2+3x) - (4x+4)$
$= x^3 + 4x^2 - x - 4$

b. $\left(x^2 - \frac{1}{x} + 1\right)(2x+5) = \left(x^2 - \frac{1}{x} + 1\right)2x + \left(x^2 - \frac{1}{x} + 1\right)5$
$= (2x^3 - 2 + 2x) + \left(5x^2 - \frac{5}{x} + 5\right)$
$= 2x^3 + 5x^2 + 2x + 3 - \frac{5}{x}$

c. $(x-y)(x-y)(x-y) = (x^2 - 2xy + y^2)(x-y)$
$= (x^2 - 2xy + y^2)x - (x^2 - 2xy + y^2)y$
$= (x^3 - 2x^2y + xy^2) - (x^2y - 2xy^2 + y^3)$
$= x^3 - 3x^2y + 3xy^2 - y^3$

Factoring Algebraic Expressions

We can think of factoring as applying the distributive law in reverse—for example,

$$2x^2 + x = x(2x+1)$$

which can be checked by using the distributive law. Factoring is an art that you will learn with experience and the help of a few useful techniques.

Factoring Using a Common Factor

To use this technique, locate a **common factor**—a term that occurs as a factor in each of the expressions being added or subtracted (for example, x is a common factor in $2x^2 + x$, because it is a factor of both $2x^2$ and x). Once you have located a common factor, "factor it out" by applying the distributive law.

quick **Examples**

1. $2x^3 - x^2 + x$ has x as a common factor, so
   $2x^3 - x^2 + x = x(2x^2 - x + 1)$
2. $2x^2 + 4x$ has $2x$ as a common factor, so
   $2x^2 + 4x = 2x(x+2)$

3. $2x^2y + xy^2 - x^2y^2$ has xy as a common factor, so

$$2x^2y + xy^2 - x^2y^2 = xy(2x + y - xy)$$

4. $(x^2 + 1)(x + 2) - (x^2 + 1)(x + 3)$ has $x^2 + 1$ as a common factor, so

$$\begin{aligned}(x^2 + 1)(x + 2) - (x^2 + 1)(x + 3) &= (x^2 + 1)[(x + 2) - (x + 3)] \\ &= (x^2 + 1)(x + 2 - x - 3) \\ &= (x^2 + 1)(-1) = -(x^2 + 1)\end{aligned}$$

5. $12x(x^2 - 1)^5(x^3 + 1)^6 + 18x^2(x^2 - 1)^6(x^3 + 1)^5$ has $6x(x^2 - 1)^5(x^3 + 1)^5$ as a common factor, so

$$\begin{aligned}&12x(x^2 - 1)^5(x^3 + 1)^6 + 18x^2(x^2 - 1)^6(x^3 + 1)^5 \\ &= 6x(x^2 - 1)^5(x^3 + 1)^5[2(x^3 + 1) + 3x(x^2 - 1)] \\ &= 6x(x^2 - 1)^5(x^3 + 1)^5(2x^3 + 2 + 3x^3 - 3x) \\ &= 6x(x^2 - 1)^5(x^3 + 1)^5(5x^3 - 3x + 2)\end{aligned}$$

We would also like to be able to reverse calculations such as $(x + 2)(2x - 5) = 2x^2 - x - 10$. That is, starting with the expression $2x^2 - x - 10$, we would like to **factor** it to get the expression $(x + 2)(2x - 5)$. An expression of the form $ax^2 + bx + c$, where a, b, and c are real numbers, is called a **quadratic** expression in x. Thus, given a quadratic expression $ax^2 + bx + c$, we would like to write it in the form $(dx + e)(fx + g)$ for some real numbers d, e, f, and g. There are some quadratics, such as $x^2 + x + 1$, that cannot be factored in this form at all. Here, we consider only quadratics that do factor, and in such a way that the numbers d, e, f and g are integers (whole numbers; other cases are discussed in Section 5). The usual technique of factoring such quadratics is a "trial and error" approach.

Factoring Quadratics by Trial and Error

To factor the quadratic $ax^2 + bx + c$, factor ax^2 as $(a_1x)(a_2x)$ (with a_1 positive) and c as c_1c_2, and then check whether $ax^2 + bx + c = (a_1x \pm c_1)(a_2x \pm c_2)$. If not, try other factorizations of ax^2 and c.

quick **Examples**

1. To factor $x^2 - 6x + 5$, first factor x^2 as $(x)(x)$, and 5 as $(5)(1)$:

$(x + 5)(x + 1) = x^2 + 6x + 5$ — No good

$(x - 5)(x - 1) = x^2 - 6x + 5$ — Desired factorization

2. To factor $x^2 - 4x - 12$, first factor x^2 as $(x)(x)$, and -12 as $(1)(-12)$, $(2)(-6)$, or $(3)(-4)$. Trying them one-by-one gives

$(x + 1)(x - 12) = x^2 - 11x - 12$ — No good

$(x - 1)(x + 12) = x^2 + 11x - 12$ — No good

$(x + 2)(x - 6) = x^2 - 4x - 12$ — Desired factorization

3. To factor $4x^2 - 25$, we can follow the above procedure, or recognize $4x^2 - 25$ as the difference of two squares:

$$4x^2 - 25 = (2x)^2 - 5^2 = (2x - 5)(2x + 5)$$

Note: Not all quadratic expressions factor. In Section 5 we look at a test that tells us whether or not a given quadratic factors.

Here are examples requiring either a little more work or a little more thought.

Example 3 Factoring Quadratics

Factor the following: **a.** $4x^2 - 5x - 6$ **b.** $x^4 - 5x^2 + 6$

Solution

a. Possible factorizations of $4x^2$ are $(2x)(2x)$ or $(x)(4x)$. Possible factorizations of -6 are $(1)(-6)$, $(2)(-3)$. We now systematically try out all the possibilities until we come up with the correct one.

$(2x)(2x)$ and $(1)(-6)$:	$(2x+1)(2x-6) = 4x^2 - 10x - 6$	No good
$(2x)(2x)$ and $(2)(-3)$:	$(2x+2)(2x-3) = 4x^2 - 2x - 6$	No good
$(x)(4x)$ and $(1)(-6)$:	$(x+1)(4x-6) = 4x^2 - 2x - 6$	No good
$(x)(4x)$ and $(2)(-3)$:	$(x+2)(4x-3) = 4x^2 + 5x - 6$	Almost!
Change signs:	$(x-2)(4x+3) = 4x^2 - 5x - 6$	Correct

b. The expression $x^4 - 5x^2 + 6$ is not a quadratic, you say? Correct, it's a quartic (a fourth degree expression). However, it looks rather like a quadratic. In fact, it is quadratic *in* x^2, meaning that it is

$$(x^2)^2 - 5(x^2) + 6 = y^2 - 5y + 6$$

where $y = x^2$. The quadratic $y^2 - 5y + 6$ factors as

$$y^2 - 5y + 6 = (y-3)(y-2)$$

so

$$x^4 - 5x^2 + 6 = (x^2 - 3)(x^2 - 2)$$

This is a sometimes useful technique.

Our last example is here to remind you why we should want to factor polynomials in the first place. We shall return to this in Section 5.

Example 4 Solving a Quadratic Equation by Factoring

Solve the equation $3x^2 + 4x - 4 = 0$.

Solution We first factor the left-hand side to get

$$(3x-2)(x+2) = 0$$

Thus, the product of the two quantities $(3x - 2)$ and $(x + 2)$ is zero. Now, if a product of two numbers is zero, one of the two must be zero. In other words, either $3x - 2 = 0$, giving $x = \frac{2}{3}$, or $x + 2 = 0$, giving $x = -2$. Thus, there are two solutions: $x = \frac{2}{3}$ and $x = -2$.

0.3 EXERCISES

Expand each expression in Exercises 1–22.

1. $x(4x+6)$

2. $(4y-2)y$

3. $(2x-y)y$

4. $x(3x+y)$

5. $(x+1)(x-3)$

6. $(y+3)(y+4)$

7. $(2y+3)(y+5)$

8. $(2x-2)(3x-4)$

9. $(2x-3)^2$

10. $(3x+1)^2$

11. $\left(x+\frac{1}{x}\right)^2$

12. $\left(y-\frac{1}{y}\right)^2$

13. $(2x-3)(2x+3)$

14. $(4+2x)(4-2x)$

15. $\left(y-\frac{1}{y}\right)\left(y+\frac{1}{y}\right)$

16. $(x-x^2)(x+x^2)$

17. $(x^2+x-1)(2x+4)$

18. $(3x+1)(2x^2-x+1)$

19. $(x^2-2x+1)^2$

20. $(x+y-xy)^2$

21. $(y^3+2y^2+y)(y^2+2y-1)$

22. $(x^3-2x^2+4)(3x^2-x+2)$

In Exercises 23–30, factor each expression and simplify as much as possible.

23. $(x+1)(x+2)+(x+1)(x+3)$

24. $(x+1)(x+2)^2+(x+1)^2(x+2)$

25. $(x^2+1)^5(x+3)^4+(x^2+1)^6(x+3)^3$

26. $10x(x^2+1)^4(x^3+1)^5+15x^2(x^2+1)^5(x^3+1)^4$

27. $(x^3+1)\sqrt{x+1}-(x^3+1)^2\sqrt{x+1}$

28. $(x^2+1)\sqrt{x+1}-\sqrt{(x+1)^3}$

29. $\sqrt{(x+1)^3}+\sqrt{(x+1)^5}$

30. $(x^2+1)\sqrt[3]{(x+1)^4}-\sqrt[3]{(x+1)^7}$

*In Exercises 31–48, **(a)** factor the given expression; **(b)** set the expression equal to zero and solve for the unknown (x in the odd-numbered exercises and y in the even-numbered exercises).*

31. $2x+3x^2$

32. y^2-4y

33. $6x^3-2x^2$

34. $3y^3-9y^2$

35. x^2-8x+7

36. y^2+6y+8

37. x^2+x-12

38. y^2+y-6

39. $2x^2-3x-2$

40. $3y^2-8y-3$

41. $6x^2+13x+6$

42. $6y^2+17y+12$

43. $12x^2+x-6$

44. $20y^2+7y-3$

45. $x^2+4xy+4y^2$

46. $4y^2-4xy+x^2$

47. x^4-5x^2+4

48. y^4+2y^2-3

0.4 Rational Expressions

Rational Expression

A **rational expression** is an algebraic expression of the form $\frac{P}{Q}$, where P and Q are simpler expressions (usually polynomials) and the denominator Q is not zero.

quick Examples

1. $\dfrac{x^2-3x}{x}$ $\quad P=x^2-3x,\ Q=x$

2. $\dfrac{x+\frac{1}{x}+1}{2x^2y+1}$ $\quad P=x+\frac{1}{x}+1,\ Q=2x^2y+1$

3. $3xy-x^2$ $\quad P=3xy-x^2,\ Q=1$

Algebra of Rational Expressions

We manipulate rational expressions in the same way that we manipulate fractions, using the following rules:

	Algebraic Rule	quick Example
Product:	$\frac{P}{Q} \cdot \frac{R}{S} = \frac{PR}{QS}$	$\frac{x+1}{x} \cdot \frac{x-1}{2x+1} = \frac{(x+1)(x-1)}{x(2x+1)} = \frac{x^2-1}{2x^2+x}$
Sum:	$\frac{P}{Q} + \frac{R}{S} = \frac{PS+RQ}{QS}$	$\frac{2x-1}{3x+2} + \frac{1}{x} = \frac{(2x-1)x+1(3x+2)}{x(3x+2)} = \frac{2x^2+2x+2}{3x^2+2x}$
Difference:	$\frac{P}{Q} - \frac{R}{S} = \frac{PS-RQ}{QS}$	$\frac{x}{3x+2} - \frac{x-4}{x} = \frac{x^2-(x-4)(3x+2)}{x(3x+2)} = \frac{-2x^2+10x+8}{3x^2+2x}$
Reciprocal:	$\frac{1}{\left(\frac{P}{Q}\right)} = \frac{Q}{P}$	$\frac{1}{\left(\frac{2xy}{3x-1}\right)} = \frac{3x-1}{2xy}$
Quotient:	$\frac{\left(\frac{P}{Q}\right)}{\left(\frac{R}{S}\right)} = \frac{P}{Q} \cdot \frac{S}{R} = \frac{PS}{QR}$	$\frac{\left(\frac{x}{x-1}\right)}{\left(\frac{y-1}{y}\right)} = \frac{xy}{(x-1)(y-1)} = \frac{xy}{xy-x-y+1}$
Cancellation:	$\frac{P\cancel{R}}{Q\cancel{R}} = \frac{P}{Q}$	$\frac{(x-1)(xy+4)}{(x^2y-8)(x-1)} = \frac{xy+4}{x^2y-8}$

Caution Cancellation of summands is *invalid.* For instance,

$$\frac{\cancel{x}+(2xy^2-y)}{\cancel{x}+4y} = \frac{(2xy^2-y)}{4y}$$ ✗ *WRONG!* Do *not* cancel a summand.

$$\frac{\cancel{x}(2xy^2-y)}{4\cancel{x}y} = \frac{(2xy^2-y)}{4y}$$ ✔ *CORRECT* Do cancel a factor.

Here are some examples that require several algebraic operations.

Example 1 Simplifying Rational Expressions

a. $$\frac{\left(\frac{1}{x+y} - \frac{1}{x}\right)}{y} = \frac{\left(\frac{x-(x+y)}{x(x+y)}\right)}{y} = \frac{\left(\frac{-y}{x(x+y)}\right)}{y} = \frac{-y}{xy(x+y)} = -\frac{1}{x(x+y)}$$

b. $$\frac{(x+1)(x+2)^2-(x+1)^2(x+2)}{(x+2)^4} = \frac{(x+1)(x+2)[(x+2)-(x+1)]}{(x+2)^4}$$

$$= \frac{(x+1)(x+2)(x+2-x-1)}{(x+2)^4} = \frac{(x+1)(x+2)}{(x+2)^4} = \frac{x+1}{(x+2)^3}$$

c. $$\frac{2x\sqrt{x+1}-\frac{x^2}{\sqrt{x+1}}}{x+1} = \frac{\left(\frac{2x\left(\sqrt{x+1}\right)^2-x^2}{\sqrt{x+1}}\right)}{x+1} = \frac{2x(x+1)-x^2}{(x+1)\sqrt{x+1}}$$

$$= \frac{2x^2+2x-x^2}{(x+1)\sqrt{x+1}} = \frac{x^2+2x}{\sqrt{(x+1)^3}} = \frac{x(x+2)}{\sqrt{(x+1)^3}}$$

0.4 EXERCISES

Rewrite each expression in Exercises 1–16 as a single rational expression, simplified as much as possible.

1. $\frac{x-4}{x+1} \cdot \frac{2x+1}{x-1}$
2. $\frac{2x-3}{x-2} \cdot \frac{x+3}{x+1}$
3. $\frac{x-4}{x+1} + \frac{2x+1}{x-1}$
4. $\frac{2x-3}{x-2} + \frac{x+3}{x+1}$
5. $\frac{x^2}{x+1} - \frac{x-1}{x+1}$
6. $\frac{x^2-1}{x-2} - \frac{1}{x-1}$
7. $\frac{1}{\left(\frac{x}{x-1}\right)} + x - 1$
8. $\frac{2}{\left(\frac{x-2}{x^2}\right)} - \frac{1}{x-2}$
9. $\frac{1}{x}\left[\frac{x-3}{xy} + \frac{1}{y}\right]$
10. $\frac{y^2}{x}\left[\frac{2x-3}{y} + \frac{x}{y}\right]$
11. $\frac{(x+1)^2(x+2)^3 - (x+1)^3(x+2)^2}{(x+2)^6}$
12. $\frac{6x(x^2+1)^2(x^3+2)^3 - 9x^2(x^2+1)^3(x^3+2)^2}{(x^3+2)^6}$
13. $\frac{(x^2-1)\sqrt{x^2+1} - \frac{x^4}{\sqrt{x^2+1}}}{x^2+1}$
14. $\frac{x\sqrt{x^3-1} - \frac{3x^4}{\sqrt{x^3-1}}}{x^3-1}$
15. $\frac{\frac{1}{(x+y)^2} - \frac{1}{x^2}}{y}$
16. $\frac{\frac{1}{(x+y)^3} - \frac{1}{x^3}}{y}$

0.5 Solving Polynomial Equations

Polynomial Equation

A **polynomial equation** in one unknown is an equation that can be written in the form

$$ax^n + bx^{n-1} + \cdots + rx + s = 0$$

where $a, b, \ldots, r$ and s are constants.

We call the largest exponent of x appearing in a nonzero term of a polynomial the **degree** of that polynomial.

quick Examples

1. $3x + 1 = 0$ has degree 1 because the largest power of x that occurs is $x = x^1$. Degree 1 equations are called **linear** equations.
2. $x^2 - x - 1 = 0$ has degree 2 because the largest power of x that occurs is x^2. Degree 2 equations are also called **quadratic equations,** or just **quadratics.**
3. $x^3 = 2x^2 + 1$ is a degree 3 polynomial (or **cubic**) in disguise. It can be rewritten as $x^3 - 2x^2 - 1 = 0$, which is in the standard form for a degree 3 equation.
4. $x^4 - x = 0$ has degree 4. It is called a **quartic.**

Now comes the question: How do we solve these equations for x? This question was asked by mathematicians as early as 1600 B.C. Let's look at these equations one degree at a time.

Solution of Linear Equations

By definition, a linear equation can be written in the form

$$ax + b = 0 \qquad a \text{ and } b \text{ are fixed numbers with } a \neq 0.$$

Solving this is a nice mental exercise: Subtract b from both sides and then divide by a, getting $x = -b/a$. Don't bother memorizing this formula; just go ahead and solve linear equations as they arise. If you feel you need practice, see the exercises at the end of the section.

Solution of Quadratic Equations

By definition, a quadratic equation has the form

$$ax^2 + bx + c = 0 \qquad a, b, \text{ and } c \text{ are fixed numbers and } a \neq 0.$$[1]

The solutions of this equation are also called the **roots** of $ax^2 + bx + c$. We're assuming that you saw quadratic equations somewhere in high school but may be a little hazy about the details of their solution. There are two ways of solving these equations—one works sometimes, and the other works every time.

Solving Quadratic Equations by Factoring (works sometimes)

If we can factor* a quadratic equation $ax^2 + bx + c = 0$, we can solve the equation by setting each factor equal to zero.

quick Examples

1. $x^2 + 7x + 10 = 0$
   $(x + 5)(x + 2) = 0$ Factor the left-hand side.
   $x + 5 = 0$ or $x + 2 = 0$ If a product is zero, one or both factors is zero.
   Solutions: $x = -5$ and $x = -2$
2. $2x^2 - 5x - 12 = 0$
   $(2x + 3)(x - 4) = 0$ Factor the left-hand side.
   $2x + 3 = 0$ or $x - 4 = 0$
   Solutions: $x = -3/2$ and $x = 4$

* See the section on factoring for a review of how to factor quadratics.

Test for Factoring

The quadratic $ax^2 + bx + c$, with a, b, and c being integers (whole numbers), factors into an expression of the form $(rx + s)(tx + u)$ with r, s, t and u integers precisely when the quantity $b^2 - 4ac$ is a perfect square (that is, it is the square of an integer). If this happens, we say that the quadratic **factors over the integers.**

quick Examples

1. $x^2 + x + 1$ has $a = 1$, $b = 1$, and $c = 1$, so $b^2 - 4ac = -3$, which is not a perfect square. Therefore, this quadratic does not factor over the integers.
2. $2x^2 - 5x - 12$ has $a = 2$, $b = -5$ and $c = -12$, so $b^2 - 4ac = 121$. Because $121 = 11^2$, this quadratic does factor over the integers (we factored it above).

[1] What happens if $a = 0$?

Solving Quadratic Equations with the Quadratic Formula (works every time)

The solutions of the general quadratic $ax^2 + bx + c = 0$ $(a \neq 0)$ are given by

$$x = \frac{-b \pm \sqrt{b^2 - 4ac}}{2a}$$

We call the quantity $\Delta = b^2 - 4ac$ the **discriminant** of the quadratic (Δ is the Greek letter delta), and we have the following general rules:

- If Δ is positive, there are two distinct real solutions.
- If Δ is zero, there is only one real solution: $x = -\dfrac{b}{2a}$. (Why?)
- If Δ is negative, there are no real solutions.

quick Examples

1. $2x^2 - 5x - 12 = 0$ has $a = 2$, $b = -5$, and $c = -12$.

$$x = \frac{-b \pm \sqrt{b^2 - 4ac}}{2a} = \frac{5 \pm \sqrt{25 + 96}}{4} = \frac{5 \pm \sqrt{121}}{4} = \frac{5 \pm 11}{4}$$

$$= \frac{16}{4} \text{ or } \frac{6}{4}, = 4 \text{ or } -3/2$$

Δ is positive in this example.

2. $4x^2 = 12x - 9$ can be rewritten as $4x^2 - 12x + 9 = 0$, which has $a = 4$, $b = -12$, and $c = 9$.

$$x = \frac{-b \pm \sqrt{b^2 - 4ac}}{2a} = \frac{12 \pm \sqrt{144 - 144}}{8} = \frac{12 \pm 0}{8} = \frac{12}{8} = \frac{3}{2}$$

Δ is zero in this example.

3. $x^2 + 2x - 1 = 0$ has $a = 1$, $b = 2$, and $c = -1$.

$$x = \frac{-b \pm \sqrt{b^2 - 4ac}}{2a} = \frac{-2 \pm \sqrt{8}}{2} = \frac{-2 \pm 2\sqrt{2}}{2} = -1 \pm \sqrt{2}$$

The two solutions are $x = -1 + \sqrt{2} = 0.414\ldots$ and $x = -1 - \sqrt{2} = -2.414\ldots$.

Δ is positive in this example.

4. $x^2 + x + 1 = 0$ has $a = 1$, $b = 1$, and $c = 1$. Since $\Delta = -3$ is negative, there are no real solutions.

Δ is negative in this example.

Q: *This is all very useful, but where does the quadratic formula come from?*

A: To see where it comes from, we will solve a general quadratic equation using "brute force." Start with the general quadratic equation.

$$ax^2 + bx + c = 0$$

First, divide out the nonzero number a to get

$$x^2 + \frac{bx}{a} + \frac{c}{a} = 0$$

Now we **complete the square:** Add and subtract the quantity $\dfrac{b^2}{4a^2}$ to get

$$x^2 + \frac{bx}{a} + \frac{b^2}{4a^2} - \frac{b^2}{4a^2} + \frac{c}{a} = 0$$

We do this to get the first three terms to factor as a perfect square:

$$\left(x + \frac{b}{2a}\right)^2 - \frac{b^2}{4a^2} + \frac{c}{a} = 0$$

(Check this by multiplying out.) Adding $\dfrac{b^2}{4a^2} - \dfrac{c}{a}$ to both sides gives:

$$\left(x + \frac{b}{2a}\right)^2 = \frac{b^2}{4a^2} - \frac{c}{a} = \frac{b^2 - 4ac}{4a^2}$$

Taking square roots gives

$$x + \frac{b}{2a} = \frac{\pm\sqrt{b^2 - 4ac}}{2a}$$

Finally, adding $-\frac{b}{2a}$ to both sides yields the result:

$$x = -\frac{b}{2a} + \frac{\pm\sqrt{b^2 - 4ac}}{2a}$$

or

$$x = \frac{-b \pm \sqrt{b^2 - 4ac}}{2a}$$

■

Solution of Cubic Equations

By definition, a cubic equation can be written in the form

$$ax^3 + bx^2 + cx + d = 0 \qquad a, b, c, \text{ and } d \text{ are fixed numbers and } a \neq 0.$$

Now we get into something of a bind. Although there is a perfectly respectable formula for the solutions, it is very complicated and involves the use of complex numbers rather heavily.[2] So we discuss instead a much simpler method that *sometimes* works nicely. Here is the method in a nutshell.

Solving Cubics by Finding One Factor

Start with a given cubic equation $ax^3 + bx^2 + cx + d = 0$.

Step 1 By trial and error, find one solution $x = s$. If a, b, c, and d are integers, the only possible *rational* solutions* are those of the form $s = \pm(\text{factor of } d)/(\text{factor of } a)$.

Step 2 It will now be possible to factor the cubic as

$$ax^3 + bx^2 + cx + d = (x - s)(ax^2 + ex + f) = 0$$

To find $ax^2 + ex + f$, divide the cubic by $x - s$, using long division.†

Step 3 The factored equation says that either $x - s = 0$ or $ax^2 + ex + f = 0$. We already know that s is a solution, and now we see that the other solutions are the roots of the quadratic. Note that this quadratic may or may not have any real solutions, as usual.

quick Example

To solve the cubic $x^3 - x^2 + x - 1 = 0$, we first find a single solution. Here, $a = 1$ and $d = -1$. Because the only factors of ± 1 are ± 1, the only possible rational solutions are $x = \pm 1$. By substitution, we see that $x = 1$ is a solution. Thus $(x - 1)$ is a factor. Dividing by $(x - 1)$ yields the quotient $(x^2 + 1)$. Thus,

$$x^3 - x^2 + x - 1 = (x - 1)(x^2 + 1) = 0$$

so that either $x - 1 = 0$ or $x^2 + 1 = 0$.

Because the discriminant of the quadratic $x^2 + 1$ is negative, we don't get any real solutions from $x^2 + 1 = 0$, so the only real solution is $x = 1$.

* There may be *irrational* solutions, however; for example $x^3 - 2 = 0$ has the single solution $x = \sqrt[3]{2}$.

† Alternatively, use "synthetic division," a shortcut that would take us too far afield to describe.

[2] It was when this formula was discovered in the 16th century that complex numbers were first taken seriously. Although we would like to show you the formula, it is too large to fit in this footnote.

Possible Outcomes When Solving a Cubic Equation

If you consider all the cases, there are three possible outcomes when solving a cubic equation:

1. One real solution (as in the Quick Example on the previous page)

2. Two real solutions (try, for example, $x^3 + x^2 - x - 1 = 0$)

3. Three real solutions (see the next example)

Example 1 Solving a Cubic

Solve the cubic $2x^3 - 3x^2 - 17x + 30 = 0$.

Solution

First we look for a single solution. Here, $a = 2$ and $d = 30$. The factors of a are ± 1 and ± 2, and the factors of d are $\pm 1, \pm 2, \pm 3, \pm 5, \pm 6, \pm 10, \pm 15$ and ± 30. This gives us a large number of possible ratios: $\pm 1, \pm 2, \pm 3, \pm 5, \pm 6, \pm 10, \pm 15, \pm 30, \pm 1/2, \pm 3/2, \pm 5/2, \pm 15/2$. Undaunted, we first try $x = 1$ and $x = -1$, getting nowhere. So we move on to $x = 2$, and we hit the jackpot, because substituting $x = 2$ gives $16 - 12 - 34 + 30 = 0$. Thus, $(x - 2)$ is a factor. Dividing yields the quotient $2x^2 + x - 15$. Here is the calculation:

$$
\begin{array}{r|l}
 & 2x^2 + x - 15 \\
\hline
x - 2 & 2x^3 - 3x^2 - 17x + 30 \\
 & \underline{2x^3 - 4x^2} \\
 & \qquad x^2 - 17x \\
 & \qquad \underline{x^2 - \ \ 2x} \\
 & \qquad\quad -15x + 30 \\
 & \qquad\quad \underline{-15x + 30} \\
 & \qquad\qquad\qquad 0
\end{array}
$$

Thus,

$$2x^3 - 3x^2 - 17x + 30 = (x - 2)(2x^2 + x - 15) = 0$$

Setting the factors equal to zero gives either $x - 2 = 0$ or $2x^2 + x - 15 = 0$. We could solve the quadratic using the quadratic formula, but luckily, we notice that it factors as

$$2x^2 + x - 15 = (x + 3)(2x - 5)$$

Thus, the solutions are $x = 2$, $x = -3$ and $x = 5/2$.

Solution of Higher-Order Polynomial Equations

Logically speaking, our next step should be a discussion of quartics, then quintics (fifth degree equations), and so on forever. Well, we've got to stop somewhere, and cubics may be as good a place as any. On the other hand, since we've gotten so far, we ought to at least tell you what is known about higher-order polynomials.

Quartics Just as in the case of cubics, there is a formula to find the solutions of quartics.[3]

[3] See, for example, *First Course in the Theory of Equations* by L. E. Dickson, (New York: Wiley, 1922), or *Modern Algebra* by B. L. van der Waerden, (New York: Frederick Ungar, 1953).

Quintics and Beyond All good things must come to an end, we're afraid. It turns out that there is no "quintic formula." In other words, there is no single algebraic formula or collection of algebraic formulas that gives the solutions to all quintics. This question was settled by the Norwegian mathematician Niels Henrik Abel in 1824 after almost 300 years of controversy about this question. (In fact, several notable mathematicians had previously claimed to have devised formulas for solving the quintic, but these were all shot down by other mathematicians—this being one of the favorite pastimes of practitioners of our art.) The same negative answer applies to polynomial equations of degree 6 and higher. It's not that these equations don't have solutions, it's just that they can't be found using algebraic formulas.[4] However, there are certain special classes of polynomial equations that can be solved with algebraic methods. The way of identifying such equations was discovered around 1829 by the French mathematician Évariste Galois.[5]

[4] What we mean by an "algebraic formula" is a formula in the coefficients using the operations of addition, subtraction, multiplication, division, and the taking of radicals. Mathematicians call the use of such formulas in solving polynomial equations "solution by radicals." If you were a math major, you would eventually go on to study this under the heading of Galois Theory.

[5] Both Abel (1802–1829) and Galois (1811–1832) died young. Abel died of tuberculosis at the age of 26, while Galois was killed in a duel at the age of 20.

0.5 EXERCISES

Solve the equations in Exercises 1–12 for x (mentally, if possible).

1. $x+1=0$
2. $x-3=1$
3. $-x+5=0$
4. $2x+4=1$
5. $4x-5=8$
6. $\frac{3}{4}x+1=0$
7. $7x+55=98$
8. $3x+1=x$
9. $x+1=2x+2$
10. $x+1=3x+1$
11. $ax+b=c\ (a\neq 0)$
12. $x-1=cx+d\ (c\neq 1)$

By any method, determine all possible real solutions of each equation in Exercises 13–30. Check your answers by substitution.

13. $2x^2+7x-4=0$
14. $x^2+x+1=0$
15. $x^2-x+1=0$
16. $2x^2-4x+3=0$
17. $2x^2-5=0$
18. $3x^2-1=0$
19. $-x^2-2x-1=0$
20. $2x^2-x-3=0$
21. $\frac{1}{2}x^2-x-\frac{3}{2}=0$
22. $-\frac{1}{2}x^2-\frac{1}{2}x+1=0$
23. $x^2-x=1$
24. $16x^2=-24x-9$
25. $x=2-\frac{1}{x}$
26. $x+4=\frac{1}{x-2}$
27. $x^4-10x^2+9=0$
28. $x^4-2x^2+1=0$
29. $x^4+x^2-1=0$
30. $x^3+2x^2+x=0$

Find all possible real solutions of each equation in Exercises 31–44.

31. $x^3+6x^2+11x+6=0$
32. $x^3-6x^2+12x-8=0$
33. $x^3+4x^2+4x+3=0$
34. $y^3+64=0$
35. $x^3-1=0$
36. $x^3-27=0$
37. $y^3+3y^2+3y+2=0$
38. $y^3-2y^2-2y-3=0$
39. $x^3-x^2-5x+5=0$
40. $x^3-x^2-3x+3=0$
41. $2x^6-x^4-2x^2+1=0$
42. $3x^6-x^4-12x^2+4=0$
43. $(x^2+3x+2)(x^2-5x+6)=0$
44. $(x^2-4x+4)^2(x^2+6x+5)^3=0$

0.6 Solving Miscellaneous Equations

Equations that are not polynomial equations of low degree often arise in calculus. Many of these complicated-looking equations can be solved easily if you remember the following, which we used in the previous section:

Solving an Equation of the Form $P \cdot Q = 0$

If a product is equal to 0, then at least one of the factors must be 0. That is, if $P \cdot Q = 0$, then either $P = 0$ or $Q = 0$.

quick Examples

1. $x^5 - 4x^3 = 0$

$x^3(x^2 - 4) = 0$ — Factor the left-hand side.

Either $x^3 = 0$ or $x^2 - 4 = 0$ — Either $P = 0$ or $Q = 0$.

$x = 0, 2$ or -2 — Solve the individual equations.

2. $(x^2 - 1)(x + 2) + (x^2 - 1)(x + 4) = 0$

$(x^2 - 1)[(x + 2) + (x + 4)] = 0$ — Factor the left-hand side.

$(x^2 - 1)(2x + 6) = 0$

Either $x^2 - 1 = 0$ or $2x + 6 = 0$ — Either $P = 0$ or $Q = 0$.

$x = -3, -1$, or 1 — Solve the individual equations.

Example 1 Solving by Factoring

Solve $12x(x^2 - 4)^5(x^2 + 2)^6 + 12x(x^2 - 4)^6(x^2 + 2)^5 = 0$.

Solution

Again, we start by factoring the left-hand side:

$$\begin{aligned} &12x(x^2 - 4)^5(x^2 + 2)^6 + 12x(x^2 - 4)^6(x^2 + 2)^5 \\ &\quad = 12x(x^2 - 4)^5(x^2 + 2)^5[(x^2 + 2) + (x^2 - 4)] \\ &\quad = 12x(x^2 - 4)^5(x^2 + 2)^5(2x^2 - 2) \\ &\quad = 24x(x^2 - 4)^5(x^2 + 2)^5(x^2 - 1) \end{aligned}$$

Setting this equal to 0, we get:

$$24x(x^2 - 4)^5(x^2 + 2)^5(x^2 - 1) = 0$$

which means that at least one of the factors of this product must be zero. Now it certainly cannot be the 24, but it could be the x: $x = 0$ is one solution. It could also be that

$$(x^2 - 4)^5 = 0$$

or

$$x^2 - 4 = 0$$

which has solutions $x = \pm 2$. Could it be that $(x^2 + 2)^5 = 0$? If so, then $x^2 + 2 = 0$, but this is impossible because $x^2 + 2 \geq 2$, no matter what x is. Finally, it could be that $x^2 - 1 = 0$, which has solutions $x = \pm 1$. This gives us five solutions to the original equation:

$$x = -2, -1, 0, 1, \text{ or } 2$$

Example 2 Solving by Factoring

Solve $(x^2 - 1)(x^2 - 4) = 10$.

Solution Watch out! You may be tempted to say that $x^2 - 1 = 10$ or $x^2 - 4 = 10$, but this does not follow. If two numbers multiply to give you 10, what must they be? There are lots of possibilities: 2 and 5, 1 and 10, $-500{,}000$ and -0.00002 are just a few. The fact that the left-hand side is factored is nearly useless to us if we want to solve this equation. What we will have to do is multiply out, bring the 10 over to the left, and hope that we can factor what we get. Here goes:

$$x^4 - 5x^2 + 4 = 10$$
$$x^4 - 5x^2 - 6 = 0$$
$$(x^2 - 6)(x^2 + 1) = 0$$

(Here we used a sometimes useful trick that we mentioned in Section 3: we treated x^2 like x and x^4 like x^2, so factoring $x^4 - 5x^2 - 6$ is essentially the same as factoring $x^2 - 5x - 6$.) *Now* we are allowed to say that one of the factors must be 0: $x^2 - 6 = 0$ has solutions $x = \pm\sqrt{6} = \pm 2.449\ldots$ and $x^2 + 1 = 0$ has no real solutions. Therefore, we get exactly two solutions, $x = \pm\sqrt{6} = \pm 2.449\ldots$.

To solve equations involving rational expressions, the following rule is very useful.

Solving an Equation of the Form $P/Q = 0$

If $\dfrac{P}{Q} = 0$, then $P = 0$.

How else could a fraction equal 0? If that is not convincing, multiply both sides by Q (which cannot be 0 if the quotient is defined).

quick **Example**

$$\frac{(x+1)(x+2)^2 - (x+1)^2(x+2)}{(x+2)^4} = 0$$

$(x+1)(x+2)^2 - (x+1)^2(x+2) = 0$ — If $\frac{P}{Q} = 0$, then $P = 0$.

$(x+1)(x+2)[(x+2) - (x+1)] = 0$ — Factor.

$(x+1)(x+2)(1) = 0$

Either $x + 1 = 0$ or $x + 2 = 0$

$x = -1$ or $x = -2$

$x = -1$ — $x = -2$ does not make sense in the original equation: it makes the denominator 0. So it is not a solution and $x = -1$ is the only solution.

Example 3 Solving a Rational Equation

Solve $1 - \dfrac{1}{x^2} = 0$.

Solution Write 1 as $\frac{1}{1}$, so that we now have a difference of two rational expressions:

$$\frac{1}{1} - \frac{1}{x^2} = 0$$

To combine these we can put both over a common denominator of x^2, which gives

$$\frac{x^2 - 1}{x^2} = 0$$

Now we can set the numerator, $x^2 - 1$, equal to zero. Thus,

$$x^2 - 1 = 0$$

so

$$(x - 1)(x + 1) = 0$$

giving $x = \pm 1$.

+ *Before we go on . . .* This equation could also have been solved by writing

$$1 = \frac{1}{x^2}$$

and then multiplying both sides by x^2. ■

Example 4 Another Rational Equation

Solve $\dfrac{2x - 1}{x} + \dfrac{3}{x - 2} = 0.$

Solution

We *could* first perform the addition on the left and then set the top equal to 0, but here is another approach. Subtracting the second expression from both sides gives

$$\frac{2x - 1}{x} = \frac{-3}{x - 2}$$

Cross-multiplying [multiplying both sides by both denominators—that is, by $x(x - 2)$] now gives

$$(2x - 1)(x - 2) = -3x$$

so

$$2x^2 - 5x + 2 = -3x$$

Adding $3x$ to both sides gives the quadratic equation

$$2x^2 - 2x + 1 = 0$$

The discriminant is $(-2)^2 - 4 \cdot 2 \cdot 1 = -4 < 0$, so we conclude that there is no real solution.

+ *Before we go on. . .* Notice that when we said that $(2x - 1)(x - 2) = -3x$, we were *not* allowed to conclude that $2x - 1 = -3x$ or $x - 2 = -3x$. ■

Example 5 A Rational Equation with Radicals

Solve $\dfrac{\left(2x\sqrt{x+1} - \frac{x^2}{\sqrt{x+1}}\right)}{x+1} = 0.$

Solution

Setting the top equal to 0 gives

$$2x\sqrt{x+1} - \frac{x^2}{\sqrt{x+1}} = 0$$

This still involves fractions. To get rid of the fractions, we could put everything over a common denominator ($\sqrt{x+1}$) and then set the top equal to 0, or we could multiply the whole equation by that common denominator in the first place to clear fractions. If we do the second, we get

$$2x(x+1) - x^2 = 0$$
$$2x^2 + 2x - x^2 = 0$$
$$x^2 + 2x = 0$$

Factoring,

$$x(x+2) = 0$$

so either $x = 0$ or $x + 2 = 0$, giving us $x = 0$ or $x = -2$. Again, one of these is not really a solution. The problem is that $x = -2$ cannot be substituted into $\sqrt{x+1}$, because we would then have to take the square root of -1, and we are not allowing ourselves to do that. Therefore, $x = 0$ is the only solution.

0.6 EXERCISES

Solve the following equations:

1. $x^4 - 3x^3 = 0$

2. $x^6 - 9x^4 = 0$

3. $x^4 - 4x^2 = -4$

4. $x^4 - x^2 = 6$

5. $(x+1)(x+2) + (x+1)(x+3) = 0$

6. $(x+1)(x+2)^2 + (x+1)^2(x+2) = 0$

7. $(x^2+1)^5(x+3)^4 + (x^2+1)^6(x+3)^3 = 0$

8. $10x(x^2+1)^4(x^3+1)^5 - 10x^2(x^2+1)^5(x^3+1)^4 = 0$

9. $(x^3+1)\sqrt{x+1} - (x^3+1)^2\sqrt{x+1} = 0$

10. $(x^2+1)\sqrt{x+1} - \sqrt{(x+1)^3} = 0$

11. $\sqrt{(x+1)^3} + \sqrt{(x+1)^5} = 0$

12. $(x^2+1)\sqrt[3]{(x+1)^4} - \sqrt[3]{(x+1)^7} = 0$

13. $(x+1)^2(2x+3) - (x+1)(2x+3)^2 = 0$

14. $(x^2-1)^2(x+2)^3 - (x^2-1)^3(x+2)^2 = 0$

15. $\dfrac{(x+1)^2(x+2)^3 - (x+1)^3(x+2)^2}{(x+2)^6} = 0$

16. $\dfrac{6x(x^2+1)^2(x^2+2)^4 - 8x(x^2+1)^3(x^2+2)^3}{(x^2+2)^8} = 0$

17. $\dfrac{2(x^2-1)\sqrt{x^2+1} - \frac{x^4}{\sqrt{x^2+1}}}{x^2+1} = 0$

18. $\dfrac{4x\sqrt{x^3-1} - \frac{3x^4}{\sqrt{x^3-1}}}{x^3-1} = 0$

19. $x - \dfrac{1}{x} = 0$

20. $1 - \dfrac{4}{x^2} = 0$

21. $\dfrac{1}{x} - \dfrac{9}{x^3} = 0$

22. $\dfrac{1}{x^2} - \dfrac{1}{x+1} = 0$

23. $\dfrac{x-4}{x+1} - \dfrac{x}{x-1} = 0$

24. $\dfrac{2x-3}{x-1} - \dfrac{2x+3}{x+1} = 0$

25. $\dfrac{x+4}{x+1} + \dfrac{x+4}{3x} = 0$

26. $\dfrac{2x-3}{x} - \dfrac{2x-3}{x+1} = 0$

1 Functions and Linear Models

CASE STUDY Modeling Spending on Internet Advertising

You are the new director of *Impact Advertising Inc.'s* Internet division, which has enjoyed a steady 0.25% of the Internet advertising market. You have drawn up an ambitious proposal to expand your division in light of your anticipation that Internet advertising will continue to skyrocket. The VP in charge of Financial Affairs feels that current projections (based on a linear model) do not warrant the level of expansion you propose. How can you persuade the VP that those projections do not fit the data convincingly?

Jeff Titcomb/Getty Images

Get a better Grade!
www.thomsonedu.com/login

Logon to your Personalized Study plan to find:

- Section by section tutorials
- A detailed chapter summary
- Additional review exercises
- Graphers, regression utilities, Excel tutorials, and other resources
- Optional section: New Functions from Old: Scaled and Shifted Functions

Introduction

To analyze recent trends in spending on Internet advertising and to make reasonable projections, we need a mathematical model of this spending. Where do we start? To apply mathematics to real-world situations like this, we need a good understanding of basic mathematical concepts. Perhaps the most fundamental of these concepts is that of a function: a relationship that shows how one quantity depends on another. Functions may be described numerically and, often, algebraically. They can also be described graphically—a viewpoint that is extremely useful.

The simplest functions—the ones with the simplest formulas and the simplest graphs—are linear functions. Because of their simplicity, they are also among the most useful functions and can often be used to model real-world situations, at least over short periods of time. In discussing linear functions, we will meet the concepts of slope and rate of change, which are the starting point of the mathematics of change.

algebra **Review**
For this chapter you should be familiar with real numbers and intervals. To review this material, see Chapter 0.

In the last section of this chapter, we discuss *simple linear regression*: construction of linear functions that best fit given collections of data. Regression is used extensively in applied mathematics, statistics, and quantitative methods in business. The inclusion of regression utilities in computer spreadsheets like Excel® makes this powerful mathematical tool readily available for anyone to use.

1.1 Functions from the Numerical and Algebraic Viewpoints

The following table gives the weights of a particular child at various ages in her first year:

Age (months)	0	2	3	4	5	6	9	12
Weight (pounds)	8	9	13	14	16	17	18	19

Let's write $W(0)$ for the child's weight at birth (in pounds), $W(2)$ for her weight at 2 months, and so on (we read $W(0)$ as "W of 0"). Thus, $W(0) = 8$, $W(2) = 9$, $W(3) = 13, \dots,$ $W(12) = 19$. More generally, if we write t for the age of the child (in months) at any time during her first year, then we write $W(t)$ for the weight of the child at age t. We call W a **function** of the variable t, meaning that for each value of t between 0 and 12, W gives us a single corresponding number $W(t)$ (the weight of the child at that age).

In general, we think of a function as a way of producing new objects from old ones. The functions we deal with in this text produce new numbers from old numbers. The numbers we have in mind are the *real* numbers, including not only positive and negative integers and fractions but also numbers like $\sqrt{2}$ or π (see Chapter 0 for more on real numbers). For this reason, the functions we use are called **real-valued functions of a real variable.** For example, the function W takes the child's age in months and returns her weight in pounds at that age (Figure 1).

Figure 1

The variable t is called the **independent** variable, while W is called the **dependent variable** as its value depends on t.

A function may be specified in several different ways. It may be specified **numerically,** by giving the values of the function for a number of values of the independent variable, as in the preceding table. It may be specified **verbally,** as in "Let $W(t)$ be the weight of the child at age t months in her first year."[1] In some cases we may be able to use an algebraic formula to calculate the function, and we say that the function is specified **algebraically.** In Section 1.2 we will see that a function may also be specified **graphically.**

Q: *For which values of t does it make sense to ask for W(t)? In other words, for which ages t is the function W defined?*

A: Since $W(t)$ refers to the weight of the child at age t months *in her first year*, $W(t)$ is defined when t is any number between 0 and 12, that is, when $0 \le t \le 12$. Using interval notation (see Appendix A), we can say that $W(t)$ is defined when t is in the interval [0, 12]. ■

The set of values of the independent variable for which a function is defined is called its **domain** and is a necessary part of the definition of the function. Notice that the preceding table gives the values of $W(t)$ at only some of the infinitely many possible values in the domain [0, 12].

The domain of a function is not always specified explicitly; if no domain is specified for a function f, we take the domain to be the largest set of numbers x for which $f(x)$ makes sense. This "largest possible domain" is sometimes called the **natural domain.**

Here is a summary of the terms we've just introduced.

Functions

A **real-valued function f of a real-valued variable x** assigns to each real number x in a specified set of numbers, called the **domain** of f, a unique real number $f(x)$, read "f of x." The variable x is called the **independent variable,** and f is called the **dependent variable.**

quick **Examples**

1. Let $W(t)$ be the weight (in pounds) at age t months of a particular child during her first year. The independent variable is t, and the dependent variable is W, the child's weight. The domain of W is [0, 12] because it was specified that W gives the child's weight during her first year.

2. Let $f(x) = \dfrac{1}{x}$. The function f is specified algebraically. Some specific values of f are

$$f(2) = \frac{1}{2} \qquad f(3) = \frac{1}{3} \qquad f(-1) = \frac{1}{-1} = -1$$

Here, $f(0)$ is not defined because there is no such number as $1/0$. The natural domain of f consists of all real numbers except zero because $f(x)$ makes sense for all values of x other than $x = 0$.

[1] Specifying a function verbally in this way is useful for understanding what the function is doing, but it gives no numerical information.

Getty Images

Example 1 A Numerically Specified Function: Airline Profits

The following table* shows the cumulative net income of U.S. domestic airlines from January 2000 to the end of year x:

Year x (Since 2000)	0	1	2	3	4
Cumulative Net Income P (\$ Billions)	12	2	−34	−51	−61

Viewing P as a function of x, give its domain and the values $P(0)$, $P(2)$, and $P(4)$. Compute $P(3) - P(2)$ and interpret the result. Also estimate and interpret the value $P(3.5)$.

Solution The domain of P is the set of numbers x with $0 \le x \le 4$—that is, [0, 4].

From the table, we have:

$P(0) = 12$ — \$12 billion net income in 2000

$P(2) = -34$ — \$34 billion cumulative loss from Jan. 2000 to Dec. 2002

$P(4) = -61$ — \$61 billion cumulative loss from Jan. 2000 to Dec. 2004

Also,

$$P(3) - P(2) = -51 - (-34) = -17$$

To interpret the result, notice that:

Cumulative net income through 2003 − Cumulative net income through 2002
= Net income in 2003

Thus, the net income in 2003 was −\$17 billion. In other words, \$17 billion was lost by the airline industry in 2003.

What about $P(3.5)$? Since $P(3) = -51$ and $P(4) = -61$, we estimate that

$P(3.5) \approx -56$ — −56 is midway between −51 and −61.

The process of estimating values for a function between points where it is already known is called **interpolation.**

To interpret $P(3.5)$, note that $P(3)$ represents the accumulated net income through 2003, and $P(4)$ represents the accumulated net income through 2004. Thus, $P(3.5)$ represents the accumulated net income through June, 2003.

*2004 figure is an estimate based on first quarter results. SOURCE: Bureau of Transportation Statistics www.bts.gov/ Nov 15 2004.

+ *Before we go on...* In Example 1 we should not use the table to estimate $P(x)$ for values of x *outside* the domain—say, for $x = 10$. Estimating values for a function outside a range where it is already known is called **extrapolation.** As a general rule, extrapolation is far less reliable than interpolation: predicting the future from current data is difficult, especially given the vagaries of the marketplace. ■

The two functions we have looked at so far were both specified numerically: we were given numerical values of the function evaluated at *certain* values of the independent variable. It would be more useful if we had a formula that would allow us to calculate the value of the function for *any* value of the independent variable we wished, that is, if the function were specified algebraically.

Example 2 An Algebraically Defined Function

Let f be the function specified by

$$f(x) = x^2 - 25x + 15$$

with domain $(-2, 10]$. When $0 \le x \le 4$, this formula gives an approximation of the airline cumulative net income function P in Example 1. Use the formula to calculate $f(0)$, $f(10)$, $f(-1)$, $f(a)$, and $f(x+h)$. Is $f(-2)$ defined?

Solution Let's check first that the values we are asked to calculate are all defined. Since the domain is stated to be $(-2, 10]$, the quantities $f(0)$, $f(10)$, and $f(-1)$ are all defined. The quantities $f(a)$ and $f(x+h)$ will also be defined if a and $x+h$ are understood to be in $(-2, 10]$. However, $f(-2)$ is not defined, since -2 is not in the domain $(-2, 10]$.

If we substitute 0 for x in the formula for $f(x)$, we get

$$f(0) = (0)^2 - 25(0) + 15 = 15$$

so $f(0) = 15$. Similarly,

$$f(10) = (10)^2 - 25(10) + 15 = 100 - 250 + 15 = -135$$

$$f(-1) = (-1)^2 - 25(-1) + 15 = 1 + 25 + 15 = 41$$

$$f(a) = a^2 - 25a + 15 \qquad \text{Substitute } a \text{ for } x.$$

$$f(x+h) = (x+h)^2 - 25(x+h) + 15 \qquad \text{Substitute } (x+h) \text{ for } x.$$

$$= x^2 + 2xh + h^2 - 25x - 25h + 15$$

Note how we placed parentheses around the number at which we are evaluating the function. If we omitted any of these parentheses, we would likely get errors:

$$f(-1) = (-1)^2 - 25(-1) + 15 \ \checkmark \qquad \text{NOT } -1^2 - 25(-1) + 15 \ \times$$

$$f(x+h) = (x+h)^2 - 25(x+h) + 15 \ \checkmark \qquad \text{NOT } x + h^2 - 25(x+h) + 15 \ \times$$

Note that there is nothing magical about the letter x. We might just as well say

$$f(t) = t^2 - 25t + 15$$

which defines *exactly the same function* as $f(x) = x^2 - 25x + 15$. For example, to calculate $f(10)$ from the formula for $f(t)$ we would substitute 10 for t, getting $f(10) = -135$, just as we did using the formula for $f(x)$.

+ *Before we go on...* We said that the function f given in the Example 2 is an approximation of the cumulative net income function P of Example 1. The following table compares some of their values:[2]

x	0	2	3	4
$P(x)$	12	–34	–51	–61
$f(x)$	15	–31	–51	–69

[2] The function f is a "best-fit," or regression quadratic curve based on the data in Example 1 (coefficients are rounded). We will learn more about regression later in this chapter.

We call the algebraic function *f* an **algebraic model** of U.S. airlines' cumulative net income from Jan. 2000 because it uses an algebraic formula to model—or mathematically represent (approximately)—the cumulative net income. The particular kind of algebraic model we used is called a **quadratic model** (see the end of this section for the names of some commonly used models). ■

Q: *The values of f(x) are close to but don't all equal those of P(x). Is this the best we can do with an algebraic model? Can't we get a formula that gives the cumulative net income data exactly?*

A: It is possible to find algebraic formulas that give the exact values of $P(x)$, but such formulas would be far more complicated than the one given, and quite possibly less useful.[3] ■

Note **Equation and Function Notation**
Instead of using *function notation*

$$f(x) = x^2 - 25x + 15 \qquad \text{Function notation}$$

we could use equation notation

$$y = x^2 - 25x + 15 \qquad \text{Equation notation}$$

(the choice of the letter y is a convention) and we say that "y is a function of x." When we write a function in this form, the variable x is the independent variable and y is the dependent variable.

We could also write the above function as $f = x^2 - 25x + 15$, in which case the dependent variable would be f.

using *Technology*

Evaluating a function can be tedious to do by hand, but various technologies make this task easier. See the Technology Guides at the end of the chapter to find out how to create a table like the one in Example 3, using a TI-83/84 or Excel. Alternatively, go online and follow:

Chapter 1
→ Tools
→ Function Evaluator & Grapher

to find a utility you can use to evaluate functions like this.

Example 3 Evaluating a Function with Technology

Evaluate the function $f(x) = -0.4x^2 + 7x - 23$ for $x = 0, 1, 2, \ldots, 10$.

Solution

The first couple of evaluations go as follows:

$$f(0) = -0.4(0)^2 + 7(0) - 23 = -23$$
$$f(1) = -0.4(1)^2 + 7(1) - 23 = -0.4 + 7 - 23 = -16.4$$

Note that to evaluate $-0.4x^2$, we first compute x^2 and then multiply by -0.4. Continuing, we get the following table.

x	0	1	2	3	4	5	6	7	8	9	10
$f(x)$	−23	−16.4	−10.6	−5.6	−1.4	2	4.6	6.4	7.4	7.6	7

Sometimes, as in Example 4, we need to use several formulas to specify a single function.

[3] One reason that more complex formulas are often less realistic than simple ones is that it is often random phenomena in the real world, rather than algebraic relationships, that cause data to fluctuate. Attempting to model these random fluctuations using algebraic formulas amounts to imposing mathematical structure where structure does not exist.

using Technology

See the Technology Guides at the end of the chapter to see how to evaluate functions like this using a TI-83/84 or Excel. The techniques shown there work for other technologies as well, including the function evaluator that you can find online. Follow:

Chapter 1
→ Tools
→ Function Evaluator & Grapher

Example 4 A Piecewise-Defined Function: EBAY Stock

The price $V(t)$ in dollars of EBAY stock during the 10-week period starting July 1, 2004 can be approximated by the following function of time t in weeks ($t = 0$ represents July 1):*

$$V(t) = \begin{cases} 90 - 4t & \text{if } 0 \le t \le 5 \\ 60 + 2t & \text{if } 5 < t \le 20 \end{cases}$$

What was the approximate price of EBAY stock after 1 week, after 5 weeks, and after 10 weeks?

Solution

We evaluate the given function at the corresponding value of t:

$t = 1$: $V(1) = 90 - 4(1) = 86$ We use the first formula since $0 \le t \le 5$.

$t = 5$: $V(5) = 90 - 4(5) = 70$ We use the first formula since $0 \le t \le 5$.

$t = 10$: $V(10) = 60 + 2(10) = 80$ We use the second formula since $5 < t \le 20$.

Thus, the price of EBAY stock was \$86 after 1 week, \$70 after 5 weeks, and \$80 after 10 weeks.

* Source for data: http://money.excite.com, November, 2004

The functions we used in Examples 1–4 above are **mathematical models** of real-life situations, because they model, or represent, situations in mathematical terms.

Mathematical Modeling

To mathematically model a situation means to represent it in mathematical terms. The particular representation used is called a **mathematical model** of the situation. Mathematical models do not always represent a situation perfectly or completely. Some (like Example 2) represent a situation only approximately, whereas others represent only some aspects of the situation.

quick Examples

Situation	***Model***
1. Albano's bank balance is twice Bravo's.	$a = 2b$ (a = Albano's balance, b = Bravo's)
2. The temperature is now 10°F and increasing by 20° per hour.	$T(t) = 10 + 20t$ (t = time in hours, T = temperature)
3. The volume of a rectangular solid with square base is obtained by multiplying the area of its base by its height.	$V = x^2h$ (h = height, x = length of a side of the base)
4. U.S. airlines' cumulative net income	The table in Example 1 is a **numerical model** of U.S. airlines' income. The function in Example 2 is an **algebraic model** of U.S. airlines' income.
5. EBAY stock price	Example 4 gives a **piecewise algebraic model** of the EBAY stock price.

Table 1 lists some common types of functions that are often used to model real world situations.

Table **1** Common Types of Algebraic Functions

	Type of Function	*Example*
Linear	$f(x) = mx + b$ m, b constant	$f(x) = 3x - 2$ Technology format: `3*x - 2`
Quadratic	$f(x) = ax^2 + bx + c$ a, b, c constant $(a \neq 0)$	$f(x) = -3x^2 + x - 1$ Technology format: `-3*x^2 + x - 1`
Cubic	$f(x) = ax^3 + bx^2 + cx + d$ a, b, c, d constant $(a \neq 0)$	$f(x) = 2x^3 - 3x^2 + x - 1$ Technology format: `2*x^3 - 3*x^2 + x - 1`
Polynomial	$f(x) = ax^n + bx^{n-1} + ... + rx + s$ $a, b, ..., r, s$ constant (Includes all of the above functions)	All the above, and $f(x) = x^6 - x^4 + x - 3$ Technology format: `x^6 - x^4 + x - 3`
Exponential	$f(x) = Ab^x$ A, b constant (b positive)	$f(x) = 3(2^x)$ Technology format: `3*2^x`
Rational	$f(x) = \dfrac{P(x)}{Q(x)}$ $P(x)$ and $Q(x)$ polynomials	$f(x) = \dfrac{x^2 - 1}{2x + 5}$ Technology format: `(x^2 - 1)/(2*x + 5)`

Functions and models other than linear ones are called **nonlinear.**

1.1 EXERCISES

● denotes basic skills exercises

tech Ex indicates exercises that should be solved using technology

In Exercises 1–4, evaluate or estimate each expression based on the following table. hint [see Example 1]

x	−3	−2	−1	0	1	2	3
$f(x)$	1	2	4	2	1	0.5	0.25

1. ● **a.** $f(0)$ **b.** $f(2)$

2. ● **a.** $f(-1)$ **b.** $f(1)$

3. ● **a.** $f(2) - f(-2)$ **b.** $f(-1)f(-2)$ **c.** $-2f(-1)$

4. ● **a.** $f(1) - f(-1)$ **b.** $f(1)f(-2)$ **c.** $3f(-2)$

5. ● Given $f(x) = 4x - 3$, find **a.** $f(-1)$ **b.** $f(0)$ **c.** $f(1)$ **d.** $f(y)$ **e.** $f(a+b)$ hint [see Example 2]

6. ● Given $f(x) = -3x + 4$, find **a.** $f(-1)$ **b.** $f(0)$ **c.** $f(1)$ **d.** $f(y)$ **e.** $f(a+b)$

7. ● Given $f(x) = x^2 + 2x + 3$, find **a.** $f(0)$ **b.** $f(1)$ **c.** $f(-1)$ **d.** $f(-3)$ **e.** $f(a)$ **f.** $f(x+h)$

8. ● Given $g(x) = 2x^2 - x + 1$, find **a.** $g(0)$ **b.** $g(-1)$ **c.** $g(r)$ **d.** $g(x+h)$

9. ● Given $g(s) = s^2 + \dfrac{1}{s}$, find **a.** $g(1)$ **b.** $g(-1)$ **c.** $g(4)$ **d.** $g(x)$ **e.** $g(s+h)$ **f.** $g(s+h) - g(s)$

10. ● Given $h(r) = \dfrac{1}{r+4}$, find **a.** $h(0)$ **b.** $h(-3)$ **c.** $h(-5)$ **d.** $h(x^2)$ **e.** $h(x^2+1)$ **f.** $h(x^2) + 1$

11. ● Given $f(t) = \begin{cases} -t & \text{if } t < 0 \\ t^2 & \text{if } 0 \le t < 4 \\ t & \text{if } t \ge 4 \end{cases}$

find **a.** $f(-1)$ **b.** $f(1)$ **c.** $f(4) - f(2)$ **d.** $f(3)f(-3)$ hint [see Example 4]

12. ● Given $f(t) = \begin{cases} t-1 & \text{if } t \le 1 \\ 2t & \text{if } 1 < t < 5 \\ t^3 & \text{if } t \ge 5 \end{cases}$

find **a.** $f(0)$ **b.** $f(1)$ **c.** $f(4) - f(2)$
d. $f(5) + f(-5)$

In Exercises 13–16, say whether $f(x)$ is defined for the given values of x. If it is defined, give its value.

13. ● $f(x) = x - \dfrac{1}{x^2}$, with domain $(0, +\infty)$ **a.** $x = 4$
b. $x = 0$ **c.** $x = -1$

14. ● $f(x) = \dfrac{2}{x} - x^2$, with domain $[2, +\infty)$
a. $x = 4$ **b.** $x = 0$ **c.** $x = 1$

15. ● $f(x) = \sqrt{x+10}$, with domain $[-10, 0)$
a. $x = 0$ **b.** $x = 9$ **c.** $x = -10$

16. ● $f(x) = \sqrt{9 - x^2}$, with domain $(-3, 3)$
a. $x = 0$ **b.** $x = 3$ **c.** $x = -3$

In Exercises 17–20, find and simplify (a) $f(x+h) - f(x)$ (b) $\dfrac{f(x+h) - f(x)}{h}$

17. $f(x) = x^2$
18. $f(x) = 3x - 1$
19. $f(x) = 2 - x^2$
20. $f(x) = x^2 + x$

In Exercises 21–24, first give the technology formula for the given function and then use technology to evaluate the function for the given values of x (when defined there).

21. tech Ex $f(x) = 0.1x^2 - 4x + 5$; $x = 0, 1, \ldots, 10$
22. tech Ex $g(x) = 0.4x^2 - 6x - 0.1$; $x = -5, -4, \ldots, 4, 5$
23. tech Ex $h(x) = \dfrac{x^2 - 1}{x^2 + 1}$; $x = 0.5, 1.5, 2.5, \ldots, 10.5$
(Round all answers to four decimal places.)
24. tech Ex $r(x) = \dfrac{2x^2 + 1}{2x^2 - 1}$; $x = -1, 0, 1, \ldots, 9$ (Round all answers to four decimal places.)

Applications

25. ● ***Employment*** The following table lists the approximate number of people employed in the U.S. during the period 1995–2001, on July 1 of each year[4] ($t = 5$ represents 1995):

Year t	5	6	7	8	9	10	11
Employment $P(t)$ (Millions)	117	120	123	125	130	132	132

a. Find or estimate $P(5)$, $P(10)$, and $P(9.5)$. Interpret your answers.
b. What is the domain of P?

[4] The given values represent nonfarm employment, and are approximate. SOURCE: Bureau of Labor Statistics/*The New York Times*, December 17, 2001, p. C3.

26. ● ***Cell Phone Sales*** The following table lists the net sales (after-tax revenue) at the Finnish cell phone company Nokia for each year in the period 1995–2001[5] ($t = 5$ represents 1995):

Year t	5	6	7	8	9	10	11
Nokia Net Sales $P(t)$ (Billions of Dollars)	8	8	10	16	20	27	28

a. Find or estimate $P(5)$, $P(10)$, and $P(7.5)$. Interpret your answers.
b. What is the domain of P?

27. ● ***Trade with China*** The value of U.S. trade with China from 1994 through 2004 can be approximated by

$$C(t) = 3t^2 - 7t + 50 \text{ billion dollars}$$

(t is time in years since 1994).[6]

a. Find an appropriate domain of C. Is $t \ge 0$ an appropriate domain? Why or why not?
b. Compute $C(10)$. What does the answer say about trade with China?

28. ● ***Scientific Research*** The number of research articles in *Physics Review* that were written by researchers in the U.S. from 1983 through 2003 can be approximated by

$$A(t) = -0.01t^2 + 0.24t + 3.4 \text{ hundred articles}$$

(t is time in years since 1983).[7]

a. Find an appropriate domain of A. Is $t \le 20$ an appropriate domain? Why or why not?
b. Compute $A(10)$. What does the answer say about the number of research articles?

29. ● ***Spending on Corrections in the 90s*** The following table shows the annual spending by all states in the U.S. on corrections ($t = 0$ represents the year 1990):[8]

Year (t)	0	2	4	6	7
Spending ($ billion)	16	18	22	28	30

a. Which of the following functions best fits the given data? (*Warning*: none of them fits exactly, but one fits more closely than the others.)
(1) $S(t) = -0.2t^2 + t + 16$
(2) $S(t) = 0.2t^2 + t + 16$
(3) $S(t) = t + 16$

[5] SOURCE: Nokia/*New York Times*, February 6, 2002, p. A3.
[6] Based on a regression by the authors. Source for data: U.S. Census Bureau/*New York Times*, September 23, 2004, p. C1.
[7] Based on a regression by the authors. Source for data: The Americal Physical Society/*New York Times*, May 3, 2003, p. A1.
[8] Data are rounded. SOURCE: National Association of State Budget Officers/*The New York Times*, February 28, 1999, p. A1.

b. Use your answer to part (a) to "predict" spending on corrections in 1998, assuming that the trend continued.

30. ● ***Spending on Corrections in the 90s*** Repeat Exercise 29, this time choosing from the following functions:

(1) $S(t) = 16 + 2t$

(2) $S(t) = 16 + t + 0.5t^2$

(3) $S(t) = 16 + t - 0.5t^2$

31. ***Demand*** The demand for Sigma Mu Fraternity plastic brownie dishes is

$$q(p) = 361{,}201 - (p+1)^2$$

where q represents the number of brownie dishes Sigma Mu can sell each month at a price of p. Use this function to determine

a. The number of brownie dishes Sigma Mu can sell each month if the price is set at 50¢,
b. The number of brownie dishes they can unload each month if they give them away,
c. The lowest price at which Sigma Mu will be unable to sell any dishes.

32. ***Revenue*** The total weekly revenue earned at Royal Ruby Retailers is given by

$$R(p) = -\frac{4}{3}p^2 + 80p$$

where p is the price (in dollars) RRR charges per ruby. Use this function to determine

a. The weekly revenue, to the nearest dollar, when the price is set at $20/ruby,
b. The weekly revenue, to the nearest dollar, when the price is set at $200/ruby (interpret your result).
c. The price RRR should charge in order to obtain a weekly revenue of $1200.

33. ● ***Processor Speeds*** The processor speed, in megahertz, of Intel processors could be approximated by the following function of time t in years since the start of 1995:[9]

$$P(t) = \begin{cases} 75t + 200 & \text{if } 0 \le t \le 4 \\ 600t - 1900 & \text{if } 4 < t \le 9 \end{cases}$$

a. Evaluate $P(0)$, $P(4)$, and $P(5)$ and interpret the results.
b. Use the model to estimate when processor speeds first hit 2.0 gigahertz (1 gigahertz = 1000 megahertz).
c. tech Ex Use technology to generate a table of values for $P(t)$ with $t = 0, 1, \ldots, 9$.

34. ● ***Leading Economic Indicators*** The value of the Conference Board Index of 10 economic indicators in the U.S. could be approximated by the following function of time t in months since the end of December, 2002:[10]

$$E(t) = \begin{cases} 0.4t + 110 & \text{if } 6 \le t \le 15 \\ -0.2t + 119 & \text{if } 15 < t \le 20 \end{cases}$$

a. Estimate $E(10)$, $E(15)$, and $E(20)$ and interpret the results.
b. Use the model to estimate when—prior to March, 2004—the index was 115.
c. tech Ex Use technology to generate a table of values for $E(t)$ with $t = 6, 7, \ldots, 20$.

35. tech Ex ***Television Advertising*** The cost, in millions of dollars, of a 30-second television ad during the Super Bowl from 1990 to 2001 can be approximated by the following piecewise linear function ($t = 0$ represents 1990):[11]

$$C(t) = \begin{cases} 0.08t + 0.6 & \text{if } 0 \le t < 8 \\ 0.355t - 1.6 & \text{if } 8 \le t \le 11 \end{cases}$$

a. Give the technology formula for C and complete the following table of values of the function C.

t	0	1	2	3	4	5	6	7	8	9	10	11
$C(t)$												

b. Between 1998 and 2000, the cost of a Super Bowl ad was increasing at a rate of $____ million per year

36. tech Ex ***Internet Purchases*** The percentage $p(t)$ of new car buyers who used the Internet for research or purchase since 1997 is given by the following function[12] ($t = 0$ represents 1997):

$$p(t) = \begin{cases} 10t + 15 & \text{if } 0 \le t < 1 \\ 15t + 10 & \text{if } 1 \le t \le 4 \end{cases}$$

a. Give the technology formula for p and complete the following table of values of the function p.

t	0	0.5	1	1.5	2	2.5	3	3.5	4
$p(t)$									

b. Between 1998 and 2000, the percentage of buyers of new cars who used the Internet for research or purchase was increasing at a rate of ____% per year

37. ***Income Taxes*** The U.S. Federal income tax is a function of taxable income. Write T for the tax owed on a taxable income

[9] SOURCE: Sandpile.org/*New York Times*, May 17, 2004, p. C1.

[10] SOURCE: The Conference Board/*New York Times*, November 19, 2004, p. C7.

[11] SOURCE: *New York Times*, January 26, 2001, p. C1.

[12] Model is based on data through 2000 (the 2000 value is estimated). SOURCE: J. D. Power Associates/*The New York Times*, January 25, 2000, p. C1.

of I dollars. For tax year 2005, the function T for a single taxpayer was specified as follows:

If your taxable income was Over—	*But not over—*	*Your tax is*	*of the amount over—*
$0	7,300	.... 10%	**$0**
7,300	29,700	**$730.00 + 15%**	**7,300**
29,700	71,950	**4,090.00 + 25%**	**29,700**
71,950	150,150	**14,652.50 + 28%**	**71,950**
150,150	326,450	**36,548.50 + 33%**	**150,150**
326,450	....	**94,727.50 + 35%**	**326,450**

What was the tax owed by a single taxpayer on a taxable income of $26,000? On a taxable income of $65,000?

38. ***Income Taxes*** The income tax function T in Exercise 37 can also be written in the following form:

$$T(I) = \begin{cases} 0.10I & \text{if } 0 < I \le 7{,}300 \\ 730 + 0.15(I - 7{,}300) & \text{if } 7{,}300 < I \le 29{,}700 \\ 4{,}090.00 + 0.25(I - 29{,}700) & \text{if } 29{,}700 < I \le 71{,}950 \\ 14{,}652.50 + 0.28(I - 71{,}950) & \text{if } 71{,}950 < I \le 150{,}150 \\ 36{,}548.50 + 0.33(I - 150{,}150) & \text{if } 150{,}150 < I \le 326{,}450 \\ 94{,}727.50 + 0.35(I - 326{,}450) & \text{if } I > 326{,}450 \end{cases}$$

What was the tax owed by a single taxpayer on a taxable income of $25,000? On a taxable income of $125,000?

39. ***Toxic Waste Treatment*** The cost of treating waste by removing PCPs goes up rapidly as the quantity of PCPs removed goes up. Here is a possible model:

$$C(q) = 2000 + 100q^2$$

where q is the reduction in toxicity (in pounds of PCPs removed per day) and $C(q)$ is the daily cost (in dollars) of this reduction.

a. Find the cost of removing 10 pounds of PCPs per day.

b. Government subsidies for toxic waste cleanup amount to

$$S(q) = 500q$$

where q is as above and $S(q)$ is the daily dollar subsidy. Calculate the net cost function $N(q)$ (the cost of removing q pounds of PCPs per day after the subsidy is taken into account), given the cost function and subsidy above, and find the net cost of removing 20 pounds of PCPs per day.

40. ***Dental Plans*** A company pays for its employees' dental coverage at an annual cost C given by

$$C(q) = 1000 + 100\sqrt{q}$$

where q is the number of employees covered and $C(q)$ is the annual cost in dollars.

a. If the company has 100 employees, find its annual outlay for dental coverage.

b. Assuming that the government subsidizes coverage by an annual dollar amount of

$$S(q) = 200q$$

calculate the net cost function $N(q)$ to the company, and calculate the net cost of subsidizing its 100 employees. Comment on your answer.

41. tech Ex ***Acquisition of Language*** The percentage $p(t)$ of children who can speak at least single words by the age of t months can be approximated by the equation[13]

$$p(t) = 100\left(1 - \frac{12{,}200}{t^{4.48}}\right) \quad (t \ge 8.5)$$

a. Give a technology formula for p.

b. Create a table of values of p for $t = 9, 10, \dots, 20$ (rounding answers to one decimal place).

c. What percentage of children can speak at least single words by the age of 12 months?

d. By what age are 90% or more children speaking at least single words?

42. tech Ex ***Acquisition of Language*** The percentage $p(t)$ of children who can speak in sentences of five or more words by the age of t months can be approximated by the equation[14]

$$p(t) = 100\left(1 - \frac{5.27 \times 10^{17}}{t^{12}}\right) \quad (t \ge 30)$$

a. Give a technology formula for p.

b. Create a table of values of p for $t = 30, 31, \dots, 40$ (rounding answers to one decimal place).

c. What percentage of children can speak in sentences of five or more words by the age of 36 months?

d. By what age are 75% or more children speaking in sentences of five or more words?

Communication and Reasoning Exercises

43. ● If the market price m of gold varies with time t, then the independent variable is ___ and the dependent variable is ___.

44. ● Complete the following sentence: If weekly profit P is specified as a function of selling price s, then the independent variable is ___ and the dependent variable is ___.

45. ● Complete the following: The function notation for the equation $y = 4x^2 - 2$ is ___.

46. ● Complete the following: The equation notation for $C(t) = -0.34t^2 + 0.1t$ is ___.

[13] The model is the authors' and is based on data presented in the article *The Emergence of Intelligence* by William H. Calvin, *Scientific American*, October, 1994, pp. 101–107.

[14] Ibid.

47. You now have 200 sound files on your hard drive, and this number is increasing by 10 sound files each day. Find a mathematical model for this situation.

48. The amount of free space left on your hard drive is now 50 gigabytes (GB) and is decreasing by 5 GB/month. Find a mathematical model for this situation.

49. Why is the following assertion false? "If $f(x) = x^2 - 1$, then $f(x + h) = x^2 + h - 1$."

50. Why is the following assertion false? "If $f(2) = 2$ and $f(4) = 4$, then $f(3) = 3$."

51. True or false: Every function can be specified numerically.

52. Which supplies more information about a situation: a numerical model or an algebraic model?

● basic skills tech Ex technology exercise

1.2 Functions from the Graphical Viewpoint

Consider again the function W discussed in Section 1.1, giving a child's weight during her first year. If we represent the data given in Section 1.1 graphically by plotting the given pairs of numbers $(t, W(t))$, we get Figure 2. (We have connected successive points by line segments.)

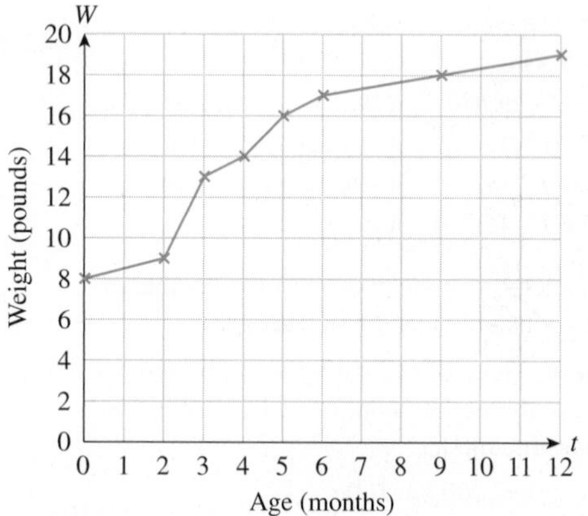

Figure **2**

Suppose now that we had only the graph without the table of data given in Section 1.1. We could use the graph to find values of W. For instance, to find $W(9)$ from the graph we do the following:

1. Find the desired value of t at the bottom of the graph ($t = 9$ in this case).
2. Estimate the height (W-coordinate) of the corresponding point on the graph (18 in this case).

Thus, $W(9) \approx 18$ pounds.[15]

We say that Figure 2 specifies the function W **graphically.** The graph is not a very accurate specification of W; the actual weight of the child would follow a smooth curve

[15] In a graphically defined function, we can never know the y-coordinates of points exactly; no matter how accurately a graph is drawn, we can only obtain *approximate* values of the coordinates of points. That is why we have been using the word *estimate* rather than *calculate* and why we say "$W(9) \approx 18$" rather than "$W(9) = 18$."

rather than a jagged line. However, the jagged line is useful in that it permits us to interpolate: for instance, we can estimate that $W(1) \approx 8.5$ pounds.

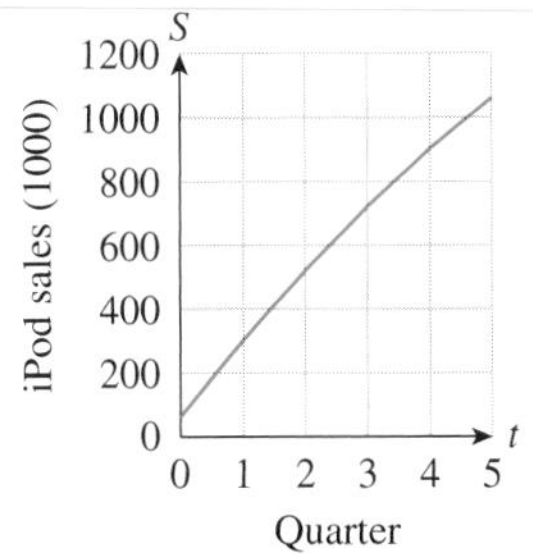

Figure 3

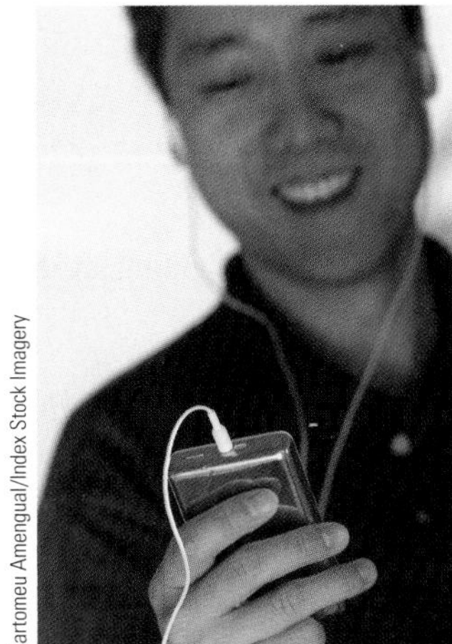

Example 1 A Function Specified Graphically: iPod Sales

Figure 3 shows the approximate quarterly sales of iPods for the second quarter in 2003 through the third quarter in 2004 ($t = 0$ represents the second quarter of 2003).*

Estimate and interpret $S(1)$, $S(4)$, and $S(5)$. What is the domain of S?

Solution We carefully estimate the S-coordinates of the points with t-coordinates 1, 4, and 5.

$$S(1) \approx 300$$

meaning that iPod sales in the third quarter of 2003 ($t = 1$) were approximately 300,000 units.

$$S(4) \approx 900$$

meaning that iPod sales in the second quarter of 2004 ($t = 4$) were approximately 900,000 units.

$$S(5) \approx 1050$$

meaning that iPod sales in the third quarter of 2004 ($t = 5$) were approximately 1,050,000 units.

The domain of S is the set of all values of t for which $S(t)$ is defined: $0 \le t \le 5$, or $[0, 5]$.

* Accurate sales figures are available from Apple financial statements, www.apple.com

Sometimes we are interested in drawing the graph of a function that has been specified in some other way—perhaps numerically or algebraically. We do this by plotting points with coordinates $(x, f(x))$.[16] Here is the formal definition of a graph.

Graph of a Function

The **graph of the function f** is the set of all points $(x, f(x))$ in the xy plane, where *we restrict the values of x to lie in the domain of f.*

quick Example

To sketch the graph of the function

$$f(x) = x^2 \qquad \text{Function notation}$$

or

$$y = x^2 \qquad \text{Equation notation}$$

with domain the set of all real numbers, first choose some convenient values of x in the domain and compute the corresponding y-coordinates.

[16] Graphing utilities typically draw graphs by plotting and connecting a large number of points.

x	−3	−2	−1	0	1	2	3
$y = x^2$	9	4	1	0	1	4	9

Plotting these points gives the picture on the left, suggesting the graph on the right.*

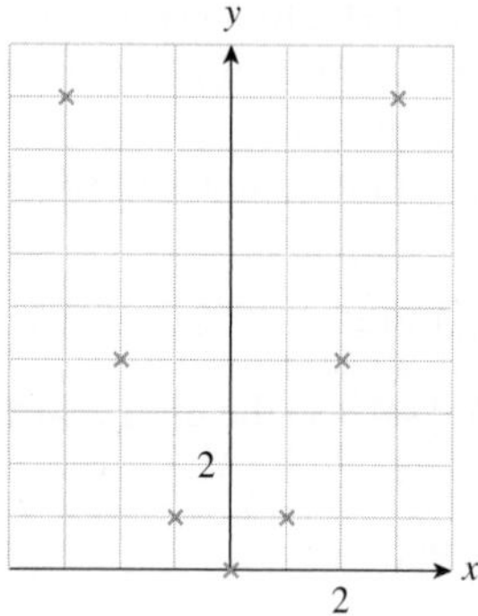

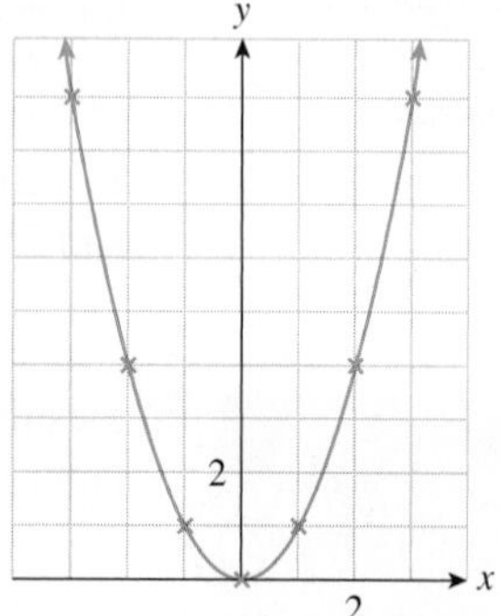

(This particular curve happens to be called a **parabola,** and its lowest point, at the origin, is called its **vertex.**)

* If you plot more points, you will find that they lie on a smooth curve as shown. That is why we did not use line segments to connect the points.

To draw the graph of a function, we often do as we did in the Quick Example above: We plot points of the form $(x, f(x))$ for several values of x in the domain of f, until we can get a good idea of the shape of the entire graph. (Calculus can give us information that allows us to draw a graph with relatively few points plotted.)

Example 2 Drawing the Graph of a Function: Web-Site Revenue

The monthly revenue† R from users logging on to your gaming site depends on the monthly access fee p you charge according to the formula

$$R(p) = -5600p^2 + 14{,}000p \qquad (0 \le p \le 2.5)$$

(R and p are in dollars.) Sketch the graph of R. Find the access fee that will result in the largest monthly revenue.

† The **revenue** resulting from one or more business transactions is the total payment received, sometimes called the gross proceeds.

using Technology

As the name suggests, graphing calculators are designed for graphing functions. Excel is also very good at drawing graphs. See the Technology Guides at the end of the chapter to find out how to graph functions using a TI-83/84 or Excel. Alternatively, there are several graphers available online.

Follow:

Chapter 1
→ Tools

and then click on any of the following:

Function Evaluator & Grapher	Gives a small graph and also values
Java Graphing Utility	A high-quality Java grapher
Excel Graphing Utility	An Excel sheet that graphs*

*Since the Excel grapher requires macros, make sure that macros are *enabled* when Excel prompts you. If macros are disabled, the grapher will not work.

Solution To sketch the graph of R by hand, we plot points of the form $(p, R(p))$ for several values of p in the domain $[0, 2.5]$ of R. First, we calculate several points:

p	0	0.5	1	1.5	2	2.5
$R(p) = -5600p^2 + 14{,}000p$	0	5600	8400	8400	5600	0

Graphing these points gives the graph shown in Figure 4(a), suggesting the parabola shown in Figure 4(b).

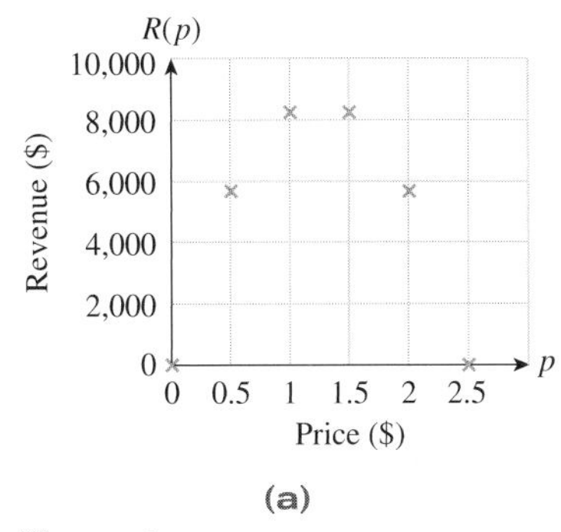

(a)

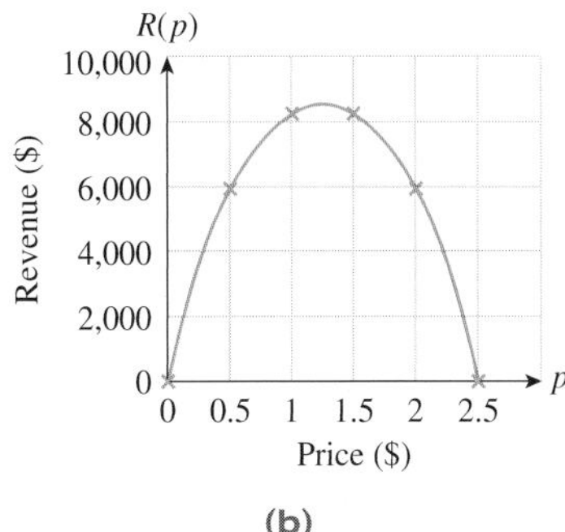

(b)

Figure 4

The revenue graph appears to reach its highest point when $p = 1.25$, so setting the access fee at \$1.25 appears to result in the largest monthly revenue.*

* We are hedging our language with words like *suggesting* and *appears* because the few points we have plotted don't, by themselves, allow us to draw these conclusions with certainty.

Note **Switching Between Equation and Function Notation**

As we discussed after Example 2 in Section 1.1, we can write the function R in Example 2 above in equation notation as

$$R = -5600p^2 + 14{,}000p \qquad \text{Equation notation}$$

The independent variable is p, and the dependent variable is R. Function notation and equation notation, using the same letter for the function name and the dependent variable, are often used interchangeably. It is important to be able to switch back and forth easily from function notation to equation notation.

Vertical Line Test

Every point in the graph of a function has the form $(x, f(x))$ for some x in the domain of f. Since f assigns a *single* value $f(x)$ to each value of x in the domain, it follows that, in the graph of f, there should be only one y corresponding to any such value of x—namely, $y = f(x)$. In other words, *the graph of a function cannot contain two or more points with the same x-coordinate—that is, two or more points on the same vertical line.*

On the other hand, a vertical line at a value of x not in the domain will not contain any points in the graph. This gives us the following rule:

Vertical-Line Test

For a graph to be the graph of a function, every vertical line must intersect the graph in *at most* one point.

quick **Examples**

As illustrated below, only graph B passes the vertical line test, so only graph B is the graph of a function.

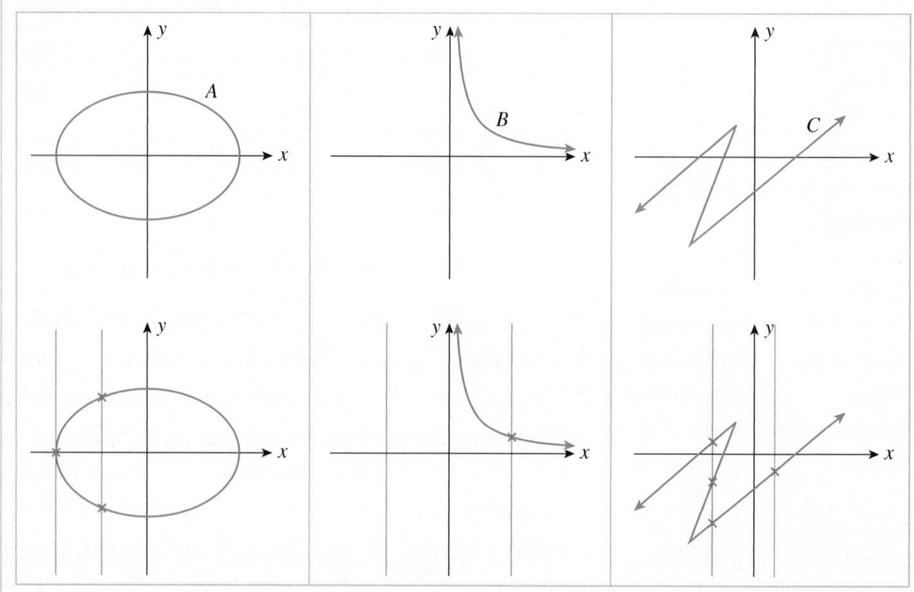

Graphing Piecewise-Defined Functions

Let us revisit the EBAY stock example from Section 1.1.

using *Technology*

To graph the function V using technology, consult the Technology Guides for Example 4 of Section 1.1 to see how to enter this piecewise-defined function. The Technology Guides for Example 2 of this section show how to then draw the graph.

Example 3 Graphing a Piecewise-Defined Function: EBAY Stock

The price $V(t)$ in dollars of EBAY stock during the 10-week period starting July 1, 2004 can be approximated by the following function of time t in weeks ($t = 0$ represents July 1):*

$$V(t) = \begin{cases} 90 - 4t & \text{if } 0 \le t \le 5 \\ 60 + 2t & \text{if } 5 < t \le 20 \end{cases}$$

Graph the function V.

Solution As in Example 2, we can sketch the graph of V by hand by computing $V(t)$ for a number of values of t, plotting these points on the graph, and then connecting them.

* Source for data: http://money.excite.com, November, 2004

t	0	5	10	15	20
$V(t)$	90	70	80	90	100

First formula (0–5) Second formula (10–20)

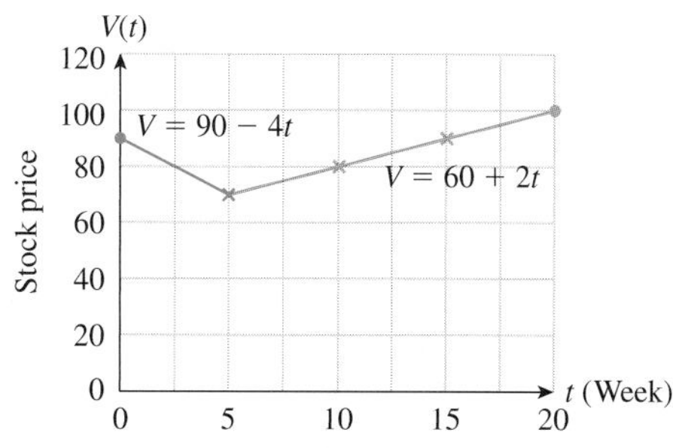

Figure **5**

The graph (Figure 5) has the following features:

1. The first formula (the descending line) is used for $0 \le t \le 5$.

2. The second formula (the ascending line) is used for $5 < t \le 20$.

3. The domain is [0, 20], so the graph is cut off at $t = 0$ and $t = 20$.

4. The heavy dots at the ends indicate the endpoints of the domain.

using *Technology*

See the Technology Guide at the end of the chapter for comments on graphing this function using a TI-83/84 or Excel. The formula with inequalities used to graph this function in Excel also works on the various graphers online.

Example **4** Graphing More Complicated Piecewise-Defined Functions

Graph the function f specified by

$$f(x) = \begin{cases} -1 & \text{if } -4 \le x < -1 \\ x & \text{if } -1 \le x \le 1 \\ x^2 - 1 & \text{if } 1 < x \le 2 \end{cases}$$

Solution The domain of f is $[-4, 2]$, since $f(x)$ is only specified when $-4 \le x \le 2$. Further, the function changes formulas when $x = -1$ and $x = 1$.

To sketch the graph by hand, we first sketch the three graphs $y = -1$, $y = x$, and $y = x^2 - 1$, and then use the appropriate portion of each (Figure 6).

Note that solid dots indicate points on the graph, whereas the open dots indicate points *not* on the graph. For example, when $x = 1$, the inequalities in the formula tell us that we are to use the middle formula (x) rather than the bottom one ($x^2 - 1$). Thus, $f(1) = 1$, not 0, so we place a solid dot at (1, 1) and an open dot at (1, 0).

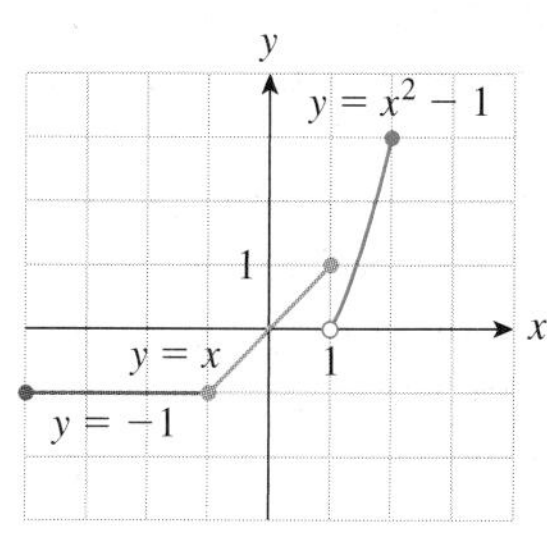

Figure **6**

We end this section with a list of some useful types of functions and their graphs (Table 2).

New Functions from Old: Scaled and Shifted Functions (Optional Section)

Online, follow:

Chapter 1
→ Online Text
→ New Functions From Old: Scaled and Shifted Functions

where you will find complete interactive text, examples, and exercises on scaling and translating the graph of a function by changing the formula.

Table **2** Functions and Their Graphs

Type of Function	*Examples*	
Linear $f(x) = mx + b$ m, b constant Graphs of linear functions are straight lines.	$y = x$ 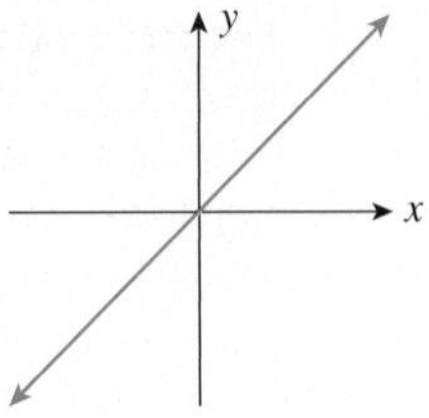	$y = -2x + 2$ 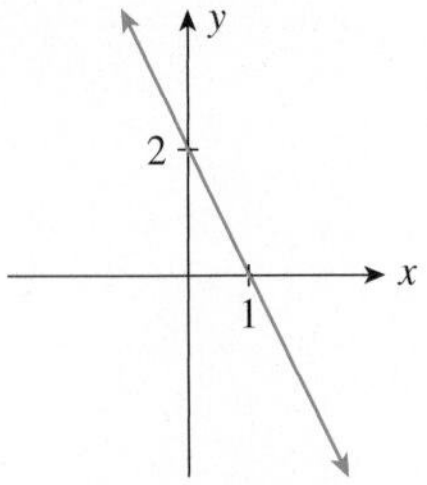
Quadratic $f(x) = ax^2 + bx + c$ a, b, c constant $(a \neq 0)$ Graphs of quadratic functions are called **parabolas.**	$y = x^2$ 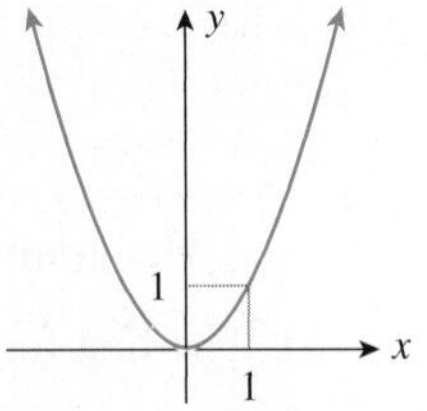	$y = -2x^2 + 2x + 4$ 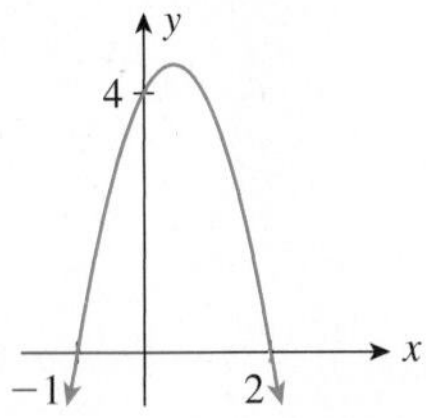
Technology formulas:	`x^2`	`-2*x^2 + 2*x + 4`
Cubic $f(x) = ax^3 + bx^2 + cx + d$ a, b, c, d constant $(a \neq 0)$	$y = x^3$ 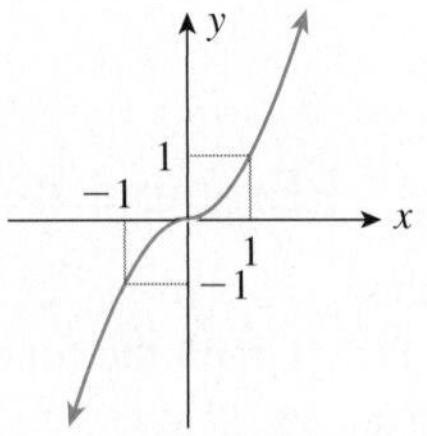	$y = -x^3 + 3x^2 + 1$ 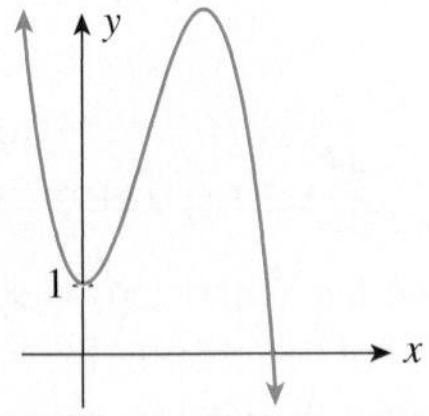
Technology formulas:	`x^3`	`-x^3 + 3*x^2 + 1`
Exponential $f(x) = Ab^x$ A, b constant $(b > 0$ and $b \neq 1)$	$y = 2^x$ 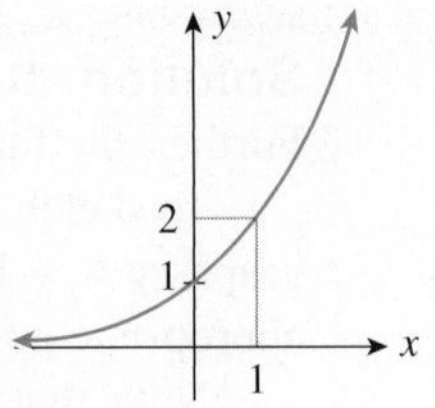	$y = 4(0.5)^x$ 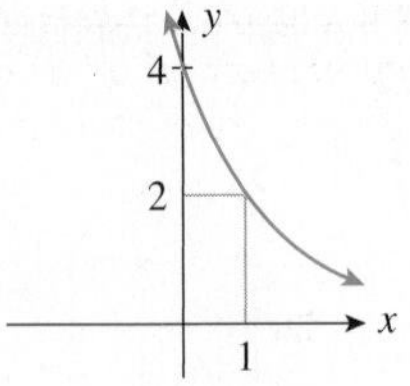
Technology formulas:	`2^x`	`4*0.5^x`
Rational $f(x) = \frac{P(x)}{Q(x)}$; $P(x)$ and $Q(x)$ polynomials The graph of $y = 1/x$ is a **hyperbola.** The domain excludes zero since $1/0$ is not defined.	$y = \frac{1}{x}$ 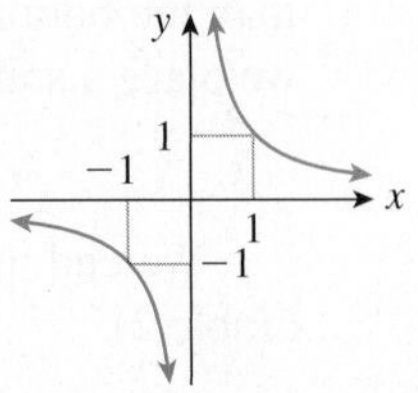	$y = \frac{x}{x-1}$ 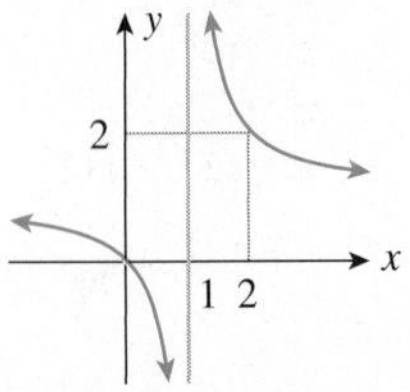
Technology formulas:	`1/x`	`x/(x - 1)`

Table **2** *(Continued)*

Type of Function	*Examples*	
Absolute value For x positive or zero, the graph of $y = \lvert x \rvert$ is the same as that of $y = x$. For x negative or zero, it is the same as that of $y = -x$.	$y = \lvert x \rvert$	$y = \lvert 2x + 2 \rvert$
Technology formulas:	`abs(x)`	`abs(2*x+2)`
Square Root The domain of $y = \sqrt{x}$ must be restricted to the nonnegative numbers, since the square root of a negative number is not real. Its graph is the top half of a horizontally oriented parabola.	$y = \sqrt{x}$	$y = \sqrt{4x - 2}$
Technology Formulas:	`x^0.5 or √(x)`	`(4*x-2)^0.5 or √(4*x-2)`

1.2 EXERCISES

● denotes basic skills exercises

tech Ex indicates exercises that should be solved using technology

In Exercises 1–4, use the graph of the function f to find approximations of the given values. hint [see Example 1]

1. ●

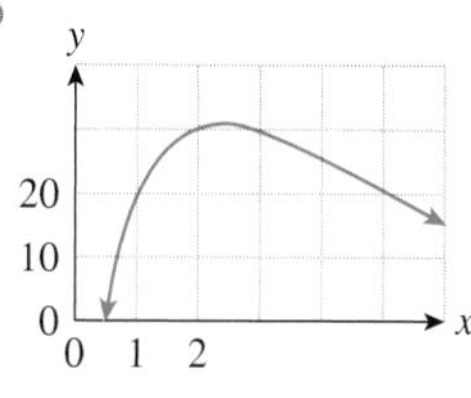

a. $f(1)$
b. $f(2)$
c. $f(3)$
d. $f(5)$
e. $f(3) - f(2)$

2. ●

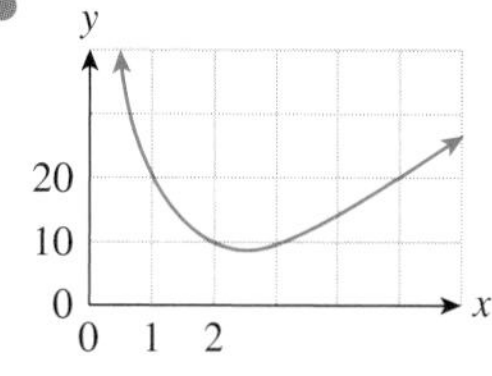

a. $f(1)$
b. $f(2)$
c. $f(3)$
d. $f(5)$
e. $f(3) - f(2)$

3. ●

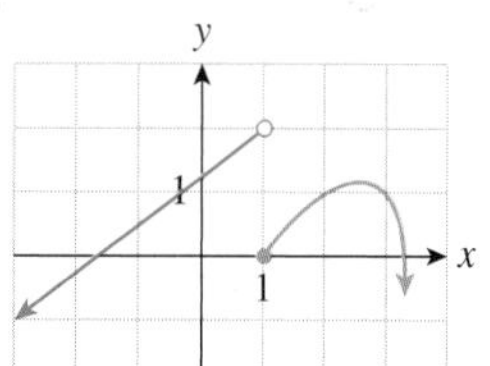

a. $f(-3)$ **b.** $f(0)$
c. $f(1)$ **d.** $f(2)$
e. $\dfrac{f(3) - f(2)}{3 - 2}$

4. ●

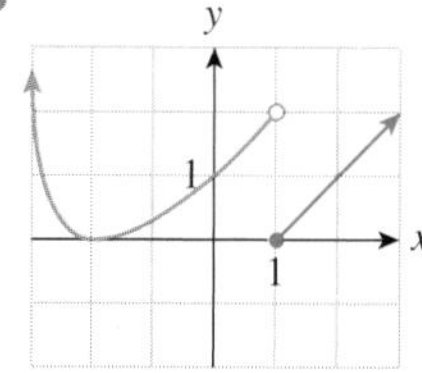

a. $f(-2)$ **b.** $f(0)$
c. $f(1)$ **d.** $f(3)$
e. $\dfrac{f(3) - f(1)}{3 - 1}$

In Exercises 5 and 6, match the functions to the graphs. Using technology to draw the graphs is suggested, but not required.

5. **tech Ex**

a. $f(x) = x \quad (-1 \le x \le 1)$
b. $f(x) = -x \quad (-1 \le x \le 1)$

c. $f(x) = \sqrt{x} \quad (0 < x < 4)$

d. $f(x) = x + \frac{1}{x} - 2 \quad (0 < x < 4)$

e. $f(x) = |x| \quad (-1 \le x \le 1)$

f. $f(x) = x - 1 \quad (-1 \le x \le 1)$

(I)

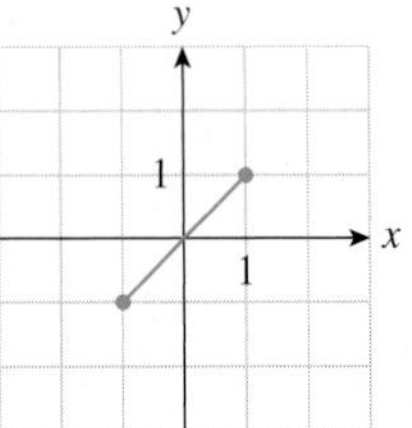

(II)

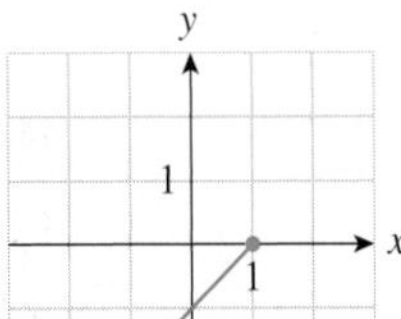

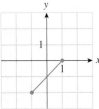

(III)

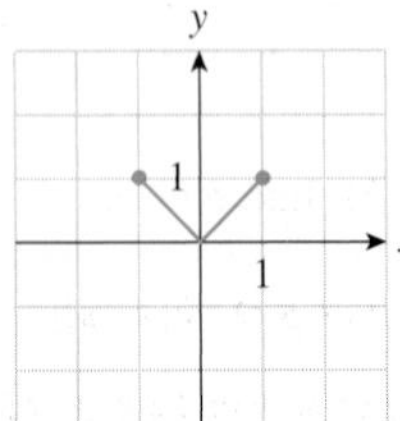

(IV)

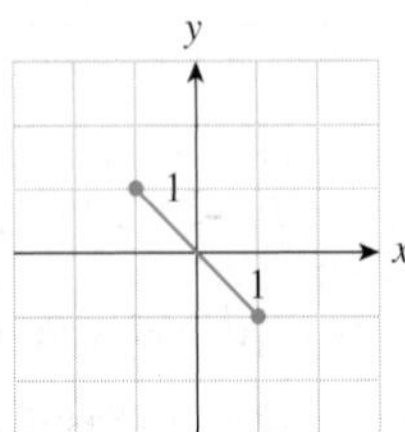

(V)

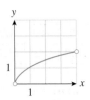

(VI)

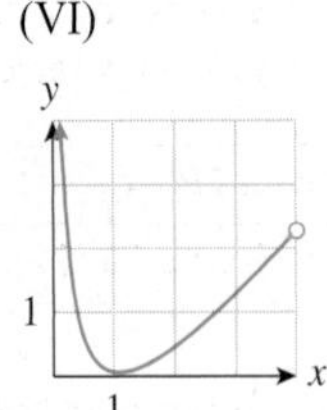

6. tech Ex

a. $f(x) = -x + 4 \quad (0 < x \le 4)$

b. $f(x) = 2 - |x| \quad (-2 < x \le 2)$

c. $f(x) = \sqrt{x+2} \quad (-2 < x \le 2)$

d. $f(x) = -x^2 + 2 \quad (-2 < x \le 2)$

e. $f(x) = \frac{1}{x} - 1 \quad (0 < x \le 4)$

f. $f(x) = x^2 - 1 \quad (-2 < x \le 2)$

(I)

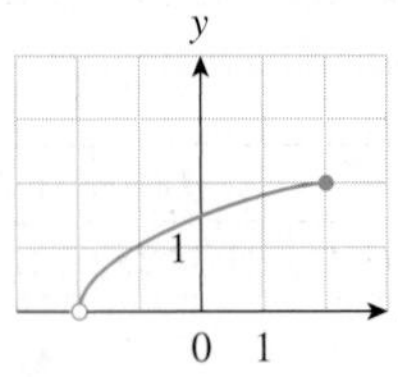

(II)

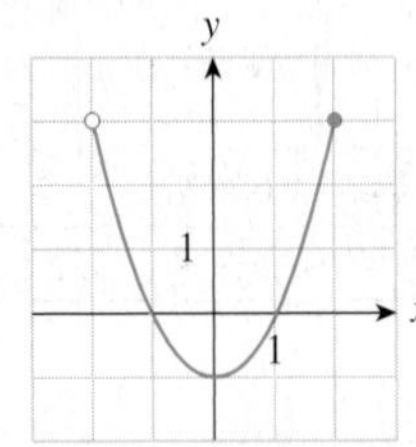

(III)

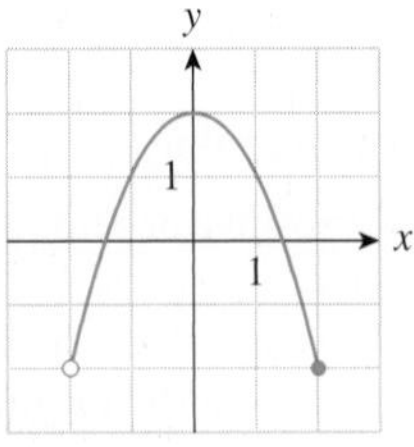

(IV)

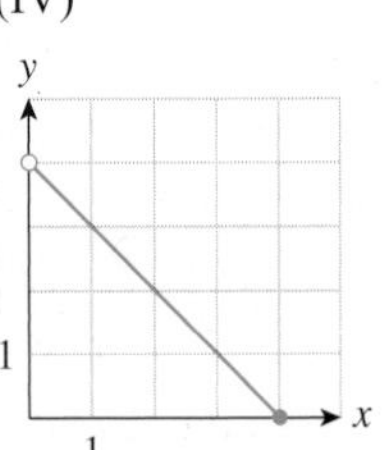

(V)

(VI)

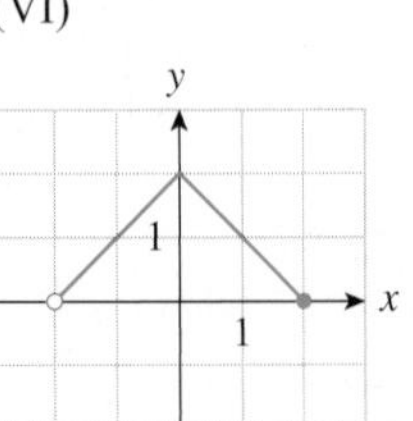

In Exercises 7–12, graph the given functions. Give the technology formula and use technology to check your graph. We suggest that you become familiar with these graphs, in addition to those in Table 2. hint [see Example 2]

7. ● $f(x) = -x^3 \quad$ (domain $(-\infty, +\infty)$)

8. ● $f(x) = x^3 \quad$ (domain $[0, +\infty)$)

9. ● $f(x) = x^4 \quad$ (domain $(-\infty, +\infty)$)

10. ● $f(x) = \sqrt[3]{x} \quad$ (domain $(-\infty, +\infty)$)

11. ● $f(x) = \frac{1}{x^2} \quad (x \ne 0)$

12. ● $f(x) = x + \frac{1}{x} \quad (x \ne 0)$

In Exercises 13–18, sketch the graph of the given function, evaluate the given expressions, and then use technology to duplicate the graphs. Give the technology formula. hint [see Example 3]

13. ● $f(x) = \begin{cases} x & \text{if } -4 \le x < 0 \\ 2 & \text{if } 0 \le x \le 4 \end{cases}$

a. $f(-1)$ **b.** $f(0)$ **c.** $f(1)$

14. ● $f(x) = \begin{cases} -1 & \text{if } -4 \le x \le 0 \\ x & \text{if } 0 < x \le 4 \end{cases}$

a. $f(-1)$ **b.** $f(0)$ **c.** $f(1)$

15. ● $f(x) = \begin{cases} x^2 & \text{if } -2 < x \le 0 \\ 1/x & \text{if } 0 < x \le 4 \end{cases}$

a. $f(-1)$ **b.** $f(0)$ **c.** $f(1)$

16. ● $f(x) = \begin{cases} -x^2 & \text{if } -2 < x \le 0 \\ \sqrt{x} & \text{if } 0 < x < 4 \end{cases}$

a. $f(-1)$ **b.** $f(0)$ **c.** $f(1)$

17. ● $f(x) = \begin{cases} x & \text{if } -1 < x \le 0 \\ x+1 & \text{if } 0 < x \le 2 \\ x & \text{if } 2 < x \le 4 \end{cases}$ hint [see Example 4]

a. $f(0)$ **b.** $f(1)$ **c.** $f(2)$ **d.** $f(3)$

18. ● $f(x) = \begin{cases} -x & \text{if } -1 < x < 0 \\ x-2 & \text{if } 0 \le x \le 2 \\ -x & \text{if } 2 < x \le 4 \end{cases}$

a. $f(0)$ **b.** $f(1)$ **c.** $f(2)$ **d.** $f(3)$

Applications

Sales of Sport Utility Vehicles *Exercises 19–22 refer to the following graph, which shows the number $f(t)$ of sports utility vehicles (SUVs) sold in the U.S. each year from 1990 through 2003 ($t = 0$ represents 1990, and $f(t)$ represents sales in year t in thousands of vehicles).*[17]

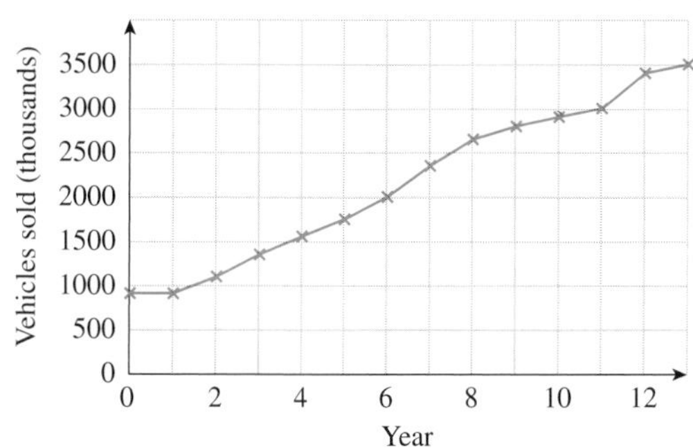

19. ● Estimate $f(6)$, $f(9)$, and $f(7.5)$. Interpret your answers.

20. ● Estimate $f(5)$, $f(11)$, and $f(1.5)$. Interpret your answers.

21. ● Which is larger: $f(6) - f(5)$ or $f(10) - f(9)$? Interpret the answer.

22. ● Which is larger: $f(10) - f(8)$ or $f(13) - f(11)$? Interpret the answer.

23. ● ***Employment*** The following graph shows the number $N(t)$ of people, in millions, employed in the U.S. (t is time in years, and $t = 0$ represents January 2000).[18]

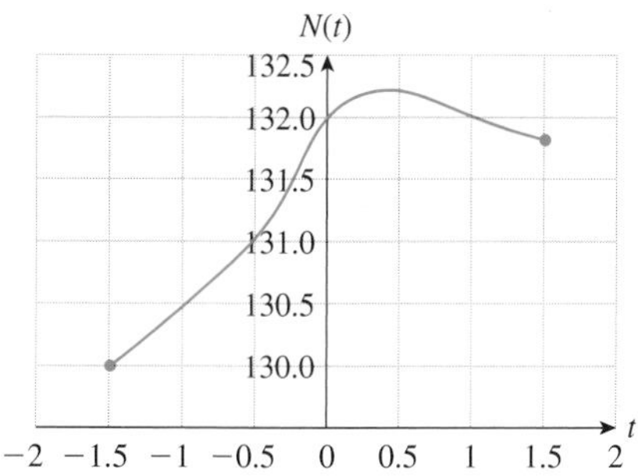

a. What is the domain of N?

b. Estimate $N(-0.5)$, $N(0)$, and $N(1)$. Interpret your answers.

c. On which interval is $N(t)$ falling? Interpret the result.

24. ● ***Productivity*** The following graph shows an index $P(t)$ of productivity in the U.S., where t is time in years, and $t = 0$ represents January 2000.[19]

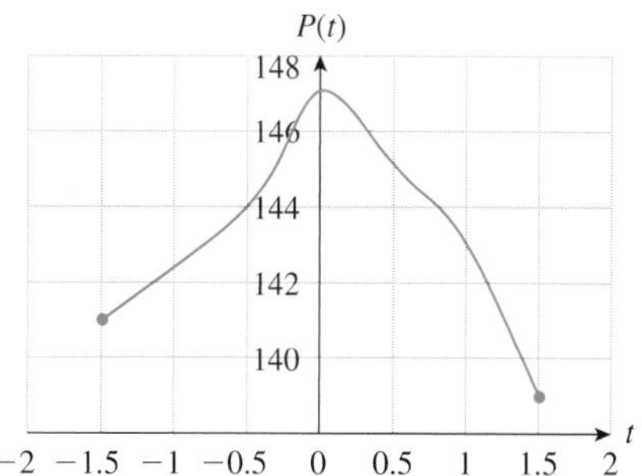

a. What is the domain of P?

b. Estimate $P(-0.5)$, $P(0)$, and $P(1.5)$. Interpret your answers.

c. On which interval is $P(t) \ge 144$? Interpret the result.

25. ● ***Soccer Gear*** The East Coast College soccer team is planning to buy new gear for its road trip to California. The cost per shirt depends on the number of shirts the team orders, as shown in the following table:

x (Shirts ordered)	5	25	40	100	125
***A*(*x*) (Cost/shirt, $)**	22.91	21.81	21.25	21.25	22.31

a. Which of the following functions best models the data?

(A) $A(x) = 0.005x + 20.75$

(B) $A(x) = 0.01x + 20 + \dfrac{25}{x}$

(C) $A(x) = 0.0005x^2 - 0.07x + 23.25$

(D) $A(x) = 25.5(1.08)^{(x-5)}$

b. tech Ex Graph the model you chose in part (a) for $10 \le x \le 100$. Use your graph to estimate the lowest cost per shirt and the number of shirts the team should order to obtain the lowest price per shirt.

26. ● ***Hockey Gear*** The South Coast College hockey team wants to purchase wool hats for its road trip to Alaska. The cost per hat depends on the number of hats the team orders, as shown in the following table:

x (Hats ordered)	5	25	40	100	125
***A*(*x*) (Cost/hat $)**	25.50	23.50	24.63	30.25	32.70

[17] 2000–2003 values were forecasts. Sources: Ford Motor Company/*The New York Times,* February 9, 1995, p. D17, Oak Ridge National Laboratory, Light Vehicle MPG and Market Shares System, AutoPacific, *The U.S. Car and Light Truck Market,* 1999, pp. 24, 120, 121.

[18] SOURCE: Haver Analytics: The Conference Board/*New York Times,* November 24, 2001.

[19] Ibid.

a. Which of the following functions best models the data?

(A) $A(x) = 0.05x + 20.75$

(B) $A(x) = 0.1x + 20 + \dfrac{25}{x}$

(C) $A(x) = 0.0008x^2 - 0.07x + 23.25$

(D) $A(x) = 25.5(1.08)^{(x-5)}$

b. tech Ex Graph the model you chose in part (a) with $5 \le x \le 30$. Use your graph to estimate the lowest cost per hat and the number of hats the team should order to obtain the lowest price per hat.

27. ● ***Value of Euro*** The following table shows the approximate value V of one Euro in U.S, dollars from its introduction in January 2000 to January 2005. ($t = 0$ represents January, 2000.)[20]

***t* (Year)**	0	2	5
***V* (Value in $)**	1.00	0.90	1.30

Which of the following kinds of models would best fit the given data? Explain your choice of model. (A, a, b, c, and m are constants.)

(A) Linear: $V(t) = mt + b$

(B) Quadratic: $V(t) = at^2 + bt + c$

(C) Exponential: $V(t) = Ab^t$

28. ● ***Household Income*** The following table shows the approximate average household income in the U.S. in 1990, 1995, and 2003. ($t = 0$ represents 1990.)[21]

***t* (Year)**	0	5	13
***H* (Household Income in $1000)**	30	35	43

Which of the following kind of model would best fit the given data? Explain your choice of model. (A, a, b, c, and m are constants.)

(A) Linear: $H(t) = mt + b$

(B) Quadratic: $H(t) = at^2 + bt + c$

(C) Exponential: $H(t) = Ab^t$

29. tech Ex ***Acquisition of Language*** The percentage $p(t)$ of children who can speak at least single words by the age of t months can be approximated by the equation[22]

$$p(t) = 100\left(1 - \frac{12{,}200}{t^{4.48}}\right) \quad (t \ge 8.5)$$

a. Give a technology formula for p.

b. Graph p for $8.5 \le t \le 20$ and $0 \le p \le 100$. Use your graph to answer parts (c) and (d).

c. What percentage of children can speak at least single words by the age of 12 months? (Round your answer to the nearest percentage point.)

d. By what age are 90% of children speaking at least single words? (Round your answer to the nearest month.)

30. tech Ex ***Acquisition of Language*** The percentage $p(t)$ of children who can speak in sentences of five or more words by the age of t months can be approximated by the equation[23]

$$p(t) = 100\left(1 - \frac{5.27 \times 10^{17}}{t^{12}}\right) \quad (t \ge 30)$$

a. Give a technology formula for p.

b. Graph p for $30 \le t \le 45$ and $0 \le p \le 100$. Use your graph to answer parts (b) and (c).

c. What percentage of children can speak in sentences of five or more words by the age of 36 months? (Round your answer to the nearest percentage point.)

d. By what age are 75% of children speaking in sentences of five or more words? (Round your answer to the nearest month.)

31. ● ***Processor Speeds*** (Compare Exercise 33 in Section 1.1.) The processor speed, in megahertz, of Intel processors could be approximated by the following function of time t in years since the start of 1995:[24]

$$P(t) = \begin{cases} 75t + 200 & \text{if } 0 \le t \le 4 \\ 600t - 1900 & \text{if } 4 < t \le 9 \end{cases}$$

Sketch the graph of P and use your graph to estimate when processor speeds first reached 2.0 gigahertz (1 gigahertz = 1000 megahertz).

32. ● ***Leading Economic Indicators*** (Compare Exercise 34 in Section 1.1.) The value of the Conference Board Index of 10 economic indicators in the U.S. could be approximated by the following function of time t in months since the end of 2002:[25]

$$E(t) = \begin{cases} 0.4t + 110 & \text{if } 6 \le t \le 15 \\ -0.2t + 119 & \text{if } 15 < t \le 20 \end{cases}$$

Sketch the graph of E and use your graph to estimate when the index first reached 115.

[20] SOURCES: Bloomberg Financial Markets, International Monetary Fund/*New York Times,* May 18, 2003, p. I7

[21] In current dollars, unadjusted for inflation. SOURCE: U.S. Census Bureau; "Table H-5. Race and Hispanic Origin of Householder—Households by Median and Mean Income: 1967 to 2003;" published August 27, 2004; www.census.gov

[22] The model is the authors' and is based on data presented in the article *The Emergence of Intelligence* by William H. Calvin, *Scientific American,* October, 1994, pp. 101–107.

[23] Ibid.

[24] SOURCE: Sandpile.org/*New York Times,* May 17, 2004, p. C1.

[25] SOURCE: The Conference Board/*New York Times,* November 19, 2004, p. C7.

33. tech Ex ***Television Advertising*** The cost, in millions of dollars, of a 30-second television ad during the Super Bowl in the years 1990–2001 can be approximated by the following piecewise linear function ($t = 0$ represents 1990):[26]

$$C(t) = \begin{cases} 0.08t + 0.6 & \text{if } 0 \le t < 8 \\ 0.355t - 1.6 & \text{if } 8 \le t \le 11 \end{cases}$$

a. Give a technology formula for C and use technology to graph the function C.
b. Based on the graph, a Superbowl ad first exceeded \$2 million in what year?

34. tech Ex ***Internet Purchases*** The percentage $p(t)$ of buyers of new cars who used the Internet for research or purchase each year since 1997 is given by the following function[27] ($t = 0$ represents 1997):

$$p(t) = \begin{cases} 10t + 15 & \text{if } 0 \le t < 1 \\ 15t + 10 & \text{if } 1 \le t \le 4 \end{cases}$$

a. Give a technology formula for p and use technology to graph the function p.
b. Based on the graph, 50% or more of all new car buyers used the Internet for research or purchase in what years?

[26] Source: *New York Times*, January 26, 2001, p. C1.

[27] Model is based on data through 2000 (the 2000 value is estimated). Source: J.D. Power Associates/*The New York Times*, January 25, 2000, p. C1.

Communication and Reasoning Exercises

35. ● True or false: Every graphically specified function can also be specified numerically. Explain.

36. ● True or false: Every algebraically specified function can also be specified graphically. Explain.

37. ● True or false: Every numerically specified function with domain [0, 10] can also be specified graphically. Explain.

38. ● True or false: Every graphically specified function can also be specified algebraically. Explain.

39. ● How do the graphs of two functions differ if they are specified by the same formula but have different domains?

40. ● How do the graphs of two functions $f(x)$ and $g(x)$ differ if $g(x) = f(x) + 10$? (Try an example.)

41. How do the graphs of two functions $f(x)$ and $g(x)$ differ if $g(x) = f(x - 5)$? (Try an example.)

42. How do the graphs of two functions $f(x)$ and $g(x)$ differ if $g(x) = f(-x)$? (Try an example.)

● basic skills   tech Ex technology exercise

1.3 Linear Functions

Linear functions are among the simplest functions and are perhaps the most useful of all mathematical functions.

Linear Function	*quick* Example
A **linear function** is one that can be written in the form	
$f(x) = mx + b$ Function form	$f(x) = 3x - 1$
or	
$y = mx + b$ Equation form	$y = 3x - 1$
where m and b are fixed numbers (the names m and b are traditional*).	

* Actually, c is sometimes used instead of b. As for m, there has even been some research lately into the question of its origin, but no one knows exactly why the letter m is used.

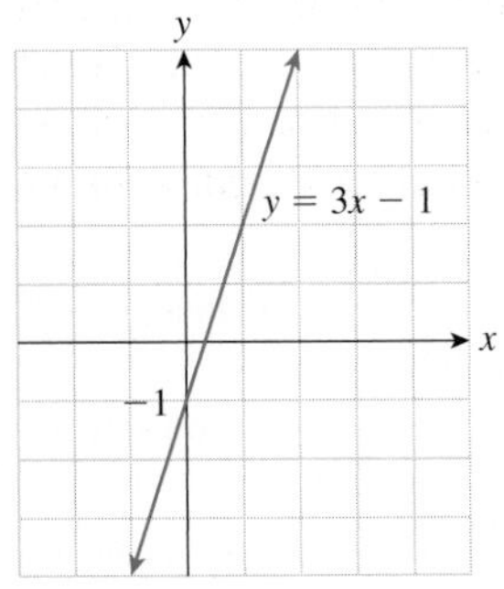

Figure 7

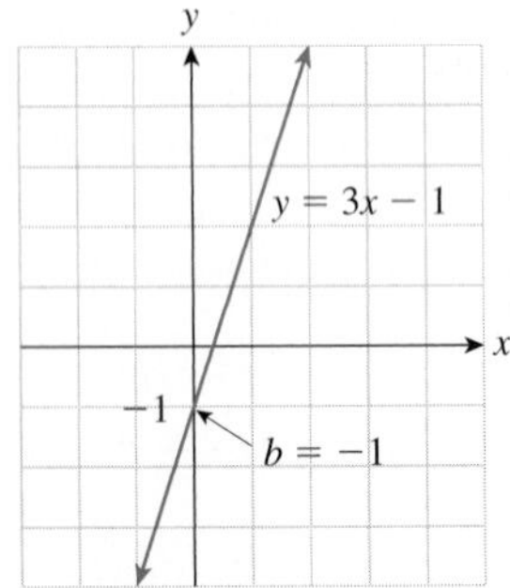

Figure 8
y-intercept = $b = -1$
Graphically, b is the y-intercept of the graph

Linear Functions from the Numerical and Graphical Point of View

The following table shows values of $y = 3x - 1$ ($m = 3$, $b = -1$) for some values of x:

x	−4	−3	−2	−1	0	1	2	3	4
y	−13	−10	−7	−4	−1	2	5	8	11

Its graph is shown in Figure 7.

Looking first at the table, notice that that setting $x = 0$ gives $y = -1$, the value of b.

Numerically, b is the value of y when x $= 0$

On the graph, the corresponding point $(0, -1)$ is the point where the graph crosses the y-axis, and we say that $b = -1$ is the ***y*-intercept** of the graph (Figure 8).

What about m? Looking once again at the table, notice that y increases by $m = 3$ units for every increase of 1 unit in x. This is caused by the term $3x$ in the formula: for every increase of 1 in x we get an increase of $3 \times 1 = 3$ in y.

Numerically, y increases by m units for every 1-unit increase of x

Likewise, for every increase of 2 in x we get an increase of $3 \times 2 = 6$ in y. In general, if x increases by some amount, y will increase by three times that amount. We write:

$$\text{Change in } y = 3 \times \text{Change in } x$$

The Change in a Quantity: Delta Notation

If a quantity q changes from q_1 to q_2, the **change in** q is just the difference:

$$\text{Change in } q = \text{Second value} - \text{First value}$$
$$= q_2 - q_1$$

Mathematicians traditionally use Δ (delta, the Greek equivalent of the Roman letter D) to stand for change, and write the change in q as Δq.

$$\Delta q = \text{Change in } q = q_2 - q_1$$

quick Examples

1. If x is changed from 1 to 3, we write

$$\Delta x = \text{Second value} - \text{First value} = 3 - 1 = 2$$

2. Looking at our linear function, we see that when x changes from 1 to 3, y changes from 2 to 8. So,

$$\Delta y = \text{Second value} - \text{First value} = 8 - 2 = 6$$

Using delta notation, we can now write, for our linear function,

$$\Delta y = 3\Delta x \qquad \text{Change in } y = 3 \times \text{Change in } x$$

or

$$\frac{\Delta y}{\Delta x} = 3$$

Because the value of y increases by exactly 3 units for every increase of 1 unit in x, the graph is a straight line rising by 3 units for every 1 unit we go to the right. We say that we have a **rise** of 3 units for each **run** of 1 unit. Because the value of y changes by $\Delta y = 3\Delta x$ units for every change of Δx units in x, in general we have a rise of $\Delta y = 3\Delta x$ units for each run of Δx units (Figure 9). Thus, we have a rise of 6 for a run of 2, a rise of 9 for a run of 3, and so on. So, $m = 3$ is a measure of the steepness of the line; we call m the **slope of the line:**

$$\text{Slope} = m = \frac{\Delta y}{\Delta x} = \frac{\text{Rise}}{\text{Run}}$$

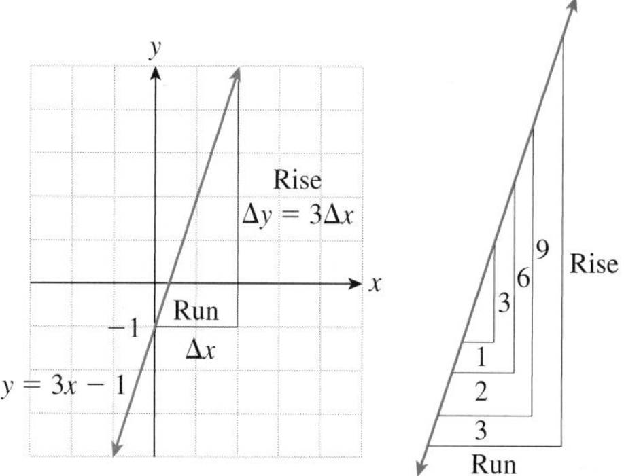

Figure 9
Slope = $m = 3$
Graphically, m is the slope of the graph.

In general (replace the number 3 by a general number m), we can say the following.

The Roles of m and b in the Linear Function $f(x) = mx + b$

Role of *m*

Numerically If $y = mx + b$, then y changes by m units for every 1-unit change in x. A change of Δx units in x results in a change of $\Delta y = m\Delta x$ units in y. Thus,

$$m = \frac{\Delta y}{\Delta x} = \frac{\text{Change in } y}{\text{Change in } x}$$

Graphically m is the slope of the line $y = mx + b$:

$$m = \frac{\Delta y}{\Delta x} = \frac{\text{Rise}}{\text{Run}} = \text{Slope}$$

For positive m, the graph rises m units for every 1-unit move to the right, and rises $\Delta y = m\Delta x$ units for every Δx units moved to the right. For negative m, the graph drops $|m|$ units for every 1-unit move to the right, and drops $|m|\Delta x$ units for every Δx units moved to the right.

Graph of $y = mx + b$

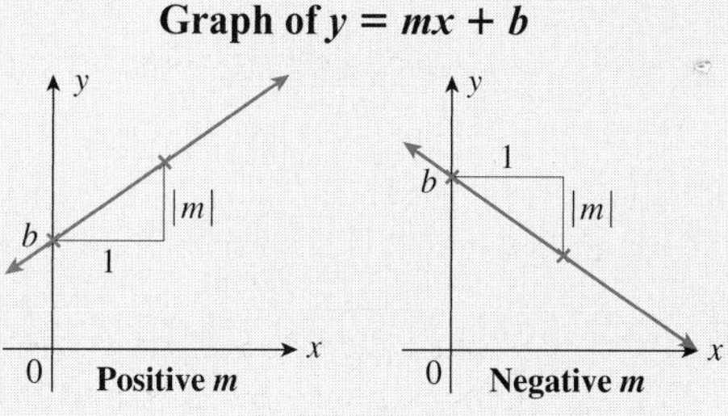

Role of b
Numerically When $x = 0$, $y = b$
Graphically b is the y-intercept of the line $y = mx + b$.

quick Examples

1. $f(x) = 2x + 1$ has slope $m = 2$ and y-intercept $b = 1$. To sketch the graph, we start at the y-intercept $b = 1$ on the y-axis, and then move 1 unit to the right and up $m = 2$ units to arrive at a second point on the graph. Now connect the two points to obtain the graph on the left.

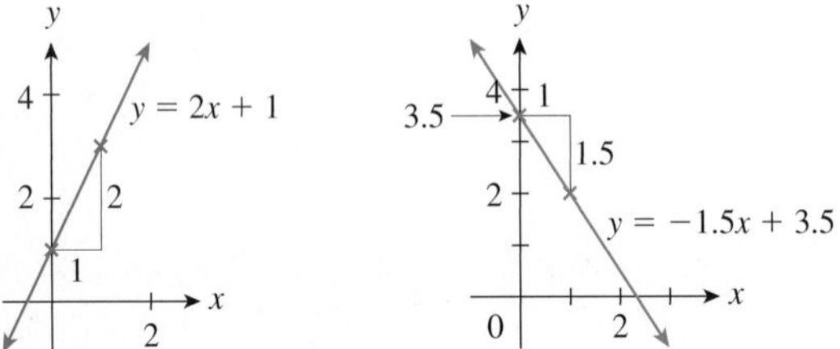

2. The line $y = -1.5x + 3.5$ has slope $m = -1.5$ and y-intercept $b = 3.5$. Since the slope is negative, the graph (above right) goes *down* 1.5 units for every 1 unit it moves to the right.

It helps to be able to picture what different slopes look like, as in Figure 10. Notice that the larger the absolute value of the slope, the steeper is the line.

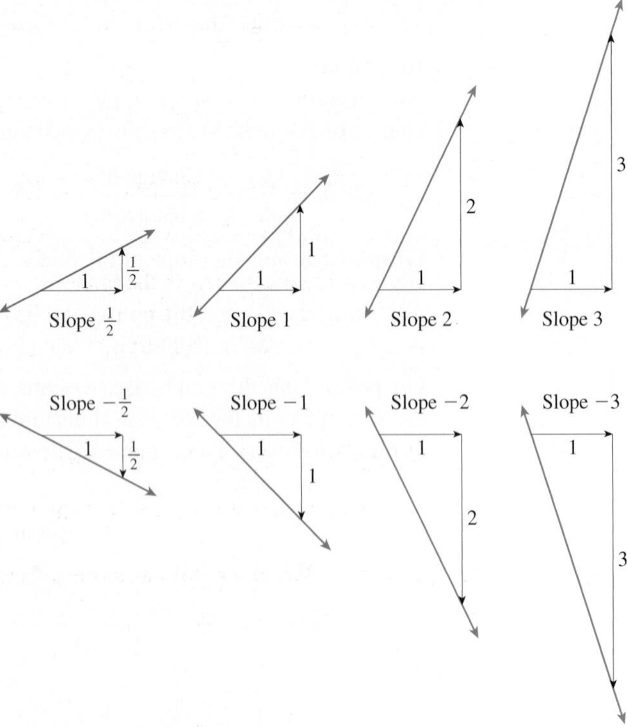

Figure **10**

Example 1 Recognizing Linear Data Numerically and Graphically

Which of the following two tables gives the values of a linear function? What is the formula for that function?

x	0	2	4	6	8	10	12
$f(x)$	3	−1	−3	−6	−8	−13	−15

x	0	2	4	6	8	10	12
$g(x)$	3	−1	−5	−9	−13	−17	−21

using *Technology*

Consult the Technology Guides at the end of the chapter to see how to generate tables showing the ratios $\Delta f/\Delta x$ and $\Delta g/\Delta x$. These tables show at a glance that *f* is not linear.

Solution The function *f* cannot be linear: If it were, we would have $\Delta f = m\Delta x$ for some fixed number m. However, although the change in x between successive entries in the table is $\Delta x = 2$ each time, the change in *f* is not the same each time. Thus, the ratio $\Delta f/\Delta x$ is not the same for every successive pair of points.

On the other hand, the ratio $\Delta g/\Delta x$ is the same each time, namely,

$$\frac{\Delta g}{\Delta x} = \frac{-4}{2} = -2$$

Δx		$2-0=2$	$4-2=2$	$6-4=2$	$8-6=2$	$10-8=2$	$12-10=2$
x	0	2	4	6	8	10	12
$g(x)$	3	−1	−5	−9	−13	−17	−21
Δg		$(-1)-3=-4$	$-5-(-1)=-4$	$-9-(-5)=-4$	$-13-(-9)=-4$	$-17-(-13)=-4$	$-21-(-17)=-4$

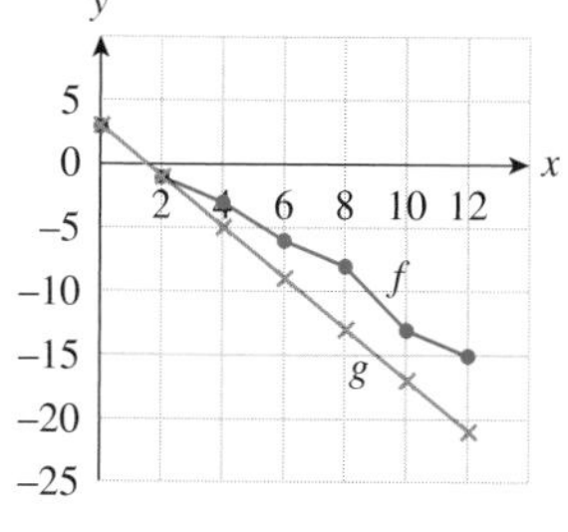

Figure 11

Thus, g is linear with slope $m = -2$. By the table, $g(0) = 3$, hence $b = 3$. Thus,

$$g(x) = -2x + 3$$ Check that this formula gives the values in the table

If you graph the points in the tables defining *f* and *g* above, it becomes easy to see that *g* is linear and *f* is not; the points of *g* lie on a straight line (with slope −2), whereas the points of *f* do not lie on a straight line (Figure 11).

Example 2 Graphing a Linear Equation by Hand: Intercepts

Graph the equation $x + 2y = 4$. Where does the line cross the x- and y-axes?

Solution We first write y as a linear function of x by solving the equation for y.

$$2y = -x + 4$$

so

$$y = -\frac{1}{2}x + 2$$

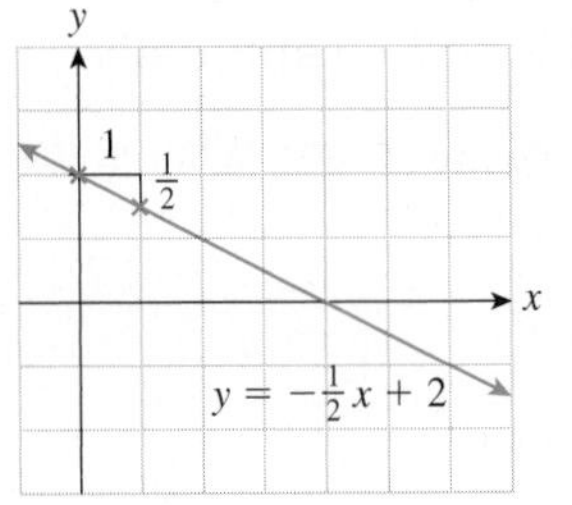

Figure **12**

Now we can see that the graph is a straight line with a slope of $-1/2$ and a y-intercept of 2. We start at 2 on the y-axis and go down 1/2 unit for every 1 unit we go to the right. The graph is shown in Figure 12.

We already know that the line crosses the y-axis at 2. Where does it cross the x-axis? Wherever that is, we know that the y-coordinate will be 0 at that point. So, we set $y = 0$ and solve for x. It's most convenient to use the equation we were originally given:

$$x + 2(0) = 4 \quad \text{Original equation with } x = 0$$

so

$$x = 4$$

The line crosses the x-axis at 4.

+ *Before we go on...* We could have graphed the equation in Example 2 another way, by first finding the intercepts. Once we know that the line crosses the y-axis at 2 and the x-axis at 4, we can draw those two points and then draw the line connecting them. ■

We now summarize the procedure for finding the intercepts of a line.

Finding the Intercepts

The x-**intercept** of a line is where it crosses the x-axis. To find it, set $y = 0$ and solve for x. The y-**intercept** is where it crosses the y-axis. If the equation of the line is written in as $y = mx + b$, then b is the y-intercept. Otherwise, set $x = 0$ and solve for y.

quick Example

Consider the equation $3x - 2y = 6$. To find its x-intercept, set $y = 0$ to find $x = 6/3 = 2$. To find its y-intercept, set $x = 0$ to find $y = 6/(-2) = -3$. The line crosses the x-axis at 2 and the y-axis at -3.

Computing the Slope of a Line

We know that the slope of a line is given by

$$\text{Slope} = m = \frac{\text{Rise}}{\text{Run}} = \frac{\Delta y}{\Delta x}$$

Recall that two points—say (x_1, y_1) and (x_2, y_2)—determine a line in the xy-plane. To find its slope, we need a run Δx and corresponding rise Δy. In Figure 13, we see that we can use $\Delta x = x_2 - x_1$, the change in the x-coordinate from the first point to the second, as our run, and $\Delta y = y_2 - y_1$, the change in the y-coordinate, as our rise. The resulting formula for computing the slope is given below.

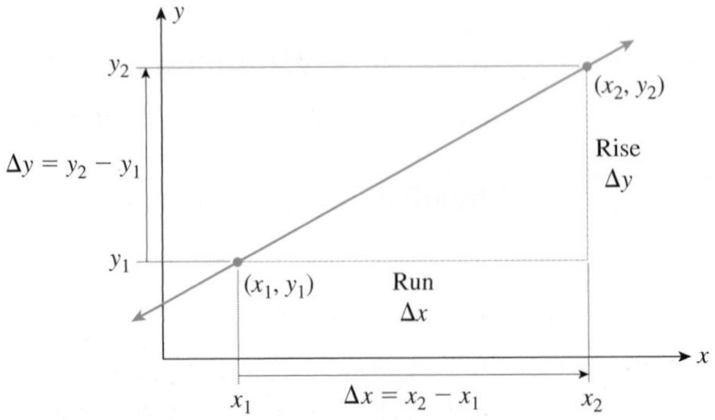

Figure **13**

Computing the Slope of a Line

We can compute the slope m of the line through the points (x_1, y_1) and (x_2, y_2) using

$$m = \frac{\Delta y}{\Delta x} = \frac{y_2 - y_1}{x_2 - x_1}$$

quick **Examples**

1. The slope of the line through $(x_1, y_1) = (1, 3)$ and $(x_2, y_2) = (5, 11)$ is

$$m = \frac{\Delta y}{\Delta x} = \frac{y_2 - y_1}{x_2 - x_1} = \frac{11 - 3}{5 - 1} = \frac{8}{4} = 2$$

2. The slope of the line through $(x_1, y_1) = (1, 2)$ and $(x_2, y_2) = (2, 1)$ is

$$m = \frac{\Delta y}{\Delta x} = \frac{y_2 - y_1}{x_2 - x_1} = \frac{1 - 2}{2 - 1} = \frac{-1}{1} = -1$$

Q: *What if we had chosen to list the two points in Quick Example 1 in reverse order? That is, suppose we had taken $(x_1, y_1) = (5, 11)$ and $(x_2, y_2) = (1, 3)$. What would have been the effect on the computation of the slope?*

A: We would have found

$$m = \frac{\Delta y}{\Delta x} = \frac{y_2 - y_1}{x_2 - x_1} = \frac{3 - 11}{1 - 5} = \frac{-8}{-4} = 2$$

the same answer. The order in which we take the points is not important, *as long as we use the same order in the numerator and the denominator.* ■

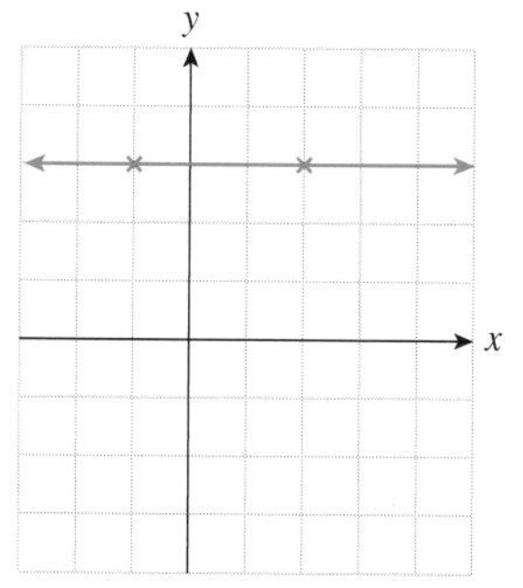

Figure **14**

Example 3 Special Slopes

Find the slope of the line through (2, 3) and (−1, 3) and the slope of the line through (3, 2) and (3, −1).

Solution The line through (2, 3) and (−1, 3) has slope

$$m = \frac{\Delta y}{\Delta x} = \frac{3 - 3}{-1 - 2} = \frac{0}{-3} = 0$$

A line of slope 0 has 0 rise, so is a *horizontal* line, as shown in Figure 14. The line through (3, 2) and (3, −1) has slope

$$m = \frac{\Delta y}{\Delta x} = \frac{-1 - 2}{3 - 3} = \frac{-3}{0}$$

which is undefined. If we plot the two points, we see that the line passing through them is *vertical,* as shown in Figure 15.

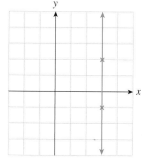

Vertical lines have undefined slope.

Figure **15**

Finding a Linear Equation from Data: How to Make a Linear Model

If we happen to know the slope and y-intercept of a line, writing down its equation is straightforward. For example, if we know that the slope is 3 and the y-intercept is −1, then the equation is $y = 3x - 1$. Sadly, the information we are given is seldom so convenient. For instance, we may know the slope and a point other than the y-intercept, two points on the line, or other information.

We describe a straightforward method for finding the equation of a line: the **point-slope** method. As the name suggests, we need two pieces of information:

- The *slope* m (which specifies the direction of the line)
- A *point* (x_1, y_1) on the line (which pins down its location in the plane)

The equation of the line through the point (x_1, y_1) with slope m must have the form

$$y = mx + b$$

for some (unknown) number b. To determine b we use the fact that the line must pass through the point (x_1, y_1), so that (x_1, y_1) satisfies the equation $y = mx + b$. In other words,

$$y_1 = mx_1 + b$$

Solving for b gives

$$b = y_1 - mx_1$$

Summarizing:

The Point-Slope Formula

An equation of the line through the point (x_1, y_1) with slope m is given by

$$y = mx + b \qquad \text{Equation form}$$

where

$$b = y_1 - mx_1$$

quick **Example** The line through (2, 3) with slope 4 has equation

$$y = 4x + b, \text{ where } b = 3 - (4)(2) = -5, \text{ so } y = 4x - 5$$

Q: *When do we use the point-slope formula rather than the slope-intercept form?*

A: Use the point-slope formula to find the equation of a line when you are given information about a point and the slope of the line. The formula does not apply if the slope is undefined, as in a vertical line; see Example 4(d) below. The slope-intercept form is more useful for graphing a line whose equation you already have. ■

Example 4 Using the Point-Slope Formula

Find equations for the following straight lines.

a. Through the points $(1, 2)$ and $(3, -1)$

b. Through $(2, -2)$ and parallel to the line $3x + 4y = 5$

c. Horizontal and through $(-9, 5)$

d. Vertical and through $(-9, 5)$

Solution In each case other than (d), we apply the point-slope formula.

a. To apply the point-slope formula, we need

- ***Point*** We have two to choose from, so we take the first, $(x_1, y_1) = (1, 2)$.
- ***Slope*** Not given directly, but we do have enough information to calculate it. Since we are given two points on the line, we can use the slope formula:

$$m = \frac{y_2 - y_1}{x_2 - x_1} = \frac{-1-2}{3-1} = -\frac{3}{2}$$

An equation of the line is therefore

$$y = -\frac{3}{2}x + b$$

where $b = y_1 - mx_1 = 2 - \left(-\frac{3}{2}\right)(1) = \frac{7}{2}$, so

$$y = -\frac{3}{2}x + \frac{7}{2}$$

b. Proceeding as before,

- ***Point*** Given here as $(2, -2)$.
- ***Slope*** We use the fact that *parallel lines have the same slope*. (Why?) We can find the slope of $3x + 4y = 5$ by solving for y and then looking at the coefficient of x:

$$y = -\frac{3}{4}x + \frac{5}{4}$$ To find the slope, solve for y.

so the slope is $-3/4$.

An equation for the desired line is

$$y = -\frac{3}{4}x + b$$

where $b = y_1 - mx_1 = -2 - \left(-\frac{3}{4}\right)(2) = -\frac{1}{2}$

so $$y = -\frac{3}{4}x - \frac{1}{2}$$

c. We are given a point: $(-9, 5)$. Furthermore, we are told that the line is horizontal, which tells us that the slope is 0. Therefore, we get

$$y = 0x + b = b$$

where $b = y_1 - mx_1 = 5 - (0)(-9) = 5$

so $y = 5$

d. We are given a point: $(-9, 5)$. This time, we are told that the line is vertical, which means that the slope is undefined. Thus, we can't use the point-slope formula. (That formula makes sense only when the slope of the line is defined.) What can we do? Well, here are some points on the desired line:

$$(-9, 1), (-9, 2), (-9, 3), \ldots,$$

so $x = -9$ and $y = \textit{anything}$. If we simply say that $x = -9$, then these points are all solutions, so the equation is $x = -9$.

1.3 EXERCISES

● denotes basic skills exercises

tech Ex indicates exercises that should be solved using technology

In Exercises 1–6, a table of values for a linear function is given. Fill in the missing value and calculate m in each case.

1. ●

x	−1	0	1
y	5	8	

2. ●

x	−1	0	1
y	−1	−3	

3. ●

x	2	3	5
$f(x)$	−1	−2	

4. ●

x	2	4	5
$f(x)$	−1	−2	

5. ●

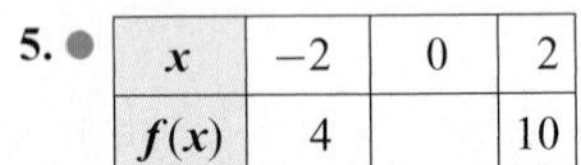

x	−2	0	2
$f(x)$	4		10

6. ●

x	0	3	6
$f(x)$	−1		−5

In Exercises 7–10, first find $f(0)$, if not supplied, and then find the equation of the given linear function.

7. ●

x	−2	0	2	4
$f(x)$	−1	−2	−3	−4

8. ●

x	−6	−3	0	3
$f(x)$	1	2	3	4

9. ●

x	−4	−3	−2	−1
$f(x)$	−1	−2	−3	−4

10. ●

x	1	2	3	4
$f(x)$	4	6	8	10

In each of Exercises 11–14, decide which of the two given functions is linear and find its equation. hint [see Example 1]

11. ●

x	0	1	2	3	4
$f(x)$	6	10	14	18	22
$g(x)$	8	10	12	16	22

12. ●

x	−10	0	10	20	30
$f(x)$	−1.5	0	1.5	2.5	3.5
$g(x)$	−9	−4	1	6	11

13. ●

x	0	3	6	10	15
$f(x)$	0	3	5	7	9
$g(x)$	−1	5	11	19	29

14. ●

x	0	3	5	6	9
$f(x)$	2	6	9	12	15
$g(x)$	−1	8	14	17	26

In Exercises 15–24, find the slope of the given line, if it is defined.

15. ● $y = -\frac{3}{2}x - 4$

16. ● $y = \frac{2x}{3} + 4$

17. ● $y = \frac{x+1}{6}$

18. ● $y = -\frac{2x-1}{3}$

19. ● $3x + 1 = 0$

20. ● $8x - 2y = 1$

21. ● $3y + 1 = 0$

22. ● $2x + 3 = 0$

23. ● $4x + 3y = 7$

24. ● $2y + 3 = 0$

In Exercises 25–38, graph the given equation. hint [see Example 2]

25. ● $y = 2x - 1$

26. ● $y = x - 3$

27. ● $y = -\frac{2}{3}x + 2$

28. ● $y = -\frac{1}{2}x + 3$

29. ● $y + \frac{1}{4}x = -4$

30. ● $y - \frac{1}{4}x = -2$

31. ● $7x - 2y = 7$

32. ● $2x - 3y = 1$

33. ● $3x = 8$

34. ● $2x = -7$

35. ● $6y = 9$

36. ● $3y = 4$

37. ● $2x = 3y$

38. ● $3x = -2y$

In Exercises 39–54, calculate the slope, if defined, of the straight line through the given pair of points. Try to do as many as you can without writing anything down except the answer. hint [see Example 3]

39. ● $(0, 0)$ and $(1, 2)$

40. ● $(0, 0)$ and $(-1, 2)$

41. ● $(-1, -2)$ and $(0, 0)$

42. ● $(2, 1)$ and $(0, 0)$

43. ● $(4, 3)$ and $(5, 1)$

44. ● $(4, 3)$ and $(4, 1)$

45. ● $(1, -1)$ and $(1, -2)$

46. ● $(-2, 2)$ and $(-1, -1)$

47. ● $(2, 3.5)$ and $(4, 6.5)$

48. ● $(10, -3.5)$ and $(0, -1.5)$

49. ● $(300, 20.2)$ and $(400, 11.2)$

50. ● $(1, -20.2)$ and $(2, 3.2)$

51. ● $(0, 1)$ and $\left(-\frac{1}{2}, \frac{3}{4}\right)$

52. ● $\left(\frac{1}{2}, 1\right)$ and $\left(-\frac{1}{2}, \frac{3}{4}\right)$

53. ● (a, b) and (c, d) $(a \neq c)$

54. ● (a, b) and (c, b) $(a \neq c)$

55. ● In the following figure, estimate the slopes of all line segments.

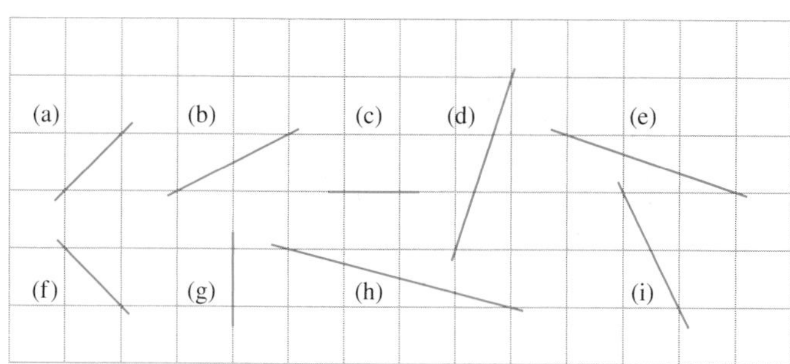

56. ● In the following figure, estimate the slopes of all line segments.

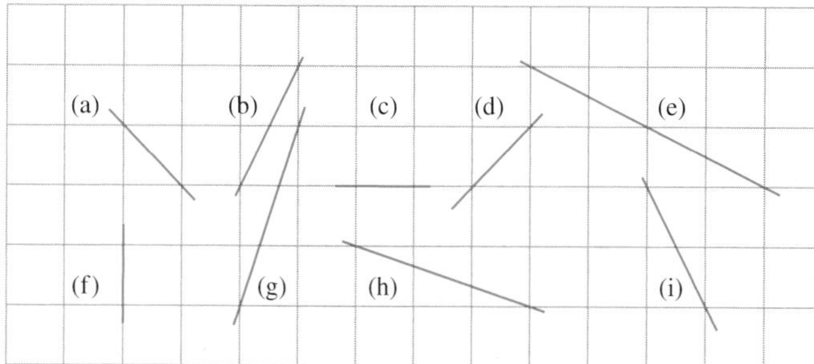

In Exercises 57–70, find a linear equation whose graph is the straight line with the given properties. hint [see Example 4]

57. ● Through $(1, 3)$ with slope 3

58. ● Through $(2, 1)$ with slope 2

59. ● Through $(1, -\frac{3}{4})$ with slope $\frac{1}{4}$

60. ● Through $(0, -\frac{1}{3})$ with slope $\frac{1}{3}$

61. ● Through $(20, -3.5)$ and increasing at a rate of 10 units of y per unit of x

62. ● Through $(3.5, -10)$ and increasing at a rate of 1 unit of y per 2 units of x.

63. ● Through $(2, -4)$ and $(1, 1)$

64. ● Through $(1, -4)$ and $(-1, -1)$

65. ● Through $(1, -0.75)$ and $(0.5, 0.75)$

66. ● Through $(0.5, -0.75)$ and $(1, -3.75)$

67. ● Through $(6, 6)$ and parallel to the line $x + y = 4$

68. ● Through $(1/3, -1)$ and parallel to the line $3x - 4y = 8$

69. ● Through $(0.5, 5)$ and parallel to the line $4x - 2y = 11$

70. ● Through $(1/3, 0)$ and parallel to the line $6x - 2y = 11$

Communication and Reasoning Exercises

71. ● How would you test a table of values of x and y to see if it comes from a linear function?

72. ● You have ascertained that a table of values of x and y corresponds to a linear function. How do you find an equation for that linear function?

73. ● To what linear function of x does the linear equation $ax + by = c\,(b \neq 0)$ correspond? Why did we specify $b \neq 0$?

74. ● Complete the following. The slope of the line with equation $y = mx + b$ is the number of units that ____ increases per unit increase in ____.

75. ● Complete the following. If, in a straight line, y is increasing three times as fast as x, then its ____ is ____.

76. ● Suppose that y is decreasing at a rate of 4 units per 3-unit increase of x. What can we say about the slope of the linear relationship between x and y? What can we say about the intercept?

77. ● If y and x are related by the linear expression $y = mx + b$, how will y change as x changes if m is positive? negative? zero?

78. ● Your friend April tells you that $y = f(x)$ has the property that, whenever x is changed by Δx, the corresponding change in y is $\Delta y = -\Delta x$. What can you tell her about f?

79. tech Ex Consider the following worksheet:

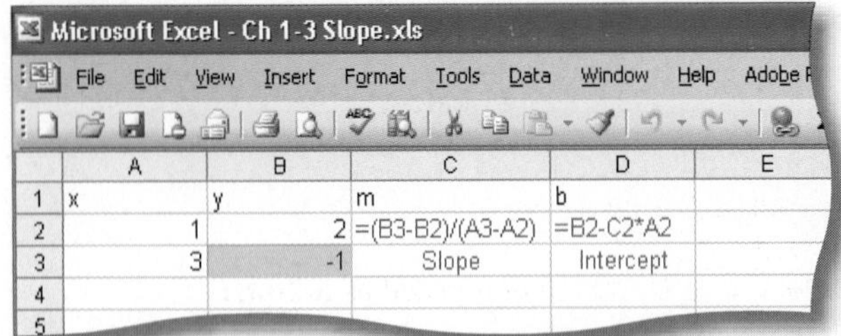

	A	B	C	D	E
1	x	y	m	b	
2	1	2	=(B3-B2)/(A3-A2)	=B2-C2*A2	
3	3	-1	Slope	Intercept	
4					
5					

What is the effect on the slope of increasing the y-coordinate of the second point (the point whose coordinates are in Row 3)? Explain.

80. tech Ex Referring to the worksheet in Exercise 79, what is the effect on the slope of increasing the x-coordinate of the second point (the point whose coordinates are in row 3)? Explain.

● basic skills   tech Ex technology exercise

1.4 Linear Models

Using linear functions to describe or approximate relationships in the real world is called **linear modeling.** We start with some examples involving cost, revenue, and profit.

Cost, Revenue, and Profit Functions

Photodisc/Getty Images

Example 1 Linear Cost Function

As of January, 2005, Yellow Cab Chicago's rates were \$1.90 on entering the cab plus \$1.60 for each mile.*

a. Find the cost C of an x-mile trip.

b. Use your answer to calculate the cost of a 40-mile trip.

c. What is the cost of the second mile? What is the cost of the tenth mile?

d. Graph C as a function of x.

Solution

a. We are being asked to find how the cost C depends on the length x of the trip, or to find C as a function of x. Here is the cost in a few cases:

Cost of a 1-mile trip: $C = 1.60(1) + 1.90 = 3.50$ 1 mile @ \$1.60 per mile plus \$1.90

Cost of a 2-mile trip: $C = 1.60(2) + 1.90 = 5.10$ 2 miles @ \$1.60 per mile plus \$1.90

Cost of a 3-mile trip: $C = 1.60(3) + 1.90 = 6.70$ 3 miles @ \$1.60 per mile plus \$1.90

Do you see the pattern? The cost of an x-mile trip is given by the linear function:

$$C(x) = 1.60x + 1.90$$

Notice that the slope 1.60 is the incremental cost per mile. In this context we call 1.60 the **marginal cost;** the varying quantity $1.60x$ is called the **variable cost.** The

*According to their website at www.yellowcabchicago.com/.

C-intercept 1.90 is the cost to enter the cab, which we call the **fixed cost.** In general, a linear cost function has the following form:

$$C(x) = \overbrace{mx}^{\text{Variable cost}} + b$$

$\uparrow$ Marginal cost $\quad\uparrow$ Fixed cost

b. We can use the formula for the cost function to calculate the cost of a 40-mile trip as:

$$C(40) = 1.60(40) + 1.90 = \$65.90$$

c. To calculate the cost of the second mile, we *could* proceed as follows:

Find the cost of a 1-mile trip: $C(1) = 1.60(1) + 1.90 = \$3.50$

Find the cost of a 2-mile trip: $C(2) = 1.60(2) + 1.90 = \$5.10$

Therefore, the cost of the second mile is $\$5.10 - \$3.50 = \$1.60$

But notice that this is just the marginal cost. In fact, the marginal cost is the cost of each additional mile, so we could have done this more simply:

Cost of second mile = Cost of tenth mile = Marginal cost = \$1.60

d. Figure 16 shows the graph of the cost function, which we can interpret as a *cost vs. miles* graph. The fixed cost is the starting height on the left, while the marginal cost is the slope of the line.

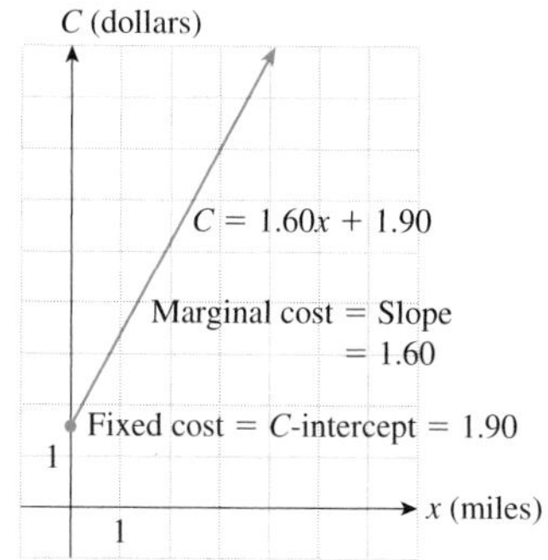

Figure **16**

+ *Before we go on...* In general, the slope m measures the number of units of change in y per 1-unit change in x, so *we measure m in units of y per unit of x:*

Units of Slope = Units of y per unit of x

In Example 1, y is the cost C, measured in dollars, and x is the length of a trip, measured in miles. Hence,

Units of Slope = Units of y per Unit of x = Dollars per mile

The y-intercept b, being a value of y, is measured in the same units as y. In Example 1, b is measured in dollars. ■

Here is a summary of the terms used in the preceding example, along with an introduction to some new terms.

Cost, Revenue, and Profit Functions

A **cost function** specifies the cost C as a function of the number of items x. Thus, $C(x)$ is the cost of x items. A cost function of the form

$$C(x) = mx + b$$

is called a **linear cost function.** The quantity mx is called the **variable cost** and the intercept b is called the **fixed cost.** The slope m, the **marginal cost,** measures the incremental cost per item.

mathematics At Work — Esteban Silva

TITLE Owner
INSTITUTION Regimen

Patrick Farace

Regimen is a retail shop and online merchant of high-end men's grooming products, a small business venture under my development. I came up with this concept in order fill the growing demand for men's grooming products from both graying baby boomers wanting to retain their competitive edge and young men who are increasingly accepting of the idea that is essential to be well styled and well groomed. The currently \$3.5 billion a year men's grooming market is ever-expanding and there is tremendous opportunity for Regimen to take advantage of this untapped potential.

In the initial stages of this business venture I have relied on math to calculate the amount of capital needed to launch and sustain the business until it becomes profitable. Using spreadsheets I input projected sales figures and estimated monthly expenses to formulate if it is possible to realistically meet targets and achieve break-even in a timely matter. With assistance from a professional interior designer, I have drawn up plans which include space acquisition, contracting, and construction costs in order budget for build-out expenses.

I have teamed up with Yahoo! Small Business Solutions and devised an online advertising strategy which allows me to reach out to the niche customers my company's products are geared towards. Using a sponsored search method of advertising I pre-determine how much I am willing to spend for each combination of keywords which drive traffic onto my website via Yahoo! I can track on a daily basis the number of matches each combination of keywords are receiving and, therefore, determine if any of them need to be altered. It's very important that I analyze these figures frequently so I can redirect the limited marketing resources of this start-up company into the most effective channels available. Thankfully, the applied mathematics techniques I learned in college have helped me live the dream of owning my own business and being my own boss.

The **revenue** resulting from one or more business transactions is the total payment received, sometimes called the gross proceeds. If $R(x)$ is the revenue from selling x items at a price of m each, then R is the linear function $R(x) = mx$ and the selling price m can also be called the **marginal revenue.**

The **profit,** on the other hand, is the *net* proceeds, or what remains of the revenue when costs are subtracted. If the profit depends linearly on the number of items, the slope m is called the **marginal profit.** Profit, revenue, and cost are related by the following formula:

$$\text{Profit} = \text{Revenue} - \text{Cost}$$
$$P = R - C$$

If the profit is negative, say $-\$500$, we refer to a **loss** (of \$500 in this case). To **break-even** means to make neither a profit nor a loss. Thus, break-even occurs when $P = 0$, or

$$R = C \qquad \text{Break-even}$$

The **break-even point** is the number of items x at which break-even occurs.

quick Example

If the daily cost (including operating costs) of manufacturing x T-shirts is $C(x) = 8x + 100$, and the revenue obtained by selling x T-shirts is $R(x) = 10x$, then the daily profit resulting from the manufacture and sale of x T-shirts is

$$P(x) = R(x) - C(x) = 10x - (8x + 100) = 2x - 100$$

Break-even occurs when $P(x) = 0$, or $x = 50$.

Example 2 Cost, Revenue, and Profit

The manager of the FrozenAir Refrigerator factory notices that on Monday it cost the company a total of \$25,000 to build 30 refrigerators and on Tuesday it cost \$30,000 to build 40 refrigerators.

a. Find a linear cost function based on this information. What is the daily fixed cost, and what is the marginal cost?

b. FrozenAir sells its refrigerators for \$1500 each. What is the revenue function?

c. What is the profit function? How many refrigerators must FrozenAir sell in a day in order to break even for that day? What will happen if it sells fewer refrigerators? If it sells more?

Solution

a. We are seeking C as a linear function of x, the number of refrigerators sold:

$$C = mx + b$$

We are told that $C = 25{,}000$ when $x = 30$, and this amounts to being told that (30, 25,000) is a point on the graph of the cost function. Similarly, (40, 30,000) is another point on the line (Figure 17).

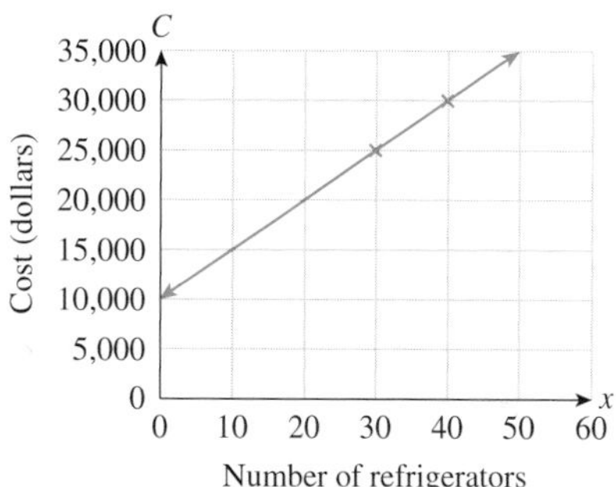

Figure **17**

We can now use the point-slope formula to construct a linear cost equation. Recall that we need two items of information: a point on the line and the slope:

- ***Point*** Let's use the first point: $(x_1, C_1) = (30{,}25{,}000)$ — *C* plays the role of *y*

- ***Slope*** $m = \dfrac{C_2 - C_1}{x_2 - x_1} = \dfrac{30{,}000 - 25{,}000}{40 - 30} = 500$ — Marginal cost = \$500

The cost function is therefore

$$C(x) = 500x + b$$

where $b = C_1 - mx_1 = 25{,}000 - (500)(30) = 10{,}000$ — Fixed cost = \$10,000

so $C(x) = 500x + 10{,}000$

Because $m = 500$ and $b = 10{,}000$ the factory's fixed cost is \$10,000 each day, and its marginal cost is \$500 per refrigerator.

b. The revenue FrozenAir obtains from the sale of a single refrigerator is \$1500. So, if it sells x refrigerators, it earns a revenue of

$$R(x) = 1500x$$

c. For the profit, we use the formula

$$\text{Profit} = \text{Revenue} - \text{Cost}$$

For the cost and revenue, we can substitute the answers from parts (a) and (b) and obtain

$$\begin{aligned} P(x) &= R(x) - C(x) && \text{Formula for profit} \\ &= 1500x - (500x + 10{,}000) && \text{Substitute } R(x) \text{ and } C(x) \\ &= 1000x - 10{,}000 \end{aligned}$$

Here, $P(x)$ is the daily profit FrozenAir makes by making and selling x refrigerators. Finally, to break even means to make zero profit. So, we need to find the x such that $P(x) = 0$. All we have to do is set $P(x) = 0$ and solve for x:

$$1000x - 10{,}000 = 0$$

giving

$$x = \frac{10{,}000}{1000} = 10$$

To break even, FrozenAir needs to manufacture and sell 10 refrigerators in a day.

For values of x less than the break-even point, 10, $P(x)$ is negative, so the company will have a loss. For values of x greater than the break-even point, $P(x)$ is positive, so the company will make a profit. This is the reason why we are interested in the point where $P(x) = 0$. Since $P(x) = R(x) - C(x)$, we can also look at the break-even point as the point where Revenue = Cost: $R(x) = C(x)$ (see Figure 18).

+ *Before we go on...* We can graph the cost and revenue functions from Example 2, and find the break-even point graphically (Figure 18):

$$\text{Cost: } C(x) = 500x + 10{,}000$$

$$\text{Revenue: } R(x) = 1500x$$

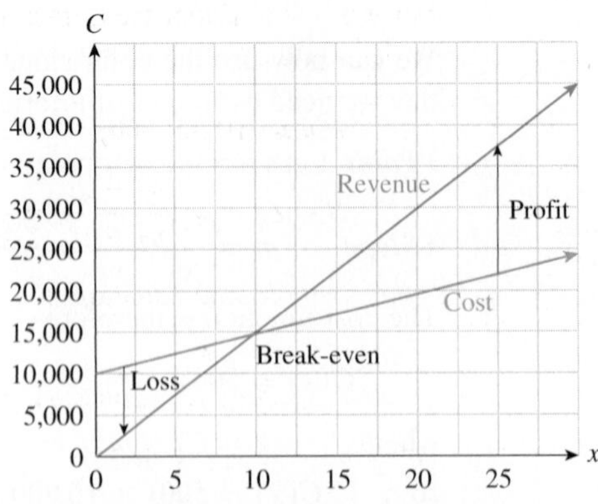

Break-even occurs at the point of intersection of the graphs of revenue and cost.

Figure **18**

The break-even point is the point where the revenue and cost are equal—that is, where the graphs of cost and revenue cross. Figure 18 confirms that break-even occurs when $x = 10$ refrigerators. Or, we can use the graph to find the break-even point in the first place. If we use technology, we can "zoom in" for an accurate estimate of the point of intersection.

Excel has an interesting feature called "Goal Seek" that can be used to find the point of intersection of two lines numerically (rather than graphically). The downloadable Excel tutorial for this section contains detailed instructions on using Goal Seek to find break-even points. ■

Demand and Supply Functions

The demand for a commodity usually goes down as its price goes up. It is traditional to use the letter q for the (quantity of) demand, as measured, for example, in weekly sales. Consider the following example.

Example 3 Linear Demand Function

You run a small supermarket, and must determine how much to charge for Hot'n'Spicy brand baked beans. The following chart shows weekly sales figures for Hot'n'Spicy at two different prices.

Price/Can (p)	\$0.50	\$0.75
Demand (cans sold/week) (q)	400	350

a. Model the data by expressing the demand q as a linear function of the price p.

b. How do we interpret the slope? The q-intercept?

c. How much should you charge for a can of Hot'n'Spicy beans if you want the demand to increase to 410 cans per week?

Solution

a. A **demand equation** or **demand function** expresses demand q (in this case, the number of cans of beans sold per week) as a function of the unit price p (in this case, price per can). We model the demand using the two points we are given: (0.50, 400) and (0.75, 350).

Point: (0.50, 400)

$$\textbf{\textit{Slope:}}\ m = \frac{q_2 - q_1}{p_2 - p_1} = \frac{350 - 400}{0.75 - 0.50} = \frac{-50}{0.25} = -200$$

Thus, the demand equation is

$$q = mp + b$$
$$= -200p + (400 - (-200)(0.50))$$

or $q = -200p + 500$

Figure 19 shows the data points and the linear model.

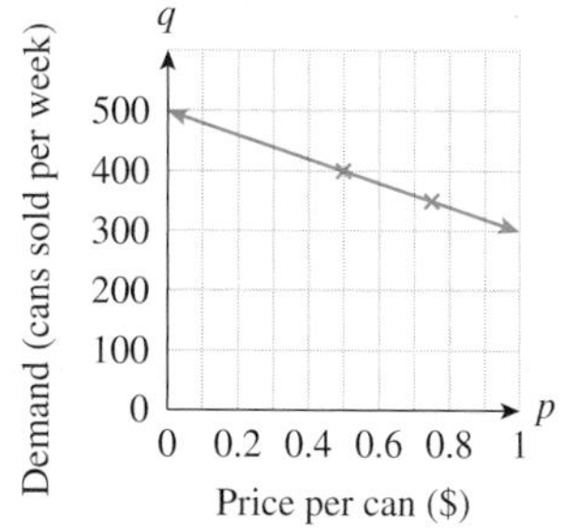

Figure 19

b. The key to interpreting the slope, $m = -200$, is to recall (see Example 1) that we measure the slope in units of y per unit of x. In this example, we mean units of q per unit of p, or the number of cans sold per dollar change in the price. Because m is negative, we see that the number of cans sold decreases as the price increases. We conclude that the weekly sales will drop by 200 cans per \$1-increase in the price.

To interpret the q-intercept, recall that it gives the q-coordinate when $p = 0$. Hence it is the number of cans the supermarket can "sell" every week if it were to give them away.*

c. If we want the demand to increase to 410 cans per week, we set $q = 410$ and solve for p:

$$410 = -200p + 500$$
$$200p = 90$$
$$p = \frac{90}{200} = \$0.45/\text{can}$$

* Does this seem realistic? Demand is not always unlimited if items were given away. For instance, campus newspapers are sometimes given away, and yet piles of them are often left untaken. Also see the "Before we go on . . ." discussion at the end of this example.

using *Technology*

A graphing calculator or Excel can be used to find the answer to part (c) numerically; consult the Technology Guides at the end of the chapter to find out how.

+ Before we go on...

Q: *Just how reliable is the linear model used in Example 3?*

A: The *actual* demand graph could in principle be obtained by tabulating new sales figures for a large number of different prices. If the resulting points were plotted on the *pq* plane, they would probably suggest a curve and not a straight line. However, if you looked at a small enough portion of this curve, you could closely *approximate* it by a straight line. In other words, *over a small range of values of p, the linear model is accurate.* Linear models of real-world situations are generally reliable only for small ranges of the variables. (This point will come up again in some of the exercises.) ■

Demand Function

A **demand equation** or **demand function** expresses demand q (the number of items demanded) as a function of the unit price p (the price per item). A **linear demand function** has the form

$$q(p) = mp + b$$

Interpretation of m

The (usually negative) slope m measures the change in demand per unit change in price. For instance, if p is measured in dollars and q in monthly sales and $m = -400$, then each \$1 increase in the price per item will result in a drop in sales of 400 items per month.

Interpretation of b

The y-intercept b gives the demand if the items were given away.

quick **Example**

If the demand for T-shirts, measured in daily sales, is given by $q(p) = -4p + 90$, where p is the sale price in dollars, then daily sales drop by four T-shirts for every \$1 increase in price. If the T-shirts were given away, the demand would be 90 T-shirts per day.

We have seen that a demand function gives the number of items consumers are willing to buy at a given price, and a higher price generally results in a lower demand. However, as the price rises, suppliers will be more inclined to produce these items (as opposed to spending their time and money on other products), so supply will generally rise. A **supply function** gives q, the number of items suppliers are willing to make available for sale[28], as a function of p, the price per item.

Example 4 Demand, Supply, and Equilibrium Price

Continuing with Example 3, consider the following chart, which shows weekly sales figures (the demand) for Hot'n'Spicy at two different prices, as well as the number of cans per week that you are prepared to place on sale (the supply) at these prices.

Price/Can	\$0.50	\$0.75
Demand (cans sold/week)	400	350
Supply (cans placed on sale/week)	300	500

a. Model these data with linear demand and supply functions.

b. How much should you charge per can of Hot'n'Spicy beans if you want the demand to equal the supply? How many cans will you sell at that price, known as the **equilibrium price?** What happens if you charge more than the equilibrium price? What happens if you charge less?

Solution

a. We have already modeled the demand function in Example 3:

$$q = -200p + 500$$

To model the supply, we use the first and third rows of the table. We are again given two points: (0.50, 300) and (0.75, 500):

Point: (0.50, 300)

$$\textbf{\textit{Slope:}}\ m = \frac{q_2 - q_1}{p_2 - p_1} = \frac{500 - 300}{0.75 - 0.50} = \frac{200}{0.25} = 800$$

So, the supply equation is

$$\begin{aligned} q &= mp + b \\ &= 800p + [300 - (800)(0.50)] \\ &= 800p - 100 \end{aligned}$$

b. To find where the demand equals the supply, we equate the two functions:

$$\begin{aligned} \text{Demand} &= \text{Supply} \\ -200p + 500 &= 800p - 100 \\ -1000p &= -600 \end{aligned}$$

so $$p = \frac{-600}{-1000} = \$0.60$$

This is the equilibrium price. We can find the corresponding demand by substituting 0.60 for p in the demand (or supply) equation.

$$\text{Equilibrium demand} = -200(0.60) + 500 = 380 \text{ cans per week}$$

[28] Although a bit confusing at first, it is traditional to use the same letter q for the quantity of supply and the quantity of demand, particularly when we want to compare them, as in the next example.

So, to balance supply and demand, you should charge \$0.60 per can of Hot'n'Spicy beans and you should place 380 cans on sale each week.

If we graph supply and demand on the same set of axes, we obtain the graphs shown in Figure 20.

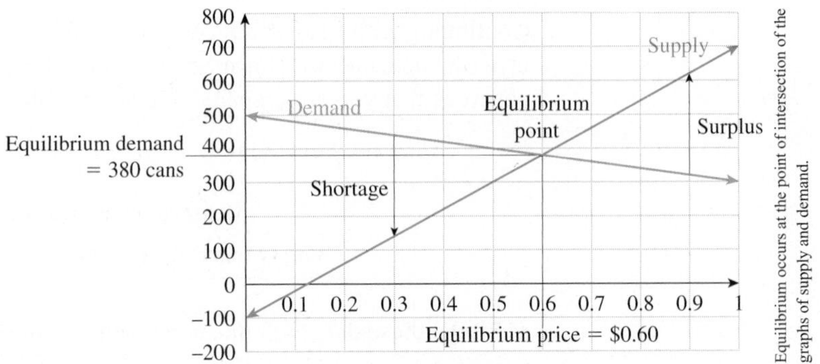

Figure **20**

Figure 20 shows what happens if you charge prices other than the equilibrium price. If you charge, say, \$0.90 per can ($p = 0.90$) then the supply will be larger than demand and there will be a weekly surplus. Similarly, if you charge less—say \$0.30 per can—then the supply will be less than the demand, and there will be a shortage of Hot'n'Spicy beans.

+ *Before we go on...* We just saw in Example 4 that if you charge less than the equilibrium price, there will be a shortage. If you were to raise your price toward the equilibrium, you would sell more items and increase revenue, since it is the supply equation—and not the demand equation—that determines what you can sell below the equilibrium price. On the other hand, if you charge more than the equilibrium price, you will be left with a possibly costly surplus of unsold items (and will want to lower prices to reduce the surplus). Prices tend to move toward the equilibrium, so supply tends to equal demand. When supply equals demand, we say that the market **clears.** ■

Supply Function and Equilibrium Price

A **supply equation** or **supply function** expresses supply q (the number of items a supplier is willing to make available) as a function of the unit price p (the price per item). A **linear supply function** has the form

$$q(p) = mp + b$$

It is usually the case that supply increases as the unit price increases, so m is usually positive.

Demand and supply are said to be in **equilibrium** when demand equals supply. The corresponding values of p and q are called the **equilibrium price** and **equilibrium demand.** To find the equilibrium price, set demand equal to supply and solve for the unit price p. To find the equilibrium demand, evaluate the demand (or supply) function at the equilibrium price.

Change Over Time

Things around us change with time. Thus, there are many quantities, such as your income or the temperature in Honolulu, that it is natural to think of as functions of time.

Example **5** Growth of Sales

The U.S. Air Force's satellite-based Global Positioning System (GPS) allows people with radio receivers to determine their exact location anywhere on earth. The following table shows the estimated total sales of U.S.-made products that use the GPS.*

Year	1994	2000
Sales ($ Billions)	0.8	8.3

a. Use these data to model total sales of GPS-based products as a linear function of time t measured in years since 1994. What is the significance of the slope?

b. Use the model to predict when sales of GPS-based products will reach $13.3 billion, assuming they continue to grow at the same rate.

Solution

a. First, notice that 1994 corresponds to $t = 0$ and 2000 to $t = 6$. Thus, we are given the coordinates of two points on the graph of sales s as a function of time t: (0, 0.8) and (6, 8.3). The slope is

$$m = \frac{s_2 - s_1}{t_2 - t_1} = \frac{8.3 - 0.8}{6 - 0} = \frac{7.5}{6} = 1.25$$

Using the point (0, 0.8), we get

$$\begin{aligned} s &= mt + b \\ &= 1.25t + 0.8 - (1.25)(0) \\ &= 1.25t + 0.8 \end{aligned}$$

Notice that we calculated the slope as the ratio (change in sales)/(change in time). Thus, m is the *rate of change* of sales and is measured in units of sales per unit of time, or billions of dollars per year. In other words, to say that $m = 1.25$ is to say that sales are increasing by $1.25 billion per year.

b. Our model of sales as a function of time is

$$s = 1.25t + 0.8$$

Sales of GPS-based products will reach $13.3 billion when $s = 13.3$, or

$$13.3 = 1.25t + 0.8$$

Solving for t,

$$1.25t = 13.3 - 0.8 = 12.5$$

$$t = \frac{12.5}{1.25} = 10$$

In 2004 ($t = 10$), sales are predicted to reach $13.3 billion.

---

* Data estimated from published graph. SOURCE: U.S. Global Positioning System Industry Council/*New York Times*, March 5, 1996, p. D1.

Example 6 Velocity

You are driving down the Ohio Turnpike, watching the mileage markers to stay awake. Measuring time in hours after you see the 20-mile marker, you see the following markers each half hour:

Time (h)	0	0.5	1	1.5	2
Marker (mi)	20	47	74	101	128

Find your location s as a function of t, the number of hours you have been driving. (The number s is also called your **position** or **displacement.**)

Solution

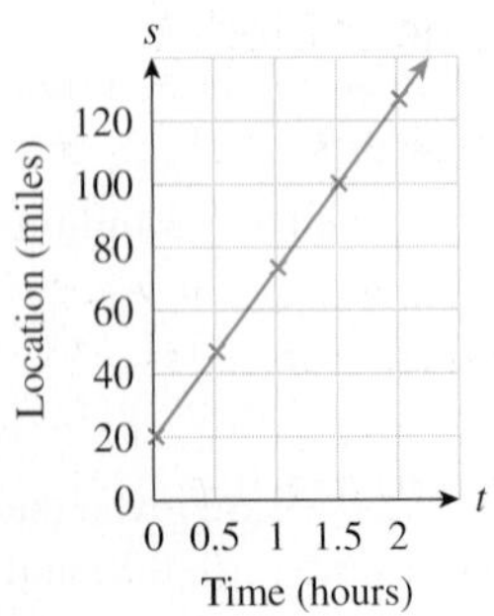

Figure **21**

If we plot the location s versus the time t, the five markers listed give us the graph in Figure 21.

These points appear to lie along a straight line. We can verify this by calculating how far you traveled in each half hour. In the first half hour, you traveled $47 - 20 = 27$ miles. In the second half hour you traveled $74 - 47 = 27$ miles also. In fact, you traveled exactly 27 miles each half hour. The points we plotted lie on a straight line that rises 27 units for every 0.5 unit we go to the right, for a slope of $27/0.5 = 54$.

To get the equation of that line, notice that we have the s-intercept, which is the starting marker of 20. From the slope intercept form (using s in place of y and t in place of x) we get:

$$s(t) = 54t + 20$$

Notice the significance of the slope: For every hour you travel, you drive a distance of 54 miles. In other words, you are traveling at a constant velocity of 54 mph. We have uncovered a very important principle:

In the graph of displacement versus time, velocity is given by the slope.

Linear Change Over Time

If a quantity q is a linear function of time t, so that

$$q(t) = mt + b$$

then the slope m measures the **rate of change** of q, and b is the quantity at time $t = 0$, the **initial quantity.** If q represents the position of a moving object, then the rate of change is also called the **velocity.**

Units of m and b

The units of measurement of m are units of q per unit of time; for instance, if q is income in dollars and t is time in years, then the rate of change m is measured in dollars per year.

The units of b are units of q; for instance, if q is income in dollars and t is time in years, then b is measured in dollars.

quick **Example**

If the accumulated revenue from sales of your video game software is given by $R(t) = 2000t + 500$ dollars, where t is time in years from now, then you have earned \$500 in revenue so far, and the accumulated revenue is increasing at a rate of \$2000 per year.

Examples 1–6 share the following common theme.

General Linear Models

If $y = mx + b$ is a linear model of changing quantities x and y, then the slope m is the rate at which y is increasing per unit increase in x, and the y-intercept b is the value of y that corresponds to $x = 0$.

Units of m and b

The slope m is measured in units of y per unit of x, and the intercept b is measured in units of y.

quick Example

If the number n of spectators at a soccer game is related to the number g of goals your team has scored so far by the equation $n = 20g + 4$, then you can expect 4 spectators if no goals have been scored and 20 additional spectators per additional goal scored.

FAQs What to Use as x and y, and How to Interpret a Linear Model

Q: *In a problem where I must find a linear relationship between two quantities, which quantity do I use as x and which do I use as y?*

A: The key is to decide which of the two quantities is the independent variable, and which is the dependent variable. Then use the independent variable as x and the dependent variable as y. In other words, *y depends on x.*

Here are examples of phrases that convey this information, usually of the form *Find y [dependent variable] in terms of x [independent variable]*:

- Find the cost in terms of the number of items. y = Cost, x = # Items
- How does color depend on wavelength? y = Color, x = Wavelength

If no information is conveyed about which variable is intended to be independent, then you can use whichever is convenient. ■

Q: *How do I interpret a general linear model $y = mx + b$?*

A: The key to interpreting a linear model is to remember the units we use to measure m and b:

The slope m is measured in units of y per unit of x; the intercept b is measured in units of y.

For instance, if $y = 4.3x + 8.1$ and you know that x is measured in feet and y in kilograms, then you can already say, "y is 8.1 kilograms when $x = 0$ feet, and increases at a rate of 4.3 kilograms per foot" without even knowing anything more about the situation! ■

1.4 EXERCISES

● denotes basic skills exercises

◆ denotes challenging exercises

tech Ex indicates exercises that should be solved using technology

Applications

1. ● ***Cost*** A piano manufacturer has a daily fixed cost of \$1200 and a marginal cost of \$1500 per piano. Find the cost $C(x)$ of manufacturing x pianos in one day. Use your function to answer the following questions: *hint* [see Example 1]

   a. On a given day, what is the cost of manufacturing 3 pianos?

   b. What is the cost of manufacturing the 3rd piano that day?

   c. What is the cost of manufacturing the 11th piano that day?

2. ● ***Cost*** The cost of renting tuxes for the Choral Society's formal is \$20 down, plus \$88 per tux. Express the cost C as a function of x, the number of tuxedos rented. Use your function to answer the following questions.

   a. What is the cost of renting 2 tuxes?

   b. What is the cost of the 2nd tux?

   c. What is the cost of the 4098th tux?

   d. What is the marginal cost per tux?

3. ● ***Cost*** The RideEm Bicycles factory can produce 100 bicycles in a day at a total cost of \$10,500 and it can produce 120 bicycles in a day at a total cost of \$11,000. What are the company's daily fixed costs, and what is the marginal cost per bicycle? hint [see Example 2]

4. ● ***Cost*** A soft-drink manufacturer can produce 1000 cases of soda in a week at a total cost of \$6000, and 1500 cases of soda at a total cost of \$8500. Find the manufacturer's weekly fixed costs and marginal cost per case of soda.

5. ● ***Break-even Analysis*** Your college newspaper, *The Collegiate Investigator,* has fixed production costs of \$70 per edition, and marginal printing and distribution costs of 40¢/copy. *The Collegiate Investigator* sells for 50¢/copy. hint [see Example 2]

   a. Write down the associated cost, revenue, and profit functions.
   b. What profit (or loss) results from the sale of 500 copies of *The Collegiate Investigator*?
   c. How many copies should be sold in order to break even?

6. ● ***Break-even Analysis*** The Audubon Society at Enormous State University (ESU) is planning its annual fund-raising "Eatathon." The society will charge students 50¢/serving of pasta. The only expenses the society will incur are the cost of the pasta, estimated at 15¢/serving, and the \$350 cost of renting the facility for the evening.

   a. Write down the associated cost, revenue, and profit functions.
   b. How many servings of pasta must the Audubon Society sell in order to break even?
   c. What profit (or loss) results from the sale of 1500 servings of pasta?

7. ● ***Demand*** Sales figures show that your company sold 1960 pen sets each week when they were priced at \$1/pen set, and 1800 pen sets each week when they were priced at \$5/pen set. What is the linear demand function for your pen sets? hint [see Example 3]

8. ● ***Demand*** A large department store is prepared to buy 3950 per month of your neon-colored shower curtains for \$5 each, but only 3700 shower curtains per month for \$10 each. What is the linear demand function for your neon-colored shower curtains?

9. ● ***Demand for Cell Phones*** The following table shows worldwide sales of Nokia® cell phones and their average wholesale prices in 2004:[29]

Quarter	*Second*	*Fourth*
Wholesale Price (\$)	111	105
Sales (millions)	45.4	51.4

   a. Use the data to obtain a linear demand function for (Nokia) cell phones, and use your demand equation to predict sales if Nokia lowered the price further to \$103.
   b. Fill in the blanks: For every ____ increase in price, sales of cell phones decrease by ____ units.

10. ● ***Demand for Cell Phones*** The following table shows projected worldwide sales of (all) cell phones and wholesale prices:[30]

Year	*2004*	*2008*
Wholesale Price (\$)	100	80
Sales (millions)	600	800

   a. Use the data to obtain a linear demand function for cell phones, and use your demand equation to predict sales if the price were set at \$85.
   b. Fill in the blanks: For every ____ increase in price, sales of cell phones decrease by ____ units.

11. ● ***Equilibrium Price*** You can sell 90 pet chias per week if they are marked at \$1 each, but only 30 each week if they are marked at \$2/chia. Your chia supplier is prepared to sell you 20 chias each week if they are marked at \$1/chia, and 100 each week if they are marked at \$2 per chia. hint [see Example 4]

   a. Write down the associated linear demand and supply functions.
   b. At what price should the chias be marked so that there is neither a surplus nor a shortage of chias?

12. ● ***Equilibrium Price*** The demand for your college newspaper is 2000 copies each week if the paper is given away free of charge, and drops to 1000 each week if the charge is 10¢/copy. However, the university is prepared to supply only 600 copies per week free of charge, but will supply 1400 each week at 20¢ per copy.

   a. Write down the associated linear demand and supply functions.
   b. At what price should the college newspapers be sold so that there is neither a surplus nor a shortage of papers?

13. ● ***Swimming Pool Sales*** The following graph shows approximate annual sales of new in-ground swimming pools in the U.S.[31]

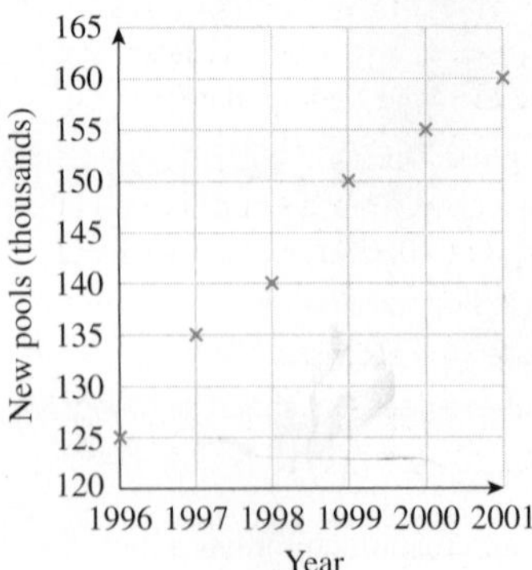

[29] SOURCE: Embedded.com/Company reports December, 2004.

[30] Wholesale price projections are the authors'. Source for sales prediction: I-Stat/NDR December, 2004.

[31] 2001 figure is an estimate. SOURCE: PK Data/*New York Times,* July 5, 2001, p. C1.

a. Find two points on the graph such that the slope of the line segment joining them is the largest possible.
b. What does your answer tell you about swimming pool sales?

14. ● ***Swimming Pool Sales*** Repeat Exercise 13 using the following graph for sales of new above-ground swimming pools in the U.S.[32]

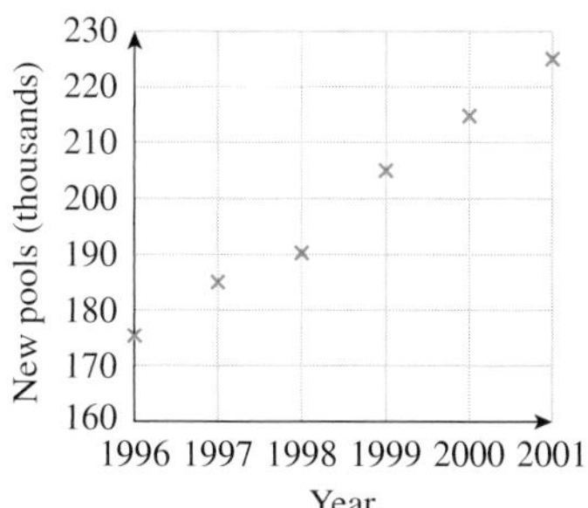

15. ● ***Online Shopping*** The number of online shopping transactions in the U.S. increased from 350 million transactions in 1999 to 450 million transactions in 2001.[33] Find a linear model for the number N of online shopping transactions in year t, with $t = 0$ corresponding to 2000. What is the significance of the slope? What are its units? *hint* [see Example 5]

16. ● ***Online Shopping*** The percentage of people in the U.S. who have ever purchased anything online increased from 20% in January, 2000 to 35% in January, 2002.[34] Find a linear model for the percentage P of people in the U.S. who have ever purchased anything online in year t, with $t = 0$ corresponding to January, 2000. What is the significance of the slope? What are its units?

17. ● ***Medicare Spending*** Annual federal spending on Medicare (in constant 2000 dollars) was projected to increase from $240 billion in 2000 to $600 billion in 2025.[35]
    a. Use this information to express s, the annual spending on Medicare (in billions of dollars), as a linear function of t, the number of years since 2000. How fast is Medicare predicted to rise in the coming years?
    b. Use your model to predict Medicare spending in 2040, assuming the spending trend continues.

18. ● ***Pasta Imports*** During the period 1990–2001, U.S. imports of pasta increased from 290 million pounds in 1990 ($t = 0$) by an average of 40 million pounds/year.[36]
    a. Use these data to express q, the annual U.S. imports of pasta (in millions of pounds), as a linear function of t, the number of years since 1990.
    b. Use your model to estimate U.S. pasta imports in 2005, assuming the import trend continued.

19. ● ***Velocity*** The position of a model train, in feet along a railroad track, is given by

$$s(t) = 2.5t + 10$$

after t seconds.
    a. How fast is the train moving?
    b. Where is the train after 4 seconds?
    c. When will it be 25 feet along the track?

20. ● ***Velocity*** The height of a falling sheet of paper, in feet from the ground, is given by

$$s(t) = -1.8t + 9$$

after t seconds.
    a. What is the velocity of the sheet of paper?
    b. How high is it after 4 seconds?
    c. When will it reach the ground?

21. ***Fast Cars*** A police car was traveling down Ocean Parkway in a high-speed chase from Jones Beach. It was at Jones Beach at exactly 10 PM ($t = 10$) and was at Oak Beach, 13 miles from Jones Beach, at exactly 10:06 PM.
    a. How fast was the police car traveling?
    b. How far was the police car from Jones Beach at time t? *hint* [see Example 6]

22. ***Fast Cars*** The car that was being pursued by the police in Exercise 21 was at Jones Beach at exactly 9:54 PM ($t = 9.9$) and passed Oak Beach (13 miles from Jones Beach) at exactly 10:06 PM, where it was overtaken by the police.
    a. How fast was the car traveling?
    b. How far was the car from Jones Beach at time t?

23. ***Fahrenheit and Celsius*** In the Fahrenheit temperature scale, water freezes at 32°F and boils at 212°F. In the Celsius scale, water freezes at 0°C and boils at 100°C. Assuming that the Fahrenheit temperature F and the Celsius temperature C are related by a linear equation, find F in terms of C. Use your equation to find the Fahrenheit temperatures corresponding to 30°C, 22°C, –10°C, and –14°C, to the nearest degree.

24. ***Fahrenheit and Celsius*** Use the information about Celsius and Fahrenheit given in Exercise 23 to obtain a linear equation for C in terms of F, and use your equation to find the Celsius temperatures corresponding to 104°F, 77°F, 14°F, and −40°F, to the nearest degree.

25. ***Income*** The well-known romance novelist Celestine A. Lafleur (a.k.a. Bertha Snodgrass) has decided to sell the screen rights to her latest book, *Henrietta's Heaving Heart,* to Boxoffice Success Productions for $50,000. In addition, the contract ensures Ms. Lafleur royalties of 5% of the net

---

[32] Ibid.

[33] Second half of 2001 data was an estimate. Source for data: Odyssey Research/*New York Times,* November 5, 2001, p. C1.

[34] January 2002 data was estimated. Source for data: Odyssey Research/*New York Times,* November 5, 2001, p. C1.

[35] Data are rounded. SOURCE: The Urban Institute's Analysis of the 1999 Trustee's Report www.urban.org

[36] Data are rounded. SOURCES: Department of Commerce/*New York Times,* September 5, 1995, p. D4, International Trade Administration (www.ita.doc.gov/) March 31, 2002.

profits.[37] Express her income I as a function of the net profit N, and determine the net profit necessary to bring her an income of \$100,000. What is her marginal income (share of each dollar of net profit)?

26. ***Income*** Due to the enormous success of the movie *Henrietta's Heaving Heart,* based on a novel by Celestine A. Lafleur (see the Exercise 25), Boxoffice Success Productions decides to film the sequel, *Henrietta, Oh Henrietta.* At this point, Bertha Snodgrass (whose novels now top the best seller lists) feels she is in a position to demand \$100,000 for the screen rights and royalties of 8% of the net profits. Express her income I as a function of the net profit N and determine the net profit necessary to bring her an income of \$1,000,000. What is her marginal income (share of each dollar of net profit)?

Exercises 27–30 are based on the following data, showing the total amount of milk and cheese, in billions of pounds, produced in the 13 Western and 12 North-Central U.S. states in 1999 and 2000.[38]

Milk	1999	2000
Western States	56	60
North-Central States	57	59
Cheese	**1999**	**2000**
Western States	2.7	3.0
North-Central States	3.9	4.0

27. Use the data from both years to find a linear relationship giving the amount of milk w produced in Western states as a function of the amount of milk n produced in North-Central states. Use your model to predict how much milk Western states will produce if North-Central states produce 50 billion pounds.

28. Use the data from both years to find a linear relationship giving the amount of cheese w produced in Western states as a function of the amount of cheese n produced in North-Central states. Use your model to predict how much cheese Western states will produce if North-Central states produce 3.4 billion pounds.

29. Use the data to model cheese production c in Western states as a function of milk production m in Western states. According to the model, how many pounds of cheese are produced for every 10 pounds of milk?

30. Repeat Exercise 29 for North-Central states.

31. ***Biology*** The Snowtree cricket behaves in a rather interesting way: The rate at which it chirps depends linearly on the temperature. One summer evening you hear a cricket chirping at a rate of 140 chirps/minute, and you notice that the temperature is 80°F. Later in the evening the cricket has slowed down to 120 chirps/minute, and you notice that the temperature has dropped to 75°F. Express the temperature T as a function of the cricket's rate of chirping r. What is the temperature if the cricket is chirping at a rate of 100 chirps/ minute?

32. ***Muscle Recovery Time*** Most workout enthusiasts will tell you that muscle recovery time is about 48 hours. But it is not quite as simple as that; the recovery time ought to depend on the number of sets you do involving the muscle group in question. For example, if you do no sets of biceps exercises, then the recovery time for your biceps is (of course) zero. To take a compromise position, let's assume that if you do three sets of exercises on a muscle group, then its recovery time is 48 hours. Use these data to write a linear function that gives the recovery time (in hours) in terms of the number of sets affecting a particular muscle. Use this model to calculate how long it would take your biceps to recover if you did 15 sets of curls. Comment on your answer with reference to the usefulness of a linear model.

33. ***Profit Analysis—Aviation*** The operating cost of a Boeing 747-100, which seats up to 405 passengers, is estimated to be \$5,132 per hour.[39] If an airline charges each passenger a fare of \$100 per hour of flight, find the hourly profit P it earns operating a 747-100 as a function of the number of passengers x (be sure to specify the domain). What is the least number of passengers it must carry in order to make a profit?

34. ***Profit Analysis—Aviation*** The operating cost of a McDonnell Douglas DC 10-10, which seats up to 295 passengers, is estimated to be \$3885 per hour.[40] If an airline charges each passenger a fare of \$100 per hour of flight, find the hourly profit P it earns operating a DC 10-10 as a function of the number of passengers x (be sure to specify the domain). What is the least number of passengers it must carry in order to make a profit?

35. ***Break-even Analysis*** *(based on a question from a CPA exam)* The Oliver Company plans to market a new product. Based on its market studies, Oliver estimates that it can sell up to 5500 units in 2005. The selling price will be \$2 per unit. Variable costs are estimated to be 40% of total revenue. Fixed costs are estimated to be \$6000 for 2005. How many units should the company sell to break even?

36. ***Break-even Analysis*** *(based on a question from a CPA exam)* The Metropolitan Company sells its latest product at a unit price of \$5. Variable costs are estimated to be 30% of the total revenue, while fixed costs amount to \$7000 per month. How many units should the company sell per month in order to break even, assuming that it can sell up to 5000 units per month at the planned price?

37. ◆ ***Break-even Analysis*** *(from a CPA exam)* Given the following notations, write a formula for the break-even sales level.

[37] Percentages of net profit are commonly called "monkey points." Few movies ever make a net profit on paper, and anyone with any clout in the business gets a share of the *gross,* not the net.

[38] Figures are approximate. SOURCE: Department of Agriculture/*New York Times,* June 28, 2001, p. C1.

[39] In 1992. SOURCE: Air Transportation Association of America.

[40] Ibid.

SP = Selling price per unit

FC = Total fixed cost

VC = Variable cost per unit

38. ◆ ***Break-even Analysis*** *(based on a question from a CPA exam)* Given the following notation, give a formula for the total fixed cost.

SP = Selling price per unit

VC = Variable cost per unit

BE = Break-even sales level in units

39. ◆ ***Break-even Analysis—Organized Crime*** The organized crime boss and perfume king Butch (Stinky) Rose has daily overheads (bribes to corrupt officials, motel photographers, wages for hit men, explosives, etc.) amounting to \$20,000 per day. On the other hand, he has a substantial income from his counterfeit perfume racket: he buys imitation French perfume (Chanel N° 22.5) at \$20 per gram, pays an additional \$30 per 100 grams for transportation, and sells it via his street thugs for \$600 per gram. Specify Stinky's profit function, $P(x)$, where x is the quantity (in grams) of perfume he buys and sells, and use your answer to calculate how much perfume should pass through his hands per day in order that he break even.

40. ◆ ***Break-even Analysis—Disorganized Crime*** Butch (Stinky) Rose's counterfeit Chanel N° 22.5 racket has run into difficulties; it seems that the *authentic* Chanel N° 22.5 perfume is selling at only \$500 per gram, whereas his street thugs have been selling the counterfeit perfume for \$600 per gram, and his costs are \$400 per gram plus \$30 per gram transportation costs and commission. (The perfume's smell is easily detected by specially trained Chanel Hounds, and this necessitates elaborate packaging measures.) He therefore decides to price it at \$420 per gram in order to undercut the competition. Specify Stinky's profit function, $P(x)$, where x is the quantity (in grams) of perfume he buys and sells, and use your answer to calculate how much perfume should pass through his hands per day in order that he break even. Interpret your answer.

41. ● ***Television Advertising*** The cost, in millions of dollars, of a 30-second television ad during the Super Bowl in the years 1990 to 2001 can be approximated by the following piecewise linear function ($t = 0$ represents 1990):[41]

$$C(t) = \begin{cases} 0.08t + 0.6 & \text{if } 0 \le t < 8 \\ 0.355t - 1.6 & \text{if } 8 \le t \le 11 \end{cases}$$

How fast and in what direction was the cost of an ad during the Super Bowl changing in 1999?

42. ● ***Processor Speeds*** The processor speed, in megahertz, of Intel processors could be approximated by the following function of time t in years since the start of 1995:[42]

$$P(t) = \begin{cases} 75t + 200 & \text{if } 0 \le t \le 4 \\ 600t - 1900 & \text{if } 4 < t \le 9 \end{cases}$$

How fast and in what direction was processor speed changing in 2002?

43. ***Investment in Gold*** Following are some approximate values of the Amex Gold BUGS Index[43]

Year	1995	2000	2004
Index	200	50	250

Take t to be the year since 1995 and y to be the BUGS index.

a. Model the 1995 and 2000 data with a linear equation.
b. Model the 2000 and 2004 data with a linear equation.
c. Use the results of parts (a) and (b) to obtain a piecewise linear model of the gold BUGS index for 1995–2004.
d. Use your model to estimate the index in 2002.

44. ***Unemployment*** The following table shows the number of unemployed persons in the U.S. from 1994, 2000, and 2004.[44]

Year	1994	2000	2004
Unemployment (Millions)	9	6	8

Take t to be the year since 1994 and y to be the number (in millions) of unemployed persons.

a. Model the 1994 and 2000 data with a linear equation.
b. Model the 2000 and 2004 data with a linear equation.
c. Use the results of parts (a) and (b) to obtain a piecewise linear model of the number (in millions) of unemployed persons for 1994–2004.
d. Use your model to estimate the number of unemployed persons in 2002.

45. ***Career Choices*** In 1989 approximately 30,000 college-bound high school seniors intended to major in computer and information sciences. This number decreased to approximately 23,000 in 1994, and rose to 60,000 in 1999.[45] Model this number C as a piecewise-linear function of the time t in years since 1989, and use your model to estimate the number of college-bound high school seniors who intended to major in computer and information sciences in 1992.

46. ***Career Choices*** In 1989 approximately 100,000 college-bound high school seniors intended to major in engineering. This number decreased to approximately 85,000 in 1994, and rose to 88,000 in 1999.[46] Model this number E as a piecewise-linear function of the time t in years since 1989, and use your model to estimate the number of college-bound high school seniors who intended to major in engineering in 1995.

[41] Source: *New York Times,* January 26, 2001, p. C1.

[42] Source: Sandpile.org/*New York Times,* May 17, 2004, p. C1.

[43] BUGS stands for "basket of unhedged gold stocks." Sources: www.321gold.com, Bloomberg Financial Markets/*New York Times,* Sept 7, 2003, p. BU8.

[44] Figures are seasonally adjusted and rounded. Source: U.S. Department of Labor, December, 2004. http://data.bls.gov

[45] Source: The College Board; National Science Foundation/*The New York Times,* September 2, 1999, p. C1.

[46] Ibid.

47. ***Divorce Rates*** A study found that the divorce rate d appears to depend on the ratio r of available men to available women.[47] When the ratio was 1.3 (130 available men per 100 available women) the divorce rate was 22%. It rose to 35% if the ratio grew to 1.6, and rose to 30% if the ratio dropped to 1.1. Model these data by expressing d as a piecewise-linear function of r, and extrapolate your model to estimate the divorce rate if there are the same number of available men as women.

48. ***Retirement*** In 1950 the number N of retirees was approximately 150 per 1000 people aged 20–64. In 1990 this number rose to approximately 200 and is projected to rise to 275 in 2020.[48] Model N as a piecewise-linear function of the time t in years since 1950, and use your model to project the number of retirees per 1000 people aged 20–64 in 2010.

Communication and Reasoning Exercises

49. ● If y is measured in bootlags[49] and x is measured in $\overline{\overline{Z}}$ (zonars, the designated currency in Utarek, Mars)[50] and $y = mx + b$, then m is measured in _______ and b is measured in _______.

50. ● If the slope in a linear relationship is measured in miles per dollar, then the independent variable is measured in ______ and the dependent variable is measured in ______.

51. ● If a quantity is changing linearly with time, and it increases by 10 units in the first day, what can you say about its behavior in the third day?

52. ● The quantities Q and T are related by a linear equation of the form

$$Q = mT + b$$

When $T = 0$, Q is positive, but decreases to a negative quantity when T is 10. What are the signs of m and b? Explain your answers.

53. The velocity of an object is given by $v = 0.1t + 20$ m/sec, where t is time in seconds. The object is

(A) moving with fixed speed **(B)** accelerating
(C) decelerating **(D)** impossible to say from the given information

54. The position of an object is given by $x = 0.2t - 4$, where t is time in seconds. The object is

(A) moving with fixed speed **(B)** accelerating
(C) decelerating **(D)** impossible to say from the given information

55. Suppose the cost function is $C(x) = mx + b$ (with m and b positive), the revenue function is $R(x) = kx (k > m)$ and the number of items is increased from the break-even quantity. Does this result in a loss, a profit, or is it impossible to say? Explain your answer.

56. You have been constructing a demand equation, and you obtained a (correct) expression of the form $p = mq + b$, whereas you would have preferred one of the form $q = mp + b$. Should you simply switch p and q in the answer, should you start again from scratch, using p in the role of x and q in the role of y, or should you solve your demand equation for q? Give reasons for your decision.

[47] The cited study, by Scott J. South and associates, appeared in the *American Sociological Review* (February, 1995). Figures are rounded. SOURCE: *The New York Times*, February 19, 1995, p. 40.

[48] Source: Social Security Administration/*The New York Times*, April 4, 1999, p. WK3.

[49] An ancient Martian unit of length; one bootlag is the mean distance from a Martian's foreleg to its rearleg.

[50] SOURCE: www.marsnext.com/comm/zonars.html

● basic skills ◆ challenging tech Ex technology exercise

1.5 Linear Regression

We have seen how to find a linear model, given two data points: We find the equation of the line that passes through them. However, we often have more than two data points, and they will rarely all lie on a single straight line, but may often come close to doing so. The problem is to find the line coming *closest* to passing through all of the points.

Suppose, for example, that we are conducting research for a cable TV company interested in expanding into China and we come across the following figures showing the growth of the cable market there.[51]

[51] Data are approximate, and the 2001–2003 figures are estimates. SOURCES: HSBC Securities, Bear Sterns/ *New York Times*, March 23, 2001, p. C1.

Year (t) ($t = 0$ represents 2000)	−4	−3	−2	−1	0	1	2	3
Households with Cable (y) (Millions)	50	55	57	60	68	72	80	83

A plot of these data suggests a roughly linear growth of the market. (Figure 22A).

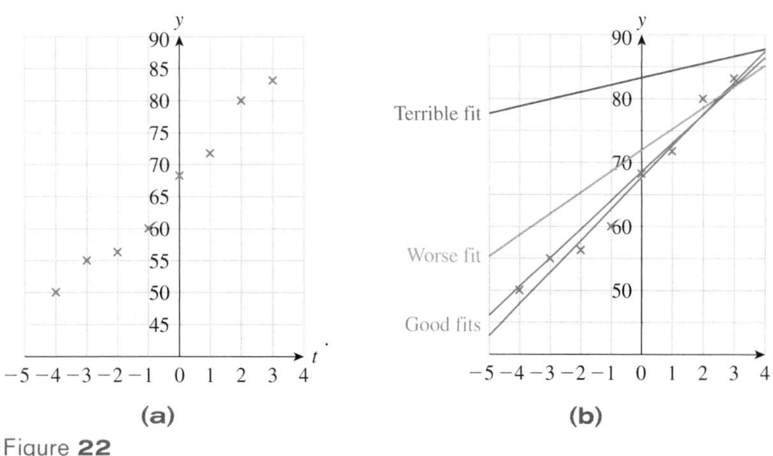

Figure **22**

These points suggest a line, although they clearly do not all lie on a single straight line. Figure 22B shows the points together with several lines, some fitting better than others. Can we precisely measure which lines fit better than others? For instance, which of the two lines labeled as "good" fits in Figure 22B models the data more accurately? We begin by considering, for each of the years 1996 through 2003, the difference between the actual number of households with cable (the **observed value**) and the number of households with cable predicted by a linear equation (the **predicted value**). The difference between the predicted value and the observed value is called the **residual.**

$$\text{Residual} = \text{Observed Value} - \text{Predicted Value}$$

On the graph, the residuals measure the vertical distances between the (observed) data points and the line (Figure 23) and they tell us how far the linear model is from predicting the number of households with cable.

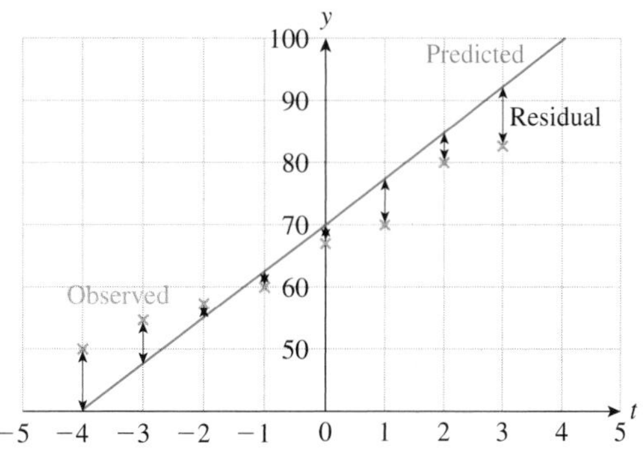

Figure **23**

The more accurate our model, the smaller the residuals should be. We can combine all the residuals into a single measure of accuracy by adding their *squares.* (We square the residuals in part to make them all positive.[52]) The sum of the squares of the residuals is called the **sum-of-squares error, SSE.** Smaller values of SSE indicate more accurate models.

Here are some definitions and formulas for what we have been discussing.

Observed and Predicted Values

Suppose we are given a collection of data points $(x_1, y_1), \ldots, (x_n, y_n)$. The n quantities $y_1, y_2, \ldots, y_n$ are called the **observed *y*-values.** If we model these data with a linear equation

$$\hat{y} = mx + b \qquad \hat{y} \text{ stands for "estimated } y\text{" or "predicted } y\text{."}$$

then the y-values we get by substituting the given x-values into the equation are called the **predicted *y*-values.**

$$\hat{y}_1 = mx_1 + b \qquad \text{Substitute } x_1 \text{ for } x.$$

$$\hat{y}_2 = mx_2 + b \qquad \text{Substitute } x_2 \text{ for } x.$$

$$\ldots$$

$$\hat{y}_n = mx_n + b \qquad \text{Substitute } x_n \text{ for } x.$$

quick **Example** Consider the three data points (0, 2), (2, 5), and (3, 6). The observed y-values are $y_1 = 2$, $y_2 = 5$, and $y_3 = 6$. If we model these data with the equation $\hat{y} = x + 2.5$, then the predicted values are:

$$\hat{y}_1 = x_1 + 2.5 = 0 + 2.5 = 2.5$$

$$\hat{y}_2 = x_2 + 2.5 = 2 + 2.5 = 4.5$$

$$\hat{y}_3 = x_3 + 2.5 = 3 + 2.5 = 5.5$$

Residuals and Sum-of-Squares Error (SSE)

If we model a collection of data $(x_1, y_1), \ldots, (x_n, y_n)$ with a linear equation $\hat{y} = mx + b$, then the **residuals** are the n quantities (Observed Value – Predicted Value):

$$(y_1 - \hat{y}_1), (y_2 - \hat{y}_2), \ldots, (y_n - \hat{y}_n)$$

The **sum-of-squares error (SSE)** is the sum of the squares of the residuals:

$$\text{SSE} = (y_1 - \hat{y}_1)^2 + (y_2 - \hat{y}_2)^2 + (y_n - \hat{y}_n)^2$$

quick **Example** For the data and linear approximation given above, the residuals are:

$$y_1 - \hat{y}_1 = 2 - 2.5 = -0.5$$

$$y_2 - \hat{y}_2 = 5 - 4.5 = 0.5$$

$$y_3 - \hat{y}_3 = 6 - 5.5 = 0.5$$

and $\quad \text{SSE} = (-0.5)^2 + (0.5)^2 + (0.5)^2 = 0.75$

[52] Why not add the absolute values of the residuals instead? Mathematically, using the squares rather than the absolute values results in a simpler and more elegant solution. Further, using the the squares always results in a *single* best-fit line in cases where the x-coordinates are all different, whereas this is not the case if we use absolute values.

Example 1 Computing the Sum-of-Squares Error

Using the data above on the cable television market in China, compute SSE, the sum-of-squares error, for the linear models $y = 8t + 72$ and $y = 5t + 68$. Which model is the better fit?

Solution We begin by creating a table showing the values of t, the observed (given) values of y, and the values predicted by the first model.

Year t	*Observed* y	*Predicted* $\hat{y} = 8t + 72$
−4	50	40
−3	55	48
−2	57	56
−1	60	64
0	68	72
1	72	80
2	80	88
3	83	96

We now add two new columns for the residuals and their squares.

using *Technology*

Consult the Technology Guides at the end of the chapter to see how to generate these tables using a TI-83/84 or Excel. We can use either technology to graph the original data points and the lines.

Year t	*Observed* y	*Predicted* $\hat{y} = 8t + 72$	*Residual* $y - \hat{y}$	*Residual*^{2} $(y - \hat{y})^2$
−4	50	40	$50 - 40 = 10$	$10^2 = 100$
−3	55	48	$55 - 48 = 7$	$7^2 = 49$
−2	57	56	$57 - 56 = 1$	$1^2 = 1$
−1	60	64	$60 - 64 = -4$	$(-4)^2 = 16$
0	68	72	$68 - 72 = -4$	$(-4)^2 = 16$
1	72	80	$72 - 80 = -8$	$(-8)^2 = 64$
2	80	88	$80 - 88 = -8$	$(-8)^2 = 64$
3	83	96	$83 - 96 = -13$	$(-13)^2 = 169$

SSE, the sum of the squares of the residuals, is then the sum of the entries in the last column,

$$\text{SSE} = 479$$

Repeating the process using the second model, $y = 5t + 68$, yields $\text{SSE} = 23$. Thus, the second model is a better fit.

+ *Before we go on...*

Q: *It seems clear from the figures that the second model in Example 1 gives a better fit. Why bother to compute SSE to tell me this?*

A: The difference between the two models we chose is so dramatic that it is clear from the graphs which is the better fit. However, if we used a third model with $m = 5$ and $b = 68.1$, then its graph would be almost indistinguishable from that of the second, but a better fit as measured by SSE $= 22.88$. ■

Among all possible lines, there ought to be one with the least possible value of SSE—that is, the greatest possible accuracy as a model. The line (and there is only one such line) that minimizes the sum of the squares of the residuals is called the **regression line,** the **least-squares line,** or the **best-fit line.**

To find the regression line, we need a way to find values of m and b that give the smallest possible value of SSE. As an example, let us take the second linear model in the example above. We said in the "Before we go on . . ." discussion that increasing b from 68 to 68.1 had the desirable effect of decreasing SSE from 23 to 22.88. We could then decrease m to 4.9, further reducing SSE to 22.2. Imagine this as a kind of game: Alternately alter the values of m and b by small amounts until SSE is as small as you can make it. This works, but is extremely tedious and time-consuming.

Fortunately, there is an algebraic way to find the regression line. Here is the calculation. To justify it rigorously requires calculus of several variables or linear algebra.

Regression Line

The **regression line (least squares line, best-fit line)** associated with the points (x_1, y_1), $(x_2, y_2), \ldots, (x_n, y_n)$ is the line that gives the minimum sum-of-squares error (SSE). The regression line is

$$y = mx + b$$

where m and b are computed as follows:

$$m = \frac{n(\Sigma xy) - (\Sigma x)(\Sigma y)}{n(\Sigma x^2) - (\Sigma x)^2}$$

$$b = \frac{\Sigma y - m(\Sigma x)}{n}$$

$n =$ number of data points

The quantities m and b are called the **regression coefficients.**

Here, "Σ" means "the sum of." Thus, for example,

$$\Sigma x = \text{Sum of the } x\text{-values} = x_1 + x_2 + \cdots + x_n$$

$$\Sigma xy = \text{Sum of products} = x_1y_1 + x_2y_2 + \cdots + x_ny_n$$

$$\Sigma x^2 = \text{Sum of the squares of the } x\text{-values} = x_1{}^2 + x_2{}^2 + \cdots + x_n{}^2$$

On the other hand,

$$(\Sigma x)^2 = \text{Square of } \Sigma x = \text{Square of the sum of the } x\text{-values}$$

Example 2 The Cable Television Market in China

In Example 1 we considered the following data about the growth of the cable TV market in China.

Year (x) **($x = 0$ represents 2000)**	-4	-3	-2	-1	0	1	2	3
Households with Cable (y) **(Millions)**	50	55	57	60	68	72	80	83

Find the best-fit linear model for these data and use the model to predict the number of Chinese households with cable in 2005.

Solution Let's organize our work in the form of a table, where the original data are entered in the first two columns and the bottom row contains the column sums.

using Technology

Consult the Technology Guides at the end of the chapter to see how to use built-in features of the TI-83/84 or Excel to find the regression line. Online, follow:

Chapter 1
→ Tools
→ Simple Regression

	x	y	xy	x^2
	-4	50	-200	16
	-3	55	-165	9
	-2	57	-114	4
	-1	60	-60	1
	0	68	0	0
	1	72	72	1
	2	80	160	4
	3	83	249	9
$\sum$ (Sum)	-4	525	-58	44

Since there are $n = 8$ data points, we get

$$m = \frac{n(\Sigma xy) - (\Sigma x)(\Sigma y)}{n(\Sigma x^2) - (\Sigma x)^2} = \frac{8(-58) - (-4)(525)}{8(44) - (-4)^2} \approx 4.87$$

and

$$b = \frac{\Sigma y - m(\Sigma x)}{n} \approx \frac{525 - (4.87)(-4)}{8} \approx 68.1$$

So, the regression line is

$$y = 4.87x + 68.1$$

To predict the number of Chinese households with cable in 2005 we substitute $x = 5$ and get $y \approx 92$ million households.

Coefficient of Correlation

If all the data points do not lie on one straight line, we would like to be able to measure how closely they can be approximated by a straight line. Recall that SSE measures the sum of the squares of the deviations from the regression line; therefore it constitutes a measurement of goodness of fit. (For instance, if SSE $= 0$, then all the points lie on a straight line.) However, SSE depends on the units we use to measure y, and also on the number of data points (the more data points we use, the larger SSE tends to be). Thus, while we can (and do) use SSE to compare the goodness of fit of two lines to the same data, we cannot use it to compare the goodness of fit of one line to one set of data with that of another to a different set of data.

To remove this dependency, statisticians have found a related quantity that can be used to compare the goodness of fit of lines to different sets of data. This quantity, called the **coefficient of correlation** or **correlation coefficient,** and usually denoted r, is between -1 and 1. The closer r is to -1 or 1, the better the fit. For an *exact* fit, we would have $r = -1$ (for a line with negative slope) or $r = 1$ (for a line with positive slope). For a bad fit, we would have r close to 0. Figure 24 shows several collections of data points with least squares lines and the corresponding values of r.

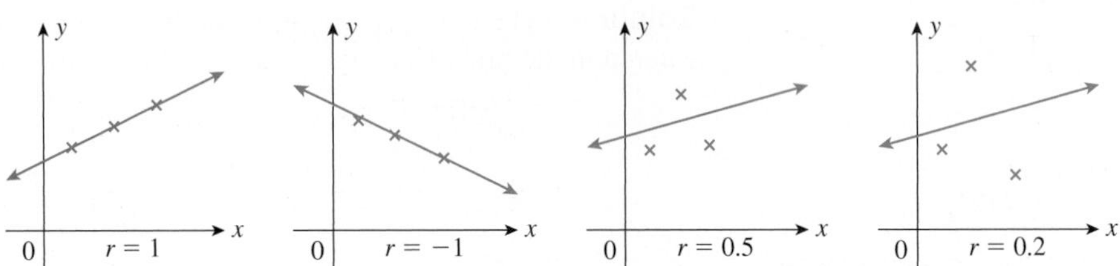

Figure **24**

Correlation Coefficient

The coefficient of correlation of the n data points $(x_1, y_1), (x_2, y_2), \ldots, (x_n, y_n)$ is

$$r = \frac{n(\Sigma xy) - (\Sigma x)(\Sigma y)}{\sqrt{n(\Sigma x^2) - (\Sigma x)^2} \cdot \sqrt{n(\Sigma y^2) - (\Sigma y)^2}}$$

It measures how closely the data points $(x_1, y_1), (x_2, y_2), \ldots, (x_n, y_n)$ fit the regression line.

Interpretation

If r is positive, the regression line has positive slope; if r is negative, the regression line has negative slope.

If $r = 1$ or -1, then all the data points lie exactly on the regression line; if it is close to ± 1, then all the data points are close to the regression line.

If r is close to 0, then y does not depend linearly on x.

Example 3 Computing the Coefficient of Correlation

Find the correlation coefficient for the data in Example 2. Is the regression line a good fit?

Solution

The formula for r requires Σx, Σx^2, Σxy, Σy, and Σy^2. We have all of these except for Σy^2, which we find in a new column, as shown.

	x	y	xy	x^2	y^2
	−4	50	−200	16	2500
	−3	55	−165	9	3025
	−2	57	−114	4	3249
	−1	60	−60	1	3600
	0	68	0	0	4624
	1	72	72	1	5184
	2	80	160	4	6400
	3	83	249	9	6889
$\sum$ (Sum)	−4	525	−58	44	35,471

using Technology

Consult the Technology Guides at the end of the chapter to see how to use built-in features of the TI-83/84 or Excel to find the correlation coefficient. Alternatively, the online utility gives the correlation coefficient. Follow:

Chapter 1
→ Tools
→ Simple Regression

Substituting these values into the formula we get

$$r = \frac{n(\Sigma xy) - (\Sigma x)(\Sigma y)}{\sqrt{n(\Sigma x^2) - (\Sigma x)^2} \cdot \sqrt{n(\Sigma y^2) - (\Sigma y)^2}}$$
$$= \frac{8(-58) - (-4)(525)}{\sqrt{8(44) - (-4)^2} \cdot \sqrt{8(35{,}471) - 525^2}}$$
$$\approx 0.989$$

Thus, the fit is a fairly good one; that is, the original points lie nearly along a straight line, as can be confirmed by graphing the data in Example 2.

1.5 EXERCISES

● denotes basic skills exercises

tech Ex indicates exercises that should be solved using technology

In Exercises 1–4, compute the sum-of-squares error (SSE) by hand *for the given set of data and linear model.* hint [see Example 1]

1. ● (1, 1), (2, 2), (3, 4); $y = x - 1$
2. ● (0, 1), (1, 1), (2, 2); $y = x + 1$
3. ● (0, −1), (1, 3), (4, 6), (5, 0); $y = -x + 2$
4. ● (2, 4), (6, 8), (8, 12), (10, 0); $y = 2x - 8$

tech Ex *In Exercises 5–8, use technology to compute the sum-of-squares error (SSE) for the given set of data and linear models. Indicate which linear model gives the better fit.*

5. ● (1, 1), (2, 2), (3, 4);
   a. $y = 1.5x - 1$ **b.** $y = 2x - 1.5$
6. ● (0, 1), (1, 1), (2, 2);
   a. $y = 0.4x + 1.1$ **b.** $y = 0.5x + 0.9$
7. ● (0, −1), (1, 3), (4, 6), (5, 0);
   a. $y = 0.3x + 1.1$ **b.** $y = 0.4x + 0.9$
8. ● (2, 4), (6, 8), (8, 12), (10, 0);
   a. $y = -0.1x + 7$ **b.** $y = -0.2x + 6$

Find the regression line associated with each set of points in Exercises 9–12. Graph the data and the best-fit line. (Round all coefficients to 4 decimal places.) hint [see Example 2]

9. ● (1, 1), (2, 2), (3, 4)
10. ● (0, 1), (1, 1), (2, 2)
11. ● (0, −1), (1, 3), (4, 6), (5, 0)
12. ● (2, 4), (6, 8), (8, 12), (10, 0)

In the next two exercises, use correlation coefficients to determine which of the given sets of data is best fit by its associated regression line and which is fit worst. Is it a perfect fit for any of the data sets? hint [see Example 3]

13. ● **a.** {(1, 3), (2, 4), (5, 6)}
    b. {(0, −1), (2, 1), (3, 4)}
    c. {(4, −3), (5, 5), (0, 0)}
14. ● **a.** {(1, 3), (−2, 9), (2, 1)}
    b. {(0, 1), (1, 0), (2, 1)}
    c. {(0, 0), (5, −5), (2, −2.1)}

Applications

15. ● ***Worldwide Cell Phone Sales*** Following are forecasts of worldwide annual cell phone handset sales:[53]

Year x	3	5	7
Sales y (Millions)	500	600	800

($x = 3$ represents 2003). Complete the following table and obtain the associated regression line. (Round coefficients to 2 decimal places.)

	x	y	xy	x^2
	3	500		
	5	600		
	7	800		
Totals				

Use your regression equation to project the 2008 sales. *hint* [see Example 2]

16. ● ***Investment in Gold*** Following are approximate values of the Amex Gold BUGS Index:[54]

Year x	0	2	4
Index y	50	100	250

($x = 0$ represents 2000). Complete the following table and obtain the associated regression line. (Round coefficients to 2 decimal places.)

	x	y	xy	x^2
	0	50		
	2	100		
	4	250		
Totals				

Use your regression equation to estimate the 2003 index.

17. ● ***E-Commerce*** The following chart shows second quarter total retail e-commerce sales in the U.S. in 2000, 2002, and 2004 ($t = 0$ represents 2000):[55]

Year t	0	2	4
Sales ($ Billion)	6	10	16

Find the regression line (round coefficients to two decimal places) and use it to estimate second quarter retail e-commerce sales in 2003.

18. ● ***Retail Inventories*** The following chart shows total January retail inventories in U.S. department stores in 2000, 2002, and 2004 ($t = 0$ represents 2000):[56]

Year t	0	2	4
Inventory ($ Billion)	2.3	2.1	2.1

Find the regression line (round coefficients to two decimal places) and use it to estimate January retail inventories in 2001.

19. ● ***Oil Recovery*** In 2004 the Texas Bureau of Economic Geology published a study on the economic impact of using carbon dioxide enhanced oil recovery (EOR) technology to extract additional oil from fields that have reached the end of their conventional economic life. The following table gives the approximate number of jobs for the citizens of Texas that would be created at various levels of recovery.[57]

Percent Recovery (%)	20	40	80	100
Jobs Created (Millions)	3	6	9	15

Find the regression line and use it to estimate the number of jobs that would be created at a recovery level of 50%.

20. ● ***Oil Recovery*** (Refer to Exercise 19.) The following table gives the approximate economic value associated with various levels of oil recovery in Texas.[58]

Percent Recovery (%)	10	40	50	80
Economic Value ($ Billions)	200	900	1000	2000

[53] SOURCE: In-StatMDR, www.in-stat.com/ July, 2004.

[54] BUGS stands for "basket of unhedged gold stocks." SOURCES: www.321gold.com, Bloomberg Financial Markets/*New York Times*, Sept 7, 2003, p. BU8.

[55] SOURCE: U.S. Census Bureau www.census.gov December, 2004.

[56] SOURCE: U.S. Census Bureau www.census.gov December, 2004

[57] SOURCE: "CO_2 –Enhanced Oil Recovery Resource Potential in Texas: Potential Positive Economic Impacts" Texas Bureau of Economic Geology, April 2004 www.rrc.state.tx.us/tepc/CO_2-EOR_white_paper.pdf

[58] SOURCE: "CO_2 –Enhanced Oil Recovery Resource Potential in Texas: Potential Positive Economic Impacts" Texas Bureau of Economic Geology, April 2004 www.rrc.state.tx.us/tepc/CO_2-EOR_white_paper.pdf

Find the regression line and use it to estimate the economic value associated with a recovery level of 70%.

21. tech Ex ***Soybean Production*** The following table shows soybean production, in millions of tons, in Brazil's *Cerrados* region, as a function of the cultivated area, in millions of acres.[59]

Area (Millions of Acres)	25	30	32	40	52
Production (Millions of Tons)	15	25	30	40	60

a. Use technology to obtain the regression line, and to show a plot of the points together with the regression line. (Round coefficients to two decimal places.)

b. Interpret the slope of the regression line.

22. tech Ex ***Trade with Taiwan*** The following table shows U.S. exports to Taiwan as a function of U.S. imports from Taiwan, based on trade figures in the period 1990–2003.[60]

Imports ($ Billions)	22	24	27	35	25
Exports ($ Billions)	12	15	20	25	17

a. Use technology to obtain the regression line, and to show a plot of the points together with the regression line. (Round coefficients to two decimal places.)

b. Interpret the slope of the regression line.

tech Ex *Exercises 23 and 24 are based on the following table comparing the median household income in the U.S. with the unemployment and poverty rates for various years from 1990 to 2003.*[61]

Year	***Median Household Income ($1000)***	***Unemployment Rate (%)***	***Poverty Rate (%)***
1990	39	5.6	13
1992	38	7.5	14
1994	39	6.1	14
1996	41	5.4	13
1998	44	4.5	12
2000	42	4	11
2002	41	5.8	12
2003	40	6	12

23. tech Ex ***Poverty and Household Income***

a. Use x = median household income and y = poverty rate, and use technology to obtain the regression equation and graph the associated points and regression line. Round coefficients to two significant digits. Does the graph suggest a relationship between x and y?

b. What does the slope tell you about the relationship between the median household income and the poverty rate?

c. Use technology to obtain the coefficient of correlation r. Does the value of r suggest a strong correlation between x and y?

24. tech Ex ***Poverty and Unemployment***

a. Use x = unemployment rate and y = poverty rate, and use technology to obtain the regression equation and graph the associated points and regression line. Round coefficients to two significant digits. Does the graph suggest a relationship between x and y?

b. What does the slope tell you about the relationship between the unemployment rate and the poverty rate?

c. Use technology to obtain the coefficient of correlation r. Does the value of r suggest a strong correlation between x and y?

25. tech Ex ***New York City Housing Costs: Downtown*** The following table shows the average price of a two-bedroom apartment in downtown New York City from 1994 to 2004. ($t = 0$ represents 1994)[62]

Year t	0	2	4	6	8	10
Price p ($ million)	0.38	0.40	0.60	0.95	1.20	1.60

a. Use technology to obtain the linear regression line, with regression coefficients rounded to two decimal places, and plot the regression line and the given points.

b. Does the graph suggest that a non-linear relationship between t and p would be more appropriate than a linear one? Why?

c. Use technology to obtain the residuals. What can you say about the residuals in support of the claim in part (b)?

26. tech Ex ***Fiber-Optic Connections*** The following table shows the number of fiber-optic cable connections to homes in the U.S. from 2000–2004 ($t = 0$ represents 2000):[63]

Year t	0	1	2	3	4
Connections c (Thousands)	0	10	25	65	150

[59] Source: Brazil Agriculture Ministry/*New York Times,* December 12, 2004, p. N32.

[60] Source: Taiwan Directorate General of Customs/*New York Times,* December 13, 2004, p. C7.

[61] Household incomes are in constant 2002 dollars. 2003 Figures for median income and poverty rate are estimates. The poverty threshold is approximately $18,000 for a family of four and $9200 for an individual. Sources: Census Bureau Current Population Survey/New York Times Sept 27, 2003, p. A10/ U.S. Department of Labor Bureau of Labor Statistics stats.bls.gov June 17, 2004.

[62] Data are rounded and 2004 figure is an estimte. Source: Miller Samuel/ *New York Times,* March 28, 2004, p. RE 11.

[63] Source: Render, Vanderslice & Associates/*New York Times,* October 11, 2004, p. C1.

a. Use technology to obtain the linear regression line, with regression coefficients rounded to two decimal places, and plot the regression line and the given points.

b. Does the graph suggest that a non-linear relationship between t and p would be more appropriate than a linear one? Why?

c. Use technology to obtain the residuals. What can you say about the residuals in support of the claim in part (b)?

Communication and Reasoning Exercises

27. ● Why is the regression line associated with the two points (a, b) and (c, d) the same as the line that passes through both? (Assume that $a \neq c$.)

28. ● What is the smallest possible sum-of-squares error if the given points happen to lie on a straight line? Why?

29. ● If the points $(x_1, y_1), (x_2, y_2), \ldots, (x_n, y_n)$ lie on a straight line, what can you say about the regression line associated with these points?

30. ● If all but one of the points $(x_1, y_1), (x_2, y_2), \ldots, (x_n, y_n)$ lie on a straight line, must the regression line pass through all but one of these points?

31. Verify that the regression line for the points $(0, 0)$, $(-a, a)$, and (a, a) has slope 0. What is the value of r? (Assume that $a \neq 0$.)

32. Verify that the regression line for the points $(0, a)$, $(0, -a)$, and $(a, 0)$ has slope 0. What is the value of r? (Assume that $a \neq 0$.)

33. Must the regression line pass through at least one of the data points? Illustrate your answer with an example.

34. Why must care be taken when using mathematical models to extrapolate?

Chapter 1 Review

KEY CONCEPTS

1.1 Functions from the Numerical and Algebraic Viewpoints

Real-valued function f of a real-valued variable x, domain *p. 35*
Independent and dependent variables *p. 35*
Numerically specified function *p. 36*
Algebraically defined function *p. 37*
Piecewise-defined function *p. 39*
Mathematical model *p. 39*
Common types of algebraic functions *p. 40*

1.2 Functions from the Graphical Viewpoint

Graphically specified function *p. 45*
Graph of the function f *p. 45*
Drawing the graph of a function *p. 46*
Vertical line test *p. 48*
Graphing a piecewise-defined function *p. 48*
Graphs of common functions *p. 50*

1.3 Linear Functions

Linear function *p. 55*

Slope of a line: $m = \dfrac{\Delta y}{\Delta x} = \dfrac{\text{Change in } y}{\text{Change in } x}$

Interpretations of m *p. 57*

Interpretation of b: y-intercept *p. 58*
Recognizing linear data *p. 59*
Graphing a linear equation *p. 59*
x- and y-intercepts *p. 60*

Computing the slope: $m = \dfrac{y_2 - y_1}{x_2 - x_1}$ *p. 61*

Slopes of horizontal and vertical lines *p. 61*
Point-slope formula: $y = mx + b$ where $b = y_1 - mx_1$ *p. 62*

1.4 Linear Models

Linear modeling *p. 66*
Cost, revenue, and profit; marginal cost, revenue, and profit; break-even point *p. 67*
Demand *p. 72*
Supply; equilibrium *p. 74*
Linear change over time; rate of change; velocity: In the graph of displacement versus time, velocity is given by the slope. *p. 76*
General linear models *p. 77*

1.5 Linear Regression

Observed and predicted values *p. 84*
Residuals and sum-of-squares error (SSE) *p. 84*
Regression line (least squares line, best-fit line) *p. 86*
Correlation coefficient *p. 88*

REVIEW EXERCISES

In each of Exercises 1–4, use the graph of the function f to find approximations of the given values.

1.

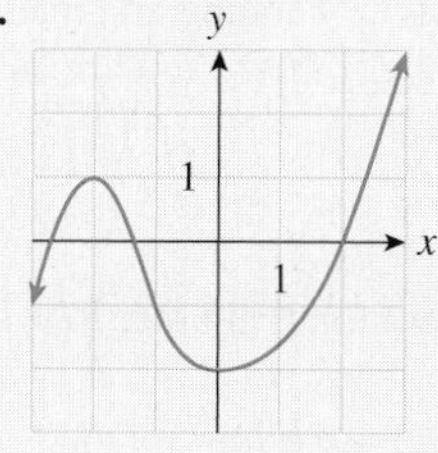

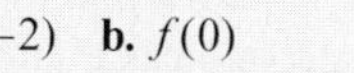

a. $f(-2)$ **b.** $f(0)$
c. $f(2)$ **d.** $f(2) - f(-2)$

2.

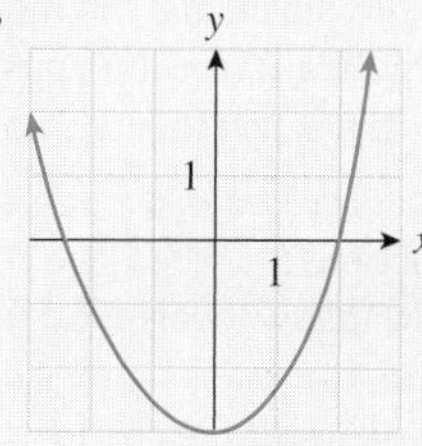

a. $f(-2)$ **b.** $f(0)$
c. $f(2)$ **d.** $f(2) - f(-2)$

3.

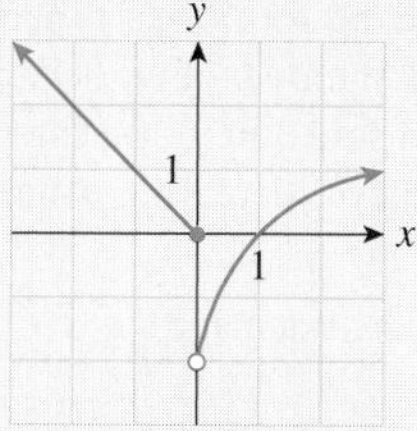

a. $f(-1)$ **b.** $f(0)$
c. $f(1)$ **d.** $f(1) - f(-1)$

4.

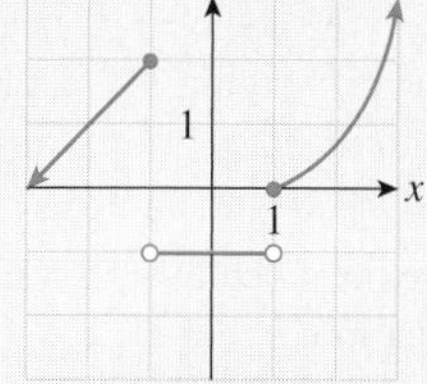

a. $f(-1)$ **b.** $f(0)$
c. $f(1)$ **d.** $f(1) - f(-1)$

In each of Exercises 5–8, graph the given function or equation.

5. $y = -2x + 5$

6. $2x - 3y = 12$

7. $y = \begin{cases} \frac{1}{2}x & \text{if } -1 \le x \le 1 \\ x - 1 & \text{if } 1 < x \le 3 \end{cases}$

8. $(x) = 4x - x^2$ with domain [0, 4]

In each of Exercises 9–13, decide whether the specified values come from a linear, quadratic, exponential, or absolute value function.

In each of Exercises 14–17, find the equation of the specified line.

	x	−2	0	1	2	4
9.	$f(x)$	4	2	1	0	2
10.	$g(x)$	−5	−3	−2	−1	1
11.	$h(x)$	1.5	1	0.75	0.5	0
12.	$k(x)$	0.25	1	2	4	16
13.	$u(x)$	0	4	3	0	−12

14. Through (3, 2) with slope −3

15. Through (−1, 2) and (1, 0)

16. Through (1, 2) parallel to $x - 2y = 2$

17. With slope 1/2 crossing $3x + y = 6$ at its x-intercept

In Exercises 18 and 19, determine which of the given lines better fits the given points.

18. $(-1, 1), (1, 2), (2, 0)$; $y = -x/2 + 1$ or $y = -x/4 + 1$

19. $(-2, -1), (-1, 1), (0, 1), (1, 2), (2, 4), (3, 3)$; $y = x + 1$ or $y = x/2 + 1$

In Exercises 20 and 21, find the line that best fits the given points and compute the correlation coefficient.

20. $(-1, 1), (1, 2), (2, 0)$

21. $(-2, -1), (-1, 1), (0, 1), (1, 2), (2, 4), (3, 3)$

Applications

22. As your online bookstore, OHaganBooks.com, has grown in popularity, you have been monitoring book sales as a function of the traffic at your site (measured in "hits" per day) and have obtained the following model:

$$n(x) = \begin{cases} 0.02x & \text{if } 0 \le x \le 1000 \\ 0.025x - 5 & \text{if } 1000 < x \le 2000 \end{cases}$$

where $n(x)$ is the average number of books sold in a day in which there are x hits at the site.

a. On average, how many books per day does your model predict you will sell when you have 500 hits in a day? 1000 hits in a day? 1500 hits in a day?

b. What does the coefficient 0.025 tell you about your book sales?

c. According to the model, how many hits per day will be needed in order to sell an average of 30 books per day?

23. Your monthly books sales have increased quite dramatically over the past few months, but now appear to be leveling off. Here are the sales figures for the past 6 months.

Month t	1	2	3	4	5	6
Daily Book Sales	12.5	37.5	62.5	72.0	74.5	75.0

a. Which of the following models best approximates the data?

(A) $S(t) = \dfrac{300}{4 + 100(5^{-t})}$ **(B)** $S(t) = 13.3t + 8.0$

(C) $S(t) = -2.3t^2 + 30.0t - 3.3$ **(D)** $S(t) = 7(3^{0.5t})$

b. What do each of the above models predict for the sales in the next few months: rising, falling, or leveling off?

24. To increase business at OHaganBooks.com, you plan to place more banner ads at well-known Internet portals. So far, you have the following data on the average number of hits per day at OHaganBooks.com versus your monthly advertising expenditures:

Advertising Expenditure (\$/Month)	\$2000	\$5000
Website Traffic (Hits/Day)	1900	2050

You decide to construct a linear model giving the average number of hits h per day as a function of the advertising expenditure c.

a. What is the model you obtain?

b. Based on your model, how much traffic can you anticipate if you budget \$6000 per month for banner ads?

c. Your goal is to eventually increase traffic at your site to an average of 2500 hits per day. Based on your model, how much do you anticipate you will need to spend on banner ads in order to accomplish this?

25. A month ago you increased expenditure on banner ads to \$6000 per month, and you have noticed that the traffic at OHaganBooks.com has not increased to the level predicted by the linear model in Exercise 24. Fitting a quadratic function to the data you have gives the model

$$h = -0.000005c^2 + 0.085c + 1750$$

where h is the daily traffic (hits) at your website, and c is the monthly advertising expenditure.

a. According to this model, what is the current traffic at your site?

b. Does this model give a reasonable prediction of traffic at expenditures larger than \$8500 per month? Why?

26. Besides selling books, you are generating additional revenue at OHaganBooks.com through your new online publishing service. Readers pay a fee to download the entire text of a novel. Author royalties and copyright fees cost you an average of \$4 per novel, and the monthly cost of operating and maintaining the service amounts to \$900 per month. You are currently charging readers \$5.50 per novel.

a. What are the associated cost, revenue, and profit functions?

b. How many novels must you sell per month in order to break even?

c. If you lower the charge to \$5.00 per novel, how many books will you need to sell in order to break even?

27. In order to generate a profit from your online publishing service, you need to know how the demand for novels depends on the price you charge. During the first month of the service, you were charging \$10 per novel, and sold 350. Lowering the price to \$5.50 per novel had the effect of increasing demand to 620 novels per month.

a. Use the given data to construct a linear demand equation.

b. Use the demand equation you constructed in part (a) to estimate the demand if you raised the price to \$15 per novel.

c. Using the information on cost given in Exercise 26, determine which of the three prices (\$5.50, \$10 and \$15) would result in the largest profit, and the size of that profit.

28. It is now several months later and you have tried selling your online novels at a variety of prices, with the following results:

Price	\$5.50	\$10	\$12	\$15
Demand (Monthly sales)	620	350	300	100

a. Use the given data to obtain a linear regression model of demand. (Round coefficients to four decimal places.)

b. Use the demand model you constructed in part (a) to estimate the demand if you charged \$8 per novel. (Round the answer to the nearest novel.)

vMentor™ Do you need a live tutor for homework problems? Access vMentor on the ThomsonNOW! website at **www.thomsonedu.com** for one-on-one tutoring from a mathematics expert.

CASE STUDY: Modeling Spending on Internet Advertising

Jeff Titcomb/Getty Images

You are the new director of Impact Advertising Inc.'s Internet division, which has enjoyed a steady 0.25% of the Internet advertising market. You have drawn up an ambitious proposal to expand your division in light of your anticipation that Internet advertising will continue to skyrocket. However, upper management sees things differently and, based on the following e-mail, does not seem likely to approve the budget for your proposal.

TO: JCheddar@impact.com (J. R. Cheddar)
CC: CVODoylePres@impact.com. (C. V. O'Doyle, CEO)
FROM: SGLombardoVP@impact.com (S. G. Lombardo, VP Financial Affairs)
SUBJECT: Your Expansion Proposal
DATE: August 3, 2005

Hi John:

Your proposal reflects exactly the kind of ambitious planning and optimism we like to see in our new upper management personnel. Your presentation last week was most impressive, and obviously reflected a great deal of hard work and preparation.

I am in full agreement with you that Internet advertising is on the increase. Indeed, our Market Research department informs me that, based on a regression of the most recently available data, Internet advertising revenue in the U.S. will continue grow at a rate of approximately \$1 billion per year. This translates into approximately \$2.5 million in increased revenues per year for Impact, given our 0.25% market share. This rate of expansion is exactly what our planned 2006 budget anticipates. Your proposal, on the other hand, would require a budget of approximately *twice* the 2006 budget allocation, even though your proposal provides no hard evidence to justify this degree of financial backing.

At this stage, therefore, I am sorry to say that I am inclined not to approve the funding for your project, although I would be happy to discuss this further with you. I plan to present my final decision on the 2006 budget at next week's divisional meeting.

Regards, Sylvia

Refusing to admit defeat, you contact the Market Research department and request the details of their projections on Internet advertising. They fax you the following information:[64]

Year	1999	2000	2001	2002	2003	2004	2005
Spending on Advertising ($ Billion)	0	0.3	0.8	1.9	3	4.3	5.8

Regression Model: $y = 0.9857x - 0.6571$ (x = years since 1999)

Correlation Coefficient: $r = 0.9781$

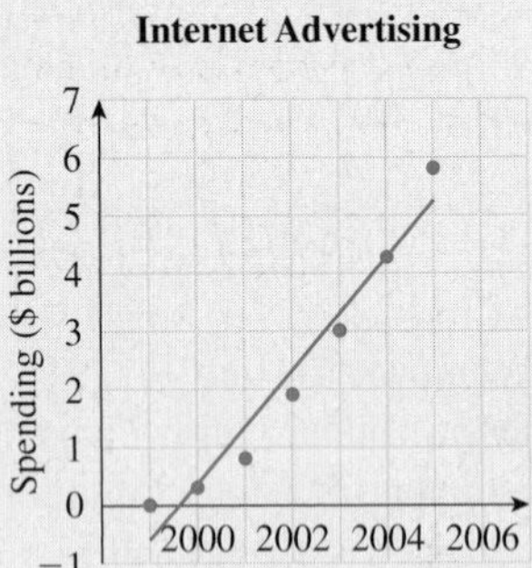

Figure **25**

Now you see where the VP got that $1 billion figure: The slope of the regression equation is close to 1, indicating a rate of increase of just under $1 billion per year. Also, the correlation coefficient is very high—an indication that the linear model fits the data well. In view of this strong evidence, it seems difficult to argue that revenues will increase by significantly more than the projected $1 billion per year.

To get a better picture of what's going on, you decide to graph the data together with the regression line in your spreadsheet program. What you get is shown in Figure 25.

You immediately notice that the data points seem to suggest a curve, and not a straight line. Then again, perhaps the suggestion of a curve is an illusion. Thus there are, you surmise, two possible interpretations of the data:

1. (Your first impression) As a function of time, spending on Internet advertising is non-linear, and is in fact accelerating (the rate of change is increasing), so a linear model is inappropriate.
2. (Devil's advocate) Spending on Internet advertising *is* a linear function of time; the fact that the points do not lie on the regression line is simply a consequence of random factors, such as the state of the economy, the stock market performance, etc.

You suspect that the VP will probably opt for the second interpretation and discount the graphical evidence of accelerating growth by claiming that it is an illusion: a "statistical fluctuation." That is, of course, a possibility, but you wonder how likely it really is.

For the sake of comparison, you decide to try a regression based on the simplest non-linear model you can think of—a quadratic function.

$$y = ax^2 + bx + c$$

Your spreadsheet allows you to fit such a function with a click of the mouse. The result is the following.

$$y = 0.1190x^2 + 0.2714x - 0.0619 \qquad (x = \text{number of years since 1999})$$

$$r = 0.9992 \qquad \text{See Note.*}$$

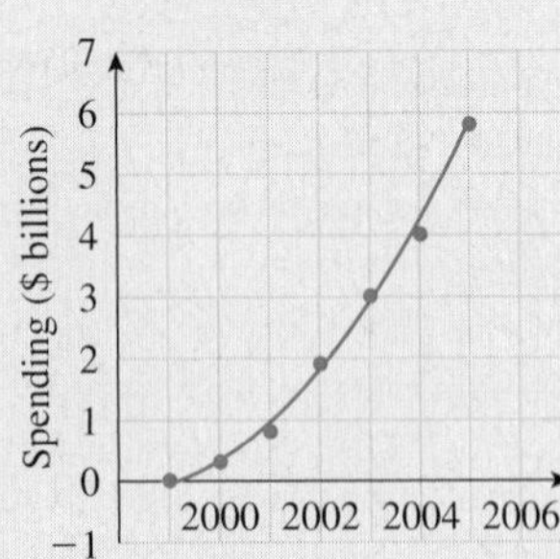

Figure **26**

Figure 26 shows the graph of the regression function together with the original data. Aha! The fit is visually far better, and the correlation coefficient is even higher! Further, the quadratic model predicts 2006 spending as

$$y = 0.1190(7)^2 + 0.2714(7) - 0.0619 \approx \$7.67 \text{ billion}$$

[64] Figures are approximate, and the 1999–2001 figures are projected. SOURCE: Nielsen NetRatings/*The New York Times,* June 7, 1999, p. C17.

*Note that this r is *not* the linear correlation coefficient we defined on p. 92; what this r measures is how closely the *quadratic* regression model fits the data.

which is \$1.87 billion above the 2005 spending figure in the table above. Given Impact Advertising's 0.25% market share, this translates into an increase in revenues of \$4.7 million, which is almost double the estimate predicted by the linear model!

You quickly draft an e-mail to Lombardo, and are about to press "send" when you decide, as a precaution, to check with a statistician. He tells you to be cautious: the value of r will always tend to increase if you pass from a linear model to a quadratic one due to an increase in "degrees of freedom."[65] A good way to test whether a quadratic model is more appropriate than a linear one is to compute a statistic called the "p-value" associated with the coefficient of x^2. A low value of p indicates a high degree of confidence that the coefficient of x^2 cannot be zero (see below). Notice that if the coefficient of x^2 *is* zero, then you have a linear model.

You can, your friend explains, obtain the p-value using Excel as follows. First, set up the data in columns, with an extra column for the values of x^2.

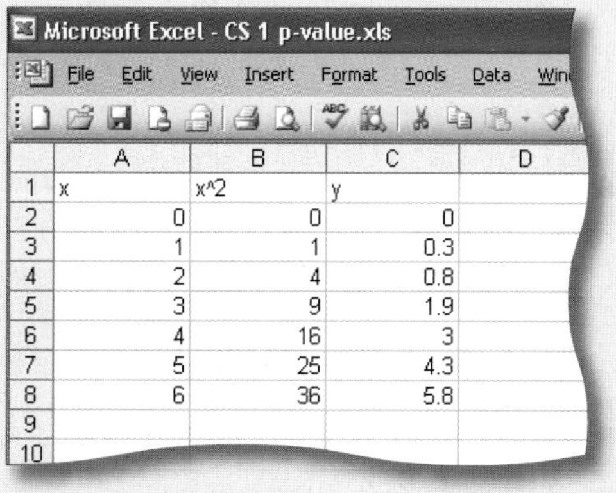

Microsoft Excel - CS 1 p-value.xls

File Edit View Insert Format Tools Data Win

	A	B	C	D
1	x	x^2	y	
2	0	0	0	
3	1	1	0.3	
4	2	4	0.8	
5	3	9	1.9	
6	4	16	3	
7	5	25	4.3	
8	6	36	5.8	
9				
10				

Next, choose "Data analysis" from the "Tools" menu, and choose "Regression." In the dialogue box, give the location of the data as shown in Figure 27.

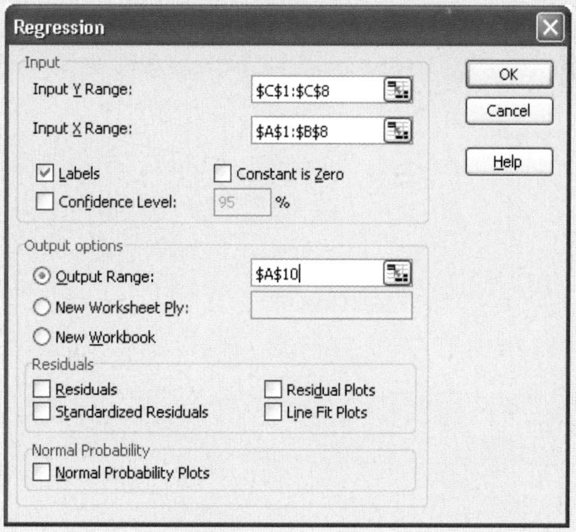

Regression

Input

Input Y Range: \$C\$1:\$C\$8

Input X Range: \$A\$1:\$B\$8

☑ Labels ☐ Constant is Zero

☐ Confidence Level: 95 %

OK

Cancel

Help

Output options

◉ Output Range: \$A\$10

○ New Worksheet Ply:

○ New Workbook

Residuals

☐ Residuals ☐ Residual Plots

☐ Standardized Residuals ☐ Line Fit Plots

Normal Probability

☐ Normal Probability Plots

Figure **27**

[65] The number of degrees of freedom in a regression model is 1 less than the number of coefficients. For a linear model, it is 1 (there are two coefficients: the slope m and the intercept b), and for a quadratic model it is 2. For a detailed discussion, consult a text on regression analysis.

Clicking "OK" then gives you a large chart of statistics. The p-value you want is in the very last row of the data: $p = 0.000478$.

Q: *What does p actually measure?*

A: *Roughly speaking,* $1 - p = .999522$ gives the degree of confidence you can have (99.9522%) in asserting that the coefficient of x^2 is not zero. (Technically, p is the probability—allowing for random fluctuation in the data—that, if the coefficient of x^2 were in fact zero, the "t-statistic" (10.4257, right next to the p-value on the spreadsheet) could be as large as it is. ■

In short, you can go ahead and send your e-mail with 99% confidence!

Exercises

Suppose you are given the following data:

Year	1999	2000	2001	2002	2003	2004	2005
Spending on Advertising ($ Billion)	0	0.3	1.5	2.6	3.4	4.3	5.0

1. Obtain a linear regression model and the correlation coefficient r. According to the model, at what rate is spending on Internet Advertising increasing in the U.S.? How does this translate to annual revenues for Impact Advertising?
2. Use a spreadsheet or other technology to graph the data together with the best-fit line. Does the graph suggest a quadratic model (parabola)?
3. Test your impression in the preceding exercise by using technology to fit a quadratic function and graphing the resulting curve together with the data. Does the graph suggest that the quadratic model is appropriate?
4. Perform a regression analysis and find the associated p-value. What does it tell you about the appropriateness of a quadratic model?

Section 1.1

Example 3 Evaluate the function $f(x) = -0.4x^2 + 7x - 23$ for $x = 0, 1, 2, \ldots, 10$.

Solution with Technology There are several ways to evaluate an algebraically defined function on a graphing calculator such as the TI-83/84.

1. Enter the function in the Y = screen, as

   `Y1 = -0.4*X^2+7*X-23`

   Negative (-) and minus (−) are different keys on the TI-83/84.

   or `Y1 = -0.4X²+7X-23`

   (See Chapter 0 for a discussion of technology formulas.)

2. To evaluate $f(0)$, for example, enter the following in the home screen:

   `Y1(0)` This evaluates the function Y_1 at 0.

Alternatively, you can use the table feature:

1. After entering the function under Y_1, press [2ND] [TBLSET], and set `Indpnt` to Ask. (You do this once and for all; it will permit you to specify values for x in the table screen.)
2. Press [2ND] [TABLE], and you will be able to evaluate the function at several values of x. Here is a table showing some of the values requested:

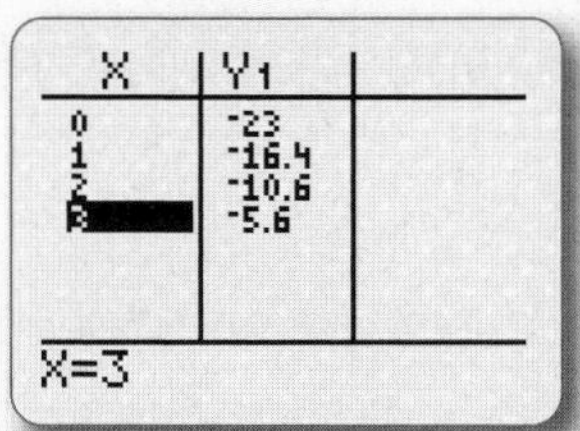

Example 4 The price $V(t)$ in dollars of EBAY stock during the 10-week period starting July 1, 2004 can be approximated by the following function of time t in weeks ($t = 0$ represents July 1):[66]

$$V(t) = \begin{cases} 90 - 4t & \text{if } 0 \le t \le 5 \\ 60 + 2t & \text{if } 5 < t \le 20 \end{cases}$$

What was the approximate price of EBAY stock after 1 week, after 5 weeks, and after 10 weeks?

[66] Source for data: http://money.excite.com, November, 2004

Solution with Technology The following formula defines the function V on the TI-83/84:

`(X≤5)*(90-4*X)+(X>5)*(60+2*X)`

The logical operators (≤ and >, for example) can be found by pressing [2ND] [TEST].

When `x` is less than or equal to 5, the logical expression `(x≤5)` evaluates to 1 because it is true, and the expression `(x>5)` evaluates to 0 because it is false. The value of the function is therefore given by the expression `(90-4*x)`. When x is greater than 5, the expression `(x≤5)` evaluates to 0 while the expression `(x>5)` evaluates to 1, so the value of the function is given by the expression `(60+2*x)`.

As in Example 3, you can use the Table feature to compute several values of the function at once:

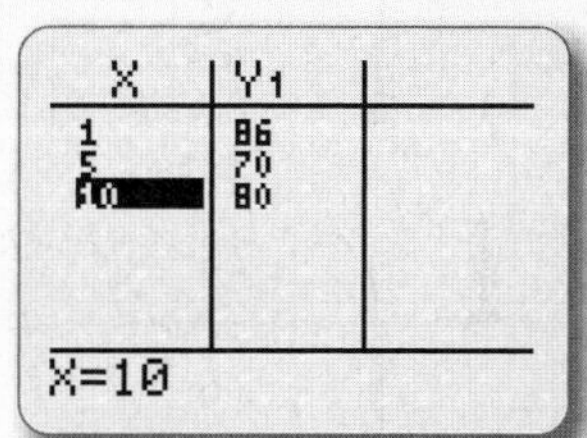

Section 1.2

Example 2 The monthly revenue R from users logging on to your gaming site depends on the monthly access fee p you charge according to the formula

$$R(p) = -5600p^2 + 14{,}000p \qquad (0 \le p \le 2.5)$$

(R and p are in dollars.) Sketch the graph of R. Find the access fee that will result in the largest monthly revenue.

Solution with Technology You can reproduce the graph shown in Figure 4(b) in Section 1.2 as follows:

1. Enter

   `Y1 = -5600*X^2+14000*X`

   in the Y= screen.
2. Set the window coordinates: Xmin = 0, Xmax = 2.5, Ymin = 0, Ymax = 10000.
3. Press [GRAPH].

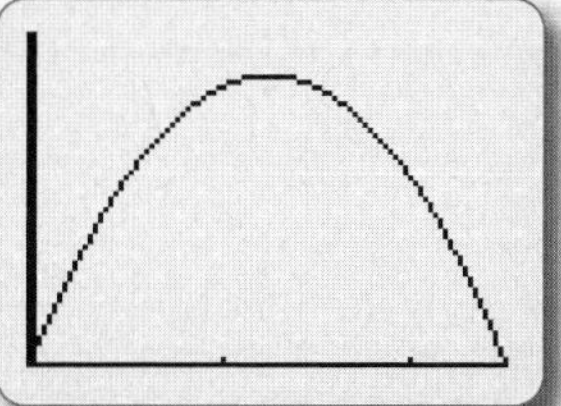

If you want to plot individual points (as in Figure 4(a) in Section 1.2) on the TI-83/84:

1. Enter the data in the stat list editor (STAT EDIT) with the values of p in L_1, and the value of $R(p)$ in L_2.
2. Go to the Y= window and turn Plot1 on by selecting it and pressing ENTER.
3. Now press ZoomStat (GRAPH 9) to obtain the plot.

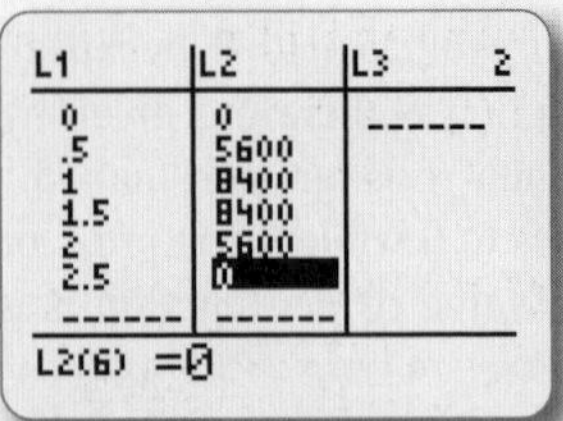

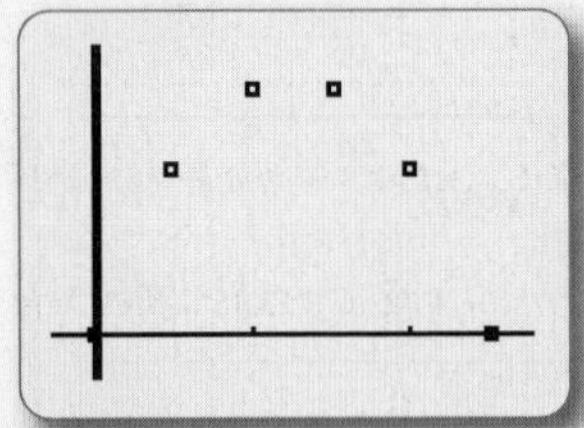

Example 4 Graph the function f specified by

$$f(x) = \begin{cases} -1 & \text{if } -4 \le x < -1 \\ x & \text{if } -1 \le x \le 1 \\ x^2 - 1 & \text{if } 1 < x \le 2 \end{cases}$$

Solution with Technology You can enter this function as

(X<-1)*(-1)+(-1≤X and X≤1)*X+(1<X)*(X²-1)

First part — Second part — Third part

The logical operator and is found in the TEST LOGIC menu. The following alternative formula will also work:

(X<-1)*(-1)+(-1≤X)*(X≤1)*X+(1<X)*(X²-1)

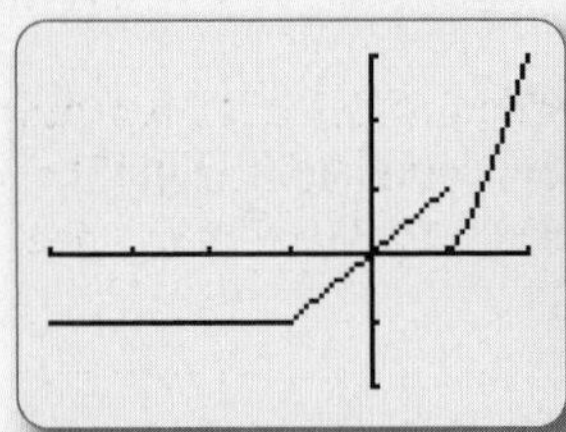

Section 1.3

Example 1 Which of the following two tables gives the values of a linear function? What is the formula for that function?

x	0	2	4	6	8	10	12
$f(x)$	3	−1	−3	−6	−8	−13	−15

x	0	2	4	6	8	10	12
$f(x)$	3	−1	−5	−9	−13	−17	−21

Solution with Technology You can compute the successive quotients $m = \Delta y/\Delta x$ as follows, using the TI-83/84.

1. Enter the values of x and $f(x)$ in the lists L_1 and L_2, which is most easily done using the stat list editor (STAT EDIT).

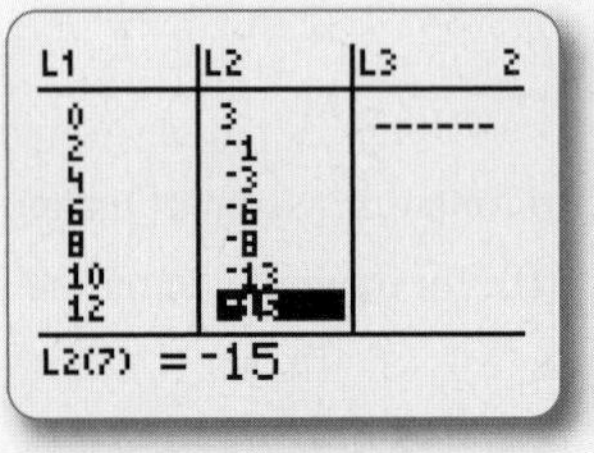

2. Highlight the heading L_3 and enter the following formula (with the quotes, as explained below):

"ΔList(L₂)/ΔList(L₁)"

The "ΔList" function is found under LIST OPS and computes the differences between successive elements of a list, returning a list with one less element. The formula above then computes the quotients $\Delta y/\Delta x$ in the list L_3.

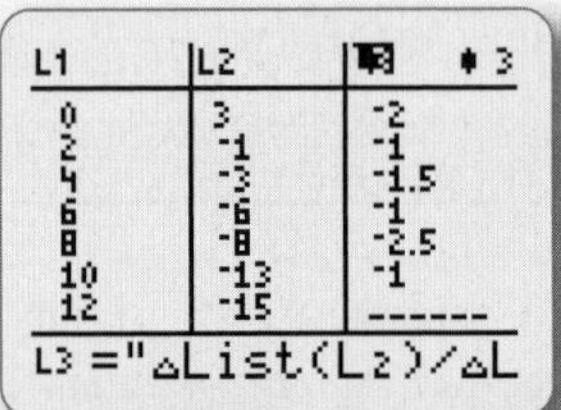

As you can see in the third column, $f(x)$ is not linear. To redo the computation for $g(x)$, all you need to do is edit the values of L_2 in the stat list editor. By putting quotes around the formula we used for L_3, we "attached" the formula to L_3 so that it would update automatically.

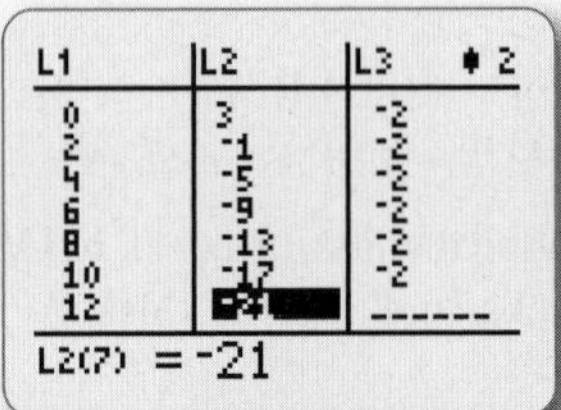

Section 1.4

Example 3(c) The following chart shows weekly sales figures for Hot'n'Spicy brand baked beans at two different prices.

Price/Can (p)	\$0.50	\$0.75
Demand (cans sold/week) (q)	400	350

How much should you charge for a can of Hot'n'Spicy beans if you want the demand to increase to 410 cans per week?

Solution with Technology In part (c) we can find p numerically using the Table feature in the TI-83/84.

1. Make sure that the table settings permit you to enter values of x: Press 2ND TBLSET and set `Indpnt` to `Ask`.
2. Enter

   `Y1 = -200*X + 500`   Demand equation

   and press 2ND TABLE.
3. You will now be able to adjust the price (x) until you find the value at which the demand equals 410.

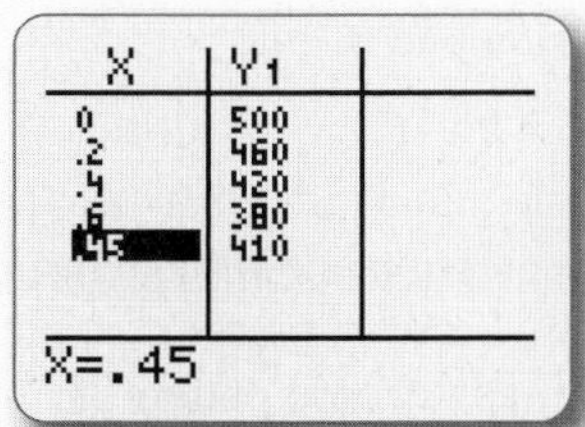

Section 1.5

Example 1 Using the data at the beginning of the section on the cable television market in China, compute SSE, the sum-of-squares error, for the linear models $y = 8t + 72$ and $y = 5t + 68$. Which model is the better fit?

Solution with Technology We can use the "List" feature in the TI-83/84 to automate the computation of SSE.

1. Use the stat list editor (STAT EDIT) to enter the given data in the first two columns, called L_1 and L_2. (If there is already data in a column you want to use, you can clear it by highlighting the column heading (e.g., L_1), using the arrow key, and pressing CLEAR ENTER.)
2. To compute the predicted values, highlight the heading L_3 using the arrow keys, and enter the formula for the predicted values:

   `8*L1+72` L_1 is 2ND [1]

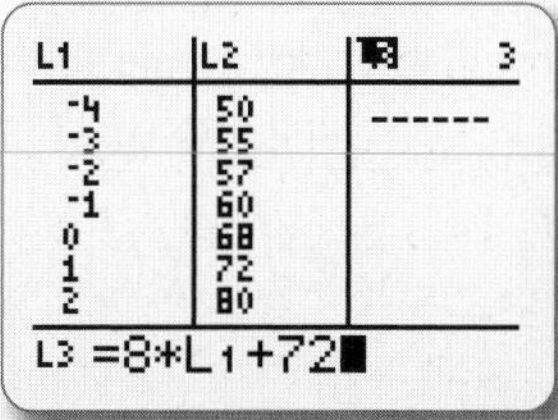

Pressing ENTER again will fill column 3 with the predicted values. (Note that only seven of the eight data points can be seen on the screen at one time.)

```
L1   L2   L3
-4   50   40
-3   55   48
-2   57   56
-1   60   64
0    68   72
1    72   80
2    80   88
L3(1)=40
```

3. Highlight the heading L_4 and enter the following formula (with the quotes):

   `"(L2-L3)^2"`   Squaring the residuals

   Pressing ENTER will fill column 4 with the squares of the residuals. (Putting quotes around the formula will allow us to easily check the second model, as we shall see.)

```
L2   L3   L4
50   40   100
55   48   49
57   56   1
60   64   16
68   72   16
72   80   64
80   88   64
L4 ="(L2-L3)^2"
```

4. To compute SSE, the sum of the entries in L_4, go to the home screen and enter `sum(L4)`. The sum function is found by pressing 2ND LIST and selecting MATH.

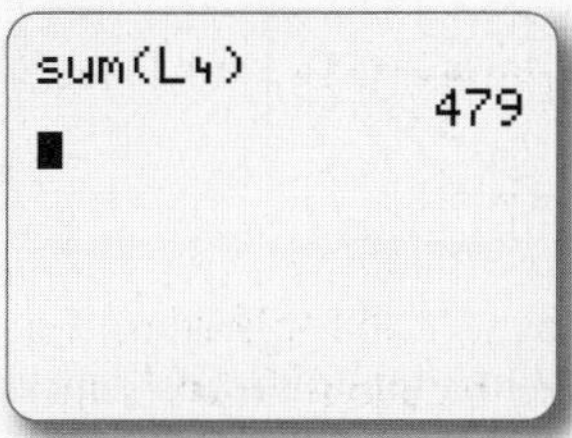

5. To check the second model, go back to the List screen, highlight the heading L_3, enter the formula for the second model, `5*L1+68`, and press ENTER.

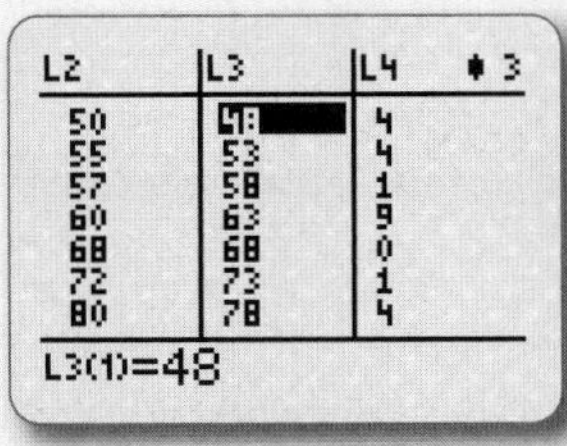

Because we put quotes around the formula for the residuals in L_4, the TI-83/84 remembered the formula and automatically recalculated the values. On the home screen we can again calculate `sum(L4)` to get SSE for the second model.

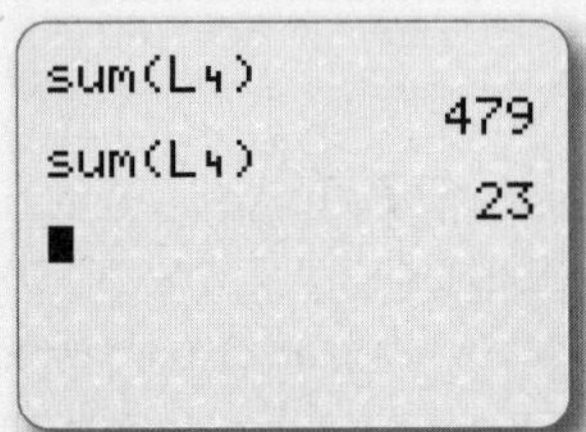

The second model gives a much smaller SSE, so is the better fit.

You can also use the TI-83/84 to plot both the original data points and the two lines.

1. Turn PLOT1 on in the STAT PLOTS window, obtained by pressing 2ND STAT PLOT.
2. To show the lines, enter them in the "Y=" screen as usual.
3. To obtain a convenient window showing all the points and the lines, press ZOOM and choose option #9: `ZoomStat`.

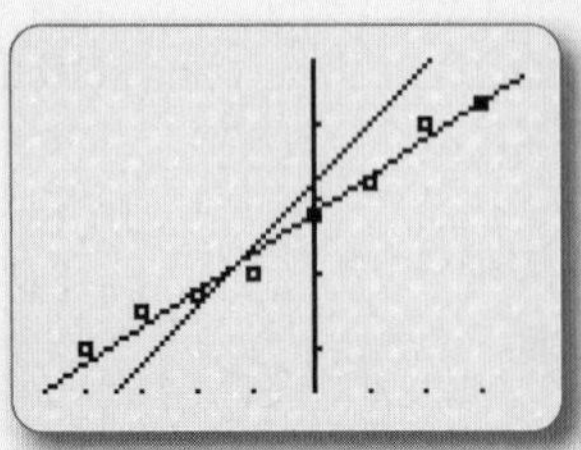

Example **2** Consider the following data about the growth of the cable TV market in China.

Year (t) ($t = 0$ represents 2000)	−4	−3	−2	−1	0	1	2	3
Households with Cable (y) (Millions)	50	55	57	60	68	72	80	83

Find the best-fit linear model for these data.

Solution with Technology

1. Enter the data in the TI-83/84 using the List feature, putting the x-coordinates in L_1 and the y-coordinates in L_2, just as in Example 1.
2. Press STAT, select CALC, and choose option #4: `LinReg(ax+b)`. Pressing ENTER will cause the equation of the regression line to be displayed in the home screen:

So, the regression line is

$$y \approx 4.87x + 68.1$$ Coefficients rounded to 3 significant digits[67]

3. To graph the regression line without having to enter it by hand in the "`Y=`" screen, press Y =, clear the contents of Y_1, press VARS, choose option #5: `Statistics`, select `EQ, and then choose #1: RegEQ`. The regression equation will then be entered under Y_1.
4. To simultaneously show the data points, press 2ND STAT PLOT and turn PLOT1 on as in Example 1.
5. To obtain a convenient window showing all the points and the line, press ZOOM and choose option #9: `ZoomStat`.

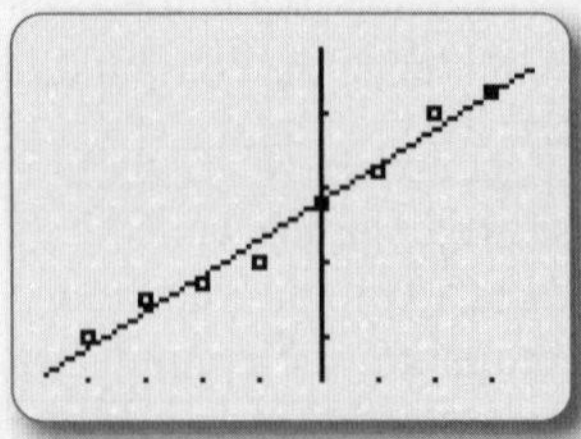

[67] The original data only gives 2 significant digits, so we rounded the coefficients to one more digit than that to give us a "safety margin" of one digit. Further digits are probably meaningless.

Example **3** Find the correlation coefficient for the data in Example 2.

Solution with Technology A utility that will calculate linear regression lines will also calculate the correlation coefficient. To find the correlation coefficient using a TI-83/84, you need to tell the calculator to show you the coefficient at the same time that it shows you the regression line. To do this, press [CATALOG] and select "`Diagnosticon`" from the list. The command will be pasted to the home screen, and you should then press [ENTER] to execute the command. Once you have done this, the "`LinReg (ax+b)`" command will show you not only a and b, but r and r^2 as well.

```
LinReg
 y=ax+b
 a=4.869047619
 b=68.05952381
 r²=.9782343
 r=.9890572784
```


EXCEL Technology Guide

Section **1.1**

Example **3** Evaluate the function $f(x) = -0.4x^2 + 7x - 23$ for $x = 0, 1, 2, \ldots, 10$.

Solution with Technology To create a table of values of f using Excel:

1. Set up two columns—one for the values of x and one for the values of $f(x)$.
2. To enter the sequence of values 0, 1, . . . , 10 in the x column, start by entering the first two values, 0 and 1, highlight both of them, and drag the **fill handle** (the little dot at the lower right-hand corner of the selection) down until you reach Row 12. (Why 12?)

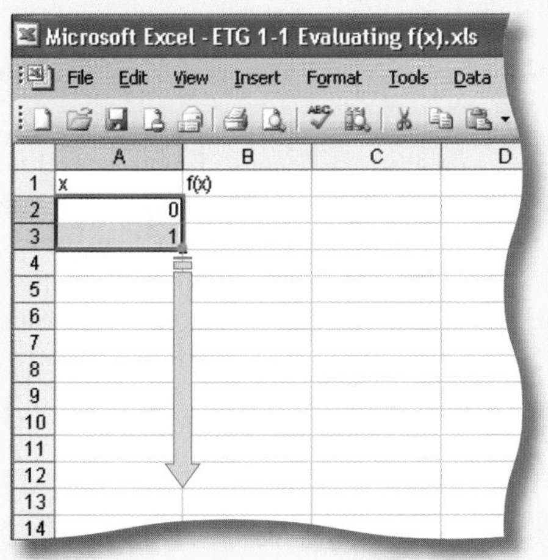

3. Enter the formula for f in cell B2. The technology formula (see Chapter 0) for f is

   `-0.4*x^2+7*x-23` Technology formula

   To get the formula to use for Excel, replace each occurrence of x by the name of the cell holding the value of x (cell A2 in this case) and obtain

   `=-0.4*A2^2+7*A2-23` A2 refers to the cell containing the value of x

Note: Instead of typing in the name of the cell "A2" each time, you can simply click on the cell A2, and "A2" will be automatically inserted. The formula

`=-0.4*x^2+7*x-23`

will also work in many versions of Excel, provided you have entered the heading x in cell A1 as shown. Try it!

Enter this formula in cell B2, press Enter, and then drag the resulting value down (using the fill handle) to cell B12, as shown below (center), to obtain the result shown at the bottom.

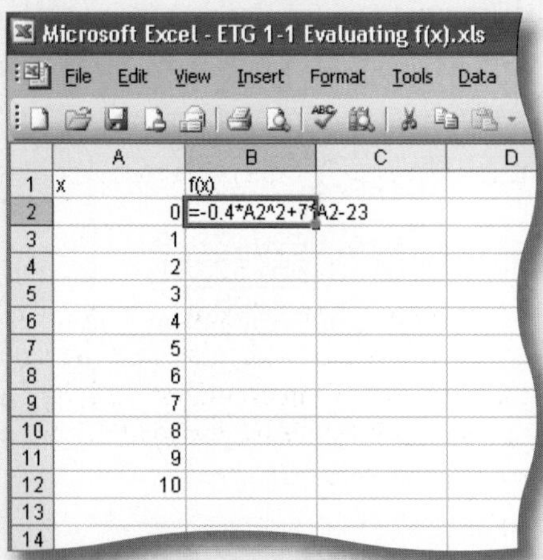

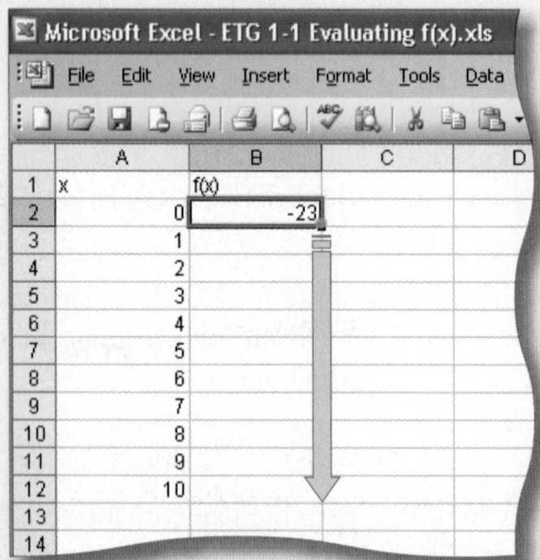

Microsoft Excel - ETG 1-1 Evaluating f(x).xls

	A	B
1	x	f(x)
2	0	-23
3	1	-16.4
4	2	-10.6
5	3	-5.6
6	4	-1.4
7	5	2
8	6	4.6
9	7	6.4
10	8	7.4
11	9	7.6
12	10	7

Warning: In interpreting a negative sign at the start of an expression, Excel uses a different convention from the usual mathematical one and the one used by almost all other technology and programming languages:

Excel Formula	*Usual Interpretation*	*Excel Interpretation*	
`-x^2`	$-x^2$	$(-x)^2$	Same as x^2 Different
`2-x^2`	$2-x^2$	$2-x^2$	The same
`-1*x^2`	$-x^2$	$-x^2$	The same
`-(x^2)`	$-x^2$	$-x^2$	The same

Thus, if a formula begins with $-x^2$, you should enter it in Excel as

`=-1*x^2` or `-(x^2)` With x replaced by the cell holding x

For example:

1. To enter $-x^2+4x-3$ in Excel, type `=-1*x^2+4*x-3`.

2. To enter $-3x^2+4x-3$ in Excel, type `=-3*x^2+4*x-3`.

3. To enter $4x-x^2$ in Excel, type `=4*x-x^2`.

In short, you need to be careful only when the expression you want to use begins with a negative sign in front of an x.

Example 4 The price $V(t)$ in dollars of EBAY stock during the 10-week period starting July 1, 2004 can be approximated by the following function of time t in weeks ($t=0$ represents July 1):[68]

$$V(t)=\begin{cases} 90-4t & \text{if } 0\le t\le 5 \\ 60+2t & \text{if } 5<t\le 20 \end{cases}$$

What was the approximate price of EBAY stock after 1 week, after 5 weeks, and after 10 weeks?

Solution with Technology The following formula defines the function V in Excel:

```
(x<=5)*(90-4*x)+(x>5)*(60+2*x)
```

When `x` is less than or equal to 5, the logical expression `(x<=5)` evaluates to 1 because it is true, and the expression `(x>5)` evaluates to 0 because it is false. The value of the function is therefore given by the expression `(90-4*x)`. When `x` is greater than 5, the expression `(x<=5)` evaluates to 0 while the expression `(x>5)` evaluates to 1, so the value of the function is given by the expression `(60+2*x)`.

We can set up a worksheet as shown (see Example 3 for instructions on using a formula to obtain values of a function in Excel).

[68] Source for data: http://money.excite.com, November, 2004.

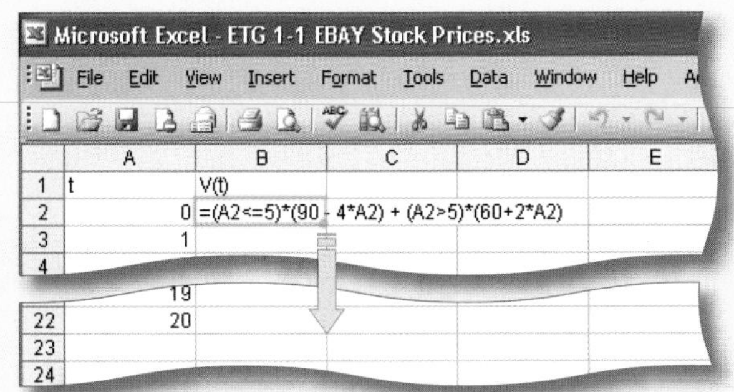

	A	B	C	D	E
1	t	V(t)			
2	0	=(A2<=5)*(90 - 4*A2) + (A2>5)*(60+2*A2)			
3	1				
4					
	19				
22	20				
23					
24					

Using the IF Function in Excel

The following worksheet shows how we can get the same result using the IF function in Excel:

Microsoft Excel - ETG 1-1 EBAY Stock Prices.xls

	A	B	C	D
1	t	V(t)		
2	0	=IF(A2<=5, 90-4*A2,60+2*A2)		
3	1			
4				
	19			
22	20			
23				
24				

The `IF` function evaluates its first argument, which tests to see if the value of t is in the range $t \leq 5$. If the first argument is true, `IF` returns the result of evaluating its second argument: `90-4*A2`; if not, it returns the result of evaluating its third argument: `60+2*A2`.

In either case, the final result will look something like this:

Microsoft Excel - ETG 1-1 EBAY Stock Prices.xls

	A	B	C	D
1	t	V(t)		
2	0	90		
3	1	86		
4				
	19	98		
22	20	100		
23				
24				

Section 1.2

Example 2 The monthly revenue R from users logging on to your gaming site depends on the monthly access fee p you charge according to the formula

$$R(p) = -5600p^2 + 14{,}000p \qquad (0 \leq p \leq 2.5)$$

(R and p are in dollars.) Sketch the graph of R. Find the access fee that will result in the largest monthly revenue.

Solution with Technology

1. Begin by creating a table of values for the function, as in Example 3 of Section 1.1, by entering the values of the independent variable p in column A and the formula for the function in cell B2, then copying the formula into the cells beneath it as shown.

Microsoft Excel - ETG 1-2 Monthly Revenue R.xls

	A	B	C	D
1	p	R		
2	0	=-5600*A2^2+14000*A2		
3	0.5			
4	1			
5	1.5			
6	2			
7	2.5			
8				
9				

2. To draw the graph shown in Figure 4(a) of Section 1.2, select (highlight) both columns of data and then ask Excel to insert a chart.
3. When it asks you to specify what type of chart, select the `XY (Scatter)` option. This tells the program that your data specify the x- and y-coordinates of a sequence of points. In the same dialogue box, select the option that shows points connected by lines.
4. Press `Next` to bring up a new dialogue called `Data Type`, where you should make sure that the `Series in Columns` option is selected, telling the program that the x- and y-coordinates are arranged vertically, down columns.
5. You can then set various other options, add labels, and otherwise fiddle with it until it looks nice.

To get a smoother curve, you need to plot many more points. Here is a method of plotting 100 points (in addition to the starting point), similar to the Excel worksheet posted online that you can find by following:

Chapter 1 → Excel Tutorials → Section 1.2: Functions from the Graphical Viewpoint

Moreover, if you decide to follow this method, you can save the resulting spreadsheet and use it as an "Excel graphing calculator" to graph any other function (see below).

1. Set up your worksheet as follows:

Microsoft Excel - ETG 1-2 Monthly Revenue R.xls

File Edit View Insert Format Tools Data Window Help Adobe PDF

	A	B	C	D	E	F	G
1	p	R					
2	=$F$2	=-5600*A2^2 + 14000*A2			Xmin	0	
3	=A2+$F$5				Xmax	2.5	
4					Points	100	
5					Delta X	=(F3-F2)/F4	
6							
7							
101							
102							
103							
104							

(Columns C and D are empty in case you want to add additional functions to graph.) The 101 values of the x-coordinate (the price p) will appear in column A. The corresponding values of the y-coordinate (the revenue R) will appear in column B. In column F you see some settings: Xmin = 0 and Xmax = 2.5 (see Figure 4). Delta X (in cell F5) is the amount by which the x-coordinate is increased as you go from one x-value in column A to the next, starting with Xmin in A2. Enter the formula for $R(p)$ in Cell B2 and copy it into the other cells in column B as shown.

2. When done, graph the data in columns A and B, choosing the scatter plot option with subtype `Points connected by lines with no markers`.

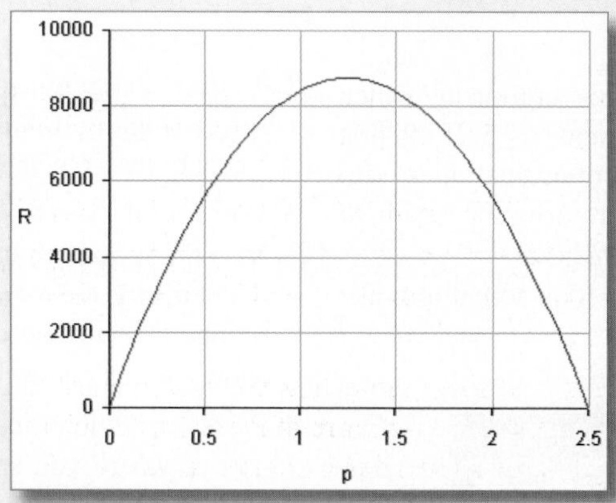

Save this worksheet with its graph and you can use it to graph new functions as follows:

1. Enter the new values for Xmin and Xmax in column F.

2. Enter the new function in cell B2 (using A2 in place of x).

3. Copy the contents of cell B2 to cells B3–B102.

The graph will be updated automatically.

Example **4** Graph the function f specified by

$$f(x) = \begin{cases} -1 & \text{if } -4 \le x < -1 \\ x & \text{if } -1 \le x \le 1 \\ x^2 - 1 & \text{if } 1 < x \le 2 \end{cases}$$

Solution with Technology You can use either of the following formulas:

```
=(x<-1)*(-1) + (-1<=x)*(x<=1)*x + (1<x)*(x^2-1)
```

First part Second part Third part

or

```
=IF(x<-1,-1,IF(x<=1,x,x^2-1))
```

Since the third part of the formula specifying f is not linear, we need to plot many points in Excel to get a smooth graph. Here is one possible setup (for a smoother curve, plot more points):

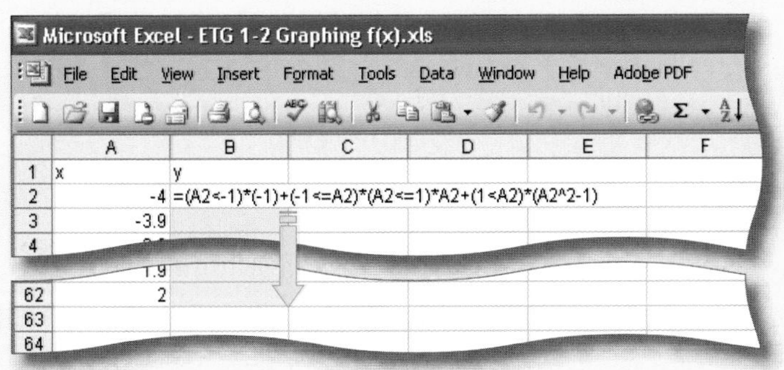

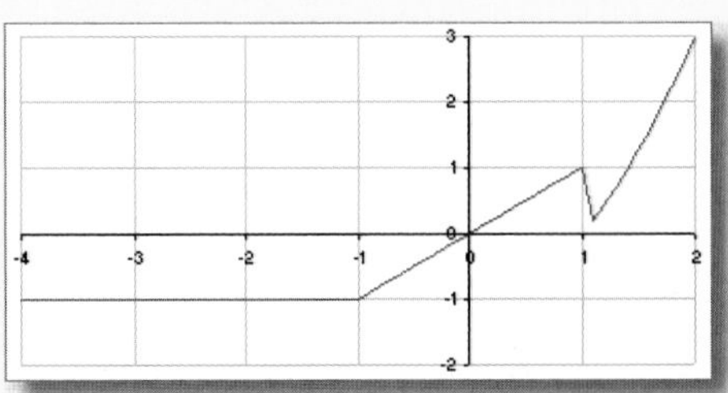

Notice that Excel does not handle the transition at $x = 1$ correctly and connects the two parts of the graph with a spurious line segment.

Section 1.3

Example 1 Which of the following two tables gives the values of a linear function? What is the formula for that function?

x	0	2	4	6	8	10	12
$f(x)$	3	−1	−3	−6	−8	−13	−15

x	0	2	4	6	8	10	12
$f(x)$	3	−1	−5	−9	−13	−17	−21

Solution with Technology The following worksheet shows how you can compute the successive quotients $m = \Delta y/\Delta x$, and hence check whether a given set of data shows a linear relationship, in which case all the quotients will be the same. (The shading indicates that the formula is to be copied down only as far as cell C7. Why not cell C8?)

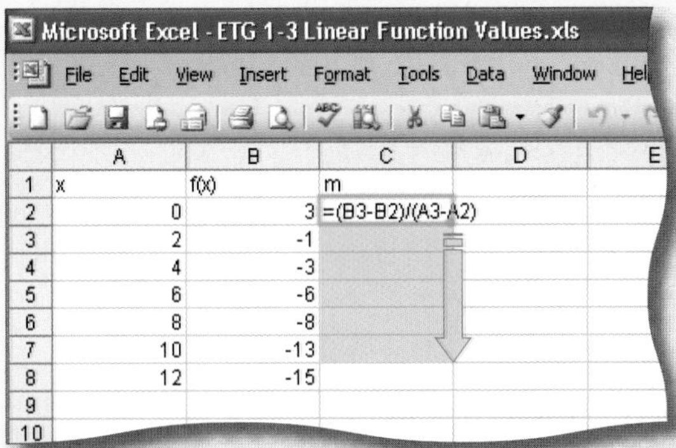

Here are the results for both $f(x)$ and $g(x)$:

Microsoft Excel - ETG 1-3 Linear Function Values.xls

	A	B	C	D
1	x	f(x)	m	
2	0	3	-2	
3	2	-1	-1	
4	4	-3	-1.5	
5	6	-6	-1	
6	8	-8	-2.5	
7	10	-13	-1	
8	12	-15		
9				
10				

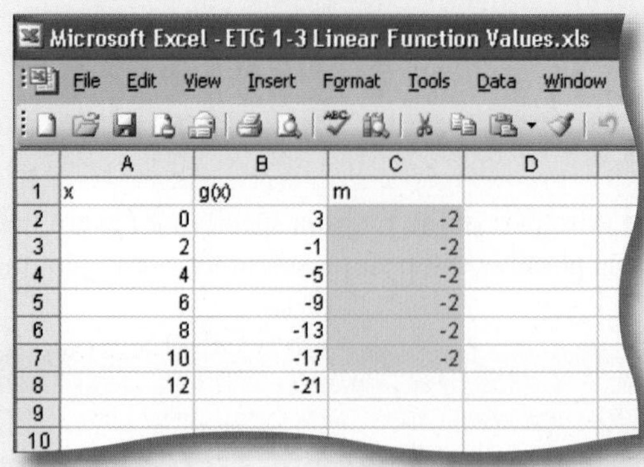

Microsoft Excel - ETG 1-3 Linear Function Values.xls

	A	B	C	D
1	x	g(x)	m	
2	0	3	-2	
3	2	-1	-2	
4	4	-5	-2	
5	6	-9	-2	
6	8	-13	-2	
7	10	-17	-2	
8	12	-21		
9				
10				

Section 1.4

Example **3(c)** The following chart shows weekly sales figures for Hot'n'Spicy brand baked beans at two different prices.

Price/Can (p)	\$0.50	\$0.75
Demand (cans sold/week) (q)	400	350

How much should you charge for a can of Hot'n'Spicy beans if you want the demand to increase to 410 cans per week?

Solution with Technology In part (c), we can find p numerically by using a worksheet like the following to compute the demand for many prices starting at $p = \$0.00$, until we find the price at which the demand equals 410.

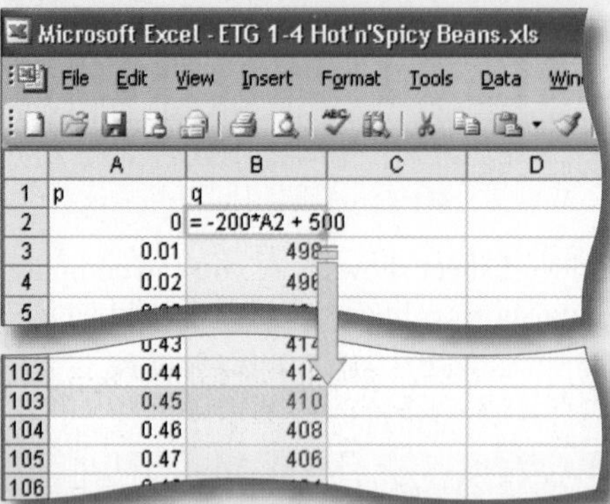

Microsoft Excel - ETG 1-4 Hot'n'Spicy Beans.xls

	A	B	C	D
1	p	q		
2	0	=-200*A2 + 500		
3	0.01	498		
4	0.02	496		
5				
	0.43	414		
102	0.44	412		
103	0.45	410		
104	0.46	408		
105	0.47	406		
106				

Section 1.5

Example **1** Using the data at the beginning of Section 1.5 on the cable television market in China, compute SSE, the sum-of-squares error, for the linear models $y = 8t + 72$ and $y = 5t + 68$. Which model is the better fit?

Solution with Technology

1. Begin by setting up your worksheet with the observed data in two columns, t and y, and the predicted data for the first model in the third.

Microsoft Excel - ETG 1-5 Cable Television Market in China.xls

	A	B	C	D	E	F	G
1	t	y (Observed)	y (Predicted)		m	b	
2	-4	50	=$E$2*A2+$F$2		8	72	
3	-3	55					
4	-2	57					
5	-1	60					
6	0	68					
7	1	72					
8	2	80					
9	3	83					
10							
11							

Notice that instead of using the numerical equation for the first model in column C, we used absolute references to the cells containing the slope *m* and the intercept *b*. This way, we can switch from one linear model to the next by changing only *m* and *b* in cells E2 and F2. (We have deliberately left column D empty in anticipation of the next step.)

2. In column D we compute the squares of the residuals using the Excel formula

```
=(B2-C2)^2
```

Microsoft Excel - ETG 1-5 Cable Television Market in China.xls

	A	B	C	D	E	F	G
1	t	y (Observed)	y (Predicted)	Residual^2	m	b	
2	-4	50	40	=(B2-C2)^2	8	72	
3	-3	55	48				
4	-2	57	56		SSE:	=SUM(D2:D9)	
5	-1	60	64				
6	0	68	72				
7	1	72	80				
8	2	80	88				
9	3	83	96				
10							
11							

Here is the completed worksheet, with SSE in cell F4.

Microsoft Excel - ETG 1-5 Cable Television Market in China.xls

	A	B	C	D	E	F	G
1	t	y (Observed)	y (Predicted)	Residual^2	m	b	
2	-4	50	40	100	8	72	
3	-3	55	48	49			
4	-2	57	56	1	SSE:	479	
5	-1	60	64	16			
6	0	68	72	16			
7	1	72	80	64			
8	2	80	88	64			
9	3	83	96	169			
10							
11							

Changing m to 5 and b to 68 gives the sum of squares error for the second model, SSE = 23.

Microsoft Excel - ETG 1-5 Cable Television Market in China.xls

File Edit View Insert Format Tools Data Window Help Adobe PDF

	A	B	C	D	E	F	G
1	t	y (Observed)	y (Predicted)	Residual^2	m	b	
2	-4	50	48	4	5	68	
3	-3	55	53	4			
4	-2	57	58	1	SSE:	23	
5	-1	60	63	9			
6	0	68	68	0			
7	1	72	73	1			
8	2	80	78	4			
9	3	83	83	0			
10							
11							

Thus, the second model is a better fit.

You can also use Excel to plot both the original data points and each of the two lines. Use a scatter plot to graph the data in columns A through C in each of the last two worksheets above.

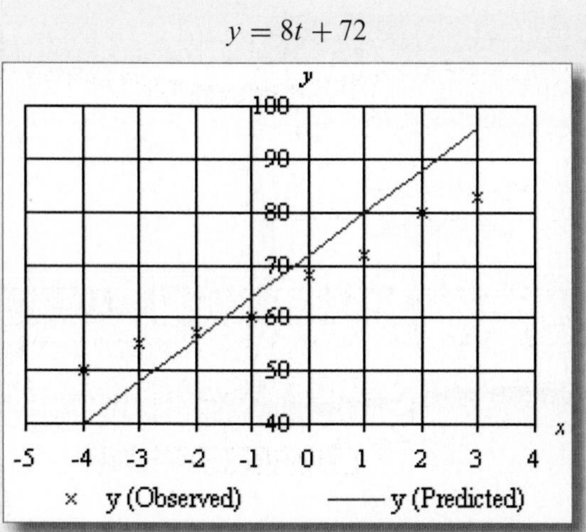

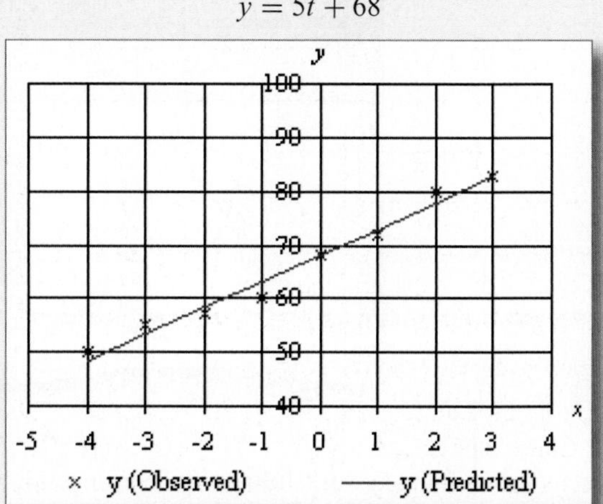

Example **2** Consider the following data about the growth of the cable TV market in China.

Year (t) ($t = 0$ represents 2000)	−4	−3	−2	−1	0	1	2	3
Households with Cable (y) (Millions)	50	55	57	60	68	72	80	83

Find the best-fit linear model for these data.

Solution with Technology Here are two Excel shortcuts for linear regression; one graphical and one based on an Excel formula.

Using the Trendline

1. Start with the original data and a "scatter plot."

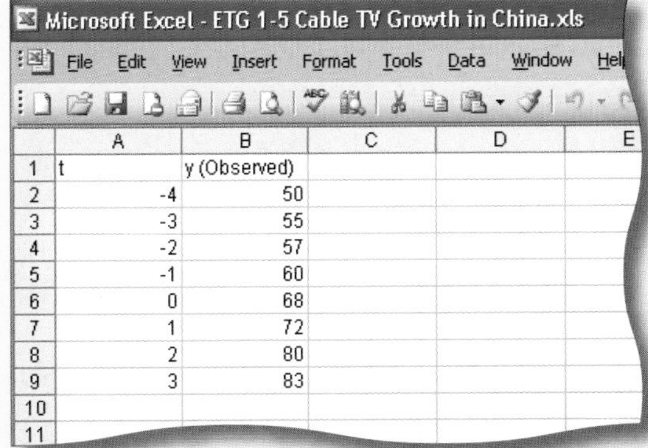

Microsoft Excel - ETG 1-5 Cable TV Growth in China.xls

	A	B	C	D	E
1	t	y (Observed)			
2	-4	50			
3	-3	55			
4	-2	57			
5	-1	60			
6	0	68			
7	1	72			
8	2	80			
9	3	83			
10					
11					

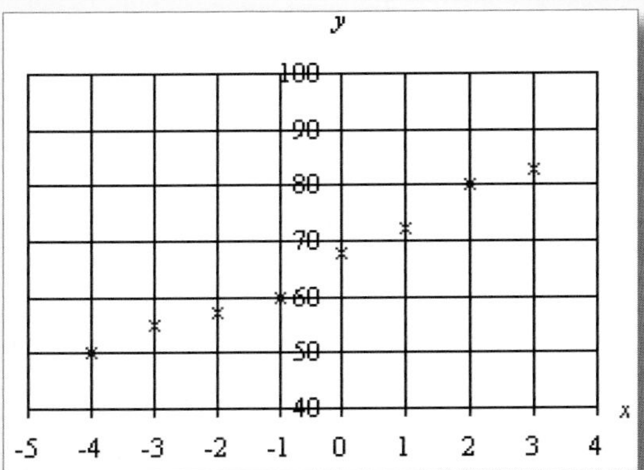

2. Click on the chart, and select "Add Trendline . . ." from the Chart menu. Then select a "Linear" type (the default) and, under "Options", check the option "Display equation on chart".

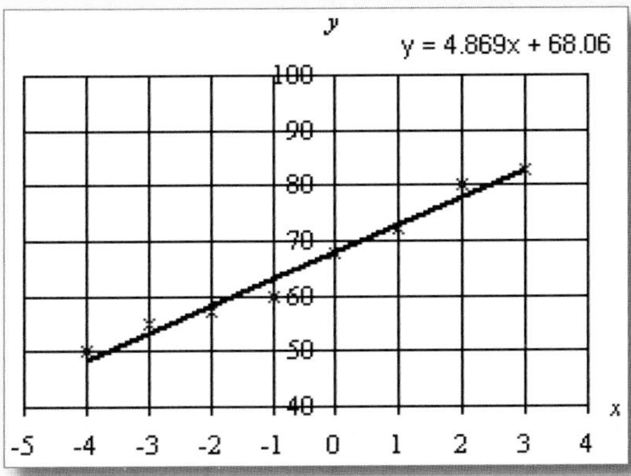

Using a Formula

Alternatively, you can use the "LINEST" function (for "linear estimate"):

1. Enter your data as above, and select a block of unused cells two wide and one tall; for example C2:D2.

2. Enter the formula

```
=LINEST(B2:B9,A2:A9)
```

as shown, and press Control-Shift-Enter.

Microsoft Excel - ETG 1-5 Cable TV Growth in China.xls

	A	B	C	D	E
1	t	y (Observed)	m	b	
2	-4	50	=LINEST(B2:B9, A2:A9)		
3	-3	55			
4	-2	57			
5	-1	60			
6	0	68			
7	1	72			
8	2	80			
9	3	83			
10					
11					

The result should look like this.

Microsoft Excel - ETG 1-5 Cable TV Growth in China.xls

	A	B	C	D	E
1	t	y (Observed)	m	b	
2	-4	50	4.869047619	68.05952381	
3	-3	55			
4	-2	57			
5	-1	60			
6	0	68			
7	1	72			
8	2	80			
9	3	83			
10					
11					

The values of m and b appear in cells C2 and D2 as shown,

Example 3 Find the correlation coefficient for the data in Example 2.

Solution with Technology In Excel, when you add a trend line to a chart you can select the option "Display r-squared value on chart" to show the value of r^2 on the chart (it is common to examine r^2, which takes on values between 0

and 1, instead of r). Alternatively, the LINEST function we used in Example 2 can be used to display quite a few statistics about a best fit line, including r^2:

1. Instead of selecting a block of cells two wide and one tall as we did in Example 2, we select one two wide and *five* tall.
2. We now enter the requisite LINEST formula with two additional arguments set to "TRUE" as shown, and press Control-Shift-Enter.

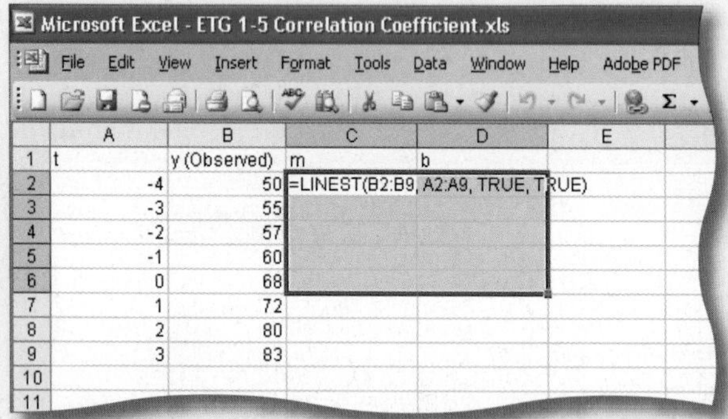

Microsoft Excel - ETG 1-5 Correlation Coefficient.xls

	A	B	C	D	E
1	t	y (Observed)	m	b	
2	-4	50	=LINEST(B2:B9, A2:A9, TRUE, TRUE)		
3	-3	55			
4	-2	57			
5	-1	60			
6	0	68			
7	1	72			
8	2	80			
9	3	83			
10					
11					

The result should look something like this:

Microsoft Excel - ETG 1-5 Correlation Coefficient.xls

	A	B	C	D	E
1	t	y (Observed)	m	b	
2	-4	50	4.869047619	68.05952381	
3	-3	55	0.296505855	0.695367867	
4	-2	57	0.9782343	1.92157756	
5	-1	60	269.6630844	6	
6	0	68	995.7202381	22.1547619	
7	1	72			
8	2	80			
9	3	83			
10					
11					

The values of m and b appear in cells C2 and D2 as before, and the value of r^2 in cell C4. (Among the other numbers shown is SSE in cell D6. For the meanings of the remaining numbers shown, see the on-line help for LINEST in Excel; a good course in statistics wouldn't hurt, either.)

2 Nonlinear Models

CASE STUDY Checking up on Malthus

In 1798 Thomas R. Malthus (1766–1834) published an influential pamphlet, later expanded into a book, titled *An Essay on the Principle of Population as It Affects the Future Improvement of Society*. One of his main contentions was that population grows geometrically (exponentially), while the supply of resources such as food grows only arithmetically (linearly). Some 200 years later, you have been asked to check the validity of Malthus's contention. How do you go about doing so?

Park Street/PhotoEdit

Introduction

To see if Malthus was right, we need to see if the data fit the models (linear and exponential) that he suggested or if other models would be better. We saw in Chapter 1 how to fit a linear model. In this chapter we discuss how to construct models using various *nonlinear* functions.

The nonlinear functions we consider in this chapter are the *quadratic* functions, the simplest nonlinear functions; the *exponential* functions, essential for discussing many kinds of growth and decay, including the growth (and decay) of money in finance and the initial growth of an epidemic; the *logarithmic* functions, needed to fully understand the exponential functions; and the *logistic* functions, used to model growth with an upper limit, such as the spread of an epidemic.

algebra Review
For this chapter, you should be familiar with the algebra reviewed in Chapter 0, Section 2.

2.1 Quadratic Functions and Models

In Chapter 1 we studied linear functions. Linear functions are useful, but in real-life applications, they are often accurate for only a limited range of values of the variables. The relationship between two quantities is often best modeled by a curved line rather than a straight line. The simplest function with a graph that is not a straight line is a *quadratic* function.

Quadratic Function

A **quadratic function** of the variable x is a function that can be written in the form

$$f(x) = ax^2 + bx + c \qquad \text{Function form}$$

or

$$y = ax^2 + bx + c \qquad \text{Equation form}$$

where a, b, and c are fixed numbers (with $a \neq 0$).

quick Examples

1. $f(x) = 3x^2 - 2x + 1$ — $a = 3, b = -2, c = 1$

2. $g(x) = -x^2$ — $a = -1, b = 0, c = 0$

3. $R(p) = -5600p^2 + 14{,}000p$ — $a = -5600, b = 14{,}000, c = 0$

Every quadratic function $f(x) = ax^2 + bx + c$ ($a \neq 0$) has a **parabola** as its graph. Following is a summary of some features of parabolas that we can use to sketch the graph of any quadratic function.[1]

[1] We shall not fully justify the formula for the vertex and the axis of symmetry until we have studied some calculus, although it is possible to do so with just algebra.

Features of a Parabola

The graph of $f(x) = ax^2 + bx + c\,(a \neq 0)$ is a **parabola.** If $a > 0$ the parabola opens upward (concave up) and if $a < 0$ it opens downward (concave down):

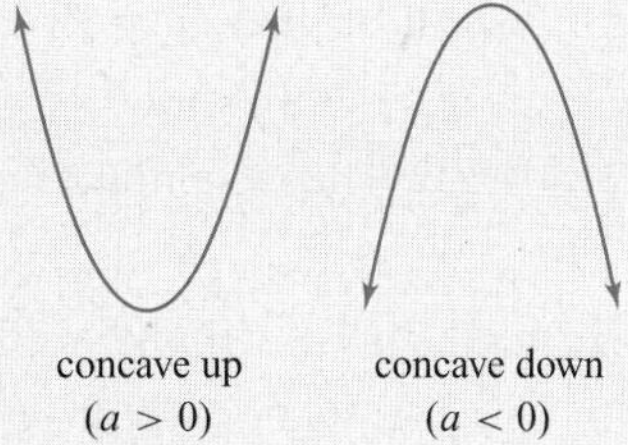

Vertex, Intercepts, and Symmetry

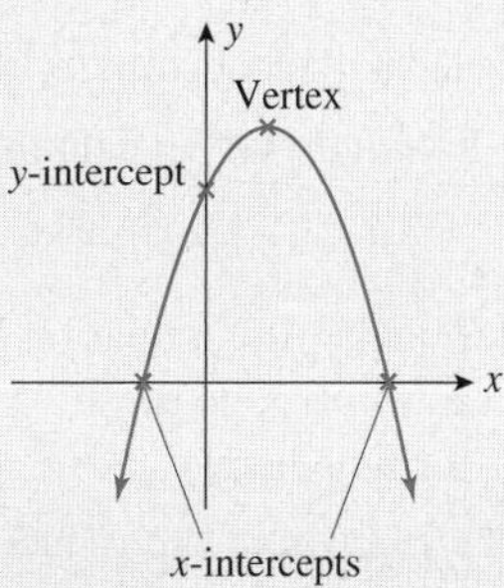

Vertex The vertex is the turning point of the parabola (see the above figure). Its x-coordinate is $-\dfrac{b}{2a}$. Its y-coordinate is $f\left(-\dfrac{b}{2a}\right)$.

x-Intercepts (if any) These occur when $f(x) = 0$; that is, when

$$ax^2 + bx + c = 0$$

Solve this equation for x by either factoring or using the quadratic formula. The x-intercepts are

$$x = \frac{-b \pm \sqrt{b^2 - 4ac}}{2a}$$

If the **discriminant** $b^2 - 4ac$ is positive, there are two x-intercepts. If it is zero, there is a single x-intercept (at the vertex). If it is negative, there are no x-intercepts (so the parabola doesn't touch the x-axis at all).

y-Intercept This occurs when $x = 0$, so

$$y = a(0)^2 + b(0) + c = c$$

Symmetry The parabola is symmetric with respect to the vertical line through the vertex, which is the line $x = -\dfrac{b}{2a}$.

Note that the x-intercepts can also be written as

$$x = -\frac{b}{2a} \pm \frac{\sqrt{b^2 - 4ac}}{2a}$$

making it clear that they are located symmetrically on either side of the line $x = -b/(2a)$. This partially justifies the claim that the whole parabola is symmetric with respect to this line.

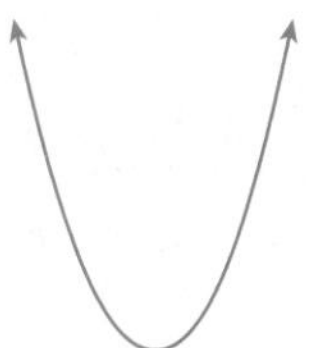

Figure **1**

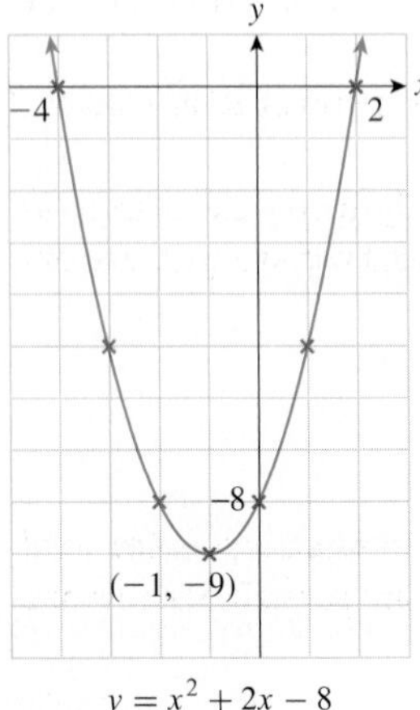

$y = x^2 + 2x - 8$

Figure **2**

Example 1 Sketching the Graph of a Quadratic Function

Sketch the graph of $f(x) = x^2 + 2x - 8$ by hand.

Solution Here, $a = 1, b = 2$, and $c = -8$. Because $a > 0$, the parabola is concave up (Figure 1).

Vertex: The x-coordinate of the vertex is

$$x = -\frac{b}{2a} = -\frac{2}{2} = -1$$

To get its y-coordinate, we substitute the value of x back into $f(x)$ to get

$$y = f(-1) = (-1)^2 + 2(-1) - 8 = 1 - 2 - 8 = -9$$

Thus, the coordinates of the vertex are $(-1, -9)$.

x-Intercepts: To calculate the x-intercepts (if any), we solve the equation

$$x^2 + 2x - 8 = 0$$

Luckily, this equation factors as $(x + 4)(x - 2) = 0$. Thus, the solutions are $x = -4$ and $x = 2$, so these values are the x-intercepts. (We could also have used the quadratic formula here.)

y-Intercept: The y-intercept is given by $c = -8$.

Symmetry: The graph is symmetric around the vertical line $x = -1$.

Now we can sketch the curve as in Figure 2. (As we see in the figure, it is helpful to plot additional points using the equation $y = x^2 + 2x - 8$, and to use symmetry to obtain others.)

Example 2 One *x*-Intercept and No *x*-Intercepts

Sketch the graph of each quadratic function, showing the location of the vertex and intercepts.

a. $f(x) = 4x^2 - 12x + 9$

b. $g(x) = -\frac{1}{2}x^2 + 4x - 12$

using *Technology*

See the Technology Guides at the end of the chapter to find out how to do the calculations and the graph in part (a) using a TI-83/84 or Excel.

Solution

a. We have $a = 4, b = -12$, and $c = 9$. Because $a > 0$, this parabola is concave up.

Vertex: $x = -\frac{b}{2a} = \frac{12}{8} = \frac{3}{2}$ x-coordinate of vertex

$$y = f\left(\frac{3}{2}\right) = 4\left(\frac{3}{2}\right)^2 - 12\left(\frac{3}{2}\right) + 9 = 0 \quad y\text{-coordinate of vertex}$$

Thus, the vertex is at the point $(3/2, 0)$.

x-Intercepts: $4x^2 - 12x + 9 = 0$

$$(2x - 3)^2 = 0$$

The only solution is $2x - 3 = 0$, or $x = 3/2$. Note that this coincides with the vertex, which lies on the x-axis.

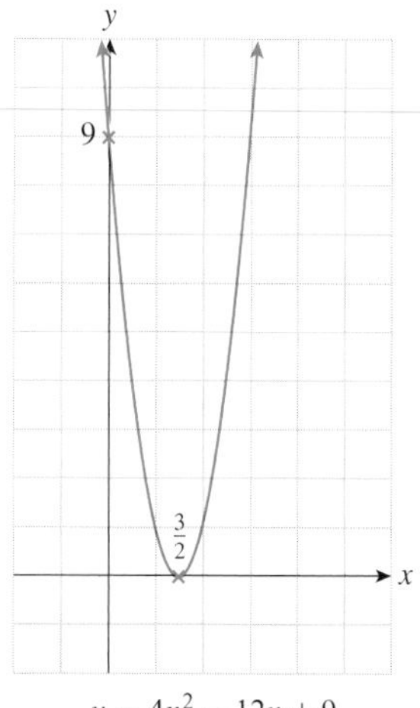

$y = 4x^2 - 12x + 9$

Figure **3**

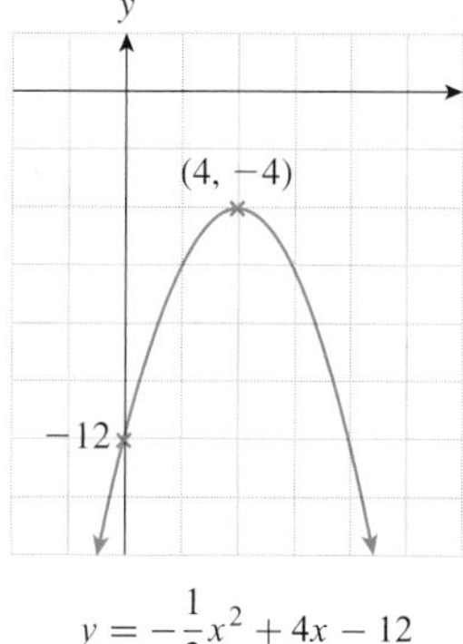

$y = -\frac{1}{2}x^2 + 4x - 12$

Figure **4**

y-Intercept: $c = 9$

Symmetry: The graph is symmetric around the vertical line $x = 3/2$.

The graph is the narrow parabola shown in Figure 3. (As we remarked in Example 1, plotting additional points and using symmetry helps us obtain an accurate sketch.)

b. Here, $a = -1/2$, $b = 4$, and $c = -12$. Because $a < 0$, the parabola is concave down. The vertex has x-coordinate $-b/(2a) = 4$, with corresponding y-coordinate $f(4) = -\frac{1}{2}(4)^2 + 4(4) - 12 = -4$. Thus, the vertex is at $(4, -4)$.

For the x-intercepts, we must solve $-\frac{1}{2}x^2 + 4x - 12 = 0$. If we try to use the quadratic formula, we discover that the discriminant is $b^2 - 4ac = 16 - 24 = -8$. Because the discriminant is negative, there are no solutions of the equation, so there are no x-intercepts.

The y-intercept is given by $c = -12$, and the graph is symmetric around the vertical line $x = 4$.

Because there are no x-intercepts, the graph lies entirely below the x-axis, as shown in Figure 4. (Again, you should plot additional points and use symmetry to ensure that your sketch is accurate.)

Applications

Recall that the **revenue** resulting from one or more business transactions is the total payment received. Thus, if q units of some item are sold at p dollars per unit, the revenue resulting from the sale is

$$\text{revenue} = \text{price} \times \text{quantity}$$
$$R = pq$$

Example **3** Demand and Revenue

Alien Publications, Inc., predicts that the demand equation for the sale of its latest illustrated sci-fi novel *Episode 93: Yoda vs. Alien* is

$$q = -2000p + 150{,}000$$

where q is the number of books it can sell each year at a price of \$$p$ per book. What price should Alien Publications, Inc., charge to obtain the maximum annual revenue?

Solution The total revenue depends on the price, as follows:

$$\begin{aligned} R &= pq && \text{Formula for revenue} \\ &= p(-2000p + 150{,}000) && \text{Substitute for } q \text{ from demand equation.} \\ &= -2000p^2 + 150{,}000p && \text{Simplify.} \end{aligned}$$

We are after the price p that gives the maximum possible revenue. Notice that what we have is a quadratic function of the form $R(p) = ap^2 + bp + c$, where $a = -2000$, $b = 150{,}000$, and $c = 0$. Because a is negative, the graph of the function is a parabola, concave down, so its vertex is its highest point (Figure 5). The p-coordinate of the vertex is

$$p = -\frac{b}{2a} = -\frac{150{,}000}{-4000} = 37.5$$

This value of p gives the highest point on the graph and thus gives the largest value of $R(p)$. We may conclude that Alien Publications, Inc., should charge \$37.50 per book to maximize its annual revenue.

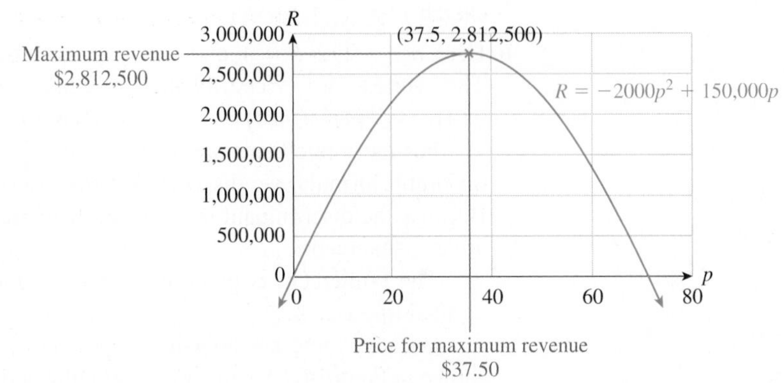

Figure **5**

+Before we go on... You might ask what the maximum annual revenue is for the publisher in Example 3. Because $R(p)$ gives us the revenue at a price of \$$p$, the answer is $R(37.5) = -2000(37.5)^2 + 150{,}000(37.5) = 2{,}812{,}500$. In other words, the company will earn total annual revenues from this book amounting to \$2,812,500. ■

Example **4** Demand, Revenue, and Profit

As the operator of Workout Fever Health Club, you calculate your demand equation to be

$$q = -0.06p + 84$$

where q is the number of members in the club and p is the annual membership fee you charge.

a. Your annual operating costs are a fixed cost of \$20,000 per year plus a variable cost of \$20 per member. Find the annual revenue and profit as functions of the membership price p.

b. At what price should you set the annual membership fee to obtain the maximum revenue? What is the maximum possible revenue?

c. At what price should you set the annual membership fee to obtain the maximum profit? What is the maximum possible profit? What is the corresponding revenue?

Solution

a. The annual revenue is given by

$R = pq$	Formula for revenue
$= p(-0.06p + 84)$	Substitute for q from demand equation.
$= -0.06p^2 + 84p$	Simplify.

The annual cost C is given by

$$C = 20{,}000 + 20q \qquad \text{\$20,000 plus \$20 per member}$$

However, this is a function of q, and not p. To express C as a function of p we substitute for q using the demand equation $q = -0.06p + 84$:

$$\begin{aligned} C &= 20{,}000 + 20(-0.06p + 84) \\ &= 20{,}000 - 1.2p + 1680 \\ &= -1.2p + 21{,}680 \end{aligned}$$

Thus, the profit function is

$$\begin{aligned} P &= R - C && \text{Formula for profit} \\ &= -0.06p^2 + 84p - (-1.2p + 21{,}680) && \text{Substitute for revenue and cost.} \\ &= -0.06p^2 + 85.2p - 21{,}680 \end{aligned}$$

b. From part (a) the revenue function is given by

$$R = -0.06p^2 + 84p$$

This is a quadratic function ($a = -0.06$, $b = 84$, $c = 0$) whose graph is a concave-down parabola (Figure 6).

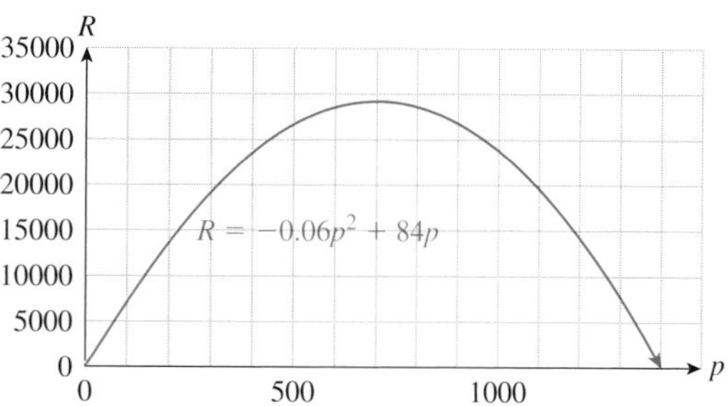

Figure **6**

The maximum revenue corresponds to the highest point of the graph: the vertex, of which the p-coordinate is

$$p = -\frac{b}{2a} = -\frac{84}{2(-0.06)} \approx \$700$$

This is the membership fee you should charge for the maximum revenue. The corresponding maximum revenue is given by the y-coordinate of the vertex in Figure 6:

$$R(700) = -0.06(700)^2 + 84(700) = \$29{,}400$$

c. From part (a), the profit function is given by

$$P = -0.06p^2 + 85.2p - 21{,}680$$

Like the revenue function, the profit function is quadratic ($a = -0.06$, $b = 85.2$, $c = -21{,}680$). Figure 7 shows both the revenue and profit functions.

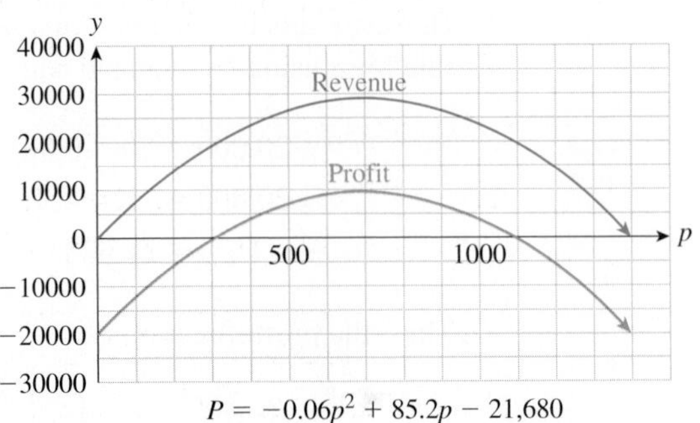

Figure 7

The maximum profit corresponds to the vertex, whose p-coordinate is

$$p = -\frac{b}{2a} = -\frac{85.2}{2(-0.06)} \approx \$710$$

This is the membership fee you should charge for the maximum profit. The corresponding maximum profit is given by the y-coordinate of the vertex of the profit curve in Figure 7:

$$P(710) = -0.06(710)^2 + 85.2(710) - 21{,}680 = \$8{,}566$$

The corresponding revenue is

$$R(710) = -0.06(710)^2 + 84(710) = \$29{,}394$$

slightly less than the maximum possible revenue of \$29,400.

+ *Before we go on...* The result of part (c) of Example 4 tells us that the vertex of the profit curve in Figure 7 is slightly to the right of the vertex in the revenue curve. However, the difference is tiny compared to the scale of the graphs, so the graphs appear to be parallel. ■

Q: *Charging \$710 membership brings in less revenue than charging \$700. So why charge \$710?*

A: A membership fee of \$700 does bring in slightly larger revenue than a fee of \$710, but it also brings in a slightly larger membership which in turn raises the operating expense and has the effect of *lowering* the profit slightly (to \$8560). In other words, the slightly higher fee, while bringing in less revenue, also lowers the cost, and the net result is a larger profit. ■

Fitting a Quadratic Function to Data: Quadratic Regression

In Section 1.5 we saw how to fit a regression line to a collection of data points. Here, we see how to use technology to obtain the **quadratic regression curve** associated with a set of points. The quadratic regression curve is the quadratic curve $y = ax^2 + bx + c$ that best fits the data points in the sense that the associated sum-of-squares error (SSE—see Section 1.5) is a minimum. Although there are algebraic methods for obtaining the quadratic regression curve, it is normal to use technology to do this.

Example 5 Currency

The following table shows the value of the euro (€) in U.S. dollars since it began trading in January, 1999 ($t = 0$ represents January 2000).*

Year t	-1	0	1	2	3	4	4.5
Value ($)	1.2	1	0.9	0.9	1.1	1.3	1.2

a. Is a linear model appropriate for these data?

b. Find the quadratic model

$$V(t) = at^2 + bt + c$$

that best fits the data.

Solution

a. To see whether a linear model is appropriate, we plot the data points and the regression line using one of the methods of Example 3 in Section 1.5 (Figure 8).

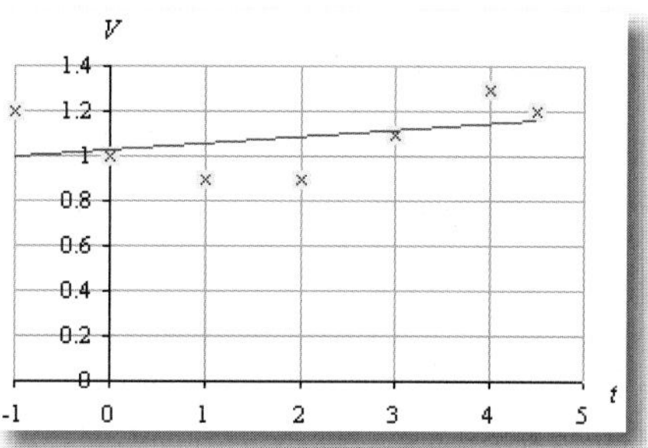

Figure **8**

From the graph, we can see that the given data suggest a curve and not a straight line: The observed points are above the regression line at the ends but below in the middle. (We would expect the data points from a linear relation to fall randomly above and below the regression line.)

b. The quadratic model that best fits the data is the quadratic regression model. As with linear regression, there are algebraic formulas to compute a, b, and c, but they are rather involved. However, we exploit the fact that these formulas are built into graphing calculators, spreadsheets, and other technology, and obtain the regression curve using technology (see Figure 9):

$$V(t) = 0.0399t^2 - 0.1150t + 1.0154 \quad \text{Coefficients rounded to four decimal places}$$

using *Technology*

See the Technology Guides at the end of the chapter for detailed instructions on using a TI-83/84 or Excel to find quadratic regression curves. Alternatively, go online and follow:

Chapter 2
→ Tools
→ Simple Regression

to find a utility for finding regression curves of various sorts.

*Prices are rounded 20-day averages. Source for data: http://finance.yahoo.com/.

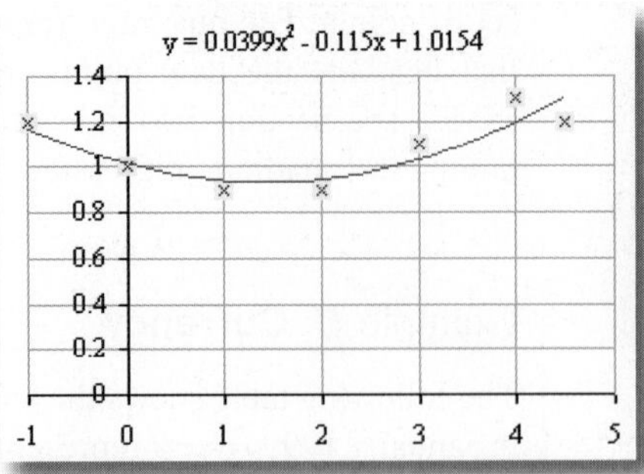

Figure 9

Notice from the graphs above that the quadratic regression model appears to give a far better fit than the linear regression model. This impression is supported by the values of SSE. For the linear regression model, SSE ≈ 0.13. For the quadratic regression model, SSE is much smaller, approximately 0.03, indicating a much better fit.

2.1 EXERCISES

● denotes basic skills exercises

tech Ex indicates exercises that should be solved using technology

In Exercises 1–10, sketch the graphs of the quadratic functions, indicating the coordinates of the vertex, the y-intercept, and the x-intercepts (if any). hint [see Example 1]

1. ● $f(x) = x^2 + 3x + 2$

2. ● $f(x) = -x^2 - x$

3. ● $f(x) = -x^2 + 4x - 4$

4. ● $f(x) = x^2 + 2x + 1$

5. ● $f(x) = -x^2 - 40x + 500$

6. ● $f(x) = x^2 - 10x - 600$

7. ● $f(x) = x^2 + x - 1$

8. ● $f(x) = x^2 + \sqrt{2}x + 1$

9. ● $f(x) = x^2 + 1$

10. ● $f(x) = -x^2 + 5$

In Exercises 11–14, for each demand equation, express the total revenue R as a function of the price p per item, sketch the graph of the resulting function, and determine the price p that maximizes total revenue in each case. hint [see Example 3]

11. ● $q = -4p + 100$

12. ● $q = -3p + 300$

13. ● $q = -2p + 400$

14. ● $q = -5p + 1200$

tech Ex *In Exercises 15–18, use technology to find the quadratic regression curve through the given points. (Round all coefficients to four decimal places.)* hint [see Example 5]

15. tech Ex $\{(1, 2), (3, 5), (4, 3), (5, 1)\}$

16. tech Ex $\{(-1, 2), (-3, 5), (-4, 3), (-5, 1)\}$

17. tech Ex $\{(-1, 2), (-3, 5), (-4, 3)\}$

18. tech Ex $\{(2, 5), (3, 5), (5, 3)\}$

Applications

19. ● ***Trade with China*** The following chart shows the value of U.S. trade with China for the period 1994–2004 ($t = 0$ represents 1994).[2] hint [see "Features of a Parabola" p. 115]

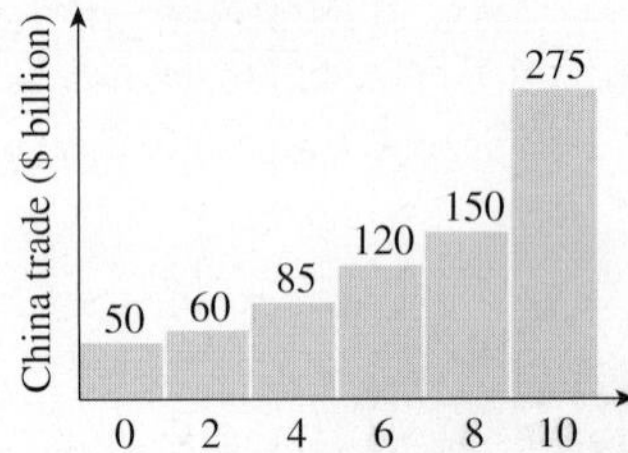

a. If you want to model the trade figures with a function of the form,

$$f(t) = at^2 + bt + c$$

would you expect the coefficient a to be positive or negative? Why?

b. Which of the following models best approximates the data given? (Try to answer this without actually computing values.)

(A) $f(t) = 3t^2 - 7t - 50$

(B) $f(t) = -3t^2 - 7t + 50$

(C) $f(t) = 3t^2 - 7t + 50$

(D) $f(t) = -3t^2 - 7t - 50$

[2] 2004 figure is an estimate. SOURCE: U.S. Census Bureau/*New York Times*, September 23, 2004, p. C1.

c. What is the nearest year that would correspond to the vertex of the graph of the correct model from part (b)? What is the danger of extrapolating the data backwards?

20. ● ***Scientific Research*** The following chart shows the number of research articles in the prominent journal *Physics Review* that were written by researchers in the U.S. for the period 1983–2003 ($t = 0$ represents 1983).[3]

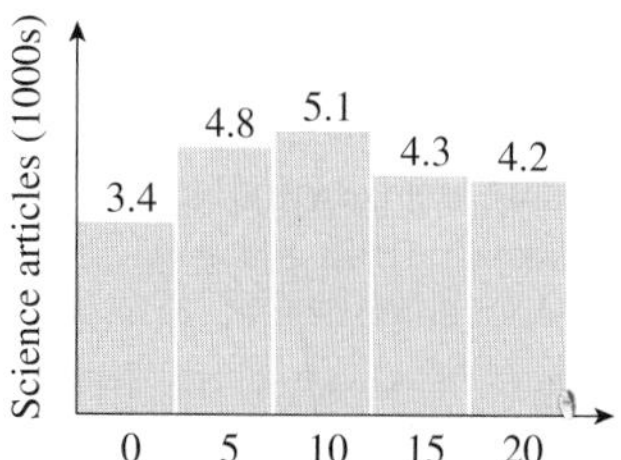

a. If you want to model the publication figures with a function of the form,

$$f(t) = at^2 + bt + c$$

would you expect the coefficient a to be positive or negative? Why?

b. Which of the following models best approximates the data given? (Try to answer this without actually computing values.)
(A) $f(t) = -0.01t^2 + 0.24t + 3.4$
(B) $f(t) = 0.01t^2 + 0.24t + 3.4$
(C) $f(t) = -0.01t^2 + 0.24t - 3.4$
(D) $f(t) = 0.01t^2 + 0.24t - 3.4$

c. In which year or years does the model in part (b) predict the number of articles published was greatest? What is the danger of extrapolating the data forwards?

21. ● ***Sport Utility Vehicles*** The average weight of an SUV could be approximated by

$$W = 3t^2 - 90t + 4200 \quad (5 \le t \le 27)$$

where t is its year of manufacture ($t = 0$ represents 1970) and W is the average weight of an SUV in pounds.[4] Sketch the graph of W as a function of t. According to the model, in what year were SUVs the lightest? What was their average weight in that year? hint [see Example 1]

22. ● ***Sedans*** The average weight of a sedan could be approximated by

$$W = 6t^2 - 240t + 4800 \quad (5 \le t \le 27)$$

where t is its year of manufacture ($t = 0$ represents 1970) and W is the average weight of a sedan in pounds.[5] Sketch the graph of W as a function of t. According to the model, in what year were sedans the lightest? What was their average weight in that year?

23. ● ***Fuel Efficiency*** The fuel efficiency (in miles per gallon) of an SUV depends on its weight according to the formula[6]

$$E = 0.000\,001\,6x^2 - 0.016x + 54 \quad (1800 \le x \le 5400)$$

where x is the weight of an SUV in pounds. According to the model, what is the weight of the least fuel-efficient SUV? Would you trust the model for weights greater than the answer you obtained? Explain.

24. ● ***Global Warming*** The amount of carbon dioxide (in pounds per 15,000 miles) released by a typical SUV depends on its fuel efficiency according to the formula[7]

$$W = 32x^2 - 2080x + 44{,}000 \quad (12 \le x \le 33)$$

where x is the fuel efficiency of an SUV in miles per gallon. According to the model, what is the fuel efficiency of the SUV with the least carbon dioxide pollution? Comment on the reliability of the model for fuel efficiencies that exceed your answer.

25. ● ***Revenue*** The market research department of the Better Baby Buggy Co. predicts that the demand equation for its buggies is given by $q = -0.5p + 140$, where q is the number of buggies it can sell in a month if the price is \$$p$ per buggy. At what price should it sell the buggies to get the largest revenue? What is the largest monthly revenue?

26. ● ***Revenue*** The Better Baby Buggy Co. has just come out with a new model, the Turbo. The market research department predicts that the demand equation for Turbos is given by $q = -2p + 320$, where q is the number of buggies it can sell in a month if the price is \$$p$ per buggy. At what price should it sell the buggies to get the largest revenue? What is the largest monthly revenue? hint [see Example 3]

27. ● ***Revenue*** Pack-Em-In Real Estate is building a new housing development. The more houses it builds, the less people will be willing to pay, due to the crowding and smaller lot sizes. In fact, if it builds 40 houses in this particular development, it can sell them for \$200,000 each, but if it builds 60 houses, it will only be able to get \$160,000 each. Obtain a linear demand equation and hence determine how many houses Pack-Em-In should build to get the largest revenue. What is the largest possible revenue?

28. ● ***Revenue*** Pack-Em-In has another development in the works. If it builds 50 houses in this development, it will be

[3] SOURCE: The American Physical Society/*New York Times* May 3, 2003, p. A1.

[4] The quadratic model is based on data published in *The New York Times,* November 30, 1997, p. 43.

[5] Ibid.

[6] Fuel efficiency assumes 50% city driving and 50% highway driving. The model is based on a quadratic regression using data from 18 models of SUV. Source for data: Environmental Protection Agency, National Highway Traffic Safety Administration, American Automobile Manufacturers' Association, Ford Motor Company/*The New York Times,* November 30, 1997, p. 43.

[7] Ibid.

able to sell them at \$190,000 each, but if it builds 70 houses, it will get only \$170,000 each. Obtain a linear demand equation and hence determine how many houses it should build to get the largest revenue. What is the largest possible revenue?

29. ● ***Website Profit*** You operate a gaming website, www.mudbeast.net, where users must pay a small fee to log on. When you charged \$2 the demand was 280 log-ons per month. When you lowered the price to \$1.50, the demand increased to 560 log-ons per month. *hint* [see Example 4]

   a. Construct a linear demand function for your website and hence obtain the monthly revenue R as a function of the log-on fee x.

   b. Your Internet provider charges you a monthly fee of \$30 to maintain your site. Express your monthly profit P as a function of the log-on fee x, and hence determine the log-on fee you should charge to obtain the largest possible monthly profit. What is the largest possible monthly profit?

30. ● ***T-Shirt Profit*** Two fraternities, Sig Ep and Ep Sig, plan to raise money jointly to benefit homeless people on Long Island. They will sell Yoda vs. Alien T-shirts in the student center, but are not sure how much to charge. Sig Ep treasurer Augustus recalls that they once sold 400 shirts in a week at \$8 per shirt, but Ep Sig treasurer Julius has solid research indicating that it is possible to sell 600 per week at \$4 per shirt.

   a. Based on this information, construct a linear demand equation for Yoda vs. Alien T-shirts, and hence obtain the weekly revenue R as a function of the unit price x.

   b. The university administration charges the fraternities a weekly fee of \$500 for use of the Student Center. Write down the monthly profit P as a function of the unit price x, and hence determine how much the fraternities should charge to obtain the largest possible weekly profit. What is the largest possible weekly profit?

31. ● ***Website Profit*** The latest demand equation for your gaming website, www.mudbeast.net, is given by

$$q = -400x + 1200$$

where q is the number of users who log on per month and x is the log-on fee you charge. Your Internet provider bills you as follows:

Site maintenance fee:	\$20 per month
High-volume access fee:	50¢ per log-on

Find the monthly cost as a function of the log-on fee x. Hence, find the monthly profit as a function of x and determine the log-on fee you should charge to obtain the largest possible monthly profit. What is the largest possible monthly profit?

32. ● ***T-Shirt Profit*** The latest demand equation for your Yoda vs. Alien T-shirts is given by

$$q = -40x + 600$$

where q is the number of shirts you can sell in one week if you charge \$$x$ per shirt. The Student Council charges you \$400 per week for use of their facilities, and the T-shirts cost you \$5 each. Find the weekly cost as a function of the unit price x. Hence, find the weekly profit as a function of x and determine the unit price you should charge to obtain the largest possible weekly profit. What is the largest possible weekly profit?

33. ***Nightclub Management*** You have just opened a new nightclub, Russ' Techno Pitstop, but are unsure of how high to set the cover charge (entrance fee). One week you charged \$10 per guest and averaged 300 guests per night. The next week you charged \$15 per guest and averaged 250 guests per night.

   a. Find a linear demand equation showing the number of guests q per night as a function of the cover charge p.

   b. Find the nightly revenue R as a function of the cover charge p.

   c. The club will provide two free nonalcoholic drinks for each guest, costing the club \$3 per head. In addition, the nightly overheads (rent, salaries, dancers, DJ, etc.) amount to \$3000. Find the cost C as a function of the cover charge p.

   d. Now find the profit in terms of the cover charge p, and hence determine the cover charge you should charge for a maximum profit.

34. ***Television Advertising*** As Sales Manager for Montevideo Productions, Inc., you are planning to review the prices you charge clients for television advertisement development. You currently charge each client an hourly development fee of \$2500. With this pricing structure, the demand, measured by the number of contracts Montevideo signs per month, is 15 contracts. This is down 5 contracts from the figure last year, when your company charged only \$2000.

   a. Construct a linear demand equation giving the number of contracts q as a function of the hourly fee p Montevideo charges for development.

   b. On average, Montevideo bills for 50 hours of production time on each contract. Give a formula for the total revenue obtained by charging \$$p$ per hour

   c. The costs to Montevideo Productions are estimated as follows:

Fixed costs:	\$120,000 per month
Variable costs:	\$80,000 per contract

   Express Montevideo Productions' monthly cost (**i**) as a function of the number q of contracts and (**ii**) as a function of the hourly production charge p.

   d. Express Montevideo Productions' monthly profit as a function of the hourly development fee p and find the price it should charge to maximize the profit.

35. tech Ex ***Trade with China*** The following table shows the value of U.S. trade with China in 1994, 1999, and 2004 (see Exercise 19; $t = 0$ represents 1994).[8]

Year t	0	5	10
China Trade ($ Billion)	50	95	275

Find a quadratic model for these data, and use your model to estimate the value of U.S. trade with China in 2000. Compare your answer with the actual figure shown in Exercise 19. *hint* [see Example 5]

36. tech Ex ***Scientific Research*** The following table shows the number of research articles in *Physics Review* that were written by researchers in the U.S. in 1983, 1993, and 2003 (See Exercise 20; $t = 0$ represents 1983).[9]

Year t	0	10	20
Science Articles (Hundreds)	34	51	42

Find a quadratic model for these data, and use your model to estimate the number of articles published in 1998. Compare your answer with the actual figure shown in Exercise 20.

37. tech Ex ***iPod Sales*** The following table shows Apple iPod sales from the second quarter in 2003 through the third quarter in 2004 ($t = 0$ represents the second quarter of 2003):[10]

Quarter t	0	1	2	3	4	5
iPod Sales (Thousands)	80	304	336	733	807	860

a. Find a quadratic regression model for these data. (Round coefficients to two decimal places.) Graph the model together with the data.

b. Assuming the trend had continued, estimate iPod sales in the fourth quarter of 2004 ($t = 6$) to the nearest 1000 units.

c. Actual sales of iPods in the fourth quarter of 2004 exceeded 2 million units. What does this fact suggest about using regression curves to predict sales?

38. tech Ex ***Fiber-Optic Connections*** Phone companies have been scrambling to install fiber-optic cable in order to compete with television cable companies. The following table shows the number of fiber-optic cable connections to homes in the U.S. from 2000 to 2004 ($t = 0$ represents 2000):[11]

Year t	0	1	2	3	4
Connections (Thousands)	0	10	25	65	150

a. Find a quadratic regression model for these data. Graph the model, together with the data.

b. Assuming the trend had continued, estimate the number of connections in 2005 to the nearest 1000 homes.

c. Is the quadratic model appropriate for long-term prediction of the number of network connections? Why?

Communication and Reasoning Exercises

39. ● Suppose the graph of revenue as a function of unit price is a parabola that is concave down. What is the significance of the coordinates of the vertex, the x-intercepts, and the y-intercept?

40. ● Suppose the height of a stone thrown vertically upward is given by a quadratic function of time. What is the significance of the coordinates of the vertex, the (possible) x-intercepts, and the y-intercept?

41. ● How might you tell, roughly, whether a set of data should be modeled by a quadratic rather than by a linear equation?

42. ● A member of your study group tells you that, because the following set of data does not suggest a straight line, the data are best modeled by a quadratic.

x	0	2	4	6	8
y	1	2	1	0	1

Comment on her suggestion.

43. Explain why, if demand is a linear function of unit price p (with negative slope) then there must be a *single value of p* that results in the maximum revenue.

44. Explain why, if the average cost of a commodity is given by $y = 0.1x^2 - 4x - 2$, where x is the number of units sold, there is a single choice of x that results in the lowest possible average cost.

45. If the revenue function for a particular commodity is $R(p) = -50p^2 + 60p$, what is the (linear) demand function? Give a reason for your answer.

46. If the revenue function for a particular commodity is $R(p) = -50p^2 + 60p + 50$, can the demand function be linear? What is the associated demand function?

[8] 2004 figure is an estimate. SOURCE: U.S. Census Bureau/*New York Times*, September 23, 2004, p. C1.

[9] SOURCE: The American Physical Society/*New York Times* May 3, 2003, p. A1.

[10] SOURCE: Apple financial statements, www.apple.com

[11] SOURCE: Render, Vanderslice & Associates/*New York Times*, October 11, 2004, p. C1.

2.2 Exponential Functions and Models

The quadratic functions we discussed in Section 2.1 can be used to model many nonlinear situations. However, exponential functions give better models in some applications, including population growth, radioactive decay, the growth or depreciation of financial investments, and many other phenomena.

To work effectively with exponential functions, we need to know the laws of exponents. The following list, similar to the one in the algebra review in Chapter 0, gives the laws of exponents we will be using.

The Laws of Exponents

If b and c are positive and x and y are any real numbers, then the following laws hold:

Law	quick Examples	
1. $b^x b^y = b^{x+y}$	$2^3 2^2 = 2^5 = 32$	$2^{3-x} = 2^3 2^{-x}$
2. $\dfrac{b^x}{b^y} = b^{x-y}$	$\dfrac{4^3}{4^2} = 4^{3-2} = 4^1 = 4$	$3^{x-2} = \dfrac{3^x}{3^2} = \dfrac{3^x}{9}$
3. $\dfrac{1}{b^x} = b^{-x}$	$9^{-0.5} = \dfrac{1}{9^{0.5}} = \dfrac{1}{3}$	$2^{-x} = \dfrac{1}{2^x}$
4. $b^0 = 1$	$(3.3)^0 = 1$	$x^0 = 1$ if $x \neq 0$
5. $(b^x)^y = b^{xy}$	$(2^3)^2 = 2^6 = 64$	$\left(\dfrac{1}{2}\right)^x = (2^{-1})^x = 2^{-x}$
6. $(bc)^x = b^x c^x$	$(4 \cdot 2)^2 = 4^2 2^2 = 64$	$10^x = 5^x 2^x$
7. $\left(\dfrac{b}{c}\right)^x = \dfrac{b^x}{c^x}$	$\left(\dfrac{4}{3}\right)^2 = \dfrac{4^2}{3^2} = \dfrac{16}{9}$	$\left(\dfrac{1}{2}\right)^x = \dfrac{1^x}{2^x} = \dfrac{1}{2^x}$

Here are the functions we will study in this section.

Exponential Function

An **exponential function** has the form

$$f(x) = Ab^x$$

Technology: `A*b^x`

where A and b are constants with $A \neq 0$ and b positive. We call b the **base** of the exponential function.

quick Examples

1. $f(x) = 2^x$ — $A = 1, b = 2$; Technology: `2^x`

   $f(1) = 2^1 = 2$ — `2^1`

   $f(-3) = 2^{-3} = \dfrac{1}{8}$ — `2^(-3)`

   $f(0) = 2^0 = 1$ — `2^0`

2. $g(x) = 20(3^x)$	$A = 20$, $b = 3$; Technology: `20*3^x`
$g(2) = 20(3^2) = 20(9) = 180$	`20*3^2`
$g(-1) = 20(3^{-1}) = 20\left(\frac{1}{3}\right) = 6\frac{2}{3}$	`20*3^(-1)`
3. $h(x) = 2^{-x} = \left(\frac{1}{2}\right)^x$	$A = 1$, $b = \frac{1}{2}$; Technology: `2^(-x)` or `(1/2)^x`
$h(1) = 2^{-1} = \frac{1}{2}$	`2^(-1)` or `(1/2)^1`
$h(2) = 2^{-2} = \frac{1}{4}$	`2^(-2)` or `(1/2)^2`
4. $k(x) = 3 \cdot 2^{-4x} = 3(2^{-4})^x$	$A = 3$, $b = 2^{-4}$; Technology: `3*2^(-4*x)`
$k(-2) = 3 \cdot 2^{-4(-2)}$ $= 3 \cdot 2^8 = 3 \cdot 256 = 768$	`3*2^(-4*(-2))`

Exponential Functions from the Numerical and Graphical Points of View

The following table shows values of $f(x) = 3(2^x)$ for some values of x ($A = 3$, $b = 2$):

x	-3	-2	-1	0	1	2	3
$f(x)$	$\frac{3}{8}$	$\frac{3}{4}$	$\frac{3}{2}$	3	6	12	24

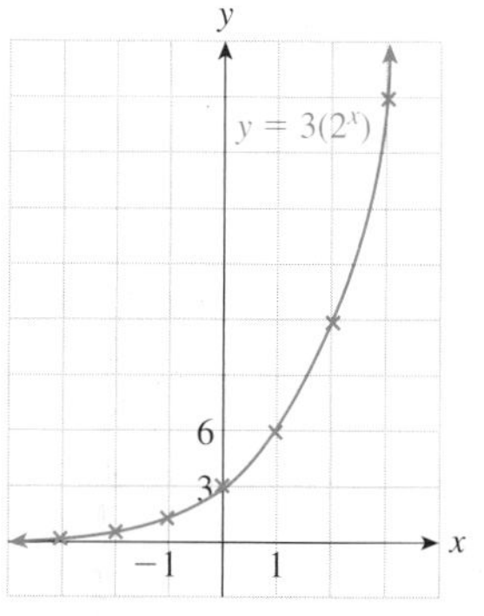

3*2^x

Figure **10**

Its graph is shown in Figure 10.

Notice that the y-intercept is $A = 3$ (obtained by setting $x = 0$). In general:

In the graph of $f(x) = Ab^x$, A is the y-intercept, or the value of y when $x = 0$.

What about b? Notice from the table that the value of y is multiplied by $b = 2$ for every increase of 1 in x. If we decrease x by 1, the y-coordinate gets *divided* by $b = 2$.

The value of y is multiplied by b for every one-unit increase of x.

x	-3	-2	-1	0	1	2	3
$f(x)$	$\frac{3}{8}$	$\frac{3}{4}$	$\frac{3}{2}$	3	6	12	24

Multiply by 2

On the graph, if we move one unit to the right from any point on the curve, the y doubles. Thus, the curve becomes dramatically steeper as the value of x in phenomenon is called **exponential growth.**

Exponential Function Numerically and Graphically

For the exponential function $f(x) = Ab^x$:

Role of A

$f(0) = A$, so A is the y-intercept of the graph of f.

Role of b

If x increases by 1, $f(x)$ is multiplied by b.

If x increases by 2, $f(x)$ is multiplied by b^2.

$\vdots$

If x increases by Δx, $f(x)$ is multiplied by $b^{\Delta x}$.

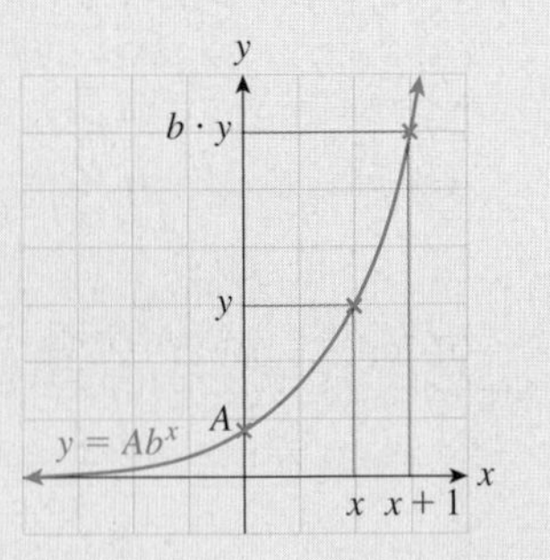

If x increases by 1, y is multiplied by b.

quick Examples

1. $f_1(x) = 2^x,\ f_2(x) = \left(\frac{1}{2}\right)^x = 2^{-x}$

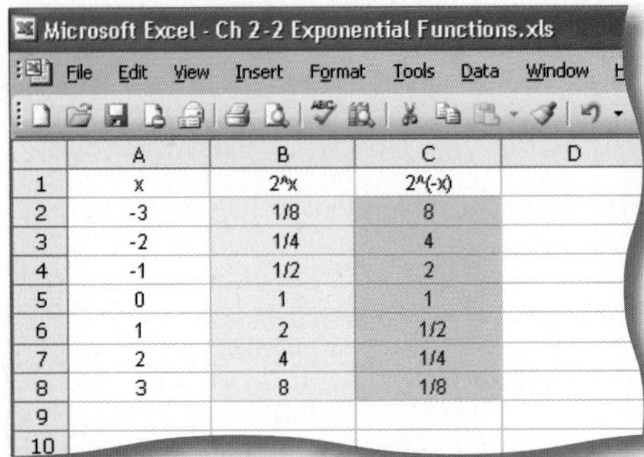
Microsoft Excel - Ch 2-2 Exponential Functions.xls

	A	B	C	D
1	x	2^x	2^(-x)	
2	-3	1/8	8	
3	-2	1/4	4	
4	-1	1/2	2	
5	0	1	1	
6	1	2	1/2	
7	2	4	1/4	
8	3	8	1/8	
9				
10				

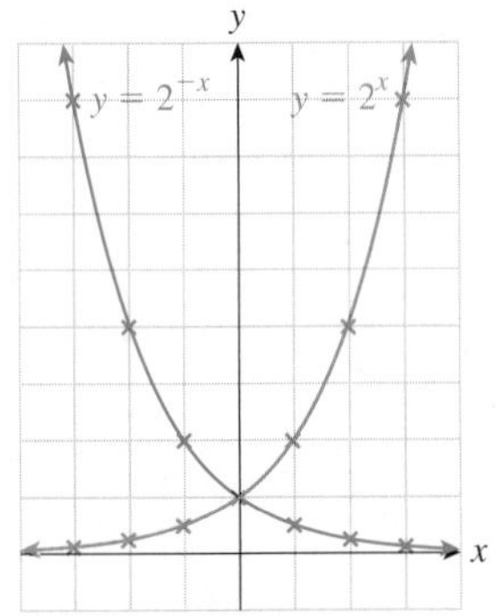

When x increases by 1, $f_2(x)$ is multiplied by $\frac{1}{2}$. The function $f_1(x) = 2^x$ illustrates exponential growth, while $f_2(x) = \left(\frac{1}{2}\right)^x$ illustrates the opposite phenomenon: **exponential decay.**

2. $f_1(x) = 2^x,\ f_2(x) = 3^x,\ f_3(x) = 1^x$

Microsoft Excel - Ch 2-2 Exponential Functions.xls

	A	B	C	D	E
1	x	2^x	3^x	1^x	
2	-3	1/8	1/27	1	
3	-2	1/4	1/9	1	
4	-1	1/2	1/3	1	
5	0	1	1	1	
6	1	2	3	1	
7	2	4	9	1	
8	3	8	27	1	
9					
10					

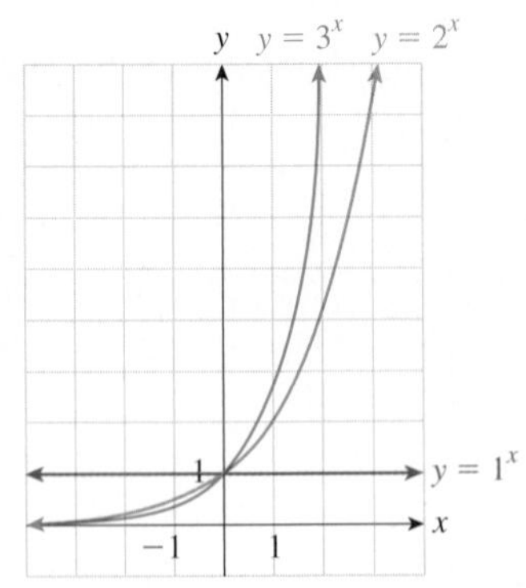

If x increases by 1, 3^x is multiplied by 3. Note also that all the graphs pass through (0, 1). (Why?)

Example 1 Recognizing Exponential Data Numerically and Graphically

Some of the values of two functions, f and g, are given in the following table:

x	-2	-1	0	1	2
$f(x)$	-7	-3	1	5	9
$g(x)$	$\frac{2}{9}$	$\frac{2}{3}$	2	6	18

One of these functions is linear, and the other is exponential. Which is which?

Solution

Remember that a linear function increases (or decreases) by the same amount every time x increases by 1. The values of f behave this way: Every time x increases by 1, the value of $f(x)$ increases by 4. Therefore, f is a linear function with a *slope* of 4. Since $f(0) = 1$, we see that

$$f(x) = 4x + 1$$

is a linear formula that fits the data.

On the other hand, every time x increases by 1, the value of $g(x)$ is *multiplied* by 3. Since $g(0) = 2$, we find that

$$g(x) = 2(3^x)$$

is an exponential function fitting the data.

We can visualize the two functions f and g by plotting the data points (Figure 11).

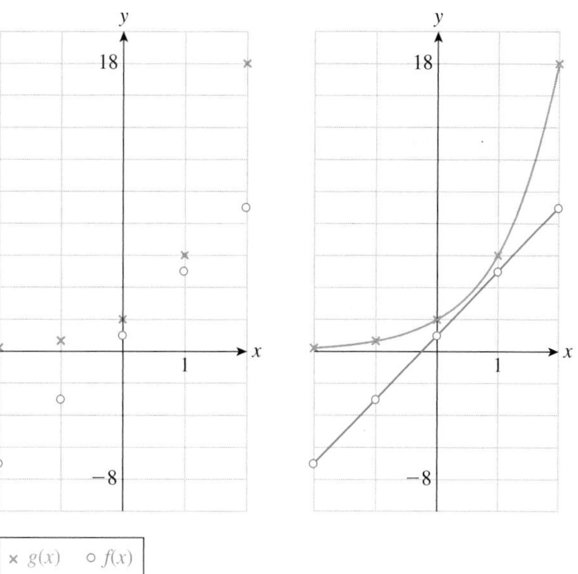

Figure 11

The data points for $f(x)$ clearly lie along a straight line, whereas the points for $g(x)$ lie along a curve, as shown in the graph on the right. The y-coordinate of each point for $g(x)$ is three times the y-coordinate of the preceding point, demonstrating that the curve is an exponential one.

In Section 1.3, we discussed a method for calculating the equation of the line that passes through two given points. In the following example, we show a method for calculating the equation of the exponential curve through two given points.

Example 2 Finding the Exponential Curve through Two Points

Find an equation of the exponential curve through (1, 6) and (3, 24).

Solution

We want an equation of the form

$$y = Ab^x \quad (b > 0)$$

Substituting the coordinates of the given points, we get

$$6 = Ab^1 \qquad \text{Substitute (1, 6).}$$

$$24 = Ab^3 \qquad \text{Substitute (3, 24).}$$

If we now divide the second equation by the first, we get

$$\frac{24}{6} = \frac{Ab^3}{Ab} = b^2$$

$$b^2 = 4$$

$$b = 2 \qquad b \text{ is positive in an exponential function}$$

Now that we have b, we can substitute its value into the first equation to obtain

$$6 = 2A \qquad \text{Substitute } b = 2 \text{ into the equation } 6 = Ab.$$

$$A = 3$$

We have both constants, $A = 3$ and $b = 2$, so the model is

$$y = 3(2^x)$$

Example 7 will show how to use technology to fit an exponential function to two or more data points.

Applications

Recall some terminology we mentioned earlier: A quantity y experiences **exponential growth** if $y = Ab^t$ with $b > 1$. (Here we use t for the independent variable, thinking of time.) It experiences **exponential decay** if $y = Ab^t$ with $0 < b < 1$. Here we discuss examples of the numerous applications of exponential growth and decay. Our first application is to public health.

Example 3 Exponential Growth: Epidemics

In the early stages of the AIDS epidemic during the 1980s, the number of cases in the U.S. was increasing by about 50% every six months. By the start of 1983, there were approximately 1600 AIDS cases in the U.S.*

*Data based on regression of the 1982–1986 figures. Source for data: Centers for Disease Control and Prevention. HIV/AIDS Surveillance Report, 2000;12 (No. 2).

a. Assuming an exponential growth model, find a function that predicts the number of people infected t years after the start of 1983.

b. Use the model to estimate the number of people infected by October 1, 1986, and also by the end of that year.

Solution

a. One way of finding the desired exponential function is to reason as follows: At time $t = 0$ (January 1, 1983), the number of people infected was 1600, so $A = 1600$. Every six months, the number of cases increased to 150% of the number six months earlier—that is, to 1.50 times that number. Each year, it therefore increased to $(1.50)^2 = 2.25$ times the number one year earlier. Hence, after t years, we need to multiply the original 1600 by 2.25^t, so the model is

$$y = 1600(2.25^t) \text{ cases}$$

Alternatively, if we wish to use the method of Example 2, we need two data points. We are given one point: (0, 1600). Since y increased by 50% every six months, six months later it reached $1600 + 800 = 2400$ ($t = 0.5$). This information gives a second point: (0.5, 2400). We can now apply the method in Example 2 to find the model above.

b. October 1, 1986, corresponds to $t = 3.75$ (because October 1 is 9 months, or $9/12 = 0.75$ of a year after January 1). Substituting this value of t in the model gives

$$y = 1600(2.25^{3.75}) \approx 33{,}481 \text{ cases}$$ `1600*2.25^3.75`

By the end of 1986, the model predicts that

$$y = 1600(2.25^4) = 41{,}006 \text{ cases}$$

(The actual number of cases was around 41,700.)

+ *Before we go on...* Increasing the number of cases by 50% every six months couldn't continue for very long and this is borne out by observations. If increasing by 50% every six months did continue, then by January 2003 ($t = 20$), the number of infected people would have been

$$1600(2.25^{20}) \approx 17{,}700{,}000{,}000$$

a number that is more than 50 times the size of the U.S. population! Thus, although the exponential model is fairly reliable in the early stages of the epidemic, it is unreliable for predicting long-term trends. ■

Epidemiologists use more sophisticated models to measure the spread of epidemics, and these models predict a leveling-off phenomenon as the number of cases becomes a significant part of the total population. We discuss such a model, the **logistic function,** in Section 2.4.

Exponential functions arise in finance and economics mainly through the idea of **compound interest.** Suppose you invest \$500 (the **present value**) in an investment account with an annual yield of 15%, and the interest is reinvested at the end of every year (we say that the interest is **compounded** once a year). Let t represent the number of years since you made the initial \$500 investment. Each year, the investment is worth 115% (or 1.15 times) its value the previous year. The **future value** A of your investment changes over time t, so we think of A as a function of t. The following table illustrates how we can calculate the future value for several values of t:

t	0	1	2	3
Future Value $A(t)$	500	575	661.25	760.44
	A	$500(1.15)$	$500(1.15)^2$	$500(1.15)^3$

$\times 1.15$ $\times 1.15$ $\times 1.15$

Thus, $A(t) = 500(1.15)^t$. A traditional way to write this formula is

$$A(t) = P(1+r)^t$$

where P is the present value ($P = 500$) and r is the annual interest rate ($r = 0.15$).

If, instead of compounding the interest once a year, we compound it every three months (four times a year), we would earn one quarter of the interest ($r/4$ of the current investment) every three months. Because this would happen $4t$ times in t years, the formula for the future value becomes

$$A(t) = P\left(1+\frac{r}{4}\right)^{4t}$$

Compound Interest

If an amount (**present value**) P is invested for t years at an annual rate of r, and if the interest is compounded (reinvested) m times per year, then the **future value** A is

$$A(t) = P\left(1+\frac{r}{m}\right)^{mt}$$

A special case is **interest compounded once a year:**

$$A(t) = P(1+r)^t$$

quick **Example** If \$2000 is invested for two and a half years in a mutual fund with an annual yield of 12.6% and the earnings are reinvested each month, then $P = 2000$, $r = 0.126$, $m = 12$, and $t = 2.5$, which gives

$$A(2.5) = 2000\left(1+\frac{0.126}{12}\right)^{12\times 2.5}$$

```
2000*(1+0.126/12)^(12*2.5)
```

$$= 2000(1.0105)^{30} = \$2736.02$$

Example 4 Compound Interest: Investments

Consider the scenario in the preceding Quick Example: you invest \$2000 in a mutual fund with an annual yield of 12.6% and the interest is reinvested each month.

a. Find the associated exponential model.

tech Ex

b. Use the model to estimate the year when the value of your investment will reach \$5000.

Solution

a. Apply the formula

$$A(t) = P\left(1+\frac{r}{m}\right)^{mt}$$

using *Technology*

See the Technology Guides at the end of the chapter for detailed instructions on using a TI-83/84 or Excel to create the tables shown here. Alternatively, go online and follow:

Chapter 2
→ Tools
→ Function Evaluator & Grapher

to use the function evaluator to create a table.

TI-83/84

with $P = 2000$, $r = 0.126$, and $m = 12$. We get

$$A(t) = 2000\left(1 + \frac{0.126}{12}\right)^{12t} \qquad \texttt{2000*(1+0.126/12)^(12*t)}$$

$$A(t) = 2000(1.0105)^{12t}$$

This is the exponential model. (What would happen if we left out the last set of parentheses in the technology formula?)

b. We need to find the value of t for which $A(t) = \$5000$, so we need to solve the equation

$$5000 = 2000(1.0105)^{12t}$$

In Section 2.3 we will learn how to use logarithms to do this algebraically, but we can answer the question now using a graphing calculator, a spreadsheet, or the Function Evaluator and Grapher tool at the website. Just enter the model and compute the balance at the end of several years. Here are examples of tables obtained using various forms of technology:

Microsoft Excel - Ch 2-2 Compound Interest of Investments.xls

	A	B	C	D	E
1	t	A			
2	0	$2,000.00			
3	1	$2,267.07			
4	2	$2,569.81			
5	3	$2,912.98			
6	4	$3,301.97			
7	5	$3,742.91			
8	6	$4,242.72			
9	7	$4,809.29			
10	8	$5,451.51			
11	9	$6,179.49			
12					
13					

Excel

Values of x:	Values of f(x)
1	2267.074593
2	2569.813606
3	2912.979567
4	3301.970984
5	3742.907262
6	4242.724979
7	4809.287003
8	5451.506188
9	6179.485587
10	7004.677386

Website

Because the balance first exceeds \$5000 in year 8, the answer is $t = 8$ years.

Carbon-14, an unstable isotope of carbon, decays exponentially to nitrogen. Because carbon-14 decay is extremely slow, it has important applications in the dating of fossils.

Example 5 Exponential Decay: Carbon Dating

The amount of carbon-14 remaining in a sample that originally contained A grams is approximately

$$C(t) = A(0.999879)^t$$

where t is time in years. A fossilized plant unearthed in an archaeological dig contains 0.50 gram of carbon-14 and is known to be 50,000 years old. How much carbon-14 did the plant originally contain?

Solution We are given the following information: $C = 0.50$, $A =$ the unknown, and $t = 50{,}000$. Substituting gives

$$0.50 = A(0.999879)^{50{,}000}$$

Solving for A gives

$$A = \frac{0.5}{0.999879^{50,000}} \approx 212 \text{ grams}$$

Thus, the plant originally contained 212 grams of carbon-14.

+*Before we go on...* The formula we used for A in Example 5 has the form

$$A(t) = \frac{C}{0.999879^t}$$

which gives the original amount of carbon-14 t years ago in terms of the amount C that is left now. A similar formula can be used in finance to find the present value, given the future value. ■

The Number e and More Applications

In nature we find examples of growth that occurs *continuously*, as though "interest" is being added more often than every second or fraction of a second. To model this, we need to see what happens to our compound interest formula as we let m (the number of times interest is added per year) become extremely large. Something very interesting does happen: we end up with a more compact and elegant formula than we began with. To see why, let's look at a very simple situation.

Suppose we invest \$1 in the bank for 1 year at 100% interest, compounded m times per year. If $m = 1$, then 100% interest is added every year, and so our money doubles at the end of the year. In general, the accumulated capital at the end of the year is

$$A = 1\left(1 + \frac{1}{m}\right)^m = \left(1 + \frac{1}{m}\right)^m \qquad \texttt{(1+1/m)^m}$$

Now, we are interested in what A becomes for large values of m. Here is an Excel sheet showing the quantity $\left(1 + \frac{1}{m}\right)^m$ for larger and larger values of m:

Microsoft Excel - Ch 2-2 The Number e.xls

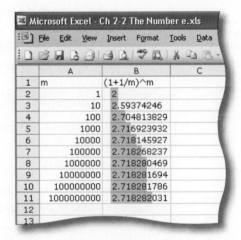

	A	B	C
1	m	(1+1/m)^m	
2	1	2	
3	10	2.59374246	
4	100	2.704813829	
5	1000	2.716923932	
6	10000	2.718145927	
7	100000	2.718268237	
8	1000000	2.718280469	
9	10000000	2.718281694	
10	100000000	2.718281786	
11	1000000000	2.718282031	
12			
13			

Something interesting *does* seem to be happening! The numbers appear to be getting closer and closer to a specific value. In mathematical terminology, we say that the numbers **converge** to a fixed number, 2.71828 . . . , called the **limiting value**[12] of the quantities $\left(1+\frac{1}{m}\right)^m$. This number, called e, is one of the most important in mathematics. The number e is irrational, just as the more familiar number π is, so we cannot write down its exact numerical value. To 20 decimal places,

$$e = 2.71828182845904523536....$$

We now say that, if \$1 is invested for 1 year at 100% interest **compounded continuously,** the accumulated money at the end of that year will amount to $\$e = \$2.72$ (to the nearest cent). But what about the following more general question?

Q: *What about a more general scenario: If we invest an amount \$P for t years at an interest rate of r, compounded continuously, what will be the accumulated amount A at the end of that period?*

A: In the special case above, (P, t, and r all equal to 1) we took the compound interest formula and let m get larger and larger. We do the same more generally, after a little preliminary work with the algebra of exponentials.

$$A = P\left(1+\frac{r}{m}\right)^{mt}$$

$$= P\left(1+\frac{1}{(m/r)}\right)^{mt} \qquad \text{Substituting } \frac{r}{m} = \frac{1}{(m/r)}.$$

$$= P\left(1+\frac{1}{(m/r)}\right)^{(m/r)rt} \qquad \text{Substituting } m = \left(\frac{m}{r}\right)r.$$

$$= P\left[\left(1+\frac{1}{(m/r)}\right)^{(m/r)}\right]^{rt} \qquad \text{Using the rule } a^{bc} = (a^b)^c$$

For continuous compounding of interest, we let m, and hence m/r, get very large. This affects only the term in brackets, which converges to e, and we get the formula

$$A = Pe^{rt} \quad ■$$

Q: *How do I obtain powers of e or e itself on a TI-83/84 or in Excel?*

A: On the TI-83/84, enter e^x as `e^(x)`, where `e^(` can be obtained by pressing 2nd LN. Excel has a built-in function called `EXP`; `EXP(x)` gives the value of e^x. To obtain the number e on the TI-83/84, enter `e^(1)`. In Excel, enter `=EXP(1)`. ■

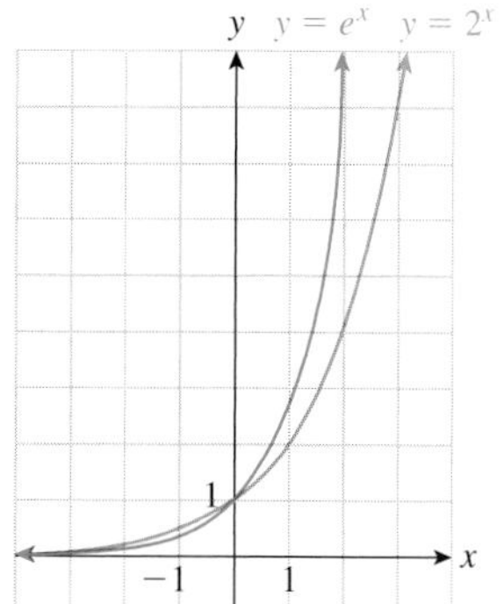

Technology formula: `e^(x)` or `EXP(x)`

Figure **12**

Figure 12 shows the graph of $y = e^x$ with that of $y = 2^x$ for comparison.

The Number e and Continuous Compounding

The number e is the limiting value of the quantities $\left(1+\frac{1}{m}\right)^m$ as m gets larger and larger, and has the value 2.71828182845904523536 . . .

If \$P is invested at an annual interest rate r compounded continuously, the accumulated amount after t years is

$$A(t) = Pe^{rt} \qquad \texttt{P*e^(r*t)} \text{ or } \texttt{P*EXP(r*t)}$$

[12] See Chapter 3 for more on limits.

quick **Examples**

1. If \$100 is invested in an account that bears 15% interest compounded continuously, at the end of 10 years the investment will be worth

$$A(10) = 100e^{(0.15)(10)} = \$448.17$$ `100*e^(0.15*10)` or `100*EXP(0.15*10)`

2. If \$1 is invested in an account that bears 100% interest compounded continuously, at the end of x years, the investment will be worth

$$A(x) = e^x \text{ dollars}$$

Example 6 Continuous Compounding

a. You invest \$10,000 at Fastrack Savings & Loan, which pays 6% compounded continuously. Express the balance in your account as a function of the number of years t and calculate the amount of money you will have after five years.

b. Your friend has just invested \$10,000 in Constant Growth Funds, whose stocks are continuously declining at a rate of 6% per year. How much will her investment be worth in five years?

Solution

a. We use the continuous growth formula with $P = 10{,}000$, $r = 0.06$, and t variable, getting

$$A(t) = Pe^{rt} = 10{,}000e^{0.06t}$$

In five years,

$$\begin{aligned} A(5) &= 10{,}000e^{0.06(5)} \\ &= 10{,}000e^{0.3} \\ &\approx \$13{,}498.59 \end{aligned}$$

b. Because the investment is depreciating, we use a negative value for r and take $P = 10{,}000$, $r = -0.06$, and $t = 5$, getting

$$\begin{aligned} A(t) &= Pe^{rt} = 10{,}000e^{-0.06t} \\ A(5) &= 10{,}000e^{-0.06(5)} \\ &= 10{,}000e^{-0.3} \\ &\approx \$7408.18 \end{aligned}$$

+*Before we go on...*

Q: *How does continuous compounding compare with monthly compounding?*

A: To repeat the calculation in part (a) of Example 6 using monthly compounding instead of continuous compounding, we use the compound interest formula with $P = 10{,}000$, $r = 0.06$, $m = 12$, and $t = 5$ and find

$$A(5) = 10{,}000(1 + 0.06/12)^{60} \approx \$13{,}488.50$$

Thus, continuous compounding earns you approximately \$10 more than monthly compounding on a five-year, \$10,000 investment. This is little to get excited about. ■

If we write the continuous compounding formula $A(t) = Pe^{rt}$ as $A(t) = P(e^r)^t$, we see that $A(t)$ is an exponential function of t, where the base is $b = e^r$, so we have really not introduced a new kind of function. In fact, exponential functions are often written in this way:

Exponential Functions: Alternative Form

We can write any exponential function in the following alternative form:

$$f(x) = Ae^{rx}$$

where A and r are constants. If r is positive, f models exponential growth; if r is negative, f models exponential decay.

quick **Examples**

1. $f(x) = 100e^{0.15x}$ — Exponential growth $A = 100$, $r = 0.15$
2. $f(t) = Ae^{-0.000\,121\,01t}$ — Exponential decay of carbon-14; $r = -0.000\,121\,01$
3. $f(t) = 100e^{0.15t} = 100\left(e^{0.15}\right)^t$
   $= 100(1.1618)^t$ — Converting Ae^{rt} to the form Ab^t

We will see in Chapter 4 that the exponential function with base e exhibits some interesting properties when we measure its rate of change, and this is the real mathematical importance of e.

Exponential Regression

Starting with a set of data that suggests an exponential curve, we can use technology to compute the exponential regression curve in much the same way as we did for the quadratic regression curve in Example 5 of Section 2.1.

tech Ex

Example 7 Exponential Regression: Health Expenditures

The following table shows annual expenditure on health in the U.S. from 1980 through 2010 ($t = 0$ represents 1980).*

Year t	0	5	10	15	20	25	30
Expenditure ($ Billion)	246	427	696	990	1310	1920	2750

a. Find the exponential regression model

$$C(t) = Ab^t$$

for the annual expenditure.

b. Use the regression model to estimate the expenditure in 2002 ($t = 22$; the actual expenditure was approximately $1550 billion).

using *Technology*

See the Technology Guides at the end of the chapter for detailed instructions on using a TI-83/84 or Excel to find exponential regression curves. Alternatively, go online and follow:

Chapter 2
→ Tools
→ Simple Regression

to find a utility for finding regression curves of various sorts.

Solution

a. We use technology to obtain the exponential regression curve (See Figure 13):

$$C(t) \approx 282.33(1.0808)^t \quad \text{Coefficients rounded}$$

*Data are rounded. 2005 and 2010 figures are projections. SOURCE: Centers for Medicare and Medicaid Services, "National Health Expenditures," 2002 version, released January 2004; www.cms.hhs.gov/statistics/nhe/

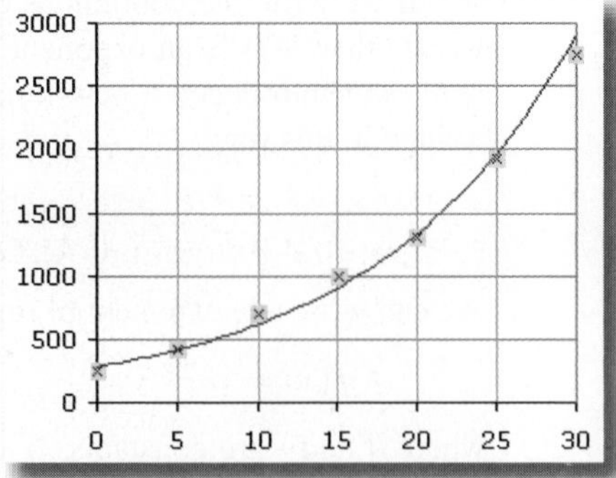

Figure **13**

b. Using the model $C(t) \approx 282.33(1.0808)^t$ we find that

$$C(22) \approx 282.33(1.0808)^{22} \approx \$1560 \text{ billion}$$

which is close to the actual number of around \$1550 billion.

+*Before we go on...* We said in the preceding section that the regression curve gives the smallest value of the sum-of-squares error, SSE (the sum of the squares of the residuals). However, exponential regression as computed via technology generally minimizes the sum of the squares of the residuals of the *logarithms* (logarithms are discussed in the next section). Using logarithms allows one easily to convert an exponential function into a linear one and then use linear regression formulas. However, in Section 2.4, we will discuss a way of using Excel's Solver to minimize SSE directly, which allows us to find the best-fit exponential curve directly without the need for devices to simplify the mathematics. If we do this, we obtain a very different equation:

$$C(t) \approx 316.79(1.0747^t)$$

If you plot this function, you will notice that it seems to fit the data more closely than the regression curve. ■

FAQs When to Use an Exponential Model for Data Points, and When to Use *e* in Your Model

Q: *Given a set of data points that appear to be curving upwards, how can I tell whether to use a quadratic model or an exponential model?*

A: Here are some things to look for:

- Do the data values appear to double at regular intervals? (For example, do the values approximately double every five units?) If so, then an exponential model is appropriate. If it takes longer and longer to double, then a quadratic model may be more appropriate.
- Do the values first decrease to a low point and then increase? If so, then a quadratic model is more appropriate.

It is also helpful to use technology to graph both the regression quadratic and exponential curves and to visually inspect the graphs to determine which gives the closest fit to the data. ■

Q: *We have two ways of writing exponential functions: $f(x) = Ab^x$ and $f(x) = Ae^{rx}$. How do we know which one to use?*

A: The two forms are equivalent, and it is always possible to convert from one form to the other.* So, use whichever form seems to be convenient for a particular situation. For instance, $f(t) = A(3^t)$ conveniently models exponential growth that is tripling every unit of time, whereas $f(t) = Ae^{0.06t}$ conveniently models an investment with continuous compounding at 6%. ■

*Quick Example 3 on p. 137 shows how to convert Ae^{rx} to Ab^x. Conversion from Ab^x to Ae^{rx} involves logarithms: $r = \ln b$.

2.2 EXERCISES

● denotes basic skills exercises

tech Ex indicates exercises that should be solved using technology

For each function in Exercises 1–12, compute the missing values in the following table and supply a valid technology formula for the given function: hint [see Quick Examples on p. 126]

x	−3	−2	−1	0	1	2	3
$f(x)$							

1. ● $f(x) = 4^x$

2. ● $f(x) = 3^x$

3. ● $f(x) = 3^{-x}$

4. ● $f(x) = 4^{-x}$

5. ● $g(x) = 2(2^x)$

6. ● $g(x) = 2(3^x)$

7. ● $h(x) = -3(2^{-x})$

8. ● $h(x) = -2(3^{-x})$

9. ● $r(x) = 2^x - 1$

10. ● $r(x) = 2^{-x} + 1$

11. ● $s(x) = 2^{x-1}$

12. ● $s(x) = 2^{1-x}$

Using a chart of values, graph each of the functions in Exercises 13–18. (Use $-3 \le x \le 3$.)

13. ● $f(x) = 3^{-x}$

14. ● $f(x) = 4^{-x}$

15. ● $g(x) = 2(2^x)$

16. ● $g(x) = 2(3^x)$

17. ● $h(x) = -3(2^{-x})$

18. ● $h(x) = -2(3^{-x})$

In Exercises 19–24, the values of two functions, f and g, are given in a table. One, both, or neither of them may be exponential. Decide which, if any, are exponential, and give the exponential models for those that are. hint [see Example 1]

19. ●

x	−2	−1	0	1	2
$f(x)$	0.5	1.5	4.5	13.5	40.5
$g(x)$	8	4	2	1	$\frac{1}{2}$

20. ●

x	−2	−1	0	1	2
$f(x)$	$\frac{1}{2}$	1	2	4	8
$g(x)$	3	0	−1	0	3

21. ●

x	−2	−1	0	1	2
$f(x)$	22.5	7.5	2.5	7.5	22.5
$g(x)$	0.3	0.9	2.7	8.1	16.2

22. ●

x	−2	−1	0	1	2
$f(x)$	0.3	0.9	2.7	8.1	24.3
$g(x)$	3	1.5	0.75	0.375	0.1875

23. ●

x	−2	−1	0	1	2
$f(x)$	100	200	400	600	800
$g(x)$	100	20	4	0.8	0.16

24. ●

x	−2	−1	0	1	2
$f(x)$	0.8	0.2	0.1	0.05	0.025
$g(x)$	80	40	20	10	2

tech Ex *For each function in Exercises 25–30, supply a valid technology formula and then use technology to compute the missing values in the following table:*

x	−3	−2	−1	0	1	2	3
$f(x)$							

25. ● $f(x) = e^{-2x}$

26. ● $g(x) = e^{x/5}$

27. ● $h(x) = 1.01(2.02^{-4x})$

28. ● $h(x) = 3.42(3^{-x/5})$

29. ● $r(x) = 50\left(1 + \frac{1}{3.2}\right)^{2x}$

30. ● $r(x) = 0.043\left(4.5 - \frac{5}{1.2}\right)^{-x}$

In Exercises 31–38, supply a valid technology formula for the given function.

31. ● 2^{x-1}

32. ● 2^{-4x}

33. ● $\frac{2}{1 - 2^{-4x}}$

34. ● $\frac{2^{3-x}}{1 - 2^x}$

35. ● $\frac{(3 + x)^{3x}}{x + 1}$

36. ● $\frac{20.3^{3x}}{1 + 20.3^{2x}}$

37. ● $2e^{(1+x)/x}$

38. ● $\frac{2e^{2/x}}{x}$

tech Ex *On the same set of axes, use technology to graph the pairs of functions in Exercises 39–46 with $-3 \le x \le 3$. Identify which graph corresponds to which function.*

39. ● $f_1(x) = 1.6^x$, $f_2(x) = 1.8^x$

40. ● $f_1(x) = 2.2^x$, $f_2(x) = 2.5^x$

41. ● $f_1(x) = 300(1.1^x)$, $f_2(x) = 300(1.1^{2x})$

42. ● $f_1(x) = 100(1.01^{2x})$, $f_2(x) = 100(1.01^{3x})$

43. ● $f_1(x) = 2.5^{1.02x}$, $f_2(x) = e^{1.02x}$

44. ● $f_1(x) = 2.5^{-1.02x}$, $f_2(x) = e^{-1.02x}$

45. ● $f_1(x) = 1000(1.045^{-3x})$, $f_2(x) = 1000(1.045^{3x})$

46. ● $f_1(x) = 1202(1.034^{-3x})$, $f_2(x) = 1202(1.034^{3x})$

For Exercises 47–54, model the data using an exponential function $f(x) = Ab^x$. hint [see Example 1]

47. ●

x	0	1	2
$f(x)$	500	250	125

48. ●

x	0	1	2
$f(x)$	500	1000	2000

49. ●

x	0	1	2
$f(x)$	10	30	90

50. ●

x	0	1	2
$f(x)$	90	30	10

51. ●

x	0	1	2
$f(x)$	500	225	101.25

52. ●

x	0	1	2
$f(x)$	5	3	1.8

53. ●

x	1	2
$f(x)$	−110	−121

54. ●

x	1	2
$f(x)$	−41	−42.025

Find equations for exponential functions that pass through the pairs of points given in Exercises 55–62. (Round all coefficients to four decimal places when necessary.) hint [see Example 2]

55. ● Through (2, 36) and (4, 324)

56. ● Through (2, –4) and (4, –16)

57. ● Through (–2, –25) and (1, –0.2)

58. ● Through (1, 1.2) and (3, 0.108)

59. ● Through (1, 3) and (3, 6)

60. ● Through (1, 2) and (4, 6)

61. ● Through (2, 3) and (6, 2)

62. ● Through (−1, 2) and (3, 1)

Obtain exponential functions in the form $f(t) = Ae^{rt}$ in Exercises 63–66. hint [see Example 6]

63. ● $f(t)$ is the value after t years of a \$5000 investment earning 10% interest compounded continuously.

64. ● $f(t)$ is the value after t years of a \$2000 investment earning 5.3% interest compounded continuously.

65. ● $f(t)$ is the value after t years of a \$1000 investment depreciating continuously at an annual rate of 6.3%.

66. ● $f(t)$ is the value after t years of a \$10,000 investment depreciating continuously at an annual rate of 60%.

tech Ex *In Exercises 67–70, use technology to find the exponential regression function through the given points. (Round all coefficients to 4 decimal places.)* hint [see Example 7]

67. ● {(1, 2), (3, 5), (4, 9), (5, 20)}

68. ● {(−1, 2), (−3, 5), (−4, 9), (−5, 20)}

69. ● {(−1, 10), (−3, 5), (−4, 3)}

70. ● {(3, 3), (4, 5), (5, 10)}

Applications

71. ● ***Bacteria*** A bacteria culture starts with 1000 bacteria and doubles in size every three hours. Find an exponential model for the size of the culture as a function of time t in hours and use the model to predict how many bacteria there will be after two days. hint [see Example 3]

72. ● ***Bacteria*** A bacteria culture starts with 1000 bacteria. Two hours later there are 1500 bacteria. Find an exponential model for the size of the culture as a function of time t in hours, and use the model to predict how many bacteria there will be after two days.

73. ● ***Investments*** In 2004, the Scottish Widows Bank in the United Kingdom offered 4.39% interest on its savings accounts, with interest reinvested annually.[13] Find the associated exponential model for the value of a £5000 deposit after t years. Assuming this rate of return continued for five years, how much would a deposit of £5000 at the beginning of 2004 be worth at the start of 2009? (Answer to the nearest £1.) hint [see Example 4]

74. ● ***Investments*** In 2004, the Northern Rock Bank in the United Kingdom offered 4.76% interest on its online accounts, with interest reinvested annually.[14] Find the associated exponential model for the value of a £4000 deposit after t years. Assuming this rate of return continued for four years, how much would a deposit of £4000 made at the beginning of 2004 be worth at the start of 2008? (Answer to the nearest £1.)

75. tech Ex ***Investments*** Refer to Exercise 73. When will an investment of £5000 made at the beginning of 2004 first exceed £7500?

76. tech Ex ***Investments*** Refer to Exercise 74. In which year will an investment of £4000 made at the beginning of 2004 first exceed £6000?

77. ● ***Carbon Dating*** A fossil originally contained 104 grams of carbon-14. Refer to the formula for $C(t)$ in Example 5 and estimate the amount of carbon-14 left in the sample after 10,000 years, 20,000 years, and 30,000 years. hint [see Example 5]

[13] SOURCE: www.rate.co.uk, October, 2004.

[14] Ibid.

78. ● ***Carbon Dating*** A fossil presently contains 4.06 grams of carbon-14. Refer to the formula for $A(t)$ in Example 5 and estimate the amount of carbon-14 in the sample 10,000 years, 20,000 years, and 30,000 years ago.

79. ● ***Carbon Dating*** A fossil presently contains 4.06 grams of carbon-14. It is estimated that the fossil originally contained 46 grams of carbon-14. By calculating the amount left after 5000 years, 10,000 years, . . . , 35,000 years, estimate the age of the sample to the nearest 5000 years. (Refer to the formula for $C(t)$ in Example 5.)

80. ● ***Carbon Dating*** A fossil presently contains 2.8 grams of carbon-14. It is estimated that the fossil originally contained 104 grams of carbon-14. By calculating the amount 5000 years, 10,000 years, . . . , 35,000 years ago, estimate the age of the sample to the nearest 5000 years. (Refer to the formula for $A(t)$ in Example 5.)

81. ● ***Aspirin*** Soon after taking an aspirin, a patient has absorbed 300 mg of the drug. If the amount of aspirin in the bloodstream decays exponentially, with half being removed every two hours, find the amount of aspirin in the bloodstream after five hours.

82. ● ***Alcohol*** After several drinks, a person has a blood alcohol level of 200 mg/dL (milligrams per deciliter). If the amount of alcohol in the blood decays exponentially, with one fourth being removed every hour, find the person's blood alcohol level after four hours.

83. ● ***Profit*** South African Breweries (SAB) reported profits of \$360 million in 1997 ($t = 0$) and \$480 million in 2000 ($t = 3$).[15] Use this information to find **a.** a linear model and **b.** an exponential model for SAB's profit P as a function of time t since 1997. (Round all coefficients to four decimal places.) Which, if either, of these models would you judge to be applicable to the data shown below?

t	0 (1997)	1	2	3	4 (2001)
Profit (\$ million)	360	380	320	480	360

84. ● ***Assets*** South African Breweries (SAB) reported fixed assets of R9500 million in 1997 ($t = 0$) and R29,300 million in 2001 ($t = 4$).[16] Use this information to find **a.** a linear model and **b.** an exponential model for SAB's fixed assets as a function of time t since 1997. (Round all coefficients to four significant digits.) Which, if either, of these models would you judge to be applicable to the data shown below?

t	0 (1997)	1	2	3	4 (2001)
Fixed Assets (R million)	9500	11,100	16,100	22,900	29,300

[15] SOURCE: South African Breweries corporate website www.sab.co.za/investfr.asp, April, 2002.

[16] Ibid.

85. ***U.S. Population.*** The U.S. population was 180 million in 1960 and 294 million in 2004.[17]

a. Use these data to give an exponential growth model showing the U.S. population P as a function of time t in years since 1960. Round coefficients to five decimal places.
b. By experimenting, determine the smallest number of decimal places to which you should round the coefficients in part (a) in order to obtain the correct 2004 population figure accurate to three significant digits.
c. Using the model in part (a), predict the population in 2020.

86. ***World Population.*** World population was estimated at 2.56 billion people in 1950 and 6.40 billion people in 2004.[18]

a. Use these data to give an exponential growth model showing the world population P as a function of time t in years since 1950. Round coefficients to five decimal places.
b. By experimenting, determine the smallest number of decimal places to which you should round the coefficients in part (a) in order to obtain the correct 2004 population figure to three significant digits.
c. Assuming the exponential growth model from part (a), estimate the world population in 1000 AD. Comment on your answer.

87. ***Frogs*** Frogs in Nassau County have been breeding like flies! Each year, the pledge class of Epsilon Delta is instructed by the brothers to tag all the frogs residing on the ESU campus (Nassau County Branch) as an educational exercise. Two years ago they managed to tag all 50,000 of them (with little Epsilon Delta Fraternity tags). This year's pledge class discovered that last year's tags had all fallen off, and they wound up tagging a total of 75,000 frogs.

a. Find an exponential model for the frog population.
b. Assuming exponential population growth, and that all this year's tags have fallen off, how many tags should Epsilon Delta order for next year's pledge class?

88. ***Flies*** Flies in Suffolk County have been breeding like frogs! Three years ago the Health Commission caught 4000 flies in a trap in one hour. This year it caught 7000 flies in one hour.

a. Find an exponential model for the fly population.
b. Assuming exponential population growth, how many flies should the commission expect to catch next year?

89. ● ***Investments*** Rock Solid Bank & Trust is offering a CD (certificate of deposit) that pays 4% compounded continuously. How much interest would a \$1000 deposit earn over 10 years? *hint* [see Example 6]

90. ● ***Savings*** FlybynightSavings.com is offering a savings account that pays 31% interest compounded continuously. How much interest would a deposit of \$2000 earn over 10 years?

[17] Figures are rounded to three significant digits. SOURCE: *Statistical Abstract of the United States,* Population Reference Bureau, October 2004 www.prb.org

[18] Figures are rounded to three significant digits. SOURCE: U.S. Census Bureau, October 2004, www.census.gov/.

91. ● ***Global Warming*** The most abundant greenhouse gas is carbon dioxide. According to a United Nations "worst-case scenario" prediction, the amount of carbon dioxide in the atmosphere (in parts of volume per million) can be approximated by

$$C(t) \approx 277e^{0.00353t} \text{ parts per million} \quad (0 \le t \le 350)$$

where t is time in years since 1750.[19]

a. Use the model to estimate the amount of carbon dioxide in the atmosphere in 1950, 2000, 2050, and 2100.

b. According to the model, when, to the nearest decade, will the level surpass 700 parts per million?

92. ● ***Global Warming*** Repeat Exercise 91 using the United Nations "midrange scenario" prediction:

$$C(t) \approx 277e^{0.00267t} \text{ parts per million} \quad (0 \le t \le 350)$$

where t is time in years since 1750.

93. tech Ex ***New York City Housing Costs: Downtown*** The following table shows the average price of a two-bedroom apartment in downtown New York City from 1994 to 2004.[20] *hint* [see Example 7]

t	0 (1994)	2	4	6	8	10 (2004)
Price ($ million)	0.38	0.40	0.60	0.95	1.20	1.60

a. Use exponential regression to model the price $P(t)$ as a function of time t since 1994. Include a sketch of the points and the regression curve. (Round the coefficients to three decimal places.)

b. Extrapolate your model to estimate the cost of a two-bedroom downtown apartment in 2005.

94. tech Ex ***New York City Housing Costs: Uptown*** The following table shows the average price of a two-bedroom apartment in uptown New York City from 1994 to 2004.[21]

t	0 (1994)	2	4	6	8	10 (2004)
Price ($ million)	0.18	0.18	1.19	0.2	0.35	0.4

a. Use exponential regression to model the price $P(t)$ as a function of time t since 1994. Include a sketch of the points and the regression curve. (Round the coefficients to three decimal places.)

b. Extrapolate your model to estimate the cost of a two-bedroom uptown apartment in 2005.

95. tech Ex ***Grants*** The following table shows the annual spending on grants by U.S. foundations from 1976 to 2001.[22]

t	0 (1976)	5	10	15	20	25 (2001)
Spending ($ billion)	6	7	10	12	15	29

a. Use exponential regression to model the annual spending on grants by U.S. foundations as a function of time in years since 1976, and graph the data points and regression curve. (Round coefficients to four decimal places.)

b. According to your model, by what annual percentage has spending on grants by U.S. foundations been increasing over the period shown?

c. Use your model to estimate 1994 spending to the nearest $1 billion.

96. tech Ex ***Foundations*** The following table shows the total number of active grant-making foundations in the U.S. from 1975 to 2000.[23]

t	0 (1975)	5	10	15	20	25 (2000)
Foundations (thousands)	22	22	25	32	40	57

a. Use exponential regression to model the number of active grant-making foundations in the U.S. as a function of time in years since 1975, and graph the data points and regression curve. (Round coefficients to four decimal places.)

b. According to your model, by what annual percentage has the number of grant-making foundations been increasing over the period shown?

c. Use your model to estimate, to the nearest 1000, the number of active grant-making foundations in 1994.

Communication and Reasoning Exercises

97. ● Which of the following three functions will be largest for large values of x?
(A) $f(x) = x^2$ **(B)** $r(x) = 2^x$ **(C)** $h(x) = x^{10}$

98. ● Which of the following three functions will be smallest for large values of x?
(A) $f(x) = x^{-2}$ **(B)** $r(x) = 2^{-x}$ **(C)** $h(x) = x^{-10}$

99. ● What limitations apply to using an exponential function to model growth in real-life situations? Illustrate your answer with an example.

100. ● Explain in words why 5% per year compounded continuously yields more interest than 5% per year compounded monthly.

101. ● Describe two real-life situations in which a linear model would be more appropriate than an exponential model, and two situations in which an exponential model would be more appropriate than a linear model.

102. ● Describe a real-life situation in which a quadratic model would be more appropriate than an exponential model and one in which an exponential model would be more appropriate than a quadratic model.

[19] Exponential regression based on the 1750 figure and the 2100 UN prediction. SOURCES: Tom Boden/Oak Ridge National Laboratory, Scripps Institute of Oceanography/University of California, International Panel on Climate Change/*The New York Times,* December 1, 1997, p. F1.

[20] Data are rounded and 2004 figure is an estimate. SOURCE: Miller Samuel/*New York Times,* March 28, 2004, p. RE 11.

[21] Ibid.

[22] Figures are rounded and adjusted for inflation. SOURCE: The Foundation Center/*New York Times,* April 2, 2002, p. A21.

[23] Figures are rounded. SOURCE: Ibid.

103. ● How would you check whether data points of the form $(1, y_1)$, $(2, y_2)$, $(3, y_3)$ lie on an exponential curve?

104. You are told that the points $(1, y_1)$, $(2, y_2)$, $(3, y_3)$ lie on an exponential curve. Express y_3 in terms of y_1 and y_2.

105. Your local banker tells you that the reason his bank doesn't compound interest continuously is that it would be too demanding of computer resources because the computer would need to spend a great deal of time keeping all accounts updated. Comment on his reasoning.

106. Your other local banker tells you that the reason *her* bank doesn't offer continuously compounded interest is that it is equivalent to offering a fractionally higher interest rate compounded daily. Comment on her reasoning.

● basic skills   tech Ex technology exercise

2.3 Logarithmic Functions and Models

Logarithms were invented by John Napier (1550–1617) in the late 16th century as a means of aiding calculation. His invention made possible the prodigious hand calculations of astronomer Johannes Kepler (1571–1630), who was the first to describe accurately the orbits and the motions of the planets. Today, computers and calculators have done away with that use of logarithms, but many other uses remain. In particular, the logarithm is used to model real-world phenomena in numerous fields, including physics, finance, and economics.

From the equation

$$2^3 = 8$$

we can see that the power to which we need to raise 2 in order to get 8 is 3. We abbreviate the phrase "the power to which we need to raise 2 in order to get 8" as "$\log_2 8$." Thus, another way of writing the equation $2^3 = 8$ is

$$\log_2 8 = 3 \qquad \text{The power to which we need to raise 2 in order to get 8 is 3.}$$

This is read "the base 2 logarithm of 8 is 3" or "the log, base 2, of 8 is 3."

Here is the general definition.

Base *b* Logarithm

The **base *b* logarithm of *x***, $\log_b x$, is the power to which we need to raise b in order to get x. Symbolically,

$$\log_b x = y \qquad \text{means} \qquad b^y = x$$

Logarithmic form — *Exponential form*

quick Examples

1. The following table lists some exponential equations and their equivalent logarithmic forms:

Exponential Form	$10^3 = 1000$	$4^2 = 16$	$3^3 = 27$	$5^1 = 5$	$7^0 = 1$	$4^{-2} = \frac{1}{16}$	$25^{1/2} = 5$
Logarithmic Form	$\log_{10} 1000 = 3$	$\log_4 16 = 2$	$\log_3 27 = 3$	$\log_5 5 = 1$	$\log_7 1 = 0$	$\log_4 \frac{1}{16} = -2$	$\log_{25} 5 = \frac{1}{2}$

2. $\log_3 9 =$ the power to which we need to raise 3 in order to get 9. Because $3^2 = 9$, this power is 2, so $\log_3 9 = 2$.

3. $\log_{10} 10{,}000 =$ the power to which we need to raise 10 in order to get 10,000. Because $10^4 = 10{,}000$, this power is 4, so $\log_{10} 10{,}000 = 4$.

4. $\log_3 \frac{1}{27}$ is the power to which we need to raise 3 in order to get $\frac{1}{27}$. Because $3^{-3} = \frac{1}{27}$ this power is –3, so $\log_3 \frac{1}{27} = -3$.

5. $\log_b 1 = 0$ for every positive number b other than 1 because $b^0 = 1$.

Note The number $\log_b x$ is defined only if b and x are both positive and $b \neq 1$. Thus, it is impossible to compute, say, $\log_3(-9)$ (because there is no power of 3 that equals -9), or $\log_1(2)$ (because there is no power of 1 that equals 2). ■

Logarithms with base 10 and base e are frequently used, so they have special names and notations.

Common Logarithm, Natural Logarithm

The following are standard abbreviations.

		TI-83/84 & Excel Formula
Base 10: $\log_{10} x = \log x$	*Common Logarithm*	`log(x)`
Base *e*: $\log_e x = \ln x$	*Natural Logarithm*	`ln(x)`

quick Examples

Logarithmic Form	**Exponential Form**
1. $\log 10{,}000 = 4$	$10^4 = 10{,}000$
2. $\log 10 = 1$	$10^1 = 10$
3. $\log \dfrac{1}{10{,}000} = -4$	$10^{-4} = \dfrac{1}{10{,}000}$
4. $\ln e = 1$	$e^1 = e$
5. $\ln 1 = 0$	$e^0 = 1$
6. $\ln 2 = 0.69314718\ldots$	$e^{0.69314718\ldots} = 2$

Some technologies (such as calculators) do not permit direct calculation of logarithms other than common and natural logarithms. To compute logarithms with other bases with these technologies, we can use the following formula:

Change-of-Base Formula

$$\log_b a = \frac{\log a}{\log b} = \frac{\ln a}{\ln b}$$

Change-of-base formula*

quick Examples

1. $\log_{11} 9 = \dfrac{\log 9}{\log 11} \approx 0.91631$ `log(9)/log(11)`

2. $\log_{11} 9 = \dfrac{\ln 9}{\ln 11} \approx 0.91631$ `ln(9)/ln(11)`

3. $\log_{3.2}\left(\dfrac{1.42}{3.4}\right) \approx -0.75065$ `log(1.42/3.4)/log(3.2)`

Using Technology to Compute Logarithms

To compute $\log_b x$ using technology, use the following formulas:

TI-83:	`log(x)/log(b)`	Example: $\log_2(16)$ is `log(16)/log(2)`
Excel:	`=LOG(x,b)`	Example: $\log_2(16)$ is `=LOG(16,2)`

* Here is a quick explanation of why this formula works: To calculate $\log_b a$, we ask, "to what power must we raise b to get a?" To check the formula, we try using $\log a/\log b$ as the exponent.

$$b^{\frac{\log a}{\log b}} = (10^{\log b})^{\frac{\log a}{\log b}} \qquad \text{(because } b = 10^{\log b}\text{)}$$
$$= 10^{\log a} = a$$

so this exponent works!

One important use of logarithms is to solve equations in which the unknown is in the exponent.

Example 1 Solving Equations with Unknowns in the Exponent

Solve the following equations

a. $5^{-x} = 125$ **b.** $3^{2x-1} = 6$ **c.** $100(1.005)^{3x} = 200$

Solution

a. Write the given equation $5^{-x} = 125$ in logarithmic form:

$$-x = \log_5 125$$

This gives $x = -\log_5 125 = -3$.

b. In logarithmic form, $3^{2x-1} = 6$ becomes

$$2x - 1 = \log_3 6$$

$$2x = 1 + \log_3 6$$

giving $$x = \frac{1 + \log_3 6}{2} \approx \frac{1 + 1.6309}{2} \approx 1.3155$$

c. We cannot write the given equation, $100(1.005)^{3x} = 200$, directly in exponential form. We must first divide both sides by 100:

$$1.005^{3x} = \frac{200}{100} = 2$$

$$3x = \log_{1.005} 2$$

$$x = \frac{\log_{1.005} 2}{3} \approx \frac{138.9757}{3} \approx 46.3252$$

Now that we know what logarithms are, we can talk about functions based on logarithms:

Logarithmic Function

A **logarithmic function** has the form

$$f(x) = \log_b x + C \qquad (b \text{ and } C \text{ are constants with } b > 0, b \neq 1)$$

or, alternatively,

$$f(x) = A \ln x + C \qquad (A, C \text{ constants with } A \neq 0)$$

quick Examples

1. $f(x) = \log x$

2. $g(x) = \ln x - 5$

3. $h(x) = \log_2 x + 1$

Q: What is the difference between the two forms of the logarithmic function?

A: None, really, they're equivalent: We can start with an equation in the first form and use the change-of-base formula to rewrite it:

$$f(x) = \log_b x + C$$

$$= \frac{\ln x}{\ln b} + C \qquad \text{Change-of-base formula}$$

$$= \left(\frac{1}{\ln b}\right) \ln x + C$$

Our function now has the form $f(x) = A \ln x + C$, where $A = 1/\ln b$. We can go the other way as well, to rewrite $A \ln x + C$ in the form $\log_b x + C$. ■

Example 2 Graphs of Logarithmic Functions

a. Sketch the graph of $f(x) = \log_2 x$ by hand.

b. Use technology to compare the graph in part (a) with the graphs of $\log_b x$ for $b = 1/4, 1/2$, and 4.

Solution

a. To sketch the graph of $f(x) = \log_2 x$ by hand, we begin with a table of values. Because $\log_2 x$ is not defined when $x = 0$, we choose several values of x close to zero and also some larger values, all chosen so that their logarithms are easy to compute:

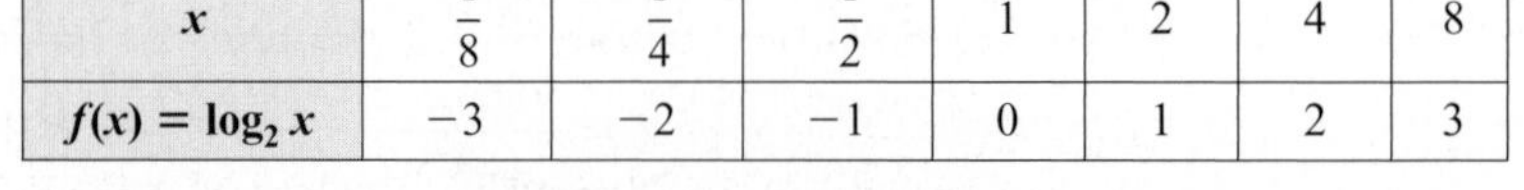

x	$\frac{1}{8}$	$\frac{1}{4}$	$\frac{1}{2}$	1	2	4	8
$f(x) = \log_2 x$	−3	−2	−1	0	1	2	3

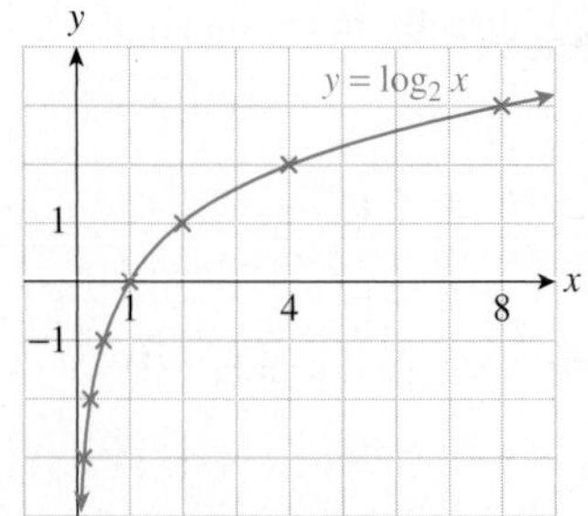

Figure **14**

Graphing these points and joining them by a smooth curve gives us Figure 14.

b. We enter the logarithmic functions in graphing utilities as follows (note the use of the change-of-base formula in the TI-83 version):

TI-83	**Excel**
`Y1=log(X)/log(0.25)`	`=LOG(x,0.25)`
`Y2=log(X)/log(0.5)`	`=LOG(x,0.5)`
`Y3=log(X)/log(2)`	`=LOG(x,2)`
`Y4=log(X)/log(4)`	`=LOG(x,4)`

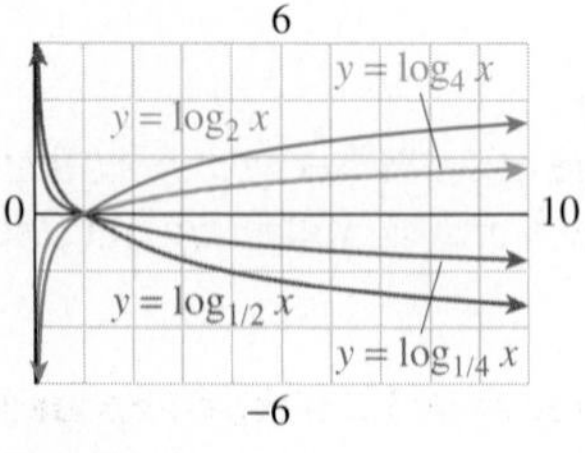

Figure **15**

Figure 15 shows the resulting graphs.

+ *Before we go on...* Notice that the graphs of the logarithmic functions in Example 2 all pass through the point (1, 0). (Why?) Notice further that the graphs of the logarithmic functions with bases less than 1 are upside-down versions of the others. Finally, how are these graphs related to the graphs of exponential functions? ■

The following lists some important algebraic properties of logarithms.

Logarithm Identities

The following identities hold for all positive bases $a \neq 1$ and $b \neq 1$, all positive numbers x and y, and every real number r. These identities follow from the laws of exponents.

Identity	**Quick Examples**
1. $\log_b(xy) = \log_b x + \log_b y$	$\log_2 16 = \log_2 8 + \log_2 2$
2. $\log_b\left(\frac{x}{y}\right) = \log_b x - \log_b y$	$\log_2\left(\frac{5}{3}\right) = \log_2 5 - \log_2 3$
3. $\log_b(x^r) = r \log_b x$	$\log_2(6^5) = 5 \log_2 6$
4. $\log_b b = 1$; $\log_b 1 = 0$	$\log_2 2 = 1$; $\ln e = 1$; $\log_{11} 1 = 0$
5. $\log_b\left(\frac{1}{x}\right) = -\log_b x$	$\log_2\left(\frac{1}{3}\right) = -\log_2 3$
6. $\log_b x = \frac{\log_a x}{\log_a b}$	$\log_2 5 = \frac{\log_{10} 5}{\log_{10} 2} = \frac{\log 5}{\log 2}$

Online, follow:

Chapter 2

→ Using and Deriving Algebraic Properties of Logarithms

to find a list of logarithmic identities and a discussion on where they come from. Follow:

Chapter 2

→ Inverse Functions

for a general discussion of inverse functions, including further discussion of the relationship between logarithmic and exponential functions.

Relationship with Exponential Functions

The following two identities demonstrate that the operations of taking the base b logarithm and raising b to a power are "inverse" to each other.*

Identity	**Quick Example**
1. $\log_b(b^x) = x$	$\log_2(2^7) = 7$

In words: The power to which you raise b in order to get b^x is x (!)

2. $b^{\log_b x} = x$	$5^{\log_5 8} = 8$

In words: Raising b to the power to which it must be raised to get x, yields x (!)

* See the online topic on inverse functions mentioned in the margin.

Applications

Example 3 Investments: How Long?

Ten-year government bonds in Italy are yielding an average of 5.2% per year.* At that interest rate, how long will it take a €1000 investment to be worth €1500 if the interest is compounded monthly?

Solution Substituting $A = 1500$, $P = 1000$, $r = 0.052$, and $m = 12$ in the compound interest equation gives

$$A(t) = P\left(1 + \frac{r}{m}\right)^{mt}$$

$$1500 = 1000\left(1 + \frac{0.052}{12}\right)^{12t}$$

$$\approx 1000(1.004333)^{12t}$$

* In 2001. SOURCE: *ECB, Reuters and BE.*

and we must solve for t. We first divide both sides by 1000, getting an equation in exponential form:

$$1.5 = 1.004333^{12t}$$

In logarithmic form, this becomes

$$12t = \log_{1.004333}(1.5)$$

We can now solve for t:

$$t = \frac{\log_{1.004333}(1.5)}{12} \approx 7.8 \text{ years}$$

```
log(1.5)/(log(1.004333)*12)
```

Thus, it will take approximately 7.8 years for a €1000 investment to be worth €1500.

Example 4 Half-Life

a. The weight of carbon-14 that remains in a sample that originally contained A grams is given by

$$C(t) = A(0.999879)^t$$

where t is time in years. Find the **half-life,** the time it takes half of the carbon-14 in a sample to decay.

b. Repeat part (a) using the following alternative form of the exponential model in part (a):

$$C(t) = Ae^{-0.000\,121\,01t}$$

See p. 137.

c. Another radioactive material has a half-life of 7000 years. Find an exponential decay model in the form

$$R(t) = Ae^{-kt}$$

for the amount of undecayed material remaining. (The constant k is called the **decay constant.**)

d. How long will it take for 99.95% of the substance in a sample of the material in part (c) to decay?

Solution

a. We want to find the value of t for which $C(t)$ = the weight of undecayed carbon-14 left = half the original weight = $0.5A$. Substituting, we get

$$0.5A = A(0.999879)^t$$

Dividing both sides by A gives

$$0.5 = 0.999879^t \quad \text{Exponential form}$$

$$t = \log_{0.999879} 0.5 \approx 5728 \text{ years} \quad \text{Logarithmic form}$$

b. This is similar to part (a): We want to solve the equation

$$0.5A = Ae^{-0.000\,121\,01t}$$

for t. Dividing both sides by A gives

$$0.5 = e^{-0.000\,121\,01t}$$

Taking the natural logarithm of both sides gives

$$\ln(0.5) = \ln(e^{-0.000\,121\,01t}) = -0.000\,121\,01t \qquad \ln(e^a) = a \ln e = a$$

$$t = \frac{\ln(0.5)}{-0.000\,121\,01} \approx 5728 \text{ years}$$

as we obtained in part (a).

c. This time we are given the half-life, which we can use to find the exponential model $R(t) = Ae^{-kt}$. At time $t = 0$, the amount of radioactive material is

$$R(0) = Ae^0 = A$$

Because half of the sample decays in 7000 years, this sample will decay to $0.5A$ grams in 7000 years ($t = 7000$). Substituting this information gives

$$0.5A = Ae^{-k(7000)}$$

Canceling A and taking natural logarithms gives

$$\ln(0.5) = -7000k$$

so the decay constant k is

$$k = -\frac{\ln(0.5)}{7000} \approx 0.000\,099\,021$$

Therefore, the model is

$$R(t) = Ae^{-0.000\,099\,021t}$$

d. If 99.95% of the substance in a sample has decayed, then the amount of undecayed material left is 0.05% of the original amount $= 0.0005A$. We have

$$0.0005A = Ae^{-0.000\,099\,021t}$$

$$0.0005 = e^{-0.000\,099\,021t}$$

$$\ln(0.0005) = -0.000\,099\,021t$$

$$t = \frac{\ln(0.0005)}{-0.000\,099\,021} \approx 76{,}760 \text{ years}$$

+*Before we go on...*

Q: *In parts (a) and (b) of Example 4 we were given two different forms of the model for carbon-14 decay. How do we convert an exponential function in one form to the other?*

A: We have already seen (See Quick Example 3 on p. 137) how to convert from the form $f(t) = Ae^{rt}$ in part (b) to the form $f(t) = Ab^t$ in part (a). To go the other way, start with the model in part (a), and equate it to the desired form:

$$C(t) = A(0.999\,879)^t = Ae^{rt}$$

To solve for r, cancel the As and take the natural logarithm of both sides:

$$t \ln(0.999\,879) = rt \ln e = rt$$

so

$$r = \ln(0.999\,879) \approx -0.000\,121\,01$$

giving

$$C(t) = Ae^{-0.000\,121\,01t}$$

as in part (b). ■

We can use the work we did in parts (b) and (c) of the above example to obtain a formula for the decay constant in an exponential decay model for any radioactive substance when we know its half-life. Write the half-life as t_h. Then the calculation in part (b) gives

$$k = -\frac{\ln(0.5)}{t_h} = \frac{\ln 2}{t_h} \qquad -\ln(0.5) = -\ln\left(\frac{1}{2}\right) = \ln 2$$

Multiplying both sides by t_h gives us the relationship $t_h k = \ln 2$.

Exponential Decay Model and Half-Life

An **exponential decay function** has the form

$$Q(t) = Q_0 e^{-kt} \qquad Q_0,\ k \text{ both positive}$$

Q_0 represents the value of Q at time $t = 0$, and k is the **decay constant.** The decay constant k and half-life t_h for Q are related by

$$t_h k = \ln 2$$

quick **Examples**

1. $Q(t) = Q_0 e^{-0.000\,121\,01t}$ is the decay function for carbon-14 (see Example 4b).
2. If $t_h = 10$ years, then $10k = \ln 2$, so $k = \dfrac{\ln 2}{10} \approx 0.06931$ so the decay model is

$$Q(t) = Q_0 e^{-0.06931t}$$

3. If $k = 0.0123$, then $t_h(0.0123) = \ln 2$, so the half-life is $t_h = \dfrac{\ln 2}{0.0123} \approx 56.35$ years.

We can repeat the analysis above for exponential growth models:

Exponential Growth Model and Doubling Time

An **exponential growth function** has the form

$$Q(t) = Q_0 e^{kt} \qquad Q_0,\ k \text{ both positive}$$

Q_0 represents the value of Q at time $t = 0$, and k is the **growth constant.** The growth constant k and doubling time t_d for Q are related by

$$t_d k = \ln 2$$

quick **Examples**

1. $P(t) = 1000e^{0.05t}$ $1000 invested at 5% annually with interest compounded continuously
2. If $t_d = 10$ years, then $10k = \ln 2$, so $k = \dfrac{\ln 2}{10} \approx 0.06931$ so the growth model is

$$Q(t) = Q_0 e^{0.06931t}$$

3. If $k = 0.0123$, then $t_d(0.0123) = \ln 2$, so the doubling time is $t_d = \dfrac{\ln 2}{0.0123} \approx 56.35$ years.

Logarithmic Regression

If we start with a set of data that suggests a logarithmic curve we can, by repeating the methods from previous sections, use technology to find the logarithmic regression curve $y = \log_b x + C$ approximating the data.

Example 5 Research & Development

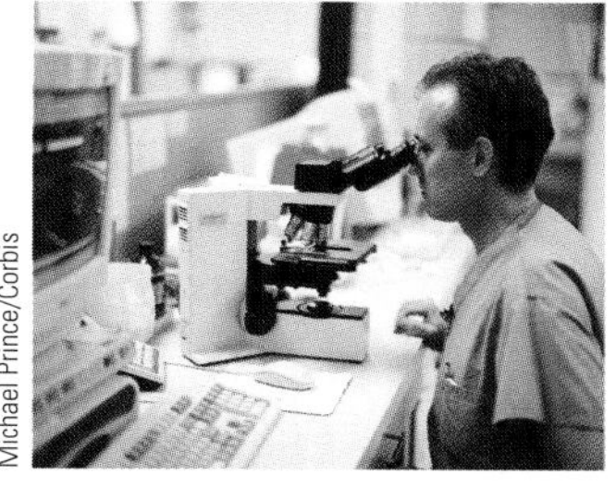

Michael Prince/Corbis

using Technology

See the Technology Guides at the end of the chapter for detailed instructions on using a TI-83/84 or Excel to find logarithmic regression curves. Alternatively, go online and follow:

Chapter 2
→ Tools
→ Simple Regression

to find a utility for finding regression curves of various sorts.

The following table shows the total spent on research and development in the U.S., in billions of dollars, for the period 1995–2005 ($t = 5$ represents 1995).*

Year t	5	6	7	8	9	10
Spending ($ billions)	187	197	208	219	232	248
Year t	11	12	13	14	15	
Spending ($ billions)	250	250	253	260	265	

Find the best-fit logarithmic model of the form

$$S(t) = A \ln t + C$$

and use the model to project total spending on research in 2010, assuming the trend continues.

Solution

We use technology to get the following regression model:

$$S(t) = 73.77 \ln t + 67.75 \qquad \text{Coefficients rounded}$$

Because 2010 is represented by $t = 20$, we have

$$S(20) = 73.77 \ln(20) + 67.75 \approx 289$$

Why did we round the result to three significant digits?

So, research and development spending is predicted to be around $289 billion in 2010.

* Data are approximate and are given in constant 1996 dollars. 2004 and 2005 figures are projections. SOURCE: National Science Foundation, Division of Science Resource Statistics, National Patterns of R&D Resources. www.nsf.gov/sbe/srs/nprdr/start.hrm October 2004.

+*Before we go on...* The model in Example 5 seems to give reasonable estimates when we extrapolate forward, but extrapolating backward is quite another matter: The logarithm curve drops sharply to the left of the given range and becomes negative for small values of t (Figure 16).

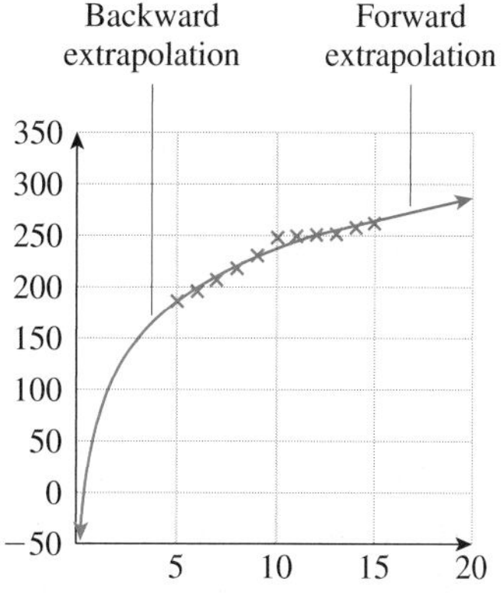

Figure **16**

■

2.3 EXERCISES

● denotes basic skills exercises

tech Ex indicates exercises that should be solved using technology

In Exercises 1–4, complete the given tables. hint [see Quick Example on p. 143]

1. ●

Exponential Form	$10^4 = 10{,}000$	$4^2 = 16$	$3^3 = 27$	$5^1 = 5$	$7^0 = 1$	$4^{-2} = \frac{1}{16}$
Logarithmic Form						

2. ●

Exponential form	$4^3 = 64$	$10^{-1} = 0.1$	$2^8 = 256$	$5^0 = 1$	$(0.5)^2 = 0.25$	$6^{-2} = \frac{1}{36}$
Logarithmic form						

3. ●

Exponential form						
Logarithmic form	$\log_{0.5} 0.25 = 2$	$\log_5 1 = 0$	$\log_{10} 0.1 = -1$	$\log_4 64 = 3$	$\log_2 256 = 8$	$\log_2 \frac{1}{4} = -2$

4. ●

Exponential form						
Logarithmic form	$\log_5 5 = 1$	$\log_4 \frac{1}{16} = -2$	$\log_4 16 = 2$	$\log_{10} 10{,}000 = 4$	$\log_3 27 = 3$	$\log_7 1 = 0$

In Exercises 5–12, use logarithms to solve the given equation. (Round answers to four decimal places.) hint [see Example 1]

5. ● $3^x = 5$ **6.** ● $4^x = 3$

7. ● $5^{-2x} = 40$ **8.** ● $6^{3x+1} = 30$

9. ● $4.16e^x = 2$ **10.** ● $5.3(10^x) = 2$

11. ● $5(1.06^{2x+1}) = 11$ **12.** ● $4(1.5^{2x-1}) = 8$

In Exercises 13–18, graph the given function. hint [see Example 2]

13. ● $f(x) = \log_4 x$ **14.** ● $f(x) = \log_5 x$

15. ● $f(x) = \log_4(x-1)$ **16.** ● $f(x) = \log_5(x+1)$

17. ● $f(x) = \log_{1/4} x$ **18.** ● $f(x) = \log_{1/5} x$

In Exercises 19–22 find the associated exponential decay or growth model. hint [see Quick Examples on p. 150]

19. ● $Q = 1000$ when $t = 0$; Half-life $= 1$

20. ● $Q = 2000$ when $t = 0$; Half-life $= 5$

21. ● $Q = 1000$ when $t = 0$; Doubling time $= 2$

22. ● $Q = 2000$ when $t = 0$; Doubling time $= 5$

In Exercises 23–26 find the associated half-life or doubling time.

23. ● $Q = 1000e^{0.5t}$ **24.** ● $Q = 1000e^{-0.025t}$

25. ● $Q = Q_0e^{-4t}$ **26.** ● $Q = Q_0e^{t}$

In Exercises 27–32 convert the given exponential function to the form indicated. Round all coefficients to four significant digits. hint [see Example 4 Before we go on]

27. ● $f(x) = 4e^{2x}$; $f(x) = Ab^x$

28. ● $f(x) = 2.1e^{-0.1x}$; $f(x) = Ab^x$

29. ● $f(t) = 2.1(1.001)^t$; $f(t) = Q_0e^{kt}$

30. ● $f(t) = 23.4(0.991)^t$; $f(t) = Q_0e^{-kt}$

31. ● $f(t) = 10(0.987)^t$; $f(t) = Q_0e^{-kt}$

32. ● $f(t) = 2.3(2.2)^t$; $f(t) = Q_0e^{kt}$

Applications

33. ● ***Investments*** How long will it take a \$500 investment to be worth \$700 if it is continuously compounded at 10% per year? (Give the answer to two decimal places.) hint [see Example 3]

34. ● ***Investments*** How long will it take a \$500 investment to be worth \$700 if it is continuously compounded at 15% per year? (Give the answer to two decimal places.)

35. ● ***Investments*** How long, to the nearest year, will it take an investment to triple if it is continuously compounded at 10% per year?

36. ● ***Investments*** How long, to the nearest year, will it take me to become a millionaire if I invest \$1000 at 10% interest compounded continuously?

37. ● ***Investments*** I would like my investment to double in value every three years. At what rate of interest would I need to invest it, assuming the interest is compounded continuously? *hint* [see Quick Examples on p. 150]

38. ● ***Depreciation*** My investment in OHaganBooks.com stocks is losing half its value every two years. Find and interpret the associated decay rate.

39. ● ***Carbon Dating*** The amount of carbon-14 remaining in a sample that originally contained A grams is given by

$$C(t) = A(0.999879)^t$$

where t is time in years. If tests on a fossilized skull reveal that 99.95% of the carbon-14 has decayed, how old, to the nearest 1000 years, is the skull?

40. ● ***Carbon Dating*** Refer back to Exercise 39. How old, to the nearest 1000 years, is a fossil in which only 30% of the carbon-14 has decayed?

Long-Term Investments *Exercises 41–48 are based on the following table, which lists interest rates on long-term investments (based on 10-year government bonds) in several countries in 2004–2005.*[24]

Country	U.S.	Japan	Canada	Korea	Australia
Yield	5.3%	1.5%	5.2%	5.4%	6.0%

41. ● Assuming that you invest \$10,000 in the U.S., how long (to the nearest year) must you wait before your investment is worth \$15,000 if the interest is compounded annually?

42. ● Assuming that you invest \$10,000 in Japan, how long (to the nearest year) must you wait before your investment is worth \$15,000 if the interest is compounded annually?

43. ● If you invest \$10,400 in Canada and the interest is compounded monthly, how many months will it take for your investment to grow to \$20,000?

44. ● If you invest \$10,400 in the U.S., and the interest is compounded monthly, how many months will it take for your investment to grow to \$20,000?

45. ● How long, to the nearest year, will it take an investment in Australia to double its value if the interest is compounded every six months?

46. ● How long, to the nearest year, will it take an investment in Korea to double its value if the interest is compounded every six months?

47. ● If the interest on a long-term U.S. investment is compounded continuously, how long will it take the value of an investment to double? (Give the answer correct to two decimal places.)

48. ● If the interest on a long-term Australia investment is compounded continuously, how long will it take the value of an investment to double? (Give an answer correct to two decimal places.)

[24] Approximate interest rates based on 10-year government bonds and similar investments. SOURCE: Organization for Economic Co-operation and Development, www.oecd.org.

49. ● ***Half-life*** The amount of radium-226 remaining in a sample that originally contained A grams is approximately

$$C(t) = A(0.999\,567)^t$$

where t is time in years. Find the half-life to the nearest 100 years. *hint* [see Example 4a]

50. ● ***Half-life*** The amount of iodine-131 remaining in a sample that originally contained A grams is approximately

$$C(t) = A(0.9175)^t$$

where t is time in days. Find the half-life to two decimal places.

51. ● ***Automobiles*** The rate of auto thefts triples every six months.

a. Determine, to two decimal places, the base b for an exponential model $y = Ab^t$ of the rate of auto thefts as a function of time in months.

b. Find the doubling time to the nearest tenth of a month.

52. ● ***Televisions*** The rate of television thefts is doubling every four months.

a. Determine, to two decimal places, the base b for an exponential model $y = Ab^t$ of the rate of television thefts as a function of time in months.

b. Find the tripling time to the nearest tenth of a month.

53. ● ***Half-life*** The half-life of cobalt-60 is five years.

a. Obtain an exponential decay model for cobalt-60 in the form $Q(t) = Q_0e^{-kt}$. (Round coefficients to three significant digits.) *hint* [see Quick Examples on p. 150]

b. Use your model to predict, to the nearest year, the time it takes one third of a sample of cobalt-50 to decay.

54. ● ***Half-life*** The half-life of strontium-90 is 28 years.

a. Obtain an exponential decay model for strontium-90 in the form $Q(t) = Q_0e^{-kt}$. (Round coefficients to three significant digits.)

b. Use your model to predict, to the nearest year, the time it takes three-fifths of a sample of strontium-90 to decay.

55. ● ***Radioactive Decay*** Uranium-235 is used as fuel for some nuclear reactors. It has a half-life of 710 million years. How long will it take 10 grams of uranium-235 to decay to 1 gram? (Round your answer to three significant digits.)

56. ● ***Radioactive Decay*** Plutonium-239 is used as fuel for some nuclear reactors, and also as the fissionable material in atomic bombs. It has a half-life of 24,400 years. How long would it take 10 grams of Plutonium-239 to decay to 1 gram? (Round your answer to three significant digits.)

57. ● ***Aspirin*** Soon after taking an aspirin, a patient has absorbed 300 mg of the drug. If the amount of aspirin in the bloodstream decays exponentially, with half being removed every two hours, find, to the nearest 0.1 hour, the time it will take for the amount of aspirin in the bloodstream to decrease to 100 mg.

58. ***Alcohol*** After several drinks, a person has a blood alcohol level of 200 mg/dL (milligrams per deciliter). If the amount of

alcohol in the blood decays exponentially, with one fourth being removed every hour, find the time it will take for the person's blood alcohol level to decrease to 80 mg/dL.

59. ***Radioactive Decay*** You are trying to determine the half-life of a new radioactive element you have isolated. You start with 1 gram, and two days later you determine that it has decayed down to 0.7 grams. What is its half-life? (Round your answer to three significant digits.)

60. ***Radioactive Decay*** You have just isolated a new radioactive element. If you can determine its half-life, you will win the Nobel Prize in physics. You purify a sample of 2 grams. One of your colleagues steals half of it, and three days later you find that 0.1 gram of the radioactive material is still left. What is the half-life? (Round your answer to three significant digits.)

61. tech Ex ***Population Aging*** The following table shows the percentage of U.S. residents over the age of 65 in 1950, 1960, . . . , 2010 (t is time in years since 1900):[25]

***t* (Year since 1900)**	50	60	70	80	90	100	110
***P* (% over 65)**	8.2	9.2	9.9	11.3	12.6	12.6	13

a. Find the logarithmic regression model of the form $P(t) = A \ln t + C$. (Round the coefficients to four significant digits).

b. In 1940, 6.9% of the population was over 65. To how many significant digits does the model reflect this figure?

c. Which of the following is correct? The model, if extrapolated into the indefinite future, predicts that

(A) The percentage of U.S. residents over the age of 65 will increase without bound.

(B) The percentage of U.S. residents over the age of 65 will level off at around 14.2%.

(C) The percentage of U.S. residents over the age of 65 will eventually decrease. *hint* [see Example 5]

62. tech Ex ***Population Aging*** The following table shows the percentage of U.S. residents over the age of 85 in 1950, 1960, . . . , 2010 (t is time in years since 1900):[26]

***t* (Year since 1900)**	50	60	70	80	90	100	110
***P* (% over 85)**	0.4	0.5	0.7	1	1.2	1.6	1.9

a. Find the logarithmic regression model of the form $P(t) = A \ln t + C$. (Round the coefficients to four significant digits).

b. In 2020, 2.1% of the population is projected to be over 85. To how many significant digits does the model reflect this figure?

c. Which of the following is correct? If you increase A by 0.1 and decrease C by 0.1 in the logarithmic model, then

(A) The new model predicts eventually lower percentages.

(B) The long-term prediction is essentially the same.

(C) The new model predicts eventually higher percentages.

63. tech Ex ***Market Share*** The following table shows the U.S. market share of sport utility vehicles (SUVs) (including "crossover utility vehicles"—smaller SUVs based on car designs) for the period 1994–2001.[27]

Year *t*	4 (1994)	5	6	7	8	9	10	11 (2001)
Market share	10%	11.5	12	15	17.5	19	19.5	21

Find the logarithmic regression model of the form $M(t) = A \ln t + C$. Comment on the long-term suitability of the model.

64. tech Ex ***Market Share*** The following table shows the U.S. market share of large size sport utility vehicles (SUVs) for the period 1994–2001.[28]

Year *t*	4 (1994)	5	6	7	8	9	10	11 (2001)
Market Share	1.5%	2	2.5	3.5	4.5	5	5	5

Find the logarithmic regression model of the form $M(t) = A \ln t + C$. Comment on the suitability of the model to estimate the market share during the period 1990–1993.

65. ***Richter Scale*** The **Richter scale** is used to measure the intensity of earthquakes. The Richter scale rating of an earthquake is given by the formula

$$R = \frac{2}{3}(\log E - 11.8)$$

where E is the energy released by the earthquake (measured in ergs[29]).

a. The San Francisco earthquake of 1906 registered $R = 8.2$ on the Richter scale. How many ergs of energy were released?

[25] SOURCE: U.S. Census Bureau.

[26] Ibid.

[27] Market share is given as a percentage of all vehicles sold in the U.S. 2001 figure is based on sales through April. SOURCE: Ward's Auto Infobank/ *New York Times,* May 19, 2001, p. C1.

[28] Ibid.

[29] An erg is a unit of energy. One erg is the amount of energy it takes to move a mass of one gram one centimeter in one second.

b. In 1989 another San Francisco earthquake registered 7.1 on the Richter scale. Compare the two: The energy released in the 1989 earthquake was what percentage of the energy released in the 1906 quake?

c. Show that if two earthquakes registering R_1 and R_2 on the Richter scale release E_1 and E_2 joules of energy, respectively, then

$$\frac{E_2}{E_1} = 10^{1.5(R_2 - R_1)}$$

d. Fill in the blank: If one earthquake registers 2 points more on the Richter scale than another, then it releases ___ times the amount of energy.

66. ***Sound Intensity*** The loudness of a sound is measured in **decibels.** The decibel level of a sound is given by the formula

$$D = 10 \log \frac{I}{I_0}$$

where D is the decibel level (dB), I is its intensity in watts per square meter (W/m^2), and $I_0 = 10^{-12}$ W/m^2 is the intensity of a barely audible "threshold" sound. A sound intensity of 90 dB or greater causes damage to the average human ear.

a. Find the decibel levels of each of the following, rounding to the nearest decibel:

Whisper:	115×10^{-12} W/m^2
TV (average volume from 10 feet):	320×10^{-7} W/m^2
Loud music:	900×10^{-3} W/m^2
Jet aircraft (from 500 feet):	100 W/m^2

b. Which of the sounds above damages the average human ear?

c. Show that if two sounds of intensity I_1 and I_2 register decibel levels of D_1 and D_2 respectively, then

$$\frac{I_2}{I_1} = 10^{0.1(D_2 - D_1)}$$

d. Fill in the blank: If one sound registers one decibel more than another, then it is ___ times as intense.

67. ***Sound Intensity*** The decibel level of a TV set decreases with the distance from the set according to the formula

$$D = 10 \log \left(\frac{320 \times 10^7}{r^2} \right)$$

where D is the decibel level and r is the distance from the TV set in feet.

a. Find the decibel level (to the nearest decibel) at distances of 10, 20, and 50 feet.

b. Express D in the form $D = A + B \log r$ for suitable constants A and B. (Round A and D to two significant digits.)

c. How far must a listener be from a TV so that the decibel level drops to 0? (Round the answer to two significant digits.)

68. ***Acidity*** The acidity of a solution is measured by its pH, which is given by the formula

$$pH = -\log(H^+)$$

where H^+ measures the concentration of hydrogen ions in moles per liter.[30] The pH of pure water is 7. A solution is referred to as *acidic* if its pH is below 7 and as *basic* if its pH is above 7.

a. Calculate the pH of each of the following substances.

Blood:	3.9×10^{-8} moles/liter
Milk:	4.0×10^{-7} moles/liter
Soap solution:	1.0×10^{-11} moles/liter
Black coffee:	1.2×10^{-7} moles/liter

b. How many moles of hydrogen ions are contained in a liter of acid rain that has a pH of 5.0?

c. Complete the following sentence: If the pH of a solution increases by 1.0, then the concentration of hydrogen ions ________.

Communication and Reasoning Exercises

69. ● Why is the logarithm of a negative number not defined?

70. ● Of what use are logarithms, now that they are no longer needed to perform complex calculations?

71. ● If $y = 4^x$, then $x =$ _______.

72. ● If $y = \log_6 x$, then $x =$ _______.

73. ● Simplify: $2^{\log_2 8}$.

74. ● Simplify: $e^{\ln x}$.

75. ● Simplify: $\ln(e^x)$.

76. ● Simplify: $\ln \sqrt{a}$.

77. ● Your company's market share is undergoing steady growth. Explain why a logarithmic function is *not* appropriate for long-term future prediction of your market share.

78. ● Your company's market share is undergoing steady growth. Explain why a logarithmic function is *not* appropriate for long-term backward extrapolation of your market share.

79. If a town's population is increasing exponentially with time, how is time increasing with population? Explain.

80. If a town's population is increasing logarithmically with time, how is time increasing with population? Explain.

[30] A mole corresponds to about 6.0×10^{23} hydrogen ions. (This number is known as Avogadro's number.)

2.4 Logistic Functions and Models

Figure 17 shows the percentage of U.S. households with personal computers as a function of time t in years ($t = 0$ represents 1994).[31]

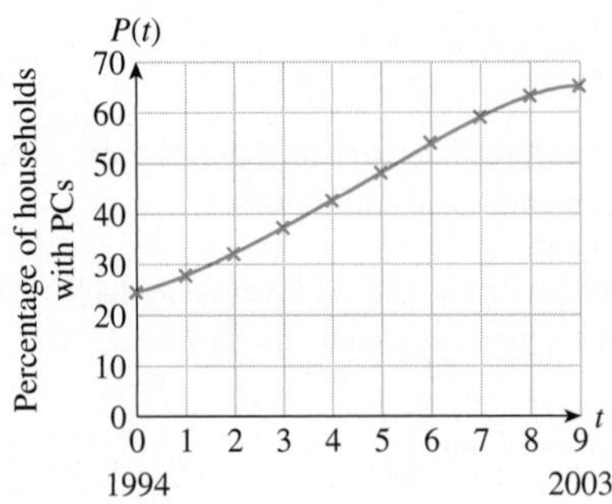

Figure **17**

The left-hand part of the curve in Figure 17, from $t = 0$ to, say, $t = 4$, looks like exponential growth: P behaves (roughly) like an exponential function, growing at a rate of around 15% per year. Then, as the market starts to become saturated, the growth of P slows and its value approaches a "saturation" point. **Logistic** functions have just this kind of behavior, growing exponentially at first and then leveling off. In addition to modeling the demand for a new technology or product, logistic functions are often used in epidemic and population modeling. In an epidemic, the number of infected people often grows exponentially at first and then slows when a significant proportion of the entire susceptible population is infected and the epidemic has "run its course." Similarly, populations may grow exponentially at first and then slow as they approach the capacity of the available resources.

Logistic Function

A **logistic function** has the form

$$f(x) = \frac{N}{1 + Ab^{-x}}$$

for some constants A, N, and b ($b > 0$ and $b \neq 1$).

quick **Example**

$$N = 6,\ A = 2,\ b = 1.1 \text{ gives } f(x) = \frac{6}{1 + 2(1.1^{-x})}$$ 6/(1+2*1.1^-x)

$$f(0) = \frac{6}{1+2} = 2$$ The y-intercept is $N/(1 + A)$

$$f(1000) = \frac{6}{1 + 2(1.1^{-1000})} \approx \frac{6}{1+0} = 6 = N$$ When x is large, $f(x) \approx N$

[31] SOURCE: NTIA/Census Bureau/Pegasus Research International, LLC www.pegasusresearch.com/metrics/growthus.htm

Graph of a Logistic Function

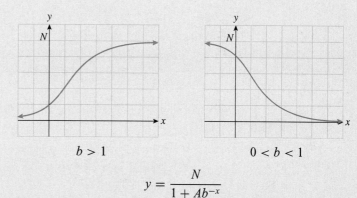

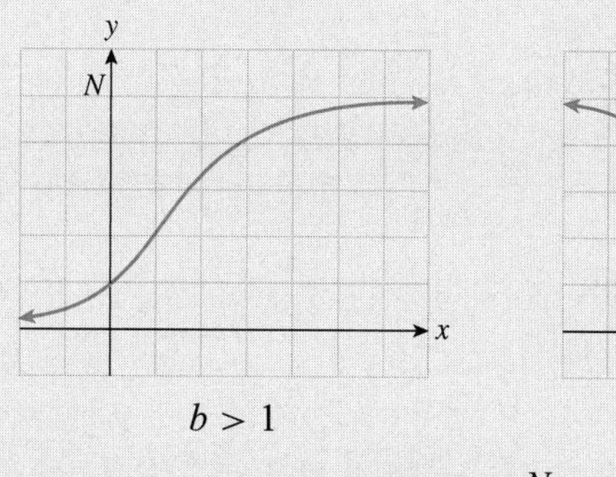

$b > 1$ $\qquad$ $0 < b < 1$

$$y = \frac{N}{1 + Ab^{-x}}$$

Properties of the Logistic Curve $y = \dfrac{N}{1 + Ab^{-x}}$

- The graph is an S-shaped curve sandwiched between the horizontal lines $y = 0$ and $y = N$. N is called the **limiting value** of the logistic curve.
- If $b > 1$ the graph rises; if $b < 1$, the graph falls.
- The y-intercept is $\dfrac{N}{1 + A}$.

Note If we write b^{-x} as e^{-kx} (where $k = \ln b$), we get the following alternative form of the logistic function:

$$f(x) = \frac{N}{1 + Ae^{-kx}}$$

■

Q: *How does the constant b affect the graph?*

A: To understand the role of b, we first rewrite the logistic function by multiplying top and bottom by b^x:

$$\begin{aligned} f(x) &= \frac{N}{1 + Ab^{-x}} \\ &= \frac{Nb^x}{(1 + Ab^{-x})b^x} \\ &= \frac{Nb^x}{b^x + A} \qquad \text{Because } b^{-x}b^x = 1 \end{aligned}$$

For values of x close to 0, the quantity b^x is close to 1, so the denominator is approximately $1 + A$, giving

$$f(x) \approx \frac{Nb^x}{1 + A} = \left(\frac{N}{1 + A}\right) b^x$$

■

In other words, $f(x)$ is approximately exponential with base b for values of x close to 0. Put another way, if x represents time, then initially the logistic function behaves like an exponential function.

To summarize:

Logistic Function for Small *x* and the Role of *b*

For small values of x, we have

$$\frac{N}{1 + Ab^{-x}} \approx \left(\frac{N}{1 + A}\right) b^x$$

Thus, for small x, the logistic function grows approximately exponentially with base b.

quick Example

Let

$$f(x) = \frac{50}{1 + 24(3^{-x})} \qquad N = 50,\ A = 24,\ b = 3$$

Then

$$f(x) \approx \left(\frac{50}{1 + 24}\right)(3^x) = 2(3^x)$$

for small values of x. The following figure compares their graphs:

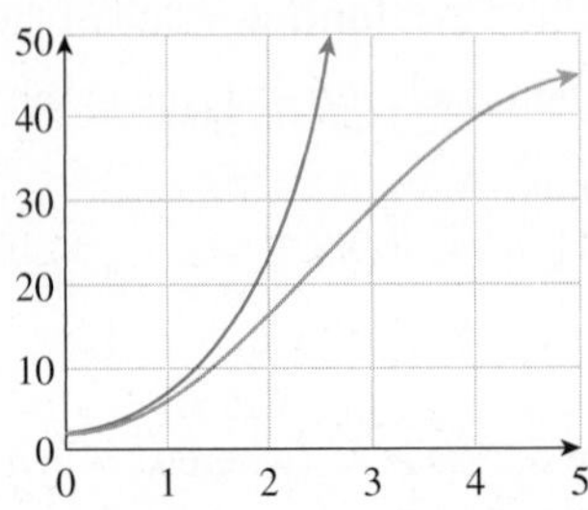

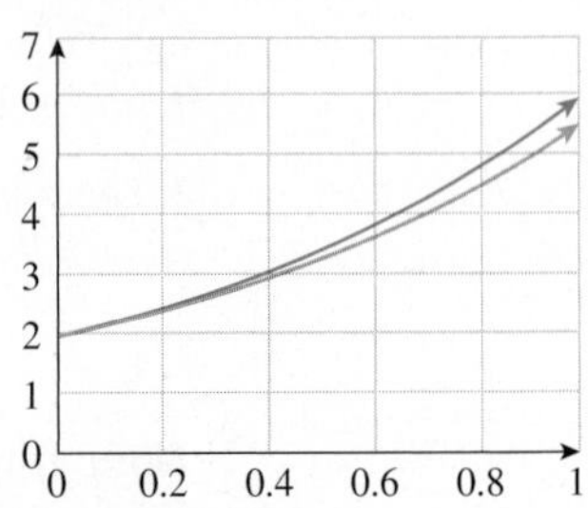

The upper curve is the exponential curve.

Modeling with the Logistic Function

Example 1 Epidemics

A flu epidemic is spreading through the U.S. population. An estimated 150 million people are susceptible to this particular strain, and it is predicted that all susceptible people will eventually become infected. There are 10,000 people already infected, and the number is doubling every two weeks. Use a logistic function to model the number of people infected. Hence predict when, to the nearest week, 1 million people will be infected.

Solution Let t be time in weeks, and let $P(t)$ be the total number of people infected at time t. We want to express P as a logistic function of t, so that

$$P(t) = \frac{N}{1 + Ab^{-t}}$$

We are told that, in the long run, 150 million people will be infected, so that

$$N = 150{,}000{,}000 \qquad \text{Limiting value of } P$$

At the current time ($t = 0$), 10,000 people are infected, so

$$10{,}000 = \frac{N}{1 + A} = \frac{150{,}000{,}000}{1 + A} \qquad \text{Value of } P \text{ when } t = 0$$

Solving for A gives

$$\begin{aligned} 10{,}000(1 + A) &= 150{,}000{,}000 \\ 1 + A &= 15{,}000 \\ A &= 14{,}999 \end{aligned}$$

What about b? At the beginning of the epidemic (t near 0), P is growing approximately exponentially, doubling every two weeks. Using the technique of Section 2.2, we find that the exponential curve passing through the points (0, 10,000) and (2, 20,000) is

$$y = 10{,}000(\sqrt{2})^t$$

giving us $b = \sqrt{2}$. Now that we have the constants N, A, and b, we can write down the logistic model:

$$P(t) = \frac{150{,}000{,}000}{1 + 14{,}999(\sqrt{2})^{-t}}$$

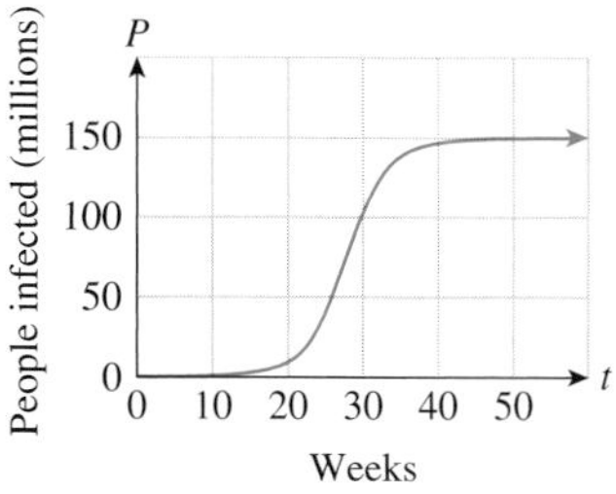

Figure **18**

The graph of this function is shown in Figure 18.

Now we tackle the question of prediction: When will 1 million people be infected? In other words: When is $P(t) = 1{,}000{,}000$?

$$\begin{aligned} 1{,}000{,}000 &= \frac{150{,}000{,}000}{1 + 14{,}999(\sqrt{2})^{-t}} \\ 1{,}000{,}000[1 + 14{,}999(\sqrt{2})^{-t}] &= 150{,}000{,}000 \\ 1 + 14{,}999(\sqrt{2})^{-t} &= 150 \\ 14{,}999(\sqrt{2})^{-t} &= 149 \\ (\sqrt{2})^{-t} &= \frac{149}{14{,}999} \\ -t &= \log_{\sqrt{2}}\left(\frac{149}{14{,}999}\right) \approx -13.31 \qquad \text{Logarithmic form} \end{aligned}$$

Thus, 1 million people will be infected by about the 13th week.

Logistic Regression

Let us go back to the data on the percentage of households with PCs and try to estimate the percentage of households that will have PCs in the long term. In order to be able to make predictions such as this, we require a model for the data, so we will need to do some form of regression.

Example 2 Households with PCs

Here are the data graphed in Figure 17:

Year (t)	0	1	2	3	4	5	6	7	8	9
Households with PCs (%) (P)	24	28	32	37	42	48	54	59	63	65

Find a logistic regression curve of the form

$$P(t) = \frac{N}{1 + Ab^{-t}}$$

In the long term, what percentage of households with PCs does the model predict?

Solution We can use technology to obtain the following regression model:

$$P(t) \approx \frac{84.573}{1 + 2.6428(1.2845)^{-t}}$$

Its graph and the original data are shown in Figure 19.

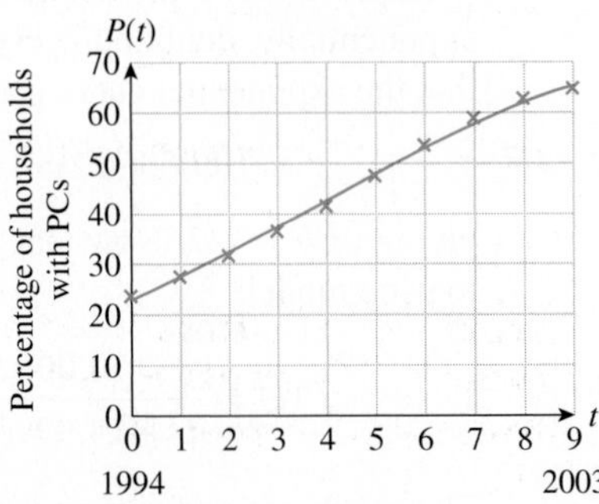

Figure **19**

using *Technology*

See the Technology Guides at the end of the chapter for detailed instructions on using a TI-83/84 or Excel to find logistic regression curves.

Because $N \approx 85$, the model predicts that about 85% of all households will have PCs in the long term.

Note Logistic regression estimates all three constants N, A, and b for a model $y = \dfrac{N}{1 + Ab^{-x}}$. However, there are times, as in Example 1, when we already know the limiting value N and require estimates of only A and b. In such cases, we can use exponential regression to compute these estimates: First rewrite the logistic equation as

$$\frac{N}{y} = 1 + Ab^{-x}$$

so that

$$\frac{N}{y} - 1 = Ab^{-x} = A(b^{-1})^x$$

This equation gives $N/y - 1$ as an exponential function of x. Thus, if we do exponential regression using the data points $(x, N/y - 1)$, we can obtain estimates for A and b^{-1} (and hence b). This is done in Exercises 33 and 34. ■

2.4 EXERCISES

● denotes basic skills exercises

◆ denotes challenging exercises

tech Ex indicates exercises that should be solved using technology

In Exercises 1–6, find N, A, and b, give a technology formula for the given function, and use technology to sketch its graph for the given range of values of x. hint [see Quick Example on p. 156]

1. ● $f(x) = \dfrac{7}{1 + 6(2^{-x})}$; [0, 10]

2. ● $g(x) = \dfrac{4}{1 + 0.333(4^{-x})}$; [0, 2]

3. ● $f(x) = \dfrac{10}{1 + 4(0.3^{-x})}$; [−5, 5]

4. ● $g(x) = \dfrac{100}{1 + 5(0.5^{-x})}$; [−5, 5]

5. ● $h(x) = \dfrac{2}{0.5 + 3.5(1.5^{-x})}$; [0, 15]
(First divide top and bottom by 0.5.)

6. ● $k(x) = \dfrac{17}{2 + 6.5(1.05^{-x})}$; [0, 100]

(First divide top and bottom by 2.)

In Exercises 7–10, find the logistic function f with the given properties. hint [see Example 1]

7. ● $f(0) = 10$, f has limiting value 200, and for small values of x, f is approximately exponential and doubles with every increase of 1 in x.

8. ● $f(0) = 1$, f has limiting value 10, and for small values of x, f is approximately exponential and grows by 50% with every increase of 1 in x.

9. ● f has limiting value 6 and passes through (0, 3) and (1, 4).

10. ● f has limiting value 4 and passes through (0, 1) and (1, 2).

In Exercises 11–16, choose the logistic function that best approximates the given curve.

11. ●

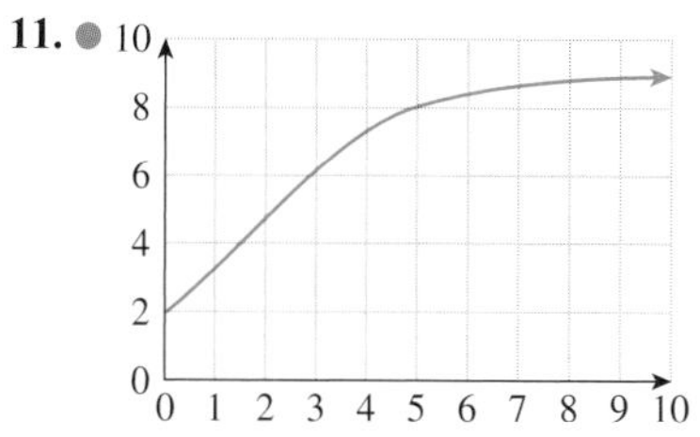

(A) $f(x) = \dfrac{6}{1 + 0.5(3^{-x})}$ (B) $f(x) = \dfrac{9}{1 + 3.5(2^{-x})}$

(C) $f(x) = \dfrac{9}{1 + 0.5(1.01)^{-x}}$

12. ●

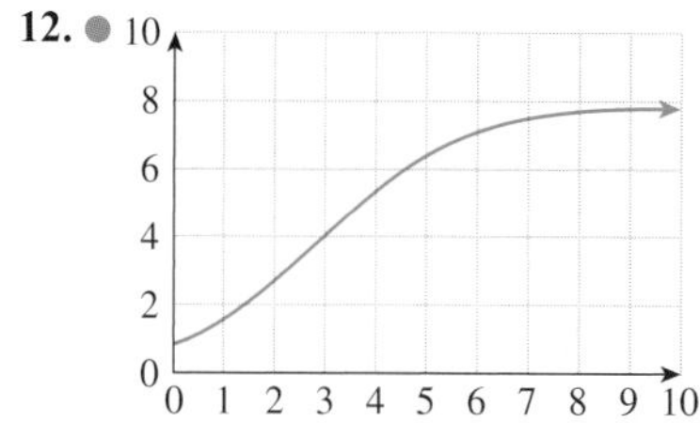

(A) $f(x) = \dfrac{8}{1 + 7(2)^{-x}}$ (B) $f(x) = \dfrac{8}{1 + 3(2)^{-x}}$

(C) $f(x) = \dfrac{6}{1 + 11(5)^{-x}}$

13. ●

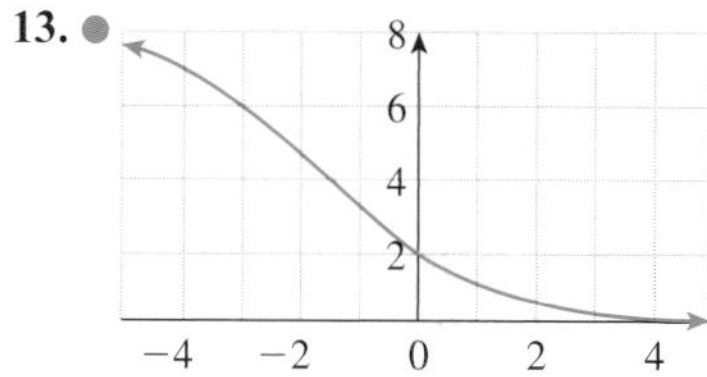

(A) $f(x) = \dfrac{8}{1 + 7(0.5)^{-x}}$ (B) $f(x) = \dfrac{8}{1 + 3(0.5)^{-x}}$

(C) $f(x) = \dfrac{8}{1 + 3(2)^{-x}}$

14. ●

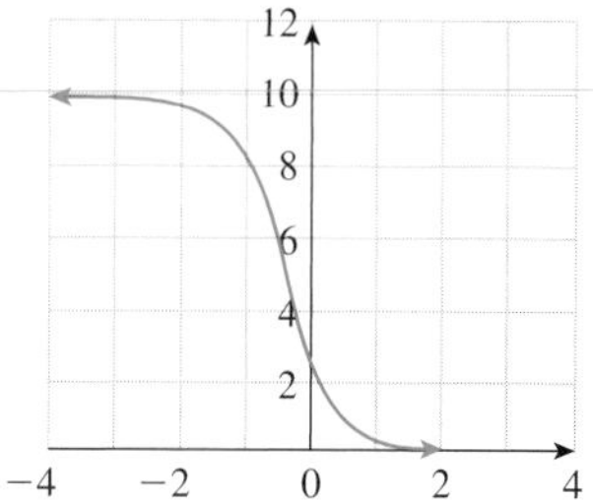

(A) $f(x) = \dfrac{10}{1 + 3(1.01)^{-x}}$ (B) $f(x) = \dfrac{8}{1 + 7(0.1)^{-x}}$

(C) $f(x) = \dfrac{10}{1 + 3(0.1)^{-x}}$

15. ●

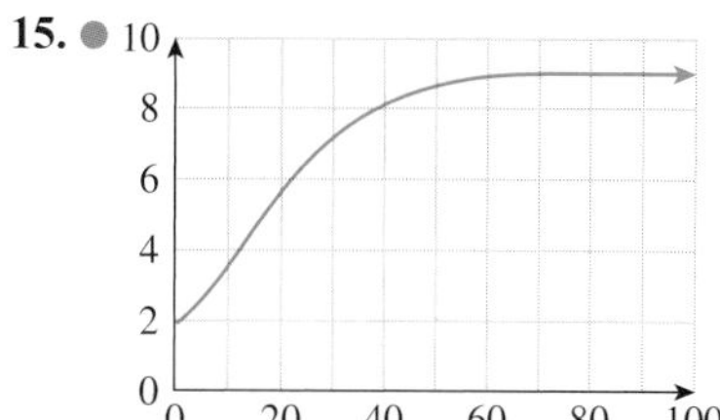

(A) $f(x) = \dfrac{18}{2 + 7(5)^{-x}}$ (B) $f(x) = \dfrac{18}{2 + 3(1.1)^{-x}}$

(C) $f(x) = \dfrac{18}{2 + 7(1.1)^{-x}}$

16. ●

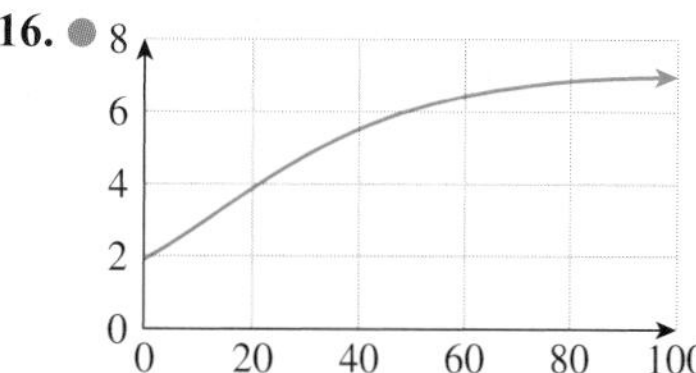

(A) $f(x) = \dfrac{14}{2 + 5(15)^{-x}}$ (B) $f(x) = \dfrac{14}{1 + 13(1.05)^{-x}}$

(C) $f(x) = \dfrac{14}{2 + 5(1.05)^{-x}}$

tech Ex *In Exercises 17–20, use technology to find a logistic regression curve* $y = \dfrac{N}{1 + Ab^{-x}}$ *approximating the given data. Draw a graph showing the data points and regression curve. (Round b to three significant digits and A and N to two significant digits.)* hint [see Example 2]

17. ●

x	0	20	40	60	80	100
y	2.1	3.6	5.0	6.1	6.8	6.9

18. ●

x	0	30	60	90	120	150
y	2.8	5.8	7.9	9.4	9.7	9.9

19. ●

x	0	20	40	60	80	100
y	30.1	11.6	3.8	1.2	0.4	0.1

20. ●

x	0	30	60	90	120	150
y	30.1	20	12	7.2	3.8	2.4

Applications

21. ● ***Scientific Research*** The following chart shows the number of research articles in the prominent journal *Physics Review* that were written by researchers in Europe during 1983–2003 ($t = 0$ represents 1983).[32] *hint* [see Properties of Logistic Curves on p. 157.]

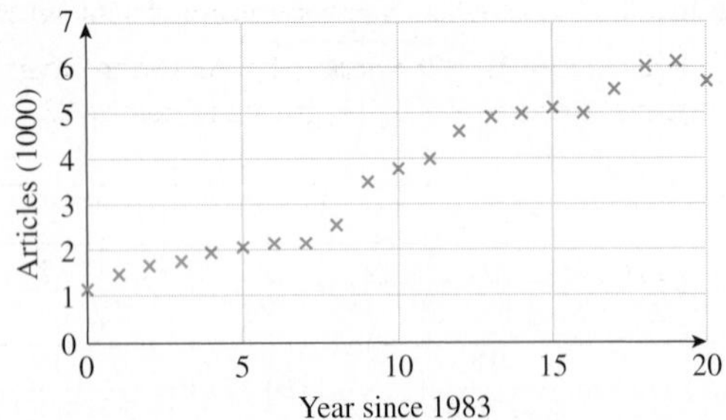

a. Which of the following logistic functions best models the data? (t is the number of years since 1983.) Try to determine the correct model without actually computing data points.

(A) $A(t) = \dfrac{7.0}{1 + 5.4(1.2)^{-t}}$ **(B)** $A(t) = \dfrac{4.0}{1 + 3.4(1.2)^{-t}}$

(C) $A(t) = \dfrac{4.0}{1 + 3.4(0.8)^{-t}}$ **(D)** $A(t) = \dfrac{7.0}{1 + 5.4(0.8)^{-t}}$

b. According to the model you selected, at what percentage was the number of articles growing around 1985?

22. ● ***Scientific Research*** The following chart shows the percentage, above 25%, of research articles in the prominent journal *Physics Review* that were written by researchers in the U.S. during 1983–2003 ($t = 0$ represents 1983).[33]

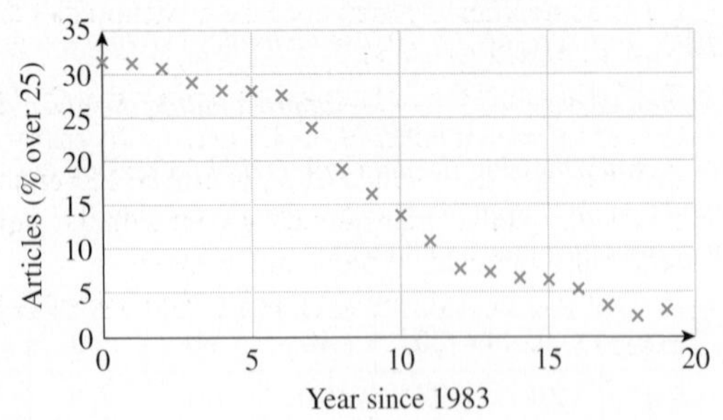

a. Which of the following logistic functions best models the data? (t is the number of years since 1983.) Try to determine the correct model without actually computing data points.

(A) $P(t) = \dfrac{36}{1 + 0.06(1.7)^{-t}}$

(B) $P(t) = \dfrac{12}{1 + 0.06(1.7)^{-t}}$

(C) $P(t) = \dfrac{12}{1 + 0.06(0.7)^{-t}}$

(D) $P(t) = \dfrac{36}{1 + 0.06(0.7)^{-t}}$

b. According to the model you selected, how fast was the value of P declining around 1985?

23. ● ***Computer Use*** The following graph shows the actual percentage of U.S. households with a computer as a function of household income (the data points) and a logistic model of these data (the curve).[34]

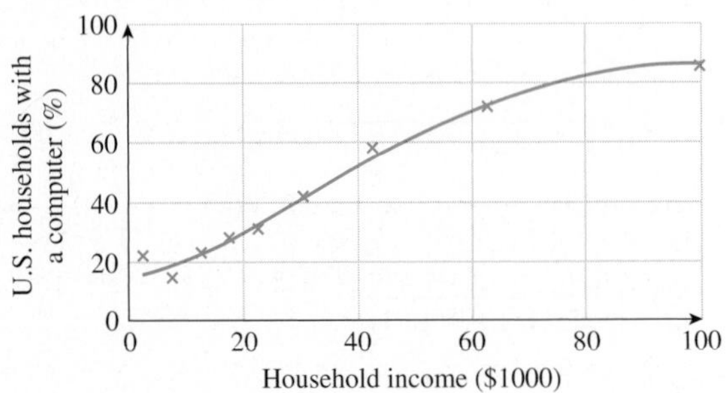

The logistic model is

$$P(x) = \frac{91}{1 + 5.35(1.05)^{-x}} \text{ percent}$$

where x is the household income in thousands of dollars.

a. According to the model, what percentage of extremely wealthy households had computers?

b. For low incomes, the logistic model is approximately exponential. Which exponential model best approximates $P(x)$ for small x?

c. According to the model, 50% of households of what income had computers in 2000? (Round the answer to the nearest $1000.)

24. ● ***Internet Use*** The following graph shows the actual percentage of U.S. residents who used the Internet at home as a function of income (the data points) and a logistic model of these data (the curve).[35]

32 Source: The American Physical Society/*New York Times* May 3, 2003, p. A1.

33 Ibid.

34 Income levels are midpoints of income brackets. (The top income level is an estimate.) Source: NTIA and ESA, U.S. Department of Commerce, using U.S. Bureau of the Census Current Population, 2000.

35 Ibid.

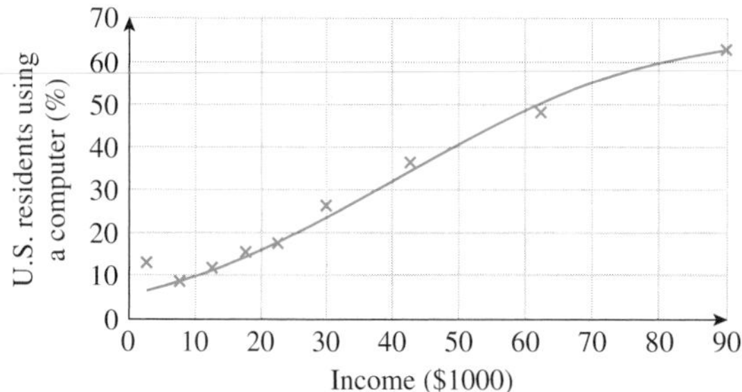

The logistic model is given by

$$P(x) = \frac{64.2}{1 + 9.6(1.06)^{-x}} \text{ percent}$$

where x is an individual's income in thousands of dollars.

a. According to the model, what percentage of extremely wealthy people used the Internet at home?

b. For low incomes, the logistic model is approximately exponential. Which exponential model best approximates $P(x)$ for small x?

c. According to the model, 50 percent of individuals with what income used the Internet at home in 2000? (Round the answer to the nearest $1000.)

25. ● ***Epidemics*** There are currently 1000 cases of Venusian flu in a total susceptible population of 10,000 and the number of cases is increasing by 25 percent each day. Find a logistic model for the number of cases of Venusian flu and use your model to predict the number of flu cases a week from now. *hint* [see Example 1]

26. ● ***Epidemics*** Last year's epidemic of Martian flu began with a single case in a total susceptible population of 10,000. The number of cases was increasing initially by 40 percent per day. Find a logistic model for the number of cases of Martian flu and use your model to predict the number of flu cases three weeks into the epidemic.

27. ● ***Sales*** You have sold 100 "I ♥ Calculus" T-shirts and sales appear to be doubling every five days. You estimate the total market for "I ♥ Calculus" T-shirts to be 3000. Give a logistic model for your sales and use it to predict, to the nearest day, when you will have sold 700 T-shirts.

28. ● ***Sales*** In Russia the average consumer drank two servings of Coca-Cola® in 1993. This amount appeared to be increasing exponentially with a doubling time of two years.[36] Given a long-range market saturation estimate of 100 servings per year, find a logistic model for the consumption of Coca-Cola in Russia and use your model to predict when, to the nearest year, the average consumption will be 50 servings per year.

29. tech Ex ***Scientific Research*** The following chart shows some the data shown in the graph in Exercise 21:

Year, t	0	5	10	15	20
Research Articles, A (1000)	1.2	2.1	3.8	5.1	5.7

($t = 0$ represents 1983.)[37]

a. What is the logistic regression model for the data? (Round all coefficients to two significant digits.) At what value does the model predict that the number of research articles will level off? *hint* [see Example 2]

b. According to the model, how many *Physics Review* articles were published by U.S. researchers in 2000 ($t = 17$)? (The actual number was about 5500 articles.)

30. tech Ex ***Scientific Research*** The following chart shows some of the data shown in the graph in Exercise 22:

Year, t	0	5	10	15	20
Percentage, P (Percentage over 25)	36	28	16	7	3

($t = 0$ represents 1983.)[38]

a. What is the logistic regression model for the data? (Round all coefficients to two significant digits.)

b. According to the model, what percentage of *Physics Review* articles were published by researchers in the U.S. in 2000 ($t = 17$)? (The actual figure was about 30.1%.)

31. tech Ex ***Online Book Sales*** The following table shows the number of books sold online in the U.S. in the period 1997–2000 ($t = 0$ represents 1997).[39]

***t* (Year)**	0	1	2	3
Book sales (millions)	4.5	20.0	58.2	78.0

a. What is the logistic regression model for the data? (Round all coefficients to three significant digits.) At what value (to three significant digits) does the model predict that book sales will level off?

b. The 2000 figure ($t = 3$) represents approximately 7 percent of the total number of books sold. Some analysts predict that book sales will level off at around 15 percent of the market. Is this prediction consistent with the logistic regression model? Comment on the answer.

c. In what year does the model predict that book sales first exceed 80 million?

---

[36] The doubling time is based on retail sales of Coca-Cola products in Russia. Sales in 1993 were double those in 1991, and were expected to double again by 1995. SOURCE: *The New York Times,* September 26, 1994, p. D2.

[37] SOURCE: The American Physical Society/*New York Times* May 3, 2003, p. A1.

[38] Ibid.

[39] SOURCE: Ipsos-NPD Book Trends/*New York Times,* April 16, 2001, p. C1.

32. tech Ex ***South African Exports*** The following table shows the value of South African exports to African nations for the period 1991–1999 ($t = 0$ represents 1990).[40]

t (Year)	1	2	3	4	5	6	7	8	9
Exports (billions of Rand)	5	6	7	9	13	18	20	20	22

a. What is the logistic regression model for the data? (Round all coefficients to three significant digits.) At what value does the model predict that the exports will level off?

b. In 2000, South Africa exported approximately R29 billion to African nations. Comment on this figure in light of your model.

tech Ex *Exercises 33 and 34 are based on the discussion following Example 2. If the limiting value N is known, then*

$$\frac{N}{y} - 1 = A(b^{-1})^x$$

and so $N/y - 1$ is an exponential function of x. In Exercises 33 and 34, use the given value of N and the data points $(x, N/y - 1)$ to obtain A and b, and hence a logistic model.

33. ◆ tech Ex ***Education*** The following chart shows the number of high-school graduates in the U.S. over the period 1993–1999.[41]

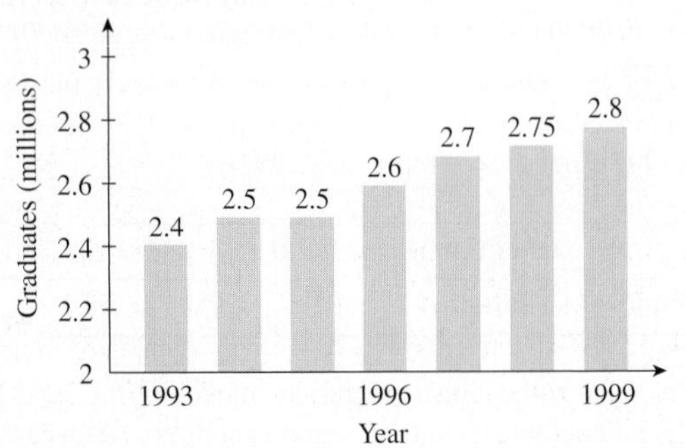

Take t to be the number of years since 1993, and find a logistic model based on the assumption that, eventually, the number of high school graduates will grow to 5 million per year. In what year does your model predict the number of high school graduates will first reach 3.5 million?

34. ◆ tech Ex ***College Athletics*** The percentage of college athletes who are women tended to increase over the preceding 20 years, as shown in the following chart.

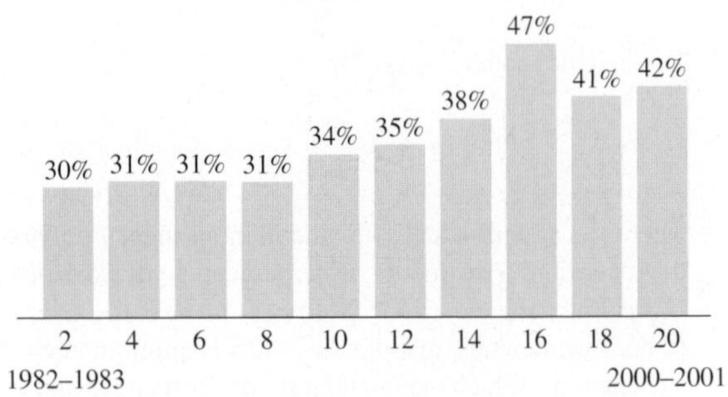

The long-term goal of many athletic policy makers is to attain a parity level of 50% women in college athletics. Using $N = 50$, find a logistic model for the percentage of women college athletes as a function of time t in years ($t = 2$ represents the 1982–1983 academic year). In which year does your model predict that 45% of all college athletes will be women?

Communication and Reasoning Exercises

35. ● Logistic functions are commonly used to model the spread of epidemics. Given this fact, explain why a logistic function is also useful to model the spread of a new technology.

36. ● Why is a logistic function more appropriate than an exponential function for modeling the spread of an epidemic?

37. ● Give one practical use for logistic regression.

38. ● What happens to the function $P(t) = \dfrac{N}{1 + Ab^{-t}}$ if $A = 0$? if $A < 0$?

[40] Data are approximate. SOURCE: ABSA: "South Africa's Foreign Trade, 2001 Edition"/*New York Times,* February 17, 2002, p. 14.

[41] Data are rounded. SOURCE: Western Interstate Commission for Higher Education and the College Board/*The New York Times,* February 17, 1999, p. B9.

Chapter 2 Review

KEY CONCEPTS

2.1 Quadratic Functions and Models

A **quadratic function** has the form $f(x) = ax^2 + bx + c$ *p. 114*

The graph of $f(x) = ax^2 + bx + c$ $(a \neq 0)$ is a **parabola** *p. 115*

The x-coordinate of the **vertex** is $-\frac{b}{2a}$. The y-coordinate is $f\left(-\frac{b}{2a}\right)$ *p. 115*

x-intercepts (if any) occur at

$$x = \frac{-b \pm \sqrt{b^2 - 4ac}}{2a} \quad p.\ 115$$

The **y-intercept** occurs at $y = c$ *p. 115*

The parabola is **symmetric** with respect to the vertical line through the vertex. *p. 115*

Sketching the graph of a quadratic function *p. 116*

Application to maximizing revenue *p. 117*

Application to maximizing profit *p. 118*

Finding the quadratic regression curve *p. 120*

2.2 Exponential Functions and Models

An **exponential function** has the form $f(x) = Ab^x$ *p. 126*

Recognizing exponential data *p. 127*

Roles of the constants A and b in an exponential function $f(x) = Ab^x$ *p. 128*

Finding the exponential curve through two points *p. 130*

Application to exponential growth (epidemics) *p. 130*

Application to compound interest *p. 132*

Application to exponential decay (carbon dating) *p. 133*

The number e and continuous compounding *p. 134*

Alternative form of an exponential function: $f(x) = Ae^{rx}$ *p. 137*

Finding the exponential regression curve *p. 137*

2.3 Logarithmic Functions and Models

The **base b logarithm of x**: $y = \log_b x$ means $b^y = x$ *p. 143*

Common logarithm, $\log x = \log_{10} x$, and **natural logarithm,** $\ln x = \log_e x$ *p. 144*

Change of base formula *p. 144*

Solving equations with unknowns in the exponent *p. 145*

A **logarithmic function** has the form $f(x) = Ab^x$ *p. 145*

Graphs of logarithmic functions *p. 146*

Logarithm identities *p. 147*

Application to investments (how long?) *p. 147*

Application to half-life *p. 148*

Exponential growth and decay models and half-life *p. 150*

Finding the logarithmic regression curve *p. 150*

2.4 Logistic Functions and Models

A **logistic function** has the form

$$f(x) = \frac{N}{1 + Ab^{-x}} \quad p.\ 156$$

Properties of the logistic curve *p. 157*

Logistic function for small x, and the role of b *p. 158*

Application to epidemics *p. 158*

Finding the logistic regression curve *p. 159*

REVIEW EXERCISES

Sketch the graph of the quadratic functions in Exercises 1 and 2, indicating the coordinates of the vertex, the y-intercept, and the x-intercepts (if any).

1. $f(x) = x^2 + 2x - 3$ **2.** $f(x) = -x^2 - x - 1$

In Exercises 3 and 4, the values of two functions, f and g, are given in a table. One, both, or neither of them may be exponential. Decide which, if any, are exponential, and give the exponential models for those that are.

3.

x	−2	−1	0	1	2
$f(x)$	20	10	5	2.5	1.25
$g(x)$	8	4	2	1	0

4.

x	−2	−1	0	1	2
$f(x)$	8	6	4	2	1
$g(x)$	$\frac{3}{4}$	$\frac{3}{2}$	3	6	12

In Exercises 5 and 6 graph the given pairs of functions on the same set of axes with $-3 \leq x \leq 3$.

5. $f(x) = \frac{1}{2}(3^x)$; $g(x) = \frac{1}{2}(3^{-x})$

6. $f(x) = 2(4^x)$; $g(x) = 2(4^{-x})$

tech Ex *On the same set of axes, use technology to graph the pairs of functions in Exercises 7 and 8 for the given range of x. Identify which graph corresponds to which function.*

7. $f(x) = e^x$; $g(x) = e^{0.8x}$; $-3 \leq x \leq 3$

8. $f(x) = 2(1.01)^x$; $g(x) = 2(0.99)^x$; $-100 \leq x \leq 100$

In Exercises 9–14, compute the indicated quantity.

9. A \$3000 investment earns 3% interest, compounded monthly. Find its value after 5 years.

10. A \$10,000 investment earns 2.5% interest, compounded quarterly. Find its value after 10 years.

11. An investment earns 3% interest, compounded monthly and is worth \$5000 after 10 years. Find its initial value.

12. An investment earns 2.5% interest, compounded quarterly and is worth \$10,000 after 10 years. Find its initial value.

13. A \$3000 investment earns 3% interest, compounded continuously. Find its value after 5 years.

14. A \$10,000 investment earns 2.5% interest, compounded continuously. Find its value after 10 years.

In Exercises 15–18, find a formula of the form $f(x) = Ab^x$ using the given information.

15. $f(0) = 4.5$; the value of f triples for every half-unit increase in x.

16. $f(0) = 5$; the value of f decreases by 75% for every one-unit increase in x.

17. $f(1) = 2,\ f(3) = 18$

18. $f(1) = 10,\ f(3) = 5$

In Exercises 19–22, use logarithms to solve the given equation for x.

19. $3^{-2x} = 4$ **20.** $2^{2x^2-1} = 2$

21. $300(10^{3x}) = 315$ **22.** $P(1+i)^{mx} = A$

On the same set of axes, graph the pairs of functions in Exercises 23 and 24.

23. $f(x) = \log_3 x;\ g(x) = \log_{(1/3)} x$

24. $f(x) = \log x;\ g(x) = \log_{(1/10)} x$

In Exercises 25–28, use the given information to find an exponential model of the form $Q = Q_0e^{-kt}$ or $Q = Q_0e^{kt}$, as appropriate. Round all coefficients to three significant digits when rounding is necessary.

25. Q is the amount of radioactive substance with a half-life of 100 years in a sample originally containing 5g (t is time in years).

26. Q is the number of cats on an island whose cat population was originally 10,000 but is being cut in half every five years (t is time in years).

27. Q is the diameter (in cm) of a circular patch of mold on your roommate's damp towel that you have been monitoring with morbid fascination. You measured the patch at 2.5 cm across four days ago, and have observed that it is doubling in diameter every two days (t is time in days).

28. Q is the population of cats on another island whose cat population was originally 10,000 but is doubling every 15 months (t is time in months).

In Exercises 29–32, find the time required, to the nearest 0.1 year, for the investment to reach the desired goal.

29. \$2000 invested at 4% , compounded monthly; goal: \$3000.

30. \$2000 invested at 6.75%, compounded daily; goal: \$3000.

31. \$2000 invested at 3.75%, compounded continuously; goal: \$3000.

32. \$1000 invested at 100%, compounded quarterly; goal: \$1200.

In Exercises 33–36, find equations for the logistic functions of x with the stated properties.

33. Through (0, 100), initially increasing by 50% per unit of x, and limiting value 900.

34. Initially exponential of the form $y = 5(1.1)^x$ with limiting value 25.

35. Passing through (0, 5) and decreasing from a limiting value of 20 to 0 at a rate of 20% per unit of x when x is near 0.

36. Initially exponential of the form $y = 2(0.8)^x$ with a value close to 10 when $x = -60$.

Applications

37. ***Website Traffic*** The daily traffic ("hits per day") at OHaganBooks.com seems to depend on the monthly expenditure on advertising through banner ads on well-known Internet portals. The following model, based on information you have collected over the past few months, shows the approximate relationship:

$$h = -0.000005c^2 + 0.085c + 1750$$

where h is the average number of hits per day at OHaganBooks.com, and c is the monthly advertising expenditure.

a. According to the model, what monthly advertising expenditure will result in the largest volume of traffic at OHaganBooks.com? What is that volume?

b. In addition to predicting a maximum volume of traffic, the model predicts that the traffic will eventually drop to zero if the advertising expenditure is increased too far. What expenditure (to the nearest dollar) results in no website traffic?

c. What feature of the formula for this quadratic model indicates that it will predict an eventual decline in traffic as advertising expenditure increases?

38. ***Broadband Access*** Pablo Pelogrande, a new summer intern at OHaganBooks.com, argues that broadband access to the Internet is increasing as a rate that justifies the website upgrades (video and audio content for broadband) that the company is planning: indeed the rate of growth of broadband was approximately $n(t) = 2t^2 - 2t + 8$ million new American adults with broadband per year, where t is time in years since the beginning of 2001.[42]

a. According to the model, when was the rate of growth at a minimum?

b. Does the model predict a zero rate of growth at any particular time? If so, when?

[42] Based on data for 2001–2003. Source for data: Pew Internet and American Life Project data memos dated May 18, 2003 and April 19, 2004, available at www.pewinternet.org.

c. What feature of the formula for this quadratic model indicates that the rate of growth eventually increases?

d. Does the fact that $n(t)$ decreases for $t \le 0.5$ suggest that the number of broadband users actually declined in early 2001? Explain.

39. ***Revenue*** Some time ago, you formulated the following linear model of demand:

$$q = -60p + 950$$

where q is the monthly demand for OHaganBooks.com's online novels at a price of p dollars per novel. Use this model to express the monthly revenue as a function of the unit price p, and hence determine the price you should charge for a maximum monthly revenue.

40. ***Profit*** Refer to the linear demand model in Exercise 39 for online novels. Author royalties and copyright fees cost the company an average of \$4 per novel, and the monthly cost of operating and maintaining the online publishing service amounts to \$900 per month. Express the monthly profit P as a function of the unit price p, and hence determine the unit price you should charge for a maximum monthly profit. What is the resulting profit (or loss)?

41. ***Lobsters*** Marjory Duffin is particularly fond of having steamed lobster at working lunches with executives from OHaganBooks.com, and is therefore alarmed by the news that the yearly lobster harvest from New York's Long Island Sound has been decreasing dramatically since 1997. Indeed, the size of the annual harvest can be approximated by

$$n(t) = 10(0.66^t) \text{ million pounds}$$

where t is time in years since June, 1997.[43]

a. The model tells us that the harvest was ____ million pounds in 1997 and decreasing by ___% each year.

b. What does the model predict for the 2005 harvest?

42. ***Stock Prices*** In the period immediately following its initial public offering (IPO), OHaganBooks.com's stock is doubling in value every three hours. If you bought \$10,000 worth of the stock when it was first offered, how much was your stock worth after eight hours?

43. ***Lobsters*** (See Exercise 41.) Marjory Duffin has just left John O'Hagan, CEO of OHaganBooks.com, a frantic phone message to the effect that yearly lobster harvest from New York's Long Island Sound has just dipped below 100,000 pounds, making that planned lobster working lunch more urgent than ever. What year is it?

44. ***Stock Prices*** We saw in Exercise 42 that OHaganBooks.com's stock was doubling in value every three hours, following its IPO. If you bought \$10,000 worth of the stock when it was first offered, how long from the initial offering did it take your investment to reach \$50,000?

45. ***Stock Prices*** We saw in Exercise 42 that OHaganBooks.com's stock was doubling in value every three hours, following its IPO. After 10 hours of trading, the stock turns around and starts losing one third of its value every four hours. How long (from the initial offering) will it be before your stock is once again worth \$10,000?

46. tech Ex ***Lobsters*** The model in Exercise 41 was based on the data shown in the following chart:

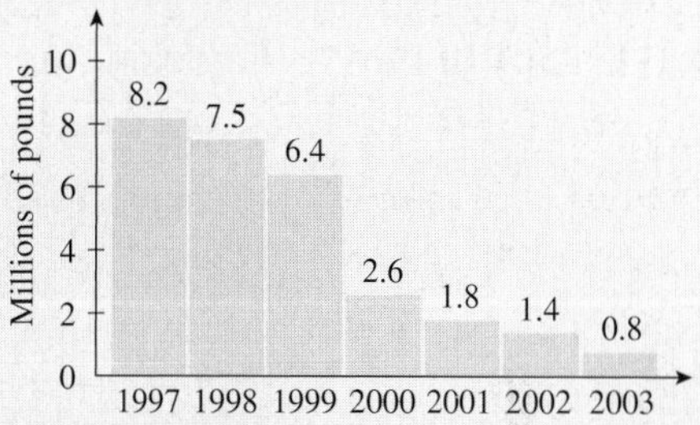

Use the data to obtain an exponential regression curve of the form $n(t) = Ab^t$, with $t = 0$ corresponding to 1997 and coefficients rounded to two significant digits.

47. ***Hardware Life*** *(Based on a question from the GRE economics exam)* To estimate the rate at which new computer hard drives will have to be retired, OHaganBooks.com uses the "survivor curve":

$$L_x = L_0 e^{-x/t}$$

where

L_x = number of surviving hard drives at age x
L_0 = number of hard drives initially
t = average life in years

All of the following are implied by the curve *except:*

(A) Some of the equipment is retired during the first year of service.

(B) Some equipment survives three average lives.

(C) More than half the equipment survives the average life.

(D) Increasing the average life of equipment by using more durable materials would increase the number surviving at every age.

(E) The number of survivors never reaches zero.

48. ***Sales*** OHaganBooks.com modeled its weekly sales over a period of time with the function

$$s(t) = 6050 + \frac{4470}{1 + 14(1.73^{-t})}$$

[43] Based on a regression model. Source for data: NY State Department of Environmental Conservation/*Newsday*, October 6, 2004, p. A4.

as shown in the following graph (t is measured in weeks):

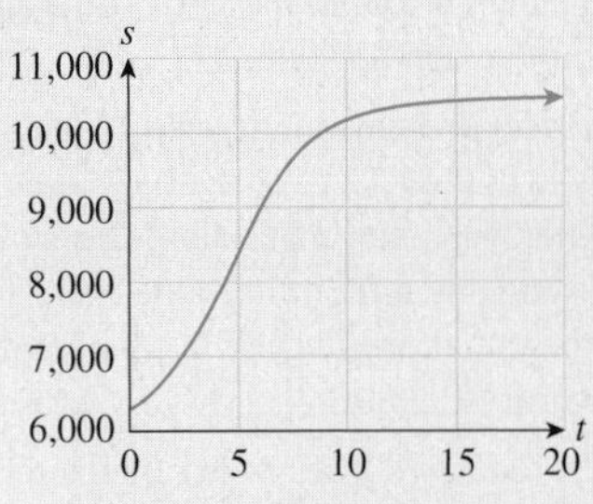

a. As time goes on, it appears that weekly sales are leveling off. At what value are they leveling off?

b. When did weekly sales rise above 10,000?

vMentor™ Do you need a live tutor for homework problems? Access vMentor on the ThomsonNOW! website at **www.thomsonedu.com** for one-on-one tutoring from a mathematics expert.

CASE STUDY: Checking up on Malthus

In 1798 Thomas R. Malthus (1766–1834) published an influential pamphlet, later expanded into a book, titled *An Essay on the Principle of Population As It Affects the Future Improvement of Society*. One of his main contentions was that population grows geometrically (exponentially) while the supply of resources such as food grows only arithmetically (linearly). This led him to the pessimistic conclusion that population would always reach the limits of subsistence and precipitate famine, war, and ill-health, unless population could be checked by other means. He advocated "moral restraint," which includes the pattern of late marriage common in Western Europe at the time and is now common in most developed countries, and which leads to a lower reproduction rate.

Two hundred years later, you have been asked to check the validity of Malthus's contention. That population grows geometrically, at least over short periods of time, is commonly assumed. That resources grow linearly is more questionable. You decide to check the actual production of a common crop, wheat, in the United States. Agricultural statistics like these are available from the U.S. government on the Internet, through the U.S. Department of Agriculture's National Agricultural Statistics Service (NASS). As of 2006, this service was available at http://www.nass.usda.gov/. Looking through this site, you locate data on the annual production of all wheat in the U.S. from 1866 through 2001.

A current link to NASS, as well as the data, are available online. Follow:

Chapter 2
→ Case Study

Year	1866	1867	. . .	2000	2001
Thousands of Bushels	169,703	210,878	. . .	2,232,460	1,957,643

Graphing these data (using Excel, for example), you obtain the graph in Figure 20.

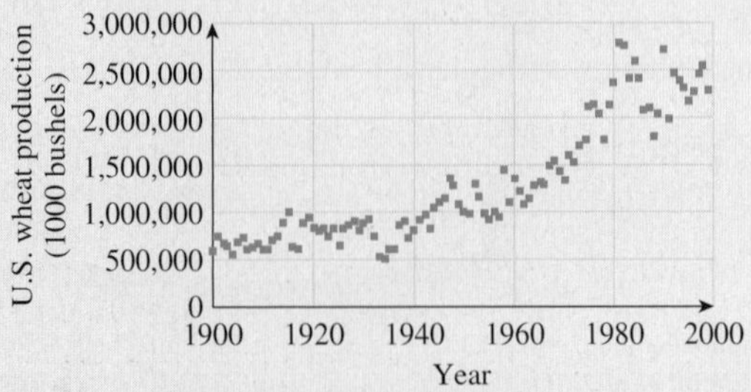

Figure **20**

This does not look very linear, particularly in the last half of the 20th century, but you continue checking the mathematics. Using Excel's built-in linear regression capabilities, you find that the line that best fits these data, shown in Figure 21, has $r^2 = 0.8002$. (Recall the discussion of the correlation coefficient r in Section 1.5. A similar statistic is available for other types of regression as well.)

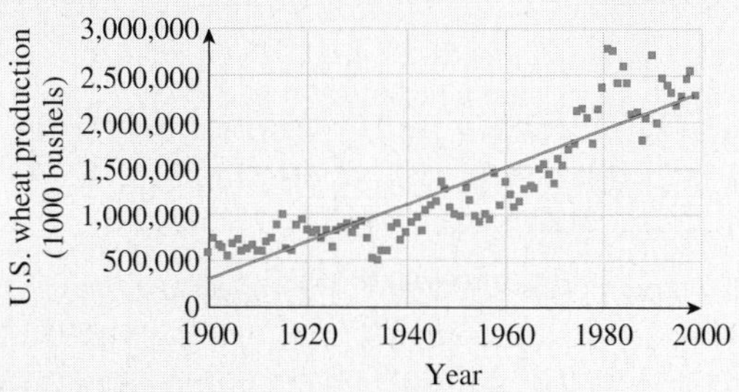

Figure **21**

Although that is a fairly high correlation, you notice that the residuals are not distributed randomly: The actual wheat production starts out higher than the line, is below the line from about 1920 to about 1970, and then is mostly above the line. This suggests that you would get a better fit from a function whose graph bends upwards. But what kind of curve? You decide to compare three different models: quadratic, exponential, and logistic.

Following is a comparison of the results of fitting the three proposed models. (Coefficients are rounded to six significant digits. SSE is the sum-of-squares error and r^2 is called the coefficient of determination, and measures how closely the regression curve fits the data.)

Model and Graph	***SSE***	r^2
Quadratic $P(t) \approx 245.067t^2 - 4319.47t + 711{,}703$	4.941×10^{12}	0.8807
Exponential $P(t) \approx 510{,}833(1.01672)^t$	5.485×10^{12}	0.8676

Model and Graph	*SSE*	r^2
Logistic $P(t) \approx \dfrac{1.15135 \times 10^{15}}{1 + 2.25867 \times 10^9 \times 1.01672^{-t}}$ $(N \approx 1.15135 \times 10^{15},\ A \approx 2.25867 \times 10^9,\ b \approx 1.01672)$ 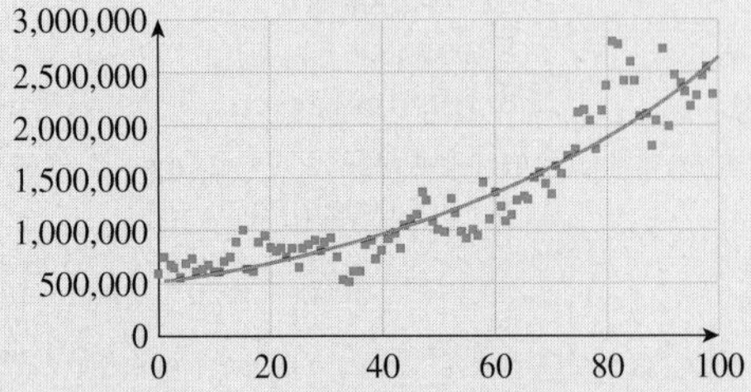	5.485×10^{12}	0.8676

Q: *Because the quadratic model gives a slightly higher value for r^2, it follows that the quadratic model is more appropriate than the exponential model, right?*

A: The quadratic model does give a better fit to the data than the exponential model (as evidenced by the values of both SSE and r^2). However, a better fit does not necessarily imply a more appropriate model. ■

Q: *Why not?*

A: Suppose, for arguments' sake, that production of wheat *was* growing exponentially according to the above regression model *on average*, but that due to random fluctuations in market conditions and weather patterns, the actual output varied from the predicted output by a random amount. This randomness would explain the fact that the observed values do not lie exactly on the regression curve, but are instead scattered about in its vicinity. Moreover, because the scatter is due to random factors, any attempt to obtain a mathematical curve that fits the actual data more closely would be questionable, given our assumption. (For example, we *could* find a degree 99 polynomial whose graph passes through every data point!) ■

Q: *Could you not then argue that the linear model might be the most appropriate of all three, and that the illusion of curvature is caused by those same random fluctuations?*

A: That could conceivably be happening, but two factors argue against it: First, the positive-negative-positive pattern of the residuals in the linear model (Figure 21) strongly suggest that something other than a linear relationship is going on. Second (and we will be vague here) there are rigorous statistical tests one can perform to support the hypothesis that there is curvature.[44] ■

Although neither the quadratic nor the exponential model has a clear advantage over the other, the good fit of both models provides reasonable evidence that wheat production, at least, is better described as increasing quadratically or exponentially than linearly, contradicting Malthus.

[44] These hypothesis tests are generally discussed in statistics courses.

If you compare the exponential and logistic models, you get additional interesting information. The logistic model seems as though it *ought* to be the most appropriate, because wheat production cannot reasonably be expected to continue increasing exponentially forever; eventually resource limitations must lead to a leveling-off of wheat production. Such a leveling off, if it occurred before the population started to level off, would seem to vindicate Malthus's pessimistic predictions.[45]

However, the logistic regression model looks suspect: It predicts a leveling-off value (N) that is orders of magnitude higher than what seems reasonable. Moreover, the logistic model (as well as SSE and r^2) looks almost indistinguishable from the exponential model, suggesting that it is no better. You are forced to conclude that wheat production—even if it is logistic—is still in the early (exponential) stage of growth, and thus shows no sign, as yet, of leveling off. In general, for a logistic model to be reliable in its prediction of the leveling-off value N, we would need to see significant evidence of leveling-off in the data.

You tentatively conclude that wheat production for the past 100 years is better described as increasing quadratically or exponentially than linearly, contradicting Malthus, and moreover that it shows no sign of leveling off as yet.

Exercises

1. Find the best-fit line for wheat production for the period 1866–1940. How good a fit is the line?

2. Find the best-fit line for wheat production for the period 1940–1997. How good a fit is the line?

3. Find the production figures for another common crop grown in the U.S. Compare the linear, quadratic, exponential, and logistic models. What can you conclude?

4. Below are the census figures for the population of the U.S. (in thousands) from 1800 to 2000.[46] Compare the linear, quadratic, and exponential models. What can you conclude?

Population of the U.S. (1000)

1810	**1820**	**1830**	**1840**	**1850**	**1860**	**1870**	**1880**	**1890**	**1900**
7,240	9,638	12,861	17,063	23,192	31,443	38,558	50,189	62,980	76,212
1910	**1920**	**1930**	**1940**	**1950**	**1960**	**1970**	**1980**	**1990**	**2000**
92,228	106,022	123,203	132,165	151,326	179,323	203,302	226,542	248,710	281,422

[45] See the exercise set for data on population.

[46] Source: Bureau of the Census, U.S. Department of Commerce.

Section 2.1

Example **2** Sketch the graph of each quadratic function, showing the location of the vertex and intercepts.

a. $f(x) = 4x^2 - 12x + 9$ **b.** $g(x) = -\frac{1}{2}x^2 + 4x - 12$

Solution with Technology We will do part (a).

1. Start by storing the coefficients a, b, c using

    `4→A:-12→B:9→C`

    STO> gives the arrow ALPHA . gives the colon

2. Save your quadratic as Y_1 using the Y= screen:

    `Y1=AX^2+BX+C`

3. To obtain the x-coordinate of the vertex, enter its formula as shown:

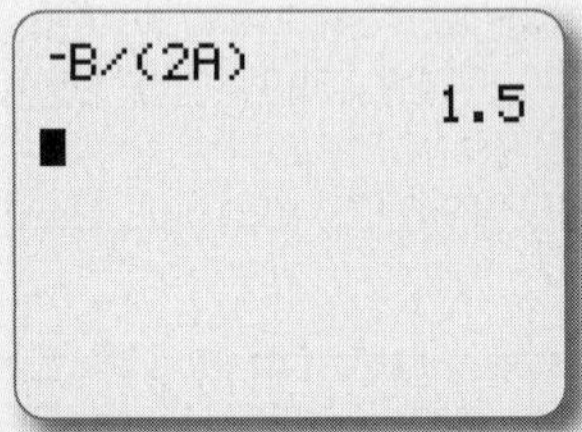

4. The y-coordinate of the vertex can be obtained from the table screen by entering $x = 1.5$ as shown. (If you can't enter values of x, press 2ND TBLSET, and set `Indpnt` to Ask.)

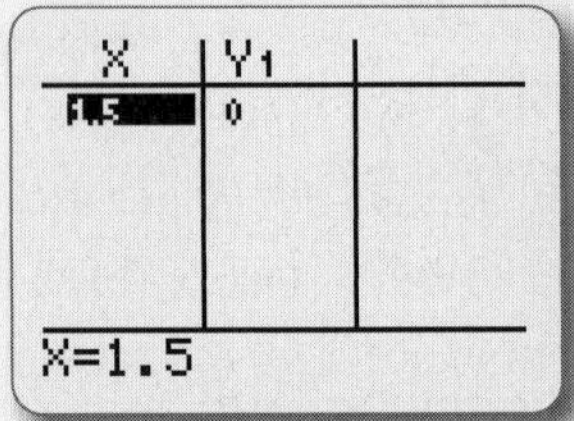

From the table, we see that the vertex is at the point (1.5, 0).

5. To obtain the x-intercepts, enter the quadratic formula on the home screen as shown:

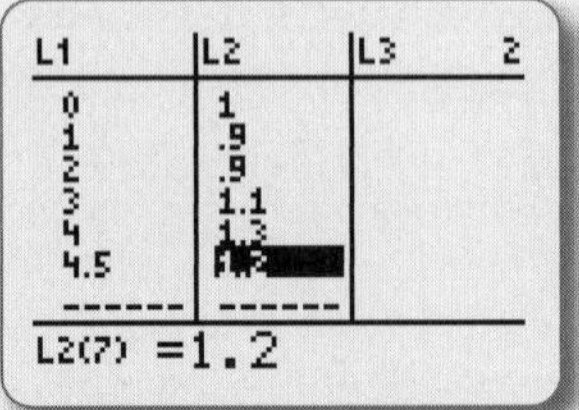

Because both intercepts agree, we conclude that the graph intersects the x-axis on a single point (at the vertex).

6. To graph the function, we need to select good values for Xmin and Xmax. In general, we would like our graph to show the vertex as well as all the intercepts. To see the vertex, make sure that its x-coordinate (1.5) is between Xmin and Xmax. To see the *x-intercepts,* make sure that they are also between Xmin and Xmax (also 1.5). To see the y-intercept, make sure that $x = 0$ is between Xmin and Xmax. Thus, to see everything, choose Xmin and Xmax so that the interval [xMin, xMax] contains the x-coordinate of the vertex, the x-intercepts, and 0. For this example, we can choose an interval like $[-1, 3]$.

7. Once xMin and xMax are chosen, you can obtain convenient values of yMin and yMax by pressing ZOOM and selecting the option `ZoomFit`. (Make sure that your quadratic equation is entered in the Y= screen before doing this!)

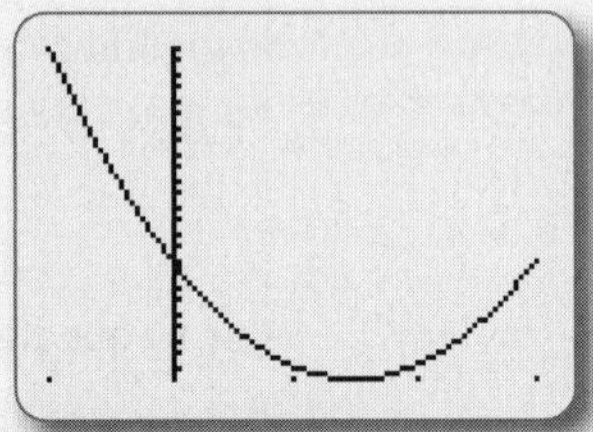

Example **5b** The following table shows the value of the euro (€) in U.S. dollars since it began trading in January, 1999 ($t = 0$ represents January, 2000).[47]

Year t	−1	0	1	2	3	4	4.5
Value ($)	1.2	1	0.9	0.9	1.1	1.3	1.2

Find the quadratic regression model.

Solution with Technology

1. Using STAT `EDIT` enter the data in the TI-83/84 putting the x-coordinates (values of t) in L_1 and the y-coordinates (values of the euro) in L_2, just as in Section 1.5:

[47] Prices are rounded 20-day averages. Source for data: http://finance.yahoo.com/.

2. Press STAT, select CALC, and choose the option QuadReg. Pressing ENTER gives the quadratic regression curve in the home screen:

   $y \approx 0.0399x^2 - 0.1150x + 1.0154$

   Coefficients rounded to four decimal places

3. To graph the points and regression line in the same window, turn Stat Plot on by pressing 2ND STAT PLOT, selecting 1 and turning PLOT1 on:

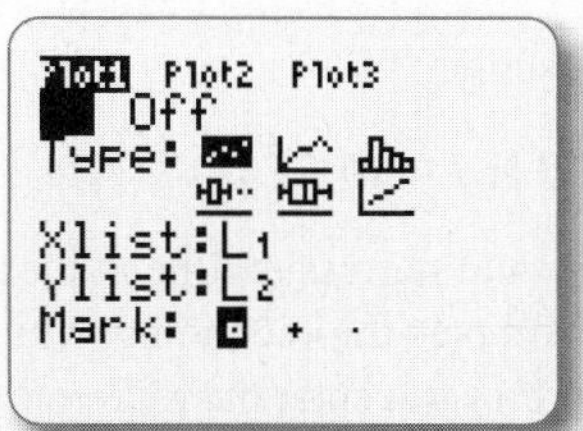

4. Next, enter the regression equation in the Y= screen by pressing Y=, clearing out whatever function is there, and pressing VARS 5 and selecting EQ (Option 1: RegEq):

```
Plot1 Plot2 Plot3
\Y1=.03989475003
132X^2+-.1149730
6101993X+1.01536
14835234
\Y2=
\Y3=
\Y4=
```

5. To obtain a convenient window showing all the points and the lines, press ZOOM and choose option #9: ZoomStat:

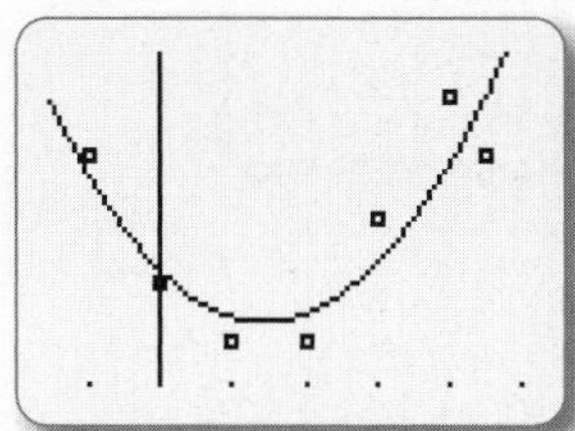

Note When you are done viewing the graph, it is a good idea to turn PLOT1 off again to avoid errors in graphing or data points showing up in your other graphs. ■

Section 2.2

Example 4b You invest \$2000 in a mutual fund with an annual yield of 12.6% and the interest is reinvested each month. Use the model to estimate the year when the value of your investment will reach \$5000.

Solution with Technology We need to find the value of t for which $A(t) = \$5000$, so we need to solve the equation $5000 = 2000(1.0105)^{12t}$ for t.

1. In the Y= screen, enter

   `Y1=2000*1.0105^(12X)`

2. Go to the Table screen, where you can list values of this function for various values of X:

```
X    Y1
5    3742.9
6    4242.7
7    4809.3
8    5451.5
9    6179.5
10   7004.7
11   7940.1
Y1=5451.50618802
```

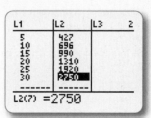

Because the balance first exceeds \$5000 in year 8, the answer is $t = 8$ years.

Example 7a The following table shows annual expenditure on health in the U.S. from 1980 through 2010 ($t = 0$ represents 1980).[48]

Year t	0	5	10	15	20	25	30
Expenditure (\$ Billion)	246	427	696	990	1310	1920	2750

Find the exponential regression model $C(t) = Ab^t$.

Solution with Technology This is very similar to Example 5 in Section 2.1 (see the Technology Guide for Section 2.1):

1. Use STAT EDIT to enter the above table of values.

```
L1     L2     L3   2
5      427
10     696
15     990
20     1310
25     1920
30     2750
------ ------
L2(7) =2750
```

[48] Data are rounded. The 2005 and 2010 figures are projections.
SOURCE: Centers for Medicare and Medicaid Services, "National Health Expenditures," 2002 version, released January 2004; www.cms.hhs.gov/statistics/nhe/.

TECHNOLOGY GUIDE

2. Press STAT, select `CALC`, and choose the option `ExpReg`. Pressing ENTER gives the exponential regression curve in the home screen:

$$C(t) \approx 282.33(1.0808)^t \quad \text{Coefficients rounded}$$

3. To graph the points and regression line in the same window, turn Stat Plot on (see the Technology Guide for Example 5 in Section 2.1) and enter the regression equation in the Y= screen by pressing Y=, clearing out whatever function is there, and pressing VARS 5 and selecting `EQ` (Option 1: `RegEq`). Then press ZOOM and choose option #9: `ZoomStat` to see the graph.

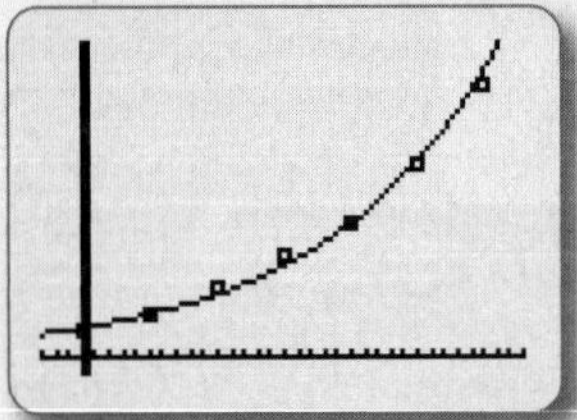

Note When you are done viewing the graph, it is a good idea to turn PLOT1 off again to avoid errors in graphing or data points showing up in your other graphs. ■

Section 2.3

Example **5** The following table shows the total spent on research and development in the U.S., in billions of dollars, for the period 1995–2005 ($t = 5$ represents 1995).[49]

Year t	5	6	7	8	9	10
Spending ($ billions)	187	197	208	219	232	248
Year t	11	12	13	14	15	
Spending ($ billions)	250	250	253	260	265	

Find the best-fit logarithmic model of the form:

$$S(t) = A \ln t + C$$

Solution with Technology This is very similar to Example 5 in Section 2.1 and Example 7 in Section 2.2 (see the Technology Guide for Section 2.1):

1. Use STAT `EDIT` to the enter above table of values.
2. Press STAT, select `CALC`, and choose the option `LnReg`. Pressing ENTER gives the quadratic regression curve in the home screen:

$$S(t) = 73.77 \ln t + 67.75 \quad \text{Coefficients rounded}$$

3. To graph the points and regression line in the same window, turn Stat Plot on (see the Technology Guide for Example 5 in Section 2.1) and enter the regression equation in the Y= screen by pressing Y=, clearing out whatever function is there, and pressing VARS 5 and selecting `EQ` (Option 1: `RegEq`). To see the graph, press ZOOM and choose option #9: `ZoomStat`:

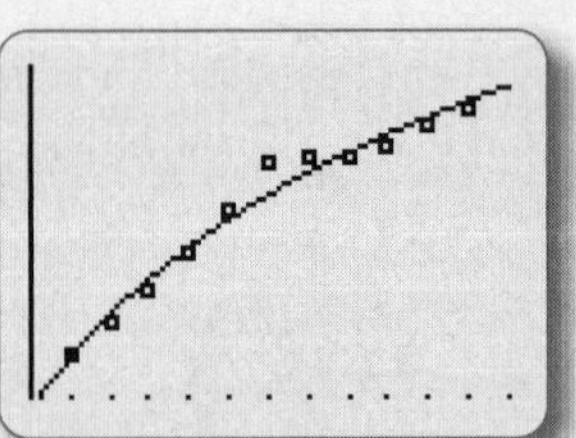

Section 2.4

Example **2** Here are the data graphed in Figure 17:

Year (t)	0	1	2	3	4	5	6	7	8	9
Households with PCs (%) (P)	24	28	32	37	42	48	54	59	63	65

Find a logistic regression curve of the form

$$P(t) = \frac{N}{1 + Ab^{-t}}$$

[49] Data are approximate and are given in constant 1996 dollars. 2004 and 2005 figures are projections. SOURCE: National Science Foundation, Division of Science Resource Statistics, National Patterns of R&D Resources. www.nsf.gov/sbe/srs/nprdr/start.hrm October 2004.

Solution with Technology This is very similar to Example 5 in Section 2.1 (see the Technology Guide for Section 2.1):

1. Use STAT EDIT to enter the above table of values.

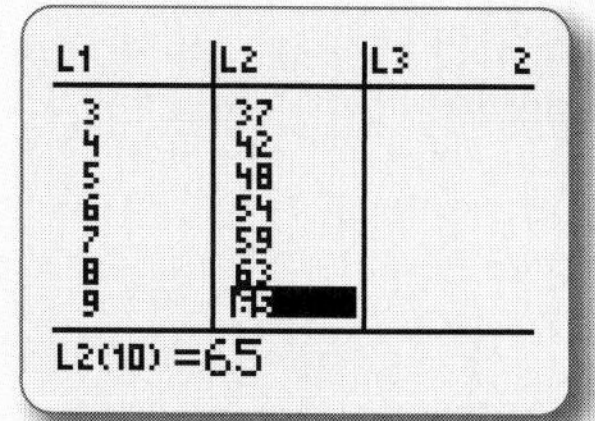

2. Press STAT, select CALC, and choose the option Logistic. Pressing ENTER gives the exponential regression curve in the home screen:

$$P(t) \approx \frac{84.573}{1 + 2.6428e^{-0.250363t}} \quad \text{Coefficients rounded}$$

This is not exactly the form we are seeking, but we can convert it to that form by writing

$$e^{-0.250363t} = (e^{0.250363})^{-t} \approx 1.2845^{-t}$$

so

$$P(t) \approx \frac{84.573}{1 + 2.6428(1.2845)^{-t}}$$

3. To graph the points and regression line in the same window, turn Stat Plot on (see the Technology Guide for Example 5 in Section 2.1) and enter the regression equation in the Y= screen by pressing Y=, clearing out whatever function is there, and pressing VARS 5 and selecting EQ (Option 1: RegEq):

To obtain a convenient window showing all the points and the lines, press ZOOM and choose option #9: ZoomStat:

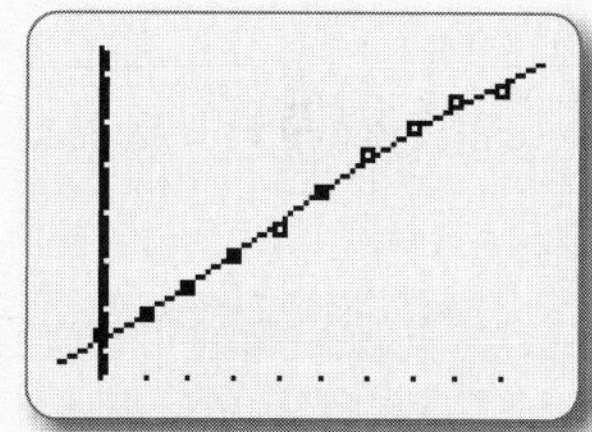

Note When you are done viewing the graph, it is a good idea to turn PLOT1 off again to avoid errors in graphing or data points showing up in your other graphs. ■

EXCEL Technology Guide

Section 2.1

Example 2 Sketch the graph of each quadratic function, showing the location of the vertex and intercepts.

a. $f(x) = 4x^2 - 12x + 9$ **b.** $g(x) = -\frac{1}{2}x^2 + 4x - 12$

Solution with Technology We can set up a worksheet so that all we have to enter are the coefficients a, b, and c, and a range of x values for the graph. Here is a possible layout that will plot 100 points using the coefficients for part (a) (similar to the Excel Graphing Worksheet we used in Example 2 of Section 1.2).

TECHNOLOGY GUIDE

1. First, we compute the x-coordinates:

Microsoft Excel - ETG 2-1 Graph of Quadratic Function.xls

File Edit View Insert Format Tools Data Window Help Adobe

	A	B	C	D	E
1	x	y	a	4	
2	=$D$4		b	-12	
3	=A2+$D$6		c	9	
4			Xmin	-10	
5			Xmax	10	
6			Delta X	=(D5-D4)/100	
7					
102					
103					

2. To add the y-coordinates, we use the technology formula

```
a*x^2+b*x+c
```

replacing a, b, and c with (absolute) references to the cells containing their values.

Microsoft Excel - ETG 2-1 Graph of Quadratic Function.xls

File Edit View Insert Format Tools Data Window Help Adobe PDF

	A	B	C	D	E
1	x	y	a	4	
2	-10	=$D$1*A2^2+$D$2*A2+$D$3	b	-12	
3	-9.8		c	9	
4	-9.6		Xmin	-10	
5	-9.4		Xmax	10	
6	-9.2		Delta X	0.2	
7					
102	10				
103					
104					

3. Graphing the data in columns A and B gives the graph shown here:

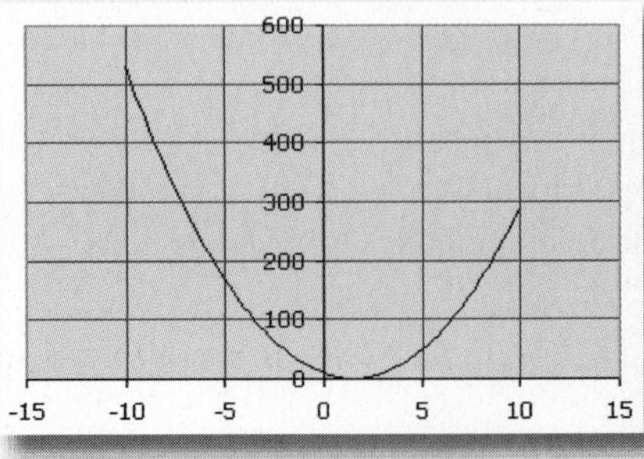

$y = 4x^2 - 12x + 9$

4. We can go further and compute the exact coordinates of the vertex and intercepts:

Microsoft Excel - ETG 2-1 Graph of Quadratic Function.xls

File Edit View Insert Format Tools Data Window Help Adobe PDF

	A	B	C	D	E	F
1	x	y	a	4	Vertex (x)	=-D2/(2*D1)
2	-10	529	b	-12	Vertex (y)	=D1*F1^2+D2*F1+D3
3	-9.8	510.76	c	9	X Intercept 1	=(-D2-SQRT(D2^2-4*D1*D3))/(2*D1)
4	-9.6	492.84	Xmin	-10	X Intercept 2	=(-D2+SQRT(D2^2-4*D1*D3))/(2*D1)
5	-9.4	475.24	Xmax	10	Y Intercept	=D3
6	-9.2	457.96	Delta X	0.2		
7	-9	441				
8	-9.8	424.36				

The completed sheet should look like this:

Microsoft Excel - ETG 2-1 Graph of Quadratic Function.xls

File Edit View Insert Format Tools Data Window Help Adobe PDF

	A	B	C	D	E	F
1	x	y	a	4	Vertex (x)	1.5
2	-10	529	b	-12	Vertex (y)	0
3	-9.8	510.76	c	9	X Intercept 1	1.5
4	-9.6	492.84	Xmin	-10	X Intercept 2	1.5
5	-9.4	475.24	Xmax	10	Y Intercept	9
6	-9.2	457.96	Delta X	0.2		
7	-9	441				
8	-9.8	424.36				

We can now save this sheet as a template to handle all quadratic functions. For instance, to do part (b), we just change the values of a, b, and c in column D to $a = -1/2$, $b = 4$, and $c = -12$.

Example 5b The following table shows the value of the euro (€) in U.S. dollars since it began trading in January, 1999 ($t = 0$ represents January, 2000).[50]

Year t	-1	0	1	2	3	4	4.5
Value ($)	1.2	1	0.9	0.9	1.1	1.3	1.2

Find the quadratic regression model.

Solution with Technology As in Section 1.5, Example 3, we start with a scatter plot of the original data, and add a trendline:

[50] Prices are rounded 20-day averages. Source for data: http://finance.yahoo.com/.

TECHNOLOGY GUIDE

1. Start with the original data and a "Scatter plot."

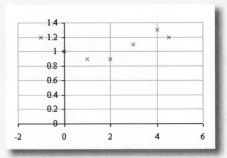

Microsoft Excel - ETG 2-1 Value of the Euro in US Dollars.xls

	A	B	C	D
1	t	Value		
2	-1	1.2		
3	0	1		
4	1	0.9		
5	2	0.9		
6	3	1.1		
7	4	1.3		
8	4.5	1.2		
9				
10				

2. Click on the chart, and select "Add Trendline . . ." from the Chart menu. Then select a "Polynomial" type, set the order to 2, and, under "Options," check the option "Display equation on chart".

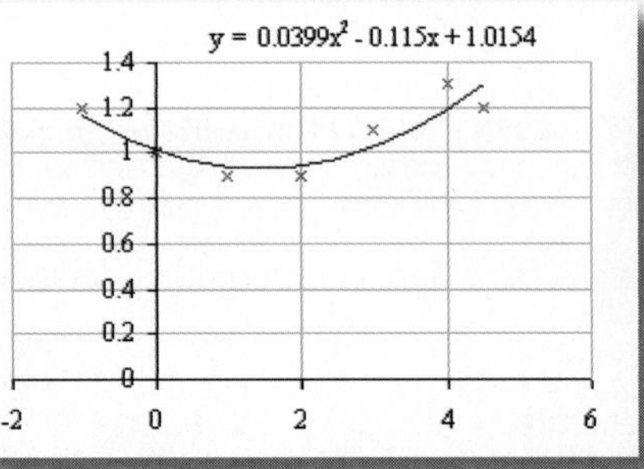

Section 2.2

Example **4b** You invest \$2000 in a mutual fund with an annual yield of 12.6% and the interest is reinvested each month. Use the model to estimate the year when the value of your investment will reach \$5000.

Solution with Technology We need to find the value of t for which $A(t) = \$5000$, so we need to solve the equation $5000 = 2000(1.0105)^{12t}$ for t. Here is a table you can obtain in Excel (to format a cell as currency, highlight the cell and use the Format menu: Format → Cells → Currency):

Microsoft Excel - ETG 2-2 Value of Investment in a Mutual Fund.xls

	A	B	C
1	t	A	
2	0	=2000*(1 + 0.126/12)^(12*A2)	
3	1		
4	2		
5	3		
6	4		
7	5		
8	6		
9	7		
10	8		
11	9		
12			
13			

Microsoft Excel - ETG 2-2 Value of Investment in a Mutual Fund.xls

	A	B	C	D	E
1	t	A			
2	0	\$2,000.00			
3	1	\$2,267.07			
4	2	\$2,569.81			
5	3	\$2,912.98			
6	4	\$3,301.97			
7	5	\$3,742.91			
8	6	\$4,242.72			
9	7	\$4,809.29			
10	8	\$5,451.51			
11	9	\$6,179.49			
12					
13					

Because the balance first exceeds \$5000 in year 8, the answer is $t = 8$ years.

Example **7a** The following table shows annual expenditure on health in the U.S. from 1980 through 2010 ($t = 0$ represents 1980).[51]

Year t	0	5	10	15	20	25	30
Expenditure (\$ Billion)	246	427	696	990	1310	1920	2750

Find the exponential regression model $C(t) = Ab^t$.

Solution with Technology This is very similar to Example 5 in Section 2.1 (see the Technology Guide for Section 2.1):

1. Start with a "Scatter plot" of the observed data, click on the chart, and select "Add Trendline . . ." from the Chart menu.
2. In the dialogue box that now appears, select the "Exponential" type and, under "Options", check the option "Display equation on chart":

Microsoft Excel - ETG 2-2 Annual Expenditure on Health in the US.xls

File Edit View Insert Format Tools Data Window Help Adobe PDF

	A	B	C	D	E
1	t	Expenditures			
2	0	246			
3	5	427			
4	10	696			
5	15	990			
6	20	1310			
7	25	1920			
8	30	2750			
9					
10					

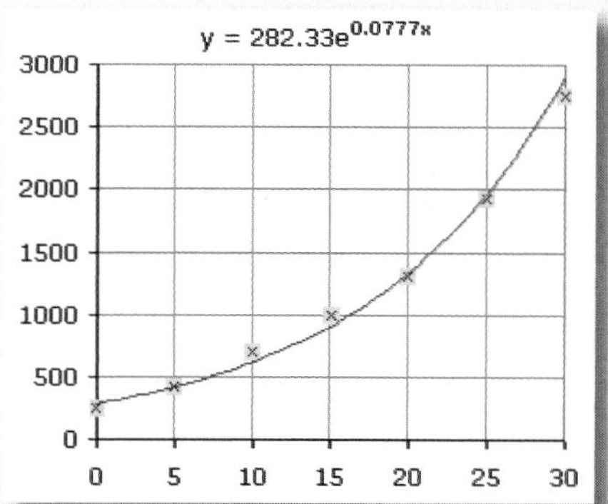

Notice that the regression curve is given in the form Ae^{kt} rather than Ab^t. To transform it, write

$$\begin{aligned} 282.33e^{0.0777t} &= 282.33(e^{0.0777})^t \\ &\approx 282.33(1.0808)^t \end{aligned} \qquad e^{0.0777} \approx 1.0808$$

Section 2.3

Example **5** The following table shows the total spent on research and development in the U.S., in billions of dollars, for the period 1995–2005 ($t = 5$ represents 1995).[52]

Year t	5	6	7	8	9	10
Spending (\$ billions)	187	197	208	219	232	248
Year t	11	12	13	14	15	
Spending (\$ billions)	250	250	253	260	265	

[51] Data are rounded. 2005 and 2010 figures are projections. SOURCE: Centers for Medicare and Medicaid Services, "National Health Expenditures," 2002 version, released January 2004; www.cms.hhs.gov/statistics/nhe/

[52] Data are approximate and are given in constant 1996 dollars. The 2004 and 2005 figures are projections. SOURCE: National Science Foundation, Division of Science Resource Statistics, National Patterns of R&D Resources. www.nsf.gov/sbe/srs/nprdr/start.hrm October 2004.

Find the best-fit logarithmic model of the form

$$S(t) = A \ln t + C$$

Solution with Technology This is very similar to Example 5 in Section 2.1 and Example 7 in Section 2.2 (see the Technology Guide for Section 2.1): We start, as usual, with a "Scatter plot" of the observed data and add a `Logarithmic` trendline. Here is the result:

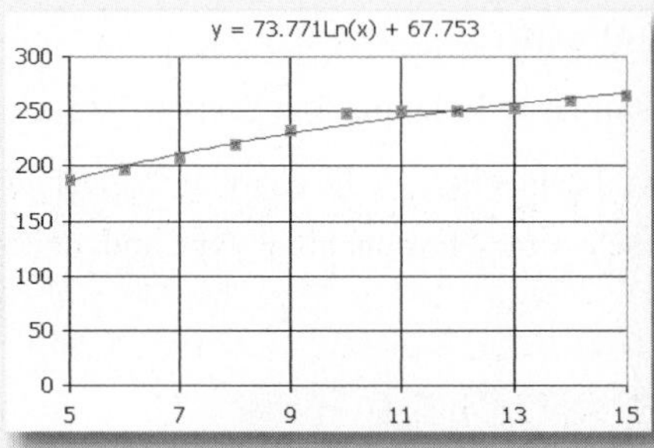

Section 2.4

Example 2 Here are the data graphed in Figure 17:

Year (t)	0	1	2	3	4	5	6	7	8	9
Households with PCs (%) (P)	24	28	32	37	42	48	54	59	63	65

Find a logistic regression curve of the form

$$P(t) = \frac{N}{1 + Ab^{-t}}$$

Solution with Technology Excel does not have a built-in logistic regression calculation, so we use an alternative method that works for any type of regression curve.

1. First use rough estimates for N, A, and b, and compute the sum-of-squares error (SSE; see Section 1.5) directly:

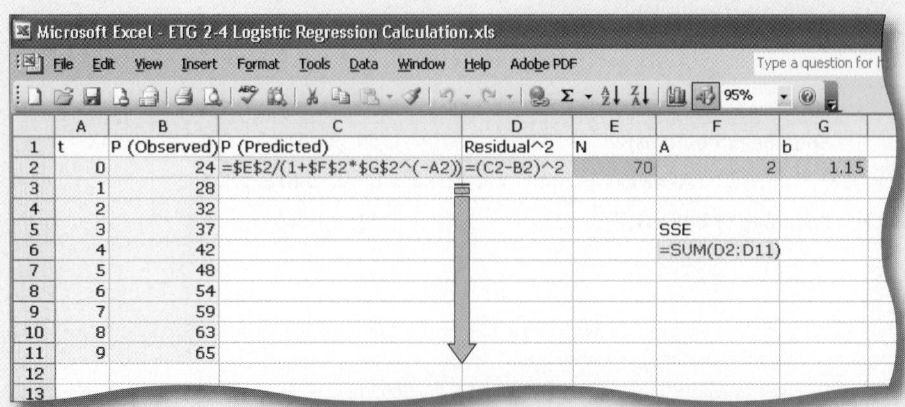

	A	B	C	D	E	F	G
1	t	P (Observed)	P (Predicted)	Residual^2	N	A	b
2	0	24	=$E$2/(1+$F$2*$G$2^(-A2))	=(C2-B2)^2	70	2	1.15
3	1	28					
4	2	32					
5	3	37				SSE	
6	4	42				=SUM(D2:D11)	
7	5	48					
8	6	54					
9	7	59					
10	8	63					
11	9	65					
12							
13							

Cells E2:G2 contain our initial rough estimates of *N*, *A*, and *b*. For *N*, we used 70 (notice that the *y*-coordinates do appear to level off around 70). For *A*, we used the fact that the *y*-intercept is $N/(1 + A)$. In other words,

$$24 = \frac{70}{1 + A}$$

Because a very rough estimate is all we are after, using $A = 2$ will do just fine. For *b*, we chose 1.15 as the values of *P* appear to be increasing by around 15% per year initially (again this is rough—we could equally have use 1.1 or 1.2).

2. Cell C2 contains the formula for $P(t)$, and the square of the resulting residual is computed in D2.

3. Cell F6 will contain SSE. The completed spreadsheet should look like this:

Microsoft Excel - ETG 2-4 Logistic Regression Calculation.xls

	A	B	C	D	E	F	G
1	t	P (Observed)	P (Predicted	Residual^2	N	A	b
2	0	24	23.3333333	0.44444444	70	2	1.15
3	1	28	25.5555556	5.97530864			
4	2	32	27.8630549	17.1143145			
5	3	37	30.237157	45.736046		SSE	
6	4	42	32.6567707	87.2959335		1798.95213	
7	5	48	35.099094	166.433375			
8	6	54	37.5404527	270.916698			
9	7	59	39.9572097	362.627862			
10	8	63	42.3266718	427.386498			
11	9	65	44.6279198	415.021653			
12							
13							

The best-fit curve will result from values of *N*, *A*, and *b* that give a minimum value for SSE. We shall use Excel's "Solver," found in the "Tools" menu, to find these values for us. (If "Solver" does not appear in the Tools menu, select Add-Ins in the Tools menu and install it.) Figure 22 shows the dialogue box with the necessary fields completed to solve the problem.

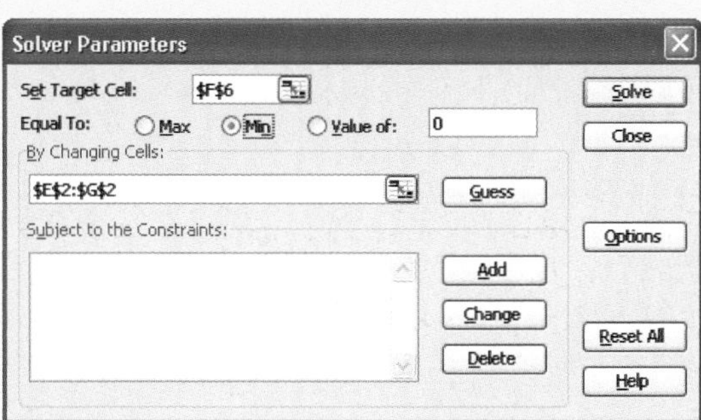

Figure **22**

- The Target Cell refers to the cell that contains SSE
- "Min" is selected because we are minimizing SSE.
- "Changing Cells" are obtained by selecting the cells that contain the current values of N, A, and b.

4. When you have filled in the values for the three items above, press "Solve" and tell Solver to Keep Solver Solution when done. You will find $N \approx 84.573$, $A \approx 2.6428$, and $b \approx 1.2845$ so that

$$P(t) \approx \frac{84.573}{1 + 2.6428(1.2845)^{-t}}$$

If you use a scatter plot to graph the data in columns A, B and C, you will obtain the following graph:

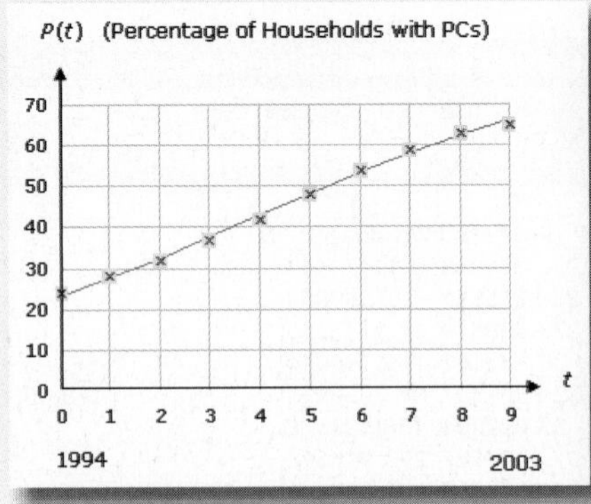

3 Introduction to the Derivative

Get a better Grade!
www.thomsonedu.com/login

Logon to your Personalized Study plan to find:

- Section by section tutorials
- A detailed chapter summary
- Additional review exercises
- Graphers, Excel tutorials, and other resources
- Optional sections:
  Sketching the Graph of the Derivative
  Proof of the Power Rule
  Continuity and Differentiability

CASE STUDY Reducing Sulfur Emissions

The Environmental Protection Agency (EPA) wants to formulate a policy that will encourage utilities to reduce sulfur emissions. Its goal is to reduce annual emissions of sulfur dioxide by a total of 10 million tons from the current level of 25 million tons by imposing a fixed charge for every ton of sulfur released into the environment per year. The EPA has some data showing the marginal cost to utilities of reducing sulfur emissions. As a consultant to the EPA, you must determine the amount to be charged per ton of sulfur emissions in light of these data.

Creatas/Superstock

Introduction

In the world around us, everything is changing. The mathematics of change is largely about the rate of change: how fast and in which direction the change is occurring. Is the Dow Jones average going up, and if so, how fast? If I raise my prices, how many customers will I lose? If I launch this missile, how fast will it be traveling after two seconds, how high will it go, and where will it come down?

We have already discussed the concept of rate of change for linear functions (straight lines), where the slope measures the rate of change. But this works only because a straight line maintains a constant rate of change along its whole length. Other functions rise faster here than there—or rise in one place and fall in another—so that the rate of change varies along the graph. The first achievement of calculus is to provide a systematic and straightforward way of calculating (hence the name) these rates of change. To describe a changing world, we need a language of change, and that is what calculus is.

The history of calculus is an interesting story of personalities, intellectual movements, and controversy. Credit for its invention is given to two mathematicians: Isaac Newton (1642–1727) and Gottfried Leibniz (1646–1716). Newton, an English mathematician and scientist, developed calculus first, probably in the 1660s. We say "probably" because, for various reasons, he did not publish his ideas until much later. This allowed Leibniz, a German mathematician and philosopher, to publish his own version of calculus first, in 1684. Fifteen years later, stirred up by nationalist fervor in England and on the continent, controversy erupted over who should get the credit for the invention of calculus. The debate got so heated that the Royal Society (of which Newton and Leibniz were both members) set up a commission to investigate the question. The commission decided in favor of Newton, who happened to be president of the society at the time. The consensus today is that both mathematicians deserve credit because they came to the same conclusions working independently. This is not really surprising: Both built on well-known work of other people, and it was almost inevitable that someone would put it all together at about that time.

algebra Review
For this chapter, you should be familiar with the algebra reviewed in Chapter 0, Section 2.

3.1 Limits: Numerical and Graphical Approaches (OPTIONAL)

Rates of change are calculated by derivatives, but an important part of the definition of the derivative is something called a **limit.** Arguably, much of mathematics since the 18th century has revolved around understanding, refining, and exploiting the idea of the limit. The basic idea is easy, but getting the technicalities right is not.

Evaluating Limits Numerically

Start with a very simple example: Look at the function $f(x) = 2 + x$ and ask: What happens to $f(x)$ as x approaches 3? The following table shows the value of $f(x)$ for values of x close to and on either side of 3:

x approaching 3 from the left → ← x approaching 3 from the right

x	2.9	2.99	2.999	2.9999	3	3.0001	3.001	3.01	3.1
$f(x) = 2 + x$	4.9	4.99	4.999	4.9999		5.0001	5.001	5.01	5.1

We have left the entry under 3 blank to emphasize that when calculating the limit of $f(x)$ as x *approaches* 3, we are not interested in its value when x *equals* 3.

Notice from the table that the closer x gets to 3 from either side, the closer $f(x)$ gets to 5. We write this as

$$\lim_{x \to 3} f(x) = 5 \qquad \text{The limit of } f(x)\text{, as } x \text{ approaches 3, equals 5.}$$

Q: *Why all the fuss? Can't we simply substitute $x = 3$ and avoid having to use a table?*

A: This happens to work for *some* functions, but not for *all* functions. The following example illustrates this point. ■

Example 1 Estimating a Limit Numerically

Use a table to estimate the following limits:

a. $\lim_{x \to 2} \dfrac{x^3 - 8}{x - 2}$ **b.** $\lim_{x \to 0} \dfrac{e^{2x} - 1}{x}$

Solution

a. We cannot simply substitute $x = 2$, because the function $f(x) = \dfrac{x^3 - 8}{x - 2}$ is not defined at $x = 2$. (Why?)* Instead, we use a table of values as we did above, with x approaching 2 from both sides.

x approaching 2 from the left → ← x approaching 2 from the right

x	1.9	1.99	1.999	1.9999	2	2.0001	2.001	2.01	2.1
$f(x) = \dfrac{x^3 - 8}{x - 2}$	11.41	11.9401	11.9940	11.9994		12.0006	12.0060	12.0601	12.61

We notice that as x approaches 2 from either side, $f(x)$ appears to be approaching 12. This suggests that the limit is 12, and we write

$$\lim_{x \to 2} \frac{x^3 - 8}{x - 2} = 12$$

b. The function $g(x) = \dfrac{e^{2x} - 1}{x}$ is not defined at $x = 0$ (nor can it even be simplified to one which *is* defined at $x = 0$). In the following table, we allow x to approach 0 from both sides:

x approaching 0 from the left → ← x approaching 0 from the right

x	−0.1	−0.01	−0.001	−0.0001	0	0.0001	0.001	0.01	0.1
$g(x) = \dfrac{e^{2x} - 1}{x}$	1.8127	1.9801	1.9980	1.9998		2.0002	2.0020	2.0201	2.2140

The table suggests that $\lim_{x \to 0} \dfrac{e^{2x} - 1}{x} = 2$.

using *Technology*

We can automate these computations using a graphing calculator or Excel. See the Technology Guides at the end of the chapter to find out how to create tables like these using a TI-83/84 or Excel.

*However, if you factor $x^3 - 8$, you will find that $f(x)$ can be simplified to a function which *is* defined at $x = 2$. This point will be discussed (and this example redone) in Section 3.3. The function in part (b) cannot be simplified by factoring.

+Before we go on... Although the table *suggests* that the limit in Example 1 part (b) is 2, it by no means establishes that fact conclusively. It is *conceivable* (though not in fact the case here) that putting $x = 0.000000087$ could result in $g(x) = 426$. Using a table can only suggest a value for the limit. In the next two sections we shall discuss algebraic techniques for finding limits. ■

Before we continue, let us make a more formal definition.

Definition of a Limit

If $f(x)$ approaches the number L as x approaches (but is not equal to) a from both sides, then we say that $f(x)$ **approaches L as $x \to a$** ("x approaches a") or that the **limit** of $f(x)$ as $x \to a$ is L. We write

$$\lim_{x \to a} f(x) = L$$

or

$$f(x) \to L \text{ as } x \to a$$

If $f(x)$ *fails* to approach *a single fixed number* as x approaches a from both sides, then we say that $f(x)$ **has no limit** as $x \to a$, or

$$\lim_{x \to a} f(x) \textbf{ does not exist.}$$

quick Examples

1. $\lim_{x \to 3}(2 + x) = 5$ — See discussion before Example 1.
2. $\lim_{x \to -2}(3x) = -6$ — As x approaches -2, $3x$ approaches -6.
3. $\lim_{x \to 0}(x^2 - 2x + 1)$ exists. — In fact, the limit is 1.
4. $\lim_{x \to 5} \frac{1}{x} = \frac{1}{5}$ — As x approaches 5, $\frac{1}{x}$ approaches $\frac{1}{5}$.
5. $\lim_{x \to 2} \frac{x^3 - 8}{x - 2} = 12$ — See Example 1. (We cannot just put $x = 2$ here.)

(For examples where the limit does not exist, see Example 2.)

Notes

1. It is important that $f(x)$ approach the same number as x approaches a from either side. For instance, if $f(x)$ approaches 5 for $x = 1.9, 1.99, 1.999, \ldots$, but approaches 4 for $x = 2.1, 2.01, 2.001, \ldots$, then the limit as $x \to 2$ does not exist. (See Example 2 for such a situation.)
2. It may happen that $f(x)$ does not approach any fixed number at all as $x \to a$ from either side. In this case, we also say that the limit does not exist.
3. We are being deliberately vague as to exactly what we mean by the word "approaches"; instead, we trust your intuition. However, the following phrasing of the definition of the limit is close to the more technical one used by mathematicians. ■

Verbal Form of the Mathematical Definition of a Limit

We can make $f(x)$ be as close to L as we like by choosing any x sufficiently close to (but not equal to) a.

The following example gives instances in which a stated limit does not exist.

Example 2 Limits Do Not Always Exist

Do the following limits exist?

a. $\lim_{x\to 0} \frac{1}{x^2}$ **b.** $\lim_{x\to 0} \frac{|x|}{x}$ **c.** $\lim_{x\to 2} \frac{1}{x-2}$

Solution

a. Here is a table of values for $f(x) = \frac{1}{x^2}$, with x approaching 0 from both sides.

x approaching 0 from the left → ← x approaching 0 from the right

x	−0.1	−0.01	−0.001	−0.0001	0	0.0001	0.001	0.01	0.1
$f(x) = \frac{1}{x^2}$	100	10,000	1,000,000	100,000,000		100,000,000	1,000,000	10,000	100

The table shows that as x gets closer to zero on either side, $f(x)$ gets larger and larger **without bound**—that is, if you name any number, no matter how large, $f(x)$ will be even larger than that if x is sufficiently close to 0. Because $f(x)$ is not approaching any real number, we conclude that $\lim_{x\to 0} \frac{1}{x^2}$ does not exist. Because $f(x)$ is becoming arbitrarily large, we also say that $\lim_{x\to 0} \frac{1}{x^2}$ **diverges to** $+\infty$, or just

$$\lim_{x\to 0} \frac{1}{x^2} = +\infty$$

Note This is not meant to imply that the limit exists; the symbol $+\infty$ does not represent any real number. We write $\lim_{x\to a} f(x) = +\infty$ to indicate two things: (1) the limit does not exist and (2) the function gets large without bound as x approaches a. ■

b. Here is a table of values for $f(x) = \frac{|x|}{x}$, with x approaching 0 from both sides.

x approaching 0 from the left → ← x approaching 0 from the right

x	−0.1	−0.01	−0.001	−0.0001	0	0.0001	0.001	0.01	0.1
$f(x) = \frac{\lvert x\rvert}{x}$	−1	−1	−1	−1		1	1	1	1

The table shows that $f(x)$ does not approach the same limit as x approaches 0 from both sides. There appear to be two *different* limits: the limit as we approach 0 from the left and the limit as we approach from the right. We write

$$\lim_{x\to 0^-} f(x) = -1$$

read as "the limit as x approaches 0 from the left (or from below) is −1" and

$$\lim_{x\to 0^+} f(x) = 1$$

read as "the limit as x approaches 0 from the right (or from above) is 1." These are called the **one-sided limits** of $f(x)$. In order for f to have a **two-sided limit**, the two one-sided limits must be equal. Because they are not, we conclude that $\lim_{x\to 0} f(x)$ does not exist.

c. Near $x = 2$, we have the following table of values for $f(x) = \dfrac{1}{x-2}$:

x approaching 2 from the left → ← x approaching 2 from the right

x	1.9	1.99	1.999	1.9999	2	2.0001	2.001	2.01	2.1
$f(x) = \dfrac{1}{x-2}$	−10	−100	−1000	−10,000		10,000	1000	100	10

Because $\dfrac{1}{x-2}$ is approaching no (single) real number as $x \to 2$, we see that $\lim_{x \to 2} \dfrac{1}{x-2}$ does not exist. Notice also that $\dfrac{1}{x-2}$ diverges to $+\infty$ as $x \to 2$ from the positive side (right half of the table) and to $-\infty$ as $x \to 2$ from the left (left half of the table). In other words,

$$\lim_{x \to 2^-} \frac{1}{x-2} = -\infty$$

$$\lim_{x \to 2^+} \frac{1}{x-2} = +\infty$$

$$\lim_{x \to 2} \frac{1}{x-2} \text{ does not exist}$$

In another useful kind of limit, we let x approach either $+\infty$ or $-\infty$, by which we mean that we let x get arbitrarily large or let x become an arbitrarily large negative number. The next example illustrates this.

Example 3 Limits at Infinity

Use a table to estimate: **a.** $\lim_{x \to +\infty} \dfrac{2x^2 - 4x}{x^2 - 1}$ and **b.** $\lim_{x \to -\infty} \dfrac{2x^2 - 4x}{x^2 - 1}$.

Solution

a. By saying that x is "approaching $+\infty$," we mean that x is getting larger and larger without bound, so we make the following table:

x approaching $+\infty$ →

x	10	100	1,000	10,000	100,000
$f(x) = \dfrac{2x^2 - 4x}{x^2 - 1}$	1.6162	1.9602	1.9960	1.9996	2.0000

(Note that we are only approaching $+\infty$ from the left because we can hardly approach it from the right!) What seems to be happening is that $f(x)$ is approaching 2. Thus we write

$$\lim_{x \to +\infty} f(x) = 2$$

b. Here, x is approaching $-\infty$, so we make a similar table, this time with x assuming negative values of greater and greater magnitude (read this table from right to left):

← x approaching $-\infty$

x	−100,000	−10,000	−1,000	−100	−10
$f(x) = \dfrac{2x^2 - 4x}{x^2 - 1}$	2.0000	2.0004	2.0040	2.0402	2.4242

Once again, $f(x)$ is approaching 2. Thus, $\lim_{x \to -\infty} f(x) = 2$.

Estimating Limits Graphically

We can often estimate a limit from a graph, as the next example shows.

Example 4 Estimating Limits Graphically

The graph of a function f is shown in Figure 1. (Recall that the solid dots indicate points on the graph, and the hollow dots indicate points not on the graph.)

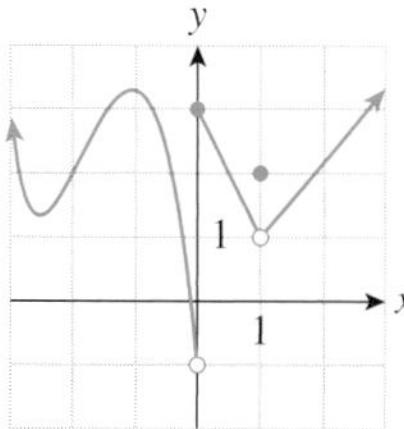

Figure **1**

From the graph, analyze the following limits.

a. $\lim_{x\to -2} f(x)$ **b.** $\lim_{x\to 0} f(x)$ **c.** $\lim_{x\to 1} f(x)$ **d.** $\lim_{x\to +\infty} f(x)$

Solution Since we are given only a graph of f, we must analyze these limits graphically.

a. Imagine that Figure 1 was drawn on a graphing calculator equipped with a trace feature that allows us to move a cursor along the graph and see the coordinates as we go. To simulate this, place a pencil point on the graph to the left of $x = -2$, and move it along the curve so that the x-coordinate approaches -2. (See Figure 2.) We evaluate the limit numerically by noting the behavior of the y-coordinates.*

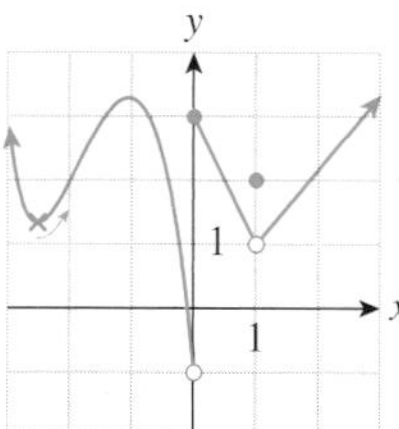

Figure **2**

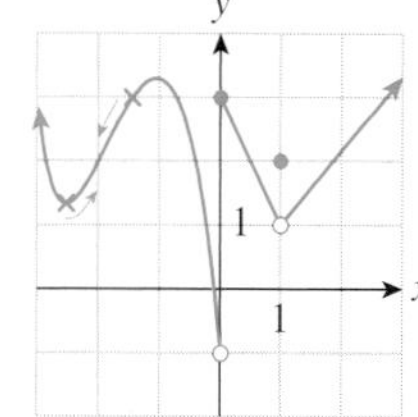

Figure **3**

However, we can see directly from the graph that the y-coordinate approaches 2. Similarly, if we place our pencil point to the right of $x = -2$ and move it to the left, the y-coordinate will approach 2 from that side as well (Figure 3). Therefore, as x approaches -2 from either side, $f(x)$ approaches 2, so

$$\lim_{x\to -2} f(x) = 2$$

b. This time we move our pencil point toward $x = 0$. Referring to Figure 4, if we start from the left of $x = 0$ and approach 0 (by moving right), the y-coordinate

*For a visual animation of this process, look at the online tutorial for this section.

approaches -1. However, if we start from the right of $x = 0$ and approach 0 (by moving left), the y-coordinate approaches 3. Thus (see Example 2),

$$\lim_{x \to 0^-} f(x) = -1$$

and

$$\lim_{x \to 0^+} f(x) = 3$$

Because these limits are not equal, we conclude that

$$\lim_{x \to 0} f(x) \text{ does not exist}$$

In this case there is a "break" in the graph at $x = 0$, and we say that the function is **discontinuous** at $x = 0$ (see Section 3.7).

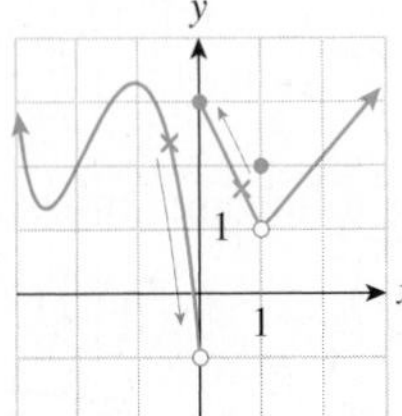

Figure 4

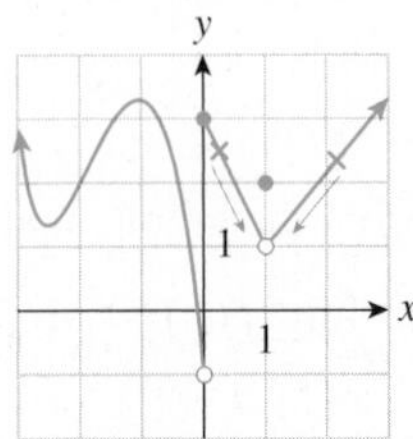

Figure 5

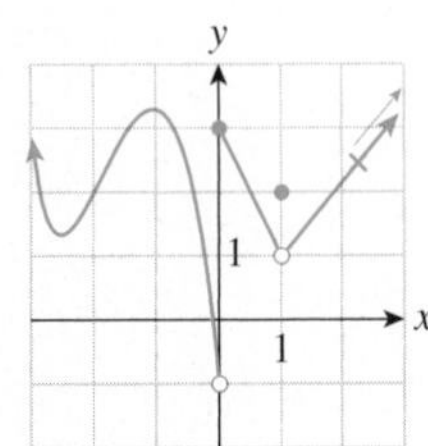

Figure 6

c. Once more we think about a pencil point moving along the graph with the x-coordinate this time approaching $x = 1$ from the left and from the right (Figure 5). As the x-coordinate of the point approaches 1 from either side, the y-coordinate approaches 1 also. Therefore,

$$\lim_{x \to 1} f(x) = 1$$

d. For this limit, x is supposed to approach infinity. We think about a pencil point moving along the graph further and further to the right as shown in Figure 6.

As the x-coordinate gets larger, the y-coordinate also gets larger and larger without bound. Thus, $f(x)$ diverges to $+\infty$:

$$\lim_{x \to +\infty} f(x) = +\infty$$

Similarly,

$$\lim_{x \to -\infty} f(x) = +\infty$$

+*Before we go on...* In Example 4(c) $\lim_{x \to 1} f(x) = 1$ but $f(1) = 2$ (why?). Thus, $\lim_{x \to 1} f(x) \neq f(1)$. In other words, the limit of $f(x)$ as x *approaches* 1 is not the same as the value of f at $x = 1$. Always keep in mind that when we evaluate a limit as $x \to a$, *we do not care about the value of the function at* $x = a$. We only care about the value of $f(x)$ as x *approaches* a. In other words, $f(a)$ may or may not equal $\lim_{x \to a} f(x)$. ■

Here is a summary of the graphical method we used in Example 4, together with some additional information:

Evaluating Limits Graphically

To decide whether $\lim_{x \to a} f(x)$ exists and to find its value if it does:

1. Draw the graph of $f(x)$ by hand or with graphing technology.
2. Position your pencil point (or the Trace cursor) on a point of the graph to the right of $x = a$.
3. Move the point *along the graph* toward $x = a$ from the right and read the y-coordinate as you go. The value the y-coordinate approaches (if any) is the limit $\lim_{x \to a^+} f(x)$.
4. Repeat Steps 2 and 3, this time starting from a point on the graph to the left of $x = a$, and approaching $x = a$ along the graph from the left. The value the y-coordinate approaches (if any) is $\lim_{x \to a^-} f(x)$.
5. If the left and right limits both exist and have the same value L, then $\lim_{x \to a} f(x) = L$. Otherwise, the limit does not exist. The value $f(a)$ has no relevance whatsoever.
6. To evaluate $\lim_{x \to +\infty} f(x)$, move the pencil point toward the far right of the graph and estimate the value the y-coordinate approaches (if any). For $\lim_{x \to -\infty} f(x)$, move the pencil point toward the far left.
7. If $x = a$ happens to be an endpoint of the domain of f, then only a one-sided limit is possible at $x = a$. For instance, if the domain is $(-\infty, 4]$, then $\lim_{x \to 4^-} f(x)$ can be computed, but not $\lim_{x \to 4} f(x)$ or $\lim_{x \to 4^+} f(x)$.

In the next example we use both the numerical and graphical approaches.

Example 5 Infinite Limit

Does $\lim\limits_{x \to 0^+} \dfrac{1}{x}$ exist?

Solution

Numerical Method Because we are asked for only the right-hand limit, we need only list values of x approaching 0 from the right.

← x approaching 0 from the right

x	0	0.0001	0.001	0.01	0.1
$f(x) = \dfrac{1}{x}$		10,000	1000	100	10

What seems to be happening as x approaches 0 from the right is that $f(x)$ is increasing without bound, as in Example 4(d). That is, if you name any number, no matter how large, $f(x)$ will be even larger than that if x is sufficiently close to zero. Thus, the limit diverges to $+\infty$, so

$$\lim_{x \to 0^+} \frac{1}{x} = +\infty$$

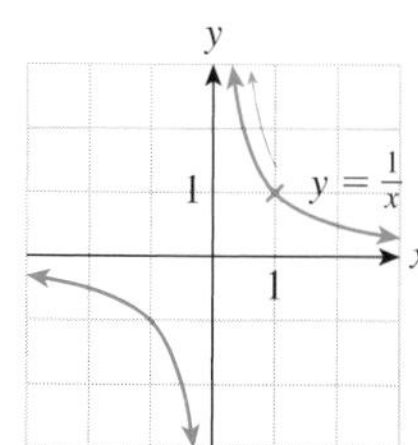

Figure 7

Graphical Method Recall that the graph of $f(x) = \dfrac{1}{x}$ is the standard hyperbola shown in Figure 7.

The figure also shows the pencil point moving so that its x-coordinate approaches 0 from the right. Because the point moves along the graph, it is forced to go higher and higher. In other words, its y-coordinate becomes larger and larger, approaching $+\infty$. Thus, we conclude that

$$\lim_{x\to 0^+} \frac{1}{x} = +\infty$$

+Before we go on... In Example 5(a) you should also check that

$$\lim_{x\to 0^-} \frac{1}{x} = -\infty$$

We say that as x approaches 0 from the left, $\frac{1}{x}$ diverges to $-\infty$. Also, check that

$$\lim_{x\to +\infty} \frac{1}{x} = \lim_{x\to -\infty} \frac{1}{x} = 0$$

■

Application

Example 6 Internet Connectivity

The number of U.S. households connected to the Internet can be modeled by*

$$N(t) = \frac{80}{1 + 2.2(3.68)^{-t}} \qquad (t \geq 0)$$

where t is time in years since 1999.

a. Estimate $\lim_{t\to +\infty} N(t)$ and interpret the answer.

b. Estimate $\lim_{t\to 0^+} N(t)$ and interpret the answer.

Solution

a. Figure 8 shows a plot of $N(t)$ for $0 < t < 10$:

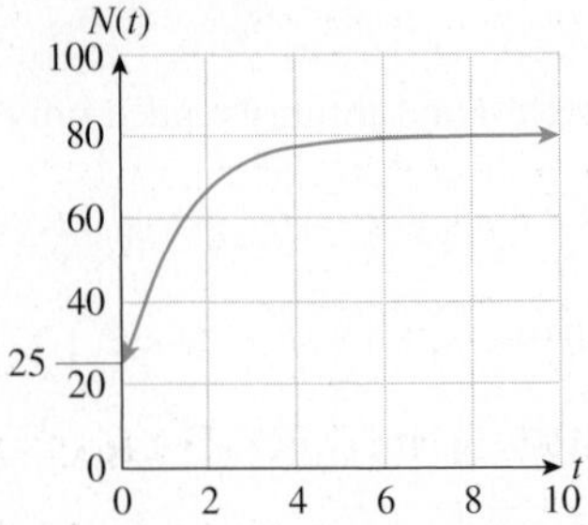

Using either the numerical or graphical approach, we find

$$\lim_{t\to +\infty} N(t) = \lim_{t\to +\infty} \frac{80}{1 + 2.2(3.68)^{-t}} = 80$$

Thus, in the long term (as t gets larger and larger) the percentage of U.S. households connected to the Internet is expected to approach 80%.

Figure **8**

b. The limit here is

$$\lim_{t\to 0^+} N(t) = \lim_{t\to 0^+} \frac{80}{1 + 2.2(3.68)^{-t}} = 25$$

(Notice that in this case, we can simply put $t = 0$ to evaluate this limit.) Thus, the closer t gets to 0 (representing 1999) the closer $N(t)$ gets to 25%, meaning that, in 1999, 25% of U.S. households were connected to the Internet.

* Based on a regression model by the authors. Sources for data: Telecommunications Reports International/ *New York Times,* May 21, 2001, p. C9.

FAQs Determining When a Limit Does or Does Not Exist

Q: If I substitute $x = a$ in the formula for a function and find that the function is not defined there, it means that $\lim_{x\to a} f(x)$ does not exist, right?

A: Wrong. The limit may still exist, as in Example 1, or may not exist, as in Example 2. In general, whether or not $\lim_{x\to a} f(x)$ exists has nothing to do with $f(a)$, but rather the value of f when x is *very close to, but not equal to a*. ■

Q: Is there a quick and easy way of telling from a graph whether $\lim_{x\to a} f(x)$ exists?

A: Yes. If you cover up the portion of the graph corresponding to $x = a$, and it appears as though the visible part of the graph could be made into a continuous line by filling in a suitable point at $x = a$, then the limit exists. (The "suitable point" need not be $(a, f(a))$.) Otherwise, it does not. Try this method with the curves in Example 4. ■

3.1 EXERCISES

● denotes basic skills exercises

◆ denotes challenging exercises

Estimate the limits in Exercises 1–18 numerically.

1. ● $\lim_{x\to 0} \dfrac{x^2}{x+1}$ *hint* [see Example 1]

2. ● $\lim_{x\to 0} \dfrac{x-3}{x-1}$

3. ● $\lim_{x\to 2} \dfrac{x^2-4}{x-2}$

4. ● $\lim_{x\to 2} \dfrac{x^2-1}{x-2}$

5. ● $\lim_{x\to -1} \dfrac{x^2+1}{x+1}$

6. ● $\lim_{x\to -1} \dfrac{x^2+2x+1}{x+1}$

7. ● $\lim_{x\to +\infty} \dfrac{3x^2+10x-1}{2x^2-5x}$ *hint* [see Example 3]

8. ● $\lim_{x\to +\infty} \dfrac{6x^2+5x+100}{3x^2-9}$

9. ● $\lim_{x\to -\infty} \dfrac{x^5-1,000x^4}{2x^5+10,000}$

10. ● $\lim_{x\to -\infty} \dfrac{x^6+3{,}000x^3+1{,}000{,}000}{2x^6+1{,}000x^3}$

11. ● $\lim_{x\to +\infty} \dfrac{10x^2+300x+1}{5x+2}$

12. ● $\lim_{x\to +\infty} \dfrac{2x^4+20x^3}{1{,}000x^6+6}$

13. ● $\lim_{x\to +\infty} \dfrac{10x^2+300x+1}{5x^3+2}$

14. ● $\lim_{x\to +\infty} \dfrac{2x^4+20x^3}{1{,}000x^3+6}$

15. ● $\lim_{x\to 2} e^{x-2}$

16. ● $\lim_{x\to +\infty} e^{-x}$

17. ● $\lim_{x\to +\infty} xe^{-x}$

18. ● $\lim_{x\to -\infty} xe^{x}$

In each of Exercises 19–30, the graph of f is given. Use the graph to compute the quantities asked for. *hint* [see Example 4]

19. ●

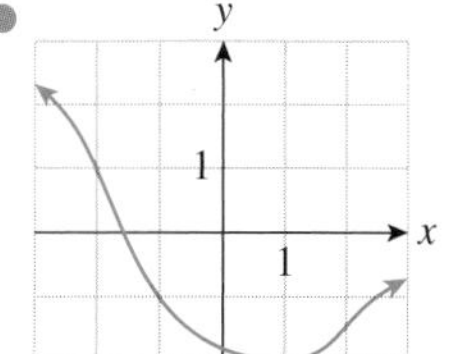

a. $\lim_{x\to 1} f(x)$ b. $\lim_{x\to -1} f(x)$

20. ●

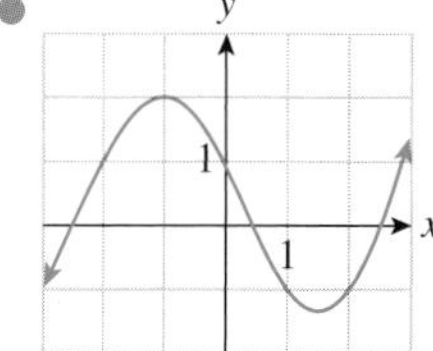

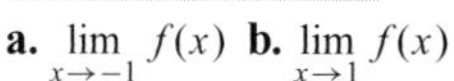

a. $\lim_{x\to -1} f(x)$ b. $\lim_{x\to 1} f(x)$

21. ●

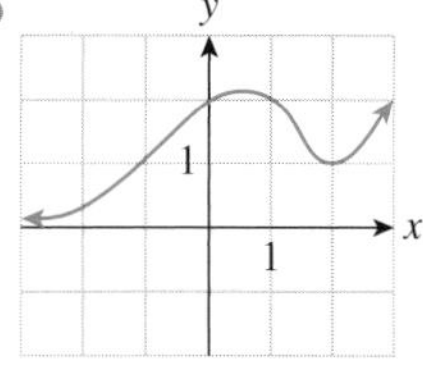

a. $\lim_{x\to 0} f(x)$ b. $\lim_{x\to 2} f(x)$

c. $\lim_{x\to -\infty} f(x)$ d. $\lim_{x\to +\infty} f(x)$

22. ●

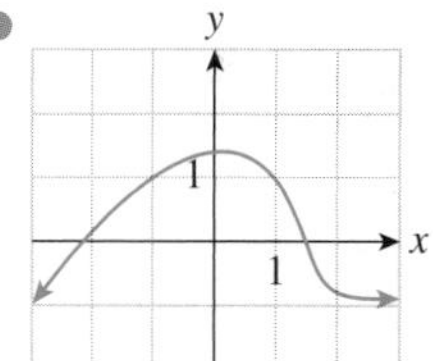

a. $\lim_{x\to -1} f(x)$ b. $\lim_{x\to 1} f(x)$

c. $\lim_{x\to +\infty} f(x)$ d. $\lim_{x\to -\infty} f(x)$

23. ●

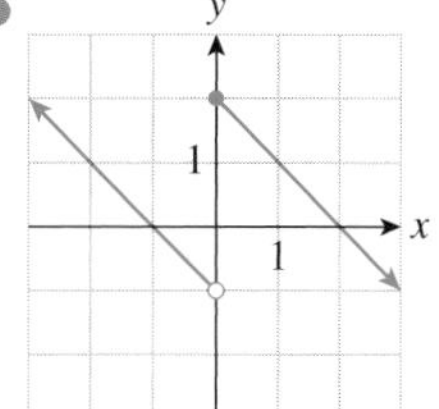

a. $\lim_{x\to 2} f(x)$ b. $\lim_{x\to 0^+} f(x)$

c. $\lim_{x\to 0^-} f(x)$ d. $\lim_{x\to 0} f(x)$

e. $f(0)$ f. $\lim_{x\to -\infty} f(x)$

24. ●

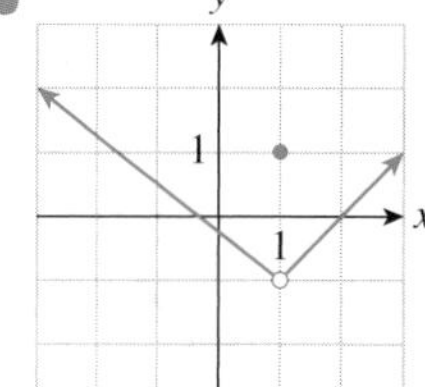

a. $\lim_{x\to 3} f(x)$ b. $\lim_{x\to 1^+} f(x)$

c. $\lim_{x\to 1^-} f(x)$ d. $\lim_{x\to 1} f(x)$

e. $f(1)$ f. $\lim_{x\to +\infty} f(x)$

25. ●

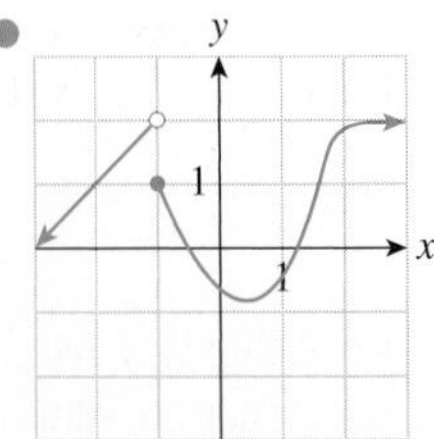

a. $\lim_{x\to -2} f(x)$ **b.** $\lim_{x\to -1^+} f(x)$
c. $\lim_{x\to -1^-} f(x)$ **d.** $\lim_{x\to -1} f(x)$
e. $f(-1)$ **f.** $\lim_{x\to +\infty} f(x)$

26. ●

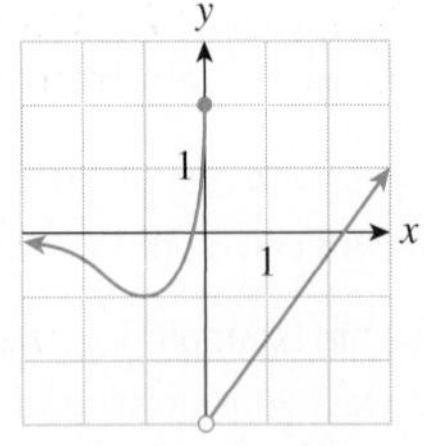

a. $\lim_{x\to -1} f(x)$ **b.** $\lim_{x\to 0^+} f(x)$
c. $\lim_{x\to 0^-} f(x)$ **d.** $\lim_{x\to 0} f(x)$
e. $f(0)$ **f.** $\lim_{x\to -\infty} f(x)$

27. ●

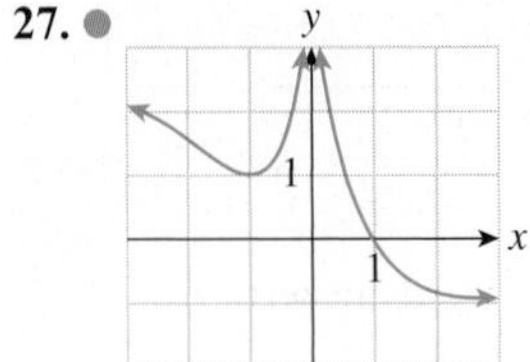

a. $\lim_{x\to -1} f(x)$ **b.** $\lim_{x\to 0^+} f(x)$
c. $\lim_{x\to 0^-} f(x)$ **d.** $\lim_{x\to 0} f(x)$
e. $f(0)$ **f.** $\lim_{x\to +\infty} f(x)$

28. ●

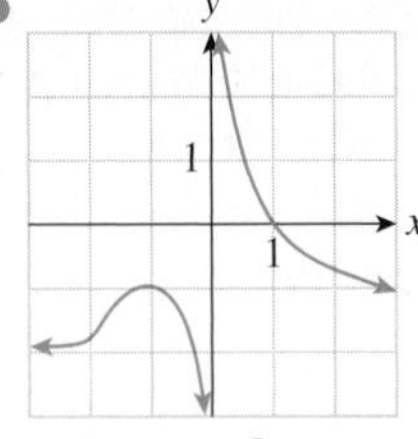

a. $\lim_{x\to 1} f(x)$ **b.** $\lim_{x\to 0^+} f(x)$
c. $\lim_{x\to 0^-} f(x)$ **d.** $\lim_{x\to 0} f(x)$
e. $f(0)$ **f.** $\lim_{x\to -\infty} f(x)$

29. ●

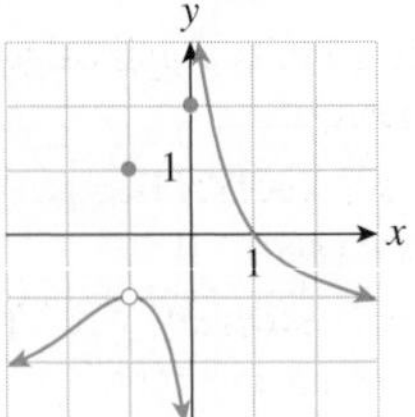

a. $\lim_{x\to -1} f(x)$ **b.** $\lim_{x\to 0^+} f(x)$
c. $\lim_{x\to 0^-} f(x)$ **d.** $\lim_{x\to 0} f(x)$
e. $f(0)$ **f.** $f(-1)$

30. ●

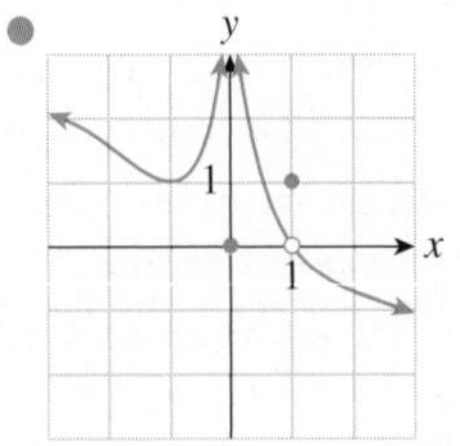

a. $\lim_{x\to 0^-} f(x)$ **b.** $\lim_{x\to 1^+} f(x)$
c. $\lim_{x\to 0} f(x)$ **d.** $\lim_{x\to 1} f(x)$
e. $f(0)$ **f.** $f(1)$

Applications

31. ● ***Scientific Research*** The number of research articles per year, in thousands, in the prominent journal *Physics Review* written by researchers in Europe can be modeled by

$$A(t) = \frac{7.0}{1 + 5.4(1.2)^{-t}}$$

where t is time in years ($t = 0$ represents 1983).[1] Estimate $\lim_{t\to +\infty} A(t)$ and interpret the answer. hint [see Example 6]

32. ● ***Scientific Research*** The percentage of research articles in the prominent journal *Physics Review* written by researchers in the U.S. can be modeled by

$$A(t) = 25 + \frac{36}{1 + 0.6(0.7)^{-t}}$$

where t is time in years ($t = 0$ represents 1983).[2] Estimate $\lim_{t\to +\infty} A(t)$ and interpret the answer.

33. ● ***SAT Scores by Income*** The following bar graph shows U.S. verbal SAT scores as a function of parents' income level:[3]

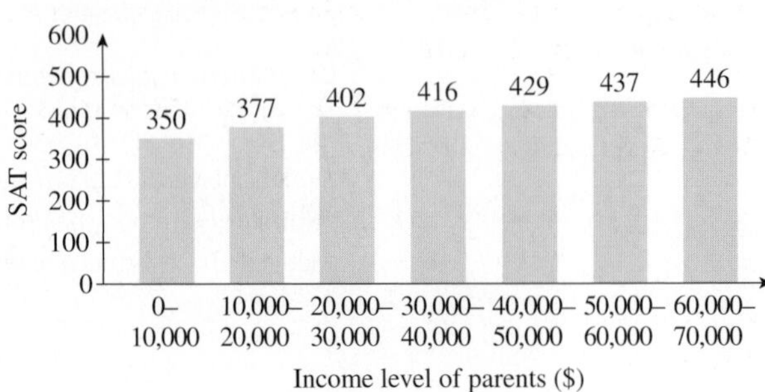

These data can be modeled by

$$S(x) = 470 - 136(0.974)^x$$

where $S(x)$ is the average SAT verbal score of a student whose parents' income is x thousand dollars per year. Evaluate $\lim_{x\to +\infty} S(x)$ and interpret the result.

34. ● ***SAT Scores by Income*** The following bar graph shows U.S. math SAT scores as a function of parents' income level:[4]

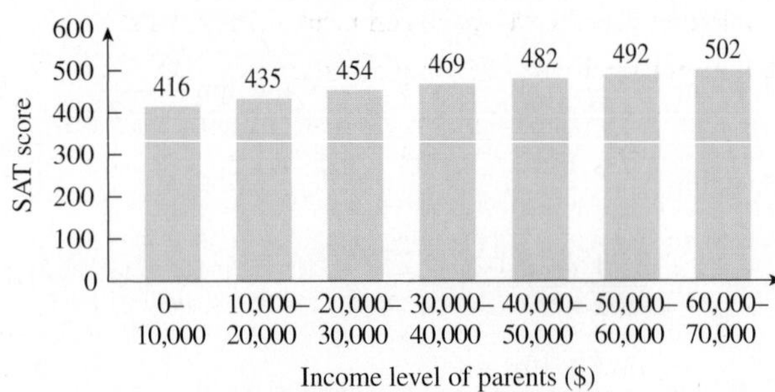

These data can be modeled by

$$S(x) = 535 - 136(0.979)^x$$

where $S(x)$ is the average math SAT score of a student whose parents' income is x thousand dollars per year. Evaluate $\lim_{x\to +\infty} S(x)$ and interpret the result.

35. ● ***Electric Rates*** The cost of electricity in Portland, Oregon, for residential customers increased suddenly on October 1, 2001, from around \$0.06 to around \$0.08 per kilowatt hour.[5]

---

[1] Based on data from 1983 to 2003. SOURCE: The American Physics Society/*New York Times*, May 3, 2003, p. A1.

[2] Based on data from 1983 to 2003. SOURCE: The American Physics Society/*New York Times*, May 3, 2003, p. A1.

[3] Based on 1994 data. SOURCE: The College Board/*New York Times*, March 5, 1995, p. E16.

[4] Ibid.

[5] SOURCE: Portland General Electric/*New York Times*, February 2, 2002, p. C1.

Let $C(t)$ be this cost at time t, and take $t = 1$ to represent October 1, 2001. What does the given information tell you about $\lim_{t\to 1} C(t)$? *hint* [see Example 4b]

36. ● ***Airline Stocks*** Prior to the September 11, 2001 attacks, United Airlines stock was trading at around \$35 per share. Immediately following the attacks, the share price dropped by \$15.[6] Let $U(t)$ be this cost at time t, and take $t = 11$ to represent September 11, 2001. What does the given information tell you about $\lim_{t\to 11} U(t)$?

Foreign Trade Annual U.S. imports from China in the years 1996 through 2003 could be approximated by

$$I(t) = t^2 + 3.5t + 50 \quad (1 \le t \le 9)$$

billion dollars, where t represents time in years since 1995. Annual U.S. exports to China in the same years could be approximated by

$$E(t) = 0.4t^2 - 1.6t + 14 \quad (0 \le t \le 10)$$

billion dollars.[7] Exercises 37 and 38 are based on these models.

37. Assuming the trends shown in the above models continue indefinitely, numerically estimate

$$\lim_{t\to+\infty} I(t) \text{ and } \lim_{t\to+\infty} \frac{I(t)}{E(t)}$$

interpret your answers, and comment on the results.

38. Repeat Exercise 37, this time calculating

$$\lim_{t\to+\infty} E(t) \text{ and } \lim_{t\to+\infty} \frac{E(t)}{I(t)}$$

39. ***Online Sales*** The following graph shows the approximate annual sales of books online in the U.S. for the period 1997–2004.[8]

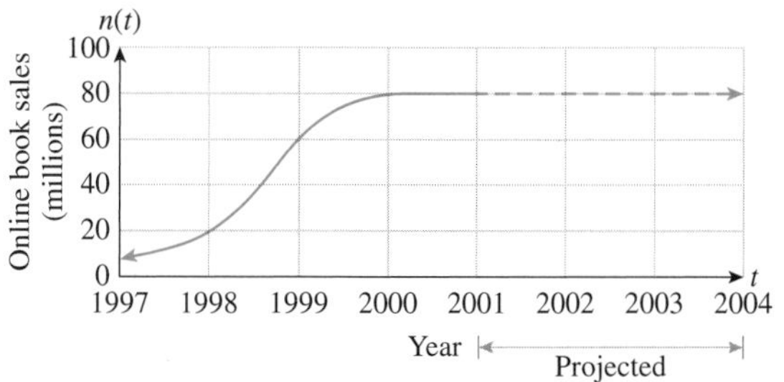

Estimate $\lim_{t\to+\infty} n(t)$ and interpret your answer.

40. ***Employment*** The following graph shows the number of new employees per year at Amerada Hess Corp. from 1984 ($t = 0$).[9]

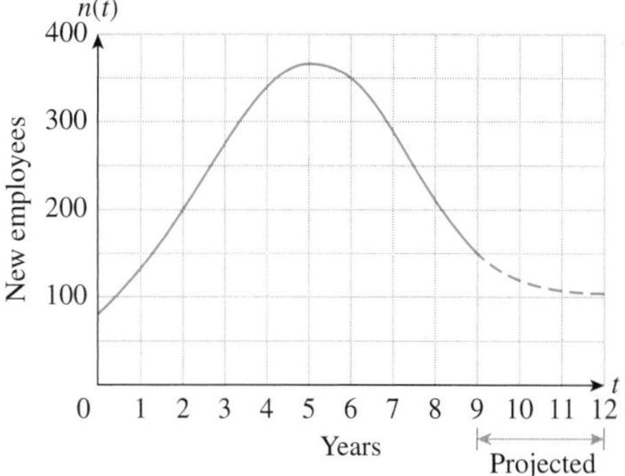

Estimate $\lim_{t\to+\infty} n(t)$ and interpret your answer.

Communication and Reasoning Exercises

41. ● Describe the method of evaluating limits numerically. Give at least one disadvantage of this method.

42. ● Describe the method of evaluating limits graphically. Give at least one disadvantage of this method.

43. What is wrong with the following statement? "Because $f(a)$ is not defined, $\lim_{x\to a} f(x)$ does not exist."

44. What is wrong with the following statement? "If $f(a)$ is defined, then $\lim_{x\to a} f(x)$ exists, and equals $f(a)$."

45. Your friend Dion, a business student, claims that the study of limits that do not exist is completely unrealistic and has nothing to do with the world of business. Give two examples from the world of business that might convince him that he is wrong.

46. If $D(t)$ is the Dow Jones Average at time t and $\lim_{t\to+\infty} D(t) = +\infty$, is it possible that the Dow will fluctuate indefinitely into the future?

47. ◆ Give an example of a function f with $\lim_{x\to 1} f(x) = f(2)$.

48. ◆ If $S(t)$ represents the size of the universe in billions of light years at time t years since the big bang and $\lim_{t\to+\infty} S(t) = 130{,}000$, is it possible that the universe will continue to expand forever?

[6] Stock prices are approximate.

[7] Based on quadratic regression using data from the U.S. Census Bureau Foreign Trade Division website www.census.gov/foreign-trade/sitc1/ as of December 2004.

[8] Source for 1997–2000 data: Ipsos-NPD Book Trends/*New York Times*, April 16, 2001, p. C1. (2001–2004 data were projections.)

[9] The projected part of the curve (from $t = 9$ on) is fictitious. The model is based on a best-fit logistic curve. Source for data: Hoover's Handbook Database (World Wide website), The Reference Press, Inc., Austin, Texas, 1995.

3.2 Limits and Continuity (OPTIONAL)

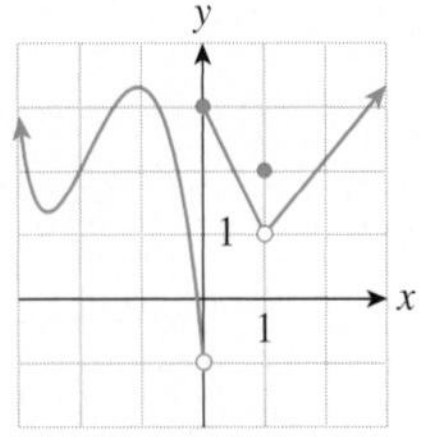

Figure 9

In Section 3.1 we saw examples of graphs that had various kinds of "breaks" or "jumps." For instance, in Example 4 we looked at the graph in Figure 9.

This graph appears to have breaks, or **discontinuities,** at $x = 0$ and at $x = 1$. At $x = 0$ we saw that $\lim_{x\to 0} f(x)$ does not exist because the left- and right-hand limits are not the same. Thus, the discontinuity at $x = 0$ seems to be due to the fact that the limit does not exist there. On the other hand, at $x = 1$, $\lim_{x\to 1} f(x)$ *does* exist (it is equal to 1), but is not equal to $f(1) = 2$.

Thus, we have identified two kinds of discontinuity:

(1) Points where the limit of the function does not exist. $x = 0$ in Figure 9 because $\lim_{x\to 0} f(x)$ does not exist.

(2) Points where the limit exists but does not equal the value of the function. $x = 1$ in Figure 9 because $\lim_{x\to 1} f(x) = 1 \neq f(1)$

On the other hand, there is no discontinuity at, say, $x = -2$, where we find that $\lim_{x\to -2} f(x)$ exists and equals 2 and $f(-2)$ is also equal to 2. In other words,

$$\lim_{x\to -2} f(x) = 2 = f(-2)$$

The point $x = -2$ is an example of a point where f is **continuous.** (Notice that you can draw the portion of the graph near $x = -2$ without lifting your pencil from the paper.) Similarly, f is continuous at *every* point other than $x = 0$ and $x = 1$. Here is the mathematical definition.

Continuous Function

Let f be a function and let a be a number in the domain of f. Then f is **continuous at** a if

a. $\lim_{x\to a} f(x)$ exists, and

b. $\lim_{x\to a} f(x) = f(a)$.

The function f is said to be **continuous on its domain** if it is continuous at each point in its domain.

If f is not continuous at a particular a in its domain, we say that f is **discontinuous** at a or that f has a **discontinuity** at a. Thus, a discontinuity can occur at $x = a$ if either

a. $\lim_{x\to a} f(x)$ does not exist, or

b. $\lim_{x\to a} f(x)$ exists but is not equal to $f(a)$.

quick Examples

1. The function shown in Figure 9 is continuous at $x = -1$ and $x = 2$. It is discontinuous at $x = 0$ and $x = 1$, and so is not continuous on its domain.
2. The function $f(x) = x^2$ is continuous on its domain. (Think of its graph, which contains no breaks.)
3. The function f whose graph is shown on the left in the following figure is continuous on its domain. (Although the graph breaks at $x = 2$, that is not a point of its domain.) The function g whose graph is shown on the right is not continuous on its

domain because it has a discontinuity at $x = 2$. (Here, $x = 2$ is a point of the domain of g.)

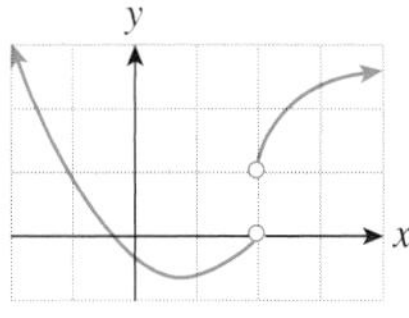

$y = f(x)$: Continuous on its domain

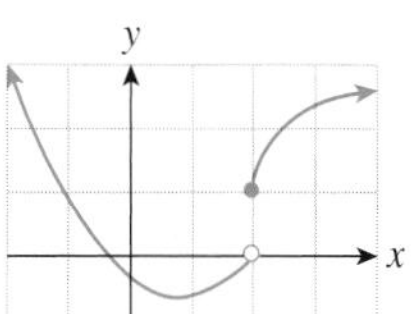

$y = g(x)$: Not continuous on its domain

Note If the number a is not in the domain of f—that is, if $f(a)$ is not defined—we will not consider the question of continuity at a. A function cannot be continuous at a point not in its domain, and it cannot be discontinuous there either. ■

Example 1 Continuous and Discontinuous Functions

Which of the following functions are continuous on their domains?

a. $h(x) = \begin{cases} x + 3 & \text{if } x \le 1 \\ 5 - x & \text{if } x > 1 \end{cases}$ **b.** $k(x) = \begin{cases} x + 3 & \text{if } x \le 1 \\ 1 - x & \text{if } x > 1 \end{cases}$

c. $f(x) = \dfrac{1}{x}$ **d.** $g(x) = \begin{cases} \frac{1}{x} & \text{if } x \neq 0 \\ 0 & \text{if } x = 0 \end{cases}$

Solution

a. and **b.** The graphs of h and k are shown in Figure 10.

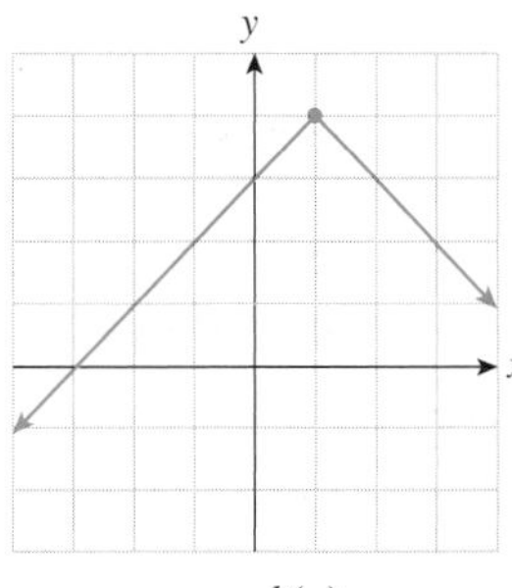

$y = h(x)$

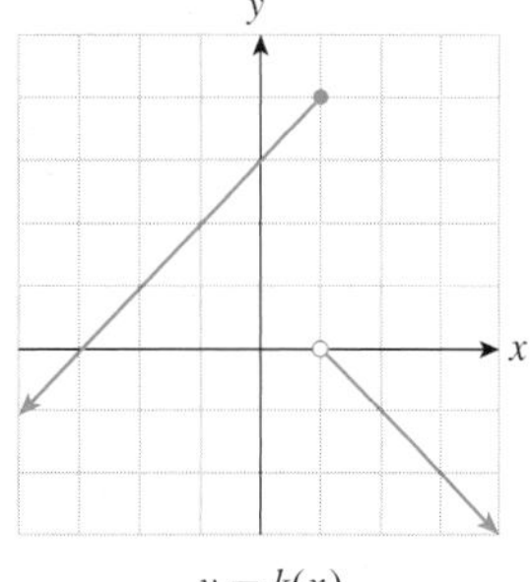

$y = k(x)$

Figure **10**

Even though the graph of h is made up of two different line segments, it is continuous at every point of its domain, including $x = 1$ because

$$\lim_{x \to 1} h(x) = 4 = h(1)$$

On the other hand, $x = 1$ is also in the domain of k, but $\lim_{x\to 1} k(x)$ does not exist. Thus, k is discontinuous at $x = 1$ and thus not continuous on its domain.

c. and **d.** The graphs of f and g are shown in Figure 11.

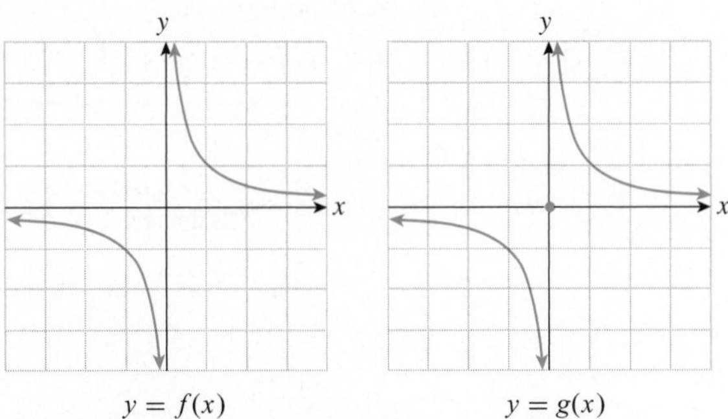

Figure **11**

The domain of f consists of all real numbers except 0 and f is continuous at all such numbers. (Notice that 0 is not in the domain of f, so the question of continuity at 0 does not arise.) Thus, f is continuous on its domain.

The function g, on the other hand, has its domain expanded to include 0, so we now need to check whether g is continuous at 0. From the graph, it is easy to see that g is discontinuous there because $\lim_{x\to 0} g(x)$ does not exist. Thus, g is not continuous on its domain because it is discontinuous at 0.

+Before we go on...

Q: *Wait a minute! How can a function like $f(x) = 1/x$ be continuous when its graph has a break in it?*

A: We are not claiming that f is continuous *at every real number.* What we are saying is that f is continuous *on its domain;* the break in the graph occurs at a point not in the domain of f. In other words, f is continuous on the set of all nonzero real numbers; it is not continuous on the set of *all* real numbers because it is not even defined on the set. ■

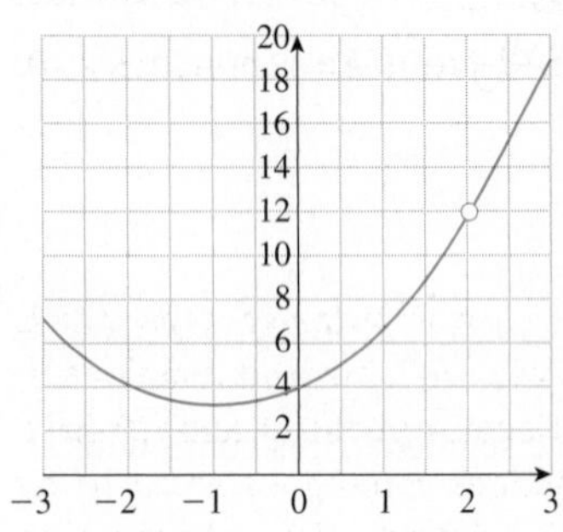

Figure **12**

Example 2 Continuous Except at a Point

In each case, say what, if any, value of $f(a)$ would make f continuous at a.

a. $f(x) = \dfrac{x^3 - 8}{x - 2}$; $a = 2$ **b.** $f(x) = \dfrac{e^{2x} - 1}{x}$; $a = 0$ **c.** $f(x) = \dfrac{|x|}{x}$; $a = 0$

Solution

a. In Figure 12 we see the graph of $f(x) = \dfrac{x^3 - 8}{x - 2}$. The point corresponding to $x = 2$ is missing because f is not (yet) defined there. (Your graphing utility will probably miss this subtlety and render a continuous curve.)

To turn f into a function that is continuous at $x = 2$, we need to "fill in the gap" so as to obtain a continuous curve. Since the graph suggests that the missing point is (2, 12), let us define $f(2) = 12$.

Does f now become continuous if we take $f(2) = 12$? From the graph, or Example 1(a) of Section 3.1,

$$\lim_{x\to 2} f(x) = \lim_{x\to 2} \frac{x^3 - 8}{x - 2} = 12$$

which is now equal to $f(2)$. Thus, $\lim_{x\to 2} f(x) = f(2)$, showing that f is now continuous at $x = 2$.

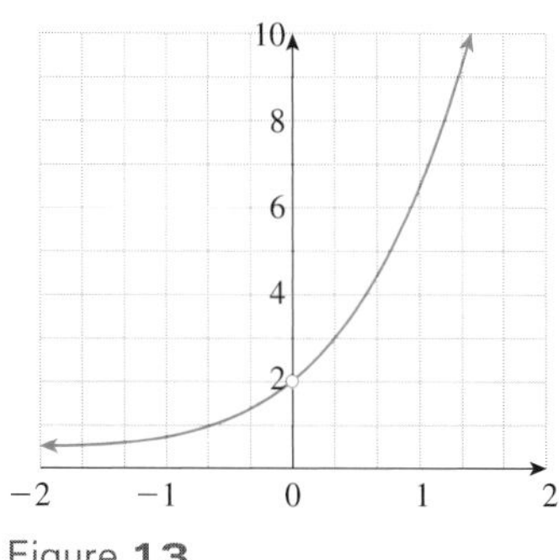

Figure **13**

b. In Example 1(b) of the preceding section, we saw that

$$\lim_{x\to 0} f(x) = \lim_{x\to 0} \frac{e^{2x} - 1}{x} = 2$$

and so, as in part (a), we must define $f(0) = 2$. This is confirmed by the graph shown in Figure 13.

c. We considered the function $f(x) = |x|/x$ in Example 2 in Section 3.1. Its graph is shown in Figure 14.

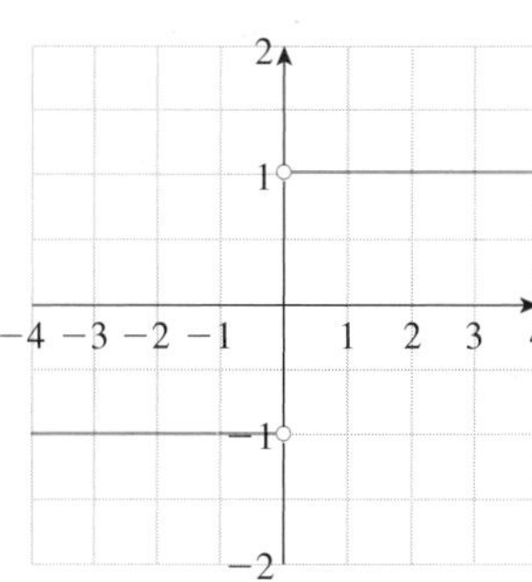

Figure **14**

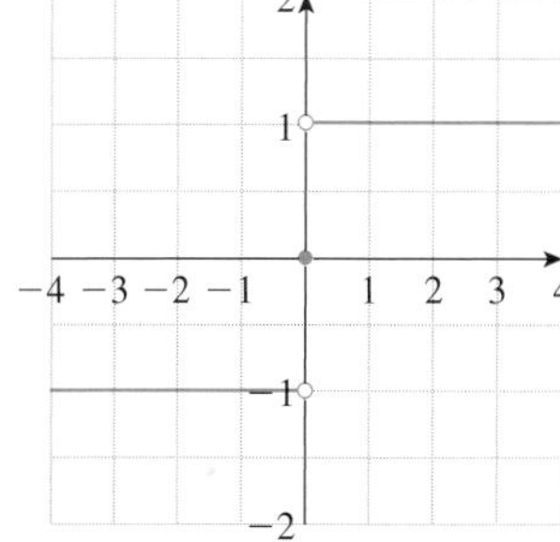

Figure **15**

Now we encounter a problem: No matter how we try to fill in the gap at $x = 0$, the result will be a discontinuous function. For example, setting $f(0) = 0$ will result in the discontinuous function shown in Figure 15.

We conclude that it is impossible to assign any value to $f(0)$ to turn f into a function that is continuous at $x = 0$.

We can also see this result algebraically: In Example 2 of Section 3.1, we saw that $\lim_{x\to 0} \frac{|x|}{x}$ does not exist. Thus, the resulting function will fail to be continuous at 0, no matter how we define $f(0)$.

A function not defined at an isolated point is said to have a **singularity** at that point. The function in part (a) of Example 2 has a singularity at $x = 2$, and the functions in parts (b) and (c) have singularities at $x = 0$. The functions in parts (a) and (b) have *removable* singularities because we can make these functions continuous at $x = a$ by properly defining $f(a)$. The function in part (c) has an **essential singularity** because we cannot make f continuous at $x = a$ just by defining $f(a)$ properly.

3.2 EXERCISES

● denotes basic skills exercises

In Exercises 1–12, the graph of a function f is given. Determine whether f is continuous on its domain. If it is not continuous on its domain, say why. hint [see Quick Examples p. 196]

1. ●

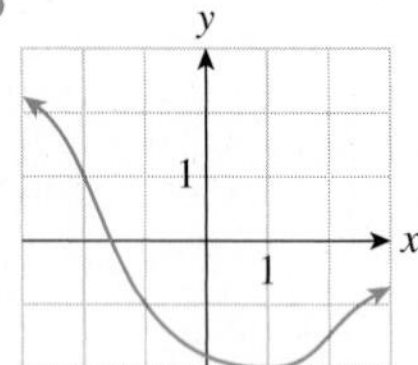

2. ●

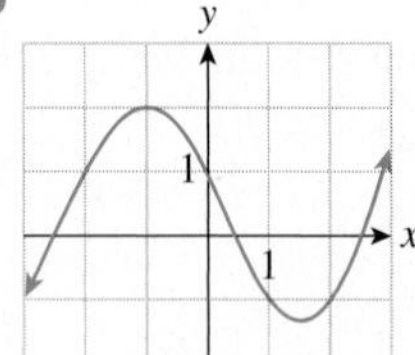

3. ●

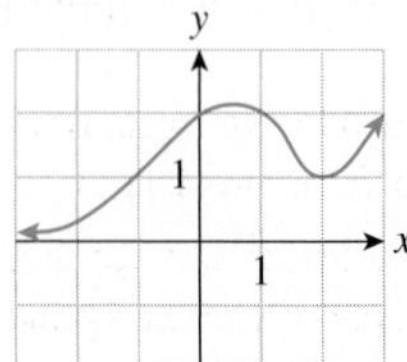

4. ●

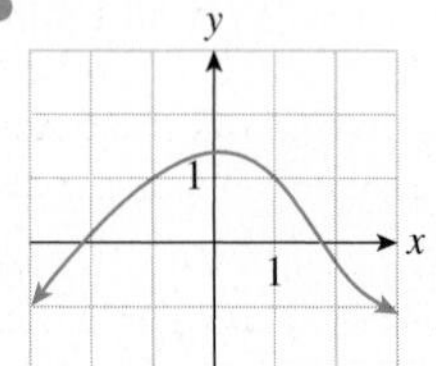

5. ●

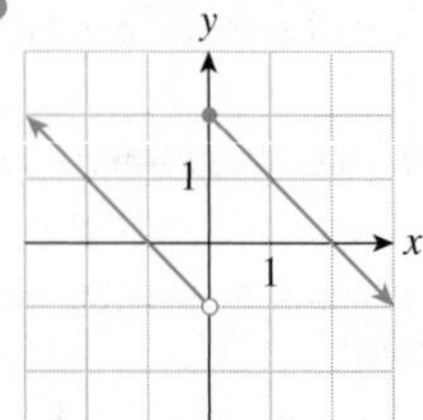

6. ●

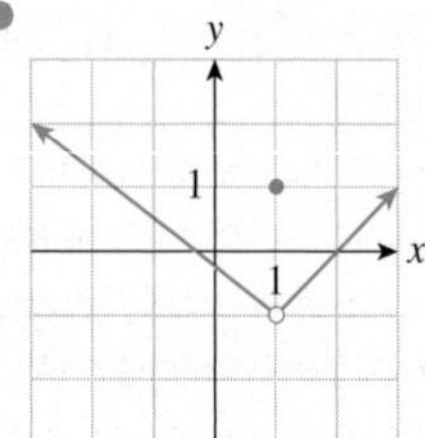

7. ●

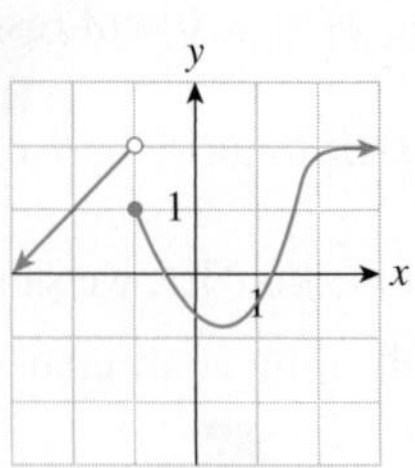

8. ●

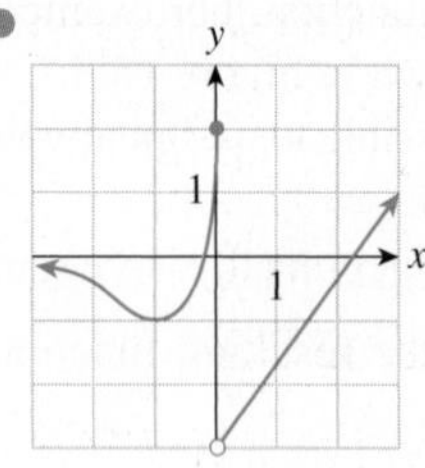

9. ●

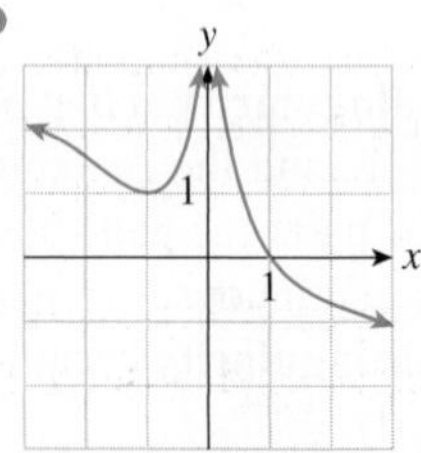

10. ●

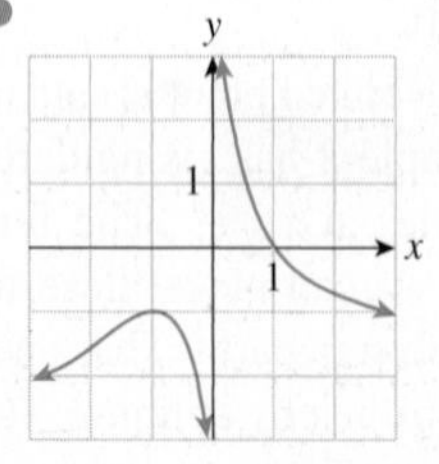

11. ●

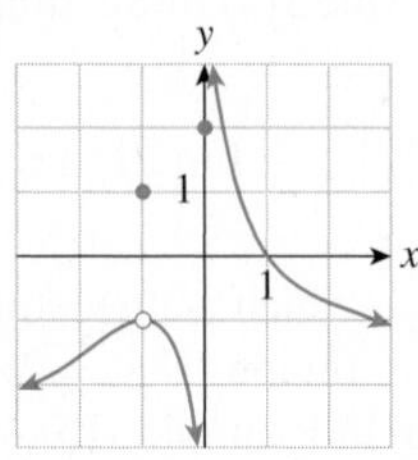

12. ●

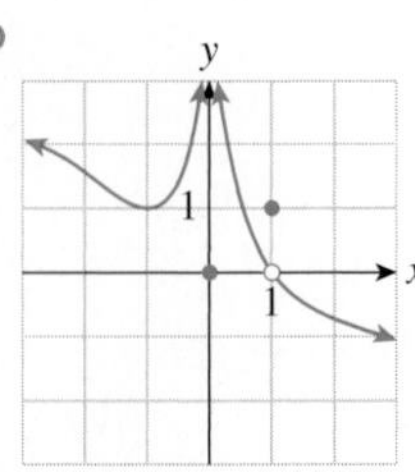

In Exercises 13 and 14, identify which (if any) of the given graphs represent functions continuous on their domains. hint [see Example 1]

13. ●

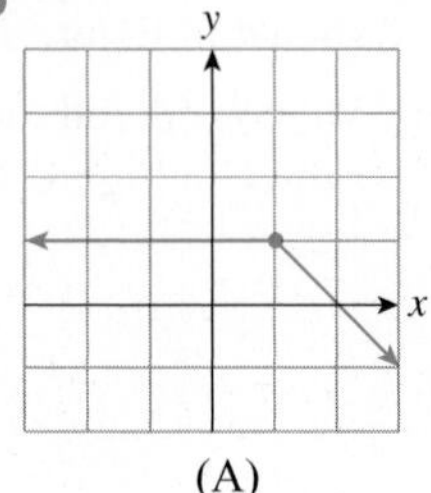

(A)

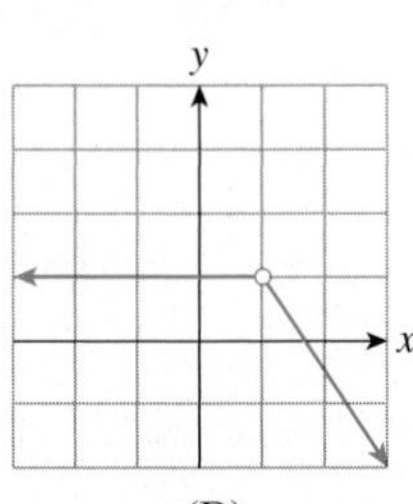

(B)

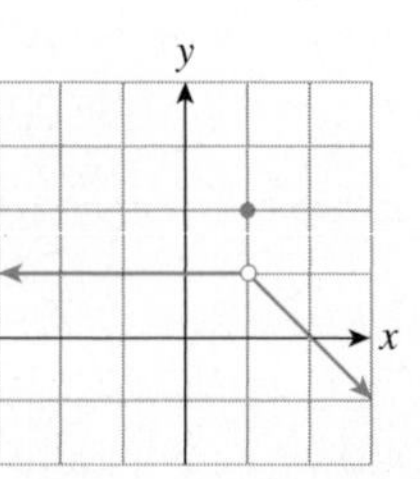

(C)

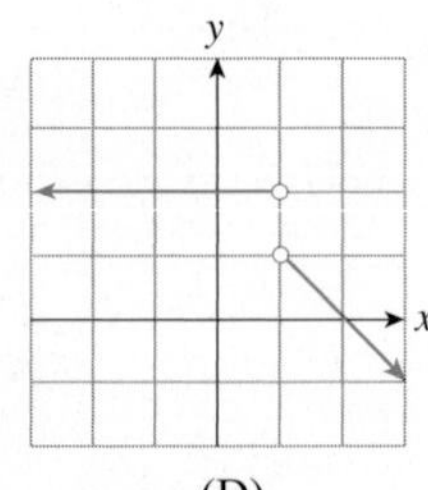

(D)

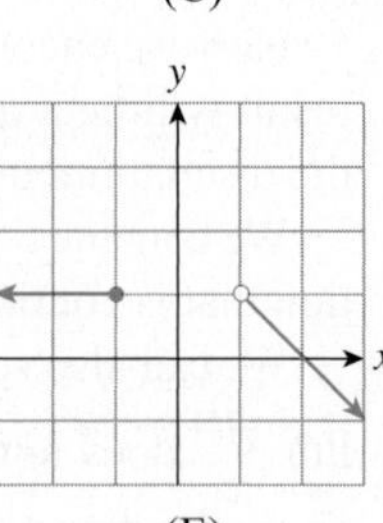

(E)

14. ●

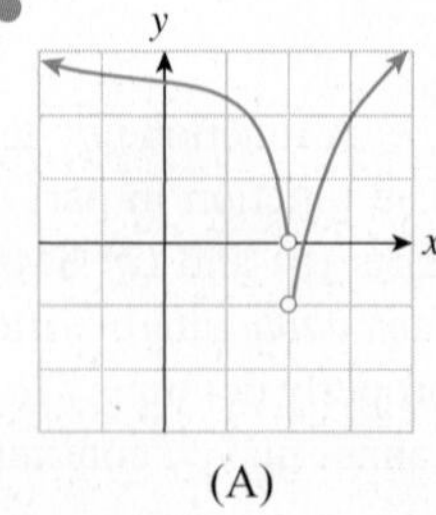

(A)

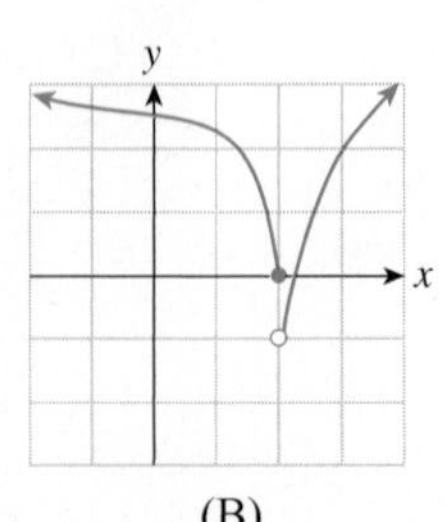

(B)

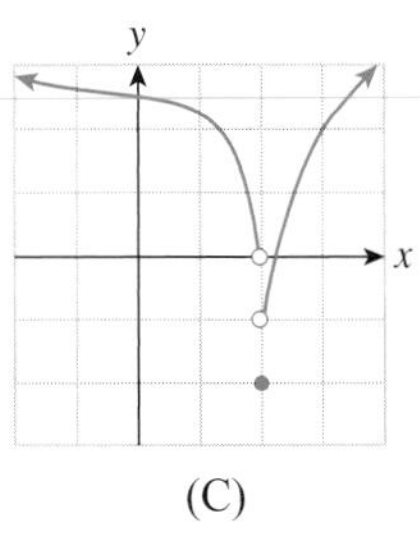

(C)

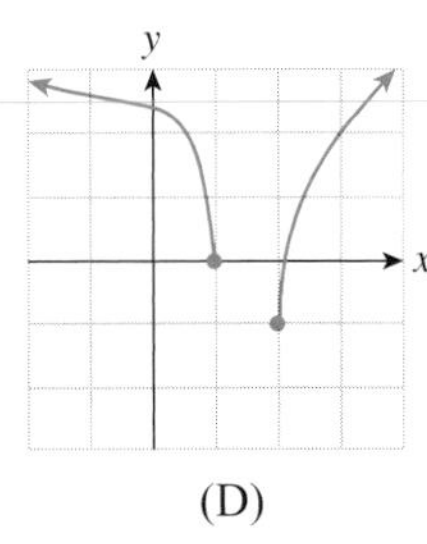

(D)

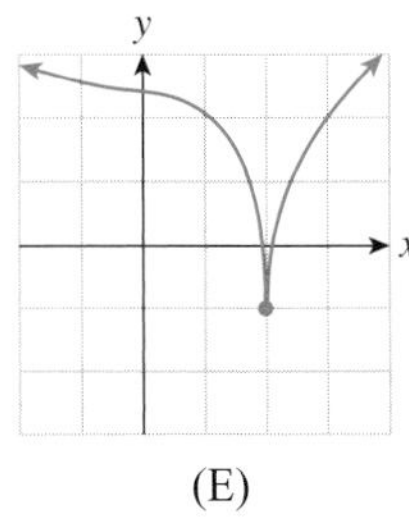

(E)

In Exercises 15–22, use a graph of f or some other method to determine what, if any, value to assign to $f(a)$ to make f continuous at $x = a$.

15. ● $f(x) = \dfrac{x^2 - 2x + 1}{x - 1}$; $a = 1$ *hint* [see Example 2]

16. ● $f(x) = \dfrac{x^2 + 3x + 2}{x + 1}$; $a = -1$

17. ● $f(x) = \dfrac{x}{3x^2 - x}$; $a = 0$

18. ● $f(x) = \dfrac{x^2 - 3x}{x + 4}$; $a = -4$

19. ● $f(x) = \dfrac{3}{3x^2 - x}$; $a = 0$

20. ● $f(x) = \dfrac{x - 1}{x^3 - 1}$; $a = 1$

21. ● $f(x) = \dfrac{1 - e^x}{x}$; $a = 0$

22. ● $f(x) = \dfrac{1 + e^x}{1 - e^x}$; $a = 0$

In Exercises 23–32, use a graph to determine whether the given function is continuous on its domain. If it is not continuous on its domain, list the points of discontinuity.

23. ● $f(x) = |x|$

24. ● $f(x) = \dfrac{|x|}{x}$

25. ● $g(x) = \dfrac{1}{x^2 - 1}$

26. ● $g(x) = \dfrac{x - 1}{x + 2}$

27. ● $f(x) = \begin{cases} x + 2 & \text{if } x < 0 \\ 2x - 1 & \text{if } x \geq 0 \end{cases}$

28. ● $f(x) = \begin{cases} 1 - x & \text{if } x \leq 1 \\ x - 1 & \text{if } x > 1 \end{cases}$

29. ● $h(x) = \begin{cases} \frac{|x|}{x} & \text{if } x \neq 0 \\ 0 & \text{if } x = 0 \end{cases}$

30. ● $h(x) = \begin{cases} \frac{1}{x^2} & \text{if } x \neq 0 \\ 2 & \text{if } x = 0 \end{cases}$

31. ● $g(x) = \begin{cases} x + 2 & \text{if } x < 0 \\ 2x + 2 & \text{if } x \geq 0 \end{cases}$

32. ● $g(x) = \begin{cases} 1 - x & \text{if } x \leq 1 \\ x + 1 & \text{if } x > 1 \end{cases}$

Communication and Reasoning Exercises

33. ● If a function is continuous on its domain, is it continuous at every real number? Explain.

34. ● True or false: The graph of a function that is continuous on its domain is a continuous curve with no breaks in it.

35. ● True or false: The graph of a function that is continuous at every real number is a continuous curve with no breaks in it.

36. Give an example of a function that is not continuous at $x = -1$ but is not discontinuous there either.

37. Draw the graph of a function that is discontinuous at every integer.

38. Draw the graph of a function that is continuous on its domain but not continuous at any integer,

39. Describe a real-life scenario in the stock market that can be modeled by a discontinuous function.

40. Describe a real-life scenario in your room that can be modeled by a discontinuous function.

● basic skills

3.3 Limits and Continuity: Algebraic Approach (OPTIONAL)

Although numerical and graphical estimation of limits is effective, the estimates these methods yield may not be perfectly accurate. The algebraic method, when it can be used, will always yield an exact answer. Moreover, algebraic analysis of a function often enables us to take a function apart and see "what makes it tick."

Let's start with the function $f(x) = 2 + x$ and ask: What happens to $f(x)$ as x approaches 3? To answer this algebraically, notice that as x gets closer and closer to 3, the quantity $2 + x$ must get closer and closer to $2 + 3 = 5$. Hence,

$$\lim_{x\to 3} f(x) = \lim_{x\to 3}(2 + x) = 2 + 3 = 5$$

Q: *Is that all there is to the algebraic method? Just substitute $x = a$?*

A: Under certain circumstances: Notice that by substituting $x = 3$ we *evaluated the function at* $x = 3$. In other words, we relied on the fact that

$$\lim_{x \to 3} f(x) = f(3)$$

In Section 3.2 we said that a function satisfying this equation is *continuous* at $x = 3$. ■

Thus,

If we know that the function f is continuous at a point a, we can compute $\lim_{x \to a} f(x)$ *by simply substituting* $x = a$ *into* $f(x)$.

To use this fact, we need to know how to recognize continuous functions when we see them. Geometrically, they are easy to spot: A function is continuous at $x = a$ if its graph has no break at $x = a$. Algebraically, a large class of functions are known to be continuous on their domains—those, roughly speaking, that are *specified by a single formula*.

We can be more precise: A **closed-form function** is any function that can be obtained by combining constants, powers of x, exponential functions, radicals, logarithms, and trigonometric functions (and some other functions we do not encounter in this text) into a *single* mathematical formula by means of the usual arithmetic operations and composition of functions. (They can be as complicated as we like.)

Closed-Form Functions

A **closed-form function** is any function that can be obtained by combining constants, powers of x, exponential functions, radicals, logarithms, and trigonometric functions (and some other functions we do not encounter in this text) into a *single* mathematical formula by means of the usual arithmetic operations and composition of functions.

quick **Examples**

1. $3x^2 - x + 1$, $\dfrac{\sqrt{x^2 - 1}}{6x - 1}$, $e^{\frac{-4x^2-1}{x}}$, and $\sqrt{\log_3(x^2 - 1)}$ are all closed form functions.

2. $f(x) = \begin{cases} -1 & \text{if } x \le -1 \\ x^2 + x & \text{if } -1 < x \le 1 \\ 2 - x & \text{if } 1 < x \le 2 \end{cases}$ is *not* a closed-form function because $f(x)$ is not specified by a *single* mathematical formula.

What is so special about closed-form functions is the following theorem:

Theorem: Continuity of Closed-Form Functions

Every closed-form function is continuous on its domain. Thus, if f is a closed-form function and $f(a)$ is defined, we have $\lim_{x \to a} f(x) = f(a)$.

quick **Example**

$f(x) = 1/x$ is a closed-form function, and its natural domain consists of all real numbers except 0. Thus, f is continuous at every nonzero real number. That is,

$$\lim_{x \to a} \frac{1}{x} = \frac{1}{a}$$

provided $a \neq 0$.

Mathematics majors spend a great deal of time studying the proof of this theorem. We ask you to accept it without proof.

Example 1 Limit of a Closed-Form Function

Evaluate $\lim_{x\to 1} \frac{x^3-8}{x-2}$ algebraically.

Solution

First, notice that $(x^3-8)/(x-2)$ is a closed-form function because it is specified by a single algebraic formula. Also, $x = 1$ is in the domain of this function. Therefore,

$$\lim_{x\to 1} \frac{x^3-8}{x-2} = \frac{1^3-8}{1-2} = 7$$

+*Before we go on...* In Example 1, the point $x = 2$ is not in the domain of the function $(x^3-8)/(x-2)$, so we cannot evaluate $\lim_{x\to 2} \frac{x^3-8}{x-2}$ by substituting $x = 2$. However—and this is the key to finding such limits—some preliminary algebraic simplification will allow us to obtain a closed-form function with $x = 2$ in its domain, as we shall see in Example 2. ■

Example 2 Simplifying to Obtain the Limit

Evaluate $\lim_{x\to 2} \frac{x^3-8}{x-2}$ algebraically.

Solution

Again, although $(x^3-8)/(x-2)$ is a closed-form function, $x = 2$ is not in its domain. Thus, we cannot obtain the limit by substitution. Instead, we first simplify $f(x)$ to obtain a new function with $x = 2$ in its domain. To do this, notice first that the numerator can be factored as

$$x^3 - 8 = (x-2)(x^2+2x+4)$$

Thus,

$$\frac{x^3-8}{x-2} = \frac{(x-2)(x^2+2x+4)}{x-2} = x^2+2x+4$$

Once we have canceled the offending $(x-2)$ in the denominator, we are left with a closed-form function *with 2 in its domain*. Thus,

$$\begin{aligned}\lim_{x\to 2} \frac{x^3-8}{x-2} &= \lim_{x\to 2}(x^2+2x+4) \\ &= 2^2 + 2(2) + 4 = 12 \quad \text{Substitute } x = 2.\end{aligned}$$

This confirms the answer we found numerically in Example 1 in Section 3.1.

If the given function fails to simplify, we can always approximate the limit numerically. It may very well be that the limit does not exist in such a case.

Q: There is something suspicious about Example 2. If 2 was not in the domain before simplifying but was in the domain after simplifying, we must have changed the function, right?

A: Correct. In fact, when we said that

$$\frac{x^3 - 8}{x - 2} = x^2 + 2x + 4$$

Domain excludes 2 Domain includes 2

we were lying a little bit. What we really meant is that these two expressions are equal *where both are defined.* The functions $(x^3 - 8)/(x - 2)$ and $x^2 + 2x + 4$ are different functions. The difference is that $x = 2$ is not in the domain of $(x^3 - 8)/(x - 2)$ and is in the domain of $x^2 + 2x + 4$. Since $\lim_{x \to 2} f(x)$ explicitly *ignores* any value that f may have at 2, this does not affect the limit. From the point of view of the limit at 2, these functions *are* equal. In general we have the following rule. ■

Functions with Equal Limits

If $f(x) = g(x)$ for all x except possibly $x = a$, then

$$\lim_{x \to a} f(x) = \lim_{x \to a} g(x).$$

quick Example

$$\frac{x^2 - 1}{x - 1} = x + 1 \text{ for all } x \text{ except } x = 1. \quad \text{Write } \frac{x^2 - 1}{x - 1} \text{ as } \frac{(x+1)(x-1)}{x - 1} \text{ and cancel the } (x - 1).$$

Therefore,

$$\lim_{x \to 1} \frac{x^2 - 1}{x - 1} = \lim_{x \to 1} (x + 1) = 1 + 1 = 2$$

We can also use algebraic techniques to analyze functions that are not given in closed form.

Example 3 Nonclosed-Form Function

For which values of x are the following piecewise defined functions continuous?

a. $f(x) = \begin{cases} x^2 + 2 & \text{if } x < 1 \\ 2x - 1 & \text{if } x \ge 1 \end{cases}$ **b.** $g(x) = \begin{cases} x^2 - x + 1 & \text{if } x \le 0 \\ 1 - x & \text{if } 0 < x \le 1 \\ x - 3 & \text{if } x > 1 \end{cases}$

Solution

a. The function $f(x)$ is given in closed form over the intervals $(-\infty, 1)$ and $[1, +\infty)$. At $x = 1$, $f(x)$ suddenly switches from one closed-form formula to another, so $x = 1$ is the only place where there is a potential problem with continuity. To investigate the continuity of $f(x)$ at $x = 1$, let's calculate the limit there:

$$\begin{aligned} \lim_{x \to 1^-} f(x) &= \lim_{x \to 1^-} (x^2 + 2) && f(x) = x^2 + 2 \text{ for } x < 1. \\ &= (1)^2 + 2 = 3 && x^2 + 2 \text{ is closed-form.} \\ \lim_{x \to 1^+} f(x) &= \lim_{x \to 1^+} (2x - 1) && f(x) = 2x - 1 \text{ for } x > 1. \\ &= 2(1) - 1 = 1 && 2x - 1 \text{ is closed-form.} \end{aligned}$$

Because the left and right limits are different, $\lim_{x\to 1} f(x)$ does not exist, and so $f(x)$ is discontinuous at $x = 1$.

b. The only potential points of discontinuity for $g(x)$ occur at $x = 0$ and $x = 1$:

$$\lim_{x\to 0^-} g(x) = \lim_{x\to 0^-} x^2 - x + 1 = 1$$

$$\lim_{x\to 0^+} g(x) = \lim_{x\to 0^+} 1 - x = 1$$

Thus, $\lim_{x\to 0} g(x) = 1$. Further, $g(0) = 0^2 - 0 + 1 = 1$ from the formula, and so

$$\lim_{x\to 0} g(x) = g(0)$$

which shows that $g(x)$ is continuous at $x = 0$. At $x = 1$ we have

$$\lim_{x\to 1^-} g(x) = \lim_{x\to 1^-} 1 - x = 0$$

$$\lim_{x\to 1^+} g(x) = \lim_{x\to 1^+} x - 3 = -2$$

so that $\lim_{x\to 1} g(x)$ does not exist. Thus, $g(x)$ is discontinuous at $x = 1$. We conclude that $g(x)$ is continuous at every real number x except $x = 1$.

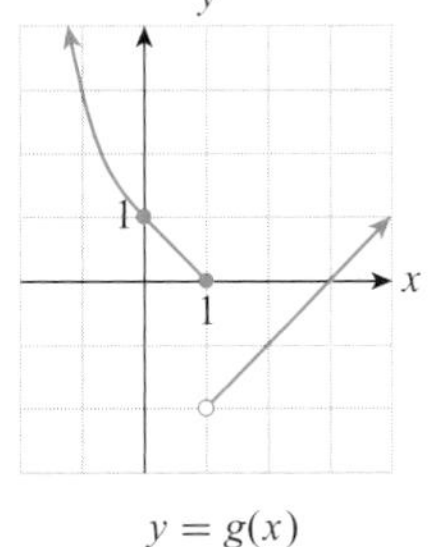

$y = g(x)$

Figure **16**

+*Before we go on...* Figure 16 shows the graph of g from Example 3(b). Notice how the discontinuity at $x = 1$ shows up as a break in the graph, whereas at $x = 0$ the two pieces "fit together" at the point (0, 1). ■

Limits at Infinity

Let's look once again at Example 3 in Section 3.1 and some similar limits.

Example **4** Limits at Infinity

Compute the following limits, if they exist:

a. $\lim_{x\to +\infty} \frac{2x^2 - 4x}{x^2 - 1}$ **b.** $\lim_{x\to -\infty} \frac{2x^2 - 4x}{x^2 - 1}$

c. $\lim_{x\to +\infty} \frac{-x^3 - 4x}{2x^2 - 1}$ **d.** $\lim_{x\to +\infty} \frac{2x^2 - 4x}{5x^3 - 3x + 5}$

Solution

a. and **b.** While calculating the values for the tables used in Example 3 in Section 3.1, you might have noticed that the highest power of x in both the numerator and denominator dominated the calculations. For instance, when $x = 100{,}000$, the term $2x^2$ in the numerator has the value of 20,000,000,000, whereas the term $4x$ has the comparatively insignificant value of 400,000. Similarly, the term x^2 in the denominator overwhelms the term -1. In other words, for large values of x (or negative values with large magnitude),

$$\frac{2x^2 - 4x}{x^2 - 1} \approx \frac{2x^2}{x^2} \quad \text{Use only the highest powers top \& bottom.}$$

$$= 2$$

Therefore,

$$\lim_{x\to \pm\infty} \frac{2x^2 - 4x}{x^2 - 1} = 2$$

The procedure of using only the highest powers of x to compute the limit is stated formally and justified after this example.

c. Applying the above technique of looking only at highest powers gives

$$\frac{-x^3-4x}{2x^2-1} \approx \frac{-x^3}{2x^2} \quad \text{Use only the highest powers top \& bottom.}$$

$$= \frac{-x}{2} \quad \text{Simplify.}$$

As x gets large, $-x/2$ gets large and negative, so

$$\lim_{x\to+\infty} \frac{-x^3-4x}{2x^2-1} = -\infty$$

d. $\frac{2x^2-4x}{5x^3-3x+5} \approx \frac{2x^2}{5x^3} = \frac{2}{5x}$. As x gets large, $2/(5x)$ gets close to zero, so

$$\lim_{x\to+\infty} \frac{2x^2-4x}{5x^3-3x+5} = 0$$

Let's look again at the limits (a) and (b) in Example 4. We say that the graph of f has a **horizontal asymptote** at $y = 2$ because of the limits we have just calculated. This means that the graph approaches the horizontal line $y = 2$ far to the right or left (in this case, to both the right and left). Figure 17 shows the graph of f together with the line $y = 2$.

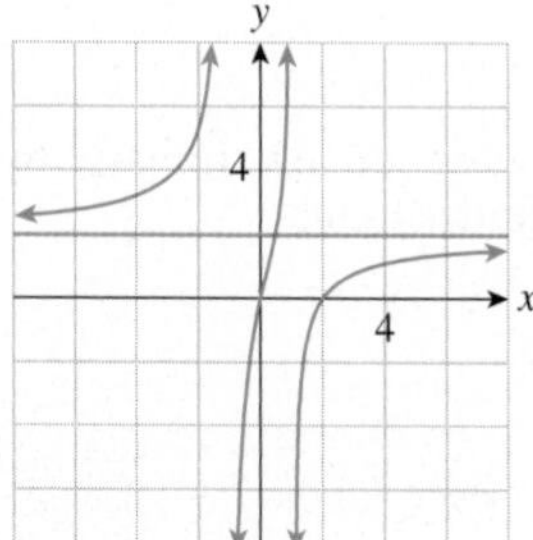

Figure 17

The graph reveals some additional interesting information: as $x \to 1^+$, $f(x) \to -\infty$, and as $x \to 1^-$, $f(x) \to +\infty$. Thus,

$$\lim_{x\to 1} f(x) \text{ does not exist}$$

See if you can determine what happens as $x \to -1$.

If you graph the function in part (d) of Example 4, you will again see a horizontal asymptote at $y = 0$. Does the limit in part (c) show a horizontal asymptote?

In Example 4, $f(x)$ was a **rational function:** a quotient of polynomial functions. We calculated the limit of $f(x)$ at $\pm\infty$ by ignoring all powers of x in both the numerator and denominator except for the largest. Following is a theorem that justifies this procedure:

Theorem: Evaluating the Limit of a Rational Function at ±∞

If $f(x)$ has the form

$$f(x) = \frac{c_n x^n + c_{n-1}x^{n-1} + \cdots + c_1 x + c_0}{d_m x^m + d_{m-1}x^{m-1} \cdots + d_1 x + d_0}$$

with the c_i and d_i constants ($c_n \neq 0$ and $d_m \neq 0$), then we can calculate the limit of $f(x)$ as $x \to \pm\infty$ by ignoring all powers of x except the highest in both the numerator and denominator. Thus,

$$\lim_{x\to\pm\infty} f(x) = \lim_{x\to\pm\infty} \frac{c_n x^n}{d_m x^m}$$

quick **Examples** (See Example 4)

1. $\lim_{x\to+\infty} \frac{2x^2-4x}{x^2-1} = \lim_{x\to+\infty} \frac{2x^2}{x^2} = \lim_{x\to+\infty} 2 = 2$

2. $\displaystyle\lim_{x\to+\infty} \frac{-x^3-4x}{2x^2-1} = \lim_{x\to+\infty} \frac{-x^3}{2x^2} = \lim_{x\to+\infty} \frac{-x}{2} = -\infty$

3. $\displaystyle\lim_{x\to+\infty} \frac{2x^2-4x}{5x^3-3x+5} = \lim_{x\to+\infty} \frac{2x^2}{5x^3} = \lim_{x\to+\infty} \frac{2}{5x} = 0$

Proof Our function $f(x)$ is a polynomial of degree n divided by a polynomial of degree m. If n happens to be larger than m, then dividing the top and bottom by the largest power x^n of x gives

$$f(x) = \frac{c_n x^n + c_{n-1}x^{n-1} + \cdots + c_1 x + c_0}{d_m x^m + d_{m-1}x^{m-1} \cdots + d_1 x + d_0}$$

$$= \frac{c_n x^n/x^n + c_{n-1}x^{n-1}/x^n + \cdots + c_1 x/x^n + c_0/x^n}{d_m x^m/x^n + d_{m-1}x^{m-1}/x^n + \cdots + d_1 x/x^n + d_0/x^n}$$

Canceling powers of x in each term and remembering that $n > m$ leaves us with

$$f(x) = \frac{c_n + c_{n-1}/x + \cdots + c_1/x^{n-1} + c_0/x^n}{d_m/x^{n-m} + d_{m-1}/x^{n-m+1} + \cdots + d_1/x^{n-1} + d_0/x^n}$$

As $x \to \pm\infty$, all the terms shown in red approach 0, so we can ignore them in taking the limit. (The first term in the denominator happens to approach zero as well, but we retain it for convenience.) Thus,

$$\lim_{x\to\pm\infty} f(x) = \lim_{x\to\pm\infty} \frac{c_n}{d_m/x^{n-m}} = \lim_{x\to\pm\infty} \frac{c_n x^n}{d_m x^m}$$

as required. The cases when n is smaller than m and $m = n$ are proved similarly by dividing top and bottom by the largest power of x in each case.

FAQs Strategy for Evaluating Limits Algebraically

Q: *Is there a systematic way to evaluate a limit $\lim_{x\to a} f(x)$ algebraically?*

A: The following approach is often successful:

Case 1: a Is a Finite Number (Not $\pm\infty$)

1. Decide whether f is a closed-form function. If it is not, then find the left and right limits at the values of x where the function changes from one formula to another.

2. If f is a closed-form function, try substituting $x = a$ in the formula for $f(x)$. Then one of three things will happen:

$f(a)$ is defined. Then $\lim_{x\to a} f(x) = f(a)$.

$f(a)$ is not defined and has the form 0/0. Try to simplify the expression for f to cancel one of the terms that gives 0.

$f(a)$ is not defined and has the form $k/0$ where k is not zero. Then the function diverges to $\pm\infty$ as x approaches a from each side. Check this graphically, as in Example 4 (see "Before we go on").

Case 2: $a = \pm\infty$

If the given function is a polynomial or ratio of polynomials, use the technique of Example 4: Focus only on the highest powers of x. ■

There is another technique for evaluating certain difficult limits, called *L'Hospital's Rule,* but this uses derivatives, so we'll have to wait to discuss it until Section 3.7.

3.3 EXERCISES

● denotes basic skills exercises

In Exercises 1–4 complete the given sentence.

1. ● The closed-form function $f(x) = \frac{1}{x-1}$ is continuous for all x except ______. hint [see Quick Example p. 202]

2. ● The closed-form function $f(x) = \frac{1}{x^2-1}$ is continuous for all x except _______.

3. ● The closed-form function $f(x) = \sqrt{x+1}$ has $x = 3$ in its domain. Therefore, $\lim_{x\to 3}\sqrt{x+1} =$ ___. hint [see Example 1]

4. ● The closed-form function $f(x) = \sqrt{x-1}$ has $x = 10$ in its domain. Therefore, $\lim_{x\to 10}\sqrt{x-1} =$ ___.

Calculate the limits in Exercises 5–42 algebraically. If a limit does not exist, say why. hint [see Example 1]

5. ● $\lim_{x\to 0}(x+1)$

6. ● $\lim_{x\to 0}(2x-4)$

7. ● $\lim_{x\to 2}\frac{2+x}{x}$

8. ● $\lim_{x\to -1}\frac{4x^2+1}{x}$

9. ● $\lim_{x\to -1}\frac{x+1}{x}$

10. ● $\lim_{x\to 4}(x+\sqrt{x})$

11. ● $\lim_{x\to 8}(x-\sqrt[3]{x})$

12. ● $\lim_{x\to 1}\frac{x-2}{x+1}$

13. ● $\lim_{h\to 1}(h^2+2h+1)$

14. ● $\lim_{h\to 0}(h^3-4)$

15. ● $\lim_{h\to 3}2$

16. ● $\lim_{h\to 0}-5$

17. ● $\lim_{h\to 0}\frac{h^2}{h+h^2}$ hint [see Example 2]

18. ● $\lim_{h\to 0}\frac{h^2+h}{h^2+2h}$

19. ● $\lim_{x\to 1}\frac{x^2-2x+1}{x^2-x}$

20. ● $\lim_{x\to -1}\frac{x^2+3x+2}{x^2+x}$

21. ● $\lim_{x\to 2}\frac{x^3-8}{x-2}$

22. ● $\lim_{x\to -2}\frac{x^3+8}{x^2+3x+2}$

23. ● $\lim_{x\to 0^+}\frac{1}{x^2}$

24. ● $\lim_{x\to 0^+}\frac{1}{x^2-x}$

25. ● $\lim_{x\to -1}\frac{x^2+1}{x+1}$

26. ● $\lim_{x\to -1^-}\frac{x^2+1}{x+1}$

27. ● $\lim_{x\to +\infty}\frac{3x^2+10x-1}{2x^2-5x}$ hint [see Example 4]

28. ● $\lim_{x\to +\infty}\frac{6x^2+5x+100}{3x^2-9}$

29. ● $\lim_{x\to +\infty}\frac{x^5-1000x^4}{2x^5+10{,}000}$

30. ● $\lim_{x\to +\infty}\frac{x^6+3000x^3+1{,}000{,}000}{2x^6+1000x^3}$

31. ● $\lim_{x\to +\infty}\frac{10x^2+300x+1}{5x+2}$

32. ● $\lim_{x\to +\infty}\frac{2x^4+20x^3}{1000x^3+6}$

33. ● $\lim_{x\to +\infty}\frac{10x^2+300x+1}{5x^3+2}$

34. ● $\lim_{x\to +\infty}\frac{2x^4+20x^3}{1000x^6+6}$

35. ● $\lim_{x\to -\infty}\frac{3x^2+10x-1}{2x^2-5x}$

36. ● $\lim_{x\to -\infty}\frac{6x^2+5x+100}{3x^2-9}$

37. ● $\lim_{x\to -\infty}\frac{x^5-1000x^4}{2x^5+10{,}000}$

38. ● $\lim_{x\to -\infty}\frac{x^6+3000x^3+1{,}000{,}000}{2x^6+1000x^3}$

39. ● $\lim_{x\to -\infty}\frac{10x^2+300x+1}{5x+2}$

40. ● $\lim_{x\to -\infty}\frac{2x^4+20x^3}{1000x^3+6}$

41. ● $\lim_{x\to -\infty}\frac{10x^2+300x+1}{5x^3+2}$

42. ● $\lim_{x\to -\infty}\frac{2x^4+20x^3}{1000x^6+6}$

In each of Exercises 43–50, find all points of discontinuity of the given function. hint [see Example 3]

43. ● $f(x) = \begin{cases} x+2 & \text{if } x < 0 \\ 2x-1 & \text{if } x \geq 0 \end{cases}$

44. ● $g(x) = \begin{cases} 1-x & \text{if } x \leq 1 \\ x-1 & \text{if } x > 1 \end{cases}$

45. ● $g(x) = \begin{cases} x+2 & \text{if } x < 0 \\ 2x+2 & \text{if } 0 \leq x < 2 \\ x^2+2 & \text{if } x \geq 2 \end{cases}$

46. ● $f(x) = \begin{cases} 1-x & \text{if } x \leq 1 \\ x+2 & \text{if } 1 < x < 3 \\ x^2-4 & \text{if } x \geq 3 \end{cases}$

47. $h(x) = \begin{cases} x+2 & \text{if } x < 0 \\ 0 & \text{if } x = 0 \\ 2x+2 & \text{if } x > 0 \end{cases}$

48. $h(x) = \begin{cases} 1-x & \text{if } x < 1 \\ 1 & \text{if } x = 1 \\ x+2 & \text{if } x > 1 \end{cases}$

49. $f(x) = \begin{cases} 1/x & \text{if } x < 0 \\ x & \text{if } 0 \leq x \leq 2 \\ 2^{x-1} & \text{if } x > 2 \end{cases}$

50. $f(x) = \begin{cases} x^3+2 & \text{if } x \leq -1 \\ x^2 & \text{if } -1 < x < 0 \\ x & \text{if } x \geq 0 \end{cases}$

Applications

51. ● ***Movie Advertising*** Movie expenditures, in billions of dollars, on advertising in newspapers from 1995 to 2004 could be approximated by

$$f(t) = \begin{cases} 0.04t + 0.33 & \text{if } t \le 4 \\ -0.01t + 1.2 & \text{if } t > 4 \end{cases}$$

where t is time in years since 1995.[10]

a. Compute $\lim_{t\to 4^-} f(t)$ and $\lim_{t\to 4^+} f(t)$, and interpret each answer.

b. Is the function f continuous at $t = 4$? What does the answer tell you about movie advertising expenditures? *hint* [see Example 3]

52. ● ***Movie Advertising*** The percentage of movie advertising as a share of newspapers' total advertising revenue from 1995 to 2004 could be approximated by

$$p(t) = \begin{cases} -0.07t + 6.0 & \text{if } t \le 4 \\ 0.3t + 17.0 & \text{if } t > 4 \end{cases}$$

where t is time in years since 1995.[11]

a. Compute $\lim_{t\to 4^-} p(t)$ and $\lim_{t\to 4^+} p(t)$, and interpret each answer.

b. Is the function p continuous at $t = 4$? What does the answer tell you about newspaper revenues?

53. ● ***Law Enforcement*** The cost of fighting crime in the U.S. increased steadily in the period 1982–1999. Total spending on police and courts can be approximated, respectively, by[12]

$$P(t) = 1.745t + 29.84 \text{ billion dollars} \quad (2 \le t \le 19)$$
$$C(t) = 1.097t + 10.65 \text{ billion dollars} \quad (2 \le t \le 19)$$

where t is time in years since 1980. Compute $\lim_{t\to+\infty} \dfrac{P(t)}{C(t)}$ to two decimal places and interpret the result. *hint* [see Example 4]

54. ***Law Enforcement*** Refer to Exercise 53. Total spending on police, courts, and prisons can be approximated, respectively, by[13]

$$P(t) = 1.745t + 29.84 \text{ billion dollars} \quad (2 \le t \le 19)$$
$$C(t) = 1.097t + 10.65 \text{ billion dollars} \quad (2 \le t \le 19)$$
$$J(t) = 1.919x + 12.36 \text{ billion dollars} \quad (2 \le t \le 19)$$

where t is time in years since 1980. Compute $\lim_{t\to+\infty} \dfrac{P(t)}{P(t) + C(t) + J(t)}$ to two decimal places and interpret the result.

Foreign Trade Annual U.S. imports from China in the years 1996 through 2003 could be approximated by

$$I(t) = t^2 + 3.5t + 50 \quad (1 \le t \le 8)$$

billion dollars, where t represents time in years since 1995. Annual U.S. exports to China in the same years could be approximated by

$$E(t) = 0.4t^2 + 1.6t + 14 \quad (0 \le t \le 10)$$

billion dollars.[14] Exercises 55 and 56 are based on these models.

55. Assuming that the trends shown in the above models continue indefinitely, calculate the limits

$$\lim_{t\to+\infty} I(t) \quad \text{and} \quad \lim_{t\to+\infty} \frac{I(t)}{E(t)}$$

algebraically, interpret your answers, and comment on the results.

56. Repeat Exercise 55, this time calculating

$$\lim_{t\to+\infty} E(t) \quad \text{and} \quad \lim_{t\to+\infty} \frac{E(t)}{I(t)}$$

57. ***Acquisition of Language*** The percentage $p(t)$ of children who can speak in at least single words by the age of t months can be approximated by the equation[15]

$$p(t) = 100\left(1 - \frac{12{,}200}{t^{4.48}}\right) \quad (t \ge 8.5)$$

Calculate $\lim_{t\to+\infty} p(t)$ and interpret the result.

58. ***Acquisition of Language*** The percentage $q(t)$ of children who can speak in sentences of five or more words by the age of t months can be approximated by the equation[16]

$$q(t) = 100\left(1 - \frac{5.27 \times 10^{17}}{t^{12}}\right) \quad (t \ge 30)$$

If p is the function referred to in the preceding exercise, calculate $\lim_{t\to+\infty}[p(t) - q(t)]$ and interpret the result.

59. ***Television Advertising*** The cost, in millions of dollars, of a 30-second television ad during Super Bowls from 1990 to 2001 can be approximated by the following piecewise linear function ($t = 0$ represents 1990):[17]

$$C(t) = \begin{cases} 0.08t + 0.6 & \text{if } 0 \le t < 8 \\ 0.355t - 1.6 & \text{if } 8 \le t \le 11 \end{cases}$$

Is C a continuous function of t? Why?

---

[10] Model by the authors. Source for data: Newspaper Association of America Business Analysis and Research/*New York Times,* May 16, 2005.

[11] Model by the authors. Source for data: Newspaper Association of America Business Analysis and Research/*New York Times,* May 16, 2005.

[12] Spending is adjusted for inflation and shown in 1999 dollars. Models are based on a linear regression. Source for data: Bureau of Justice Statistics/*New York Times,* February 11, 2002, p. A14.

[13] Ibid.

[14] Based on quadratic regression using data from the U.S. Census Bureau Foreign Trade Division website www.census.gov/foreign-trade/sitc1/ as of December 2004.

[15] The model is the authors' and is based on data presented in the article *The Emergence of Intelligence* by William H. Calvin, *Scientific American,* October, 1994, pp. 101–107.

[16] Ibid.

[17] SOURCE: *New York Times,* January 26, 2001, p. C1.

60. ***Internet Purchases*** The percentage $p(t)$ of buyers of new cars who used the Internet for research or purchase since 1997 is given by the following function[18] ($t = 0$ represents 1997):

$$p(t) = \begin{cases} 10t + 15 & \text{if } 0 \le t < 1 \\ 15t + 10 & \text{if } 1 \le t \le 4 \end{cases}$$

Is p a continuous function of t? Why?

Communication and Reasoning Exercises

61. ● Describe the algebraic method of evaluating limits as discussed in this section and give at least one disadvantage of this method.

62. ● What is a closed-form function? What can we say about such functions?

63. Your friend Karin tells you that $f(x) = 1/(x-2)^2$ cannot be a closed-form function because it is not continuous at $x = 2$. Comment on her assertion.

64. Give an example of a function f specified by means of algebraic formulas such that the domain of f consists of all real numbers and f is not continuous at $x = 2$. Is f a closed-form function?

65. ● What is wrong with the following statement? If $f(x)$ is specified algebraically and $f(x)$ is defined, then $\lim_{x\to a} f(x)$ exists and equals $f(a)$.

66. ● What is wrong with the following statement? $\lim\limits_{x\to -2} \dfrac{x^2-4}{x+2}$ does not exist because substituting $x = -2$ yields 0/0, which is undefined.

67. Find a function that is continuous everywhere except at two points.

68. Find a function that is continuous everywhere except at three points.

● basic skills

[18] Model is based on data through 2000 (the 2000 value is estimated). SOURCE: J.D. Power Associates/*New York Times*, January 25, 2000, p. C1.

3.4 Average Rate of Change

Calculus is the mathematics of change, inspired largely by observation of continuously changing quantities around us in the real world. As an example, the New York metro area consumer confidence index C decreased from 100 points in January 2000 to 80 points in January 2002.[19] As we saw in Chapter 1, the **change** in this index can be measured as the difference:

$$\Delta C = \text{Second value} - \text{First value} = 80 - 100 = -20 \text{ points}$$

(The fact that the confidence index decreased is reflected in the negative sign of the change.) The kind of question we will concentrate on is *how fast* the confidence index was dropping. Because C decreased by 20 points in 2 years, we say it averaged a $20/2 = 10$ point drop each year. (It actually dropped less than 10 points the first year and more the second, giving an average drop of 10 points each year.)

Alternatively, we might want to measure this rate in points per month rather than points per year. Because C decreased by 20 points in 24 months, it went down at an average rate of $20/24 \approx 0.833$ points per month.

[19] Figures are approximate. SOURCE: Siena College Research Institute/*New York Times*, February 10, 2002, p. LI.

In both cases, we obtained the average rate of change by dividing the change by the corresponding length of time:

$$\text{Average rate of change} = \frac{\text{Change in } C}{\text{Change in time}} = \frac{-20}{2} = -10 \text{ points per year}$$

$$\text{Average rate of change} = \frac{\text{Change in } C}{\text{Change in time}} = \frac{-20}{24} \approx -0.833 \text{ points per month}$$

Average Rate of Change of a Function Using Numerical Data

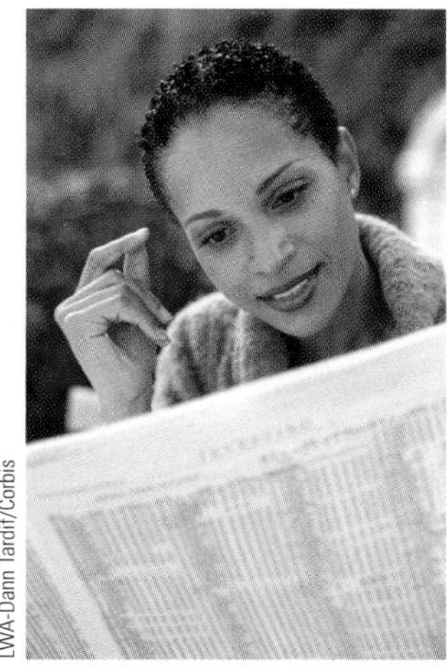

LWA-Dann Tardif/Corbis

Example **1** Average Rate of Change from a Table

The following table lists the approximate value of Standard and Poors 500 stock market index (S&P) during the 10-year period 1998–2004* ($t = 8$ represents 1998):

***t* (year)**	8	9	10	11	12	13	14
***S*(*t*)** **S&P 500 Index (points)**	1200	1350	1450	1200	950	1000	1100

a. What was the average rate of change in the S&P over the two-year period 1998–2000 (the period $8 \le t \le 10$ or [8, 10] in interval notation); over the four-year period 2000–2004 (the period $10 \le t \le 14$ or [10, 14]; and over the period [8, 11]?

b. Graph the values shown in the table. How are the rates of change reflected in the graph?

Solution

a. During the two-year period [8, 10], the S&P changed as follows:

Start of the period ($t = 8$):	$S(8) = 1200$
End of the period ($t = 10$):	$S(10) = 1450$
Change during the period [8, 10]:	$S(10) - S(8) = 250$

Thus, the S&P increased by 250 points in 2 years, giving an average rate of change of $250/2 = 125$ points per year. We can write the calculation this way:

$$\begin{aligned}\text{Average rate of change of } S &= \frac{\text{Change in } S}{\text{Change in } t}\\ &= \frac{\Delta S}{\Delta t}\\ &= \frac{S(10) - S(8)}{10 - 8}\\ &= \frac{1450 - 1200}{10 - 8} = \frac{250}{2} = 125 \text{ points per year}\end{aligned}$$

* The values are approximate values midway through the given year. SOURCE: http://money.excite.com, May, 2004.

Interpreting the result: During the period [8, 10] (that is, 1998–2000), the S&P increased at an average rate of 125 points per year.

Similarly, the average rate of change during the period [10, 14] was

$$\text{Average rate of change of } S = \frac{\Delta S}{\Delta t} = \frac{S(14) - S(10)}{14 - 10} = \frac{1100 - 1450}{14 - 10}$$

$$= -\frac{350}{4} = -87.5 \text{ points per year}$$

Interpreting the result: During the period [10, 14] the S&P *decreased* at an average rate of 87.5 points per year.

Finally, during the period [8, 11], the average rate of change was

$$\text{Average rate of change of } S = \frac{\Delta S}{\Delta t} = \frac{S(11) - S(8)}{11 - 8} = \frac{1200 - 1200}{11 - 8}$$

$$= \frac{0}{3} = 0 \text{ points per year}$$

Interpreting the result: During the period [8, 11] the average rate of change of the S&P was zero points per year (even though its value did fluctuate during that period).

b. In Chapter 1, we saw that the rate of change of a quantity that changes linearly with time is measured by the slope of its graph. However, the S&P index does not change linearly with time. Figure 18 shows the data plotted two different ways: (a) as a bar chart and (b) as a piecewise linear graph. Bar charts are more commonly used in the media, but Figure 18b on the right illustrates the changing index price more clearly.

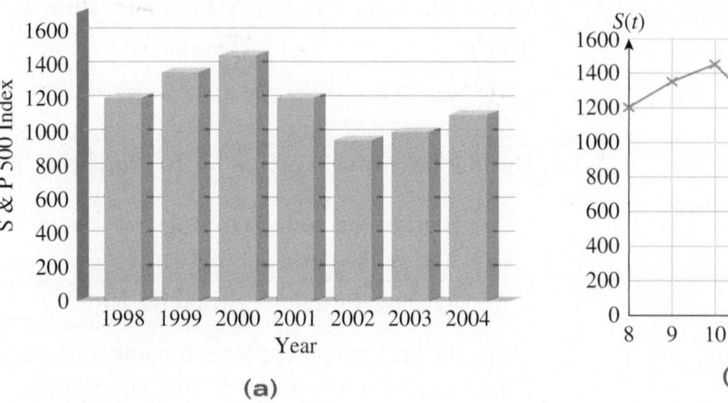

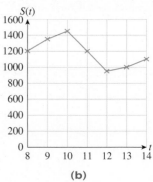

Figure **18**

We saw in part (a) that the average rate of change of S over the interval [8, 10] is the ratio

$$\text{Rate of change of } S = \frac{\Delta S}{\Delta t} = \frac{\text{Change in } S}{\text{Change in } t} = \frac{S(10) - S(8)}{10 - 8}$$

Notice that this rate of change is also the slope of the line through P and Q shown in Figure 19.

Average Rate of Change as Slope: The average rate of change of the S&P over the interval [8, 10] is the slope of the line passing through the points on the graph where $t = 8$ and $t = 10$.

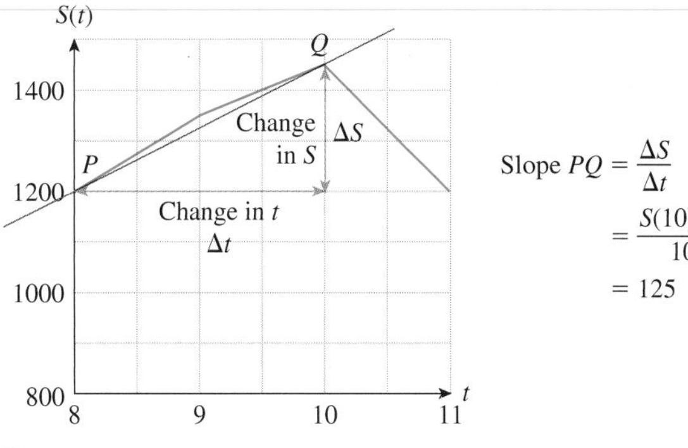

$$\text{Slope } PQ = \frac{\Delta S}{\Delta t} = \frac{S(10) - S(8)}{10 - 8} = 125$$

Figure **19**

Similarly, the average rates of change of the S&P over the intervals [10, 14] and [8, 11] are the slopes of the lines through pairs of corresponding points.

Here is the formal definition of the average rate of change of a function over an interval.

Change and Average Rate of Change of *f* over [*a*, *b*]: Difference Quotient

The **change** in $f(x)$ over the interval $[a, b]$ is

$$\begin{aligned}\text{Change in } f &= \Delta f \\ &= \text{Second value} - \text{First value} \\ &= f(b) - f(a)\end{aligned}$$

The **average rate of change** of $f(x)$ over the interval $[a, b]$ is

$$\begin{aligned}\text{Average rate of change of } f &= \frac{\text{Change in } f}{\text{Change in } x} \\ &= \frac{\Delta f}{\Delta x} = \frac{f(b) - f(a)}{b - a} \\ &= \text{Slope of line through points } P \text{ and } Q \\ &\quad \text{(see figure)}\end{aligned}$$

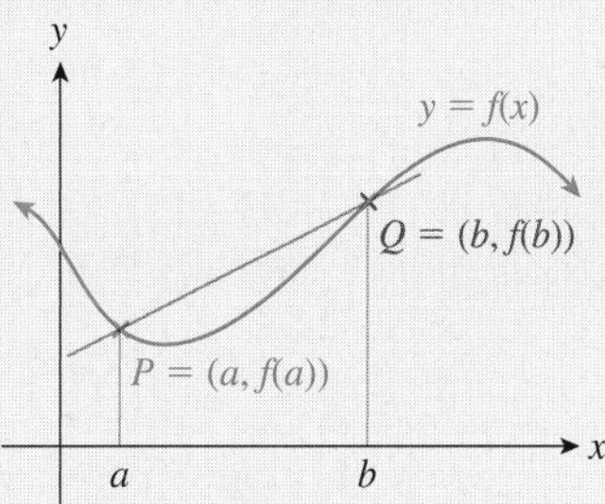

Average rate of change = Slope of PQ

We also call this average rate of change the **difference quotient** of f over the interval $[a, b]$. (It is the *quotient* of the *differences* $f(b) - f(a)$ and $b - a$.) A line through two points of a graph like P and Q is called a **secant line** of the graph.

Units

The units of the change in f are the units of $f(x)$.
The units of the average rate of change of f are units of $f(x)$ per unit of x.

quick **Example**

If $f(3) = -1$ billion dollars, $f(5) = 0.5$ billion dollars, and x is measured in years, then the change and average rate of change of f over the interval [3, 5] are given by

$$\text{Change in } f = f(5) - f(3) = 0.5 - (-1) = 1.5 \text{ billion dollars}$$

$$\text{Average rate of change} = \frac{f(5) - f(3)}{5 - 3} = \frac{0.5 - (-1)}{2} = 0.75 \text{ billion dollars/year}$$

Alternative Formula: Average Rate of Change of *f* over [*a*, *a* + *h*]

(Replace b above by $a + h$.) The average rate of change of f over the interval $[a, a + h]$ is

$$\text{Average rate of change of } f = \frac{f(a + h) - f(a)}{h}$$

Average Rate of Change of a Function Using Graphical Data

In Example 1 we saw that the average rate of change of a quantity can be determined directly from a graph. Here is an example that further illustrates the graphical approach.

Example 2 Average Rate of Change from a Graph

Figure 20 shows the number of sports utility vehicles (SUVs) sold in the U.S. each year from 1990 through 2003 ($t = 0$ represents the year 1990, and $N(t)$ represents sales in year t in thousands of vehicles).*

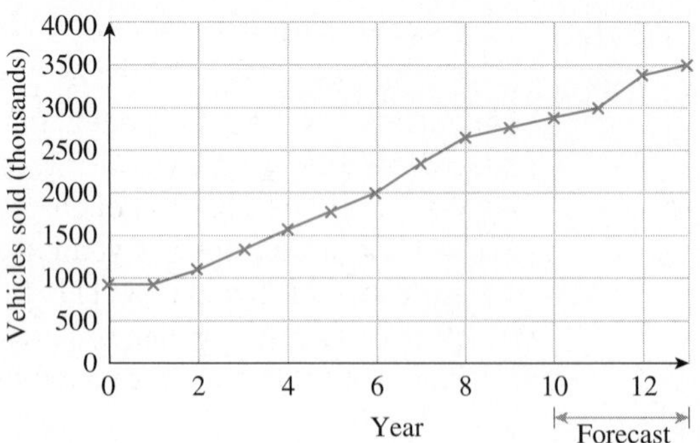

Figure **20**

a. Use the graph to estimate the average rate of change of $N(t)$ with respect to t over the interval [6, 11] and interpret the result.

b. Over which one-year period(s) was the average rate of change of $N(t)$ the greatest?

* SOURCES: Ford Motor Company/*New York Times,* February 9, 1995, p. D17, Oak Ridge National Laboratory, Light Vehicle MPG and Market Shares System, AutoPacific, *The U.S. Car and Light Truck Market,* 1999, pp. 24, 120, 121.

Solution

a. The average rate of change of N over the interval [6, 11] is given by the slope of the line through the points P and Q shown in Figure 21.

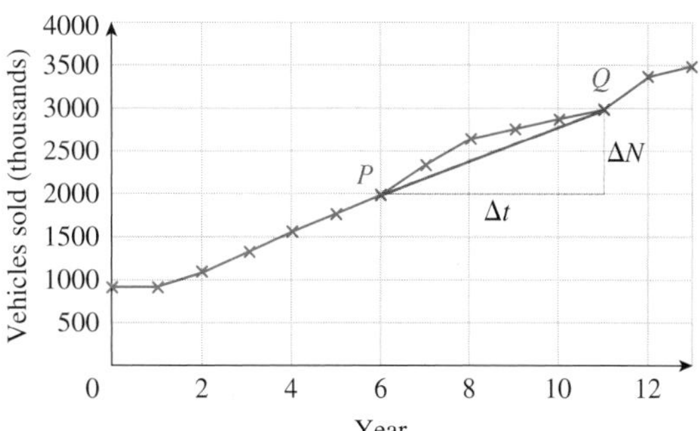

Figure **21**

From the figure,

$$\text{Average rate of change of } N = \frac{\Delta N}{\Delta t} = \text{slope } PQ \approx \frac{3000 - 2000}{11 - 6} = \frac{1000}{5} = 200$$

Thus, the rate of change of N over the interval [6, 11] is approximately 200.

Q: *How do we interpret the result?*

A: A clue is given by the units of the average rate of change: units of N per unit of t. The units of N are thousands of SUVs and the units of t are years. Thus, the average rate of change of N is measured in thousands of SUVs per year, and we can now interpret the result as follows:

Interpreting the average rate of change: Sales of SUVs were increasing at an average rate of 200,000 SUVs per year from 1996 to 2001. ■

b. The rates of change of annual sales over successive one-year periods are given by the slopes of the individual line segments that make up the graph in Figure 20. Thus, the greatest average rate of change over a single year corresponds to the segment(s) with the largest slope. If you look carefully at the figure, you will notice that the segment corresponding to [11, 12] is the steepest. (The segment corresponding to [6, 7] is slightly less steep.) Thus, the average rate of change of annual sales was largest over the one-year period from 2001 to 2002.

+*Before we go on...* Notice in Example 2 that we do not get exact answers from a graph; the best we can do is *estimate* the rates of change: Was the exact answer to part (a) closer to 201 or 202? Two people can reasonably disagree about results read from a graph, and you should bear this in mind when you check the answers to the exercises.

Perhaps the most sophisticated way to compute the average rate of change of a quantity is through the use of a mathematical formula or model for the quantity in question. ■

Average Rate of Change of a Function Using Algebraic Data

Example 3 Average Rate of Change from a Formula

You are a commodities trader and you monitor the price of gold on the New York Spot Market very closely during an active morning. Suppose you find that the price of an ounce of gold can be approximated by the function

$$G(t) = -2t^2 + 36t + 228 \text{ dollars} \quad (7.5 \le t \le 10.5)$$

where t is time in hours. (See Figure 22. $t = 8$ represents 8:00 AM.)

New York Spot Gold (bid)

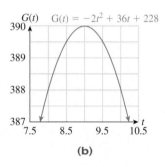

Source: www.kitco.com May 25, 2004

(a)

$G(t)$ $G(t) = -2t^2 + 36t + 228$

390 389 388 387

7.5 8.5 9.5 10.5 t

(b)

Figure **22**

Looking at the graph on the right, we can see that the price of gold rose rather rapidly at the beginning of the time period, but by $t = 8.5$ the rise had slowed, until the market faltered and the price began to fall more and more rapidly toward the end of the period. What was the average rate of change of the price of gold over the $1\frac{1}{2}$-hour period starting at 8:00 AM (the interval $[8, 9.5]$ on the t-axis)?

Solution We have

$$\text{Average rate of change of } G \text{ over } [8.\ 9.5] = \frac{\Delta G}{\Delta t} = \frac{G(9.5) - G(8)}{9.5 - 8}$$

From the formula for $G(t)$, we find

$$G(9.5) = -2(9.5)^2 + 36(9.5) + 228 = 389.5$$
$$G(8) = -2(8)^2 + 36(8) + 228 = 388$$

Thus, the average rate of change of G is given by

$$\frac{G(9.5) - G(8)}{9.5 - 8} = \frac{389.5 - 388}{1.5} = \frac{1.5}{1.5} = \$1 \text{ per hour}$$

In other words, the price of gold was increasing at an average rate of \$1 per hour over the given $1\frac{1}{2}$-hour period.

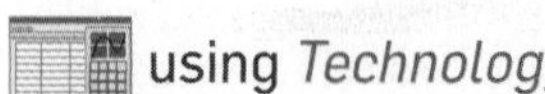

using *Technology*

See the Technology Guides at the end of the chapter to find out how we can use a TI-83/84 or Excel to compute average rates of change for a given function.

Example 4 Rates of Change over Shorter Intervals

Continuing with Example 3, use technology to compute the average rate of change of

$$G(t) = -2t^2 + 36t + 228 \qquad (7.5 \le t \le 10.5)$$

over the intervals $[8, 8 + h]$, where $h = 1, 0.1, 0.01, 0.001$, and 0.0001. What do the answers tell you about the price of gold?

Solution

We use the alternative formula

$$\text{Average rate of change of } G \text{ over } [a, a + h] = \frac{G(a + h) - G(a)}{h}$$

so

$$\text{Average rate of change of } G \text{ over } [8, 8 + h] = \frac{G(8 + h) - G(8)}{h}$$

Let us calculate this average rate of change for some of the values of h listed:

$h = 1$: $G(8 + h) = G(8 + 1) = G(9) = -2(9)^2 + 36(9) + 228 = 390$

$G(8) = -2(8)^2 + 36(8) + 228 = 388$

$$\text{Average rate of change of } G = \frac{G(9) - G(8)}{1} = \frac{390 - 388}{1} = 2$$

$h = 0.1$: $G(8 + h) = G(8 + 0.1) = G(8.1) = -2(8.1)^2 + 36(8.1) + 228 = 388.38$

$G(8) = -2(8)^2 + 36(8) + 228 = 388$

$$\text{Average rate of change of } G = \frac{G(8.1) - G(8)}{0.1} = \frac{388.38 - 388}{0.1} = 3.8$$

$h = 0.01$: $G(8 + h) = G(8 + 0.01) = G(8.01) = -2(8.01)^2 + 36(8.01) + 288$

$= 388.0398$

$G(8) = -2(8)^2 + 36(8) + 228 = 388$

$$\text{Average rate of change of } G = \frac{G(8.01) - G(8)}{0.01} = \frac{388.0398 - 388}{0.01} = 3.98$$

Continuing in this way, we get the values in the following table:

h	1	0.1	0.01	0.001	0.0001
Ave. Rate of Change $\frac{G(8 + h) - G(8)}{h}$	2	3.8	3.98	3.998	3.9998

Each value is an average rate of change of G. For example, the value corresponding to $h = 0.01$ is 3.98, which tells us:

Over the interval $[8, 8.01]$ *the price of gold was increasing at an average rate of* \$3.98 *per hour.*

In other words, during the first one-hundredth of an hour (or 36 seconds) starting at $t = 8$ AM, the price of gold was increasing at an average rate of \$3.98 per hour. Put another way, in those 36 seconds, the price of gold increased at a rate that, if continued, would have produced an increase of \$3.98 in the price of gold during the next hour. We will return to this example at the beginning of Section 3.5.

using *Technology*

This is the kind of example where the use of technology can make a huge difference. See the Technology Guides at the end of the chapter to find out how to do the above computations almost effortlessly.

FAQs Recognizing When and How to Compute the Average Rate of Change and How to Interpret the Answer

Q: *How do I know, by looking at the wording of a problem, that it is asking for an average rate of change?*

A: If a problem does not ask for an average rate of change directly, it might do so indirectly, as in "On average, how fast is quantity q increasing?" ■

Q: *If I know that a problem calls for computing an average rate of change, how should I compute it? By hand or using technology?*

A: All the computations can be done by hand, but when hand calculations are not called for, using technology might save time. ■

Q: *Lots of problems ask us to "interpret" the answer. How do I do that for questions involving average rates of change?*

A: The *units* of the average rate of change are often the key to interpreting the results:

The units of the average rate of change of f(x) are units of f(x) per unit of x.

Thus, for instance, if $f(x)$ is the cost, in dollars, of a trip of x miles in length, and the average rate of change of f is calculated to be 10, then we can say that the cost of a trip rises an average of $10 for each additional mile. ■

3.4 EXERCISES

● denotes basic skills exercises
◆ denotes challenging exercises
tech Ex indicates exercises that should be solved using technology

In Exercises 1–18, calculate the average rate of change of the given function over the given interval. Where appropriate, specify the units of measurement.

1. ●

x	0	1	2	3
$f(x)$	3	5	2	−1

Interval: [1, 3] *hint* [see Example 1]

2. ●

x	0	1	2	3
$f(x)$	−1	3	2	1

Interval: [0, 2]

3. ●

x	−3	−2	−1	0
$f(x)$	−2.1	0	−1.5	0

Interval: [−3, −1]

4. ●

x	−2	−1	0	1
$f(x)$	−1.5	−0.5	4	6.5

Interval: [−1, 1]

5. ●

t (months)	2	4	6
$R(t)$ ($ millions)	20.2	24.3	20.1

Interval: [2, 6]

6. ●

x (kilos)	1	2	3
$C(x)$ (£)	2.20	3.30	4.00

Interval: [1, 3]

7. ●

p ($)	5.00	5.50	6.00
$q(p)$ (items)	400	300	150

Interval: [5, 5.5]

8. ●

t (hours)	0	0.1	0.2
$D(t)$ (miles)	0	3	6

Interval: [0.1, 0.2]

9. ● hint [see Example 2]

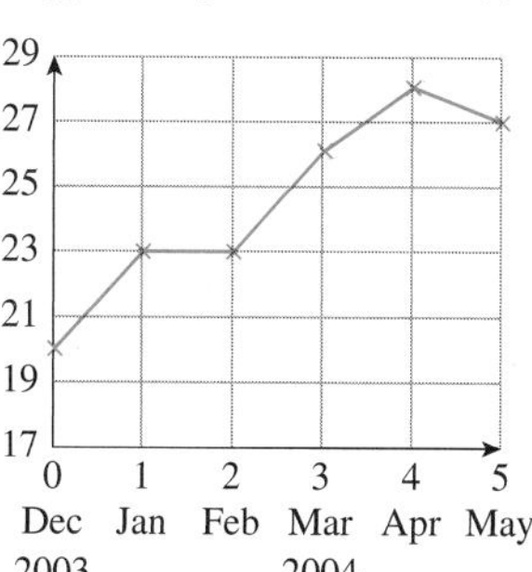

Interval: [2, 5]

10. ●

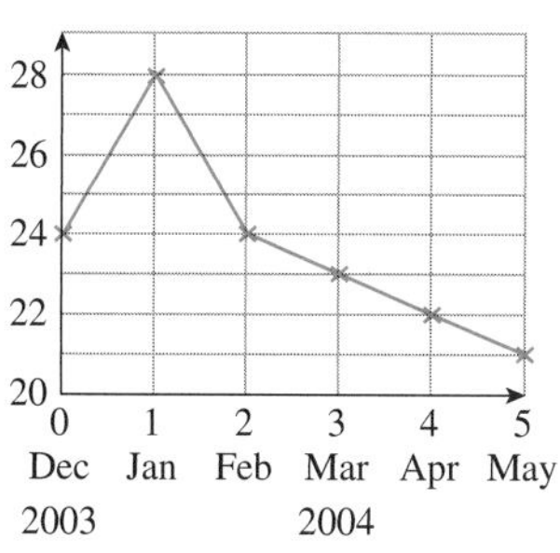

Interval: [1, 5]

11. ●

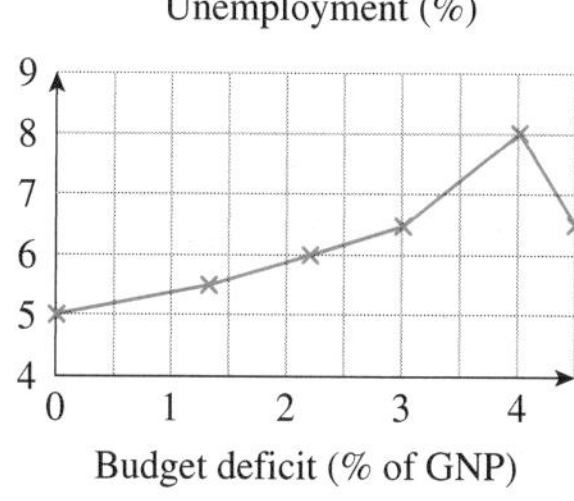

Interval: [0, 4]

12. ●

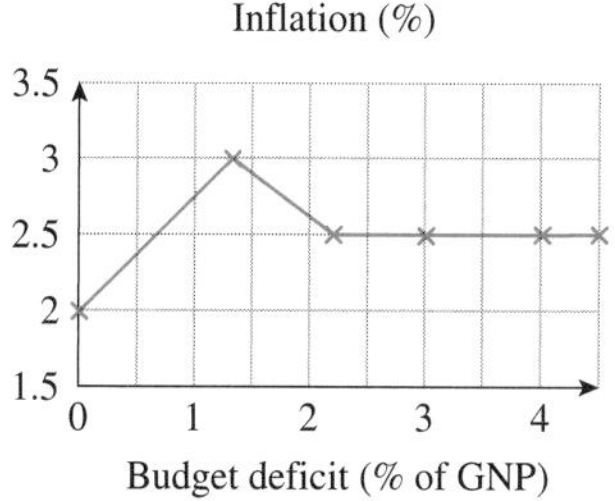

Interval: [0, 4]

13. ● $f(x) = x^2 - 3$; [1, 3] hint [see Example 3]

14. ● $f(x) = 2x^2 + 4$; [−1, 2]

15. ● $f(x) = 2x + 4$; [−2, 0]

16. ● $f(x) = \frac{1}{x}$; [1, 4]

17. ● $f(x) = \frac{x^2}{2} + \frac{1}{x}$; [2, 3]

18. ● $f(x) = 3x^2 - \frac{x}{2}$; [3, 4]

In Exercises 19–24, calculate the average rate of change of the given function f over the intervals $[a, a + h]$ where $h = 1, 0.1, 0.01, 0.001$, and 0.0001. (Technology is recommended for the cases $h = 0.01, 0.001$, and 0.0001.)

19. ● $f(x) = 2x^2$; $a = 0$ hint [see Example 4]

20. ● $f(x) = \frac{x^2}{2}$; $a = 1$

21. ● $f(x) = \frac{1}{x}$; $a = 2$

22. ● $f(x) = \frac{2}{x}$; $a = 1$

23. ● $f(x) = x^2 + 2x$; $a = 3$

24. ● $f(x) = 3x^2 - 2x$; $a = 0$

Applications

25. ● ***Employment*** The following table lists the approximate number of people employed in the U.S. during the period 1998–2004, on July 1 of each year[20] ($t = 0$ represents 2000):

Year t	−2	−1	0	1	2	3	4
Employment $P(t)$ (millions)	126	130	132	132	130	130	131

Compute and interpret the average rate of change of $P(t)$ **a.** over the period 2000–2004 (that is, [0, 4]), and **b.** over the period [−1, 2]. Be sure to state the units of measurement. hint [see Example 1]

26. ● ***Cell Phone Sales*** The following table lists the net sales (after-tax revenue) at the Finnish cell phone company Nokia during the period 1997–2003[21] ($t = 0$ represents 2000):

Year t	−3	−2	−1	0	1	2	3
Nokia net sales $P(t)$ (€ Billion)	9	14	20	31	31	30	29

Compute and interpret the average rate of change of $P(t)$ **a.** over the period [−2, 3], and **b.** over the period [0, 1]. Be sure to state the units of measurement.

27. ● ***Venture Capital*** The following table shows the number of companies that invested in venture capital each year during the period 1995–2001[22] ($t = 5$ represents 1995):

Year t	5	6	7	8	9	10	11
Number of companies $N(t)$	100	150	300	400	1000	1700	900

During which two-year interval(s) was the average rate of change of $N(t)$ **a.** greatest **b.** least? Interpret your answers by referring to the rates of change.

28. ● ***Venture Capital*** The following table shows the amount of money that companies invested in venture capital during the period 1995–2001[23] ($t = 5$ represents 1995):

Year t	5	6	7	8	9	10	11
Investment $M(t)$ (billions)	$0.05	0.5	1	2	8	16	4

During which three-year interval(s) was the average rate of change of $M(t)$ **a.** greatest **b.** least? Interpret your answers by referring to the rates of change.

29. ***Physics Research in the U.S.*** The following table shows the number of research articles in the journal *Physics Review* authored by U.S researchers during the period 1993–2003[24] ($t = 3$ represents 1993):

[20] The given (approximate) values represent nonfarm employment. SOURCE: Bureau of Labor Statistics http://stats.bls.gov/, June 10, 2004.

[21] SOURCES: *New York Times*, February 6, 2002, p. A3, Nokia June 10, 2003 www.nokia.com.

[22] 2001 figure is a projection based on data through September. SOURCE: Venture Economics/National Venture Capital Association/*New York Times*, February 3, 2002, p. BU4.

[23] Ibid.

[24] SOURCE: The American Physical Society/*New York Times* May 3, 2003, p. A1.

t (Year)	3	5	7	9	11	13
N(*t*) (Articles, thousands)	5.1	4.6	4.3	4.3	4.5	4.2

a. Find the interval(s) over which the average rate of change of *N* was the most negative. What was that rate of change? Interpret your answer.

b. The **percentage change of *N* over the interval [*a*, *b*]** is defined to be

$$\text{Percentage change of } N = \frac{\text{Change in } N}{\text{First value}} = \frac{N(b) - N(a)}{N(a)}$$

Compute the percentage change of *N* over the interval [3, 13] and also the average rate of change. Interpret the answers.

30. ***Physics Research in Europe*** The following table shows the number of research articles in the journal *Physics Review* authored by researchers in Europe during the period 1993–2003[25] ($t = 3+$ represents 1993):

t (Year)	3	5	7	9	11	13
N(*t*) (Articles, thousands)	3.8	4.6	5.0	5.0	6.0	5.7

a. Find the interval(s) over which the average rate of change of *N* was the most positive. What was that rate of change? Interpret your answer.

b. The **percentage change of *N* over the interval [*a*, *b*]** is defined to be

$$\text{Percentage change of } N = \frac{\text{Change in } N}{\text{First value}} = \frac{N(b) - N(a)}{N(a)}$$

Compute the percentage change of *N* over the interval [7, 13] and also the average rate of change. Interpret the answers.

31. ● ***Collegiate Sports*** The following chart shows the number of women's college soccer teams in the U.S. from 1982 to 2001[26] ($t = 1$ represents the 1981–1982 academic year):

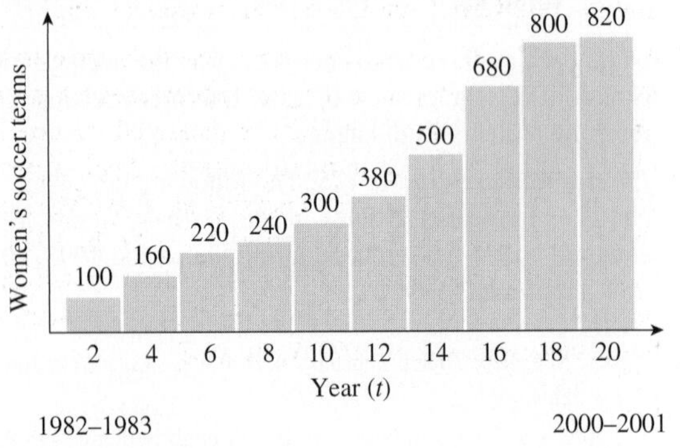

a. On average, how fast was the number of women's college soccer teams growing over the four-year period starting in the 1992–1993 academic year?

b. By inspecting the graph, determine whether the four-year average rates of change increased or decreased beginning in 1994–1995. *hint* [see Example 2]

32. ● ***Collegiate Sports.*** The following chart shows the number of men's college wrestling teams in the U.S. from 1982 to 2001[27] ($t = 1$ represents the 1981–1982 academic year):

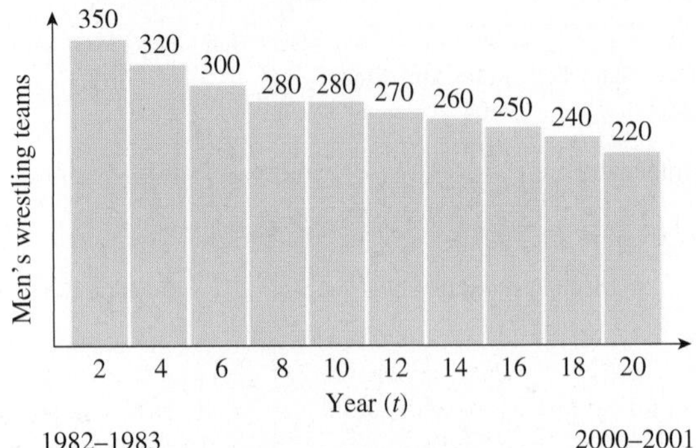

a. On average, how fast was the number of men's college wrestling teams decreasing over the eight-year period, starting in the 1984–1985 academic year?

b. By inspecting the graph, determine when the number of men's college wrestling teams was declining the fastest.

33. ● ***Online Shopping*** The following graph shows the annual number *N*(*t*) of online shopping transactions in the U.S. for the period January 2000–January 2002[28] ($t = 0$ represents January, 2000):

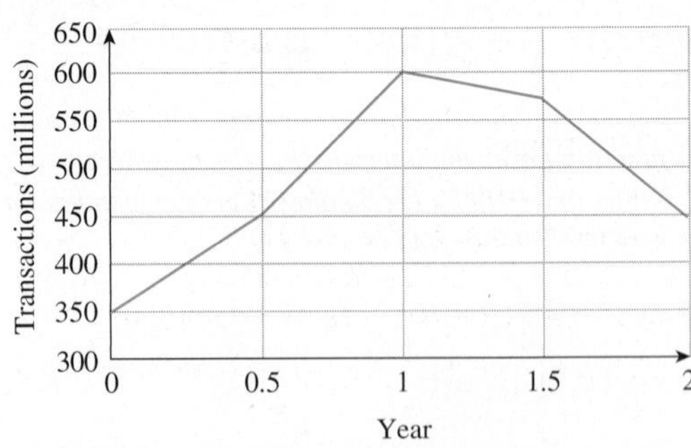

a. Estimate the average rate of change of *N*(*t*) over the intervals [0, 1], [1, 2], and [0, 2]. Interpret your answers.

b. How can the average rate of change of *N*(*t*) over [0, 2] be obtained from the rates over [0, 1] and [1, 2]?

34. ● ***Online Shopping*** The following graph shows the percentage of people in the U.S. who have ever purchased anything

[25] SOURCE: The American Physical Society/*New York Times* May 3, 2003, p. A1.

[26] SOURCE: N.C.A.A./*New York Times*, May 9, 2002, p. D4.

[27] SOURCE: N.C.A.A./*New York Times*, May 9, 2002, p. D4.

[28] Second half of 2001 data was an estimate. Source for data: Odyssey Research/*New York Times*, November 5, 2001, p. C1.

online for the period January 2000–January 2002 ($t = 0$ represents January 2000):[29]

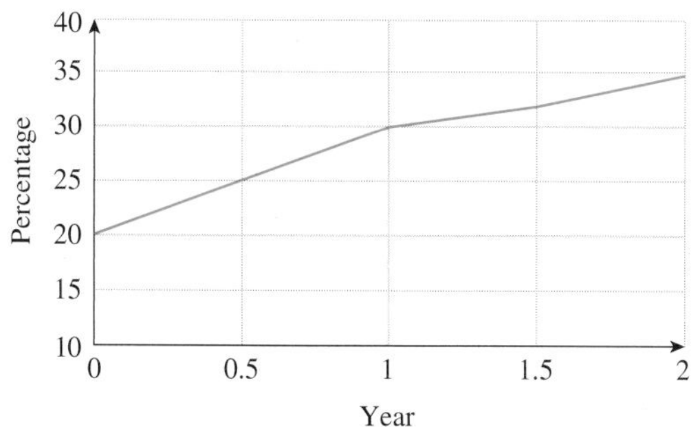

a. Estimate the average rate of change of $P(t)$ over the interval [0, 2], and interpret your answer.

b. Are any of the one-year average rates of change greater than the two-year rate? Refer in your answer to the slopes of certain lines.

35. ***Funding for the Arts*** The following chart shows the total annual support for the arts in the U.S. by federal, state, and local government in 1995–2003 as a function of time in years ($t = 0$ represents 1995) together with the regression line:[30]

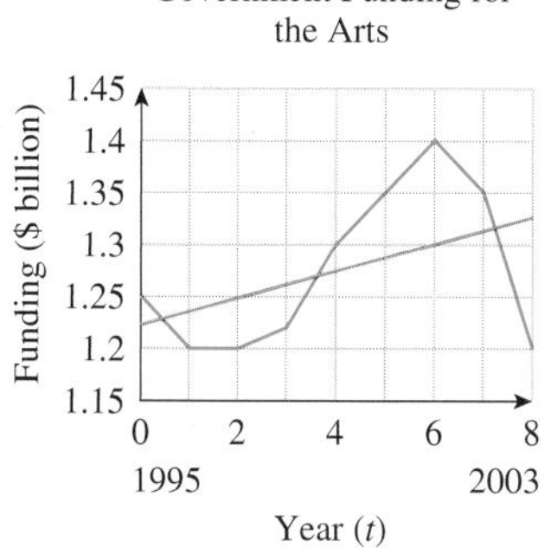

Multiple choice:

a. Over the period [0, 4] the average rate of change of government funding for the arts was
(A) less than **(B)** greater than **(C)** approximately equal to the rate predicted by the regression line.

b. Over the period [4, 8] the average rate of change of government funding for the arts was
(A) less than **(B)** greater than **(C)** approximately equal to the rate predicted by the regression line.

c. Over the period [3, 6] the average rate of change of government funding for the arts was
(A) less than **(B)** greater than **(C)** approximately equal to the rate predicted by the regression line.

d. Estimate, to two significant digits, the average rate of change of government funding for the arts over the period [0, 8]. (Be careful to state the units of measurement.) How does it compare to the slope of the regression line?

36. ***Funding for the Arts*** The following chart shows the total annual support for the arts in the U.S. by foundation endowments in 1995–2002 as a function of time in years ($t = 0$ represents 1995) together with the regression line:[31]

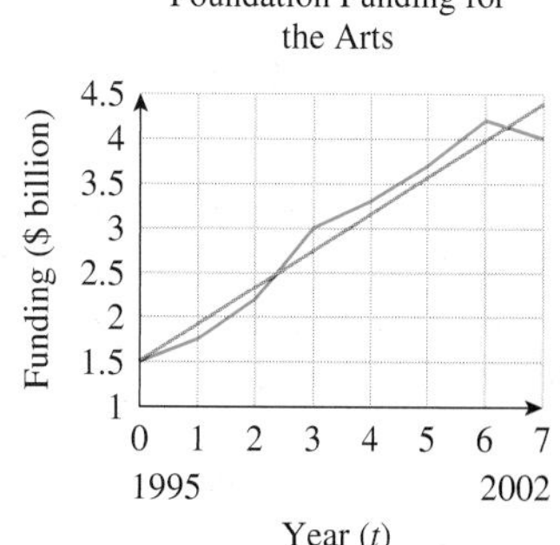

Multiple choice:

a. Over the period [0, 2.5] the average rate of change of government funding for the arts was
(A) less than **(B)** greater than **(C)** approximately equal to the rate predicted by the regression line.

b. Over the period [2, 6] the average rate of change of government funding for the arts was
(A) less than **(B)** greater than **(C)** approximately equal to the rate predicted by the regression line.

c. Over the period [3, 7] the average rate of change of government funding for the arts was
(A) less than **(B)** greater than **(C)** approximately equal to the rate predicted by the regression line.

d. Estimate, to two significant digits, the average rate of change of foundation funding for the arts over the period [0, 7]. (Be careful to state the units of measurement.) How does it compare to the slope of the regression line?

37. ***Market Volatility*** A volatility index generally measures the extent to which a market undergoes sudden changes in value. The volatility of the S&P 500 (as measured by one such index) was decreasing at an average rate of 0.2 points per year during 1991–1995, and was increasing at an average rate of about 0.3 points per year during 1995–1999. In 1995, the volatility of the S&P was 1.1.[32] Use this information to give a rough sketch of the volatility of the S&P 500 as a function of time, showing its values in 1991 and 1999.

[29] January 2002 data was estimated. Source for data: Odyssey Research/*New York Times,* November 5, 2001, p. C1.

[30] Figures are adjusted for inflation. SOURCES: Giving USA, The Foundation Center, Americans for the Arts/*New York Times,* June 19, 2004, p. B7.

[31] Figures are adjusted for inflation. SOURCES: Giving USA, The Foundation Center, Americans for the Arts/*New York Times,* June 19, 2004, p. B7.

[32] Source for data: Sanford C. Bernstein Company/*New York Times,* March 24, 2000, p. C1.

38. ***Market Volatility*** The volatility (see the preceding exercise) of the NASDAQ had an average rate of change of 0 points per year during 1992–1995, and increased at an average rate of 0.2 points per year during 1995–1998. In 1995, the volatility of the NASDAQ was 1.1.[33] Use this information to give a rough sketch of the volatility of the NASDAQ as a function of time.

39. ● ***Market Index*** Joe Downs runs a small investment company from his basement. Every week he publishes a report on the success of his investments, including the progress of the "Joe Downs Index." At the end of one particularly memorable week, he reported that the index for that week had the value $I(t) = 1000 + 1500t - 800t^2 + 100t^3$ points, where t represents the number of business days into the week; t ranges from 0 at the beginning of the week to 5 at end of the week. The graph of I is shown below.

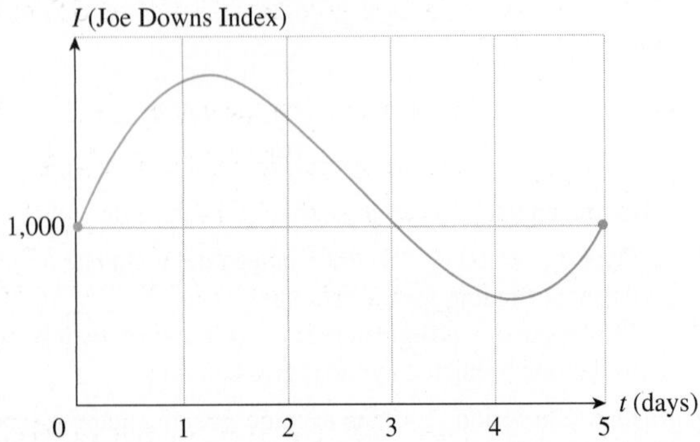

On average, how fast, and in what direction, was the index changing over the first two business days (the interval [0, 2])? *hint* [see Example 3]

40. ● ***Market Index*** Refer to the Joe Downs Index in the preceding exercise. On average, how fast, and in which direction, was the index changing over the last three business days (the interval [2, 5])?

41. ● ***Currency*** The value of the euro (€) since its introduction in January, 1999 can be approximated by

$$e(t) = 0.036t^2 - 0.10t + 1.0 \text{ U.S. dollars} \quad (-1 \le t \le 4.5)$$

where $t = 0$ represents January, 2000.[34] Compute the average rate of change of $e(t)$ over the interval [0.5, 4.5] and interpret your answer.

42. ● ***Interest Rates*** The prime lending rate (the lowest short-term interest rate charged by commercial banks to their most creditworthy clients) for the period January 1982 – June 2004 can be approximated by

$$p(t) = 0.028t^2 - 0.52t + 9.3 \text{ percentage points } (-8 \le t \le 14)$$

where $t = 0$ represents January, 1990.[35] Compute the average rate of change of $p(t)$ over the interval [−4, 4] and interpret your answer.

[33] Ibid.

[34] Sources: Bank of England, Reuters, July, 2004.

[35] Sources: Bloomberg News, www.icmarc.org July 6, 2004.

43. ***Ecology*** Increasing numbers of manatees ("sea sirens") have been killed by boats off the Florida coast. The following graph shows the relationship between the number of boats registered in Florida and the number of manatees killed each year:

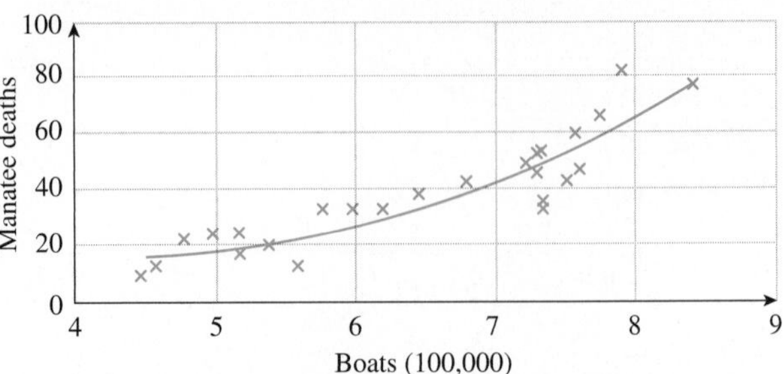

The regression curve shown is given by

$$f(x) = 3.55x^2 - 30.2x + 81 \text{ manatees} \quad (4.5 \le x \le 8.5)$$

where x is the number of boats (in hundreds of thousands) registered in Florida in a particular year, and $f(x)$ is the number of manatees killed by boats in Florida that year.[36]

a. Compute the average rate of change of f over the intervals [5, 6] and [7, 8].

b. What does the answer to part (a) tell you about the manatee deaths per boat?

44. ***Ecology*** Refer to Exercise 43,

a. Compute the average rate of change of f over the intervals [5, 7] and [6, 8].

b. Had we used a linear model instead of a quadratic one, how would the two answers in part (a) be related to each other?

45. ***Advertising Revenue*** The following table shows the annual advertising revenue earned by America Online (AOL) during the last three years of the 1990s:[37]

Year	1997	1998	1999
Revenue ($ million)	150	360	760

These data can be modeled by

$$R(t) = 95t^2 + 115t + 150 \text{ million dollars} \quad (0 \le t \le 2)$$

where t is time in years since December 1997.

a. What was the average rate of change of R over the period 1997–1999? Interpret the result.

b. Which of the following is true? From 1997 to 1999, annual online advertising revenues

(A) increased at a faster and faster rate.

(B) increased at a slower and slower rate.

[36] Regression model is based on data from 1976 to 2000. Sources for data: Florida Department of Highway Safety & Motor Vehicles, Florida Marine Institute/*New York Times,* February 12, 2002, p. F4.

[37] Figures are rounded to the nearest $10 million. Sources: AOL; Forrester Research/*New York Times,* January 31, 2000, p. C1.

(C) decreased at a faster and faster rate.
(D) decreased at a slower and slower rate.

c. Use the model to project the average rate of change of R over the one-year period ending December 2000. Interpret the result.

46. ***Religion*** The following table shows the population of Roman Catholic nuns in the U.S. during the last 25 years of the 1900s:[38]

Year	1975	1985	1995
Population	130,000	120,000	80,000

These data can be modeled by

$$P(t) = -0.15t^2 + 0.50t + 130 \quad \text{thousand nuns} \quad (0 \le t \le 20)$$

where t is time in years since December 1975.

a. What was the average rate of change of P over the period 1975–1995? Interpret the result.

b. Which of the following is true? From 1975 to 1995, the population of nuns
(A) increased at a faster and faster rate.
(B) increased at a slower and slower rate.
(C) decreased at a faster and faster rate.
(D) decreased at a slower and slower rate.

c. Use the model to project the average rate of change of P over the 10-year period ending December 2005. Interpret the result.

47. tech Ex ***Poverty vs Income*** Based on data from 1988 through 2003, the poverty rate (percentage of households with incomes below the poverty threshold) in the U.S. can be approximated by

$$p(x) = 0.092x^2 - 8.1x + 190 \text{ percentage points} \quad (38 \le x \le 44)$$

where x is the U.S. median household income in thousands of dollars.[39]

a. Use technology to complete the following table which shows the average rate of change of p over successive intervals of length $\frac{1}{2}$. (Round all answers to two decimal places.) hint [see Example 4]

Interval	[39, 39.5]	[39.5, 40]	[40, 40.5]	[40.5, 41]	[41, 41.5]	[41.5, 42]
Average Rate of change of p						

b. Interpret your answer for the interval [40, 40.5], being sure to indicate the direction of change and the units of measurement.

c. Multiple choice: As the median household income rises, the poverty rate
(A) Increases
(B) Decreases
(C) Increases, then decreases
(D) Decreases, then increases

d. Multiple choice: As the median income increases, the effect on the poverty rate is
(A) More pronounced
(B) Less pronounced

48. tech Ex ***Poverty vs Unemployment*** Based on data from 1988 through 2003, the poverty rate (percentage of households with incomes below the poverty threshold) in the U.S. can be approximated by

$$p(x) = -0.12x^2 + 2.4x + 3.2 \text{ percentage points} \quad (4 \le x \le 8)$$

where x is the unemployment rate in percentage points.[40]

a. Use technology to complete the following table which shows the average rate of change of p over successive intervals of length $\frac{1}{2}$. (Round all answers to two decimal places.)

Interval	[5.0, 5.5]	[5.5, 6.0]	[6.0, 6.5]	[6.5, 7.0]	[7.0, 7.5]	[7.5, 8.0]
Average Rate of change of p						

b. Interpret your answer for the interval [5.0, 5.5], being sure to indicate the direction of change and the units of measurement.

c. Multiple choice: As the median household income rises, the poverty rate
(A) Increases
(B) Decreases
(C) Increases, then decreases
(D) Decreases, then increases

d. Multiple choice: As the unemployment rate increases, the effect on the poverty rate is
(A) More pronounced
(B) Less pronounced

[38] Figures are rounded. SOURCE: Center for Applied Research in the Apostolate/*New York Times,* January 16, 2000, p. A1.

[39] The model is based on a quadratic regression. Household incomes are in constant 2002 dollars. The poverty threshold is approximately $18,000 for a family of four and $9200 for an individual. SOURCES: Census Bureau Current Population Survey/*New York Times,* Sept 27, 2003, p. A10, U.S. Department of Labor Bureau of Labor Statistics http://stats.bls.gov June 17, 2004.

[40] The model is based on a quadratic regression. Household incomes are in constant 2002 dollars. The poverty threshold is approximately $18,000 for a family of four and $9200 for an individual. SOURCES: Census Bureau Current Population Survey/*New York Times,* Sept 27, 2003, p. A10, U.S. Department of Labor Bureau of Labor Statistics http://stats.bls.gov June 17, 2004.

Communication and Reasoning Exercises

49. ● Describe three ways we have used to determine the average rate of change of f over an interval $[a, b]$. Which of the three ways is *least* precise? Explain.

50. ● If f is a linear function of x with slope m, what is its average rate of change over any interval $[a, b]$?

51. ● Sketch the graph of a function whose average rate of change over [0, 3] is negative but whose average rate of change over [1, 3] is positive.

52. ● Sketch the graph of a function whose average rate of change over [0, 2] is positive but whose average rate of change over [0, 1] is negative.

53. If the rate of change of quantity A is 2 units of quantity A per unit of quantity B, and the rate of change of quantity B is 3 units of quantity B per unit of quantity C, what is the rate of change of quantity A with respect to quantity C?

54. If the rate of change of quantity A is 2 units of quantity A per unit of quantity B, what is the rate of change of quantity B with respect to quantity A?

55. A certain function has the property that its average rate of change over the interval $[1, 1+h]$ (for positive h) increases as h decreases. Which of the following graphs could be the graph of f?

(A)

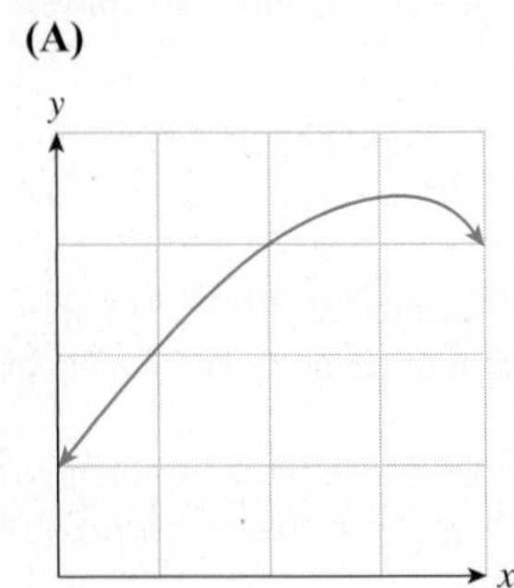

(B)

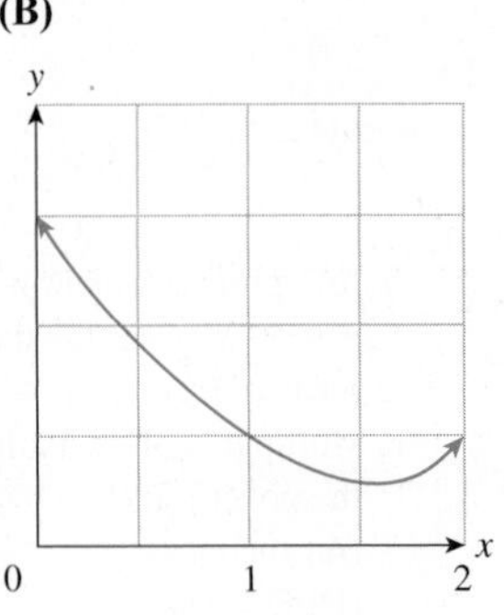

(C)

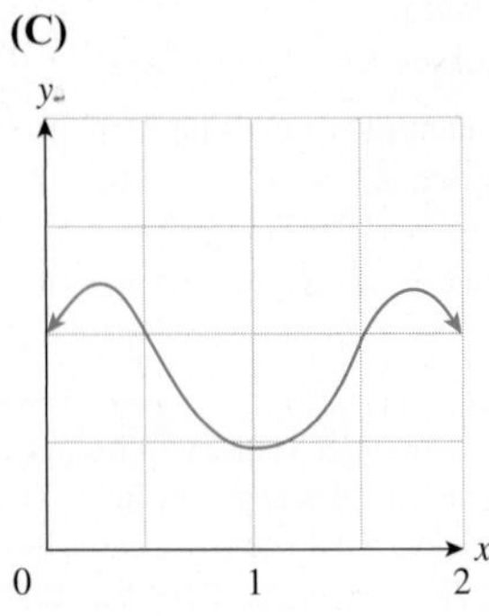

56. ● A certain function has the property that its average rate of change over the interval $[1, 1+h]$ (for positive h) decreases as h decreases. Which of the following graphs could be the graph of f?

(A)

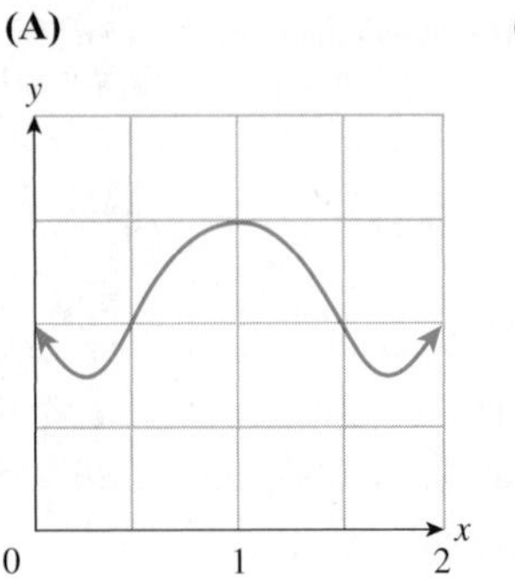

(B)

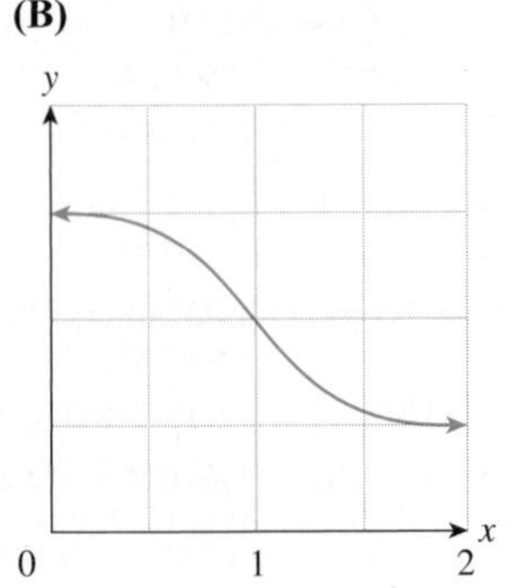

(C)

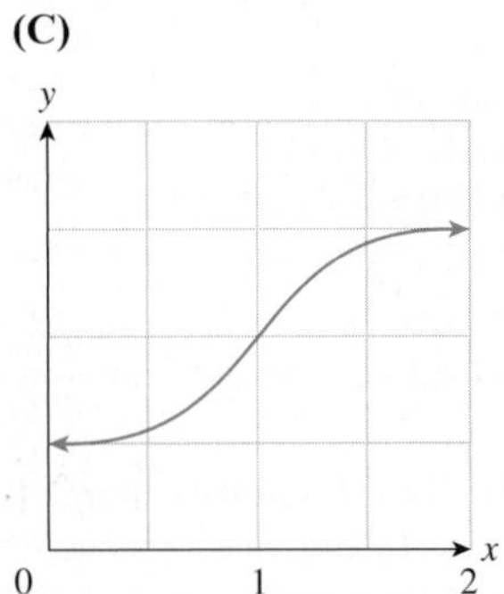

57. Is it possible for a company's revenue to have a negative three-year average rate of growth, but a positive average rate of growth in two of the three years? (If not, explain; if so, illustrate with an example.)

58. Is it possible for a company's revenue to have a larger two-year average rate of change than either of the one-year average rates of change? (If not, explain why with the aid of a graph; if so, illustrate with an example.)

59. ◆ The average rate of change of f over [1, 3] is
(A) always equal to **(B)** never equal to
(C) sometimes equal to the average of its average rates of change over [1, 2] and [2, 3].

60. ◆ The average rate of change of f over [1, 4] is
(A) always equal to **(B)** never equal to
(C) sometimes equal to the average of its average rates of change over [1, 2], [2, 3], and [3, 4].

3.5 Derivatives: Numerical and Graphical Viewpoints

In Example 4 of Section 3.4, we looked at the average rate of change of the function $G(t) = -2t^2 + 36t + 228$, approximating the price of gold on the New York Spot Market, over the intervals $[8, 8 + h]$ for successively smaller values of h. Here are some values we got:

h getting smaller; interval $[8, 8 + h]$ getting smaller →

h	0.1	0.01	0.001	0.0001
Ave. rate of change over $[8, 8 + h]$	3.8	3.98	3.998	3.9998

Rate of change approaching \$4 per hour →

The average rate of change of the price of gold over smaller and smaller periods of time, starting at the instant $t = 8$ (8 AM), appears to be getting closer and closer to \$4 per hour. As we look at these shrinking periods of time, we are getting closer to looking at what happens at the *instant* $t = 8$. So it seems reasonable to say that the average rates of change are approaching the **instantaneous rate of change** at $t = 8$, which the table suggests is \$4 per hour. This is how fast the price of gold was changing *exactly* at 8 AM.

At $t = 8$, the instantaneous rate of change of $G(t)$ is 4

We express this fact mathematically by writing $G'(8) = 4$ (which we read as "G prime of 8 equals 4"). Thus,

$G'(8) = 4$ *means that, at $t = 8$, the instantaneous rate of change of $G(t)$ is* 4

The process of letting h get smaller and smaller is called taking the **limit** as h approaches 0 (as you recognize if you've done the sections on limits). We write $h \to 0$ as shorthand for "h approaches 0." Thus, taking the limit of the average rates of change as $h \to 0$ gives us the instantaneous rate of change.

Q: *All these intervals $[8, 8 + h]$ are intervals to the right of 8. What about small intervals to the left of 8, such as $[7.9, 8]$?*

A: We can compute the average rate of change of our function for such intervals by choosing h to be negative ($h = -0.1, -0.01$, etc.) and using the same difference quotient formula we used for positive h:

$$\text{Average rate of change of } G \text{ over } [8 + h, 8] = \frac{G(8) - G(8 + h)}{8 - (8 + h)} = \frac{G(8 + h) - G(8)}{h}$$

Here are the results we get using negative h:

h getting closer to 0; interval $[8 + h, 8]$ getting smaller →

h	−0.1	−0.01	−0.001	−0.0001
Ave. rate of change over $[8 + h, 8]$	4.2	4.02	4.002	4.0002

Rate of change approaching \$4 per hour →

Notice that the average rates of change are again getting closer and closer to 4 as h approaches 0, suggesting once again that the instantaneous rate of change is \$4 per hour. ■

Instantaneous Rate of Change of $f(x)$ at $x = a$: Derivative

The **instantaneous rate of change** of $f(x)$ at $x = a$ is defined as

$$f'(a) = \lim_{h \to 0} \frac{f(a+h) - f(a)}{h}$$

f prime of a equals the limit as h approaches 0, of the ratio $\frac{f(a+h) - f(a)}{h}$

The quantity $f'(a)$ is also called the **derivative of $f(x)$ at $x = a$.** Finding the derivative of f is called **differentiating f.**

Units

The units of $f'(a)$ are the same as the units of the average rate of change: units of f per unit of x.

quick **Example** If $f(x) = -2x^2 + 36x + 228$, then the two tables above suggest that

$$f'(8) = \lim_{h \to 0} \frac{f(8+h) - f(8)}{h} = 4$$

Important Notes

1. Sections 3.1–3.3 discuss limits in some detail. If you have not (yet) covered those sections, you can trust to your intuition.
2. The formula for the derivative tells us that the instantaneous rate of change is the limit of the average rates of change $[f(a+h) - f(a)]/h$ over smaller and smaller intervals. Thus, value of $f'(a)$ can be approximated by computing the average rate of change for smaller and smaller values of h, both positive and negative.
3. In this section we will only *approximate* derivatives. In Section 3.6 we will begin to see how we find the *exact* values of derivatives.
4. $f'(a)$ is a number we can calculate, or at least approximate, for various values of a, as we have done in the example above. Since $f'(a)$ depends on the value of a, we can think of f' as *a function of* a. (We return to this idea at the end of this section.) An old name for f' is "the function *derived from* f," which has been shortened to the *derivative* of f.
5. It is because f' is a function that we sometimes refer to $f'(a)$ as "the derivative of f *evaluated* at a," or the "derivative of $f(x)$ evaluated at $x = a$."

It may happen that the average rates of change $[f(a+h) - f(a)]/h$ do not approach any fixed number at all as h approaches zero, or that they approach one number on the intervals using positive h, and another on those using negative h. If this happens, we say that f is **not differentiable** at $x = a$, or **$f'(a)$ does not exist.** When the average rates of change *do* approach a fixed limit for both positive and negative h, we say that f is **differentiable** at the point $x = a$, or $f'(a)$ **exists.** It is comforting to know that all polynomials and exponential functions are differentiable at *every* point. On the other hand, certain functions are not differentiable. Examples are $f(x) = |x|$ and $f(x) = x^{1/3}$, neither of which is differentiable at $x = 0$ (see Section 3.7).

Example 1 Instantaneous Rate of Change: Numerically and Graphically

The air temperature one spring morning, t hours after 7:00 AM, was given by the function $f(t) = 50 + 0.1t^4$ °F $(0 \le t \le 4)$.

a. How fast was the temperature rising at 9:00 AM?

b. How is the instantaneous rate of change of temperature at 9:00 AM reflected in the graph of temperature vs. time?

Solution

a. We are being asked to find the instantaneous rate of change of the temperature at $t = 2$, so we need to find $f'(2)$. To do this we examine the average rates of change

$$\frac{f(2+h) - f(2)}{h}$$ Average rate of change = difference quotient

for values of h approaching 0. Calculating the average rate of change over $[2, 2+h]$ for $h = 1, 0.1, 0.01, 0.001$, and 0.0001 we get the following values (rounded to four decimal places):*

h	1	0.1	0.01	0.001	0.0001
Ave. rate of change over [2, 2 + h]	6.5	3.4481	3.2241	3.2024	3.2002

Here are the values we get using negative values of h:

h	−1	−0.1	−0.01	−0.001	−0.0001
Ave. rate of change over [2 + h, 2]	1.5	2.9679	3.1761	3.1976	3.1998

The average rates of change are clearly approaching the number 3.2, so we can say that $f'(2) = 3.2$. Thus, at 9:00 in the morning, the temperature was rising at the rate of 3.2°F per hour.

b. We saw in Section 3.4 that the average rate of change of f over an interval is the slope of the secant line through the corresponding points on the graph of f. Figure 23 illustrates this for the intervals $[2, 2+h]$ with $h = 1, 0.5$, and 0.1.

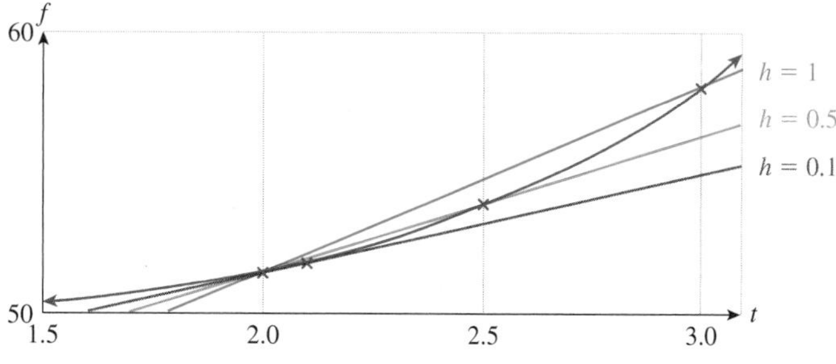

Figure **23**

* We can quickly compute these values using technology as in Example 4 in Section 3.4 (see the Technology Guides at the end of the chapter).

All three secant lines pass though the point $(2, f(2)) = (2, 51.6)$ on the graph of f. Each of them passes through a second point on the curve (the second point is different for each secant line) and this second point gets closer and closer to (2, 51.6) as h gets closer to 0. What seems to be happening is that the secant lines are getting closer and closer to a line that just touches the curve at (2, 51.6): the **tangent line** at (2, 51.6), shown in Figure 24.

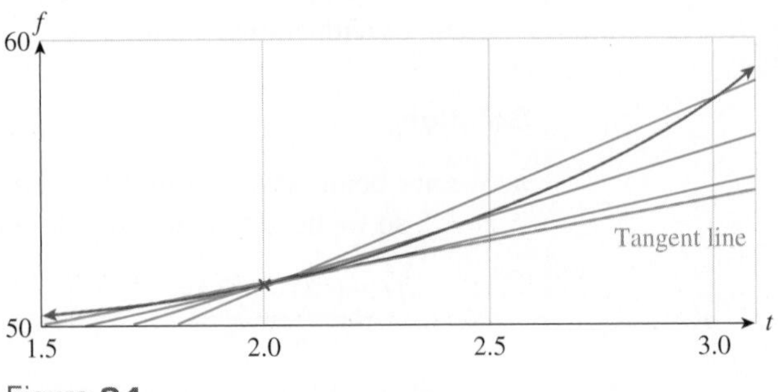

Figure **24**

Q: *What is the slope of this tangent line?*

A: Because the slopes of the secant lines are getting closer and closer to 3.2, and because the secant lines are approaching the tangent line, the tangent line must have slope 3.2. In other words,

At the point on the graph where $x = 2$, the slope of the tangent line is $f'(2)$. ■

Be sure you understand the difference between $f(2)$ and $f'(2)$: Briefly, $f(2)$ is the *value of f* when $t = 2$, while $f'(2)$ is the *rate at which f is changing* when $t = 2$. Here,

$$f(2) = 50 + 0.1(2)^4 = 51.6°\text{F}$$

Thus, at 9:00 AM ($t = 2$), the temperature was 51.6°F. On the other hand,

$$f'(2) = 3.2°\text{F/hour}$$ Units of slope are units of f per unit of t.

This means that, at 9:00 AM ($t = 2$), the temperature was increasing at a rate of 3.2°F per hour.

Because we have been talking about tangent lines, we should say more about what they *are*. A tangent line to a *circle* is a line that touches the circle in just one point. A tangent line gives the circle "a glancing blow," as shown in Figure 25.

For a smooth curve other than a circle, a tangent line may touch the curve at more than one point, or pass through it (Figure 26).

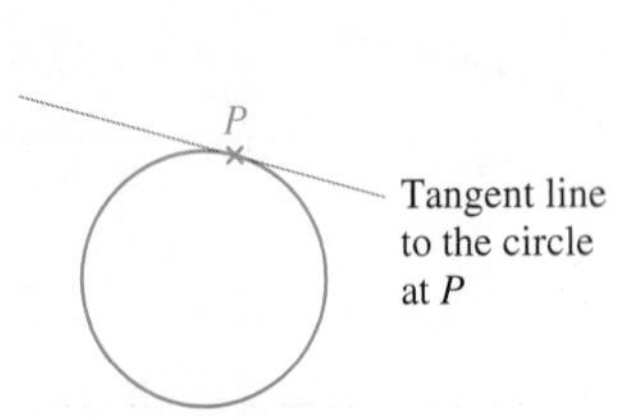

Figure **25**

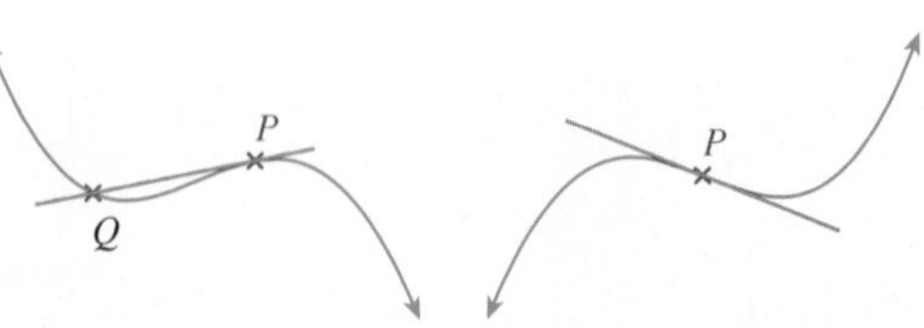

Tangent line at P intersects graph at Q

Tangent line at P passes through curve at P

Figure **26**

However, all tangent lines have the following interesting property in common: If we focus on a small portion of the curve very close to the point P—in other words, if we "zoom in" to the graph near the point P—the curve will appear almost straight, and almost indistinguishable from the tangent line. (Figure 27).

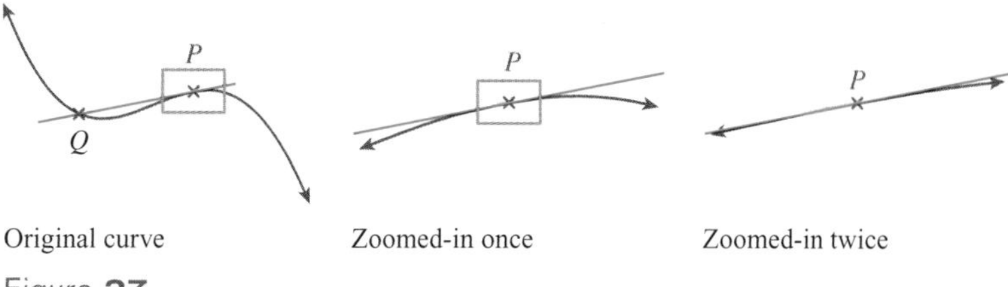

Original curve Zoomed-in once Zoomed-in twice

Figure **27**

You can check this property by zooming in on the curve shown in Figures 23 and 24 in the above example near the point where $x = 2$.

Secant and Tangent Lines

The *slope of the secant line* through the points on the graph of f where $x = a$ and $x = a + h$ is given by the average rate of change, or difference quotient,

$$m_{\text{sec}} = \text{slope of secant} = \text{average rate of change} = \frac{f(a+h) - f(a)}{h}$$

The *slope of the tangent line* through the point on the graph of f where $x = a$ is given by the instantaneous rate of change, or derivative

$$m_{\text{tan}} = \text{slope of tangent} = \text{derivative} = f'(a) = \lim_{h \to 0} \frac{f(a+h) - f(a)}{h}$$

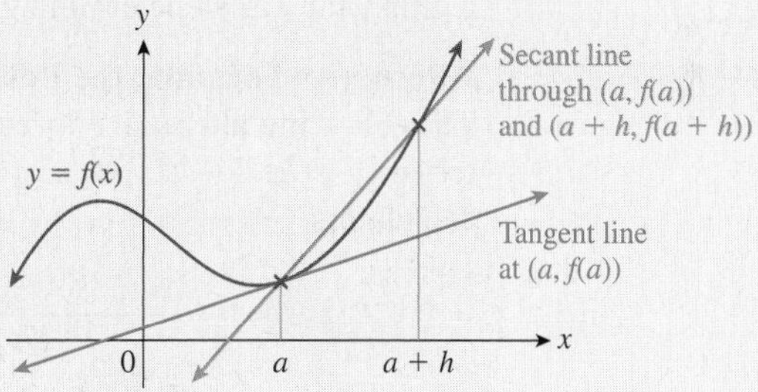

quick Example In the following graph, the tangent line at the point where $x = 2$ has slope 3. Therefore, the derivative at $x = 2$ is 3. That is, $f'(2) = 3$.

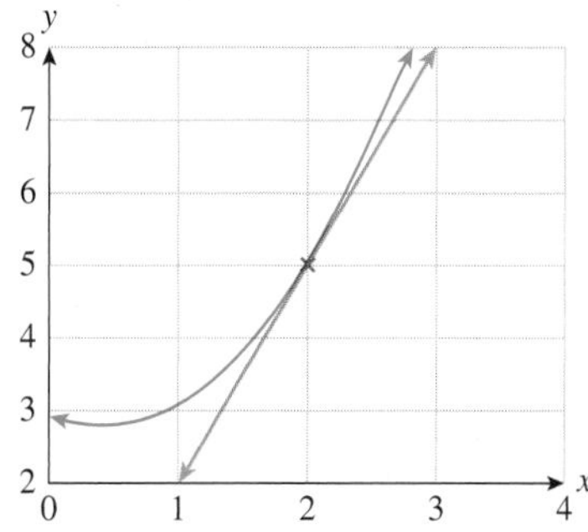

Note It might happen that the tangent line is vertical at some point or does not exist at all. These are the cases in which f is not differentiable at the given point. (See Sections 3.6 and 3.7.) ■

We can now give a more precise definition of what we mean by the tangent line to a point P on the graph of f at a given point: The **tangent line** to the graph of f at the point $P(a, f(a))$ is the straight line passing through P with slope $f'(a)$.

Quick Approximation of the Derivative

Q: *Do we always need to make tables of difference quotients as above in order to calculate an approximate value for the derivative?*

A: We can usually *approximate* the value of the derivative by using a single, small value of h. In the example above, the value $h = 0.0001$ would have given a pretty good approximation. The problems with using a fixed value of h are that (1) we do not get an *exact* answer, only an *approximation* of the derivative, and (2) how good an approximation it is depends on the function we're differentiating.[41] However, with most of the functions we'll be considering, setting $h = 0.0001$ does give us a good approximation. ■

Calculating a Quick Approximation of the Derivative

We can calculate an approximate value of $f'(a)$ by using the formula

$$f'(a) \approx \frac{f(a+h) - f(a)}{h} \qquad \text{Rate of change over } [a,\ a+h]$$

with a small value of h. The value $h = 0.0001$ often works (but see the next example for a graphical way of determining a good value to use).

Alternative Formula: the Balanced Difference Quotient
The following alternative formula, which measures the rate of change of f over the interval $[a - h, a + h]$, often gives a more accurate result, and is the one used in many calculators:

$$f'(a) \approx \frac{f(a+h) - f(a-h)}{2h} \qquad \text{Rate of change over } [a-h,\ a+h]$$

Note For the quick approximations to be valid, the function f must be differentiable; that is, $f'(a)$ must exist. ■

Example 2 Quick Approximation of the Derivative

a. Calculate an approximate value of $f'(1.5)$ if $f(x) = x^2 - 4x$.

b. Find the equation of the tangent line at the point on the graph where $x = 1.5$.

[41] In fact, no matter how small the value we decide to use for h, it is possible to craft a function f for which the difference quotient at a is not even close to $f'(a)$.

Solution

a. We shall compute both the ordinary difference quotient and the balanced difference quotient. Using $h = 0.0001$, the ordinary difference quotient is:

$$f'(1.5) \approx \frac{f(1.5 + 0.0001) - f(1.5)}{0.0001} \qquad \text{Usual difference quotient}$$

$$= \frac{f(1.5001) - f(1.5)}{0.0001}$$

$$= \frac{(1.5001^2 - 4 \times 1.5001) - (1.5^2 - 4 \times 1.5)}{0.0001} = -0.9999$$

This answer is accurate to 0.0001; in fact, $f'(1.5) = -1$.

Graphically, we can picture this approximation as follows: Zoom in on the curve using the window $1.5 \le x \le 1.5001$ and measure the slope of the secant line joining both ends of the curve segment. Figure 28 shows close-up views of the curve and tangent line near the point P in which we are interested, the third view being the zoomed-in view used for this approximation.

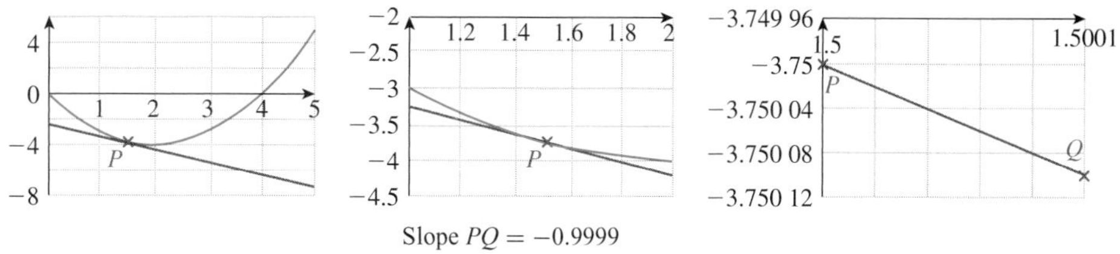

Figure **28**

Notice that in the third window the tangent line and curve are indistinguishable. Also, the point P in which we are interested is on the left edge of the window.

Turning to the balanced difference quotient, we get

$$f'(1.5) \approx \frac{f(1.5 + 0.0001) - f(1.5 - 0.0001)}{2(0.0001)} \qquad \text{Balanced difference quotient}$$

$$= \frac{f(1.5001) - f(1.4999)}{0.0002}$$

$$= \frac{(1.5001^2 - 4 \times 1.5001) - (1.4999^2 - 4 \times 1.4999)}{0.0002} = -1$$

This balanced difference quotient gives the exact answer in this case!* Graphically, it is as though we have zoomed in using a window that puts the point P in the *center* of the screen (Figure 29) rather than at the left edge.

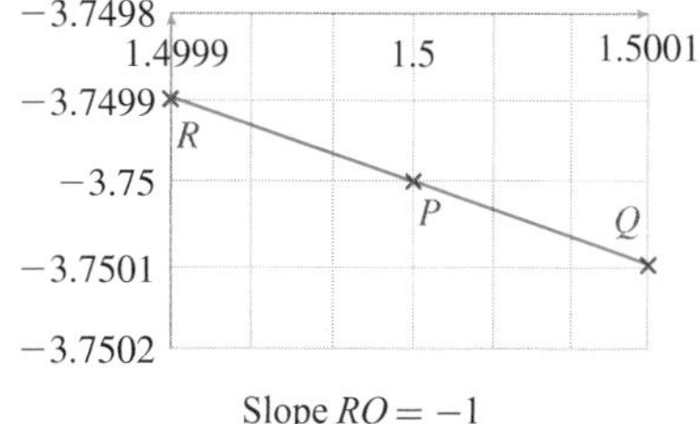

Figure **29**

*The balanced difference quotient always gives the exact derivative for a quadratic function.

using Technology

See the Technology Guides at the end of the chapter to find out how to compute the usual and balanced difference quotient very easily.

b. To find the equation of the tangent line, we use the point-slope formula from Chapter 1:

- ***Point*** $(1.5, f(1.5)) = (1.5, -3.75)$.
- ***Slope*** $m = f'(1.5) = -1$. Slope of the tangent line = derivative

The equation is

$$y = mx + b$$

where $m = -1$ and $b = y_1 - mx_1 = -3.75 - (-1)(1.5) = -2.25$. Thus, the equation of the tangent line is

$$y = -x - 2.25$$

Q: *Why can't we simply put* $h = 0.000\,000\,000\,000\,000\,000\,01$ *for an incredibly accurate approximation to the instantaneous rate of change and be done with it?*

A: This approach would certainly work if you were patient enough to do the (thankless) calculation by hand! However, doing it with the help of technology—even an ordinary calculator—will cause problems: The issue is that calculators and spreadsheets represent numbers with a maximum number of significant digits (15 in the case of Excel). As the value of h gets smaller, the value of $f(a+h)$ gets closer and closer to the value of $f(a)$. For example, if $f(x) = 50 + 0.1x^4$, Excel might compute

$$\begin{aligned} &f(2 + 0.000\,000\,000\,000\,1) - f(2) \\ &\quad = 51.600\,000\,000\,000\,3 - 51.6 \qquad \text{Rounded to 15 digits} \\ &\quad = 0.000\,000\,000\,000\,3 \end{aligned}$$

and the corresponding difference quotient would be 3, not 3.2 as it should be. If h gets even smaller, Excel will not be able to distinguish between $f(a+h)$ and $f(a)$ at all, in which case it will compute 0 for the rate of change. This loss in accuracy when subtracting two very close numbers is called **subtractive error.**

Thus, there is a trade-off in lowering the value of h: smaller values of h yield *mathematically* more accurate approximations of the derivative, but if h gets too small, subtractive error becomes a problem and decreases the accuracy of computations that use technology. ■

Leibniz *d* Notation

We introduced the notation $f'(x)$ for the derivative of f at x, but there is another interesting notation. We have written the average rate of change as

$$\text{Average rate of change} = \frac{\Delta f}{\Delta x} \qquad \frac{\text{change in } f}{\text{change in } x}$$

As we use smaller and smaller values for Δx, we approach the instantaneous rate of change, or derivative, for which we also have the notation df/dx, due to Leibniz:

$$\text{Instantaneous rate of change} = \lim_{\Delta x \to 0} \frac{\Delta f}{\Delta x} = \frac{df}{dx}$$

That is, df/dx is just another notation for $f'(x)$. Do not think of df/dx as an actual quotient of two numbers: remember that we only use an actual quotient $\Delta f/\Delta x$ to *approximate* the value of df/dx.

In Example 3, we apply the quick approximation method of estimating the derivative.

Photodisc/Getty Images

Example 3 Velocity

My friend Eric, an enthusiastic baseball player, claims he can "probably" throw a ball upward at a speed of 100 feet per second (ft/sec).* Our physicist friends tell us that its height s (in feet) t seconds later would be $s = 100t - 16t^2$. Find its average velocity over the interval [2, 3] and its instantaneous velocity exactly 2 seconds after Eric throws it.

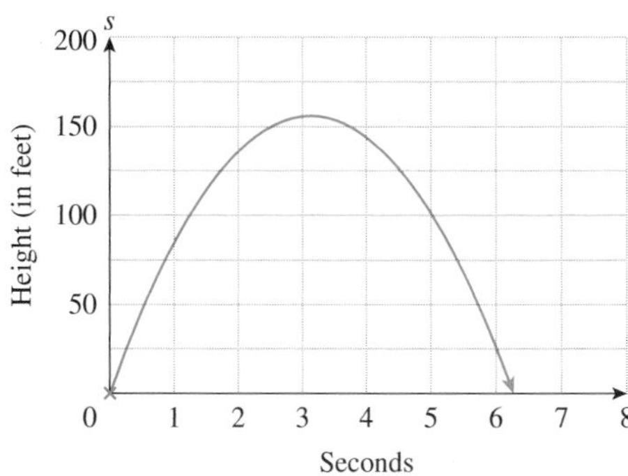

Figure **30**

Solution The graph of the ball's height as a function of time is shown in Figure 30. Asking for the velocity is really asking for the rate of change of height with respect to time. (Why?) Consider average velocity first. To compute the **average velocity** of the ball from time 2 to time 3, we first compute the change in height:

$$\Delta s = s(3) - s(2) = 156 - 136 = 20 \text{ ft}$$

Since it rises 20 feet in $\Delta t = 1$ second, we use the defining formula *speed* $=$ *distance*/*time* to get the average velocity:

$$\text{Average velocity} = \frac{\Delta s}{\Delta t} = \frac{20}{1} = 20 \text{ ft/sec}$$

from time $t = 2$ to $t = 3$. This is just the difference quotient, so

The average velocity is the average rate of change of height.

To get the **instantaneous velocity** at $t = 2$, we find the instantaneous rate of change of height. In other words, we need to calculate the derivative ds/dt at $t = 2$. Using the balanced quick approximation described above, we get

$$\begin{aligned}\frac{ds}{dt} &\approx \frac{s(2+0.0001) - s(2-0.0001)}{2(0.0001)} \\ &= \frac{s(2.0001) - s(1.9999)}{0.0002} \\ &= \frac{100(2.0001) - 16(2.0001)^2 - (100(1.9999) - 16(1.9999)^2)}{0.0002} \\ &= 36 \text{ ft/sec}\end{aligned}$$

In fact, this happens to be the exact answer; the instantaneous velocity at $t = 2$ is exactly 36 ft/sec. (Try an even smaller value of h to persuade yourself.)

*Eric's claim is difficult to believe; 100 ft/sec corresponds to around 68 mph, and professional pitchers can throw *forward* at about 100 mph.

+ *Before we go on...* If we repeat the calculation in Example 3 at time $t = 5$, we get

$$\frac{ds}{dt} = -60 \text{ ft/s}$$

The negative sign tells us that the ball is *falling* at a rate of 60 feet per second at time $t = 5$. (How does the fact that it is falling at $t = 5$ show up on the graph?)

The preceding example gives another interpretation of the derivative. ■

Average and Instantaneous Velocity

For an object moving in a straight line with position $s(t)$ at time t, the **average velocity** from time t to time $t + h$ is the average rate of change of position with respect to time:

$$v_{ave} = \frac{s(t+h) - s(t)}{h} = \frac{\Delta s}{\Delta t}$$

Average velocity = Average rate of change of position

The **instantaneous velocity** at time t is

$$v = \lim_{h \to 0} \frac{s(t+h) - s(t)}{h} = \frac{ds}{dt}$$

Instantaneous velocity = Instantaneous rate of change of position

In other words, *instantaneous velocity is the derivative of position with respect to time.*

Here is one last comment on Leibniz notation. In Example 3, we could have written the velocity either as s' or as ds/dt, as we chose to do. To write the answer to the question, that the velocity at $t = 2$ sec was 36 ft/sec, we can write either

$$s'(2) = 36$$

or

$$\left.\frac{ds}{dt}\right|_{t=2} = 36$$

The notation "$|_{t=2}$" is read "evaluated at $t = 2$." Similarly, if $y = f(x)$, we can write the instantaneous rate of change of f at $x = 5$ in either functional notation as

$$f'(5) \qquad \text{The derivative of } f \text{, evaluated at } x = 5$$

or in Leibniz notation as

$$\left.\frac{dy}{dx}\right|_{x=5} \qquad \text{The derivative of } y \text{, evaluated at } x = 5$$

The latter notation is obviously more cumbersome than the functional notation $f'(5)$, but the notation dy/dx has compensating advantages. You should practice using both notations.

The Derivative Function

The derivative $f'(x)$ is a number we can calculate, or at least approximate, for various values of x. Because $f'(x)$ depends on the value of x, we may think of f' as a function of x. This function is the **derivative function.**

Derivative Function

If f is a function, its **derivative function** f' is the function whose value $f'(x)$ is the derivative of f at x. Its domain is the set of all x at which f is differentiable. Equivalently, f' associates to each x the slope of the tangent to the graph of the function f at x, or the rate of change of f at x. The formula for the derivative function is

$$f'(x) = \lim_{h \to 0} \frac{f(x+h) - f(x)}{h} \qquad \text{Derivative function}$$

quick Examples

1. Let $f(x) = 3x - 1$. The graph of f is a straight line that has slope 3 everywhere. In other words, $f'(x) = 3$ for every choice of x; that is, f' is a constant function.

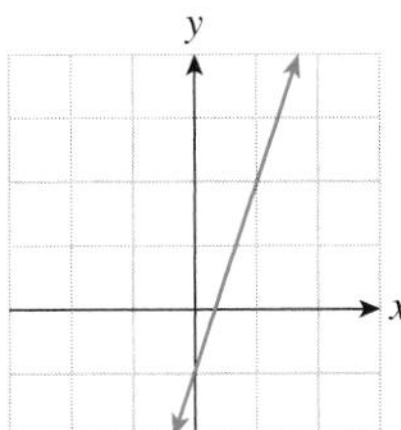

Original Function f
$f(x) = 3x - 1$

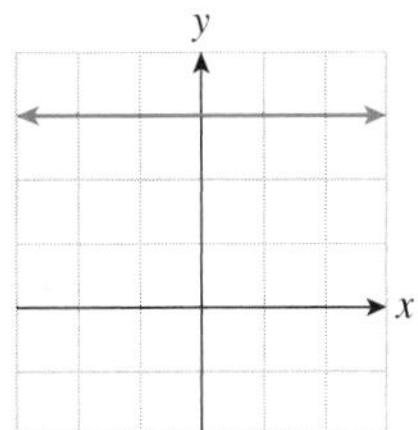

Derivative Function f'
$f'(x) = 3$

2. Given the graph of a function f, we can get a rough sketch of the graph of f' by estimating the slope of the tangent to the graph of f at several points, as illustrated below.*

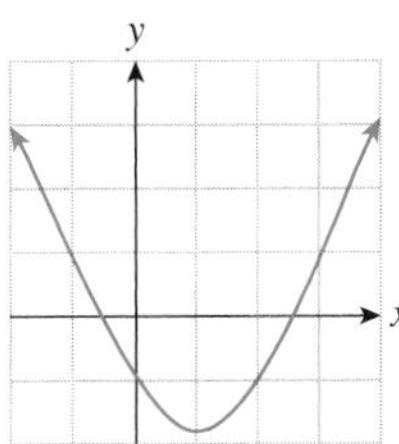

Original Function f
$y = f(x)$

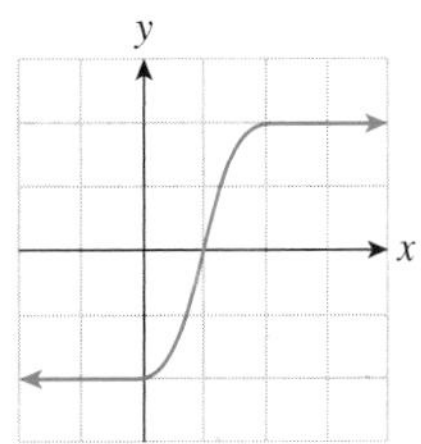

Derivative Function f'
$y = f'(x)$

For x between -2 and 0, the graph of f is linear with slope -2. As x increases from 0 to 2, the slope increases from -2 to 2. For x larger than 2, the graph of f is linear with slope 2. (Notice that, when $x = 1$, the graph of f has a horizontal tangent, so $f'(1) = 0$.)

* This method is discussed in detail online at Chapter 3 → Online Text → Sketching the Graph of the Derivative.

The following example shows how we can use technology to graph the (approximate) derivative of a function, where it exists.

Example 4 Tabulating and Graphing the Derivative with Technology

Use technology to obtain a table of values of and graph the derivative of $f(x) = -2x^2 + 6x + 5$ for values of x starting at -5.

Solution The TI-83 has a built-in function that approximates the derivative, and we can use it to graph the derivative of a function. In Excel, we need to create the approximation using one of the quick approximation formulas and we can then graph a table of its values. See the Technology Guides at the end of the chapter to find out how to graph the derivative (Figure 31) using the TI-83/84 and Excel.

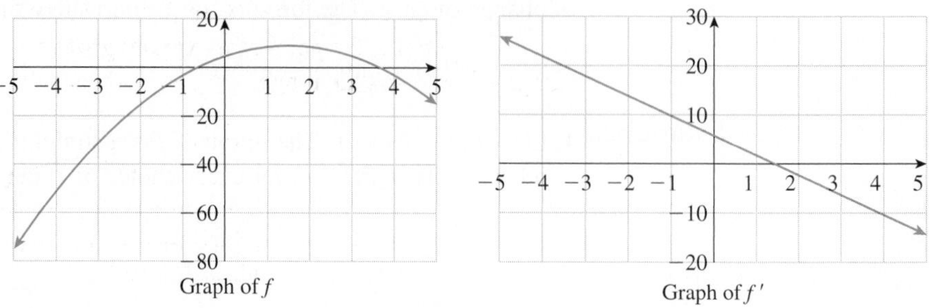

Figure **31**

We said that f' records the slope of (the tangent line to) the function f at each point. Notice that the graph of f' confirms that the slope of the graph of f is decreasing as x increases from -5 to 5. Note also that the graph of f reaches a high point at $x = 1.5$ (the vertex of the parabola). At that point, the slope of the tangent is zero; that is, $f'(1.5) = 0$ as we see in the graph of f'.

Example **5** An Application: Market Growth

The number N of U.S. households connected to the Internet from the start of 1999 could be modeled by the logistic function

$$N(t) = \frac{79.317}{1 + 2.2116(1.3854)^{-t}} \text{ million households} \qquad (0 \le t \le 9)$$

where t is the number of quarters since the start of 1999.* Graph both N and its derivative, and determine when Internet usage was growing most rapidly.

Solution Using one of the methods in Example 4, we obtain the graphs shown in Figure 32.

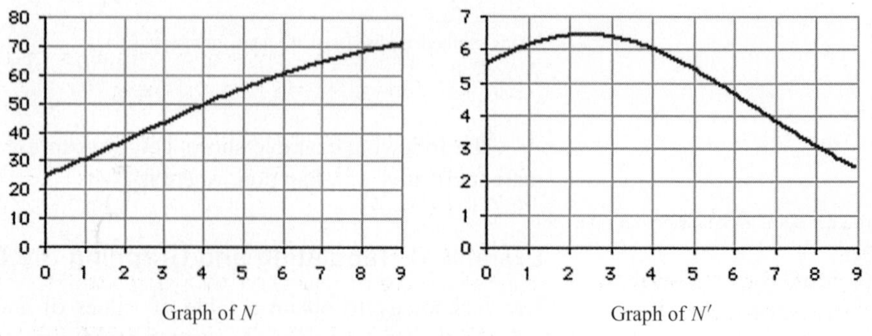

Figure **32**

*The model was obtained In Section 2.4 by logistic regression. Sources for data: Telecommunications Reports International/*New York Times,* May 21, 2001, p. C9.

From the graph on the right, we see that N' reaches a peak somewhere between $t = 2$ and $t = 3$ (sometime during the third quarter of 1999). Recalling that N' measures the *slope* of the graph of N, we can conclude that the graph of N is steepest between $t = 2$ and $t = 3$, indicating that, according to the model, the number of U.S. households connected to the Internet was growing most rapidly during the third quarter of 1999. Notice that this is not so easy to see directly on the graph of N.

To determine the point of maximum growth more accurately, we can zoom in on the graph of N' using the range $2 \le t \le 3$ (Figure 33).

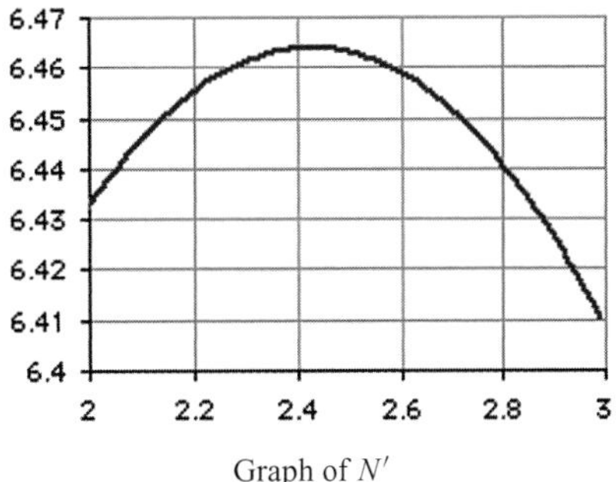

Figure **33**

We can now see that N' reaches its highest point around $t = 2.4$, so we conclude that the number of U.S. households connected to the Internet was growing most rapidly shortly before the midpoint of the third quarter of 1999.

+*Before we go on...* Besides helping us to determine the point of maximum growth, the graph of N' in Example 5 gives us a great deal of additional information. As just one example, in Figure 32 we can see that the maximum value of N' is approximately 6.5, indicating that Internet usage in the U.S. never grew at a faster rate than about 6.5 million households per quarter. ■

FAQs Recognizing When and How to Compute the Instantaneous Rate of Change

Q: *How do I know, by looking at the wording of a problem, that it is asking for an instantaneous rate of change?*

A: If a problem does not ask for an instantaneous rate of change directly, it might do so indirectly, as in "How fast is quantity *q* increasing?" or "Find the rate of increase of *q*." ■

Q: *If I know that a problem calls for estimating an instantaneous rate of change, how should I estimate it: with a table showing smaller and smaller values of h, or by using a quick approximation?*

A: For most practical purposes, a quick approximation is accurate enough. Use a table showing smaller and smaller values of *h* when you would like to check the accuracy. ■

Q: *Which should I use in computing a quick approximation: the balanced difference quotient or the ordinary difference quotient?*

A: In general, the balanced difference quotient gives a more accurate answer. ■

You can find the following optional sections:

Continuity and Differentiability

Sketching the Graph of the Derivative

Online, follow:

Chapter 3

→ Online Text

3.5 EXERCISES

● denotes basic skills exercises

◆ denotes challenging exercises

tech Ex indicates exercises that should be solved using technology

In Exercises 1–4, estimate the derivative from the table of average rates of change. hint [see discussion at the beginning of the section]

1. ●

h	1	0.1	0.01	0.001	0.0001
Ave. rate of change of f over $[5, 5+h]$	12	6.4	6.04	6.004	6.0004
h	−1	−0.1	−0.01	−0.001	−0.0001
Ave. rate of change of f over $[5+h, 5]$	3	5.6	5.96	5.996	5.9996

Estimate $f'(5)$.

2. ●

h	1	0.1	0.01	0.001	0.0001
Ave. rate of change of g over $[7, 7+h]$	4	4.8	4.98	4.998	4.9998
h	−1	−0.1	−0.01	−0.001	−0.0001
Ave. rate of change of g over $[7+h, 7]$	5	5.3	5.03	5.003	5.0003

Estimate $g'(7)$.

3. ●

h	1	0.1	0.01	0.001	0.0001
Ave. rate of change of r over $[-6, -6+h]$	−5.4	−5.498	−5.4998	−5.499982	−5.49999822
h	−1	−0.1	−0.01	−0.001	−0.0001
Ave. rate of change of r over $[-6+h, -6]$	−7.52	−6.13	−5.5014	−5.5000144	−5.500001444

Estimate $r'(-6)$.

4. ●

h	1	0.1	0.01	0.001	0.0001
Ave. rate of change of s over $[0, h]$	−2.52	−1.13	0.6014	−0.6000144	−0.600001444
h	−1	−0.1	−0.01	−0.001	−0.0001
Ave. rate of change of s over $[h, 0]$	−0.4	−0.598	−0.5998	−0.599982	−0.59999822

Estimate $s'(0)$.

Consider the functions in Exercises 5–8 as representing the value of an ounce of silver in Indian rupees as a function of the time t in days.[42] *Find the average rates of change of $R(t)$ over the time intervals $[t, t+h]$, where t is as indicated and $h = 1, 0.1,$ and 0.01 days. Hence, estimate the instantaneous rate of change of R at time t, specifying the units of measurement. (Use smaller values of h to check your estimates.)* hint [see Example 1]

5. ● $R(t) = 50t - t^2; t = 5$

6. ● $R(t) = 60t - 2t^2; t = 3$

7. ● $R(t) = 100 + 20t^3; t = 1$

8. ● $R(t) = 1000 + 50t - t^3; t = 2$

Each of the functions in Exercises 9–12 gives the cost to manufacture x items. Find the average cost per unit of manufacturing h more items (i.e., the average rate of change of the total cost) at a production level of x, where x is as indicated and $h = 10$ and 1. Hence, estimate the instantaneous rate of change of the total cost at the given production level x, specifying the units of measurement. (Use smaller values of h to check your estimates.)

9. ● $C(x) = 10{,}000 + 5x - \dfrac{x^2}{10{,}000};\ x = 1000$

10. ● $C(x) = 20{,}000 + 7x - \dfrac{x^2}{20{,}000};\ x = 10{,}000$

11. ● $C(x) = 15{,}000 + 100x + \dfrac{1000}{x};\ x = 100$

12. ● $C(x) = 20{,}000 + 50x + \dfrac{10{,}000}{x};\ x = 100$

In each of the graphs given in Exercises 13–18, say at which labeled point the slope of the tangent is (a) greatest and (b) least (in the sense that −7 is less than 1).

13. ●

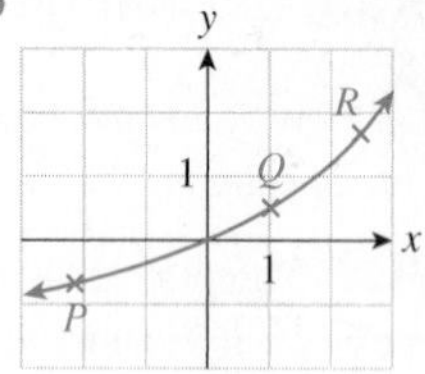

14. ●

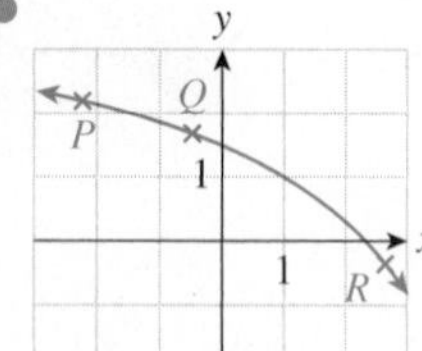

15. ●

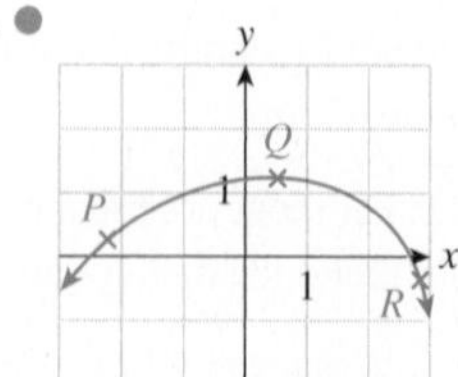

16. ●

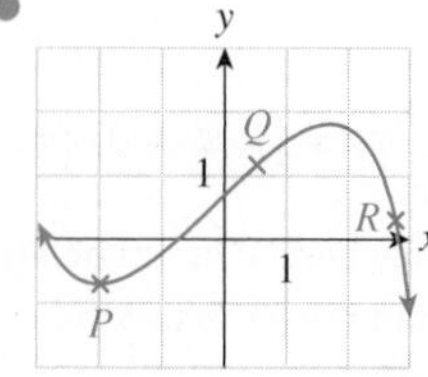

[42] Silver was trading at around 290 rupees in July, 2004.

17. ●

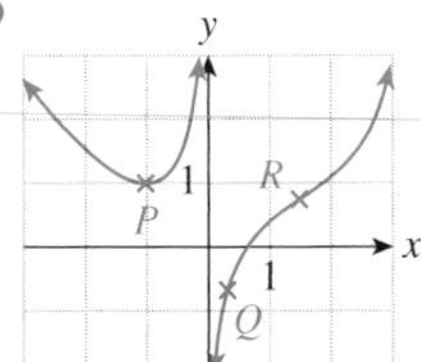

18. ●

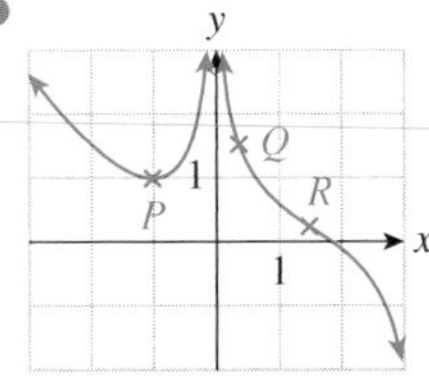

In Exercises 19–22, the graph of a function is shown together with the tangent line at a point P. Estimate the derivative of f at the corresponding x-value. hint [see Quick Example on p. 229]

19. ●

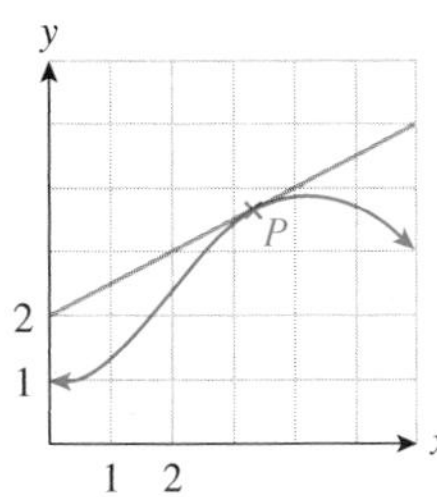

20. ●

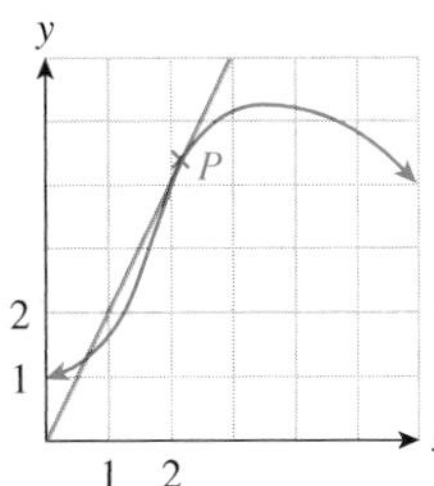

21. ●

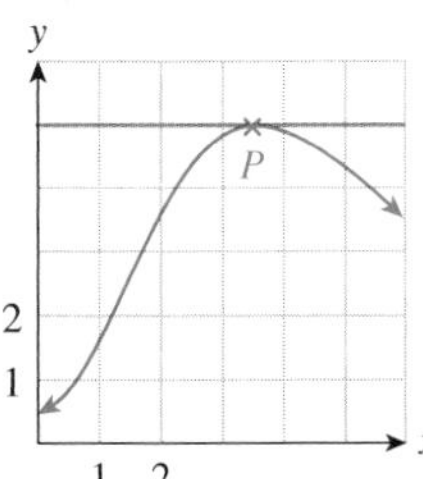

22. ●

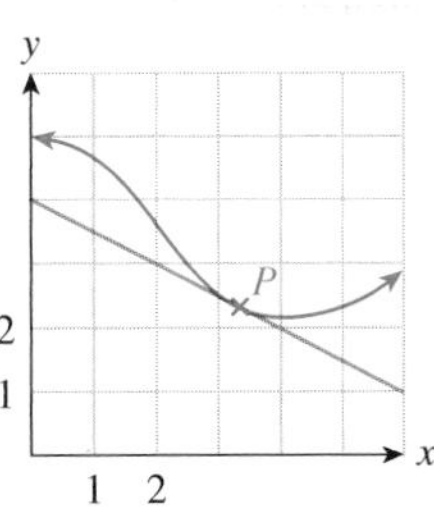

In each of Exercises 23–26, three slopes are given. For each slope, determine at which of the labeled points on the graph the tangent line has that slope.

23. ● **a.** 0 **b.** 4 **c.** −1

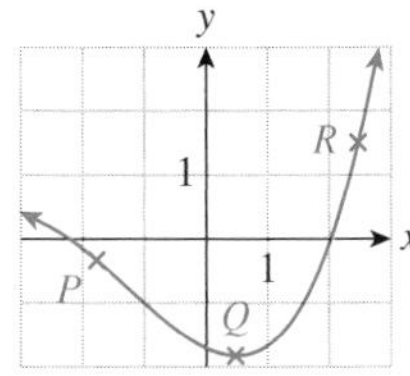

24. ● **a.** 0 **b.** 1 **c.** −1

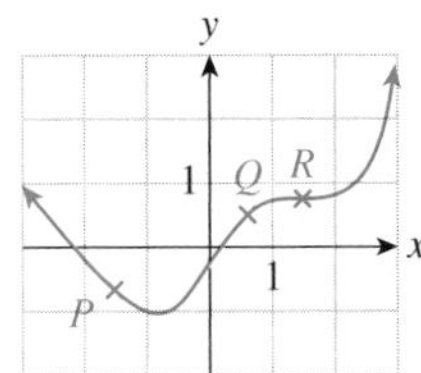

25. ● **a.** 0 **b.** 3 **c.** −3

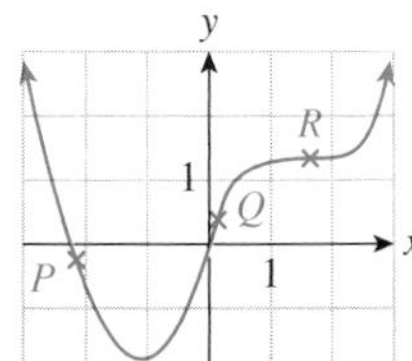

26. ● **a.** 0 **b.** 3 **c.** 1

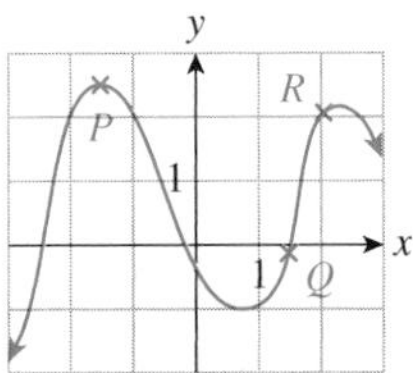

In each of Exercises 27–30, find the approximate coordinates of all points (if any) where the slope of the tangent is: ***(a)*** *0,* ***(b)*** *1,* ***(c)*** *−1.*

27. ●

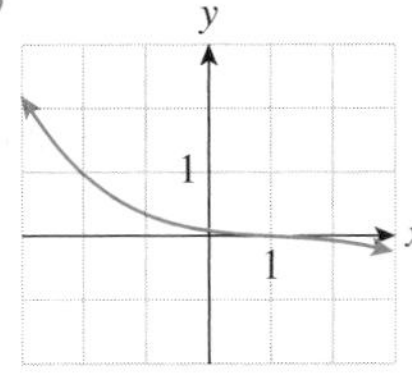

28. ●

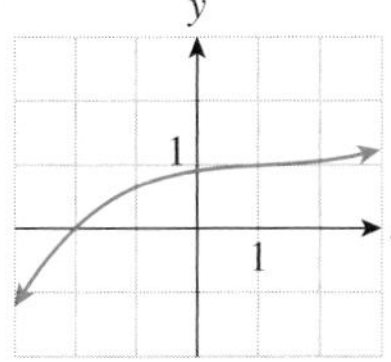

29. ●

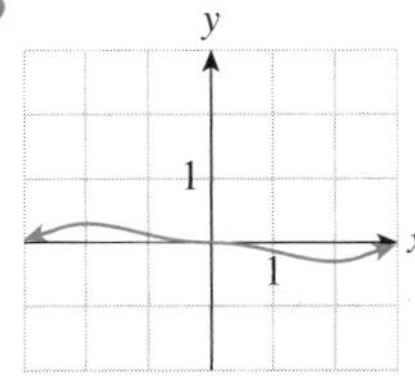

30. ●

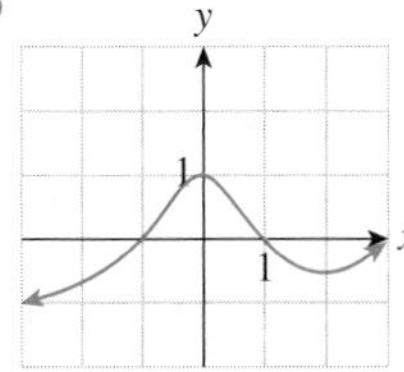

31. ● Complete the following: The tangent to the graph of the function f at the point where $x = a$ is the line passing through the point ____ with slope ____ .

32. ● Complete the following: The difference quotient for f at the point where $x = a$ gives the slope of the ____ line that passes through _____ .

33. ● Which is correct? The derivative function assigns to each value x

(A) the average rate of change of f at x.

(B) the slope of the tangent to the graph of f at $(x, f(x))$.

(C) the rate at which f is changing over the interval $[x, x + h]$ for $h = 0.0001$.

(D) the balanced difference quotient $[f(x + h) - f(x - h)]/(2h)$ for $h \approx 0.0001$.

34. ● Which is correct? The derivative function $f'(x)$ tells us

(A) the slope of the tangent line at each of the points $(x, f(x))$.

(B) the approximate slope of the tangent line at each of the points $(x, f(x))$.

(C) the slope of the secant line through $(x, f(x))$ and $(x + h, f(x + h))$ for $h = 0.0001$.

(D) the slope of a certain secant line through each of the points $(x, f(x))$.

35. Let f have the graph shown.

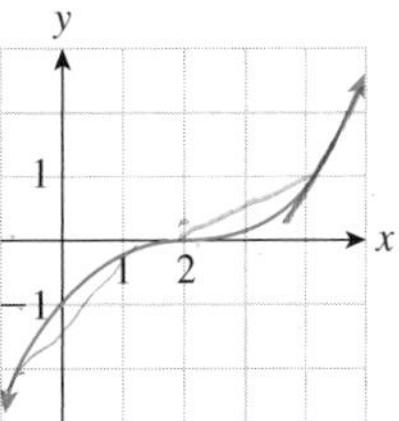

a. The average rate of change of f over the interval [2, 4] is
(A) greater than **(B)** less than
(C) approximately equal to $f'(2)$.

b. The average rate of change of f over the interval $[-1, 1]$ is
(A) greater than **(B)** less than
(C) approximately equal to $f'(0)$.

c. Over the interval [0, 2], the instantaneous rate of change of f is
(A) increasing **(B)** decreasing
(C) neither.

d. Over the interval [0, 4], the instantaneous rate of change of f is
(A) increasing, then decreasing.
(B) decreasing, then increasing.
(C) always increasing.
(D) always decreasing.

e. When $x = 4$, $f(x)$ is
(A) approximately 0, and increasing at a rate of about 0.7 units per unit of x.
(B) approximately 0, and decreasing at a rate of about 0.7 unit per unit of x.
(C) approximately 0.7, and increasing at a rate of about 1 unit per unit of x.
(D) approximately 0.7, and increasing at a rate of about 3 units per unit of x.

36. A function f has the following graph.

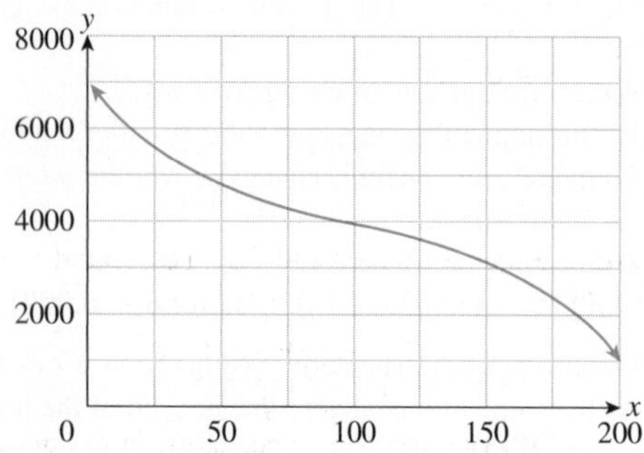

a. The average rate of change of f over [0, 200] is
(A) greater than
(B) less than
(C) approximately equal to the instantaneous rate of change at $x = 100$.

b. The average rate of change of f over [0, 200] is
(A) greater than
(B) less than
(C) approximately equal to the instantaneous rate of change at $x = 150$.

c. Over the interval [0, 50] the instantaneous rate of change of f is
(A) increasing, then decreasing.
(B) decreasing, then increasing.
(C) always increasing.
(D) always decreasing.

d. On the interval [0, 200], the instantaneous rate of change of f is
(A) Always positive. **(B)** Always negative.
(C) Negative, positive, and then negative.

e. $f'(100)$ is
(A) greater than **(B)** less than
(C) approximately equal to $f'(25)$.

In Exercises 37–40, use a quick approximation to estimate the derivative of the given function at the indicated point. hint [see Example 2a]

37. ● $f(x) = 1 - 2x;\ x = 2$ **38.** ● $f(x) = \frac{x}{3} - 1;\ x = -3$

39. ● $f(x) = \frac{x^2}{4} - \frac{x^3}{3};\ x = -1$ **40.** ● $f(x) = \frac{x^2}{2} + \frac{x}{4};\ x = 2$

In Exercises 41–48, estimate the indicated derivative by any method.

41. ● $g(t) = \frac{1}{t^5}$; estimate $g'(1)$

42. ● $s(t) = \frac{1}{t^3}$; estimate $s'(-2)$

43. ● $y = 4x^2$; estimate $\left.\frac{dy}{dx}\right|_{x=2}$

44. ● $y = 1 - x^2$; estimate $\left.\frac{dy}{dx}\right|_{x=-1}$

45. ● $s = 4t + t^2$; estimate $\left.\frac{ds}{dt}\right|_{t=-2}$

46. ● $s = t - t^2$; estimate $\left.\frac{ds}{dt}\right|_{t=2}$

47. ● $R = \frac{1}{p}$; estimate $\left.\frac{dR}{dp}\right|_{p=20}$

48. ● $R = \sqrt{p}$; estimate $\left.\frac{dR}{dp}\right|_{p=400}$

In Exercises 49–54, ***(a)*** *use any method to estimate the slope of the tangent to the graph of the given function at the point with the given x-coordinate and,* ***(b)*** *find an equation of the tangent line in part (a). In each case, sketch the curve together with the appropriate tangent line.* hint [see Example 2b]

49. ● $f(x) = x^3;\ x = -1$ **50.** ● $f(x) = x^2;\ x = 0$

51. ● $f(x) = x + \frac{1}{x};\ x = 2$ **52.** ● $f(x) = \frac{1}{x^2};\ x = 1$

53. ● $f(x) = \sqrt{x};\ x = 4$ **54.** ● $f(x) = 2x + 4;\ x = -1$

In each of Exercises 55–58, estimate the given quantity.

55. ● $f(x) = e^x$; estimate $f'(0)$

56. ● $f(x) = 2e^x$; estimate $f'(1)$

57. ● $f(x) = \ln x$; estimate $f'(1)$

58. ● $f(x) = \ln x$; estimate $f'(2)$

● basic skills ◆ challenging tech Ex technology exercise

In Exercises 59–64, match the graph of f to the graph of f' (the graphs of f' are shown after Exercise 64).

59.

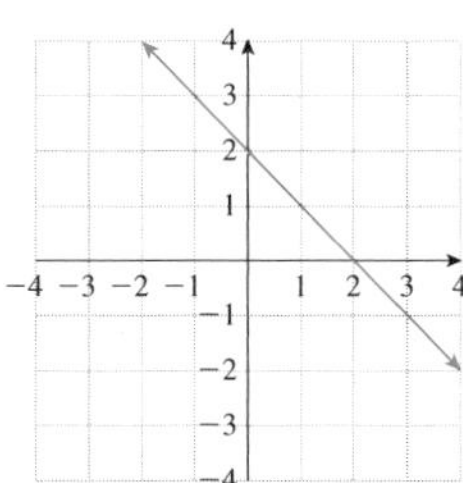

60.

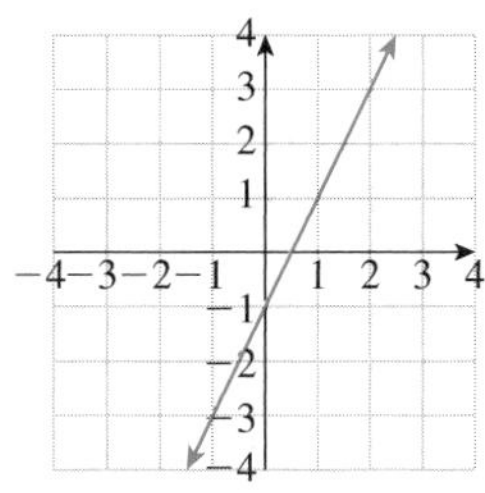

61.

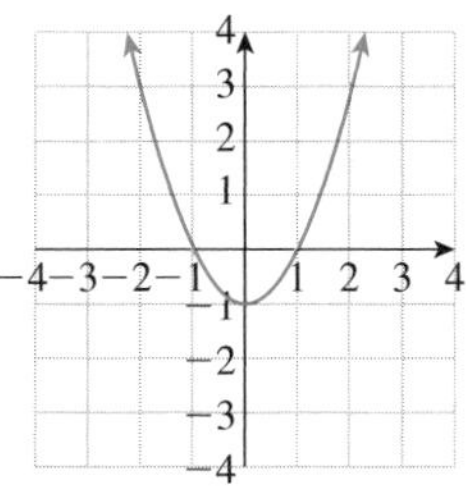

62.

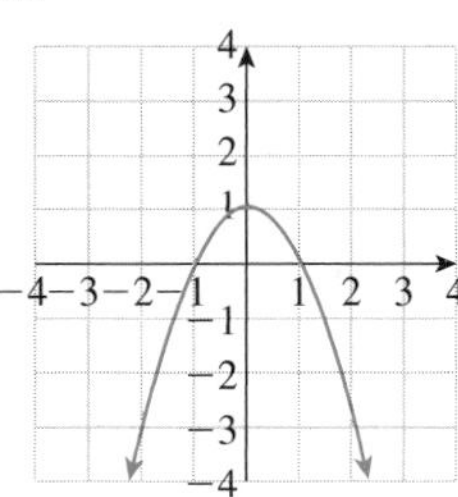

63.

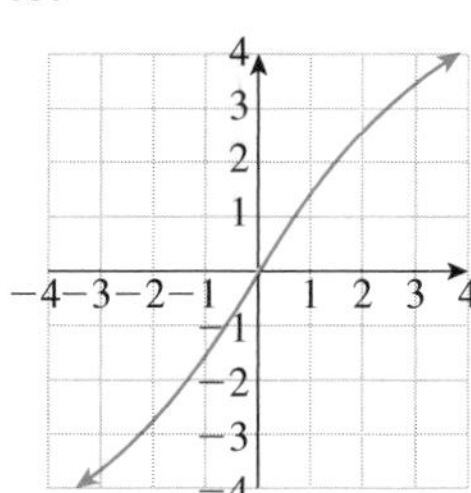

64.

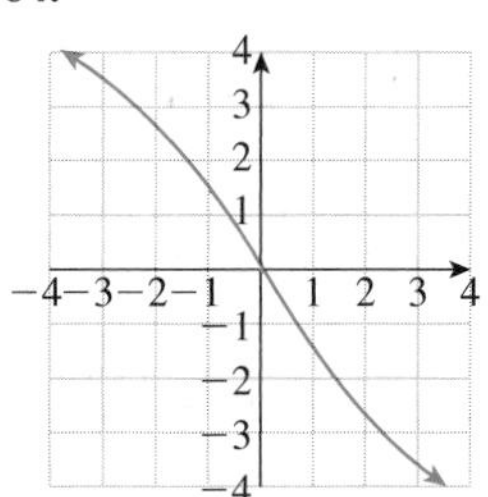

Graphs of derivatives for Exercises 59–64:

(A)

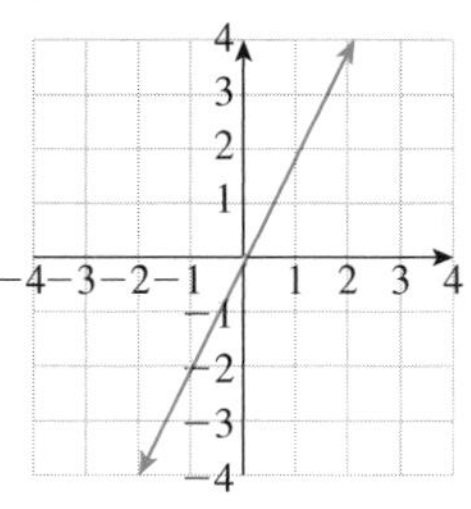

(B)

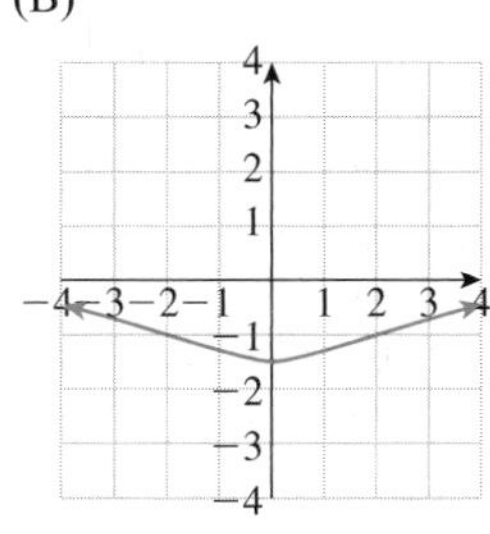

(C)

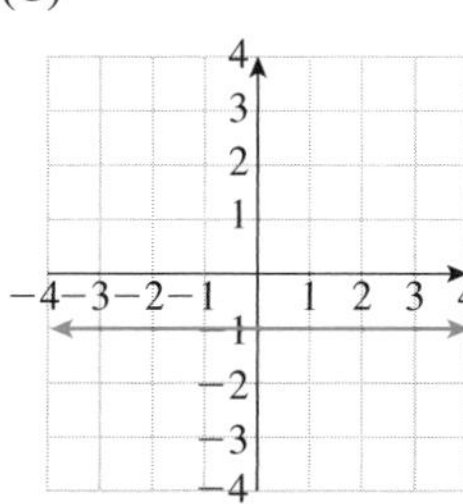

(D)

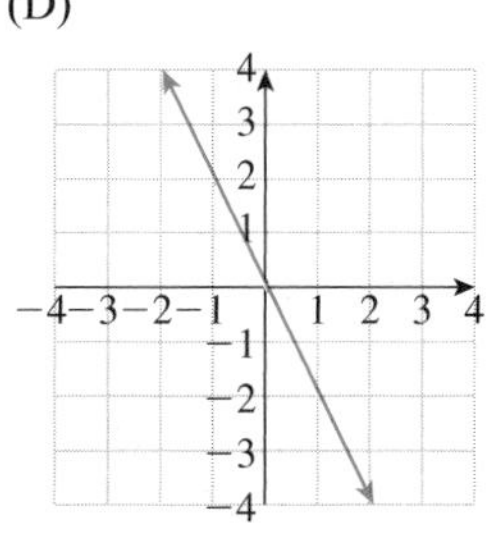

(E)

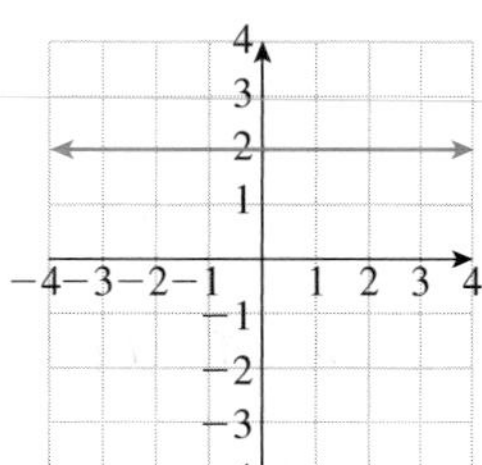

(F)

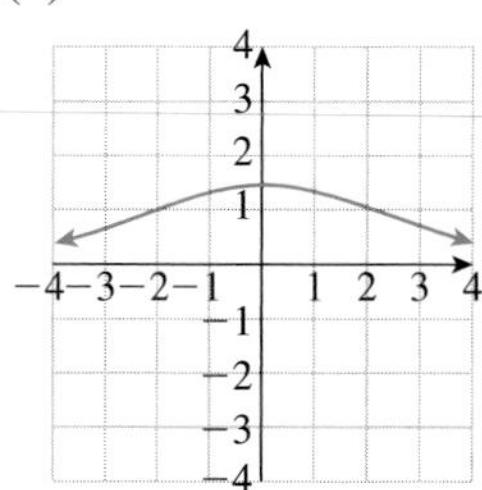

tech Ex *In Exercises 65 and 66, use technology to graph the derivative of the given function for the given range of values of x. Then use your graph to estimate all values of x (if any) where the tangent line to the graph of the given function is horizontal. Round answers to one decimal place.*
hint [see Example 1]

65. ● $f(x) = x^4 + 2x^3 - 1; -2 \leq x \leq 1$

66. ● $f(x) = -x^3 - 3x^2 - 1; -3 \leq x \leq 1$

tech Ex *In Exercises 67 and 68, use the method of Example 4 to list approximate values of $f'(x)$ for x in the given range. Graph $f(x)$ together with $f'(x)$ for x the given range.*

67. ● $f(x) = \dfrac{x+2}{x-3}; 4 \leq x \leq 5$

68. ● $f(x) = \dfrac{10x}{x-2}; 2.5 \leq x \leq 3$

Applications

69. ● ***Demand*** Suppose the demand for a new brand of sneakers is given by

$$q = \frac{5{,}000{,}000}{p}$$

where p is the price per pair of sneakers, in dollars, and q is the number of pairs of sneakers that can be sold at price p. Find $q(100)$ and estimate $q'(100)$. Interpret your answers.

70. ● ***Demand*** Suppose the demand for an old brand of TV is given by

$$q = \frac{100{,}000}{p+10}$$

where p is the price per TV set, in dollars, and q is the number of TV sets that can be sold at price p. Find $q(190)$ and estimate $q'(190)$. Interpret your answers.

71. ● ***Swimming Pool Sales*** The following graph shows the approximate annual U.S. sales of in ground swimming pools.[43]

---

[43] Based on a regression model using 1996–2002 data. Source for data: PK Data/*New York Times,* July 5, 2001, p. C1, Industry reports, June 2004 www.poolspamarketing.com/statistics/

Also shown is the tangent line (and its slope) at the point corresponding to year 2000.

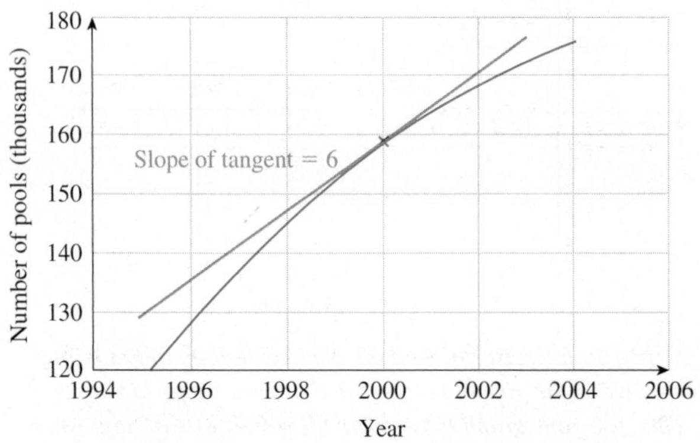

a. What does the graph tell you about swimming pool sales in 2000?

b. According to the graph, is the rate of change of swimming pool sales increasing or decreasing? Why?

72. ● ***Swimming Pool Sales*** Repeat Exercise 71 using the following graph showing approximate annual U.S. sales of above-ground swimming pools.[44]

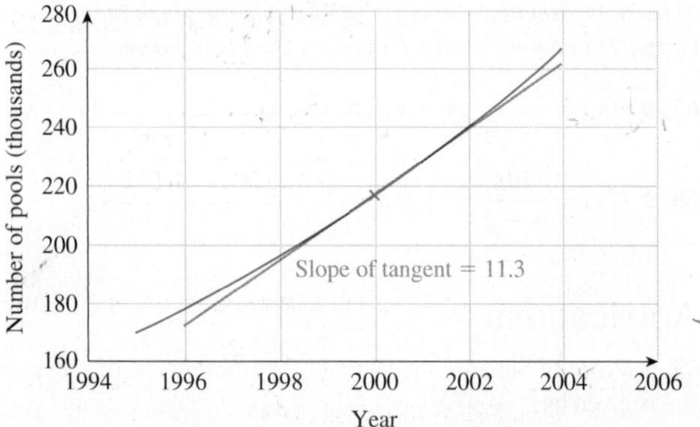

73. ***Prison Population*** The following curve is a model of the total population in state prisons as a function of time in years ($t = 0$ represents 1980).[45]

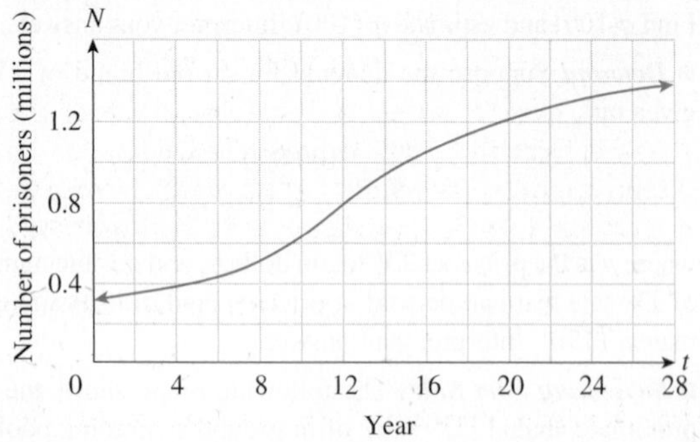

a. Which is correct? Over the period [16, 20] the instantaneous rate of change of N is

(A) increasing **(B)** decreasing.

b. Which is correct? The instantaneous rate of change of prison population at $t = 12$ was

(A) less than **(B)** greater than

(C) approximately equal to the average rate of change over the interval [0, 24].

c. Which is correct? Over the period [0, 28] the instantaneous rate of change of N is

(A) increasing, then decreasing

(B) decreasing, then increasing

(C) always increasing

(D) always decreasing

d. According to the model, the total state prison population was increasing fastest around what year?

e. Roughly estimate the instantaneous rate of change of N at $t = 16$ by using a balanced difference quotient with $h = 4$. Interpret the result.

74. ***Demand for Freon*** The demand for chlorofluorocarbon-12 (CFC-12)—the ozone-depleting refrigerant commonly known as freon[46]—has been declining significantly in response to regulation and concern about the ozone layer. The graph below represents a model for the projected demand for CFC-12 as a function of time in years ($t = 0$ represents 1990).[47]

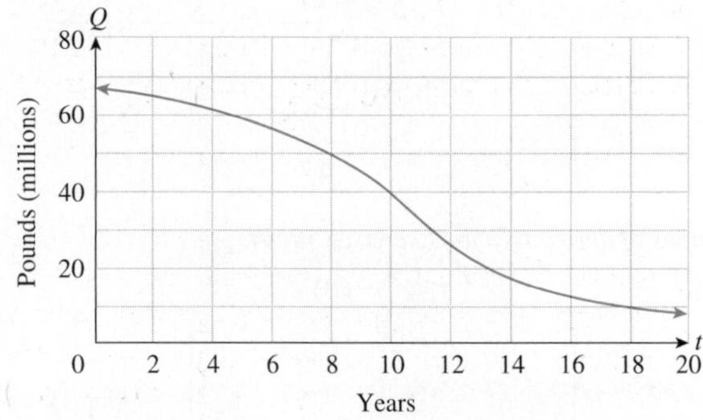

a. Which is correct? Over the period [12, 20] the instantaneous rate of change of Q is

(A) increasing **(B)** decreasing.

b. Which is correct? The instantaneous rate of change of demand for freon at $t = 10$ was

(A) less than **(B)** greater than

(C) approximately equal to the average rate of change over the interval [0, 20].

[44] Ibid.

[45] The prison population represented excludes federal prisons. Source for 1980–2000 data: Bureau of Justice Statistics/*New York Times,* June 9, 2001, p. A10.

[46] The name given to it by DuPont.

[47] Source for data: The Automobile Consulting Group/*New York Times,* December 26, 1993, p. F23. The exact figures were not given, and the chart is a reasonable facsimile of the chart that appeared in *New York Times*.

c. Which is correct? Over the period [0, 20] the instantaneous rate of change of Q is
(A) increasing, then decreasing
(B) decreasing, then increasing
(C) always increasing
(D) always decreasing

d. According to the model, the demand for freon was decreasing most rapidly around what year?

e. Roughly estimate the instantaneous rate of change of Q at $t = 13$ by using a balanced difference quotient with $h = 5$. Interpret the result.

75. ● ***Velocity*** If a stone is dropped from a height of 400 feet, its height after t seconds is given by $s = 400 - 16t^2$. *hint* [see Example 3]

a. Find its average velocity over the period [2, 4].
b. Estimate its instantaneous velocity at time $t = 4$.

76. ● ***Velocity*** If a stone is thrown down at 120 ft/sec from a height of 1000 feet, its height after t seconds is given by $s = 1000 - 120t - 16t^2$.

a. Find its average velocity over the period [1, 3].
b. Estimate its instantaneous velocity at time $t = 3$.

77. ● ***Currency*** The value of the euro (€) since its introduction in January, 1999 can be approximated by

$$e(t) = 0.036t^2 - 0.10t + 1.0 \text{ U.S. dollars} \quad (-1 \le t \le 4.5)$$

where $t = 0$ represents January, 2000.[48]

a. Compute the average rate of change of $e(t)$ over the interval [0, 4], and interpret your answer.
b. Estimate the instantaneous rate of change of $e(t)$ at $t = 0$, and interpret your answer.
c. The answers to part (a) and part (b) have opposite sign. What does this indicate about the value of the euro?

78. ● ***Interest Rates*** The prime lending rate (the lowest short-term interest rate charged by commercial banks to their most creditworthy clients) for the period January 1982–June 2004 can be approximated by

$$p(t) = 0.028t^2 - 0.52t + 9.3 \text{ percentage points} \quad (-8 \le t \le 14)$$

where $t = 0$ represents January, 1990.[49]

a. Compute the average rate of change of $p(t)$ over the interval [0, 5], and interpret your answer.
b. Estimate the instantaneous rate of change of $p(t)$ at $t = 0$, and interpret your answer.
c. The answer to part (b) has larger absolute value than the answer to part (a). What does this indicate about the prime lending rate?

79. ● ***Advertising Revenue*** The following table shows the annual advertising revenue earned by America Online (AOL) during the last three years of the 1990s.[50]

Year	1997	1998	1999
Revenue ($ million)	150	360	760

These data can be modeled by

$$R(t) = 95t^2 + 115t + 150 \text{ million dollars} \quad (0 \le t \le 2)$$

where t is time in years since December, 1997.

a. How fast was AOL's advertising revenue increasing in December 1998?
b. Which of the following is true? During 1997–1999, annual online advertising revenues
(A) increased at a faster and faster rate.
(B) increased at a slower and slower rate.
(C) decreased at a faster and faster rate.
(D) decreased at a slower and slower rate.
c. Use the model to project the instantaneous rate of change of R in December, 2000. Interpret the result.

80. ● ***Religion*** The following table shows the population of Roman Catholic nuns in the U.S. at the end of the 20th century.[51]

Year	1975	1985	1995
Population	130,000	120,000	80,000

These data can be modeled by

$$P(t) = -0.15t^2 + 0.50t + 130 \text{ thousand nuns} \quad (0 \le t \le 20)$$

where t is time in years since December, 1975.

a. How fast was the number of Roman Catholic nuns in the U.S. decreasing in December, 1995?
b. Which of the following is true? During 1975–1995, the annual population of nuns
(A) increased at a faster and faster rate.
(B) increased at a slower and slower rate.
(C) decreased at a faster and faster rate.
(D) decreased at a slower and slower rate.
c. Use the model to project the instantaneous rate of change of P in December, 2005. Interpret the result.

81. ● ***Online Services*** On January 1, 1996, America Online was the biggest online service provider, with 4.5 million subscribers, and was adding new subscribers at a rate of 60,000 per week.[52] If $A(t)$ is the number of America Online subscribers t weeks

[48] SOURCES: Bank of England, Reuters, July, 2004.

[49] SOURCE: Bloomberg News, www.icmarc.org July 6, 2004.

[50] Figures are rounded to the nearest $10 million. SOURCES: AOL; Forrester Research/*New York Times*, January 31, 2000, p. C1.

[51] Figures are rounded. SOURCE: Center for Applied Research in the Apostolate/*New York Times*, January 16, 2000, p. A1.

[52] SOURCE: Information and Interactive Services Report/*New York Times*, January 2, 1996, p. C14.

after January 1, 1996, what do the given data tell you about values of the function A and its derivative?

82. ● ***Online Services*** On January 1, 1996, Prodigy was the third-biggest online service provider, with 1.6 million subscribers, but was losing subscribers.[53] If $P(t)$ is the number of Prodigy subscribers t weeks after January 1, 1996, what do the given data tell you about values of the function P and its derivative?

83. ***Learning to Speak*** Let $p(t)$ represent the percentage of children who are able to speak at the age of t months.

a. It is found that $p(10) = 60$ and $\left.\frac{dp}{dt}\right|_{t=10} = 18.2$.[54] What does this mean?

b. As t increases, what happens to p and $\frac{dp}{dt}$?

84. ***Learning to Read*** Let $p(t)$ represent the number of children in your class who learned to read at the age of t years.

a. Assuming that everyone in your class could read by the age of 7, what does this tell you about $p(7)$ and $\left.\frac{dp}{dt}\right|_{t=7}$?

b. Assuming that 25.0% of the people in your class could read by the age of 5, and that 25.3% of them could read by the age of 5 years and one month, estimate $\left.\frac{dp}{dt}\right|_{t=5}$. Remember to give its units.

85. ● ***Sales*** Weekly sales of a new brand of sneakers are given by

$$S(t) = 200 - 150e^{-t/10}$$

pairs sold per week, where t is the number of weeks since the introduction of the brand. Estimate $S(5)$ and $\left.\frac{dS}{dt}\right|_{t=5}$ and interpret your answers.

86. ● ***Sales*** Weekly sales of an old brand of TV are given by

$$S(t) = 100e^{-t/5}$$

sets per week, where t is the number of weeks after the introduction of a competing brand. Estimate $S(5)$ and $\left.\frac{dS}{dt}\right|_{t=5}$ and interpret your answers.

87. ● ***Computer Use*** The percentage of U.S. households with a computer in 2000 as a function of household income can be modeled by the logistic function[55]

$$P(x) = \frac{91}{1 + 5.35(1.05)^{-x}} \text{ percent} \quad 0 \le x \le 100$$

where x is the household income in thousands of dollars.

a. Estimate $P(50)$ and $P'(50)$. What do the answers tell you about computer use in the U.S.? *hint* [see Example 5]

b. Graph the function and its derivative for $0 \le x \le 100$ and use your graphs to describe how the derivative behaves for values of x approaching 100.

88. ● ***Online Book Sales*** The number of books sold online in the U.S. for the period 1997–2000 can be modeled by the logistic function[56]

$$N(t) = \frac{82.8}{1 + 21.8(7.14)^{-t}} \quad 0 \le t \le 3$$

where t is time in years since the start of 1997, and $N(t)$ is the number of books sold in the year beginning at time t.

a. Estimate $N(1)$ and $N'(1)$. What do the answers tell you about online book sales?

b. Graph the function and its derivative for $0 \le t \le 3$ and use your graphs to estimate, to the nearest 6 months, when N' was greatest.

89. tech Ex ***Embryo Development*** The oxygen consumption of a turkey embryo increases from the time the egg is laid through the time the turkey chick hatches. In a brush turkey, the oxygen consumption (in milliliters per hour) can be approximated by

$$c(t) = -0.0012t^3 + 0.12t^2 - 1.83t + 3.97 \quad (20 \le t \le 50)$$

where t is the time (in days) since the egg was laid.[57] (An egg will typically hatch at around $t = 50$.) Use technology to graph $c'(t)$ and use your graph to answer the following questions.

a. Over the interval [20, 32] the derivative c' is
(A) increasing, then decreasing
(B) decreasing, then increasing
(C) decreasing
(D) increasing

b. When, to the nearest day, is the oxygen consumption increasing at the fastest rate?

c. When, to the nearest day, is the oxygen consumption increasing at the slowest rate?

90. tech Ex ***Embryo Development*** The oxygen consumption of a bird embryo increases from the time the egg is laid through the time the chick hatches. In a typical galliform bird, the oxygen consumption (in milliliters per hour) can be approximated by

$$c(t) = -0.0027t^3 + 0.14t^2 - 0.89t + 0.15 \quad (8 \le t \le 30)$$

where t is the time (in days) since the egg was laid.[58] (An egg will typically hatch at around $t = 28$.) Use technology to graph $c'(t)$ and use your graph to answer the following questions.

a. Over the interval [8, 30] the derivative c' is
(A) increasing, then decreasing
(B) decreasing, then increasing
(C) decreasing
(D) increasing

[53] Ibid.

[54] Based on data presented in the article *The Emergence of Intelligence* by William H. Calvin, *Scientific American*, October, 1994, pp. 101–107.

[55] SOURCE: NTIA and ESA, U.S. Department of Commerce, using U.S. Bureau of the Census Current Population, 2000.

[56] SOURCE: Ipsos-NPD Book Trends/*New York Times*, April 16, 2001, p. C1.

[57] Ibid.

[58] The model approximates graphical data published in the article *The Brush Turkey* by Roger S. Seymour, *Scientific American*, December, 1991, pp. 108–114.

b. When, to the nearest day, is the oxygen consumption increasing the fastest?

c. When, to the nearest day, is the oxygen consumption increasing at the slowest rate?

The next two exercises are applications of Einstein's Special Theory of Relativity and relate to objects that are moving extremely fast. In science fiction terminology, a speed of *warp 1* is the speed of light—about 3×10^8 meters per second. (Thus, for instance, a speed of warp 0.8 corresponds to 80% of the speed of light—about 2.4×10^8 meters per second.)

91. ◆ ***Lorentz Contraction*** According to Einstein's Special Theory of Relativity, a moving object appears to get shorter to a stationary observer as its speed approaches the speed of light. If a spaceship that has a length of 100 meters at rest travels at a speed of warp p, its length in meters, as measured by a stationary observer, is given by

$$L(p) = 100\sqrt{1 - p^2}$$

with domain $[0, 1)$. Estimate $L(0.95)$ and $L'(0.95)$. What do these figures tell you?

92. ◆ ***Time Dilation*** Another prediction of Einstein's Special Theory of Relativity is that, to a stationary observer, clocks (as well as all biological processes) in a moving object appear to go more and more slowly as the speed of the object approaches that of light. If a spaceship travels at a speed of warp p, the time it takes for an onboard clock to register one second, as measured by a stationary observer, will be given by

$$T(p) = \frac{1}{\sqrt{1 - p^2}} \text{ seconds}$$

with domain $[0, 1)$. Estimate $T(0.95)$ and $T'(0.95)$. What do these figures tell you?

Communication and Reasoning Exercises

93. ● Explain why we cannot put $h = 0$ in the approximation

$$f'(x) \approx \frac{f(x+h) - f(x)}{h}$$

for the derivative of f.

94. ● The balanced difference quotient

$$f'(a) \approx \frac{f(a + 0.0001) - f(a - 0.0001)}{0.0002}$$

is the average rate of change of f on what interval?

95. ● It is now eight months since the Garden City lacrosse team won the national championship, and sales of team paraphernalia, while still increasing, have been leveling off. What does this tell you about the derivative of the sales curve?

96. ● Having been soundly defeated in the national lacrosse championships, Brakpan High has been faced with decreasing sales of its team paraphernalia. However, sales, while still decreasing, appear to be bottoming out. What does this tell you about the derivative of the sales curve?

97. Company A's profits are given by $P(0) = \$1$ million and $P'(0) = -\$1$ million/month. Company B's profits are given by $P(0) = -\$1$ million and $P'(0) = \$1$ million/month. In which company would you rather invest? Why?

98. Company C's profits are given by $P(0) = \$1$ million and $P'(0) = \$0.5$ million/month. Company D's profits are given by $P(0) = \$0.5$ million and $P'(0) = \$1$ million/month. In which company would you rather invest? Why?

99. During the one-month period starting last January 1, your company's profits increased at an average rate of change of \$4 million per month. On January 1, profits were increasing at an instantaneous rate of \$5 million per month. Which of the following graphs could represent your company's profits? Why?

(A)

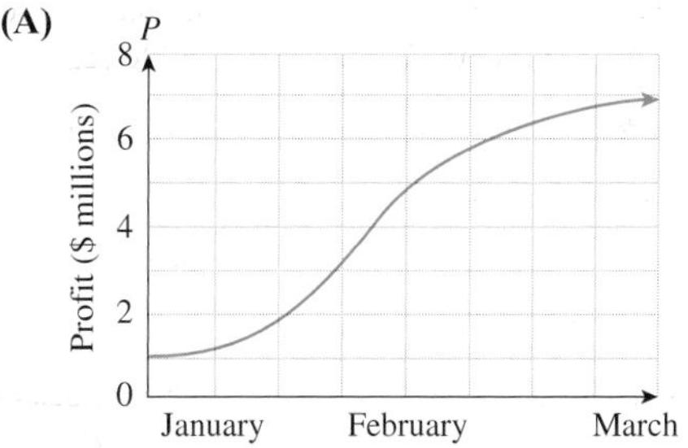

(B)

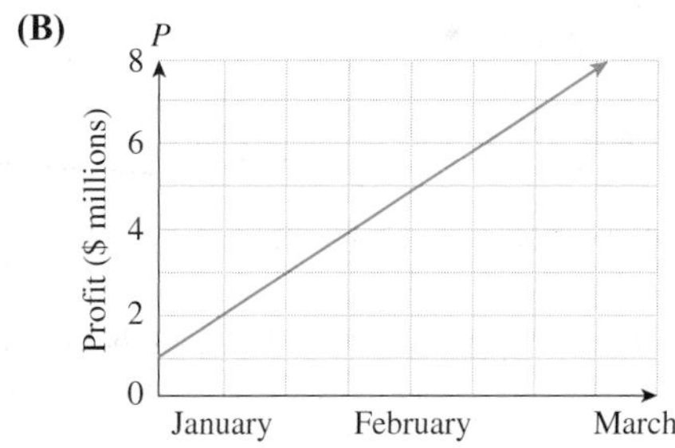

(C)

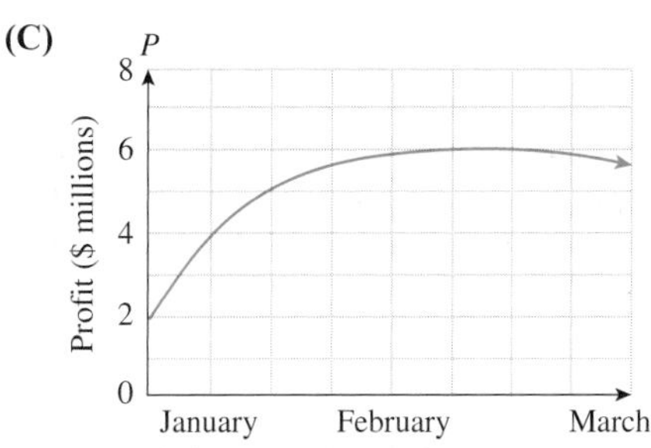

100. During the one-month period starting last January 1, your company's sales increased at an average rate of change of \$3000 per month. On January 1, sales were changing at an instantaneous rate of −\$1000 per month. Which of the following graphs could represent your company's sales? Why?

(A)

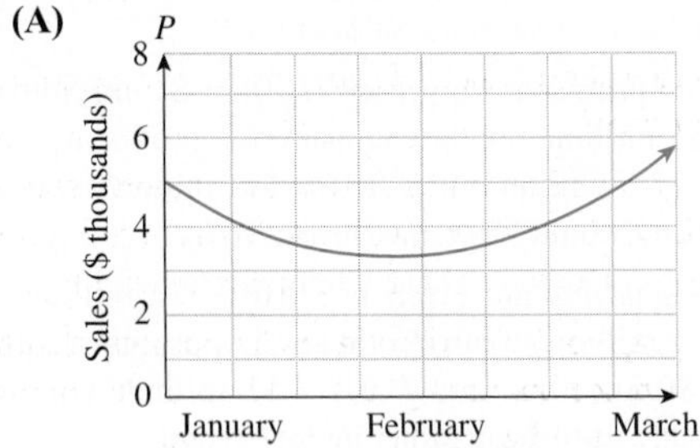

(B)

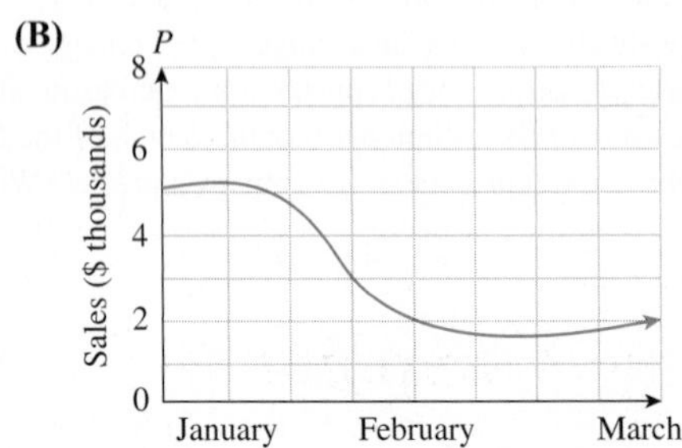

(C)

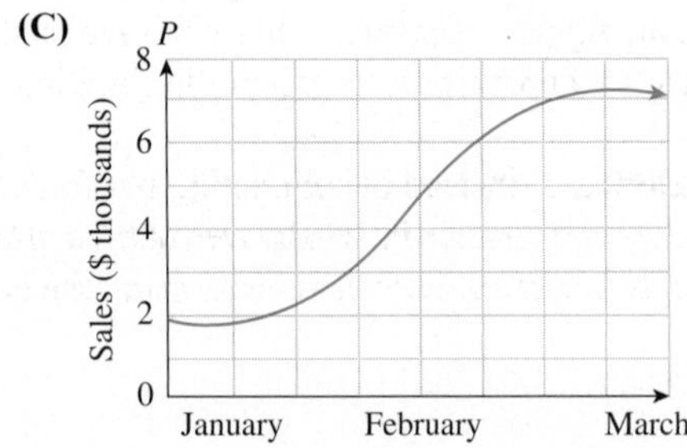

101. If the derivative of f is zero at a point, what do you know about the graph of f near that point?

102. Sketch the graph of a function whose derivative never exceeds 1.

103. Sketch the graph of a function whose derivative exceeds 1 at every point.

104. Sketch the graph of a function whose derivative is exactly 1 at every point.

105. Use the difference quotient to explain the fact that if f is a linear function, then the average rate of change over any interval equals the instantaneous rate of change at any point.

106. Give a numerical explanation of the fact that if f is a linear function, then the average rate of change over any interval equals the instantaneous rate of change at any point.

107. ◆ Consider the following values of the function f from Exercise 1.

h	0.1	0.01	0.001	0.0001
Ave. rate of change of f over $[5, 5+h]$	6.4	6.04	6.004	6.0004
h	−0.1	−0.01	−0.001	−0.0001
Ave. rate of change of f over $[5+h, 5]$	5.6	5.96	5.996	5.9996

Does the table suggests that the instantaneous rate of change of f is

(A) increasing **(B)** decreasing

as x increases toward 5?

108. ◆ Consider the following values of the function g from Exercise 2.

h	0.1	0.01	0.001	0.0001
Ave. rate of change of g over $[7, 7+h]$	4.8	4.98	4.998	4.9998
h	−0.1	−0.01	−0.001	−0.0001
Ave. rate of change of g over $[7+h, 7]$	5.3	5.03	5.003	5.0003

Does the table suggests that the instantaneous rate of change of g is

(A) increasing **(B)** decreasing

as x increases toward 7?

109. Sketch the graph of a function whose derivative is never zero but decreases as x increases.

110. Sketch the graph of a function whose derivative is never negative but is zero at exactly two points.

111. ◆ Here is the graph of the derivative f' of a function f. Give a rough sketch of the graph of f, given that $f(0) = 0$.

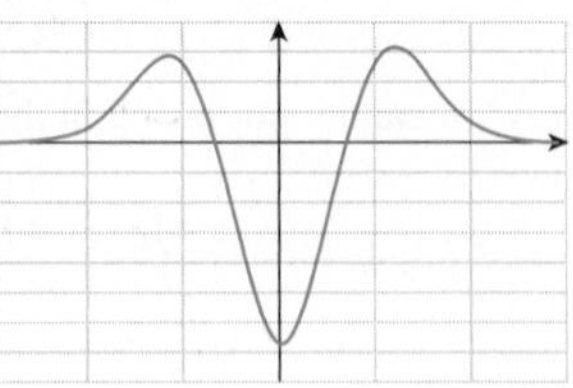

112. ◆ Here is the graph of the derivative f' of a function f. Give a rough sketch of the graph of f, given that $f(0) = 0$.

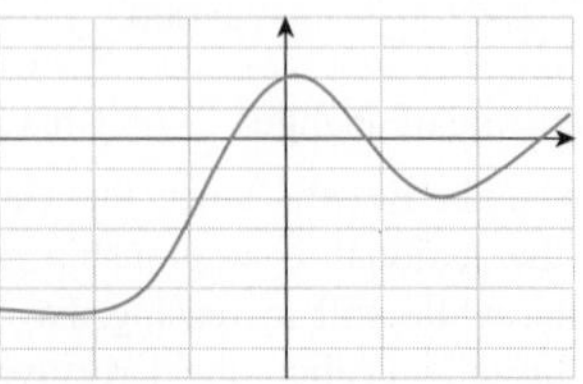

113. ◆ Professor Talker of the physics department drove a 60-mile stretch of road in exactly one hour. The speed limit along that stretch was 55 miles per hour. Which of the following must be correct:
(A) He exceeded the speed limit at no point of the journey.
(B) He exceeded the speed limit at some point of the journey.
(C) He exceeded the speed limit throughout the journey.
(D) He traveled slower than the speed limit at some point of the journey

114. ◆ Professor Silent, another physics professor, drove a 50-mile stretch of road in exactly one hour. The speed limit along that stretch was 55 miles per hour. Which of the following must be correct:
(A) She exceeded the speed limit at no point of the journey.
(B) She exceeded the speed limit at some point of the journey.
(C) She traveled slower than the speed limit throughout the journey.
(D) She traveled slower than the speed limit at some point of the journey.

115. ◆ Draw the graph of a function f with the property that the balanced difference quotient gives a more accurate approximation of $f'(1)$ than the ordinary difference quotient.

116. ◆ Draw the graph of a function f with the property that the balanced difference quotient gives a less accurate approximation of $f'(1)$ than the ordinary difference quotient.

● basic skills ◆ challenging tech Ex technology exercise

3.6 The Derivative: Algebraic Viewpoint

In Section 3.5 we saw how to estimate the derivative of a function using numerical and graphical approaches. In this section we use an algebraic approach that will give us the *exact value* of the derivative, rather than just an approximation, when the function is specified algebraically.

This algebraic approach is quite straightforward: Instead of subtracting numbers to estimate the average rate of change over smaller and smaller intervals, we subtract algebraic expressions. Our starting point is the definition of the derivative in terms of the difference quotient:

$$f'(a) = \lim_{h\to 0} \frac{f(a+h) - f(a)}{h}$$

Example 1 Calculating the Derivative at a Point Algebraically

Let $f(x) = x^2$. Use the definition of the derivative to compute $f'(3)$ algebraically.

Solution Substituting $a = 3$ into the definition of the derivative, we get:

$$f'(3) = \lim_{h\to 0} \frac{f(3+h) - f(3)}{h} \quad \text{Formula for the derivative}$$

$$= \lim_{h\to 0} \frac{\overbrace{(3+h)^2}^{f(3+h)} - \overbrace{3^2}^{f(3)}}{h} \quad \text{Substitute for } f(3) \text{ and } f(3+h)$$

$$= \lim_{h\to 0} \frac{(9 + 6h + h^2) - 9}{h} \quad \text{Expand } (3+h)^2$$

$$= \lim_{h\to 0} \frac{6h + h^2}{h} \quad \text{Cancel the 9}$$

$$= \lim_{h\to 0} \frac{h(6+h)}{h} \qquad \text{Factor out } h$$

$$= \lim_{h\to 0} (6+h) \qquad \text{Cancel the } h$$

Now we let h approach 0. As h gets closer and closer to 0, the sum $6+h$ clearly gets closer and closer to $6+0=6$. Thus,

$$f'(3) = \lim_{h\to 0} (6+h) = 6 \qquad \text{As } h \to 0, (6+h) \to 6$$

(Calculations of limits like this are discussed and justified more fully in Sections 3.2 and 3.3.)

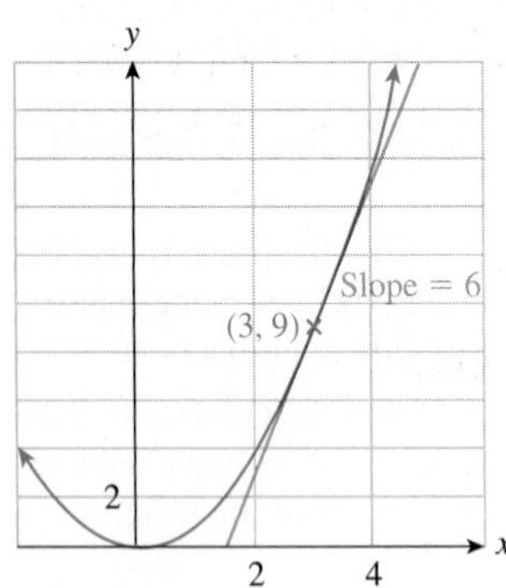

Figure **34**

+*Before we go on...* We did the following calculation in Example 1: If $f(x)=x^2$, then $f'(3)=6$. In other words, the tangent to the graph of $y=x^2$ at the point (3, 9) has slope 6 (Figure 34). ■

There is nothing very special about $a=3$ in Example 1. Let's try to compute $f'(x)$ for general x.

Example **2** Calculating the Derivative Function Algebraically

Let $f(x)=x^2$. Use the definition of the derivative to compute $f'(x)$ algebraically.

Solution Once again, our starting point is the definition of the derivative in terms of the difference quotient:

$$f'(x) = \lim_{h\to 0} \frac{f(x+h)-f(x)}{h} \qquad \text{Formula for the derivative}$$

$$= \lim_{h\to 0} \frac{\overbrace{(x+h)^2}^{f(x+h)} - \overbrace{x^2}^{f(x)}}{h} \qquad \text{Substitute for } f(x) \text{ and } f(x+h)$$

$$= \lim_{h\to 0} \frac{(x^2+2xh+h^2)-x^2}{h} \qquad \text{Expand } (x+h)^2.$$

$$= \lim_{h\to 0} \frac{2xh+h^2}{h} \qquad \text{Cancel the } x^2.$$

$$= \lim_{h\to 0} \frac{h(2x+h)}{h} \qquad \text{Factor out } h.$$

$$= \lim_{h\to 0} (2x+h) \qquad \text{Cancel the } h.$$

Now we let h approach 0. As h gets closer and closer to 0, the sum $2x+h$ clearly gets closer and closer to $2x+0=2x$. Thus,

$$f'(x) = \lim_{h\to 0} (2x+h) = 2x$$

This is the derivative function. Now that we have a *formula* for the derivative of *f*, we can obtain $f'(a)$ for any value of a we choose by simply evaluating f' there. For instance,

$$f'(3) = 2(3) = 6$$

as we saw in Example 1.

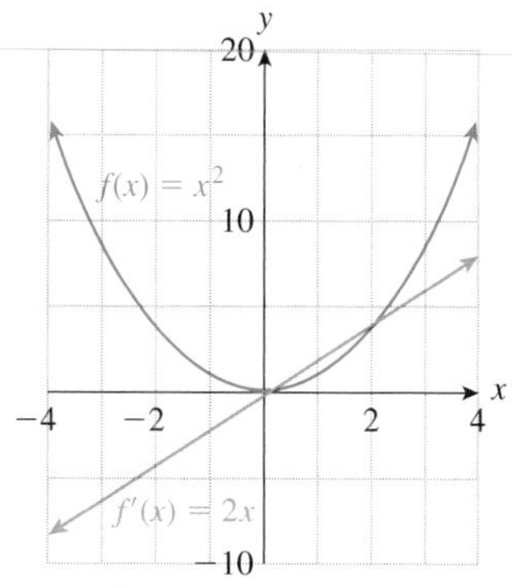

Figure **35**

Before we go on... The graphs of $f(x) = x^2$ and $f'(x) = 2x$ from Example 2 are familiar. Their graphs are shown in Figure 35.

When $x < 0$, the parabola slopes downward, which is reflected in the fact that the derivative $2x$ is negative there. When $x > 0$, the parabola slopes upward, which is reflected in the fact that the derivative is positive there. The parabola has a horizontal tangent line at $x = 0$, reflected in the fact that $2x = 0$ there. ■

Example **3** More Computations of Derivative Functions

Compute the derivative $f'(x)$ for each of the following functions:

a. $f(x) = x^3$ **b.** $f(x) = 2x^2 - x$ **c.** $f(x) = \dfrac{1}{x}$

Solution

a.
$$f'(x) = \lim_{h\to 0} \frac{f(x+h) - f(x)}{h} \quad \text{Derivative formula}$$
$$= \lim_{h\to 0} \frac{\overbrace{(x+h)^3}^{f(x+h)} - \overbrace{x^3}^{f(x)}}{h} \quad \text{Substitute for } f(x) \text{ and } f(x+h)$$
$$= \lim_{h\to 0} \frac{(x^3 + 3x^2h + 3xh^2 + h^3) - x^3}{h} \quad \text{Expand } (x+h)^3$$
$$= \lim_{h\to 0} \frac{3x^2h + 3xh^2 + h^3}{h} \quad \text{Cancel the } x^3$$
$$= \lim_{h\to 0} \frac{h(3x^2 + 3xh + h^2)}{h} \quad \text{Factor out } h$$
$$= \lim_{h\to 0} (3x^2 + 3xh + h^2) \quad \text{Cancel the } h$$
$$= 3x^2 \quad \text{Let } h \text{ approach } 0$$

b.
$$f'(x) = \lim_{h\to 0} \frac{f(x+h) - f(x)}{h} \quad \text{Derivative formula}$$
$$= \lim_{h\to 0} \frac{\overbrace{(2(x+h)^2 - (x+h))}^{f(x+h)} - \overbrace{(2x^2 - x)}^{f(x)}}{h} \quad \text{Substitute for } f(x) \text{ and } f(x+h)$$
$$= \lim_{h\to 0} \frac{(2x^2 + 4xh + 2h^2 - x - h) - (2x^2 - x)}{h} \quad \text{Expand}$$
$$= \lim_{h\to 0} \frac{4xh + 2h^2 - h}{h} \quad \text{Cancel the } 2x^2 \text{ and } x$$
$$= \lim_{h\to 0} \frac{h(4x + 2h - 1)}{h} \quad \text{Factor out } h$$
$$= \lim_{h\to 0} (4x + 2h - 1) \quad \text{Cancel the } h$$
$$= 4x - 1 \quad \text{Let } h \text{ approach } 0$$

c.
$$f'(x) = \lim_{h\to 0} \frac{f(x+h) - f(x)}{h} \quad \text{Derivative formula}$$
$$= \lim_{h\to 0} \frac{\left[\overbrace{\frac{1}{x+h}}^{f(x+h)} - \overbrace{\frac{1}{x}}^{f(x)}\right]}{h} \quad \text{Substitute for } f(x) \text{ and } f(x+h)$$

$$= \lim_{h\to 0} \frac{\left[\dfrac{x-(x+h)}{(x+h)x}\right]}{h}$$ Subtract the fractions

$$= \lim_{h\to 0} \frac{1}{h}\left[\frac{x-(x+h)}{(x+h)x}\right]$$ Dividing by h = Multiplying by $1/h$

$$= \lim_{h\to 0} \left[\frac{-h}{h(x+h)x}\right]$$ Simplify

$$= \lim_{h\to 0} \left[\frac{-1}{(x+h)x}\right]$$ Cancel the h

$$= \frac{-1}{x^2}$$ Let h approach 0

In Example 4, we redo Example 3 of Section 3.5, this time getting an exact, rather than approximate, answer.

Example 4 Velocity

My friend Eric, an enthusiastic baseball player, claims he can "probably" throw a ball upward at a speed of 100 feet per second (ft/sec). Our physicist friends tell us that its height s (in feet) t seconds later would be $s(t) = 100t - 16t^2$. Find the ball's instantaneous velocity function and its velocity exactly 2 seconds after Eric throws it.

Solution The instantaneous velocity function is the derivative ds/dt, which we calculate as follow:

$$\frac{ds}{dt} = \lim_{h\to 0} \frac{s(t+h)-s(t)}{h}$$

Let us compute $s(t+h)$ and $s(t)$ separately:

$$\begin{aligned} s(t) &= 100t - 16t^2 \\ s(t+h) &= 100(t+h) - 16(t+h)^2 \\ &= 100t + 100h - 16(t^2 + 2th + h^2) \\ &= 100t + 100h - 16t^2 - 32th - 16h^2 \end{aligned}$$

Therefore,

$$\begin{aligned} \frac{ds}{dt} &= \lim_{h\to 0} \frac{s(t+h)-s(t)}{h} \\ &= \lim_{h\to 0} \frac{100t + 100h - 16t^2 - 32th - 16h^2 - (100t - 16t^2)}{h} \\ &= \lim_{h\to 0} \frac{100h - 32th - 16h^2}{h} \\ &= \lim_{h\to 0} \frac{h(100 - 32t - 16h)}{h} \\ &= \lim_{h\to 0} 100 - 32t - 16h \\ &= 100 - 32t \text{ ft/sec} \end{aligned}$$

Thus, the velocity exactly 2 seconds after Eric throws it is

$$\left.\frac{ds}{dt}\right|_{t=2} = 100 - 32(2) = 36 \text{ ft/sec}$$

This verifies the accuracy of the approximation we made in Section 3.5.

+*Before we go on...* From the derivative function in Example 4, we can now describe the behavior of the velocity of the ball: Immediately on release ($t = 0$) the ball is traveling at 100 feet per second upward. The ball then slows down; precisely, it loses 32 feet per second of speed every second. When, exactly, does the velocity become zero and what happens after that? ■

Q: *Do we always have to calculate the limit of the difference quotient to find a formula for the derivative function?*

A: As it turns out, no. In Section 3.7 we will start to look at shortcuts for finding derivatives that allow us to bypass the definition of the derivative in many cases. ■

A Function Not Differentiable at a Point

Recall from Section 3.5 that a function is **differentiable** at a point a if $f'(a)$ exists; that is, if the difference quotient $[f(a+h) - f(a)]/h$ approaches a fixed value as h approaches 0. In Section 3.5, we mentioned that the function $f(x) = |x|$ is not differentiable at $x = 0$. In Example 5, we find out why.

Example 5 A Function Not Differentiable at 0

Numerically, graphically, and algebraically investigate the differentiability of the function $f(x) = |x|$ at the points **a.** $x = 1$ and **b.** $x = 0$.

Solution

a. We compute

$$\begin{aligned} f'(1) &= \lim_{h \to 0} \frac{f(1+h) - f(1)}{h} \\ &= \lim_{h \to 0} \frac{|1+h| - 1}{h} \end{aligned}$$

Numerically, we can make tables of the values of the average rate of change $(|1+h| - 1)/h$ for h positive or negative and approaching 0:

h	1	0.1	0.01	0.001	0.0001
Ave. rate of change over [1, 1 + h]	1	1	1	1	1

h	−1	−0.1	−0.01	−0.001	−0.0001
Ave. rate of change over [1 + h, 1]	1	1	1	1	1

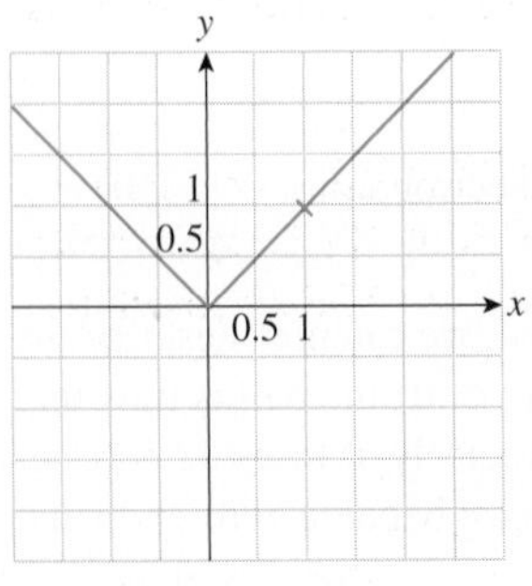

Figure **36**

From these tables it appears that $f'(1)$ is equal to 1. We can verify that algebraically: For h that is sufficiently small, $1+h$ is positive (even if h is negative) and so

$$f'(1) = \lim_{h\to 0} \frac{1+h-1}{h}$$

$$= \lim_{h\to 0} \frac{h}{h} \quad \text{Cancel the 1s}$$

$$= \lim_{h\to 0} 1 \quad \text{Cancel the } h$$

$$= 1$$

Graphically, we are seeing the fact that the tangent line at the point (1, 1) has slope 1 because the graph is a straight line with slope 1 near that point (Figure 36).

b. $$f'(0) = \lim_{h\to 0} \frac{f(0+h) - f(0)}{h}$$

$$= \lim_{h\to 0} \frac{|0+h| - 0}{h}$$

$$= \lim_{h\to 0} \frac{|h|}{h}$$

If we make tables of values in this case we get the following:

h	1	0.1	0.01	0.001	0.0001
Ave. rate of change over [0, 0 + h]	1	1	1	1	1

h	−1	−0.1	−0.01	−0.001	−0.0001
Ave. rate of change over [0 + h, 0]	−1	−1	−1	−1	−1

For the limit and hence the derivative $f'(0)$ to exist, the average rates of change should approach the same number for both positive and negative h. Because they do not, f is not differentiable at $x = 0$. We can verify this conclusion algebraically: If h is positive, then $|h| = h$, and so the ratio $|h|/h$ is 1, regardless of how small h is. Thus, according to the values of the difference quotients with $h > 0$, the limit should be 1. On the other hand if h is negative, then $|h| = -h$ (positive) and so $|h|/h = -1$, meaning that the limit should be -1. Because the limit cannot be both -1 and 1 (it must be a single number for the derivative to exist), we conclude that $f'(0)$ does not exist.

To see what is happening graphically, take a look at Figure 37, which shows zoomed-in views of the graph of f near $x = 0$.

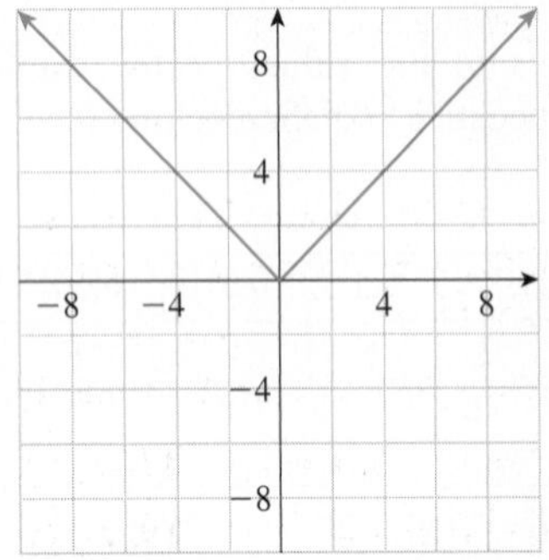

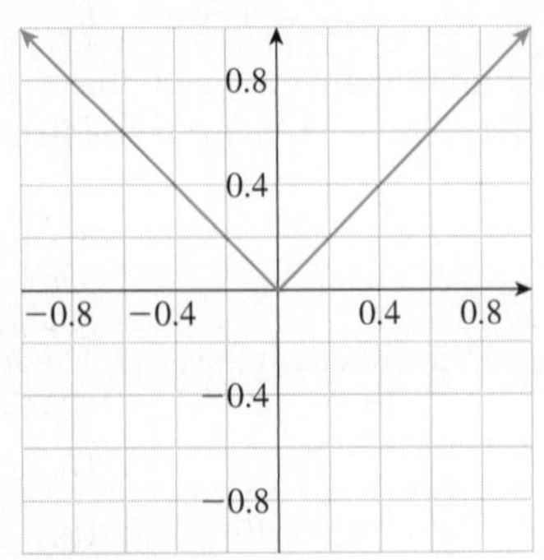

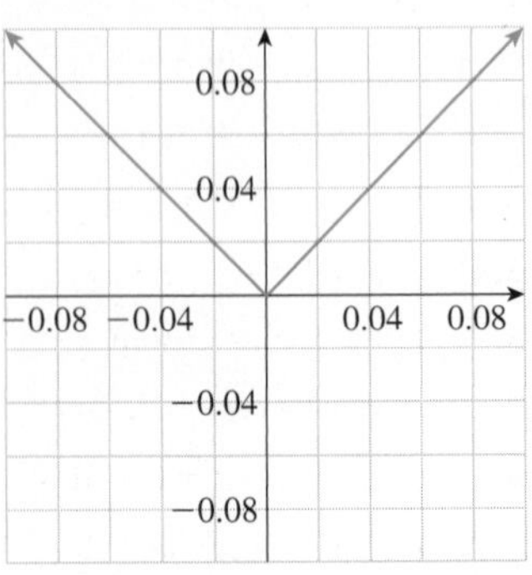

Figure **37**

No matter what scale we use to view the graph, it has a sharp corner at $x = 0$ and hence has no tangent line there. Since there is no tangent line at $x = 0$, the function is not differentiable there.

+*Before we go on...* If we repeat the computation in Example 5(a) using any nonzero value for a in place of 1, we see that f is differentiable there as well. If a is positive, we find that $f'(a) = 1$ and, if a is negative, $f'(a) = -1$. In other words, the derivative function is

$$f'(x) = \begin{cases} -1 & \text{if } x < 0 \\ 1 & \text{if } x > 0 \end{cases}$$

Of course, $f'(x)$ is not defined when $x = 0$. ■

FAQs Computing Derivatives Algebraically

Q: *The algebraic computation of $f'(x)$ seems to require a number of steps. How do I remember what to do, and when?*

A: If you examine the computations in the examples above, you will find the following pattern:

1. Write out the formula for $f'(x)$ as the limit of the difference quotient, then substitute $f(x+h)$ and $f(x)$.
2. Expand and simplify the *numerator* of the expression, but not the denominator.
3. After simplifying the numerator, factor out an h to cancel with the h in the denominator. If h does not factor out of the numerator, you might have made an error. (A frequent error is a wrong sign.)
4. After canceling the h, you should be able to see what the limit is by letting $h \to 0$. ■

3.6 EXERCISES

● denotes basic skills exercises

In Exercises 1–14, compute $f'(a)$ algebraically for the given value of a.

1. ● $f(x) = x^2 + 1$; $a = 2$ *hint* [see Example 1]

2. ● $f(x) = x^2 - 3$; $a = 1$

3. ● $f(x) = 3x - 4$; $a = -1$

4. ● $f(x) = -2x + 4$; $a = -1$

5. ● $f(x) = 3x^2 + x$; $a = 1$

6. ● $f(x) = 2x^2 + x$; $a = -2$

7. ● $f(x) = 2x - x^2$; $a = -1$

8. ● $f(x) = -x - x^2$; $a = 0$

9. ● $f(x) = x^3 + 2x$; $a = 2$

10. ● $f(x) = x - 2x^3$; $a = 1$

11. ● $f(x) = \frac{-1}{x}$; $a = 1$ *hint* [see Example 3]

12. ● $f(x) = \frac{2}{x}$; $a = 5$

13. $f(x) = mx + b$; $a = 43$

14. $f(x) = \frac{x}{k} - b$ $(k \neq 0)$; $a = 12$

In Exercises 15–28, compute the derivative function $f'(x)$ algebraically. (Notice that the functions are the same as those in Exercises 1–14.)

15. ● $f(x) = x^2 + 1$ *hint* [see Examples 2 and 3]

16. ● $f(x) = x^2 - 3$; $a = 1$

17. ● $f(x) = 3x - 4$

18. ● $f(x) = -2x + 4$

19. ● $f(x) = 3x^2 + x$

20. ● $f(x) = 2x^2 + x$

21. ● $f(x) = 2x - x^2$

22. ● $f(x) = -x - x^2$

23. ● $f(x) = x^3 + 2x$

24. ● $f(x) = x - 2x^3$

25. $f(x) = \frac{-1}{x}$

26. $f(x) = \frac{2}{x}$

27. $f(x) = mx + b$

28. $f(x) = \frac{x}{k} - b\ (k \neq 0)$

In Exercises 29–38, compute the indicated derivative.

29. ● $R(t) = -0.3t^2$; $R'(2)$

30. ● $S(t) = 1.4t^2$; $S'(-1)$

31. ● $U(t) = 5.1t^2 + 5.1$; $U'(3)$

32. ● $U(t) = -1.3t^2 + 1.1$; $U'(4)$

33. ● $U(t) = -1.3t^2 - 4.5t$; $U'(1)$

34. ● $U(t) = 5.1t^2 - 1.1t$; $U'(1)$

35. ● $L(r) = 4.25r - 5.01$; $L'(1.2)$

36. ● $L(r) = -1.02r + 5.7$; $L'(3.1)$

37. $q(p) = \frac{2.4}{p} + 3.1$; $q'(2)$

38. $q(p) = \frac{1}{0.5p} - 3.1$; $q'(2)$

In Exercises 39–44, find the equation of the tangent to the graph at the indicated point.

39. $f(x) = x^2 - 3$; $a = 2$

40. $f(x) = x^2 + 1$; $a = 2$

41. $f(x) = -2x - 4$; $a = 3$

42. $f(x) = 3x + 1$; $a = 1$

43. $f(x) = x^2 - x$; $a = -1$

44. $f(x) = x^2 + x$; $a = -1$

Applications

45. ● ***Velocity*** If a stone is dropped from a height of 400 feet, its height after t seconds is given by $s = 400 - 16t^2$. Find its instantaneous velocity function and its velocity at time $t = 4$. *hint* [see Example 4]

46. ● ***Velocity*** If a stone is thrown down at 120 feet per second from a height of 1000 feet, its height after t seconds is given by $s = 1000 - 120t - 16t^2$. Find its instantaneous velocity function and its velocity at time $t = 3$.

47. ● ***Foreign Trade*** Annual U.S. imports from China in the years 1996 through 2003 could be approximated by

$$I(t) = t^2 + 3.5t + 50 \text{ billion dollars} \quad (1 \leq t \leq 9)$$

where t represents time in years since 1995.[59] At what rate was this number increasing in 2000?

[59] Based on quadratic regression using data from the U.S. Census Bureau Foreign Trade Division website www.census.gov/foreign-trade/sitc1/ as of December 2004.

48. ● ***Foreign Trade*** Annual U.S. exports to China in the years 1995 through 2003 could be approximated by

$$E(t) = 0.4t^2 - 1.6t + 14 \text{ billion dollars} \quad (0 \leq t \leq 8)$$

where t represents time in years since 1995.[60] At what rate was this number increasing in 2000?

49. ● ***Bottled Water Sales*** Annual U.S. sales of bottled water rose through the period 1993–2003 as shown in the following chart.[61]

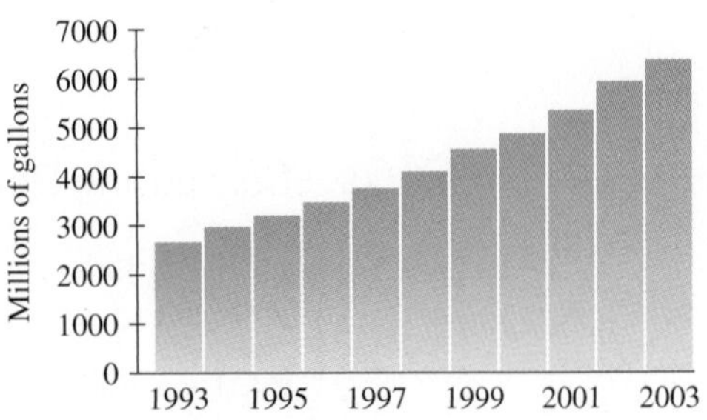

The function

$$R(t) = 17t^2 + 100t + 2300 \text{ million gallons } (3 \leq t \leq 13)$$

gives a good approximation, where t is time in years since 1990. Find the derivative function $R'(t)$. According to the model, how fast were annual sales of bottled water increasing in 2000?

50. ● ***Bottled Water Sales*** Annual U.S. per capita sales of bottled water rose through the period 1993–2003 as shown in the following chart.[62]

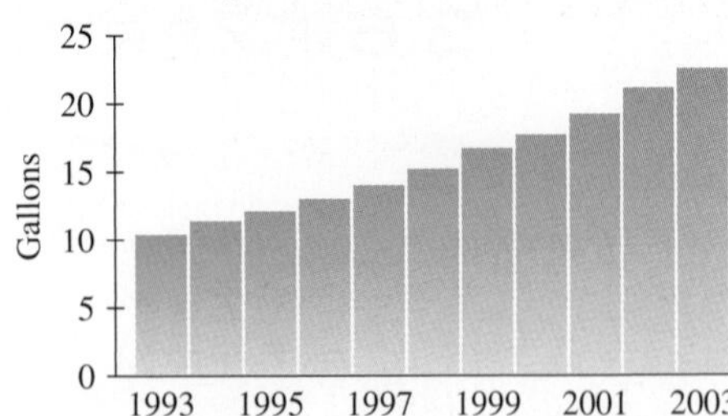

[60] Based on quadratic regression using data from the U.S. Census Bureau Foreign Trade Division website www.census.gov/foreign-trade/sitc1/ as of December 2004.

[61] SOURCE: Beverage Marketing Corporation news release, "Bottled water now number-two commercial beverage in U.S., says Beverage Marketing Corporation," April 8, 2004, available at www.beveragemarketing.com.

[62] Ibid.

The function

$$Q(t) = 0.05t^2 + 0.4t + 9 \text{ gallons}$$

gives a good approximation, where t is the time in years since 1990. Find the derivative function $Q'(t)$. According to the model, how fast were annual per capita sales of bottled water increasing in 2000?

51. ***Ecology*** Increasing numbers of manatees ("sea sirens") have been killed by boats off the Florida coast. The following graph shows the relationship between the number of boats registered in Florida and the number of manatees killed each year.

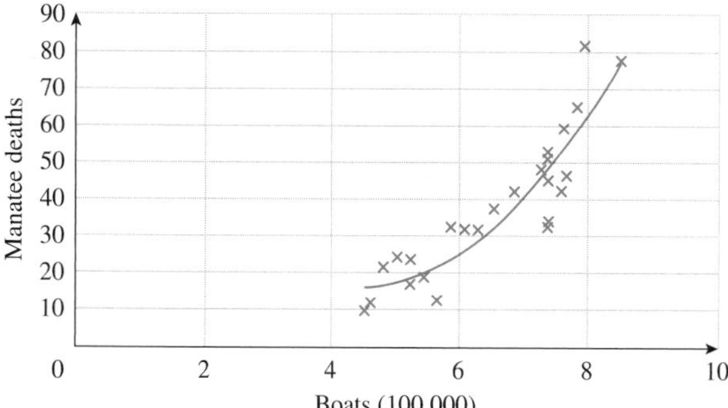

The regression curve shown is given by

$$f(x) = 3.55x^2 - 30.2x + 81 \text{ manatee deaths}$$
$$(4.5 \le x \le 8.5)$$

where x is the number of boats (hundreds of thousands) registered in Florida in a particular year and $f(x)$ is the number of manatees killed by boats in Florida that year.[63] Compute and interpret $f'(8)$.

52. ***SAT Scores by Income*** The following graph shows U.S. verbal SAT scores as a function of parents' income level.[64]

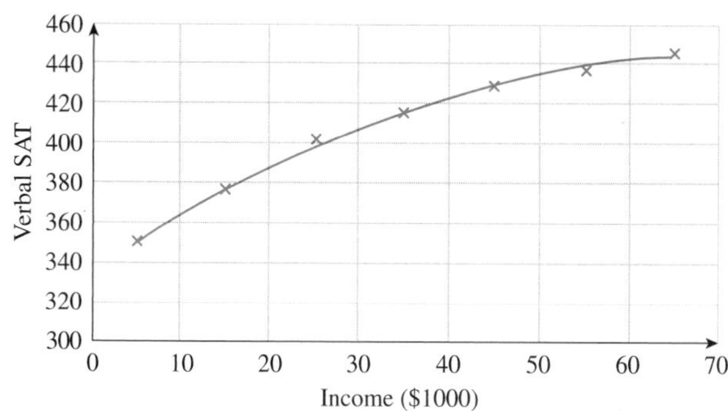

The regression curve shown is given by

$$f(x) = -0.021x^2 + 3.0x + 336 \quad (5 \le x \le 65)$$

where $f(x)$ is the average SAT verbal score of a student whose parents earn x thousand dollars per year.[65] Compute and interpret $f'(30)$.

Communication and Reasoning Exercises

53. ● Of the three methods (numerical, graphical, algebraic) we can use to estimate the derivative of a function at a given value of x, which is always the most accurate? Explain.

54. ● Explain why we cannot put $h = 0$ in the formula

$$f'(a) = \lim_{h \to 0} \frac{f(a+h) - f(a)}{h}$$

for the derivative of f.

55. ● Your friend Muffy claims that, because the balanced difference quotient is more accurate, it would be better to use that instead of the usual difference quotient when computing the derivative algebraically. Comment on this advice.

56. ● Use the balanced difference quotient formula,

$$f'(a) = \lim_{h \to 0} \frac{f(a+h) - f(a-h)}{2h}$$

to compute $f'(3)$ when $f(x) = x^2$. What do you find?

57. A certain function f has the property that $f'(a)$ does not exist. How is that reflected in the attempt to compute $f'(a)$ algebraically?

58. One cannot put $h = 0$ in the formula

$$f'(a) = \lim_{h \to 0} \frac{f(a+h) - f(a)}{h}$$

for the derivative of f. (See Exercise 54). However, in the last step of each of the computations in the text, we are effectively setting $h = 0$ when taking the limit. What is going on here?

---

[63] Regression model is based on data from 1976 to 2000. Sources for data: Florida Department of Highway Safety & Motor Vehicles, Florida Marine Institute/*New York Times,* February 12, 2002, p. F4.

[64] Based on 1994 data. SOURCE: The College Board/*New York Times,* March 5, 1995, p. E16.

[65] Regression model is based on 1994 data. SOURCE: The College Board/*New York Times,* March 5, 1995, p. E16.

3.7 Derivatives of Powers, Sums, and Constant Multiples

So far in this chapter we have approximated derivatives using difference quotients, and we have done exact calculations using the definition of the derivative as the limit of a difference quotient. In general, we would prefer to have an exact calculation, and it is also very useful to have a formula for the derivative function when we can find one. However, the calculation of a derivative as a limit is often tedious, so it would be nice to have a quicker method. We discuss the first of the shortcut rules in this section. By the end of Chapter 4, we will be able to find fairly quickly the derivative of almost any function we can write.

Shortcut Formula: The Power Rule

If you look again at Examples 2 and 3 in Section 3.6, you may notice a pattern:

$$f(x) = x^2 \quad \Rightarrow \quad f'(x) = 2x$$
$$f(x) = x^3 \quad \Rightarrow \quad f'(x) = 3x^2$$

Theorem: The Power Rule

If n is any constant and $f(x) = x^n$, then

$$f'(x) = nx^{n-1}$$

quick **Examples**

1. If $f(x) = x^2$, then $f'(x) = 2x^1 = 2x$.
2. If $f(x) = x^3$, then $f'(x) = 3x^2$.
3. If $f(x) = x$, rewrite as $f(x) = x^1$, so $f'(x) = 1x^0 = 1$.
4. If $f(x) = 1$, rewrite as $f(x) = x^0$, so $f'(x) = 0x^{-1} = 0$.

The proof of the power rule involves first studying the case when n is a positive integer, and then studying the cases of other types of exponents (negative integer, rational number, irrational number). You can find a proof at the website.

Find a proof of the power rule online.
Follow:
Chapter 3
→ Proof of the Power Rule

Example 1 Using the Power Rule for Negative and Fractional Exponents

Calculate the derivatives of the following:

a. $f(x) = \dfrac{1}{x}$ **b.** $f(x) = \dfrac{1}{x^2}$ **c.** $f(x) = \sqrt{x}$

Solution

a. Rewrite* as $f(x) = x^{-1}$. Then $f'(x) = (-1)x^{-2} = -\dfrac{1}{x^2}$.

b. Rewrite as $f(x) = x^{-2}$. Then $f'(x) = (-2)x^{-3} = -\dfrac{2}{x^3}$.

c. Rewrite as $f(x) = x^{0.5}$. Then $f'(x) = 0.5x^{-0.5} = \dfrac{0.5}{x^{0.5}}$.

Alternatively, rewrite $f(x)$ as $x^{1/2}$, so that $f'(x) = \dfrac{1}{2}x^{-1/2} = \dfrac{1}{2x^{1/2}} = \dfrac{1}{2\sqrt{x}}$.

* See the section on exponents in the algebra review to brush up on negative and fractional exponents.

By rewriting the given functions in Example 1 before taking derivatives, we converted them from **rational** or **radical form** (as in, say, $\frac{1}{x^2}$ or $\sqrt{x}$) to **exponent form** (as in x^{-2} and $x^{0.5}$) to enable us to use the power rule (see the caution below).

Caution

We cannot apply the power rule to terms in the denominators or under square roots. For example:

1. The derivative of $\frac{1}{x^2}$ is **NOT** $\frac{1}{2x}$; but is $-\frac{2}{x^3}$. — See Example 1(b)

2. The derivative of $\sqrt{x^3}$ is **NOT** $\sqrt{3x^2}$; but is $1.5x^{0.5}$. — Rewrite $\sqrt{x^3}$ as $x^{3/2}$ or $x^{1.5}$ and apply the power rule

Table **1** Table of Derivative Formulas

$f(x)$	$f'(x)$
1	0
x	1
x^2	$2x$
x^3	$3x^2$
x^n	nx^{n-1}
$\frac{1}{x}$	$-\frac{1}{x^2}$
$\frac{1}{x^2}$	$-\frac{2}{x^3}$
$\sqrt{x}$	$\frac{1}{2\sqrt{x}}$

Some of the derivatives in Example 1 are very useful to remember, so we summarize them in Table 1. We suggest that you add to this table as you learn more derivatives. It is *extremely* helpful to remember the derivatives of common functions such as $1/x$ and $\sqrt{x}$, even though they can be obtained using the power rule as in the above example.

Another Notation: Differential Notation

Here is a useful notation based on the "*d*-notation" we discussed in Section 3.5. **Differential notation** is based on an abbreviation for the phrase "the derivative with respect to x." For example, we learned that if $f(x) = x^3$, then $f'(x) = 3x^2$. When we say "$f'(x) = 3x^2$," we mean the following:

The derivative of x^3 with respect to x equals $3x^2$.

You may wonder why we sneaked in the words "with respect to x." All this means is that the variable of the function is x, and not any other variable.[66] Since we use the phrase "the derivative with respect to x" often, we use the following abbreviation.

Differential Notation; Differentiation

$\frac{d}{dx}$ means "the derivative with respect to x."

Thus, $\frac{d}{dx}[f(x)]$ is the same thing as $f'(x)$, the derivative of $f(x)$ with respect to x. If y is a function of x, then the derivative of y with respect to x is

$$\frac{d}{dx}(y) \quad \text{or, more compactly,} \quad \frac{dy}{dx}$$

[66] This may seem odd in the case of $f(x) = x^3$ because there are no other variables to worry about. But in expressions like st^3 that involve variables other than x, it is necessary to specify just what the variable of the function is. This is the same reason that we write "$f(x) = x^3$" rather than just "$f = x^3$."

To **differentiate** a function $f(x)$ with respect to x means to take its derivative with respect to x.

quick Examples

In Words	Formula
1. The derivative with respect to x of x^3 is $3x^2$.	$\frac{d}{dx}(x^3) = 3x^2$
2. The derivative with respect to t of $\frac{1}{t}$ is $-\frac{1}{t^2}$.	$\frac{d}{dt}\left(\frac{1}{t}\right) = -\frac{1}{t^2}$
3. If $y = x^4$, then $\frac{dy}{dx} = 4x^3$.	
4. If $u = \frac{1}{t^2}$, then $\frac{du}{dt} = -\frac{2}{t^3}$.	

Notes

1. $\frac{dy}{dx}$ is Leibniz notation for the derivative we discussed in Section 3.5 (see the discussion before Example 3 there).

2. Leibniz notation illustrates units nicely: units of $\frac{dy}{dx}$ are units of y per unit of x. ■

The Rules for Sums and Constant Multiples

We can now find the derivatives of more complicated functions, such as polynomials, using the following rules:

Theorem: Derivatives of Sums, Differences, and Constant Multiples

If $f(x)$ and $g(x)$ are any two differentiable functions, and if c is any constant, then the functions $f(x) + g(x)$ and $cf(x)$ are differentiable, and

$$[f(x) \pm g(x)]' = f'(x) \pm g'(x) \quad \text{Sum Rule}$$

$$[cf(x)]' = cf'(x) \quad \text{Constant Multiple Rule}$$

In Words:

- The derivative of a sum is the sum of the derivatives, and the derivative of a difference is the difference of the derivatives.
- The derivative of c times a function is c times the derivative of the function.

Differential Notation:

$$\frac{d}{dx}[f(x) \pm g(x)] = \frac{d}{dx}f(x) \pm \frac{d}{dx}g(x)$$

$$\frac{d}{dx}[cf(x)] = c\frac{d}{dx}f(x)$$

quick Examples

1. $\frac{d}{dx}[x^2 - x^4] = \frac{d}{dx}[x^2] - \frac{d}{dx}[x^4] = 2x - 4x^3$

2. $\frac{d}{dx}[7x^3] = 7\frac{d}{dx}[x^3] = 7(3x^2) = 21x^2$

In other words, we multiply the coefficient (7) by the exponent (3), and then decrease the exponent by 1.

3. $\frac{d}{dx}[12x] = 12\frac{d}{dx}[x] = 12(1) = 12$

In other words, the derivative of a constant times x is that constant.

4. $\frac{d}{dx}[-x^{0.5}] = \frac{d}{dx}[(-1)x^{0.5}] = (-1)\frac{d}{dx}[x^{0.5}] = (-1)(0.5)x^{-0.5} = -0.5x^{-0.5}$

5. $\frac{d}{dx}[12] = \frac{d}{dx}[12(1)] = 12\frac{d}{dx}[1] = 12(0) = 0.$

In other words, the derivative of a constant is zero.

6. If my company earns twice as much (annual) revenue as yours and the derivative of your revenue function is the curve on the left, then the derivative of my revenue function is the curve on the right.

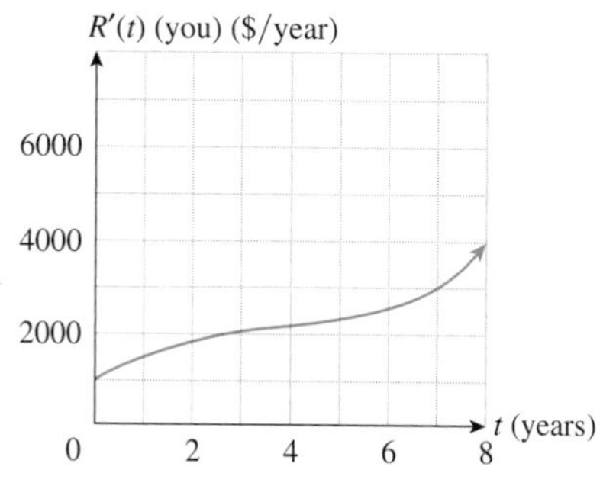

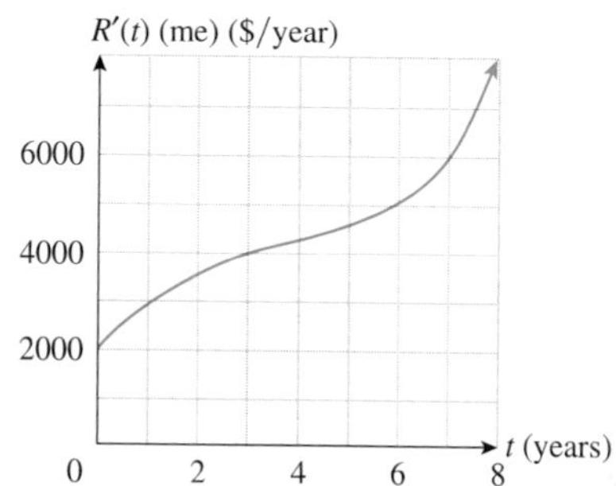

7. Suppose that a company's revenue R and cost C are changing with time. Then so is the profit, $P(t) = R(t) - C(t)$, and the rate of change of the profit is

$$P'(t) = R'(t) - C'(t)$$

In words: *The derivative of the profit is the derivative of revenue minus the derivative of cost.*

Proof of the Sum Rule

By the definition of the derivative of a function,

$$\begin{aligned}
\frac{d}{dx}[f(x)+g(x)] &= \lim_{h\to 0}\frac{[f(x+h)+g(x+h)]-[f(x)+g(x)]}{h} \\
&= \lim_{h\to 0}\frac{[f(x+h)-f(x)]+[g(x+h)-g(x)]}{h} \\
&= \lim_{h\to 0}\left[\frac{f(x+h)-f(x)}{h}+\frac{g(x+h)-g(x)}{h}\right] \\
&= \lim_{h\to 0}\frac{f(x+h)-f(x)}{h}+\lim_{h\to 0}\frac{g(x+h)-g(x)}{h} \\
&= \frac{d}{dx}[f(x)]+\frac{d}{dx}[g(x)]
\end{aligned}$$

The next-to-last step uses a property of limits: the limit of a sum is the sum of the limits. Think about why this should be true. The last step uses the definition of the derivative again (and the fact that the functions are differentiable).

The proof of the rule for constant multiples is similar.

Example 2 Combining the Sum and Constant Multiple Rules, and Dealing with x in the Denominator

Find the derivatives of the following:

a. $f(x) = 3x^2 + 2x - 4$ **b.** $f(x) = \frac{2x}{3} - \frac{6}{x} + \frac{2}{3x^{0.2}} - \frac{x^4}{2}$

Solution

a.
$$\frac{d}{dx}(3x^2 + 2x - 4) = \frac{d}{dx}(3x^2) + \frac{d}{dx}(2x - 4) \qquad \text{Rule for sums}$$
$$= \frac{d}{dx}(3x^2) + \frac{d}{dx}(2x) - \frac{d}{dx}(4) \qquad \text{Rule for differences}$$
$$= 3(2x) + 2(1) - 0 \qquad \text{See Quick Example 2}$$
$$= 6x + 2$$

b. Notice that f has x and powers of x in the denominator. We deal with these terms the same way we did in Example 1, by rewriting them in exponent form:

$$f(x) = \frac{2x}{3} - \frac{6}{x} + \frac{2}{3x^{0.2}} - \frac{x^4}{2} \qquad \text{Rational form}$$
$$= \frac{2}{3}x - 6x^{-1} + \frac{2}{3}x^{-0.2} - \frac{1}{2}x^4 \qquad \text{Exponent form}$$

We are now ready to take the derivative:

$$f'(x) = \frac{2}{3}(1) - 6(-1)x^{-2} + \frac{2}{3}(-0.2)x^{-1.2} - \frac{1}{2}(4x^3)$$
$$= \frac{2}{3} + 6x^{-2} - \frac{0.4}{3}x^{-1.2} - 2x^3 \qquad \text{Exponent form}$$
$$= \frac{2}{3} + \frac{6}{x^2} - \frac{0.4}{3x^{1.2}} - 2x^3 \qquad \text{Rational form}$$

Notice that in Example 2(a) we had three terms in the expression for $f(x)$, not just two. By applying the rule for sums and differences twice, we saw that the derivative of a sum or difference of three terms is the sum or difference of the derivatives of the terms. (One of those terms had zero derivatives, so the final answer had only two terms.) In fact, the derivative of a sum or difference of any number of terms is the sum or difference of the derivatives of the terms. Put another way, to take the derivative of a sum or difference of any number of terms, we take derivatives term by term.

Note Nothing forces us to use only x as the independent variable when taking derivatives (although it is traditional to give x preference). For instance, part (a) in Example 2 can be rewritten as

$$\frac{d}{dt}(3t^2 + 2t - 4) = 6t + 2 \qquad \frac{d}{dt} \text{ means "derivative with respect to } t\text{".}$$

or

$$\frac{d}{du}(3u^2 + 2u - 4) = 6u + 2 \qquad \frac{d}{du} \text{ means "derivative with respect to } u\text{".}$$

■

In the examples above, we saw instances of the following important facts. (Think about these graphically to see why they must be true.)

The Derivative of a Constant Times *x* and the Derivative of a Constant

If c is any constant, then:

Rule	*quick* Examples	
$\frac{d}{dx}(cx) = c$	$\frac{d}{dx}(6x) = 6$	$\frac{d}{dx}(-x) = -1$
$\frac{d}{dx}(c) = 0$	$\frac{d}{dx}(5) = 0$	$\frac{d}{dx}(\pi) = 0$

In Example 5 of Section 3.6 we saw that $f(x) = |x|$ fails to be differentiable at $x = 0$. In the next example we use the power rule and find more functions not differentiable at a point.

Example 3 Functions Not Differentiable at a Point

Find the natural domains of the derivatives of $f(x) = x^{1/3}$ and $g(x) = x^{2/3}$, and $h(x) = |x|$.

Solution Let's first look at the functions f and g. By the power rule,

$$f'(x) = \frac{1}{3}x^{-2/3} = \frac{1}{3x^{2/3}}$$

and

$$g'(x) = \frac{2}{3}x^{-1/3} = \frac{2}{3x^{1/3}}$$

$f'(x)$ and $g'(x)$ are defined only for nonzero values of x, and their natural domains consist of all real numbers except 0. Thus, the derivatives f' and g' do not exist at $x = 0$. In other words, f and g are not differentiable at $x = 0$. If we look at Figure 38, we notice why these functions fail to be differentiable at $x = 0$: The graph of f has a vertical tangent line at 0. Because a vertical line has undefined slope, the derivative is undefined at that point. The graph of g comes to a sharp point (called a **cusp**) at 0, so it is not meaningful to speak about a tangent line at that point; therefore, the derivative of g is not defined there. (Actually, there is a reasonable candidate for the tangent line at $x = 0$, but it is the vertical line again.)

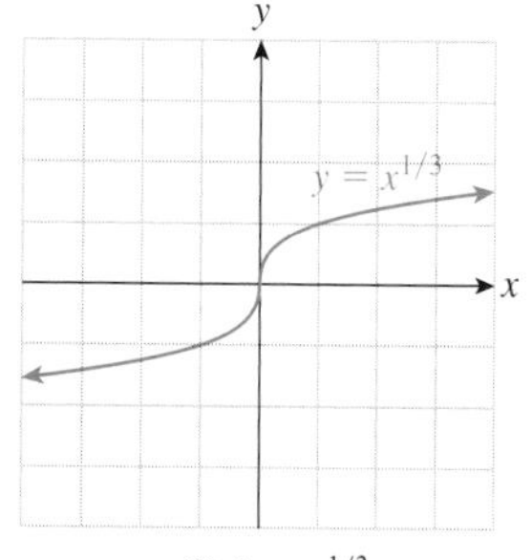

$f(x) = x^{1/3}$

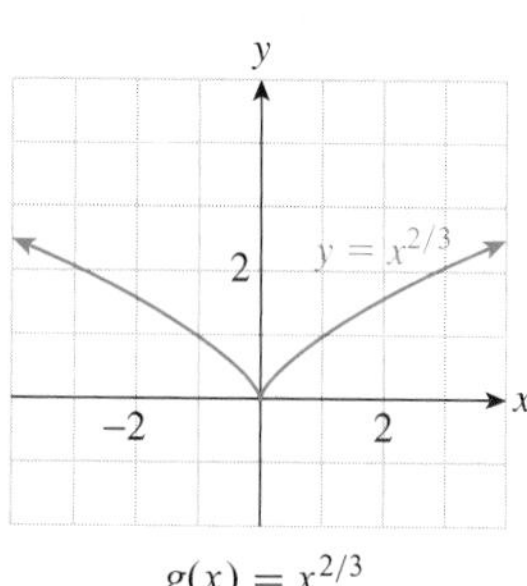

$g(x) = x^{2/3}$

Figure **38**

We can also detect this nondifferentiability by computing some difference quotients numerically. In the case of $f(x) = x^{1/3}$, we get the following table:

h	± 1	± 0.1	± 0.01	± 0.001	± 0.0001
$\frac{f(0+h) - f(0)}{h}$	1	4.6416	21.544	100	464.16

suggesting that the difference quotients $[f(0 + h) - f(0)]/h$ grow large without bound rather than approach any fixed number as h approaches 0. (Can you see how the behavior of the difference quotients in the table is reflected in the graph?)

using *Technology*

If you try to graph the function $f(x) = x^{2/3}$ using the format

```
X^(2/3)
```

you may get only the right-hand portion of Figure 38 because graphing utilities are (often) not programmed to raise negative numbers to fractional exponents. (However, many will handle `X^(1/3)` correctly, as a special case they recognize.) To avoid this difficulty, you can take advantage of the identity

$$x^{2/3} = (x^2)^{1/3}$$

so that it is always a nonnegative number that is being raised to a fractional exponent. Thus, use the format

```
(X^2)^(1/3)
```

to obtain both portions of the graph.

Now we return to the function $h(x) = |x|$ discussed in Example 5 of Section 3.6. We can write

$$|x| = \begin{cases} -x & \text{if } x < 0 \\ x & \text{if } x > 0 \end{cases}$$

Hence, by the power rule (think of x as x^1):

$$f'(x) = \begin{cases} -1 & \text{if } x < 0 \\ 1 & \text{if } x > 0 \end{cases}$$

Q: *So does that mean there is no single formula for the derivative of |x|?*

A: Actually, there *is* a convenient formula. Consider the ratio

$$\frac{|x|}{x} \quad ■$$

If x is positive then $|x| = x$, so $|x|/x = x/x = 1$. On the other hand, if x is negative then $|x| = -x$, so $|x|/x = -x/x = -1$. In other words,

$$\frac{|x|}{x} = \begin{cases} -1 & \text{if } x < 0 \\ 1 & \text{if } x > 0 \end{cases}$$

which is exactly the formula we obtained for $f'(x)$. In other words:

Derivative of |x|

$$\frac{d}{dx}|x| = \frac{|x|}{x}$$

Note that the derivative does not exist when $x = 0$.

***quick* Example**

$$\frac{d}{dx}[3|x| + x] = 3\frac{|x|}{x} + 1$$

An Application to Limits: L'Hospital's Rule (Optional)

The limits that caused us some trouble in Sections 3.1–3.3 are those of the form $\lim_{x \to a} f(x)$ in which we cannot just substitute $x = a$, such as

$$\lim_{x \to 2} \frac{x^3 - 8}{x - 2} \qquad \text{Substituting } x = 2 \text{ yields } \frac{0}{0}.$$

$$\lim_{x \to +\infty} \frac{2x - 4}{x - 1} \qquad \text{Substituting } x = +\infty \text{ yields} \frac{\infty}{\infty}.$$

L'Hospital's rule gives us an alternate way of computing limits such as these without the need to do any preliminary simplification. It also allows us to compute some limits for which algebraic simplification does not work.[67]

[67] Guillame François Antoine Marquis de L'Hospital (1661–1704) wrote the first textbook on calculus, *Analyse des infiniment petits pour l'intelligence des lignes courbes,* in 1692. The rule now known as L'Hospital's Rule appeared first in this book.

Theorem: L'Hospital's Rule

If f and g are two differentiable functions such that substituting $x = a$ in the expression $\frac{f(x)}{g(x)}$ gives either $\frac{0}{0}$ or $\frac{\infty}{\infty}$, then

$$\lim_{x \to a} \frac{f(x)}{g(x)} = \lim_{x \to a} \frac{f'(x)}{g'(x)}$$

That is, we can replace $f(x)$ and $g(x)$ with their *derivatives* and try again to take the limit.

quick Examples

1. Substituting $x = 2$ in $\frac{x^3 - 8}{x - 2}$ yields $\frac{0}{0}$. Therefore, L'Hospital's rule applies and

$$\lim_{x \to 2} \frac{x^3 - 8}{x - 2} = \lim_{x \to 2} \frac{3x^2}{1} = \frac{3(2)^2}{1} = 12$$

2. Substituting $x = +\infty$ in $\frac{2x - 4}{x - 1}$ yields $\frac{\infty}{\infty}$. Therefore, L'Hospital's rule applies and

$$\lim_{x \to +\infty} \frac{2x - 4}{x - 1} = \lim_{x \to +\infty} \frac{2}{1} = 2$$

The proof of L'Hospital's rule is beyond the scope of this text.[68]

Example 4 Applying L'Hospital's Rule

Check whether L'Hospital's rule applies to each of the following limits. If it does, use it to evaluate the limit. Otherwise, use some other method to evaluate the limit.

a. $\lim_{x \to 1} \frac{x^2 - 2x + 1}{4x^3 - 3x^2 - 6x + 5}$ **b.** $\lim_{x \to +\infty} \frac{2x^2 - 4x}{5x^3 - 3x + 5}$

c. $\lim_{x \to 1} \frac{x - 1}{x^3 - 3x^2 + 3x - 1}$ **d.** $\lim_{x \to 1} \frac{x}{x^3 - 3x^2 + 3x - 1}$

Solution

a. Setting $x = 1$ yields

$$\frac{1 - 2 + 1}{4 - 3 - 6 + 5} = \frac{0}{0}$$

Therefore L'Hospital's rule applies and

$$\lim_{x \to 1} \frac{x^2 - 2x + 1}{4x^3 - 3x^2 - 6x + 5} = \lim_{x \to 1} \frac{2x - 2}{12x^2 - 6x - 6}$$

[68] A proof of L'Hospital's rule can be found in most advanced calculus textbooks.

We are left with a closed-form function. However, we cannot substitute $x = 1$ to find the limit because the function $(2x - 2)/(12x^2 - 6x - 6)$ is still not defined at $x = 1$. In fact, if we set $x = 1$, we again get 0/0. Thus, L'Hospital's rule applies again, and

$$\lim_{x\to 1} \frac{2x - 2}{12x^2 - 6x - 6} = \lim_{x\to 1} \frac{2}{24x - 6}$$

Once again we have a closed-form function, but this time it is defined when $x = 1$, giving

$$\frac{2}{24 - 6} = \frac{1}{9}$$

Thus,

$$\lim_{x\to 1} \frac{x^2 - 2x + 1}{4x^3 - 3x^2 - 6x + 5} = \frac{1}{9}$$

b. Setting $x = +\infty$ yields $\frac{\infty}{\infty}$, so

$$\lim_{x\to +\infty} \frac{2x^2 - 4x}{5x^3 - 3x + 5} = \lim_{x\to +\infty} \frac{4x - 4}{15x^2 - 3}$$

Setting $x = +\infty$ again yields $\frac{\infty}{\infty}$, so we can apply the rule again to obtain

$$\lim_{x\to +\infty} \frac{4x - 4}{15x^2 - 3} = \lim_{x\to +\infty} \frac{4}{30x}$$

Note that we cannot apply L'Hospital's rule a third time because setting $x = +\infty$ yields $4/\infty$. However, we can easily see now that the limit is zero. (Refer to Example 4(d) in Section 3.3.)

c. Setting $x = 1$ yields 0/0 so, by L'Hospital's rule,

$$\lim_{x\to 1} \frac{x - 1}{x^3 - 3x^2 + 3x - 1} = \lim_{x\to 1} \frac{1}{3x^2 - 6x + 3}$$

We are left with a closed-form function that is still not defined at $x = 1$. Further, L'Hospital's rule no longer applies because putting $x = 1$ yields 1/0. To investigate this limit, we must either graph it or create a table of values. If we use either method, we find that

$$\lim_{x\to 1} \frac{x - 1}{x^3 - 3x^2 + 3x - 1} = +\infty$$

d. Setting $x = 1$ in the expression yields 1/0, so L'Hospital's rule does not apply here. If we graph the function or create a table of values, we find that the limit does not exist.

FAQs Using the Rules and Recognizing When a Function Is Not Differentiable

Q: *I would like to say that the derivative of $5x^2 - 8x + 4$ is just $10x - 8$ without having to go through all that stuff about derivatives of sums and constant multiples. Can I simply forget about all the rules and write down the answer?*

A: We developed the rules for sums and constant multiples precisely for that reason: so that we could simply write down a derivative without having to think about it too hard. So, you are perfectly justified in simply writing down the derivative without going through the rules, but bear in mind that what you are really doing is applying the power rule, the rule for sums, and the rule for multiples over and over. ■

Q: *Is there a way of telling from its formula whether a function f is not differentiable at a point?*

A: Here are some indicators to look for in the formula for f:

- The absolute value of some expression; f may not be differentiable at points where that expression is zero.

  Example: $f(x) = 3x^2 - |x - 4|$ is not differentiable at $x = 4$.

- A fractional power smaller than 1 of some expression; f may not be differentiable at points where that expression is zero.

  Example: $f(x) = (x^2 - 16)^{2/3}$ is not differentiable at $x = \pm 4$. ■

3.7 EXERCISES

● denotes basic skills exercises

◆ denotes challenging exercises

tech Ex indicates exercises that should be solved using technology

*In Exercises 1–10, use the shortcut rules to **mentally** calculate the derivative of the given function.*

1. ● $f(x) = x^5$ *hint* [see Quick Examples on p. 256]

2. ● $f(x) = x^4$

3. ● $f(x) = 2x^{-2}$

4. ● $f(x) = 3x^{-1}$

5. ● $f(x) = -x^{0.25}$

6. ● $f(x) = -x^{-0.5}$

7. ● $f(x) = 2x^4 + 3x^3 - 1$

8. ● $f(x) = -x^3 - 3x^2 - 1$

9. ● $f(x) = -x + \dfrac{1}{x} + 1$ *hint* [see Example 1]

10. ● $f(x) = \dfrac{1}{x} + \dfrac{1}{x^2}$

In Exercises 11–16, obtain the derivative dy/dx and state the rules that you use. *hint* [see Example 2]

11. ● $y = 10$

12. ● $y = x^3$

13. ● $y = x^2 + x$

14. ● $y = x - 5$

15. ● $y = 4x^3 + 2x - 1$

16. ● $y = 4x^{-1} - 2x - 10$

In Exercises 17–40, find the derivative of each function. *hint* [see Example 2]

17. ● $f(x) = x^2 - 3x + 5$

18. ● $f(x) = 3x^3 - 2x^2 + x$

19. ● $f(x) = x + x^{0.5}$

20. ● $f(x) = x^{0.5} + 2x^{-0.5}$

21. ● $g(x) = x^{-2} - 3x^{-1} - 2;$

22. ● $g(x) = 2x^{-1} + 4x^{-2}$

23. ● $g(x) = \dfrac{1}{x} - \dfrac{1}{x^2}$

24. ● $g(x) = \dfrac{1}{x^2} + \dfrac{1}{x^3}$

25. ● $h(x) = \dfrac{2}{x^{0.4}}$

26. ● $h(x) = -\dfrac{1}{2x^{0.2}}$

27. ● $h(x) = \dfrac{1}{x^2} + \dfrac{2}{x^3}$

28. ● $h(x) = \dfrac{2}{x} - \dfrac{2}{x^3} + \dfrac{1}{x^4}$

29. ● $r(x) = \dfrac{2}{3x} - \dfrac{1}{2x^{0.1}}$

30. ● $r(x) = \dfrac{4}{3x^2} + \dfrac{1}{x^{3.2}}$

31. ● $r(x) = \dfrac{2x}{3} - \dfrac{x^{0.1}}{2} + \dfrac{4}{3x^{1.1}} - 2$

32. ● $r(x) = \dfrac{4x^2}{3} + \dfrac{x^{3.2}}{6} - \dfrac{2}{3x^2} + 4$

33. ● $t(x) = |x| + \dfrac{1}{x}$

34. ● $t(x) = 3|x| - \sqrt{x}$

35. ● $s(x) = \sqrt{x} + \dfrac{1}{\sqrt{x}}$

36. ● $s(x) = x + \dfrac{7}{\sqrt{x}}$

[Hint: For Exercises 37–40: First expand the given function]

37. $s(x) = x\left(x^2 - \dfrac{1}{x}\right)$

38. $s(x) = x^{-1}\left(x - \dfrac{2}{x}\right)$

39. $t(x) = \dfrac{x^2 - 2x^3}{x}$

40. $t(x) = \dfrac{2x + x^2}{x}$

In Exercises 41–46, evaluate the given expression.

41. ● $\dfrac{d}{dx}(2x^{1.3} - x^{-1.2})$

42. ● $\dfrac{d}{dx}(2x^{4.3} + x^{0.6})$

43. $\dfrac{d}{dx}[1.2(x - |x|)]$

44. $\dfrac{d}{dx}[4(x^2 + 3|x|)]$

45. $\dfrac{d}{dt}(at^3 - 4at)$; ($a$ constant)

46. $\dfrac{d}{dt}(at^2 + bt + c)$ (a, b, c constant)

In Exercises 47–52, find the indicated derivative.

47. ● $y = \dfrac{x^{10.3}}{2} + 99x^{-1}$; $\dfrac{dy}{dx}$

48. ● $y = \dfrac{x^{1.2}}{3} - \dfrac{x^{0.9}}{2}$; $\dfrac{dy}{dx}$

49. ● $s = 2.3 + \dfrac{2.1}{t^{1.1}} - \dfrac{t^{0.6}}{2}$; $\dfrac{ds}{dt}$

50. ● $s = \dfrac{2}{t^{1.1}} + t^{-1.2}$; $\dfrac{ds}{dt}$

51. $V = \dfrac{4}{3}\pi r^3$; $\dfrac{dV}{dr}$

52. $A = 4\pi r^2$; $\dfrac{dA}{dr}$

In Exercises 53–58, find the slope of the tangent to the graph of the given function at the indicated point.

53. ● $f(x) = x^3$; $(-1, -1)$

54. ● $g(x) = x^4$; $(-2, 16)$

55. ● $f(x) = 1 - 2x$; $(2, -3)$

56. ● $f(x) = \dfrac{x}{3} - 1$; $(-3, -2)$

57. ● $g(t) = \dfrac{1}{t^5}$; $(1, 1)$

58. ● $s(t) = \dfrac{1}{t^3}$; $(-2, -\dfrac{1}{8})$

In Exercises 59–64, find the equation of the tangent line to the graph of the given function at the point with the indicated x-coordinate. In each case, sketch the curve together with the appropriate tangent line.

59. $f(x) = x^3$; $x = -1$

60. $f(x) = x^2$; $x = 0$

61. $f(x) = x + \dfrac{1}{x}$; $x = 2$

62. $f(x) = \dfrac{1}{x^2}$; $x = 1$

63. $f(x) = \sqrt{x}$; $x = 4$

64. $f(x) = 2x + 4$; $x = -1$

In Exercises 65–70, find all values of x (if any) where the tangent line to the graph of the given equation is horizontal.

65. $y = 2x^2 + 3x - 1$

66. $y = -3x^2 - x$

67. $y = 2x + 8$

68. $y = -x + 1$

69. $y = x + \dfrac{1}{x}$

70. $y = x - \sqrt{x}$

71. ◆ Write out the proof that $\dfrac{d}{dx}(x^4) = 4x^3$.

72. ◆ Write out the proof that $\dfrac{d}{dx}(x^5) = 5x^4$.

tech Ex *In Exercises 73–76, use technology to graph the derivative of the given function for the given range of values of x. Then use your graph to estimate all values of x (if any) where **(a)** the given function is not differentiable, and **(b)** the tangent line to the graph of the given function is horizontal. Round answers to one decimal place.*

73. ● $h(x) = |x - 3|$; $-5 \le x \le 5$

74. tech Ex $h(x) = 2x + (x - 3)^{1/3}$; $-5 \le x \le 5$

75. tech Ex $f(x) = x - 5(x - 1)^{2/5}$; $-4 \le x \le 6$

76. tech Ex $f(x) = |2x + 5| - x^2$; $-4 \le x \le 4$

tech Ex *In Exercises 77–80, investigate the differentiability of the given function at the given points numerically (that is, use a table of values). If $f'(a)$ exists, give its approximate value.* hint [see Example 3]

77. tech Ex $f(x) = x^{1/3}$ **a.** $a = 1$ **b.** $a = 0$

78. tech Ex $f(x) = x + |1 - x|$ **a.** $a = 1$ **b.** $a = 0$

79. tech Ex $f(x) = [x(1 - x)]^{1/3}$ **a.** $a = 1$ **b.** $a = 0$

80. tech Ex $f(x) = (1 - x)^{2/3}$ **a.** $a = -1$ **b.** $a = 1$

In Exercises 81–92 say whether L'Hospital's rule applies. It is does, use it to evaluate the given limit. If not, use some other method.

81. ● $\lim\limits_{x\to 1} \dfrac{x^2 - 2x + 1}{x^2 - x}$

82. ● $\lim\limits_{x\to -1} \dfrac{x^2 + 3x + 2}{x^2 + x}$

83. ● $\lim\limits_{x\to 2} \dfrac{x^3 - 8}{x - 2}$

84. ● $\lim\limits_{x\to 0} \dfrac{x^3 + 8}{x^2 + 3x + 2}$

85. ● $\lim\limits_{x\to 1} \dfrac{x^2 + 3x + 2}{x^2 + x}$

86. ● $\lim\limits_{x\to -2} \dfrac{x^3 + 8}{x^2 + 3x + 2}$

87. ● $\lim\limits_{x\to -\infty} \dfrac{3x^2 + 10x - 1}{2x^2 - 5x}$

88. ● $\lim\limits_{x\to -\infty} \dfrac{6x^2 + 5x + 100}{3x^2 - 9}$

89. ● $\lim\limits_{x\to -\infty} \dfrac{10x^2 + 300x + 1}{5x + 2}$

90. ● $\lim\limits_{x\to -\infty} \dfrac{2x^4 + 20x^3}{1000x^3 + 6}$

91. ● $\lim\limits_{x\to -\infty} \dfrac{x^3 - 100}{2x^2 + 500}$

92. ● $\lim\limits_{x\to -\infty} \dfrac{x^2 + 30x}{2x^6 + 10x}$

Applications

93. ● ***Collegiate Sports*** The number of women's college soccer teams in the U.S. from 1982 to 2001 can be modeled by

$$s(t) = 1.52t^2 + 9.45t + 82.7 \qquad 2 \le t \le 20$$

where t is time in years since the 1980–1981 academic year.[69]

[69] The model is based on a quadratic regression. Source for data: N.C.A.A./*New York Times,* May 9, 2002, p. D4.

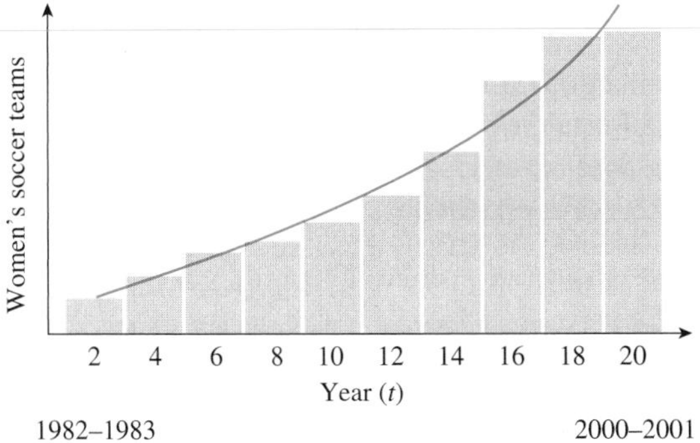

a. Find $s'(t)$.

b. How fast (to the nearest whole number) was the number of women's college soccer teams increasing in the 1994–1995 academic year?

94. ● ***Collegiate Sports*** The number of men's college wrestling teams in the U.S. from 1982 to 2001 can be modeled by

$$w(t) = 0.161t^2 - 9.75t + 360 \qquad 2 \leq t \leq 20$$

where t is time in years since the 1980–1981 academic year[70]

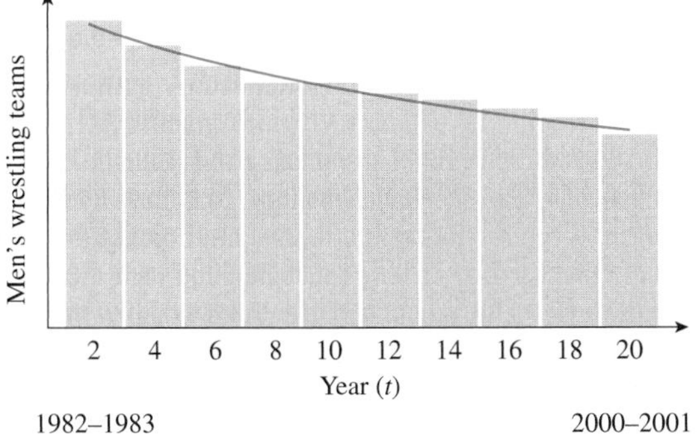

a. Find and graph $w'(t)$.

b. How fast (to the nearest whole number) was the number of men's college wrestling teams decreasing in the 1998–1999 academic year?

95. ● ***Online Shopping*** In January 2000–January 2002, the percentage of people in the U.S. who had ever purchased anything online can be approximated by

$$P(t) = -2.6t^2 + 13t + 19 \text{ percent} \quad (0 \leq t \leq 2)$$

where t is time in years since January 2000.[71] Find $P'(t)$. What does your answer tell you about online shopping transactions in January 2002?

96. ● ***Online Shopping*** The annual number of online shopping transactions in the U.S. for the period January 2000–January 2002 can be approximated by

$$N(t) = -180t^2 + 440t + 320 \text{ million transactions } (0 \leq t \leq 2)$$

where t is time in years since January 2000.[72] Find $N'(t)$. What does your answer tell you about online shopping transactions in January 2002?

97. ● ***Food Versus Education*** The following equation shows the approximate relationship between the percentage y of total personal consumption spent on food and the corresponding percentage x spent on education.[73]

$$y = \frac{35}{x^{0.35}} \text{ percentage points} \quad (6.5 \leq x \leq 17.5)$$

According to the model, spending on food is decreasing at a rate of _____ percentage points per one percentage point increase in spending on education when 10% of total consumption is spent on education. (Answer should be rounded to two significant digits.)

98. ● ***Food Versus Recreation*** The following equation shows the approximate relationship between the percentage y of total personal consumption spent on food and the corresponding percentage x spent on recreation.[74]

$$y = \frac{33}{x^{0.63}} \text{ percentage points} \quad (2.5 \leq x \leq 4.5)$$

According to the model, spending on food is decreasing at a rate of _____ percentage points per one percentage point increase in spending on recreation when 3% of total consumption is spent on recreation. (Answer should be rounded to two significant digits.)

99. ● ***Velocity*** If a stone is dropped from a height of 400 feet, its height s after t seconds is given by $s(t) = 400 - 16t^2$, with s in feet.

a. Compute $s'(t)$ and hence find its velocity at times $t = 0$, 1, 2, 3, and 4 seconds.

b. When does it reach the ground, and how fast is it traveling when it hits the ground?

100. ● ***Velocity*** If a stone is thrown down at 120 ft/sec from a height of 1000 feet, its height s after t seconds is given by $s(t) = 1000 - 120t - 16t^2$, with s in feet.

a. Compute $s'(t)$ and hence find its velocity at times $t = 0$, 1, 2, 3, and 4 seconds.

b. When does it reach the ground, and how fast is it traveling when it hits the ground?

---

[70] Ibid.

[71] Based on a regression model. (Second half of 2001 data was an estimate.) Source for data: Odyssey Research/*New York Times,* November 5, 2001, p. C1.

[72] Based on a regression model. (Second half of 2001 data was an estimate.) Source for data: Odyssey Research/*New York Times,* November 5, 2001, p. C1.

[73] Model based on historical and projected data from 1908–2010. SOURCES: Historical data, Bureau of Economic Analysis; projected data, Bureau of Labor Statistics/*New York Times,* December 1, 2003, p. C2.

[74] Ibid.

101. ● ***Currency*** The value of the euro (€) since its introduction in January, 1999 can be approximated by

$$E(t) = 0.036t^2 - 0.10t + 1.0 \text{ U.S. dollars} \quad (-1 \le t \le 4.5)$$

where $t = 0$ represents January 2000.[75]

a. Compute $E'(t)$. How fast was the value of the euro changing in January, 2004?

b. According to the model, the value of the euro
(A) increased at a faster and faster rate
(B) increased at a slower and slower rate
(C) decreased at a faster and faster rate
(D) decreased at a slower and slower rate

from January 2000 to January 2001.

102. ● ***Funding for the Arts*** Total annual support for the arts in the U.S. by federal, state, and local government for the period January 1998 – January 2003 can be approximated by

$$f(t) = -0.028t^2 + 0.031t + 1.4 \text{ billion dollars} \quad (-2 \le t \le 3)$$

where $t = 0$ represents January 2000.[76]

a. Compute $f'(t)$. How fast was annual support for the arts changing in January, 2002?

b. According to the model, annual support for the arts
(A) increased at a faster and faster rate
(B) increased at a slower and slower rate
(C) decreased at a faster and faster rate
(D) decreased at a slower and slower rate

from January 1998 to January 2000.

103. ● ***Ecology*** Increasing numbers of manatees ("sea sirens") have been killed by boats off the Florida coast. The following graph shows the relationship between the number of boats registered in Florida and the number of manatees killed each year.

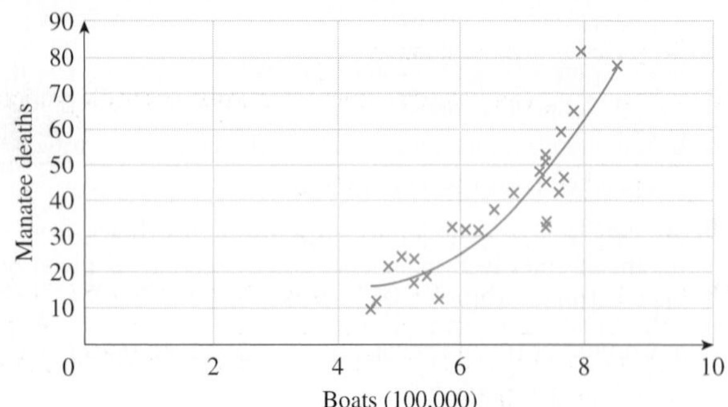

The regression curve shown is given by

$$f(x) = 3.55x^2 - 30.2x + 81 \quad (4.5 \le x \le 8.5)$$

where x is the number of boats (hundreds of thousands) registered in Florida in a particular year and $f(x)$ is the number of manatees killed by boats in Florida that year.[77]

a. Compute $f'(x)$. What are the units of measurement of $f'(x)$?

b. Is $f'(x)$ increasing or decreasing with increasing x? Interpret the answer.

c. Compute and interpret $f'(8)$.

104. ● ***SAT Scores by Income*** The following graph shows U.S. verbal SAT scores as a function of parents' income level.[78]

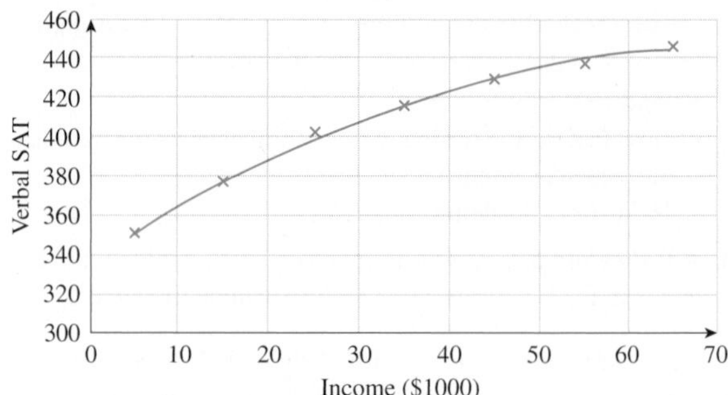

The regression curve shown is given by

$$f(x) = -0.021x^2 + 3.0x + 336 \quad (5 \le x \le 65)$$

where $f(x)$ is the average SAT verbal score of a student whose parents earn x thousand dollars per year.[79]

a. Compute $f'(x)$. What are the units of measurement of $f'(x)$?

b. Is $f'(x)$ increasing or decreasing with increasing x? Interpret the answer.

c. Compute and interpret $f'(30)$

105. ***ISP Market Share*** The following graph shows approximate market shares, in percentage points, of Microsoft's MSN Internet service provider, and the combined shares of MSN, Comcast, Earthlink, and AOL for the period 1999–2004.[80]

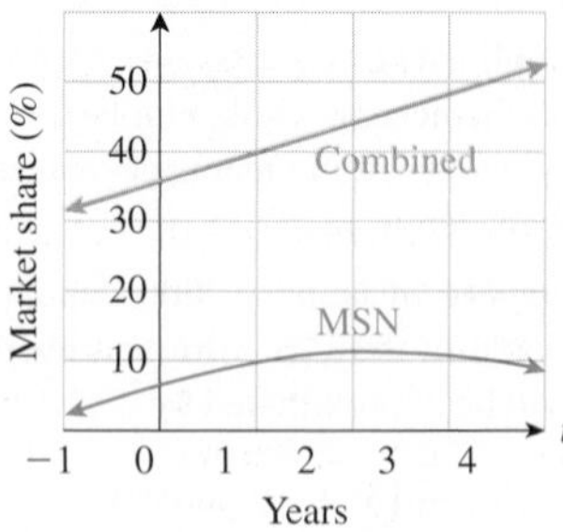

[75] Sources: Bank of England, Reuters, July, 2004.

[76] Based in a quadratic regression of original data. Figures are adjusted for inflation. Sources: Giving USA, The Foundation Center, Americans for the Arts/*New York Times,* June 19, 2004, p. B7.

[77] Regression model is based on data from 1976 to 2000. Sources for data: Florida Department of Highway Safety & Motor Vehicles, Florida Marine Institute/*New York Times,* February 12, 2002, p. F4.

[78] Based on 1994 data. Source: The College Board/*New York Times,* March 5, 1995, p. E16.

[79] Ibid.

[80] The curves are regression models. Source for data: Solomon Research, Morgan Stanley/*New York Times,* July 19, 2004.

Here, t is time in years since June, 2000. Let $c(t)$ be the combined market share at time t, and let $m(t)$ be MSN's share at time t.

a. What does the function $c(t) - m(t)$ measure? What does $c'(t) - m'(t)$ measure?

b. Based on the graphs shown, $c(t) - m(t)$ is

(A) Increasing **(B)** Decreasing
(C) Increasing, then decreasing
(D) Decreasing, then increasing

on the interval [3, 4]

c. Based on the graphs shown, $c'(t) - m'(t)$ is

(A) Positive **(B)** Negative
(C) Positive, then negative
(D) Negative, then positive

on the interval [3, 4].

d. The two market shares are approximated by

$$\text{MSN: } m(t) = -0.83t^2 + 3.8t + 6.8 \quad (-1 \le t \le 4)$$
$$\text{Combined: } c(t) = 4.2t + 36 \quad (-1 \le t \le 4)$$

Compute $c'(2) - m'(2)$. Interpret your answer.

106. ***ISP Revenue*** The following graph shows the approximate total revenue, in millions of dollars, of Microsoft's MSN Internet service provider, as well as the portion of the revenue due to advertising for the period June, 2001–January, 2004.[81]

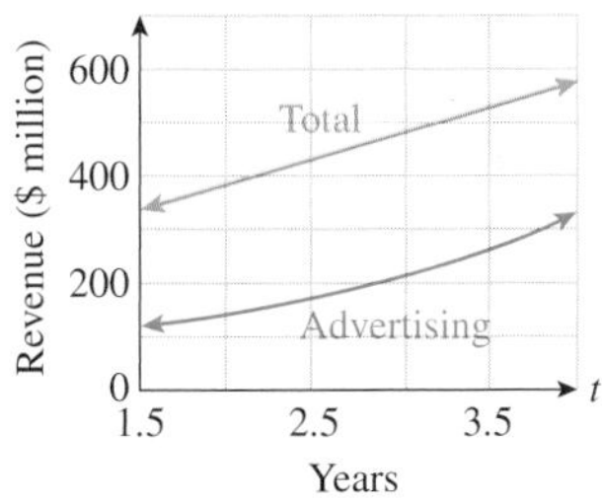

Here, t is time in years since January, 2000. Let $s(t)$ be the total revenue at time t, and let $a(t)$ be revenue due to advertising at time t.

a. What does the function $s(t) - a(t)$ measure? What does $s'(t) - a'(t)$ measure?

b. Based on the graphs shown, $s(t) - a(t)$ is

(A) Increasing **(B)** Decreasing
(C) Increasing, then decreasing
(D) Decreasing, then increasing

on the interval [2, 4]

c. Based on the graphs shown, $s'(t) - a'(t)$ is

(A) Positive **(B)** Negative
(C) Positive, then negative
(D) Negative, then positive

on the interval [2, 4].

d. The two revenue curves are approximated by

$$\text{Advertising: } a(t) = 20t^2 - 27t + 120 \quad (1.5 \le t \le 4)$$
$$\text{Total: } s(t) = 96t + 190 \quad (1.5 \le t \le 4)$$

Compute $a'(2)$, $s'(2)$, and hence $s'(2) - a'(2)$. Interpret your answer.

Communication and Reasoning Exercises

107. ● What instructions would you give to a fellow student who wanted to accurately graph the tangent line to the curve $y = 3x^2$ at the point $(-1, 3)$?

108. ● What instructions would you give to a fellow student who wanted to accurately graph a line at right angles to the curve $y = 4/x$ at the point where $x = 0.5$?

109. ● Consider $f(x) = x^2$ and $g(x) = 2x^2$. How do the slopes of the tangent lines of f and g at the same x compare?

110. ● Consider $f(x) = x^3$ and $g(x) = x^3 + 3$. How do the slopes of the tangent lines of f and g compare?

111. ● Suppose $g(x) = -f(x)$. How do the derivatives of f and g compare?

112. ● Suppose $g(x) = f(x) - 50$. How do the derivatives of f and g compare?

113. ● Following is an excerpt from your best friend's graded homework:

$3x^4 + 11x^5 = 12x^3 + 55x^4$ ✗ *WRONG* (−8)

Why was it marked wrong?

114. ● Following is an excerpt from your second best friend's graded homework:

$f(x) = \dfrac{3}{4x^2}$; $f'(x) = \dfrac{3}{8x}$ ✗ *WRONG* (−10)

Why was it marked wrong?

115. ● Following is an excerpt from your worst enemy's graded homework:

$f(x) = 4x^2$; $f'(x) = (0)(2x) = 0$ ✗ *WRONG* (−6)

Why was it marked wrong?

116. How would you respond to an acquaintance who says, "I finally understand what the derivative is: it is nx^{n-1}! Why weren't we taught that in the first place instead of the difficult way using limits?"

117. Sketch the graph of a function whose derivative is undefined at exactly two points but which has a tangent line at all but one point.

118. Sketch the graph of a function that has a tangent line at each of its points, but whose derivative is undefined at exactly two points.

[81] The curves are regression models. Source for data: Solomon Research, Morgan Stanley/*New York Times,* July 19, 2004.

3.8 A First Application: Marginal Analysis

In Chapter 1, we considered linear *cost functions* of the form $C(x) = mx + b$, where C is the total cost, x is the number of items, and m and b are constants. The slope m is the *marginal cost.* It measures the *cost of one more item.* Notice that the derivative of $C(x) = mx + b$ is $C'(x) = m$. In other words, for a linear cost function, *the marginal cost is the derivative of the cost function.*

In general, we make the following definition.

Marginal Cost

A **cost function** specifies the total cost C as a function of the number of items x. In other words, $C(x)$ is the total cost of x items. The **marginal cost function** is the derivative $C'(x)$ of the cost function $C(x)$. It measures the rate of change of cost with respect to x.

Units

The units of marginal cost are units of cost (dollars, say) per item.

Interpretation

We interpret $C'(x)$ as the approximate cost of one more item.[*]

quick Example

If $C(x) = 400x + 1000$ dollars, then the marginal cost function is $C'(x) = \$400$ per item (a constant).

[*] See Example 1 below.

Example 1 Marginal Cost

Suppose that the cost in dollars to manufacture portable CD players is given by

$$C(x) = 150{,}000 + 20x - 0.0001x^2$$

where x is the number of CD players manufactured.[†] Find the marginal cost function $C'(x)$ and use it to estimate the cost of manufacturing the 50,001st CD player.

Solution Since

$$C(x) = 150{,}000 + 20x - 0.0001x^2$$

[†] You might well ask where on earth this formula came from. There are two approaches to obtaining cost functions in real life: analytical and empirical. The analytical approach is to calculate the cost function from scratch. For example, in the above situation, we might have fixed costs of \$150,000, plus a production cost of \$20 per CD player. The term $0.0001x^2$ may reflect a cost saving for high levels of production, such as a bulk discount in the cost of electronic components. In the empirical approach, we first obtain the cost at several different production levels by direct observation. This gives several points on the (as yet unknown) cost versus production level graph. Then find the equation of the curve that best fits these points, usually using regression.

the marginal cost function is

$$C'(x) = 20 - 0.0002x$$

The units of $C'(x)$ are units of C (dollars) per unit of x (CD players). Thus, $C'(x)$ is measured in dollars per CD player.

The cost of the 50,001st CD player is the amount by which the total cost would rise if we increased production from 50,000 CD players to 50,001. Thus, we need to know the rate at which the total cost rises as we increase production. This rate of change is measured by the derivative, or marginal cost, which we just computed. At $x = 50{,}000$, we get

$$C'(50{,}000) = 20 - 0.0002(50{,}000) = \$10 \text{ per CD player}$$

In other words, we estimate that the 50,001st CD player will cost approximately \$10.

+ *Before we go on...* In Example 1, the marginal cost is really only an *approximation* to the cost of the 50,001st CD player:

$$C'(50{,}000) \approx \frac{C(50{,}001) - C(50{,}000)}{1} \qquad \text{Set } h = 1 \text{ in the definition of the derivative}$$

$$= C(50{,}001) - C(50{,}000)$$

$$= \text{Cost of the 50,001st CD player}$$

The exact cost of the 50,001st CD player is

$$C(50{,}001) - C(50{,}000) = [150{,}000 + 20(50{,}001) - 0.0001(50{,}001)^2] - [150{,}000 + 20(50{,}000) - 0.0001(50{,}000)^2] = \$9.9999$$

So, the marginal cost is a good approximation to the actual cost.

Graphically, we are using the tangent line to approximate the cost function near a production level of 50,000. Figure 39 shows the graph of the cost function together with the tangent line at $x = 50{,}000$. Notice that the tangent line is essentially indistinguishable from the graph of the function for some distance on either side of 50,000.

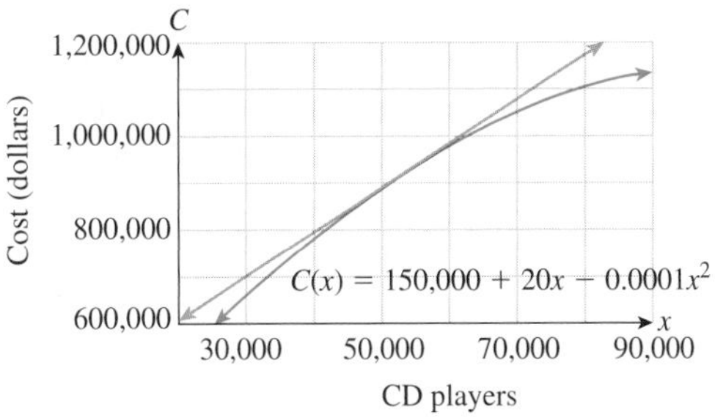

Figure 39 ■

Notes

1. In general, the difference quotient $[C(x+h) - C(x)]/h$ gives the **average cost per item** to produce h more items at a current production level of x items. (Why?)
2. Notice that $C'(x)$ is much easier to calculate than $[C(x+h) - C(x)]/h$. (Try it.) ■

We can extend the idea of marginal cost to include other functions, like revenue and profit:

Marginal Revenue and Profit

A **revenue** or **profit function** specifies the total revenue R or profit P as a function of the number of items x. The derivatives, $R'(x)$ and $P'(x)$ of these functions are called the **marginal revenue** and **marginal profit** functions. They measure the rate of change of revenue and profit with respect to x.

Units

The units of marginal revenue and profit are the same as those of marginal cost: dollars (or euros, pesos, etc.) per item.

Interpretation

We interpret $R'(x)$ and $P'(x)$ as the approximate revenue and profit from the sale of one more item.

Example 2 Marginal Revenue and Profit

You operate an *iPod* customizing service (a typical customized iPod might have a custom color case with blinking lights and a personalized logo). The cost to refurbish x iPods in a month is calculated to be

$$C(x) = 0.25x^2 + 40x + 1000 \text{ dollars}$$

You charge customers \$80 per iPod for the work.

a. Calculate the marginal revenue and profit functions. Interpret the results.

b. Compute the revenue and profit, and also the marginal revenue and profit, if you have refurbished 20 units this month. Interpret the results.

c. For which value of x is the marginal profit is zero? Interpret your answer.

Solution

a. We first calculate the revenue and profit functions:

$$R(x) = 80x \qquad \text{Revenue} = \text{Price} \times \text{Quantity}$$

$$P(x) = R(x) - C(x) \qquad \text{Profit} = \text{Revenue} - \text{Cost}$$

$$= 80x - (0.25x^2 + 40x + 1000)$$

$$P(x) = -0.25x^2 + 40x - 1000$$

The marginal revenue and profit functions are then the derivatives:

$$\text{Marginal revenue} = R'(x) = 80$$
$$\text{Marginal Profit} = P'(x) = -0.5x + 40$$

Interpretation: $R'(x)$ gives the approximate revenue from the refurbishing of one more item, and $P'(x)$ gives the approximate profit from the refurbishing of one more item. Thus, if x iPods have been refurbished in a month, you will earn a revenue of \$80 and make a profit of approximately $\$(-0.5x + 40)$ if you refurbish one more that month.

Notice that the marginal revenue is a constant, so you earn the same revenue (\$80) for each iPod you refurbish. However, the marginal profit, $\$(-0.5x + 40)$, decreases as x increases, so your additional profit is about 50¢ less for each additional iPod you refurbish.

b. From part (a), the revenue, profit, marginal revenue, and marginal profit functions are

$$R(x) = 80x$$
$$P(x) = -0.25x^2 + 40x - 1000$$
$$R'(x) = 80$$
$$P'(x) = -0.5x + 40$$

Because you have refurbished $x = 20$ iPods this month, $x = 20$, so

$R(20) = 80(20) = \$1600$ — Total revenue from 20 iPods

$P(20) = -0.25(20)^2 + 40(20) - 1000 = -\$300$ — Total profit from 20 iPods

$R'(20) = \$80$ per unit — Approximate revenue from the 21st iPod

$P'(20) = -0.5(20) + 40 = \$30$ per unit — Approximate profit from the 21st iPod

Interpretation: If you refurbish 20 iPods in a month, you will earn a total revenue of \$160 and a profit of −\$300 (indicating a loss of \$300). Refurbishing one more iPod that month will earn you an additional revenue of \$80 and an additional profit of about \$30.

c. The marginal profit is zero when $P'(x) = 0$

$$-0.5x + 40 = 0$$
$$x = \frac{40}{0.5} = 80 \text{ iPods}$$

Thus, if you refurbish 80 iPods in a month, refurbishing one more will get you (approximately) zero additional profit. To understand this further, let us take a look at the graph of the profit function, shown in Figure 40.

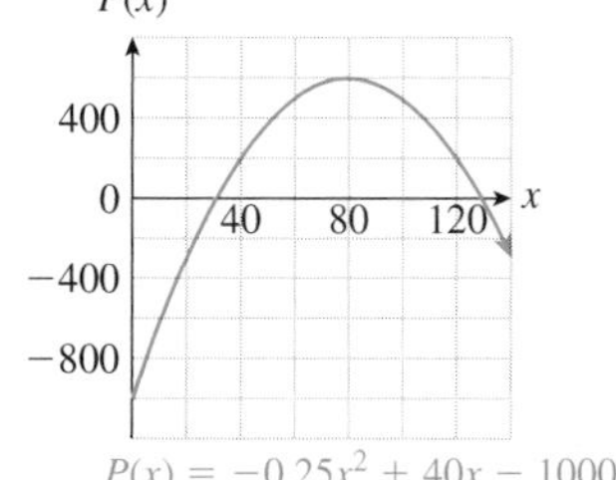

$P(x) = -0.25x^2 + 40x - 1000$

Figure **40**

Notice that the graph is a parabola (the profit function is quadratic) with vertex at the point $x = 80$, where $P'(x) = 0$, so the profit is a maximum at this value of x.

+ *Before we go on...* In general, setting $P'(x) = 0$ and solving for x will always give the exact values of x for which the profit peaks as in Figure 40, assuming there is such a value. We recommend that you graph the profit function to check whether the profit is indeed a maximum at such a point. ■

Example **3** Marginal Product

A consultant determines that Precision Manufacturers' annual profit (in dollars) is given by

$$P(n) = -200{,}000 + 400{,}000n - 4600n^2 - 10n^3 \quad (10 \le n \le 50)$$

where n is the number of assembly-line workers it employs.

a. Compute $P'(n)$. $P'(n)$ is called the **marginal product** at the employment level of n assembly-line workers. What are its units?

b. Calculate $P(20)$ and $P'(20)$, and interpret the results.

c. Precision Manufacturers currently employs 20 assembly-line workers and is considering laying off some of them. What advice would you give the company's management?

Solution

a. Taking the derivative gives

$$P'(n) = 400{,}000 - 9200n - 30n^2$$

The units of $P'(n)$ are profit (in dollars) per worker.

b. Substituting into the formula for $P(n)$, we get

$$P(20) = -200{,}000 + 400{,}000(20) - 4600(20)^2 - 10(20)^3 = \$5{,}880{,}000$$

Thus, Precision Manufacturer will make an annual profit of \$5,880,000 if it employs 20 assembly-line workers. On the other hand,

$$P'(20) = 400{,}000 - 9200(20) - 30(20)^2 = \$204{,}000/\text{worker}$$

Thus, at an employment level of 20 assembly-line workers, annual profit is increasing at a rate of \$204,000 per additional worker. In other words, if the company were to employ one more assembly-line worker, its annual profit would increase by approximately \$204,000.

c. Because the marginal product is positive, profits will increase if the company increases the number of workers and will decrease if it decreases the number of workers, so your advice would be to hire additional assembly-line workers. Downsizing their assembly-line workforce would reduce their annual profits.

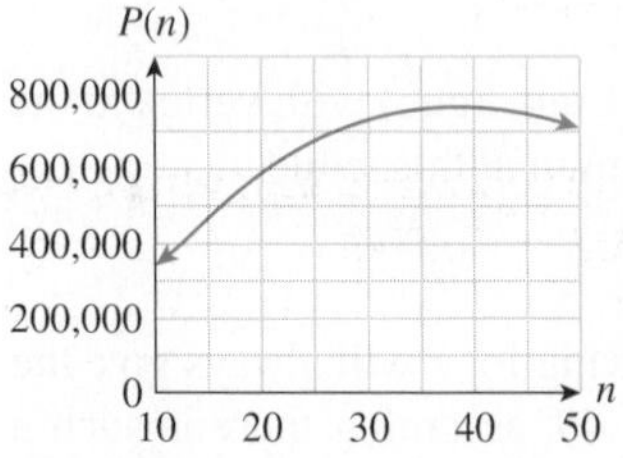

+ *Before we go on...* In Example 3, it would be interesting for Precision Manufacturers to ascertain how many additional assembly-line workers they should hire to obtain the *maximum* annual profit. Taking our cue from Example 2, we suspect that such a value of n would correspond to a point where $P'(n) = 0$. Figure 41 shows the graph of P, and on it we see that the highest point of the graph is indeed a point where the tangent line is horizontal; that is, $P'(n) = 0$, and occurs somewhere between $n = 35$ and 40.

P(n)
800,000
600,000
400,000
200,000
0
10 20 30 40 50
n

Figure **41**

To compute this value of n more accurately, set $P'(n) = 0$ and solve for n:

$$P'(n) = 400{,}000 - 9200n - 30n^2 = 0$$

$$\text{or} \quad 40{,}000 - 920n - 3n^2 = 0$$

We can now obtain n using the quadratic formula:

$$n = \frac{-b \pm \sqrt{b^2 - 4ac}}{2a} = \frac{920 \pm \sqrt{920^2 - 4(-3)(40{,}000)}}{2(-3)}$$

$$= \frac{920 \pm \sqrt{1{,}326{,}400}}{-6} \approx -345.3 \text{ or } 38.6$$

The only meaningful solution is the positive one, $n \approx 38.6$ workers, and we conclude that the company should employ between 38 and 39 assembly-line workers for a maximum profit. To see which gives the larger profit, 38 or 39, we check:

$$P(38) = \$7{,}808{,}880$$

while

$$P(39) = \$7{,}810{,}210$$

This tells us that the company should employ 39 assembly-line workers for a maximum profit. Thus, instead of laying off any of its 20 assembly-line workers, the company should hire 19 additional assembly line workers for a total of 39. ■

Average Cost

Example 4 Average Cost

Suppose the cost in dollars to manufacture portable CD players is given by

$$C(x) = 150{,}000 + 20x - 0.0001x^2$$

where x is the number of CD players manufactured. (This is the cost equation we saw in Example 1.)

a. Find the average cost per CD player if 50,000 CD players are manufactured.

b. Find a formula for the average cost per CD player if x CD players are manufactured. This function of x is called the **average cost function, $\bar{C}(x)$.**

Solution

a. The total cost of manufacturing 50,000 CD players is given by

$$\begin{aligned} C(50{,}000) &= 150{,}000 + 20(50{,}000) - 0.0001(50{,}000)^2 \\ &= \$900{,}000 \end{aligned}$$

Because 50,000 CD players cost a total of \$900,000 to manufacture, the average cost of manufacturing one CD player is this total cost divided by 50,000:

$$\bar{C}(50{,}000) = \frac{900{,}000}{50{,}000} = \$18.00 \text{ per CD player}$$

Thus, if 50,000 CD players are manufactured, each CD player costs the manufacturer an average of \$18.00 to manufacture.

b. If we replace 50,000 by x, we get the general formula for the average cost of manufacturing x CD players:

$$\begin{aligned} \bar{C}(x) &= \frac{C(x)}{x} \\ &= \frac{1}{x}(150{,}000 + 20x - 0.0001x^2) \\ &= \frac{150{,}000}{x} + 20 - 0.0001x \qquad \text{Average cost function} \end{aligned}$$

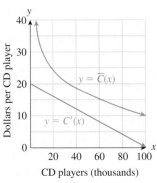

+Before we go on... Average cost and marginal cost convey different but related information. The average cost $\bar{C}(50{,}000) = \$18$ that we calculated in Example 4 is the cost per item of manufacturing the first 50,000 CD players, whereas the marginal cost $C'(50{,}000) = \$10$ that we calculated in Example 1 gives the (approximate) cost of manufacturing the *next* CD player. Thus, according to our calculations, the first 50,000 CD players cost an average of \$18 to manufacture, but it costs only about \$10 to manufacture the next one. Note that the marginal cost at a production level of 50,000 CD players is lower than the average cost. This means that the average cost to manufacture CDs is going down with increasing volume. (Think about why.)

Figure 42 shows the graphs of average and marginal cost. Notice how the decreasing marginal cost seems to pull the average cost down with it. ■

Figure **42**

To summarize:

Average Cost

Given a cost function C, the **average cost** of the first x items is given by

$$\bar{C}(x) = \frac{C(x)}{x}$$

The average cost is distinct from the **marginal cost** $C'(x)$, which tells us the approximate cost of the *next* item.

quick **Example**

For the cost function $C(x) = 20x + 100$ dollars

$$\text{Marginal Cost} = C'(x) = \$20 \text{ per additional item}$$

$$\text{Average Cost} = \bar{C}(x) = \frac{C(x)}{x} = \frac{20x + 100}{x} = \$(20 + 100/x) \text{ per item}$$

3.8 EXERCISES

● denotes basic skills exercises

◆ denotes challenging exercises

In Exercises 1–4, for each cost function, find the marginal cost at the given production level x, and state the units of measurement. (All costs are in dollars.) hint [see Example 1]

1. ● $C(x) = 10{,}000 + 5x - 0.0001x^2;\ x = 1000$

2. ● $C(x) = 20{,}000 + 7x - 0.00005x^2;\ x = 10{,}000$

3. ● $C(x) = 15{,}000 + 100x + \dfrac{1000}{x};\ x = 100$

4. ● $C(x) = 20{,}000 + 50x + \dfrac{10{,}000}{x};\ x = 100$

In Exercises 5 and 6, find the marginal cost, marginal revenue, and marginal profit functions, and find all values of x for which the marginal profit is zero. Interpret your answer. hint [see Example 2]

5. ● $C(x) = 4x;\ \ R(x) = 8x - 0.001x^2$

6. ● $C(x) = 5x^2;\ \ R(x) = x^3 + 7x + 10$

7. A certain cost function has the following graph:

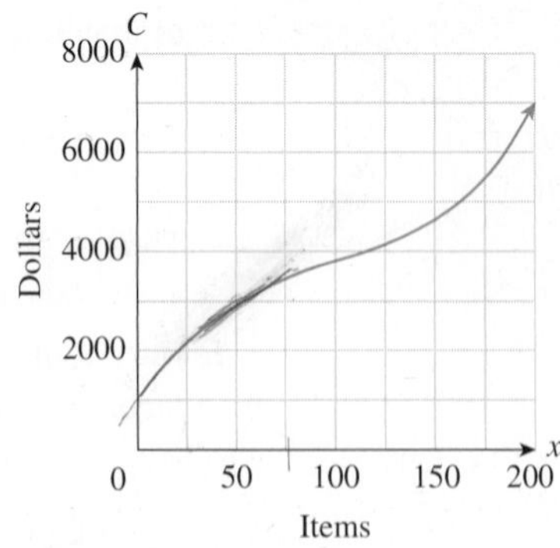

a. The associated marginal cost is
(A) increasing, then decreasing.
(B) decreasing, then increasing.
(C) always increasing.
(D) always decreasing.

b. The marginal cost is least at approximately
(A) $x = 0$ (B) $x = 50$
(C) $x = 100$ (D) $x = 150$

c. The cost of 50 items is
(A) approximately \$20, and increasing at a rate of about \$3000 per item.
(B) approximately \$0.50, and increasing at a rate of about \$3000 per item.
(C) approximately \$3000, and increasing at a rate of about \$20 per item.
(D) approximately \$3000, and increasing at a rate of about \$0.50 per item.

8. A certain cost function has the following graph:

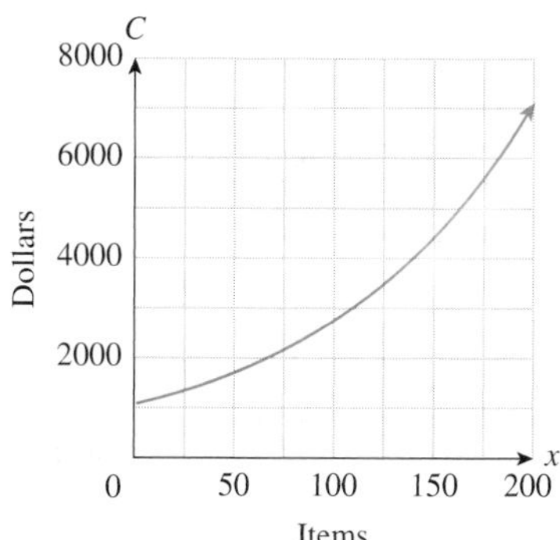

a. The associated marginal cost is
(A) increasing, then decreasing.
(B) decreasing, then increasing.
(C) always increasing.
(D) always decreasing.

b. When $x = 100$, the marginal cost is
(A) greater than (B) less than
(C) approximately equal to the average cost.

c. The cost of 150 items is
(A) approximately \$4400, and increasing at a rate of about \$40 per item.
(B) approximately \$40, and increasing at a rate of about \$4400 per item.
(C) approximately \$4400, and increasing at a rate of about \$1 per item.
(D) approximately \$1, and increasing at a rate of about \$4400 per item.

Applications

9. ● ***Advertising Costs*** The cost, in thousands of dollars, of airing x television commercials during a Super Bowl game is given by[82]

$$C(x) = 150 + 2250x - 0.02x^2$$

a. Find the marginal cost function and use it to estimate how fast the cost is increasing when $x = 4$. Compare this with the exact cost of airing the fifth commercial.

b. Find the average cost function $\bar{C}$, and evaluate $\bar{C}(4)$. What does the answer tell you? *hint* [see Example 1]

10. ● ***Marginal Cost and Average Cost*** The cost of producing x teddy bears per day at the Cuddly Companion Co. is calculated by their marketing staff to be given by the formula

$$C(x) = 100 + 40x - 0.001x^2$$

a. Find the marginal cost function and use it to estimate how fast the cost is going up at a production level of 100 teddy bears. Compare this with the exact cost of producing the 101st teddy bear.

b. Find the average cost function $\bar{C}$, and evaluate $\bar{C}(100)$. What does the answer tell you?

11. ● ***Marginal Revenue and Profit*** Your college newspaper, *The Collegiate Investigator,* sells for 90¢ per copy. The cost of producing x copies of an edition is given by

$$C(x) = 70 + 0.10x + 0.001x^2 \text{ dollars}$$

a. Calculate the marginal revenue and profit functions.

b. Compute the revenue and profit, and also the marginal revenue and profit, if you have produced and sold 500 copies of the latest edition. Interpret the results.

c. For which value of x is the marginal profit zero? Interpret your answer. *hint* [see Example 2]

12. ● ***Marginal Revenue and Profit*** The Audubon Society at Enormous State University (ESU) is planning its annual fund-raising "Eatathon." The society will charge students \$1.10 per serving of pasta. The society estimates that the total cost of producing x servings of pasta at the event will be

$$C(x) = 350 + 0.10x + 0.002x^2 \text{ dollars}$$

a. Calculate the marginal revenue and profit functions.

b. Compute the revenue and profit, and also the marginal revenue and profit, if you have produced and sold 200 servings of pasta. Interpret the results.

c. For which value of x is the marginal profit zero? Interpret your answer.

13. ● ***Marginal Profit*** Suppose $P(x)$ represents the profit on the sale of x DVDs. If $P(1000) = 3000$ and $P'(1000) = -3$, what do these values tell you about the profit?

14. ● ***Marginal Loss*** An automobile retailer calculates that its loss on the sale of type M cars is given by $L(50) = 5000$ and $L'(50) = -200$, where $L(x)$ represents the loss on the sale of x type M cars. What do these values tell you about losses?

15. ● ***Marginal Profit*** Your monthly profit (in dollars) from selling magazines is given by

$$P = 5x + \sqrt{x}$$

where x is the number of magazines you sell in a month. If you are currently selling $x = 50$ magazines per month, find your profit and your marginal profit. Interpret your answers.

[82] CBS charged an average of \$2.25 million per 30-second television spot during the 2004 Super Bowl game. This explains the coefficient of x in the cost function. SOURCE: Advertising Age Research, www.AdAge.com/.

16. ***Marginal Profit*** Your monthly profit (in dollars) from your newspaper route is given by

$$P = 2n - \sqrt{n}$$

where n is the number of subscribers on your route. If you currently have 100 subscribers, find your profit and your marginal profit. Interpret your answers.

17. ***Marginal Revenue: Pricing Tuna*** Assume that the demand function for tuna in a small coastal town is given by

$$p = \frac{20{,}000}{q^{1.5}} \qquad (200 \le q \le 800)$$

where p is the price (in dollars) per pound of tuna, and q is the number of pounds of tuna that can be sold at the price p in one month.

a. Calculate the price that the town's fishery should charge for tuna in order to produce a demand of 400 pounds of tuna per month.

b. Calculate the monthly revenue R as a function of the number of pounds of tuna q.

c. Calculate the revenue and marginal revenue (derivative of the revenue with respect to q) at a demand level of 400 pounds per month, and interpret the results.

d. If the town fishery's monthly tuna catch amounted to 400 pounds of tuna, and the price is at the level in part (a), would you recommend that the fishery raise or lower the price of tuna in order to increase its revenue?

18. ***Marginal Revenue: Pricing Tuna*** Repeat Exercise 17, assuming a demand equation of

$$p = \frac{60}{q^{0.5}} \qquad (200 \le q \le 800)$$

19. ● ***Marginal Product*** A car wash firm calculates that its daily profit (in dollars) depends on the number n of workers it employs according to the formula

$$P = 400n - 0.5n^2$$

Calculate the marginal product at an employment level of 50 workers, and interpret the result. hint [see Example 3]

20. ● ***Marginal Product*** Repeat the preceding exercise using the formula

$$P = -100n + 25n^2 - 0.005n^4$$

21. ● ***Average and Marginal Cost*** The daily cost to manufacture generic trinkets for gullible tourists is given by the cost function

$$C(x) = -0.001x^2 + 0.3x + 500 \text{ dollars}$$

where x is the number of trinkets. hint [see Example 4]

a. As x increases, the marginal cost
(A) increases **(B)** decreases
(C) increases, then decreases.
(D) decreases, then increases.

b. As x increases, the average cost
(A) increases **(B)** decreases
(C) increases, then decreases.
(D) decreases, then increases.

c. The marginal cost is
(A) greater than **(B)** equal to **(C)** less than
the average cost when $x = 100$.

22. ● ***Average and Marginal Cost*** Repeat Exercise 21, using the following cost function for imitation oil paintings (x is the number of "oil paintings" manufactured):

$$C(x) = 0.1x^2 - 3.5x + 500 \text{ dollars}$$

23. ● ***Advertising Cost*** Your company is planning to air a number of television commercials during the ABC Television Network's presentation of the Academy Awards. ABC is charging your company \$1.6 million per 30 second spot.[83] Additional fixed costs (development and personnel costs) amount to \$500,000, and the network has agreed to provide a discount of $\$10{,}000\sqrt{x}$ for x television spots.

a. Write down the cost function C, marginal cost function C', and average cost function $\bar{C}$.

b. Compute $C'(3)$ and $\bar{C}(3)$. (Round all answers to three significant digits.) Use these two answers to say whether the average cost is increasing or decreasing as x increases.

24. ● ***Housing Costs*** The cost C of building a house is related to the number k of carpenters used and the number x of electricians used by the formula[84]

$$C = 15{,}000 + 50k^2 + 60x^2$$

a. Assuming that 10 carpenters are currently being used, find the cost function C, marginal cost function C', and average cost function $\bar{C}$, all as functions of x.

b. Use the functions you obtained in part (a) to compute $C'(15)$ and $\bar{C}(15)$. Use these two answers to say whether the average cost is increasing or decreasing as the number of electricians increases.

25. ***Emission Control*** The cost of controlling emissions at a firm rises rapidly as the amount of emissions reduced increases. Here is a possible model:

$$C(q) = 4000 + 100q^2$$

where q is the reduction in emissions (in pounds of pollutant per day) and C is the daily cost (in dollars) of this reduction.

a. If a firm is currently reducing its emissions by 10 pounds each day, what is the marginal cost of reducing emissions further?

---

[83] ABC charged an average of \$1.6 million for a 30-second spot during the 2005 Academy Awards presentation. SOURCE: CNN/Reuters, www.cnn.com/, February 9, 2005.

[84] Based on an exercise in *Introduction to Mathematical Economics* by A. L. Ostrosky, Jr., and J. V. Koch (Waveland Press, Prospect Heights, Illinois, 1979).

b. Government clean-air subsidies to the firm are based on the formula

$$S(q) = 500q$$

where q is again the reduction in emissions (in pounds per day) and S is the subsidy (in dollars). At what reduction level does the marginal cost surpass the marginal subsidy?

c. Calculate the net cost function, $N(q) = C(q) - S(q)$, given the cost function and subsidy above, and find the value of q that gives the lowest net cost. What is this lowest net cost? Compare your answer to that for part (b) and comment on what you find.

26. ***Taxation Schemes*** Here is a curious proposal for taxation rates based on income:

$$T(i) = 0.001i^{0.5}$$

where i represents total annual income in dollars and $T(i)$ is the income tax rate as a percentage of total annual income. (Thus, for example, an income of \$50,000 per year would be taxed at about 22%, while an income of double that amount would be taxed at about 32%.)[85]

a. Calculate the after-tax (net) income $N(i)$ an individual can expect to earn as a function of income i.

b. Calculate an individual's marginal after-tax income at income levels of \$100,000 and \$500,000.

c. At what income does an individual's marginal after-tax income become negative? What is the after-tax income at that level, and what happens at higher income levels?

d. What do you suspect is the most anyone can earn after taxes? (See the footnote.)

27. ***Fuel Economy*** Your Porsche's gas mileage (in miles per gallon) is given as a function $M(x)$ of speed x in miles per hour. It is found that

$$M'(x) = \frac{3600x^{-2} - 1}{(3600x^{-1} + x)^2}$$

Estimate $M'(10)$, $M'(60)$, and $M'(70)$. What do the answers tell you about your car?

28. ***Marginal Revenue*** The estimated marginal revenue for sales of ESU soccer team T-shirts is given by

$$R'(p) = \frac{(8 - 2p)e^{-p^2+8p}}{10{,}000{,}000}$$

where p is the price (in dollars) that the soccer players charge for each shirt. Estimate $R'(3)$, $R'(4)$, and $R'(5)$. What do the answers tell you?

29. ◆ ***Marginal Cost (from the GRE Economics Test)*** In a multiplant firm in which the different plants have different and continuous cost schedules, if costs of production for a given output level are to be minimized, which of the following is essential?

(A) Marginal costs must equal marginal revenue.
(B) Average variable costs must be the same in all plants.
(C) Marginal costs must be the same in all plants.
(D) Total costs must be the same in all plants.
(E) Output per worker per hour must be the same in all plants.

30. ◆ ***Study Time (from the GRE economics test)*** A student has a fixed number of hours to devote to study and is certain of the relationship between hours of study and the final grade for each course. Grades are given on a numerical scale (e.g., 0 to 100), and each course is counted equally in computing the grade average. In order to maximize his or her grade average, the student should allocate these hours to different courses so that

(A) the grade in each course is the same.
(B) the marginal product of an hour's study (in terms of final grade) in each course is zero.
(C) the marginal product of an hour's study (in terms of final grade) in each course is equal, although not necessarily equal to zero
(D) the average product of an hour's study (in terms of final grade) in each course is equal.
(E) the number of hours spent in study for each course are equal.

31. ◆ ***Marginal Product (from the GRE economics test)*** Assume that the marginal product of an additional senior professor is 50% higher than the marginal product of an additional junior professor and that junior professors are paid one-half the amount that senior professors receive. With a fixed overall budget, a university that wishes to maximize its quantity of output from professors should do which of the following?

(A) Hire equal numbers of senior professors and junior professors.
(B) Hire more senior professors and junior professors.
(C) Hire more senior professors and discharge junior professors.
(D) Discharge senior professors and hire more junior professors.
(E) Discharge all senior professors and half of the junior professors.

32. ◆ ***Marginal Product (Based on a Question from the GRE Economics Test)*** Assume that the marginal product of an additional senior professor is twice the marginal product of an additional junior professor and that junior professors are paid two-thirds the amount that senior professors receive. With a fixed overall budget, a university that wishes to maximize its quantity of output from professors should do which of the following?

(A) Hire equal numbers of senior professors and junior professors.
(B) Hire more senior professors and junior professors.
(C) Hire more senior professors and discharge junior professors.

[85] This model has the following interesting feature: an income of a million dollars per year would be taxed at 100%, leaving the individual penniless!

(D) Discharge senior professors and hire more junior professors.
(E) Discharge all senior professors and half of the junior professors.

Communication and Reasoning Exercises

33. ● The marginal cost of producing the 1001st item is
(A) Equal to
(B) Approximately equal to
(C) Always slightly greater than
the actual cost of producing the 1001st item.

34. ● For the cost function $C(x) = mx + b$, the marginal cost of producing the 1001st item is
(A) Equal to
(B) Approximately equal to
(C) Always slightly greater than
the actual cost of producing the 1001st item.

35. ● What is a cost function? Carefully explain the difference between *average cost* and *marginal cost* in terms of **a.** their mathematical definition, **b.** graphs, and **c.** interpretation.

36. ● The cost function for your grand piano manufacturing plant has the property that $\bar{C}(1000) = \$3000$ per unit and $C'(1000) = \$2500$ per unit. Will the average cost increase or decrease if your company manufactures a slightly larger number of pianos? Explain your reasoning.

37. ● If the average cost to manufacture one grand piano increases as the production level increases, which is greater, the marginal cost or the average cost?

38. ● If your analysis of a manufacturing company yielded positive marginal profit but negative profit at the company's current production levels, what would you advise the company to do?

39. If the marginal cost is decreasing, is the average cost necessarily decreasing? Explain.

40. If the average cost is decreasing, is the marginal cost necessarily decreasing?

41. ◆ If a company's marginal average cost is zero at the current production level, positive for a slightly higher production level, and negative for a slightly lower production level, what should you advise the company to do?

42. ◆ The **acceleration** of cost is defined as the derivative of the marginal cost function: that is, the derivative of the derivative—or *second derivative*—of the cost function. What are the units of acceleration of cost, and how does one interpret this measure?

Chapter 3 Review

KEY CONCEPTS

3.1 Limits: Numerical and Graphical Approaches

$\lim_{x\to a} f(x) = L$ means that $f(x)$ approaches L as x approaches a. *p. 186*

What it means for a limit to exist *p. 186*

Limits at infinity *p. 188*

Estimating limits graphically *p. 189*

Interpreting limits in real-world situations *p. 192*

3.2 Limits and Continuity

f is continuous at a if $\lim_{x\to a} f(x)$ exists and $\lim_{x\to a} f(x) = f(a)$. *p. 196*

Discontinuous, continuous on domain *p. 196*

Determining whether a given function is continuous *p. 197*

3.3 Limits and Continuity Algebraic Approach

Closed-form function *p. 202*

Limits of closed form functions *p. 202*

Simplifying to obtain limits *p. 203*

Limits of piecewise defined functions *p. 204*

Limits at infinity *p. 205*

3.4 Average Rate of Change

Average rate of change of $f(x)$ over $[a, b]$: $\dfrac{\Delta f}{\Delta x} = \dfrac{f(b) - f(a)}{b - a}$ *p. 213*

Average rate of change as slope of the secant line *p. 213*

Computing the average rate of change from a graph *p. 214*

Computing the average rate of change from a formula *p. 216*

Computing the average rate of change over short intervals $[a, a + h]$ *p. 217*

3.5 The Derivative: Numerical and Graphical Viewpoints

Instantaneous rate of change of $f(x)$ (derivative of f at a);

$$f'(a) = \lim_{h\to 0} \frac{f(a+h) - f(a)}{h} \quad p.\ 226$$

The derivative as slope of the tangent line *p. 229*

Quick approximation of the derivative *p. 230*

Leibniz d notation *p. 232*

The derivative as velocity *p. 233*

Average and instantaneous velocity *p. 234*

The derivative function *p. 235*

Graphing the derivative function with technology *p. 235*

3.6 The Derivative: Algebraic Viewpoint

Derivative at the point $x = a$:

$$f'(a) = \lim_{h\to 0} \frac{f(a+h) - f(a)}{h} \quad p.\ 247$$

Derivative function:

$$f'(x) = \lim_{h\to 0} \frac{f(x+h) - f(x)}{h} \quad p.\ 248$$

Examples of the computation of $f'(x)$ *p. 248*

$f(x) = |x|$ is not differentiable at $x = 0$. *p. 251*

3.7 Derivatives of Powers, Sums and Constant Multiples

Power Rule: If n is any constant and $f(x) = x^n$, then $f'(x) = nx^{n-1}$ *p. 256*

Using the power rule for negative and fractional exponents *p. 256*

$\dfrac{d}{dx}$ Notation *p. 257*

Sums, Differences, and Constant Multiples *p. 258*

Combining the rules *p. 260*

$\dfrac{d}{dx}(cx) = c$, $\dfrac{d}{dx}(c) = 0$ *p. 261*

$f(x) = x^{1/3}$ and $g(x) = x^{2/3}$ are not differentiable at $x = 0$. *p. 261*

Derivative of $f(x) = |x|$:

$$\frac{d}{dx}|x| = \frac{|x|}{x} \quad p.\ 262$$

3.8 A First Application: Marginal Analysis

Marginal cost function $C'(x)$ *p. 270*

Marginal revenue and profit functions $R'(x)$ and $P'(x)$ *p. 272*

What it means when the marginal profit is zero *p. 272*

Marginal product *p. 273*

Average cost of the first x items:

$$\bar{C}(x) = \frac{C(x)}{x} \quad p.\ 276$$

REVIEW EXERCISES

Numerically estimate whether the limits in Exercises 1–4 exist. If a limit does exist, give its approximate value.

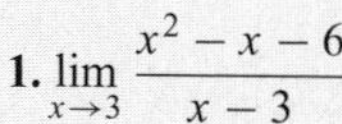

1. $\displaystyle\lim_{x\to 3} \frac{x^2 - x - 6}{x - 3}$

2. $\displaystyle\lim_{x\to 3} \frac{x^2 - 2x - 6}{x - 3}$

3. $\displaystyle\lim_{x\to -1} \frac{|x+1|}{x^2 - x - 2}$

4. $\displaystyle\lim_{x\to -1} \frac{|x+1|}{x^2 + x - 2}$

In Exercises 5 and 6, the graph of a function f is shown. Graphically determine whether the given limits exist. If a limit does exist, give its approximate value.

5.

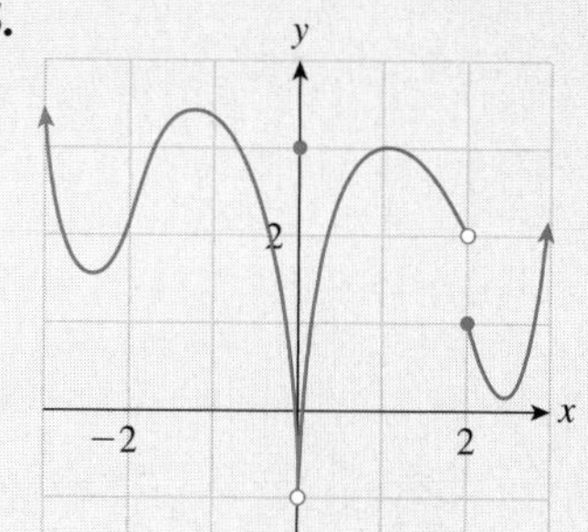

a. $\lim_{x\to 0} f(x)$

b. $\lim_{x\to 1} f(x)$

c. $\lim_{x\to 2} f(x)$

6.

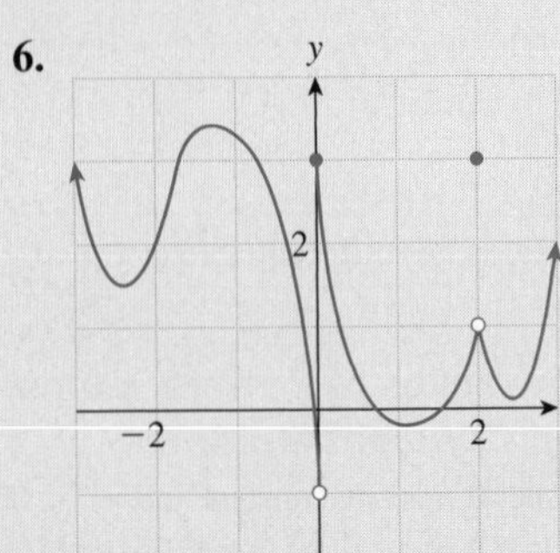

a. $\lim_{x\to 0} f(x)$

b. $\lim_{x\to -2} f(x)$

c. $\lim_{x\to 2} f(x)$

Calculate the limits in Exercises 7–12 algebraically. If a limit does not exist, say why.

7. $\lim_{x\to -2} \dfrac{x^2}{x-3}$ **8.** $\lim_{x\to 3} \dfrac{x^2-9}{2x-6}$

9. $\lim_{x\to 0} \dfrac{x}{2x^2-x}$ **10.** $\lim_{x\to 1} \dfrac{x^2-9}{x-1}$

11. $\lim_{x\to -\infty} \dfrac{x^2-x-6}{x-3}$ **12.** $\lim_{x\to \infty} \dfrac{x^2-x-6}{4x^2-3}$

In Exercises 13–16, find the average rate of change of the given function over the interval $[a, a+h]$ for $h = 1$, 0.01, and 0.001. (Round answers to four decimal places.) Then estimate the slope of the tangent line to the graph of the function at a.

13. $f(x) = \dfrac{1}{x+1}$; $a = 0$ **14.** $f(x) = x^x$; $a = 2$

15. $f(x) = e^{2x}$; $a = 0$ **16.** $f(x) = \ln(2x)$; $a = 1$

*In Exercises 17–20 you are given the graph of a function with four points marked. Determine at which (if any) of these points the derivative of the function is: **(i)** −1 **(ii)** 0 **(iii)** 1, and **(iv)** 2.*

17.

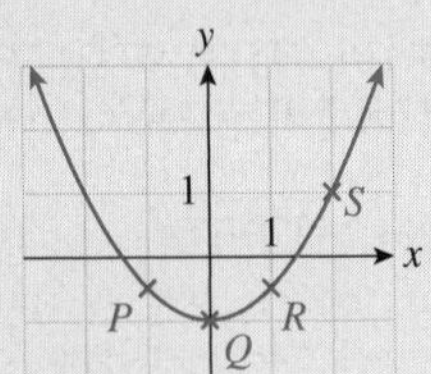

18.

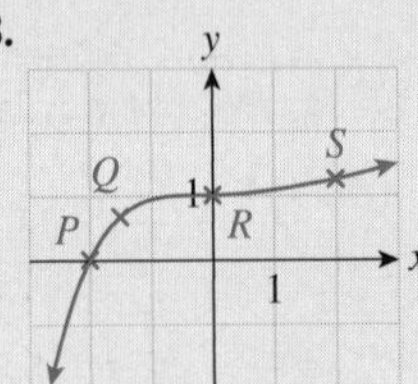

19.

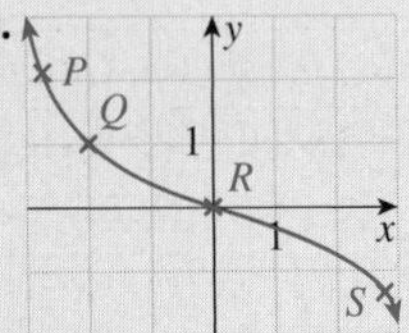

20.

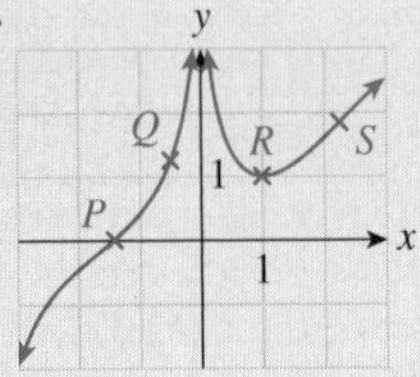

21. Let f have the graph shown.

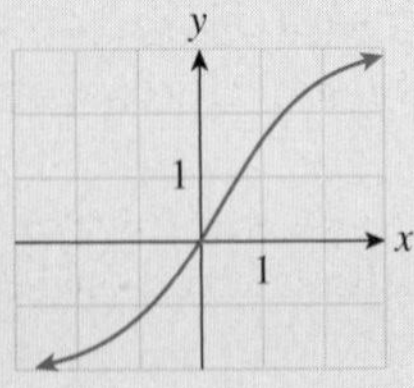

Select the correct answer.

a. The average rate of change of f over the interval [0, 2] is
(A) greater than **(B)** less than
(C) approximately equal to $f'(0)$.

b. The average rate of change of f over the interval [−1, 1] is
(A) greater than **(B)** less than
(C) approximately equal to $f'(0)$.

c. Over the interval [0, 2], the instantaneous rate of change of f is
(A) increasing **(B)** decreasing
(C) neither increasing nor decreasing

d. Over the interval [−2, 2], the instantaneous rate of change of f is
(A) increasing, then decreasing
(B) decreasing, then increasing
(C) approximately constant

e. When $x = 2$, $f(x)$ is
(A) approximately 1 and increasing at a rate of about 2.5 units per unit of x
(B) approximately 1.2 and increasing at a rate of about 1 unit per unit of x
(C) approximately 2.5 and increasing at a rate of about 0.5 units per unit of x
(D) approximately 2.5 and increasing at a rate of about 2.5 units per unit of x

22. Let f have the graph shown.

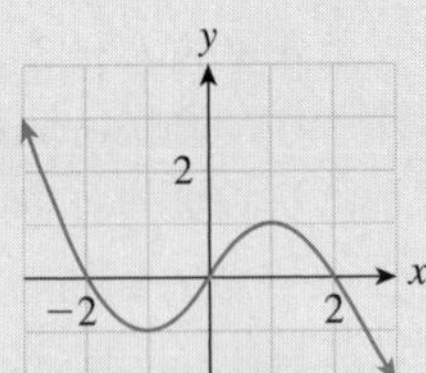

Select the correct answer.

a. The average rate of change of f over the interval [0, 1] is
(A) greater than **(B)** less than
(C) approximately equal to $f'(0)$.

b. The average rate of change of f over the interval [0, 2] is
(A) greater than **(B)** less than
(C) approximately equal to $f'(1)$.

c. Over the interval [−2, 0], the instantaneous rate of change of f is
(A) increasing **(B)** decreasing
(C) neither increasing nor decreasing

d. Over the interval [−2, 2], the instantaneous rate of change of f is
(A) increasing, then decreasing
(B) decreasing, then increasing
(C) approximately constant

e. When $x = 0$, $f(x)$ is
(A) approximately 0 and increasing at a rate of about 1.5 units per unit of x

(B) approximately 0 and decreasing at a rate of about 1.5 units per unit of x

(C) approximately 1.5 and neither increasing nor decreasing

(D) approximately 0 and neither increasing nor decreasing

In Exercises 23–26, use the definition of the derivative to calculate the derivative of each of the given functions algebraically.

23. $f(x) = x^2 + x$ **24.** $f(x) = 3x^2 - x + 1$

25. $f(x) = 1 - \frac{2}{x}$ **26.** $f(x) = \frac{1}{x} + 1$

In Exercises 27–30, find the derivative of the given function.

27. $f(x) = 10x^5 + \frac{1}{2}x^4 - x + 2$

28. $f(x) = \frac{10}{x^5} + \frac{1}{2x^4} - \frac{1}{x} + 2$

29. $f(x) = 3x^3 + 3\sqrt[3]{x}$

30. $f(x) = \frac{2}{x^{2.1}} - \frac{x^{0.1}}{2}$

In Exercises 31–34, evaluate the given expressions.

31. $\frac{d}{dx}\left(x + \frac{1}{x^2}\right)$

32. $\frac{d}{dx}\left(2x - \frac{1}{x}\right)$

33. $\frac{d}{dx}\left(\frac{4}{3x} - \frac{2}{x^{0.1}} + \frac{x^{1.1}}{3.2} - 4\right)$

34. $\frac{d}{dx}\left(\frac{4}{x} + \frac{x}{4} - |x|\right)$

tech Ex *In Exercises 35–38, use technology to graph the derivative of the given function. In each case, choose a range of x-values and y-values that shows the interesting features of the graph.*

35. $f(x) = 10x^5 + \frac{1}{2}x^4 - x + 2$

36. $f(x) = \frac{10}{x^5} + \frac{1}{2x^4} - \frac{1}{x} + 2$

37. $f(x) = 3x^3 + 3\sqrt[3]{x}$

38. $f(x) = \frac{2}{x^{2.1}} - \frac{x^{0.1}}{2}$

Applications

39. OHaganBooks.com CEO John O'Hagan has terrible luck with stocks. The following graph shows the value of Fly-By-Night Airlines stock that he bought acting on a "hot tip" from Marjory Duffin (CEO of Duffin Press and a close business associate):

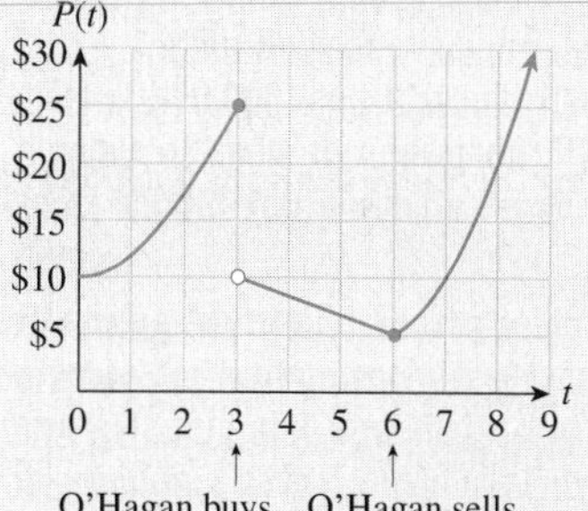

a. Compute $P(3)$, $\lim_{t\to 3^-} P(t)$ and $\lim_{t\to 3^+} P(t)$. Does $\lim_{t\to 3} P(t)$exist? Interpret your answers in terms of Fly-By-Night stocks.

b. Is P continuous at $t = 6$? Is P differentiable at $t = 6$? Interpret your answers in terms of Fly-By-Night stocks.

40. ***Advertising Costs*** OHaganBooks.com has (on further advice from Marjory Duffin) mounted an aggressive online marketing strategy. The following graph shows the weekly cost of this campaign for the six-week period since the start of July (t is time in weeks):

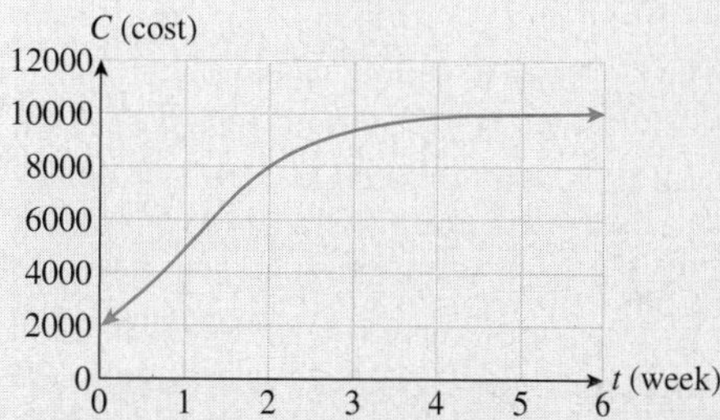

a. Assuming the trend shown in the graph were to continue indefinitely, estimate $\lim_{t\to 2} C(t)$ and $\lim_{t\to +\infty} C(t)$ and interpret the results.

b. Estimate $\lim_{t\to +\infty} C'(t)$ and interpret the result.

41. ***Sales*** Since the start of July, OHaganBooks.com has seen its weekly sales increase, as shown in the following table:

Week	1	2	3	4	5	6
Sales (Books)	6500	7000	7200	7800	8500	9000

a. What was the average rate of increase of weekly sales over this entire period?

b. During which 1-week interval(s) did the rate of increase of sales exceed the average rate?

c. During which 2-week interval(s) did the weekly sales rise at the highest average rate, and what was that average rate?

42. ***Advertising Costs*** The following graph (see Exercise 40) shows the weekly cost of OHaganBooks.com's online ad campaign for the six-week period since the start of July (t is time in weeks).

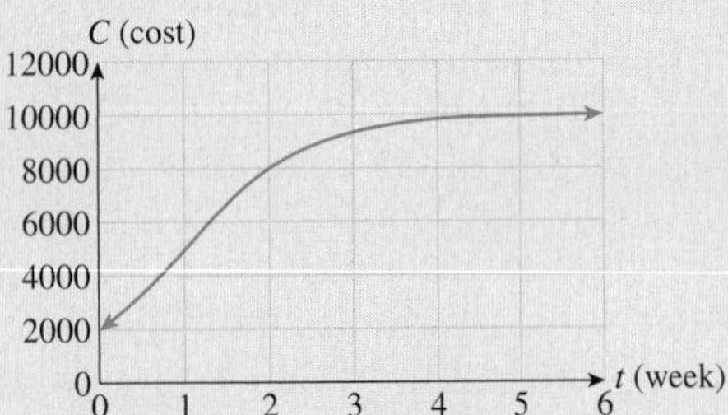

Use the graph to answer the following questions:

a. What was the average rate of change of cost over the entire six-week period?

b. What was the average rate of change of cost over the period [2, 6]?

c. Which of the following is correct? Over the period [2, 6],

(A) The rate of change of cost increased and the cost increased

(B) The rate of change of cost decreased and the cost increased

(C) The rate of change of cost increased and the cost decreased

(D) The rate of change of cost decreased and the cost decreased

43. ***Sales*** OHaganBooks.com fits the cubic curve

$$w(t) = -3.7t^3 + 74.6t^2 + 135.5t + 6300$$

to its weekly sales figures from Exercise 41, as shown in the following graph:

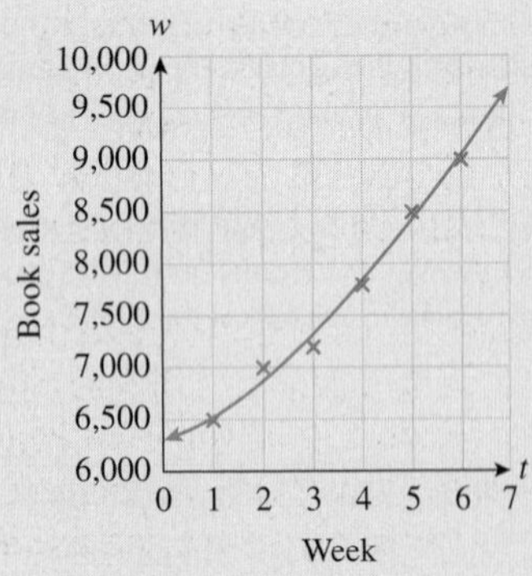

a. According to the cubic model, what was the rate of increase of sales at the beginning of the second week ($t = 1$)? (Round your answer to the nearest unit.)

b. If we extrapolate the model, what would be the rate of increase of weekly sales at the beginning of the 8th week ($t = 7$)?

c. Graph the function w for $0 \leq t \leq 20$. Would it be realistic to use the function to predict sales through week 20? Why?

44. tech Ex ***Sales*** OHaganBooks.com decided that the cubic curve in Exercise 43 was not suitable for extrapolation, so instead it tried

$$s(t) = 6053 + \frac{4474}{1 + e^{-0.55(t-4.8)}}$$

which is shown in the following graph:

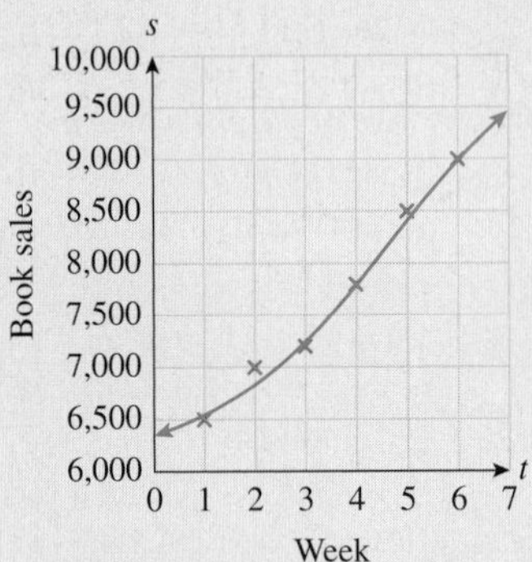

a. Using this function, estimate the rate of increase of weekly sales at the beginning of the 7th week ($t = 6$). (Round your answer to the nearest unit.)

b. If we extrapolate the model, what would be the rate of increase of weekly sales at the beginning of the 15th week ($t = 14$)?

c. Graph the function s for $0 \leq t \leq 20$. What is the long-term prediction for weekly sales? What is the long-term prediction for the rate of change of weekly sales?

45. As OHaganBooks.com's sales increase, so do its costs. If we take into account volume discounts from suppliers and shippers, the weekly cost of selling x books is

$$C(x) = -0.00002x^2 + 3.2x + 5400 \text{ dollars}$$

a. What is the marginal cost at a sales level of 8000 books per week?

b. What is the average cost per book at a sales level of 8000 books per week?

c. What is the marginal average cost at a sales level of 8000 books per week?

d. Interpret the results of parts (a)–(c).

CASE STUDY: Reducing Sulfur Emissions

Creatas/Superstock

The Environmental Protection Agency (EPA) wishes to formulate a policy that will encourage utilities to reduce sulfur emissions. Its goal is to reduce annual emissions of sulfur dioxide by a total of 10 million tons from the current level of 25 million tons by imposing a fixed charge for every ton of sulfur released into the environment per year. As a consultant to the EPA, you must determine the amount to be charged per ton of sulfur emissions.

You have the following data, which show the marginal cost to the utility industry of reducing sulfur emissions at several levels of reduction.[86]

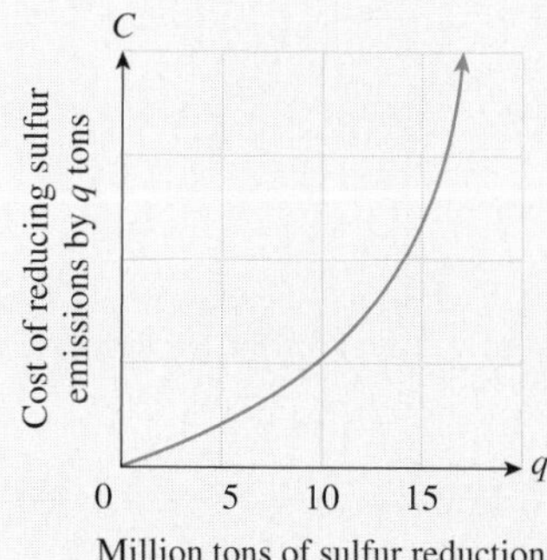

Figure **42**

Reduction (millions of tons)	8	10	12
Marginal Cost ($ per ton)	270	360	779

If $C(q)$ is the cost of removing q tons of sulfur dioxide, the table tells you that $C'(8{,}000{,}000) = \$270$ per ton, $C'(10{,}000{,}000) = \$360$ per ton, and $C'(12{,}000{,}000) = \$779$ per ton. Recalling that $C'(q)$ is the slope of the tangent to the graph of the cost function, you can see from the table that this slope is positive and increasing as q increases, so the graph of this cost function has the general shape shown in Figure 42. (Notice that the slope is increasing as you move to the right.) Thus, the utility industry has no cost incentive to reduce emissions. What you would like to do—if the goal of reducing total emissions by 10 million tons is to be reached—is to alter this cost curve so that it has the general shape shown in Figure 43.

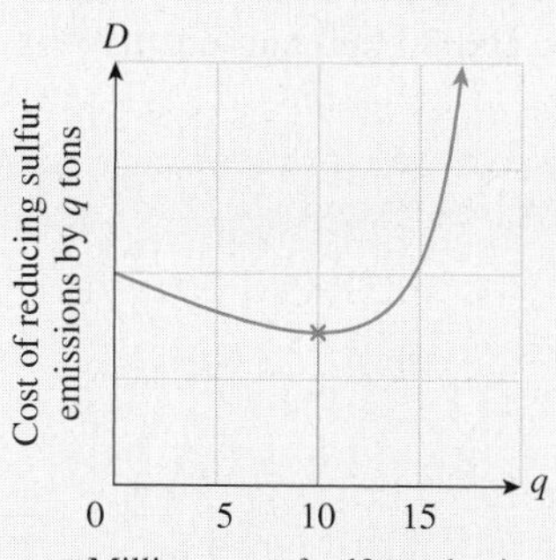

Figure **43**

In this curve, the cost D to utilities is lowest at a reduction level of 10 million tons, so if the utilities act to minimize cost, they can be expected to reduce emissions by 10 million tons, which is the EPA goal. From the graph, you can see that $D'(10{,}000{,}000) = \$0$ per ton, whereas $D'(q)$ is negative for $q < 10{,}000{,}000$.

At first you are bothered by the fact that you were not given a cost function. Only the marginal costs were supplied, but you decide to work as best you can without knowing the original cost function $C(q)$.

You now assume that the EPA will impose an annual emission charge of $\$k$ per ton of sulfur released into the environment. It is your job to calculate k. Because you are working with q as the independent variable, you decide that it would be best to formulate the emission charge as a function of q, where q represents the amount by which sulfur emissions are *reduced*. The relationship between the annual sulfur emissions and the amount q by which emissions are reduced from the original 25 million tons is given by

$$\begin{aligned}\text{Annual sulfur emissions} &= \text{original emissions} - \text{amount of reduction}\\ &= 25{,}000{,}000 - q\end{aligned}$$

[86] These figures were produced in a computerized study of reducing sulfur emissions from the 1980 level by the given amounts. Source: Congress of the United States, Congressional Budget Office, *Curbing Acid Rain: Cost, Budget and Coal Market Effects* (Washington, DC: Government Printing Office, 1986): xx, xxii, 23, 80.

Thus, the total annual emission charge to the utilities is

$$k(25{,}000{,}000 - q) = 25{,}000{,}000k - kq$$

This results in a total cost to the utilities of

$$\text{Total cost} = \text{Cost of reducing emissions} + \text{emission charge}$$

$$D(q) = C(q) + 25{,}000{,}000k - kq$$

Even though you have no idea of the form of $C(q)$, you remember that the derivative of a sum is the sum of the derivatives, so you differentiate both sides and obtain

$$\begin{aligned} D'(q) &= C'(q) + 0 - k \\ &= C'(q) - k \end{aligned}$$

The derivative of kq is k (the slope).

Remember that you want

$$D'(10{,}000{,}000) = 0$$

Thus,

$$C'(10{,}000{,}000) - k = 0$$

Referring to the table, you see that

$$360 - k = 0$$

so

$$k = \$360 \text{ per ton}$$

In other words, all you need to do is set the emission charge at $k = \$360$ per ton of sulfur emitted. Further, to ensure that the resulting curve will have the general shape shown in Figure 2, you would like to have $D'(q)$ negative for $q < 10{,}000{,}000$ and positive for $q > 10{,}000{,}000$. To check this, write

$$\begin{aligned} D'(q) &= C'(q) - k \\ &= C'(q) - 360 \end{aligned}$$

and refer to the table to obtain

$$D'(8{,}000{,}000) = 270 - 360 = -90 < 0 \quad ✔$$

and

$$D'(12{,}000{,}000) = 779 - 360 = 419 > 0 \quad ✔$$

Thus, based on the given data, the resulting curve will have the shape you require. You therefore inform the EPA that an annual emissions charge of \$360 per ton of sulfur released into the environment will create the desired incentive: to reduce sulfur emissions by 10 million tons per year.

One week later, you are informed that this charge would be unrealistic because the utilities cannot possibly afford such a cost. You are asked whether there is an alternative plan that accomplishes the 10-million-ton reduction goal and yet is cheaper to the utilities by \$5 billion per year. You then look at your expression for the emission charge

$$25{,}000{,}000k - kq$$

and notice that, if you decrease this amount by \$5 billion, the derivative will not change at all because the derivative of a constant is zero. Thus, you propose the following revised formula for the emission charge:

$$\begin{aligned} &25{,}000{,}000k - kq - 5{,}000{,}000{,}000 \\ &= 25{,}000{,}000(360) - 360q - 5{,}000{,}000{,}000 \\ &= 4{,}000{,}000{,}000 - 360q \end{aligned}$$

At the expected reduction level of 10 million tons, the total amount paid by the utilities will then be

$$4{,}000{,}000{,}000 - 360(10{,}000{,}000) = \$400{,}000{,}000$$

Thus, your revised proposal is the following: Impose an annual emissions charge of \$360 per ton of sulfur released into the environment and hand back \$5 billion in the form of subsidies. The effect of this policy will be to cause the utilities industry to reduce sulfur emissions by 10 million tons per year and will result in \$400 million in annual revenues to the government.

Notice that this policy also provides an incentive for the utilities to search for cheaper ways to reduce emissions. For instance, if they lowered costs to the point where they could achieve a reduction level of 12 million tons, they would have a total emission charge of

$$4{,}000{,}000{,}000 - 360(12{,}000{,}000) = -\$320{,}000{,}000$$

The fact that this is negative means that the government would be paying the utilities industry \$320 million more in annual subsidies than the industry is paying in per ton emission charges.

Exercises

1. Excluding subsidies, what should the annual emission charge be if the goal is to reduce sulfur emissions by 8 million tons?

2. Excluding subsidies, what should the annual emission charge be if the goal is to reduce sulfur emissions by 12 million tons?

3. What is the *marginal emission charge* in your revised proposal (as stated before the exercise set)? What is the relationship between the marginal cost of reducing sulfur emissions before emissions charges are implemented and the marginal emission charge, at the optimal reduction under your revised proposal?

4. We said that the revised policy provided an incentive for utilities to find cheaper ways to reduce emissions. How would $C(q)$ have to change to make 12 million tons the optimum reduction?

5. What change in $C(q)$ would make 8 million tons the optimum reduction?

6. If the scenario in Exercise 5 took place, what would the EPA have to do in order to make 10 million tons the optimal reduction once again?

7. Due to intense lobbying by the utility industry, you are asked to revise the proposed policy so that the utility industry will pay no charge if sulfur emissions are reduced by the desired 10 million tons. How can you accomplish this?

8. Suppose that instead of imposing a fixed charge per ton of emission, you decide to use a sliding scale, so that the total charge to the industry for annual emissions of x tons will be $\$kx^2$ for some k. What must k be to again make 10 million tons the optimum reduction? [The derivative of kx^2 is $2kx$.]

Section 3.1

Example **1** Use a table to estimate the following limits.

a. $\lim_{x\to 2} \dfrac{x^3-8}{x-2}$ **b.** $\lim_{x\to 0} \dfrac{e^{2x}-1}{x}$

Solution with Technology On the TI-83/84, use the table feature to automate these computations as follows:

1. Define `Y1=(x^3-8)/(x-2)` for part (a) or `Y1=(e^(2x)-1)/x` for part (b).
2. Press 2ND TABLE to list its values for the given values of x. (If the calculator does not allow you to enter values of x, press 2ND TBLSET and set Indpnt to Ask).

Here is the table showing some of the values for part (a):

X	Y1
1.9	11.41
1.99	11.94
1.999	11.994
1.9999	11.999

X=1.9999

For part (b) use `Y1=(e^(2*x)-1)/X` and use values of x approaching 0 from either side.

Section 3.4

Example **3** You are a commodities trader and you monitor the price of gold on the New York Spot Market very closely during an active morning. Suppose you find that the price of an ounce of gold can be approximated by the function

$$G(t) = -2t^2 + 36t + 228 \text{ dollars} \quad (7.5 \le t \le 10.5)$$

where t is time in hours. What was the average rate of change of the price of gold over the $1\frac{1}{2}$-hour period starting at 8:00 AM (the interval [8, 9.5] on the t-axis)?

Solution with Technology On the TI-83/84:

1. Enter the function G as Y1 (using X for t):

```
Y1=-2*X^2+36*X+228
```

2. Now find the average rate of change over [8, 9.5] by evaluating the following on the home screen:

```
(Y1(9.5)-Y1(8))/(9.5-8)
```

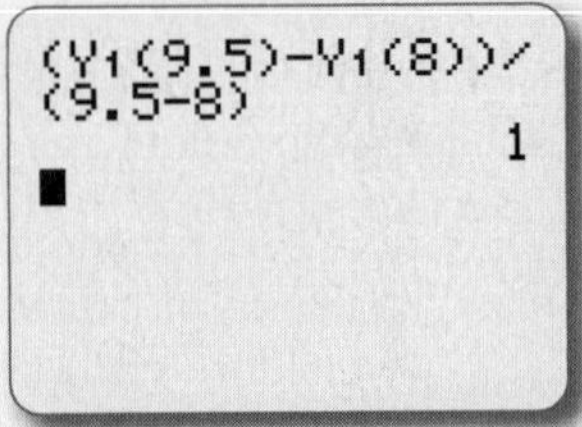

As shown on the screen, the average rate is of change is 1.

Example **4** Continuing with Example 3, use technology to compute the average rate of change of

$$G(t) = -2t^2 + 36t + 228 \quad (7.5 \le t \le 10.5)$$

over the intervals $[8, 8+h]$, where $h = 1, 0.1, 0.01, 0.001$, and 0.0001.

Solution with Technology

1. As in Example 3, enter the function G as Y1 (using X for t):

```
Y1=-2*X^2+36*X+228
```

2. Now find the average rate of change for $h = 1$ by evaluating, on the home screen,

```
(Y1(8+1)-Y1(8))/1
```

which gives 2.

3. To evaluate for $h = 0.1$, recall the expression using 2nd ENTER and then change the 1, both places it occurs, to 0.1, getting

```
(Y1(8+0.1)-Y1(8))/0.1
```

which gives 3.8.

4. Continuing, we can evaluate the average rate of change for all the desired values of h:

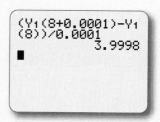

```
(Y1(8+1)-Y1(8))/
1
                2
(Y1(8+0.1)-Y1(8)
)/0.1
              3.8
```

```
(Y1(8+0.01)-Y1(8
))/0.01
             3.98
(Y1(8+0.001)-Y1(
8))/0.001
            3.998
```

```
(Y1(8+0.0001)-Y1
(8))/0.0001
           3.9998
```

We get the values in the following table:

h	1	0.1	0.01	0.001	0.0001
Ave. Rate of Change $\dfrac{G(8+h)-G(8)}{h}$	2	3.8	3.98	3.998	3.9998

Section 3.5

Example 2 Calculate an approximate value of $f'(1.5)$ if $f(x) = x^2 - 4x$, and then find the equation of the tangent line at the point on the graph where $x = 1.5$.

Solution with Technology

1. In the TI-83/84, enter the function f as Y_1

Y_1=x^2-4*x

2. Go to the home screen to compute the approximations:

(Y_1(1.5001)-Y_1(1.5))/0.0001

Usual difference quotient

(Y_1(1.5001)-Y_1(1.4999))/0.0002

Balanced difference quotient

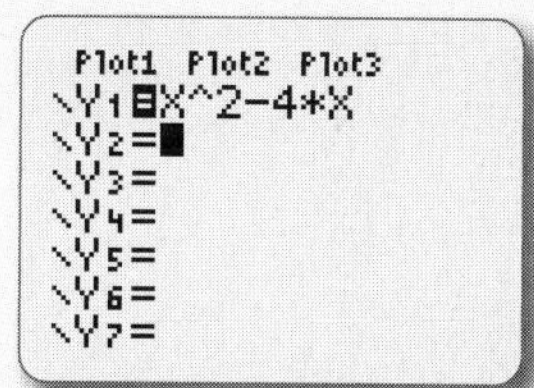

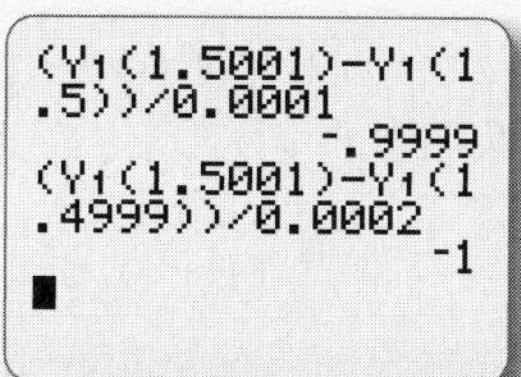

From the display on the right, we find that the difference quotient quick approximation is –0.9999 and the balanced difference quotient quick approximation is –1, which is in fact is the exact value of $f'(1.5)$. See the discussion in the text for the calculation of the equation of the tangent line.

Example 4 Use technology to obtain a table of values of and graph the derivative of $f(x) = -2x^2 + 6x + 5$ for values of x in starting at -5.

Solution with Technology On the TI-83/84, the easiest way to obtain quick approximations of the derivative of a given function is to use the built-in `nDeriv` function, which calculates balanced difference quotients.

1. On the `Y=` screen, first enter the function:

Y_1=-2x^2+6x+5

2. Then set

Y_2=nDeriv(Y_1,X,X) For `nDeriv` press MATH 8

which is the TI-83's approximation of $f'(x)$.

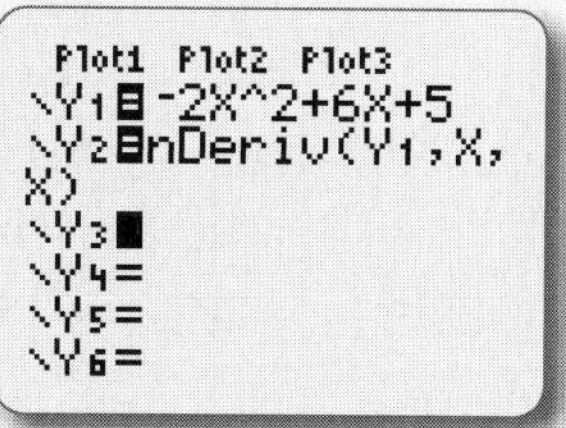

Alternatively, we can enter the balanced difference quotient directly:

Y_2=(Y_1(X+0.001)-Y_1(X-0.001))/0.002

(The TI-83 uses $h = 0.001$ by default in the balanced difference quotient when calculating `nDeriv`, but this can be changed by giving a value of h as a fourth argument, like `nDeriv(Y1,X,X,0.0001)`.) To see a table of approximate values of the derivative, we press [2ND] [TABLE] and choose a collection of values for x:

X	Y1	Y2
-3	-31	18
-2	-15	14
-1	-3	10
0	5	6
1	9	2
2	9	-2
3	5	-6

X=3

Here, Y_1 shows the value of f and Y_2 shows the values of f'.

To graph the function or its derivative, we can graph Y_1 or Y_2 in a window showing the given domain $[-5, 5]$:

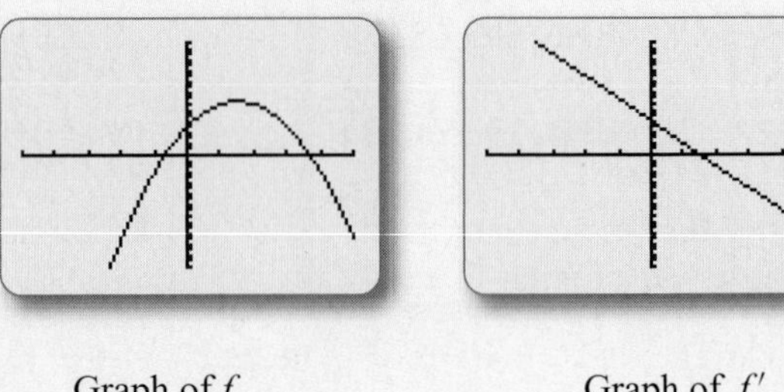

Graph of f Graph of f'

EXCEL Technology Guide

Section 3.1

Example 1 Use a table to estimate the following limits.

a. $\lim_{x\to 2} \frac{x^3-8}{x-2}$ **b.** $\lim_{x\to 0} \frac{e^{2x}-1}{x}$

Solution with Technology Set up your spreadsheet to duplicate the table in part (a) as follows:

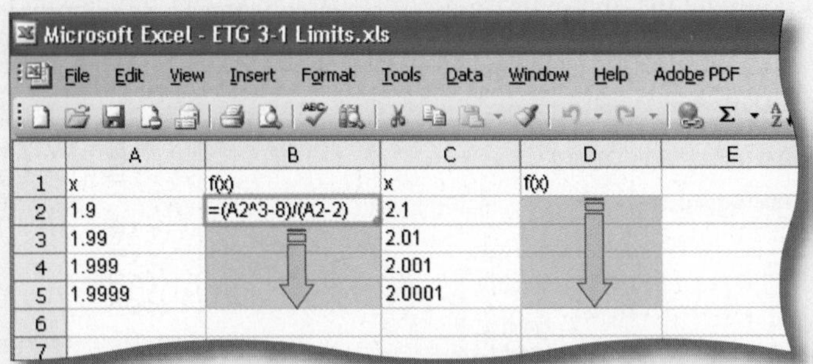

Microsoft Excel - ETG 3-1 Limits.xls

	A	B	C	D	E
1	x	f(x)	x	f(x)	
2	1.9	=(A2^3-8)/(A2-2)	2.1		
3	1.99		2.01		
4	1.999		2.001		
5	1.9999		2.0001		
6					
7					

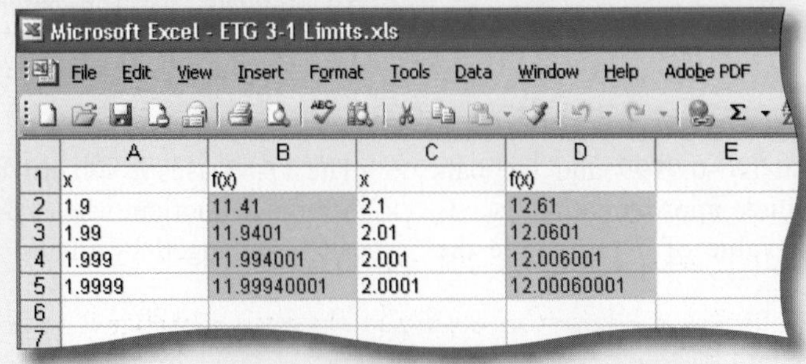

Microsoft Excel - ETG 3-1 Limits.xls

	A	B	C	D	E
1	x	f(x)	x	f(x)	
2	1.9	11.41	2.1	12.61	
3	1.99	11.9401	2.01	12.0601	
4	1.999	11.994001	2.001	12.006001	
5	1.9999	11.99940001	2.0001	12.00060001	
6					
7					

(The formula in cell B2 is copied to columns B and D as indicated by the shading.) The values of $f(x)$ will be calculated in columns B and D.

For part (b), use the formula `=(EXP(2*A2)-1)/A2` in cell B2 and, in columns A and C, use values of x approaching 0 from either side.

Section 3.4

Example **3** You are a commodities trader and you monitor the price of gold on the New York Spot Market very closely during an active morning. Suppose you find that the price of an ounce of gold can be approximated by the function

$$G(t) = -2t^2 + 36t + 228 \text{ dollars} \quad (7.5 \le t \le 10.5)$$

where t is time in hours. What was the average rate of change of the price of gold over the $1\frac{1}{2}$-hour period starting at 8:00 AM (the interval [8, 9.5] on the t-axis)?

Solution with Technology To use Excel to compute the average rate of change of G:

1. Start with two columns, one for values of t and one for values of $G(t)$, which you enter using the formula for G:

Microsoft Excel - ETG 3-4 Average Rate of Change of G.xls

	A	B	C
1	t	G(t)	
2	8	=-2*A2^2+36*A2+228	
3	8.5		
4	9		
5	9.5		
6	10		
7			
8			

2. Next, calculate the average rate of change as shown here:

Microsoft Excel - ETG 3-4 Average Rate of Change of G.xls

	A	B	C	D
1	t	G(t)		
2	8	388	Rate of change over [8, 9.5]:	
3	8.5	389.5	=(B5-B2)/(A5-A2)	
4	9	390		
5	9.5	389.5		
6	10	388		
7				
8				

Microsoft Excel - ETG 3-4 Average Rate of Change of G.xls

	A	B	C	D	E
1	t	G(t)			
2	8	388	Rate of change over [8, 9.5]:		
3	8.5	389.5	1		
4	9	390			
5	9.5	389.5			
6	10	388			
7					
8					

In Example 4, we describe another, more versatile Excel template for computing rates of change.

Example **4** Continuing with Example 3, use technology to compute the average rate of change of

$$G(t) = -2t^2 + 36t + 228 \qquad (7.5 \le t \le 10.5)$$

over the intervals $[8, 8 + h]$, where $h = 1, 0.1, 0.01, 0.001$, and 0.0001.

Solution with Technology The template we can use to compute the rates of change is an extension of what we used in Example 3:

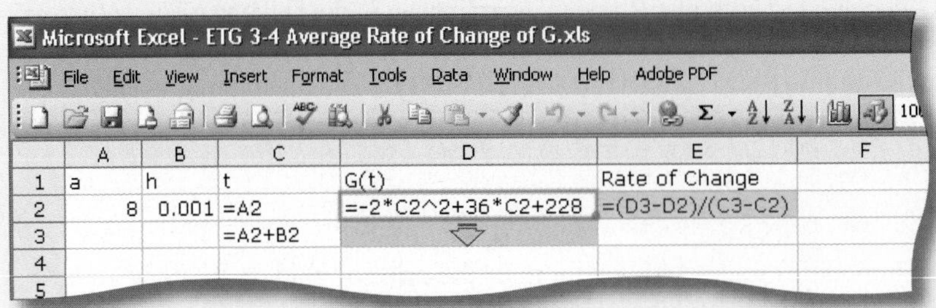

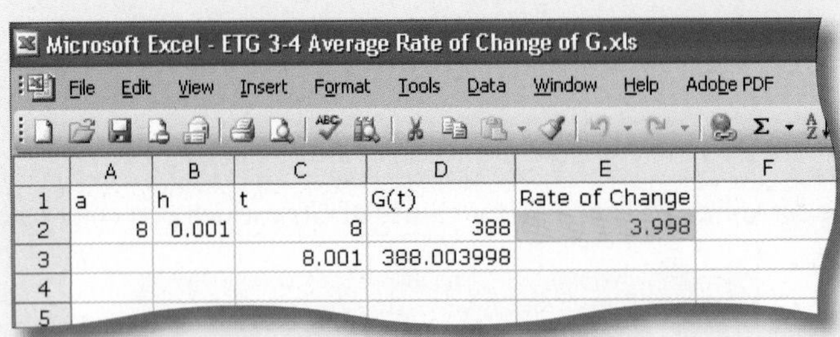

Column C contains the values $t = a$ and $t = a + h$ we are using for the independent variable. The formula in cell E2 is the average rate of change formula $\Delta G/\Delta t$. Entering the different values $h = 1$, 0.1, 0.01, 0.001, and 0.0001 gives the results shown in the following table:

h	1	0.1	0.01	0.001	0.0001
Ave. Rate of Change $\dfrac{G(8+h) - G(8)}{h}$	2	3.8	3.98	3.998	3.9998

Section 3.5

Example 2 Calculate an approximate value of $f'(1.5)$ if $f(x) = x^2 - 4x$, and then find the equation of the tangent line at the point on the graph where $x = 1.5$.

Solution with Technology You can compute both the difference quotient and the balanced difference quotient approximations in Excel using the following extension of the worksheet in Example 4 in Section 3.1.

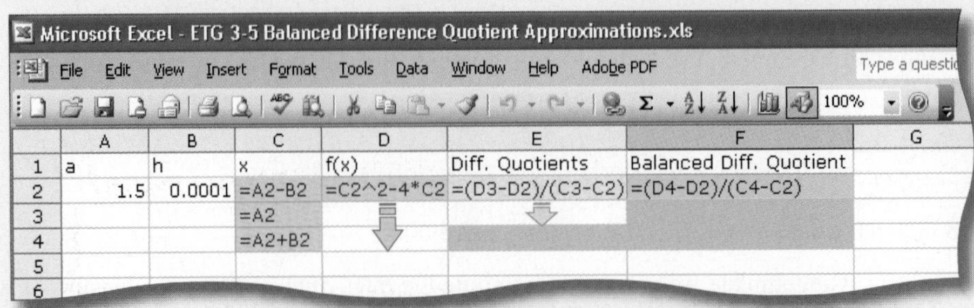

Notice that we get two difference quotients in column E. The first uses $h = -0.0001$ while the second uses $h = 0.0001$ and is the one we use for our quick approximation. The balanced quotient is their average (column F). The results are as follows.

Microsoft Excel - ETG 3-5 Balanced Difference Quotient Approximations.xls

	A	B	C	D	E	F	G
1	a	h	x	f(x)	Diff. Quotients	Balanced Diff. Quotient	
2	1.5	0.0001	1.4999	-3.7499	-1.0001	-1	
3			1.5	-3.75	-0.9999		
4			1.5001	-3.7501			
5							
6							

From the results shown above, we find that the difference quotient quick approximation is -0.9999 and that the balanced difference quotient quick approximation is -1, which is in fact it is the exact value of $f'(1.5)$. See the discussion in the text for the calculation of the equation of the tangent line.

Example **4** Use technology to obtain a table of values of and graph the derivative of $f(x) = -2x^2 + 6x + 5$ for values of x in starting at -5.

Solution with Technology

1. Start with a table of values for the function *f*, reminiscent of our graphing spreadsheet from Chapter 1:

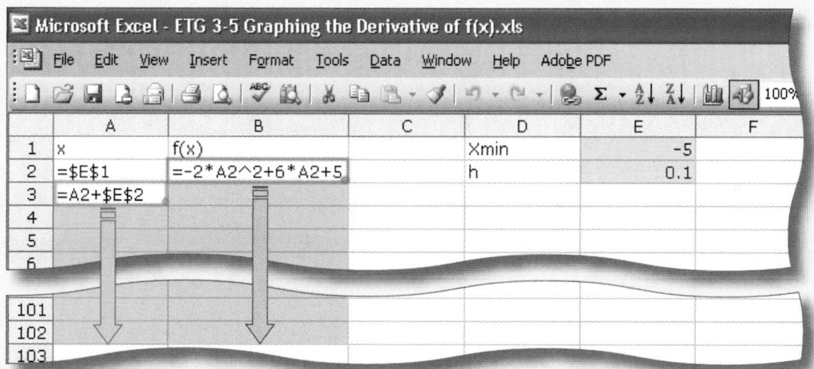

2. Next, compute approximate derivatives in Column C:

Microsoft Excel - ETG 3-5 Graphing the Derivative of f(x).xls

	A	B	C	D	E	F
1	x	f(x)	f'(x)	Xmin	-5	
2	-5	-75	=(B3-B2)/$E$2	h	0.1	
3	-4.9	-72.42				
4	-4.8	-69.88				
5	-4.7	-67.38				
6		-64.92				
	-4.8					
101	-4.9	-13.62				
102	-5	-15				
103						
104						

TECHNOLOGY GUIDE

Microsoft Excel - ETG 3-5 Graphing the Derivative of f(x).xls

File Edit View Insert Format Tools Data Window Help Adobe PDF

	A	B	C	D	E	F
1	x	f(x)	f'(x)	Xmin	-5	
2	-5	-75	25.8	h	0.1	
3	-4.9	-72.42	25.4			
4	-4.8	-69.88	25			
5	-4.7	-67.38	24.6			
101	-4.9	-13.62	-13.8			
102	-5	-15				
103						
104						

You cannot paste the difference quotient formula into cell C102. (Why?) Notice that this worksheet uses the ordinary difference quotients, $[f(x+h)-f(x)]/h$. If you prefer, you can use balanced difference quotients $[f(x+h)-f(x-h)]/(2h)$, in which case cells C2 and C102 would both have to be left blank.

We then graph the function and the derivative on different graphs as follows:

1. First, graph the function f in the usual way, using Columns A and B.

2. Make a copy of this graph and click on it once. Columns A and B should be outlined, indicating that these are the columns used in the graph.

3. By dragging from the center of the bottom edge, move the Column B box over to Column C as shown:

	A	B	C
97	4.5	-8.5	-12.2
98	4.6	-9.72	-12.6
99	4.7	-10.98	-13
100	4.8	-12.28	-13.4
101	4.9	-13.62	-13.8
102	5	-15	
103			
104			

	A	B	C
97	4.5	-8.5	-12.2
98	4.6	-9.72	-12.6
99	4.7	-10.98	-13
100	4.8	-12.28	-13.4
101	4.9	-13.62	-13.8
102	5	-15	
103			
104			

The graph will then show the derivative (Columns A and C):

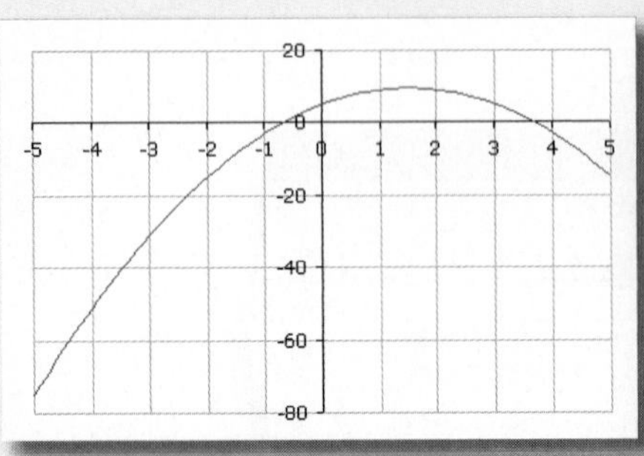

Graph of f

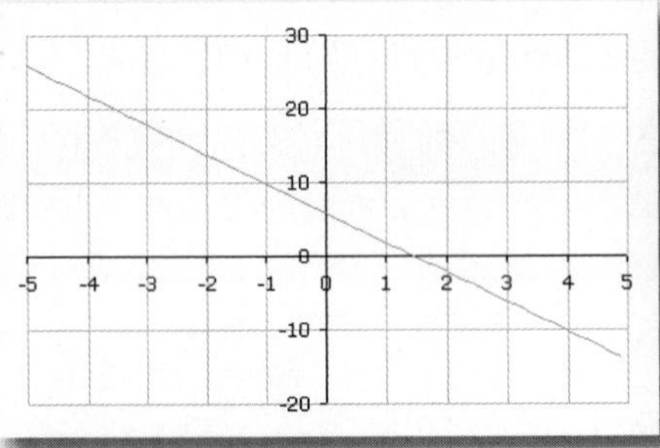

Graph of f'

4 Techniques of Differentiation

Get a better Grade!
www.thomsonedu.com/login

Logon to your Personalized Study plan to find:

- Section by section tutorials
- A detailed chapter summary
- Additional review exercises
- Graphers, Excel tutorials, and other resources
- Optional section: Linear Approximation and Error Estimation

CASE STUDY Projecting Market Growth

You are on the board of directors at Fullcourt Academic Press. The sales director of the high school division has just burst into your office with a proposal for a major expansion strategy based on the assumption that the number of high school seniors in the U.S. will be growing at a rate of at least 20,000 per year through the year 2005. Because the figures actually appear to be leveling off, you are suspicious about this estimate. You would like to devise a model that predicts this trend before tomorrow's scheduled board meeting. How do you go about doing this?

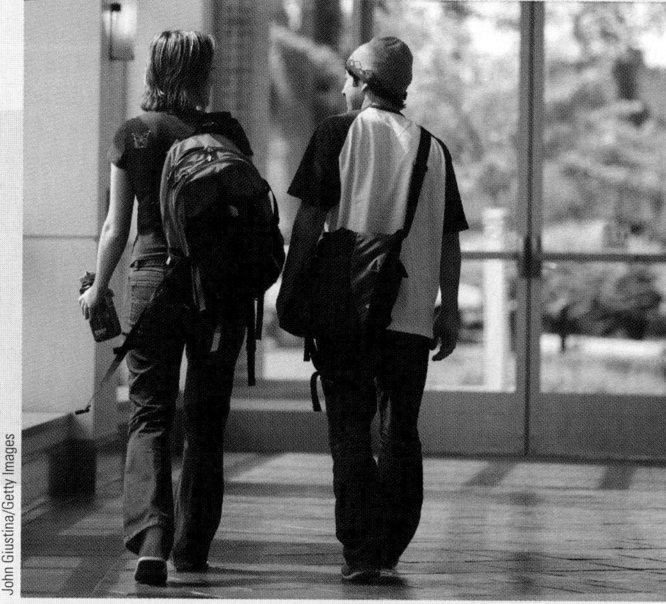

John Giustina/Getty Images

Introduction

algebra Review
For this chapter, you should be familiar with the algebra reviewed in Chapter 0, Sections 3 and 4.

In Chapter 3 we studied the concept of the derivative of a function, and we saw some of the applications for which derivatives are useful. However, the only functions we could differentiate easily were sums of terms of the form ax^n, where a and n are constants.

In this chapter we develop techniques that help us differentiate any closed-form function—that is, any function, no matter how complicated, that can be specified by a formula involving powers, radicals, exponents, and logarithms. (In a later chapter, we will discuss how to add trigonometric functions to this list.) We also show how to find the derivatives of functions that are only specified *implicitly*—that is, functions for which we are not given an explicit formula for y in terms of x but only an equation relating x and y.

4.1 The Product and Quotient Rules

We know how to find the derivatives of functions that are sums of powers, like polynomials. In general, if a function is a sum or difference of functions whose derivatives we know, then we know how to find its derivative. But what about *products and quotients* of functions whose derivatives we know? For instance, how do we calculate the derivative of something like $x^2/(x+1)$? The derivative of $x^2/(x+1)$ is not, as one might suspect, $2x/1 = 2x$. That calculation is based on an assumption that the derivative of a quotient is the quotient of the derivatives. But it is easy to see that this assumption is false: For instance, the derivative of $1/x$ is not $0/1 = 0$, but $-1/x^2$. Similarly, the derivative of a product is not the product of the derivatives: For instance, the derivative of $x = 1 \cdot x$ is not $0 \cdot 1 = 0$, but 1.

To identify the correct method of computing the derivatives of products and quotients, let's look at a simple example. We know that the daily revenue resulting from the sale of q items per day at a price of p dollars per item is given by the product, $R = pq$ dollars. Suppose you are currently selling wall posters on campus. At this time your daily sales are 50 posters, and sales are increasing at a rate of 4 per day. Furthermore, you are currently charging \$10 per poster, and you are also raising the price at a rate of \$2 per day. Let's use this information to estimate how fast your daily revenue is increasing. In other words, let us estimate the rate of change, dR/dt, of the revenue R.

There are two contributions to the rate of change of daily revenue: the increase in daily sales and the increase in the unit price. We have

$$\frac{dR}{dt} \text{ due to increasing price: \$2 per day} \times 50 \text{ posters} = \text{\$100 per day}$$

$$\frac{dR}{dt} \text{ due to increasing sales: \$10 per poster} \times 4 \text{ posters per day} = \text{\$40 per day}$$

Thus, we estimate the daily revenue to be increasing at a rate of \$100 + \$40 = \$140 per day. Let us translate what we have said into symbols:

$$\frac{dR}{dt} \text{ due to increasing price: } \frac{dp}{dt} \times q$$

$$\frac{dR}{dt} \text{ due to increasing sales: } p \times \frac{dq}{dt}$$

Thus, the rate of change of revenue is given by

$$\frac{dR}{dt} = \frac{dp}{dt}q + p\frac{dq}{dt}$$

Because $R = pq$, we have discovered the following rule for differentiating a product:

$$\frac{d}{dt}(pq) = \frac{dp}{dt}q + p\frac{dq}{dt}$$

The derivative of a product is the derivative of the first times the second, plus the first times the derivative of the second.

This rule and a similar rule for differentiating quotients are given next, and also a discussion of how these results are proved rigorously.

Product Rule

If $f(x)$ and $g(x)$ are differentiable functions of x, then so is their product $f(x)g(x)$, and

$$\frac{d}{dx}[f(x)g(x)] = f'(x)g(x) + f(x)g'(x)$$

Product Rule in Words

The derivative of a product is the derivative of the first times the second, plus the first times the derivative of the second.

quick Example

$f(x) = x^2$ and $g(x) = 3x - 1$ are both differentiable functions of x, and so their product $x^2(3x - 1)$ is differentiable, and

$$\frac{d}{dx}[x^2(3x-1)] = \underbrace{2x}_{\text{Derivative of first}} \cdot \underbrace{(3x-1)}_{\text{Second}} + \underbrace{x^2}_{\text{First}} \cdot \underbrace{(3)}_{\text{Derivative of second}}$$

Quotient Rule

If $f(x)$ and $g(x)$ are differentiable functions of x, then so is their quotient $f(x)/g(x)$ (provided $g(x) \neq 0$), and

$$\frac{d}{dx}\left(\frac{f(x)}{g(x)}\right) = \frac{f'(x)g(x) - f(x)g'(x)}{[g(x)]^2}$$

Quotient Rule in Words

The derivative of a quotient is the derivative of the top times the bottom, minus the top times the derivative of the bottom, all over the bottom squared.

quick Example

$f(x) = x^3$ and $g(x) = x^2 + 1$ are both differentiable functions of x, and so their quotient $x^3/(x^2 + 1)$ is differentiable, and

$$\frac{d}{dx}\left(\frac{x^3}{x^2+1}\right) = \frac{\overbrace{3x^2}^{\text{Derivative of top}}\overbrace{(x^2+1)}^{\text{Bottom}} - \overbrace{x^3}^{\text{Top}} \cdot \overbrace{2x}^{\text{Derivative of bottom}}}{\underbrace{(x^2+1)^2}_{\text{Bottom squared}}}$$

Notes

1. Don't try to remember the rules by the symbols we have used, but remember them in words. (The slogans are easy to remember, even if the terms are not precise.)
2. One more time: *The derivative of a product is* NOT *the product of the derivatives, and the derivative of a quotient is* NOT *the quotient of the derivatives.* To find the

derivative of a product, you must use the product rule, and to find the derivative of a quotient, you must use the quotient rule.[1]

Q: *Wait a minute! The expression $2x^3$ is a product, and we already know that its derivative is $6x^2$. Where did we use the product rule?*

A: To differentiate functions such as $2x^3$, we have used the rule from Section 3.4:
The derivative of c times a function is c times the derivative of the function.

However, the product rule gives us the same result:

	Derivative of first ↓	Second ↓		First ↓	Derivative of Second ↓	
$\frac{d}{dx}(2x^3) =$	(0)	(x^3)	$+$	(2)	$(3x^2) = 6x^2$	Product rule

$$\frac{d}{dx}(2x^3) = (2)(3x^2) = 6x^2 \qquad \text{Derivative of a constant times a function}$$

We do not recommend that you use the product rule to differentiate functions like $2x^3$; continue to use the simpler rule when one of the factors is a constant. ■

Derivation of the Product Rule

Before we look at more examples of using the product and quotient rules, let's see why the product rule is true. To calculate the derivative of the product $f(x)g(x)$ of two differentiable functions, we go back to the definition of the derivative:

$$\frac{d}{dx}[f(x)g(x)] = \lim_{h\to 0}\frac{f(x+h)g(x+h) - f(x)g(x)}{h}$$

We now rewrite this expression so that we can evaluate the limit: Notice that the numerator reflects a simultaneous change in f [from $f(x)$ to $f(x+h)$] and g [from $g(x)$ to $g(x+h)$]. To separate the two effects, we add and subtract a quantity in the numerator that reflects a change in only one of the functions:

$$\frac{d}{dx}[f(x)g(x)] = \lim_{h\to 0}\frac{f(x+h)g(x+h) - f(x)g(x)}{h}$$

$$= \lim_{h\to 0}\frac{f(x+h)g(x+h) - f(x)g(x+h) + f(x)g(x+h) - f(x)g(x)}{h} \qquad \text{We subtracted and added the quantity}^2\ f(x)g(x+h)$$

$$= \lim_{h\to 0}\frac{[f(x+h) - f(x)]g(x+h) + f(x)[g(x+h) - g(x)]}{h} \qquad \text{Common factors}$$

$$= \lim_{h\to 0}\left(\frac{f(x+h) - f(x)}{h}\right)g(x+h) + \lim_{h\to 0} f(x)\left(\frac{g(x+h) - g(x)}{h}\right) \qquad \text{Limit of sum}$$

$$= \lim_{h\to 0}\left(\frac{f(x+h) - f(x)}{h}\right)\lim_{h\to 0} g(x+h) + \lim_{h\to 0} f(x)\lim_{h\to 0}\left(\frac{g(x+h) - g(x)}{h}\right) \qquad \text{Limit of product}$$

[1] Leibniz made this mistake at first, too, so you would be in good company if you forgot to use the product or quotient rule.

[2] Adding an appropriate form of zero is an age-old mathematical ploy.

For a proof of the fact that, if g is differentiable, it must be continuous, go online and follow:

Chapter 3

→ Continuity and Differentiability

Now we already know the following four limits:

$$\lim_{h\to 0} \frac{f(x+h)-f(x)}{h} = f'(x) \qquad \text{Definition of derivative of } f;\ f \text{ is differentiable}$$

$$\lim_{h\to 0} \frac{g(x+h)-g(x)}{h} = g'(x) \qquad \text{Definition of derivative of } g;\ g \text{ is differentiable}$$

$$\lim_{h\to 0} g(x+h) = g(x) \qquad \text{If } g \text{ is differentiable, it must be continuous.}$$

$$\lim_{h\to 0} f(x) = f(x) \qquad \text{Limit of a constant}$$

The quotient rule can be proved in a very similar way. Go online and follow:

Chapter 4

→ Proof of Quotient Rule

to find a proof.

Putting these limits into the one we're calculating, we get

$$\frac{d}{dx}[f(x)g(x)] = f'(x)g(x) + f(x)g'(x)$$

which is the product rule.

Example 1 Using the Product Rule

Compute the following derivatives.

a. $\frac{d}{dx}[(x^{3.2}+1)(1-x)]$ Simplify the answer.

b. $\frac{d}{dx}[(x+1)(x^2+1)(x^3+1)]$ Do not expand the answer.

Solution

a. We can do the calculation in two ways.

Using the Product Rule:

$$\frac{d}{dx}[(x^{3.2}+1)(1-x)] = \underbrace{(3.2x^{2.2})}_{\text{derivative of first}}\underbrace{(1-x)}_{\text{second}} + \underbrace{(x^{3.2}+1)}_{\text{first}}\underbrace{(-1)}_{\text{derivative of second}}$$

$$= 3.2x^{2.2} - 3.2x^{3.2} - x^{3.2} - 1 \qquad \text{Expand the answer.}$$

$$= -4.2x^{3.2} + 3.2x^{2.2} - 1$$

Not using the Product Rule: First, expand the given expression.

$$(x^{3.2}+1)(1-x) = -x^{4.2} + x^{3.2} - x + 1$$

Thus,

$$\frac{d}{dx}[(x^{3.2}+1)(1-x)] = \frac{d}{dx}(-x^{4.2} + x^{3.2} - x + 1)$$

$$= -4.2x^{3.2} + 3.2x^{2.2} - 1$$

In this example the product rule saves us little or no work, but in later sections we shall see examples that can be done in no other way. Learn how to use the product rule now!

b. Here we have a product of *three* functions, not just two. We can find the derivative by using the product rule twice:

$$\frac{d}{dx}[(x+1)(x^2+1)(x^3+1)]$$
$$= \frac{d}{dx}(x+1)\cdot[(x^2+1)(x^3+1)] + (x+1)\cdot\frac{d}{dx}[(x^2+1)(x^3+1)]$$
$$= (1)(x^2+1)(x^3+1) + (x+1)[(2x)(x^3+1) + (x^2+1)(3x^2)]$$
$$= (1)(x^2+1)(x^3+1) + (x+1)(2x)(x^3+1) + (x+1)(x^2+1)(3x^2)$$

We can see here a more general product rule:

$$(fgh)' = f'gh + fg'h + fgh'$$

Notice that every factor has a chance to contribute to the rate of change of the product. There are similar formulas for products of four or more functions.

Example 2 Using the Quotient Rule

Compute the derivatives **a.** $\frac{d}{dx}\left[\frac{1-3.2x^{-0.1}}{x+1}\right]$ **b.** $\frac{d}{dx}\left[\frac{(x+1)(x+2)}{x-1}\right]$

Solution

a. $$\frac{d}{dx}\left[\frac{1-3.2x^{-0.1}}{x+1}\right] = \frac{\overset{\text{Derivative of top}}{(0.32x^{-1.1})}\overset{\text{Bottom}}{(x+1)} - \overset{\text{Top}}{(1-3.2x^{-0.1})}\overset{\text{Derivative of bottom}}{(1)}}{\underset{\text{Bottom squared}}{(x+1)^2}}$$

$$= \frac{0.32x^{-0.1} + 0.32x^{-1.1} - 1 + 3.2x^{-0.1}}{(x+1)^2} \qquad \text{Expand the numerator}$$

$$= \frac{3.52x^{-0.1} + 0.32x^{-1.1} - 1}{(x+1)^2}$$

b. Here we have both a product and a quotient. Which rule do we use, the product or the quotient rule? Here is a way to decide. Think about how we would calculate, step by step, the value of $(x+1)(x+2)/(x-1)$ for a specific value of x—say $x = 11$. Here is how we would probably do it:

1. Calculate $(x+1)(x+2) = (11+1)(11+2) = 156$.

2. Calculate $x - 1 = 11 - 1 = 10$.

3. Divide 156 by 10 to get 15.6.

Now ask: *What was the last operation we performed?* The last operation we performed was division, so we can regard the whole expression as a *quotient*—that is, as $(x+1)(x+2)$ *divided by* $(x-1)$. Therefore, we should use the quotient rule.

The first thing the quotient rule tells us to do is take the derivative of the numerator. Now, the numerator is a product, so we must use the product rule to take its derivative.

Here is the calculation:

$$\frac{d}{dx}\left[\frac{(x+1)(x+2)}{x-1}\right] = \frac{\overbrace{[(1)(x+2)+(x+1)(1)]}^{\text{Derivative of top}}\overbrace{(x-1)}^{\text{Bottom}} - \overbrace{[(x+1)(x+2)]}^{\text{Top}}\overbrace{(1)}^{\text{Derivative of bottom}}}{\underbrace{(x-1)^2}_{\text{Bottom squared}}}$$

$$= \frac{(2x+3)(x-1)-(x+1)(x+2)}{(x-1)^2}$$

$$= \frac{x^2-2x-5}{(x-1)^2}$$

What is important is to determine the *order of operations* and, in particular, to determine the last operation to be performed. Pretending to do an actual calculation reminds us of the order of operations; we call this technique the **calculation thought experiment.**

+ *Before we go on...* We used the quotient rule in Example 2 because the function was a quotient; we used the product rule to calculate the derivative of the numerator because the numerator was a product. Get used to this: Differentiation rules usually must be used in combination.

Here is another way we could have done this problem: Our calculation thought experiment could have taken the following form:

1. Calculate $(x+1)/(x-1) = (11+1)/(11-1) = 1.2$.

2. Calculate $x+2 = 11+2 = 13$.

3. Multiply 1.2 by 13 to get 15.6.

We would have then regarded the expression as a *product*—the product of the factors $(x+1)/(x-1)$ and $(x+2)$—and used the product rule instead. We can't escape the quotient rule however: We need to use it to take the derivative of the first factor, $(x+1)/(x-1)$. Try this approach for practice and check that you get the same answer. ■

Calculation Thought Experiment

The **calculation thought experiment** is a technique to determine whether to treat an algebraic expression as a product, quotient, sum, or difference. Given an expression, consider the steps you would use in computing its value. If the last operation is multiplication, treat the expression as a product; if the last operation is division, treat the expression as a quotient; and so on.

quick Examples

1. $(3x^2-4)(2x+1)$ can be computed by first calculating the expressions in parentheses and then multiplying. Because the last step is multiplication, we can treat the expression as a product.

2. $\dfrac{2x-1}{x}$ can be computed by first calculating the numerator and denominator and then dividing one by the other. Because the last step is division, we can treat the expression as a quotient.

3. $x^2 + (4x - 1)(x + 2)$ can be computed by first calculating x^2, then calculating the product $(4x - 1)(x + 2)$, and finally adding the two answers. Thus, we can treat the expression as a sum.

4. $(3x^2 - 1)^5$ can be computed by first calculating the expression in parentheses and then raising the answer to the fifth power. Thus, we can treat the expression as a power. (We shall see how to differentiate powers of expressions in Section 4.2.)

It often happens that the same expression can be calculated in different ways. For example, $(x + 1)(x + 2)/(x - 1)$ can be treated as either a quotient or a product; see Example 2(b).

Example 3 Using the Calculation Thought Experiment

Find $\dfrac{d}{dx}\left[6x^2 + 5\left(\dfrac{x}{x-1}\right)\right]$.

Solution

The calculation thought experiment tells us that the expression we are asked to differentiate can be treated as a *sum*. Because the derivative of a sum is the sum of the derivatives, we get

$$\frac{d}{dx}\left[6x^2 + 5\left(\frac{x}{x-1}\right)\right] = \frac{d}{dx}(6x^2) + \frac{d}{dx}\left[5\left(\frac{x}{x-1}\right)\right]$$

In other words, we must take the derivatives of $6x^2$ and $5(\frac{x}{x-1})$ separately and then add the answers. The derivative of $6x^2$ is $12x$. There are two ways of taking the derivative of $5(\frac{x}{x-1})$: we could either first multiply the expression $(\frac{x}{x-1})$ by 5 to get $(\frac{5x}{x-1})$ and then take its derivative using the quotient rule, or we could pull the 5 out, as we do next.

$$\begin{aligned}
\frac{d}{dx}\left[6x^2 + 5\left(\frac{x}{x-1}\right)\right] &= \frac{d}{dx}(6x^2) + \frac{d}{dx}\left[5\left(\frac{x}{x-1}\right)\right] && \text{Derivative of sum}\\
&= 12x + 5\frac{d}{dx}\left(\frac{x}{x-1}\right) && \text{Constant} \times \text{Function}\\
&= 12x + 5\left(\frac{(1)(x-1) - (x)(1)}{(x-1)^2}\right) && \text{Quotient rule}\\
&= 12x + 5\left(\frac{-1}{(x-1)^2}\right)\\
&= 12x - \frac{5}{(x-1)^2}
\end{aligned}$$

Applications

In the next example, we return to a scenario similar to the one discussed at the start of this section.

Example 4 Applying the Product and Quotient Rules: Revenue and Average Cost

Sales of your newly launched miniature wall posters for college dorms, *iMiniPosters,* are really taking off. (Those old-fashioned large wall posters no longer fit in today's "downsized" college dorm rooms.) Monthly sales to students at the start of this year were 1500 iMiniPosters, and since that time, sales have been increasing by 300 posters each month, even though the price you charge has also been going up.

a. The price you charge for iMiniPosters is given by:

$$p(t) = 10 + 0.05t^2 \text{ dollars per poster}$$

where t is time in months since the start of January of this year. Find a formula for the monthly revenue, and then compute its rate of change at the beginning of March.

b. The number of students who purchase iMiniPosters in a month is given by

$$n(t) = 800 + 0.2t$$

where t is as in part (a). Find a formula for the average number of posters each student buys, and hence estimate the rate at which this number was growing at the beginning of March.

Solution

a. To compute monthly revenue as a function of time t, we use

$$R(t) = p(t)q(t) \qquad \text{Revenue} = \text{Price} \times \text{Quantity}$$

We already have a formula for $p(t)$. The function $q(t)$ measures sales, which were 1500 posters/month at time $t = 0$, and rising by 300 per month:

$$q(t) = 1500 + 300t$$

Therefore, the formula for revenue is

$$R(t) = p(t)q(t)$$
$$R(t) = (10 + 0.05t^2)(1500 + 300t)$$

Rather than expand this expression, we shall leave it as a product so that we can use the product rule in computing its rate of change:

$$\begin{aligned} R'(t) &= p'(t)q(t) + p(t)q'(t) \\ &= [0.10t][1500 + 300t] + [10 + 0.05t^2][300] \end{aligned}$$

Because the beginning of March corresponds to $t = 2$, we have

$$\begin{aligned} R'(2) &= [0.10(2)][1500 + 300(2)] + [10 + 0.05(2)^2][300] \\ &= (0.2)(2100) + (10.2)(300) = \$3480 \text{ per month} \end{aligned}$$

Therefore, your monthly revenue was increasing at a rate of \$3480 per month at the beginning of March.

b. The average number of posters sold to each student is

$$k(t) = \frac{\text{Number of posters}}{\text{Number of students}}$$

$$k(t) = \frac{q(t)}{n(t)} = \frac{1500 + 300t}{800 + 0.2t}$$

The rate of change of $k(t)$ is computed with the quotient rule:

$$k'(t) = \frac{q'(t)n(t) - q(t)n'(t)}{n(t)^2}$$

$$= \frac{(300)(800 + 0.2t) - (1500 + 300t)(0.2)}{(800 + 0.2t)^2}$$

so that

$$k'(2) = \frac{(300)[800 + 0.2(2)] - [1500 + 300(2)](0.2)}{[800 + 0.2(2)]^2}$$

$$= \frac{(300)(800.4) - (2100)(0.2)}{800.4^2} \approx 0.37 \text{ posters/student per month}$$

Therefore, the average number of posters sold to each student was increasing at a rate of about 0.37 posters/student per month.

4.1 EXERCISES

● denotes basic skills exercises

◆ denotes challenging exercises

In Exercises 1–12:

a. Calculate the derivative of the given function without using either the product or quotient rule.

b. Use the product or quotient rule to find the derivative. Check that you obtain the same answer.

1. ● $f(x) = 3x$ **2.** ● $f(x) = 2x^2$ **3.** ● $g(x) = x \cdot x^2$

4. ● $g(x) = x \cdot x$ **5.** ● $h(x) = x(x+3)$ **6.** ● $h(x) = x(1+2x)$

7. ● $r(x) = 100x^{2.1}$ **8.** ● $r(x) = 0.2x^{-1}$ **9.** ● $s(x) = \dfrac{2}{x}$

10. ● $t(x) = \dfrac{x}{3}$ **11.** ● $u(x) = \dfrac{x^2}{3}$ **12.** ● $s(x) = \dfrac{3}{x^2}$

Calculate $\dfrac{dy}{dx}$ in Exercises 13–20. Simplify your answer. *hint* [see Example 1]

13. ● $y = 3x(4x^2 - 1)$ **14.** ● $y = 3x^2(2x + 1)$

15. ● $y = x^3(1 - x^2)$ **16.** ● $y = x^5(1 - x)$

17. ● $y = (2x + 3)^2$ **18.** ● $y = (4x - 1)^2$

19. ● $x\sqrt{x}$ **20.** ● $x^2\sqrt{x}$

Calculate $\dfrac{dy}{dx}$ in Exercises 21–56. You need not expand your answers.

21. ● $y = (x + 1)(x^2 - 1)$

22. ● $y = (4x^2 + x)(x - x^2)$

23. ● $y = (2x^{0.5} + 4x - 5)(x - x^{-1})$

24. ● $y = (x^{0.7} - 4x - 5)(x^{-1} + x^{-2})$

25. ● $y = (2x^2 - 4x + 1)^2$

26. ● $y = (2x^{0.5} - x^2)^2$

27. ● $y = \left(\dfrac{x}{3.2} + \dfrac{3.2}{x}\right)(x^2 + 1)$

28. ● $y = \left(\dfrac{x^{2.1}}{7} + \dfrac{2}{x^{2.1}}\right)(7x - 1)$

29. ● $x^2(2x + 3)(7x + 2)$ *hint* [see Example 1b]

30. ● $x(x^2 - 3)(2x^2 + 1)$

31. ● $(5.3x - 1)(1 - x^{2.1})(x^{-2.3} - 3.4)$

32. ● $(1.1x + 4)(x^{2.1} - x)(3.4 - x^{-2.1})$

33. $y = (\sqrt{x} + 1)\left(\sqrt{x} + \dfrac{1}{x^2}\right)$

34. $y = (4x^2 - \sqrt{x})\left(\sqrt{x} - \dfrac{2}{x^2}\right)$

35. ● $y = \dfrac{2x + 4}{3x - 1}$ *hint* [see Example 2]

36. ● $y = \dfrac{3x - 9}{2x + 4}$

37. ● $y = \dfrac{2x^2 + 4x + 1}{3x - 1}$ **38.** ● $y = \dfrac{3x^2 - 9x + 11}{2x + 4}$

39. ● $y = \dfrac{x^2 - 4x + 1}{x^2 + x + 1}$ **40.** ● $y = \dfrac{x^2 + 9x - 1}{x^2 + 2x - 1}$

41. ● $y = \dfrac{x^{0.23} - 5.7x}{1 - x^{-2.9}}$ **42.** ● $y = \dfrac{8.43x^{-0.1} - 0.5x^{-1}}{3.2 + x^{2.9}}$

43. $y = \dfrac{\sqrt{x}+1}{\sqrt{x}-1}$

44. $y = \dfrac{\sqrt{x}-1}{\sqrt{x}+1}$

45. $y = \dfrac{\left(\dfrac{1}{x}+\dfrac{1}{x^2}\right)}{x+x^2}$

46. $y = \dfrac{\left(1-\dfrac{1}{x^2}\right)}{x^2-1}$

47. ● $y = \dfrac{(x+3)(x+1)}{3x-1}$ *hint* [see Example 2b]

48. ● $y = \dfrac{x}{(x-5)(x-4)}$

49. ● $y = \dfrac{(x+3)(x+1)(x+2)}{3x-1}$

50. ● $y = \dfrac{3x-1}{(x-5)(x-4)(x-1)}$

51. ● $y = x^4 - (x^2+120)(4x-1)$ *hint* [see Example 3]

52. ● $y = x^4 - \dfrac{x^2+120}{4x-1}$

53. ● $y = x+1+2\left(\dfrac{x}{x+1}\right)$

54. ● $y = x+2-4(x^2-x)\left(x+\dfrac{1}{x}\right)$ (Do not simplify the answer)

55. ● $y = (x+1)(x-2)-2\left(\dfrac{x}{x+1}\right)$

56. ● $y = \dfrac{x+2}{x+1}+(x+1)(x-2)$

In Exercises 57–62, compute the derivatives.

57. ● $\dfrac{d}{dx}[(x^2+x)(x^2-x)]$

58. ● $\dfrac{d}{dx}[(x^2+x^3)(x+1)]$

59. ● $\dfrac{d}{dx}[(x^3+2x)(x^2-x)]\Big|_{x=2}$

60. ● $\dfrac{d}{dx}[(x^2+x)(x^2-x)]\Big|_{x=1}$

61. ● $\dfrac{d}{dt}[(t^2-t^{0.5})(t^{0.5}+t^{-0.5})]\Big|_{t=1}$

62. ● $\dfrac{d}{dt}[(t^2+t^{0.5})(t^{0.5}-t^{-0.5})]\Big|_{t=1}$

In Exercises 63–68, find the equation of the line tangent to the graph of the given function at the point with the indicated x-coordinate.

63. ● $f(x) = (x^2+1)(x^3+x)$; $x = 1$

64. ● $f(x) = (x^{0.5}+1)(x^2+x)$; $x = 1$

65. ● $f(x) = \dfrac{x+1}{x+2}$; $x = 0$

66. ● $f(x) = \dfrac{\sqrt{x}+1}{\sqrt{x}+2}$; $x = 4$

67. ● $f(x) = \dfrac{x^2+1}{x}$; $x = -1$

68. ● $f(x) = \dfrac{x}{x^2+1}$; $x = 1$

Applications

69. ● ***Revenue*** The monthly sales of Sunny Electronics' new sound system are given by $q(t) = 2000t - 100t^2$ units per month, t months after its introduction. The price Sunny charges is $p(t) = 1000 - t^2$ dollars per sound system, t months after introduction. Find the rate of change of monthly sales, the rate of change of the price, and the rate of change of monthly revenue five months after the introduction of the sound system. Interpret your answers. *hint* [see Example 4a]

70. ● ***Revenue*** The monthly sales of Sunny Electronics' new *iSun* walkman is given by $q(t) = 2000t - 100t^2$ units per month, t months after its introduction. The price Sunny charges is $p(t) = 100 - t^2$ dollars per *iSun*, t months after introduction. Find the rate of change of monthly sales, the rate of change of the price, and the rate of change of monthly revenue six months after the introduction of the *iSun*. Interpret your answers.

71. ● ***Saudi Oil Revenues*** The spot price of crude oil during the period 2000–2005 can be approximated by

$$P(t) = 5t + 25 \text{ dollars per barrel} \quad (0 \le t \le 5)$$

in year t, where $t = 0$ represents 2000. Saudi Arabia's crude oil production over the same period can be approximated by

$$Q(t) = 0.082t^2 - 0.22t + 8.2 \text{ million barrels per day}^3 \quad (0 \le t \le 5)$$

Use these models to estimate Saudi Arabia's daily oil revenue and also its rate of change in 2001. (Round your answers to the nearest \$1 million.)

72. ● ***Russian Oil Revenues*** Russia's crude oil production during the period 2000–2005 can be approximated by

$$Q(t) = -0.066t^2 + 0.96t + 6.1 \text{ million barrels per day}^4 \quad (0 \le t \le 5)$$

in year t, where $t = 0$ represents 2000. Use the model for the spot price in Exercise 71 to estimate Russia's daily oil revenue and also its rate of change in 2001.

73. ● ***Revenue*** Dorothy Wagner is currently selling 20 "I ♥ Calculus" T-shirts per day, but sales are dropping at a rate of 3 per day. She is currently charging \$7 per T-shirt, but to compensate for dwindling sales, she is increasing the unit price by \$1 per day. How fast, and in what direction is her daily revenue currently changing?

74. ● ***Pricing Policy*** Let us turn Exercise 73 around a little: Dorothy Wagner is currently selling 20 "I ♥ Calculus" T-shirts per day, but sales are dropping at a rate of 3 per day. She is currently charging \$7 per T-shirt, and she wishes to increase

[3] Source for data: EIA/Saudi British Bank (www.sabb.com). 2004 figures are based on mid-year data, and 2005 data are estimates.

[4] Source for data: Energy Information Administration (http://www.eia.doe.gov), Pravda (http://english.pravda.ru). 2004 figures are based on mid-year data, and 2005 data are estimates.

her daily revenue by \$10 per day. At what rate should she increase the unit price to accomplish this (assuming that the price increase does not affect sales)?

75. ● ***Bus Travel*** Thoroughbred Bus Company finds that its monthly costs for one particular year were given by $C(t) = 10{,}000 + t^2$ dollars after t months. After t months the company had $P(t) = 1000 + t^2$ passengers per month. How fast is its cost per passenger changing after 6 months? hint [see Example 4b]

76. ● ***Bus Travel*** Thoroughbred Bus Company finds that its monthly costs for one particular year were given by $C(t) = 100 + t^2$ dollars after t months. After t months, the company had $P(t) = 1000 + t^2$ passengers per month. How fast is its cost per passenger changing after 6 months?

77. ● ***Fuel Economy*** Your muscle car's gas mileage (in miles per gallon) is given as a function $M(x)$ of speed x in mph, where

$$M(x) = \frac{3000}{x + 3600x^{-1}}$$

Calculate $M'(x)$, and then $M'(10)$, $M'(60)$, and $M'(70)$. What do the answers tell you about your car?

78. ● ***Fuel Economy*** Your used Chevy's gas mileage (in miles per gallon) is given as a function $M(x)$ of speed x in mph, where

$$M(x) = \frac{4000}{x + 3025x^{-1}}$$

Calculate $M'(x)$ and hence determine *the sign* of each of the following: $M'(40)$, $M'(55)$, $M'(60)$. Interpret your results.

79. ***Military Spending*** The annual cost per active-duty armed service member in the U.S. increased from \$80,000 in 1995 to a projected \$120,000 in 2007. In 1995, there were 1.5 million armed service personnel, and this number was projected to decrease to 1.4 million in 2003.[5] Use linear models for annual cost and personnel to estimate, to the nearest \$10 million, the rate of change of total military personnel costs in 2002.

80. ***Military Spending in the 1990s*** The annual cost per active-duty armed service member in the U.S. increased from \$80,000 in 1995 to \$90,000 in 2000. In 1990, there were 2 million armed service personnel and this number decreased to 1.5 million in 2000.[6] Use linear models for annual cost and personnel to estimate, to the nearest \$10 million, the rate of change of total military personnel costs in 1995.

81. ***Biology—Reproduction*** The Verhulst model for population growth specifies the reproductive rate of an organism as a function of the total population according to the following formula:

$$R(p) = \frac{r}{1 + kp}$$

where p is the total population in thousands of organisms, r and k are constants that depend on the particular circumstances and the organism being studied, and $R(p)$ is the reproduction rate in thousands of organisms per hour.[7] If $k = 0.125$ and $r = 45$, find $R'(p)$ and then $R'(4)$. Interpret the result.

82. ***Biology—Reproduction*** Another model, the predator satiation model for population growth, specifies that the reproductive rate of an organism as a function of the total population varies according to the following formula:

$$R(p) = \frac{rp}{1 + kp}$$

where p is the total population in thousands of organisms, r and k are constants that depend on the particular circumstances and the organism being studied, and $R(p)$ is the reproduction rate in new organisms per hour.[8] Given that $k = 0.2$ and $r = 0.08$, find $R'(p)$ and $R'(2)$. Interpret the result.

83. ***Embryo Development*** Bird embryos consume oxygen from the time the egg is laid through the time the chick hatches. For a typical galliform bird egg, the total oxygen consumption (in milliliters) t days after the egg was laid can be approximated by[9]

$$C(t) = -0.016t^4 + 1.1t^3 - 11t^2 + 3.6t \quad (15 \le t \le 30)$$

(An egg will usually hatch at around $t = 28$.) Suppose that at time $t = 0$ you have a collection of 30 newly laid eggs and that the number of eggs decreases linearly to zero at time $t = 30$ days. How fast is the total oxygen consumption of your collection of embryos changing after 25 days? (Round your answers to 2 significant digits.) Comment on the result.

84. ***Embryo Development*** Turkey embryos consume oxygen from the time the egg is laid through the time the chick hatches. For a brush turkey, the total oxygen consumption (in milliliters) t days after the egg was laid can be approximated by[10]

$$C(t) = -0.0071t^4 + 0.95t^3 - 22t^2 + 95t \quad (25 \le t \le 50)$$

(An egg will typically hatch at around $t = 50$.) Suppose that at time $t = 0$ you have a collection of 100 newly laid eggs and that the number of eggs decreases linearly to zero at time $t = 50$ days. How fast is the total oxygen consumption of your collection of embryos changing after 40 days? (Round your answer to 2 significant digits.) Interpret the result.

85. ***ISP Market Share*** The following graphs show approximate market shares, in percentage points, of Microsoft's MSN

[5] Annual costs are adjusted for inflation. SOURCES: Department of Defense, Stephen Daggett, military analyst, Congressional Research Service/*New York Times*, April 19, 2002, p. A21.

[6] Ibid.

[7] SOURCE: *Mathematics in Medicine and the Life Sciences* by F. C. Hoppensteadt and C. S. Peskin (Springer-Verlag, New York, 1992) pp. 20–22.

[8] Ibid.

[9] The model is derived from graphical data published in the article "The Brush Turkey" by Roger S. Seymour, *Scientific American*, December, 1991, pp. 108–114.

[10] Ibid.

Internet service provider, and the combined shares of MSN, Comcast, Earthlink, and AOL for the period 1999–2004.[11]

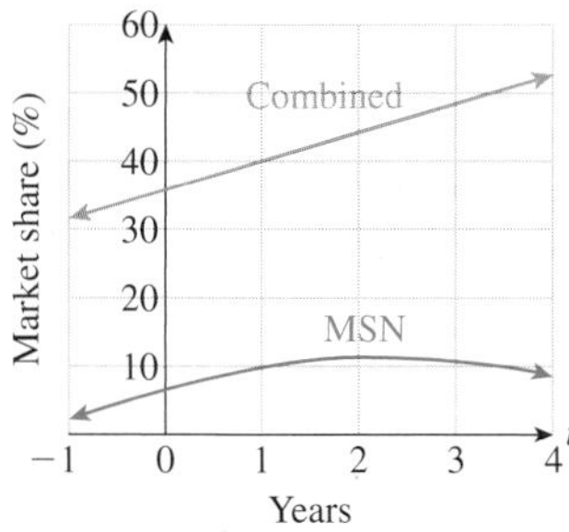

Formulas for the curves are:

MSN: $m(t) = -0.83t^2 + 3.8t + 6.8 \quad (-1 \le t \le 4)$

Combined: $c(t) = 4.2t + 36 \quad (-1 \le t \le 4)$

t is time in years since June, 2000.

a. What are represented by the functions $c(t) - m(t)$ and $m(t)/c(t)$?

b. Compute $\left.\frac{d}{dt}\left(\frac{m(t)}{c(t)}\right)\right|_{t=3}$ to two significant digits. What does the answer tell you about MSN?

86. ***ISP Revenue*** The following graphs show the approximate total revenue, in millions of dollars, of Microsoft's MSN Internet service, as well as the portion of that revenue due to advertising for the period June, 2001–January, 2004.[12]

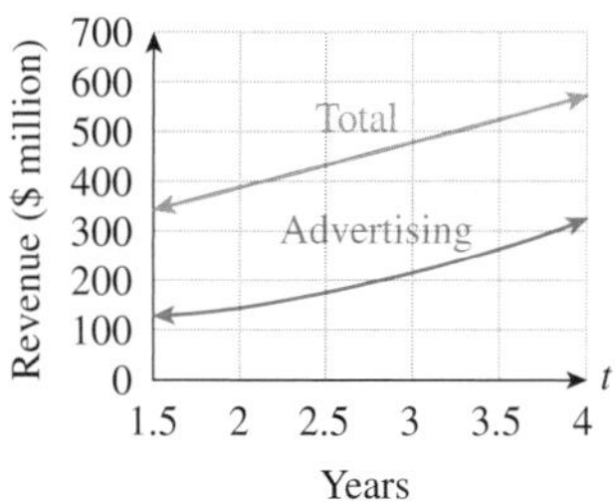

Formulas for the curves are:

Advertising: $a(t) = 20t^2 - 27t + 120 \quad (1.5 \le t \le 4)$

Total: $s(t) = 96t + 190 \quad (1.5 \le t \le 4)$

a. What are represented by the functions $s(t) - a(t)$ and $a(t)/s(t)$?

b. Compute $\left.\frac{d}{dt}\left(\frac{a(t)}{s(t)}\right)\right|_{t=2}$ to two significant digits. What does the answer tell you about MSN?

[11] The curves are regression models. Source for data: Solomon Research, Morgan Stanley/*New York Times*, July 19, 2004.

[12] Ibid.

Communication and Reasoning Exercises

87. ● You have come across the following in a newspaper article: "Revenues of HAL Home Heating Oil Inc. are rising by \$4.2 million per year. This is due to an annual increase of 70¢ per gallon in the price HAL charges for heating oil and an increase in sales of 6 million gallons of oil per year." Comment on this analysis.

88. ● Your friend says that because average cost is obtained by dividing the cost function by the number of units x, it follows that the derivative of average cost is the same as marginal cost because the derivative of x is 1. Comment on this analysis.

89. Find a demand function $q(p)$ such that, at a price per item of $p = \$100$, revenue will rise if the price per item is increased.

90. What must be true about a demand function $q(p)$ so that, at a price per item of $p = \$100$, revenue will decrease if the price per item is increased?

91. You and I are both selling a steady 20 T-shirts per day. The price I am getting for my T-shirts is increasing twice as fast as yours, but your T-shirts are currently selling for twice the price of mine. Whose revenue is increasing faster: yours, mine, or neither? Explain.

92. You and I are both selling T-shirts for a steady \$20 per shirt. Sales of my T-shirts are increasing at twice the rate of yours, but you are currently selling twice as many as I am. Whose revenue is increasing faster: yours, mine, or neither? Explain.

93. ◆ ***Marginal Product*** *(From the GRE Economics Test)* Which of the following statements about average product and marginal product is correct?

(A) If average product is decreasing, marginal product must be less than average product.

(B) If average product is increasing, marginal product must be increasing.

(C) If marginal product is decreasing, average product must be less than marginal product.

(D) If marginal product is increasing, average product must be decreasing.

(E) If marginal product is constant over some range, average product must be constant over that range.

94. ◆ ***Marginal Cost*** *(Based on a Question from the GRE Economics Test)* Which of the following statements about average cost and marginal cost is correct?

(A) If average cost is increasing, marginal cost must be increasing.

(B) If average cost is increasing, marginal cost must be decreasing.

(C) If average cost is increasing, marginal cost must be more than average cost.

(D) If marginal cost is increasing, average cost must be increasing.

(E) If marginal cost is increasing, average cost must be larger than marginal cost.

4.2 The Chain Rule

We can now find the derivatives of expressions involving powers of x combined using addition, subtraction, multiplication, and division, but we still cannot take the derivative of an expression like $(3x+1)^{0.5}$. For this we need one more rule. The function $h(x) = (3x+1)^{0.5}$ is not a sum, difference, product, or quotient. We can use the calculation thought experiment to find the last operation we would perform in calculating $h(x)$.

1. Calculate $3x + 1$.

2. Take the 0.5 power (square root) of the answer.

Thus, the last operation is "take the 0.5 power." We do not yet have a rule for finding the derivative of the 0.5 power of a quantity other than x.

There is a way to build $h(x) = (3x+1)^{0.5}$ out of two simpler functions: $u(x) = 3x + 1$ (the function that corresponds to the first step in the calculation above) and $f(x) = x^{0.5}$ (the function that corresponds to the second step):

$$\begin{aligned} h(x) &= (3x+1)^{0.5} \\ &= [u(x)]^{0.5} && u(x) = 3x + 1 \\ &= f(u(x)) && f(x) = x^{0.5} \end{aligned}$$

We say that h is the **composite** of f and u. We read $f(u(x))$ as "f of u of x."

To compute $h(1)$, say, we first compute $3 \cdot 1 + 1 = 4$ and then take the square root of 4, giving $h(1) = 2$. To compute $f(u(1))$ we follow exactly the same steps: First compute $u(1) = 4$ and then $f(u(1)) = f(4) = 2$. We always compute $f(u(x))$ numerically from the inside out: Given x, first compute $u(x)$ and then $f(u(x))$.

Now, f and u are functions *whose derivatives we know*. The *chain rule* allows us to use our knowledge of the derivatives of f and u to find the derivative of $f(u(x))$. For the purposes of stating the rule, let us avoid some of the nested parentheses by abbreviating $u(x)$ as u. Thus, we write $f(u)$ instead of $f(u(x))$ and remember that u is a function of x.

Chain Rule

If f is a differentiable function of u and u is a differentiable function of x, then the composite $f(u)$ is a differentiable function of x, and

$$\frac{d}{dx}[f(u)] = f'(u)\frac{du}{dx} \qquad \text{Chain Rule}$$

In words *The derivative of f(quantity) is the derivative of f, evaluated at that quantity, times the derivative of the quantity.*

quick Examples

1. Take $f(u) = u^2$. Then

$$\frac{d}{dx}[u^2] = 2u\frac{du}{dx} \qquad \text{Since } f'(u) = 2u$$

The derivative of a quantity squared is two times the quantity, times the derivative of the quantity.

2. Take $f(u) = u^{0.5}$. Then

$$\frac{d}{dx}[u^{0.5}] = 0.5u^{-0.5}\frac{du}{dx} \qquad \text{Since } f'(u) = 0.5u^{-0.5}.$$

The derivative of a quantity raised to the 0.5 *is* 0.5 *times the quantity raised to the* −0.5, *times the derivative of the quantity.*

As the quick examples illustrate, for every power of a function u whose derivative we know, we now get a "generalized" differentiation rule. The following table gives more examples.

Original Rule	***Generalized Rule***	***In Words***
$\frac{d}{dx}[x^2] = 2x$	$\frac{d}{dx}[u^2] = 2u\frac{du}{dx}$	The derivative of a quantity squared is twice the quantity, times the derivative of the quantity.
$\frac{d}{dx}[x^3] = 3x^2$	$\frac{d}{dx}[u^3] = 3u^2\frac{du}{dx}$	The derivative of a quantity cubed is 3 times the quantity squared, times the derivative of the quantity.
$\frac{d}{dx}\left(\frac{1}{x}\right) = -\frac{1}{x^2}$	$\frac{d}{dx}\left(\frac{1}{u}\right) = -\frac{1}{u^2}\frac{du}{dx}$	The derivative of 1 over a quantity is negative 1 over the quantity squared, times the derivative of the quantity.
Power Rule	***Generalized Power Rule***	***In Words***
$\frac{d}{dx}[x^n] = nx^{n-1}$	$\frac{d}{dx}[u^n] = nu^{n-1}\frac{du}{dx}$	The derivative of a quantity raised to the n is n times the quantity raised to the $n-1$, times the derivative of the quantity.

To motivate the chain rule, let us see why it is true in the special case when $f(u) = u^3$, where the chain rule tells us that

$$\frac{d}{dx}[u^3] = 3u^2\frac{du}{dx} \qquad \text{Generalized Power Rule with } n = 3$$

But we could have done this using the product rule instead:

$$\frac{d}{dx}[u^3] = \frac{d}{dx}[u \cdot u \cdot u] = \frac{du}{dx}u \cdot u + u\frac{du}{dx}u + u \cdot u\frac{du}{dx} = 3u^2\frac{du}{dx}$$

which gives us the same result. A similar argument works for $f(u) = u^n$ where $n = 2, 3, 4, \ldots$ We can then use the quotient rule and the chain rule for positive powers to verify the generalized power rule for *negative* powers as well. For the case of a general differentiable function f, the proof of the chain rule is beyond the scope of this book, but see the note in the margin.

For the proof of the chain rule for a general differentiable function *f*, go online and follow:

Chapter 4

→ Proof of Chain Rule

Example 1 Using the Chain Rule

Compute the following derivatives.

a. $\frac{d}{dx}[(2x^2+x)^3]$ **b.** $\frac{d}{dx}[(x^3+x)^{100}]$ **c.** $\frac{d}{dx}\sqrt{3x+1}$

Solution

a. Using the calculation thought experiment, we see that the last operation we would perform in calculating $(2x^2+x)^3$ is that of *cubing*. Thus we think of $(2x^2+x)^3$ as *a quantity cubed*. There are two similar methods we can use to calculate its derivative.

Method 1: Using the formula We think of $(2x^2+x)^3$ as u^3, where $u = 2x^2+x$. By the formula,

$$\frac{d}{dx}[u^3] = 3u^2\frac{du}{dx} \qquad \text{Generalized Power Rule}$$

Now substitute for u:

$$\begin{aligned}\frac{d}{dx}[(2x^2+x)^3] &= 3(2x^2+x)^2\frac{d}{dx}(2x^2+x)\\ &= 3(2x^2+x)^2(4x+1)\end{aligned}$$

Method 2: Using the verbal form If we prefer to use the verbal form, we get:

The derivative of $(2x^2+x)$ *cubed is three times* $(2x^2+x)$ *squared, times the derivative of* $(2x^2+x)$.

In symbols,

$$\frac{d}{dx}[(2x^2+x)^3] = 3(2x^2+x)^2(4x+1)$$

as we obtained above.

b. First, the calculation thought experiment: If we were computing $(x^3+x)^{100}$, the last operation we would perform is *raising a quantity to the power* 100. Thus we are dealing with *a quantity raised to the power* 100, and so we must again use the generalized power rule. According to the verbal form of the generalized power rule, the derivative of a quantity raised to the power 100 is 100 times that quantity to the power 99, times the derivative of that quantity. In symbols,

$$\frac{d}{dx}[(x^3+x)^{100}] = 100(x^3+x)^{99}(3x^2+1)$$

c. We first rewrite the expression $\sqrt{3x+1}$ as $(3x+1)^{0.5}$ and then use the generalized power rule as in parts (a) and (b):

The derivative of a quantity raised to the 0.5 *is* 0.5 *times the quantity raised to the* −0.5, *times the derivative of the quantity.*

Thus,

$$\frac{d}{dx}[(3x+1)^{0.5}] = 0.5(3x+1)^{-0.5}\cdot 3 = 1.5(3x+1)^{-0.5}$$

+ *Before we go on...* The following are examples of common errors in solving Example 1(b):

$$\text{“}\frac{d}{dx}[(x^3+x)^{100}] = 100(3x^2+1)^{99}\text{”} \quad ✗ \quad \textit{WRONG!}$$

$$\text{“}\frac{d}{dx}[(x^3+x)^{100}] = 100(x^3+x)^{99}\text{”} \quad ✗ \quad \textit{WRONG!}$$

Remember that the generalized power rule says that the derivative of a quantity to the power 100 is 100 times *that same quantity* raised to the power 99, *times the derivative of that quantity.* ■

Q: *It seems that there are now two formulas for the derivative of an nth power:*

$$(1) \quad \frac{d}{dx}[x^n] = nx^{n-1}$$

$$(2) \quad \frac{d}{dx}[u^n] = nu^{n-1}\frac{du}{dx}$$

Which one do I use?

A: Formula 1 is the original power rule, which applies only to a power of x. For instance, it applies to x^{10}, but it does not apply to $(2x+1)^{10}$ because the quantity that is being raised to a power is not x. Formula 2 applies to a power of any *function of* x, such as $(2x+1)^{10}$. It can even be used in place of the original power rule. For example, if we take $u = x$ in Formula 2, we obtain

$$\begin{aligned}\frac{d}{dx}[x^n] &= nx^{n-1}\frac{dx}{dx} \\ &= nx^{n-1} && \text{The derivative of } x \text{ with respect to } x \text{ is 1.}\end{aligned}$$

Thus, the generalized power rule really *is* a generalization of the original power rule, as its name suggests. ■

Example 2 More Examples Using the Chain Rule

Find: **a.** $\frac{d}{dx}[(2x^5+x^2-20)^{-2/3}]$ **b.** $\frac{d}{dx}\left[\frac{1}{\sqrt{x+2}}\right]$ **c.** $\frac{d}{dx}\left[\frac{1}{x^2+x}\right]$.

Solution

Each of the given functions is, or can be rewritten as, a power of a function whose derivative we know. Thus, we can use the method of Example 1.

a. $\frac{d}{dx}[(2x^5+x^2-20)^{-2/3}] = -\frac{2}{3}(2x^5+x^2-20)^{-5/3}(10x^4+2x)$

b. $\frac{d}{dx}\left[\frac{1}{\sqrt{x+2}}\right] = \frac{d}{dx}(x+2)^{-1/2} = -\frac{1}{2}(x+2)^{-3/2}\cdot 1 = -\frac{1}{2(x+2)^{3/2}}$

c. $\frac{d}{dx}\left[\frac{1}{x^2+x}\right] = \frac{d}{dx}(x^2+x)^{-1} = -(x^2+x)^{-2}(2x+1) = -\frac{2x+1}{(x^2+x)^2}$

+ *Before we go on...* In Example 2(c), we could have used the quotient rule instead of the generalized power rule. We can think of the quantity $1/(x^2+x)$ in two different ways using the calculation thought experiment:

1. As 1 divided by something—in other words, as a quotient

2. As something raised to the -1 power

Of course, we get the same derivative using either approach. ■

We now look at some more complicated examples.

Example 3 Harder Examples Using the Chain Rule

Find $\frac{dy}{dx}$ in each case. **a.** $y = [(x+1)^{-2.5} + 3x]^{-3}$ **b.** $y = (x+10)^3\sqrt{1-x^2}$

Solution

a. The calculation thought experiment tells us that the last operation we would perform in calculating y is raising the quantity $[(x+1)^{-2.5} + 3x]$ to the power -3. Thus, we use the generalized power rule.

$$\frac{dy}{dx} = -3[(x+1)^{-2.5} + 3x]^{-4}\frac{d}{dx}[(x+1)^{-2.5} + 3x]$$

We are not yet done; we must still find the derivative of $(x+1)^{-2.5} + 3x$. Finding the derivative of a complicated function in several steps helps to keep the problem manageable. Continuing, we have

$$\frac{dy}{dx} = -3[(x+1)^{-2.5} + 3x]^{-4}\frac{d}{dx}[(x+1)^{-2.5} + 3x]$$

$$= -3[(x+1)^{-2.5} + 3x]^{-4}\left[\frac{d}{dx}[(x+1)^{-2.5}] + \frac{d}{dx}(3x)\right] \quad \text{Derivative of a sum}$$

Now we have two derivatives left to calculate. The second of these we know to be 3, and the first is the derivative of a quantity raised to the -2.5 power. Thus

$$\frac{dy}{dx} = -3[(x+1)^{-2.5} + 3x]^{-4}[-2.5(x+1)^{-3.5}\cdot 1 + 3]$$

b. The expression $(x+10)^3\sqrt{1-x^2}$ is a product, so we use the product rule:

$$\frac{d}{dx}\left[(x+10)^3\sqrt{1-x^2}\right] = \left(\frac{d}{dx}[(x+10)^3]\right)\sqrt{1-x^2} + (x+10)^3\left(\frac{d}{dx}\sqrt{1-x^2}\right)$$

$$= 3(x+10)^2\sqrt{1-x^2} + (x+10)^3\frac{1}{2\sqrt{1-x^2}}(-2x)$$

$$= 3(x+10)^2\sqrt{1-x^2} - \frac{x(x+10)^3}{\sqrt{1-x^2}}$$

Applications

The next example is a new treatment of Example 3 from Section 3.8.

Example 4 Marginal Product

Precision Manufacturers is informed by a consultant that its annual profit is given by

$$P = -200{,}000 + 4000q - 0.46q^2 - 0.00001q^3$$

where q is the number of surgical lasers it sells each year. The consultant also informs Precision that the number of surgical lasers it can manufacture each year depends on the number n of assembly line workers it employs according to the equation

$$q = 100n \qquad \text{Each worker contributes 100 lasers per year}$$

Use the chain rule to find the marginal product $\dfrac{dP}{dn}$.

Solution

We could calculate the marginal product by substituting the expression for q in the expression for P to obtain P as a function of n (as given in Chapter 3) and then finding dP/dn. Alternatively—and this will simplify the calculation—we can use the chain rule. To see how the chain rule applies, notice that P is a function of q, where q in turn is given as a function of n. By the chain rule,

$$\begin{aligned}\frac{dP}{dn} &= P'(q)\frac{dq}{dn} && \text{Chain Rule}\\ &= \frac{dP}{dq}\frac{dq}{dn} && \text{Notice how the "quantities" } dq \text{ appear to cancel}\end{aligned}$$

Now we compute

$$\frac{dP}{dq} = 4000 - 0.92q - 0.00003q^2$$

and $$\frac{dq}{dn} = 100$$

Substituting into the equation for $\dfrac{dP}{dn}$ gives

$$\begin{aligned}\frac{dP}{dn} &= (4000 - 0.92q - 0.00003q^2)(100)\\ &= 400{,}000 - 92q - 0.003q^2\end{aligned}$$

Notice that the answer has q as a variable. We can express dP/dn as a function of n by substituting $100n$ for q:

$$\begin{aligned}\frac{dP}{dn} &= 400{,}000 - 92(100n) - 0.003(100n)^2\\ &= 400{,}000 - 9200n - 30n^2\end{aligned}$$

The equation

$$\frac{dP}{dn} = \frac{dP}{dq}\frac{dq}{dn}$$

in the example above is an appealing way of writing the chain rule because it suggests that the "quantities" dq cancel. In general, we can write the chain rule as follows.

Chain Rule in Differential Notation

If y is a differentiable function of u, and u is a differentiable function of x, then

$$\frac{dy}{dx} = \frac{dy}{du}\frac{du}{dx}$$

Notice how the units cancel:

$$\frac{\text{Units of } y}{\text{Units of } x} = \frac{\text{Units of } y}{\cancel{\text{Units of } u}}\frac{\cancel{\text{Units of } u}}{\text{Units of } x}$$

quick **Example**

If $y = u^3$, where $u = 4x + 1$, then

$$\frac{dy}{dx} = \frac{dy}{du}\frac{du}{dx} = 3u^2 \cdot 4 = 12u^2 = 12(4x + 1)^2$$

You can see one of the reasons we still use Leibniz differential notation: The chain rule looks like a simple "cancellation" of du terms.

Example 5 Marginal Revenue

Suppose a company's weekly revenue R is given as a function of the unit price p, and p in turn is given as a function of weekly sales q (by means of a demand equation). If

$$\left.\frac{dR}{dp}\right|_{q=1000} = \$40 \text{ per } \$1 \text{ increase in price}$$

and

$$\left.\frac{dp}{dq}\right|_{q=1000} = -\$20 \text{ per additional item sold per week}$$

find the marginal revenue when sales are 1000 items per week.

Solution

The marginal revenue is $\frac{dR}{dq}$. By the chain rule, we have

$$\frac{dR}{dq} = \frac{dR}{dp}\frac{dp}{dq}$$

Units: Revenue per item = Revenue per \$1 price increase × price increase per additional item

Because we are interested in the marginal revenue at a demand level of 1000 items per week, we have

$$\left.\frac{dR}{dq}\right|_{q=1000} = (40)(-20) = -\$800 \text{ per additional item sold}$$

Thus, if the price is lowered to increase the demand from 1000 to 1001 items per week, the weekly revenue will drop by approximately \$800.

Look again at the way the terms "du" appeared to cancel in the differential formula $\frac{dy}{dx} = \frac{dy}{du}\frac{du}{dx}$. In fact, the chain rule tells us more:

Manipulating Derivatives in Differential Notation

1. Suppose y is a function of x. Then, thinking of x as a function of y (as, for instance, when we can solve for x)* one has

$$\frac{dx}{dy} = \frac{1}{\left(\frac{dy}{dx}\right)}, \text{ provided } \frac{dy}{dx} \neq 0$$ Notice again how $\frac{dy}{dx}$ behaves like a fraction.

quick Example

In the demand equation $q = -0.2p - 8$, we have $\frac{dq}{dp} = -0.2$. Therefore,

$$\frac{dp}{dq} = \frac{1}{\left(\frac{dq}{dp}\right)} = \frac{1}{-0.2} = -5$$

2. Suppose x and y are functions of t. Then, thinking of y as a function of x (as, for instance, when we can solve for t as a function of x, and hence obtain y as a function of x) one has

$$\frac{dy}{dx} = \frac{dy/dt}{dx/dt}$$ The terms dt appear to cancel.

quick Example

If $x = 3 - 0.2t$ and $y = 6 + 6t$, then

$$\frac{dy}{dx} = \frac{dy/dt}{dx/dt} = \frac{6}{-0.2} = -30$$

* The notion of "thinking of x as a function of y" will be made more precise in Section 4.4.

To see why the above formulas work, notice that the second formula,

$$\frac{dy}{dx} = \frac{\left(\frac{dy}{dt}\right)}{\left(\frac{dx}{dt}\right)}$$

can be written as

$$\frac{dy}{dx}\frac{dx}{dt} = \frac{dy}{dt}$$ Multiply both sides by $\frac{dx}{dt}$

which is just the differential form of the chain rule. For the first formula, use the second formula with y playing the role of t:

$$\frac{dy}{dx} = \frac{dy/dy}{dx/dy}$$
$$= \frac{1}{dx/dy}$$ $\frac{dy}{dy} = \frac{d}{dy}[y] = 1$

FAQs Using the Chain Rule

Q: *How do I decide whether or not to use the chain rule when taking a derivative?*

A: Use the Calculation Thought Experiment (Section 4.1): Given an expression, consider the steps you would use in computing its value.

- If the last step is *raising a quantity to a power*, as in $\left(\frac{x^2-1}{x+4}\right)^4$, then the first step to use is the chain rule (in the form of the generalized power rule):

$$\frac{d}{dx}\left(\frac{x^2-1}{x+4}\right)^4 = 4\left(\frac{x^2-1}{x+4}\right)^3 \frac{d}{dx}\left(\frac{x^2-1}{x+4}\right)$$

Then use the appropriate rules to finish the computation. You may need to again use the Calculation Thought Experiment to decide on the next step (here the quotient rule):

$$= 4\left(\frac{x^2-1}{x+4}\right)^3 \frac{(2x)(x+4)-(x^2-1)(1)}{(x+4)^2}$$

- If the last step is *division*, as in $\frac{(x^2-1)}{(3x+4)^4}$, then the first step to use is the quotient rule:

$$\frac{d}{dx}\frac{(x^2-1)}{(3x+4)^4} = \frac{(2x)(3x+4)^4-(x^2-1)\frac{d}{dx}(3x+4)^4}{(3x+4)^8}$$

Then use the appropriate rules to finish the computation (here the chain rule):

$$= \frac{(2x)(3x+4)^4-(x^2-1)4(3x+4)^3(3)}{(3x+4)^8}$$

- If the last step is *multiplication, addition, subtraction, or multiplication by a constant*, then the first rule to use is the product rule, or the rule for sums, differences or constant multiples as appropriate. ■

Q: *Every time I compute the derivative, I leave something out. How do I make sure I am really done when taking the derivative of a complicated-looking expression?*

A: Until you are an expert at taking derivatives, the key is to use one rule at a time and write out each step, rather than trying to compute the derivative in a single step. To illustrate this, try computing the derivative of $(x+10)^3\sqrt{1-x^2}$ in Example 3(b) in two ways: First try to compute it in a single step, and then compute it by writing out each step as shown in the example. How do your results compare? For more practice, try Exercises 83 and 84 below. ■

4.2 EXERCISES

● denotes basic skills exercises

◆ denotes challenging exercises

tech Ex indicates exercises that should be solved using technology

Calculate the derivatives of the functions in Exercises 1–46.
hint [see Example 1]

1. ● $f(x) = (2x+1)^2$

2. ● $f(x) = (3x-1)^2$

3. ● $f(x) = (x-1)^{-1}$

4. ● $f(x) = (2x-1)^{-2}$

5. ● $f(x) = (2-x)^{-2}$

6. ● $f(x) = (1-x)^{-1}$

7. ● $f(x) = (2x+1)^{0.5}$

8. ● $f(x) = (-x+2)^{1.5}$

9. ● $f(x) = (4x-1)^{-1}$

10. ● $f(x) = (x+7)^{-2}$

11. ● $f(x) = \frac{1}{3x-1}$

12. ● $f(x) = \frac{1}{(x+1)^2}$

13. ● $f(x) = (x^2+2x)^4$

14. ● $f(x) = (x^3-x)^3$

15. ● $f(x) = (2x^2-2)^{-1}$

16. ● $f(x) = (2x^3+x)^{-2}$

17. ● $g(x) = (x^2-3x-1)^{-5}$

18. ● $g(x) = (2x^2+x+1)^{-3}$

19. ● $h(x) = \frac{1}{(x^2+1)^3}$ *hint* [see Example 2]

20. ● $h(x) = \dfrac{1}{(x^2+x+1)^2}$

21. ● $r(x) = (0.1x^2 - 4.2x + 9.5)^{1.5}$

22. ● $r(x) = (0.1x - 4.2x^{-1})^{0.5}$

23. ● $r(s) = (s^2 - s^{0.5})^4$

24. ● $r(s) = (2s + s^{0.5})^{-1}$

25. ● $f(x) = \sqrt{1-x^2}$

26. ● $f(x) = \sqrt{x+x^2}$

27. ● $h(x) = 2[(x+1)(x^2-1)]^{-1/2}$ hint [see Example 3]

28. ● $h(x) = 3[(2x-1)(x-1)]^{-1/3}$

29. ● $h(x) = (3.1x-2)^2 - \dfrac{1}{(3.1x-2)^2}$

30. ● $h(x) = \left[3.1x^2 - 2 - \dfrac{1}{3.1x-2}\right]^2$

31. ● $f(x) = [(6.4x-1)^2 + (5.4x-2)^3]^2$

32. ● $f(x) = (6.4x-3)^{-2} + (4.3x-1)^{-2}$

33. ● $f(x) = (x^2-3x)^{-2}(1-x^2)^{0.5}$

34. ● $f(x) = (3x^2+x)(1-x^2)^{0.5}$

35. ● $s(x) = \left(\dfrac{2x+4}{3x-1}\right)^2$

36. ● $s(x) = \left(\dfrac{3x-9}{2x+4}\right)^3$

37. ● $g(z) = \left(\dfrac{z}{1+z^2}\right)^3$

38. ● $g(z) = \left(\dfrac{z^2}{1+z}\right)^2$

39. ● $f(x) = [(1+2x)^4 - (1-x)^2]^3$

40. ● $f(x) = [(3x-1)^2 + (1-x)^5]^2$

41. ● $t(x) = [2 + (x+1)^{-0.1}]^{4.3}$

42. ● $t(x) = [(x+1)^{0.1} - 4x]^{-5.1}$

43. $r(x) = \left(\sqrt{2x+1} - x^2\right)^{-1}$

44. $r(x) = \left(\sqrt{x+1} + \sqrt{x}\right)^3$

45. $f(x) = \left(1 + \left(1 + (1+2x)^3\right)^3\right)^3$

46. $f(x) = 2x + \left(2x + (2x+1)^3\right)^3$

Find the indicated derivatives in Exercises 47–54. In each case, the independent variable is a (unspecified) function of t.

47. ● $y = x^{100} + 99x^{-1}$. Find $\dfrac{dy}{dt}$.

48. ● $y = x^{0.5}(1+x)$. Find $\dfrac{dy}{dt}$.

49. ● $s = \dfrac{1}{r^3} + r^{0.5}$. Find $\dfrac{ds}{dt}$.

50. ● $s = r + r^{-1}$. Find $\dfrac{ds}{dt}$.

51. ● $V = \dfrac{4}{3}\pi r^3$. Find $\dfrac{dV}{dt}$.

52. ● $A = 4\pi r^2$. Find $\dfrac{dA}{dt}$.

53. $y = x^3 + \dfrac{1}{x}$, $x = 2$ when $t = 1$, $\left.\dfrac{dx}{dt}\right|_{t=1} = -1$.
Find $\left.\dfrac{dy}{dt}\right|_{t=1}$.

54. $y = \sqrt{x} + \dfrac{1}{\sqrt{x}}$, $x = 9$ when $t = 1$, $\left.\dfrac{dx}{dt}\right|_{t=1} = -1$.
Find $\left.\dfrac{dy}{dt}\right|_{t=1}$.

In Exercises 55–60, compute the indicated derivative using the chain rule. hint [see Quick Examples on p. 315]

55. ● $y = 3x - 2; \dfrac{dx}{dy}$

56. ● $y = 8x + 4; \dfrac{dx}{dy}$

57. ● $x = 2 + 3t$, $y = -5t; \dfrac{dy}{dx}$

58. ● $x = 1 - t/2$, $y = 4t - 1; \dfrac{dy}{dx}$

59. ● $y = 3x^2 - 2x; \left.\dfrac{dx}{dy}\right|_{x=1}$

60. ● $y = 3x - \dfrac{2}{x}; \left.\dfrac{dx}{dy}\right|_{x=2}$

Applications

61. ● ***Food Versus Education*** The percentage y (of total personal consumption) an individual spends on food is approximately

$$y = 35x^{-0.25} \text{ percentage points} \quad (6.5 \le x \le 17.5)$$

where x is the percentage the individual spends on education.[13] An individual finds that she is spending

$$x = 7 + 0.2t$$

percent of her personal consumption on education, where t is time in months since January 1. Use direct substitution to express the percentage y as a function of time t (do not simplify the expression) and then use the chain rule to estimate how fast the percentage she spends on food is changing on November 1. Be sure to specify the units.

62. ● ***Food Versus Recreation*** The percentage y (of total personal consumption) an individual spends on food is approximately

$$y = 33x^{-0.63} \text{ percentage points} \quad (2.5 \le x \le 4.5)$$

where x is the percentage the individual spends on recreation.[14] A college student finds that he is spending

$$x = 3.5 + 0.1t$$

percent of his personal consumption on recreation, where t is time in months since January 1. Use direct substitution to

[13] Model based on historical and projected data from 1908–2010. SOURCES: Historical data, Bureau of Economic Analysis; projected data, Bureau of Labor Statistics/*New York Times*, December 1, 2003, p. C2.

[14] Ibid.

express the percentage y as a function of time t (do not simplify the expression) and then use the chain rule to estimate how fast the percentage he spends on food is changing on November 1. Be sure to specify the units.

63. ● ***Marginal Product*** Paramount Electronics has an annual profit given by

$$P = -100{,}000 + 5000q - 0.25q^2$$

where q is the number of laptop computers it sells each year. The number of laptop computers it can make and sell each year depends on the number n of electrical engineers Paramount employs, according to the equation

$$q = 30n + 0.01n^2$$

Use the chain rule to find $\left.\frac{dp}{dn}\right|_{n=10}$ and interpret the result. hint [see Example 4]

64. ● ***Marginal Product*** Refer back to Exercise 63. The average profit $\bar{P}$ per computer is given by dividing the total profit P by q:

$$\bar{P} = -\frac{100{,}000}{q} + 5000 - 0.25q$$

Determine the **marginal average product,** $d\bar{P}/dn$ at an employee level of 10 engineers. Interpret the result.

65. ● ***Marginal Revenue*** The weekly revenue from the sale of rubies at Royal Ruby Retailers (RRR) is increasing at a rate of \$40 per \$1 increase in price, and the price is decreasing at a rate of \$0.75 per additional ruby sold. What is the marginal revenue? (Be sure to state the units of measurement.) Interpret the result. hint [see Example 5]

66. ● ***Marginal Revenue*** The weekly revenue from the sale of emeralds at Eduardo's Emerald Emporium (EEE) is decreasing at a rate of €500 per €1 increase in price, and the price is decreasing at a rate of €0.45 per additional emerald sold. What is the marginal revenue? (Be sure to state the units of measurement.) Interpret the result.

67. ● ***Crime Statistics*** The murder rate in large cities (over 1 million residents) can be related to that in smaller cities (500,000–1,000,000 residents) by the following linear model:[15]

$$y = 1.5x - 1.9 \quad (15 \le x \le 25)$$

where y is the murder rate (in murders per 100,000 residents each year) in large cities and x is the murder rate in smaller cities. During the period 1991–1998, the murder rate in small cities was decreasing at an average rate of 2 murders per 100,000 residents each year. Use the chain rule to estimate how fast the murder rate was changing in larger cities during that period. (Show how you used the chain rule in your answer.)

68. ● ***Crime Statistics*** Following is a quadratic model relating the murder rates described in the preceding exercise:

$$y = 0.1x^2 - 3x + 39 \quad (15 \le x \le 25)$$

In 1996, the murder rate in smaller cities was approximately 22 murders per 100,000 residents each year and was decreasing at a rate of approximately 2.5 murders per 100,000 residents each year. Use the chain rule to estimate how fast the murder rate was changing for large cities. (Show how you used the chain rule in your answer.)

69. ● ***Ecology*** Manatees are grazing sea mammals sometimes referred to as "sea sirens." Increasing numbers of manatees have been killed by boats off the Florida coast, as shown in the following chart:

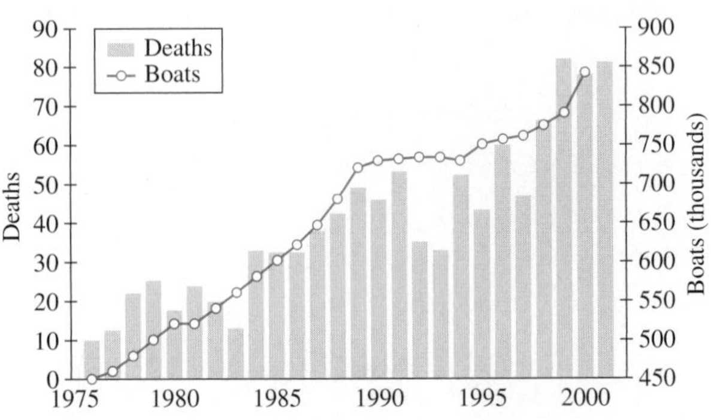

Since 1976 the number M of manatees killed by boats each year is roughly linear, with

$$M(t) = 2.48t + 6.87 \text{ manatees} \quad (1 \le t \le 26)$$

where t is the number of years since 1975.[16] Over the same period, the total number B of boats registered in Florida has also been increasing at a roughly linear rate, given by

$$B(t) = 15{,}700t + 444{,}000 \text{ boats} \quad (1 \le t \le 25)$$

Use the chain rule to give an estimate of dM/dB. What does the answer tell you about manatee deaths? hint [see Quick Examples on p. 315]

70. ● ***Ecology*** Refer to Exercise 69. If we use only the data from 1990 on, we obtain the following linear models:

$$M(t) = 3.87t + 35.0 \text{ manatees} \quad (0 \le t \le 11)$$

$$B(t) = 9020t + 712{,}000 \text{ boats} \quad (0 \le t \le 10)$$

where t is the number of years since 1990.[17] Repeat Exercise 69 using these models.

71. ***Pollution*** An offshore oil well is leaking oil and creating a circular oil slick. If the radius of the slick is growing at a rate of 2 miles/hour, find the rate at which the area is increasing when the radius is 3 miles. (The area of a disc of radius r is $A = \pi r^2$.)

[15] The model is a linear regression model. Source for data: Federal Bureau of Investigation, Supplementary Homicide Reports/*New York Times,* May 29, 2000, p. A12.

[16] Rounded regression model. Sources for data: Florida Department of Highway Safety & Motor Vehicles, Florida Marine Institute/*New York Times,* February 12, 2002, p. F4.

[17] Ibid.

72. ***Mold*** A mold culture in a dorm refrigerator is circular and growing. The radius is growing at a rate of 0.3 cm/day. How fast is the area growing when the culture is 4 centimeters in radius? (The area of a disc of radius r is $A = \pi r^2$.)

73. ***Budget Overruns*** The Pentagon is planning to build a new, spherical satellite. As is typical in these cases, the specifications keep changing, so that the size of the satellite keeps growing. In fact, the radius of the planned satellite is growing 0.5 feet per week. Its cost will be \$1000 per cubic foot. At the point when the plans call for a satellite 10 feet in radius, how fast is the cost growing? (The volume of a solid sphere of radius r is $V = \frac{4}{3}\pi r^3$.)

74. ***Soap Bubbles*** The soap bubble I am blowing has a radius that is growing at a rate of 4 cm/s. How fast is the surface area growing when the radius is 10 cm? (The surface area of a sphere of radius r is $S = 4\pi r^2$.)

75. tech Ex ***Revenue Growth*** The demand for the Cyberpunk II arcade video game is modeled by the logistic curve

$$q(t) = \frac{10{,}000}{1 + 0.5e^{-0.4t}}$$

where $q(t)$ is the total number of units sold t months after its introduction.

a. Use technology to estimate $q'(4)$.

b. Assume that the manufacturers of Cyberpunk II sell each unit for \$800. What is the company's marginal revenue dR/dq?

c. Use the chain rule to estimate the rate at which revenue is growing 4 months after the introduction of the video game.

76. tech Ex ***Information Highway*** The amount of information transmitted each month in the early years of the Internet (1988 to 1994) can be modeled by the equation

$$q(t) = \frac{2e^{0.69t}}{3 + 1.5e^{-0.4t}} \quad (0 \le t \le 6)$$

where q is the amount of information transmitted each month in billions of data packets and t is the number of years since the start of 1988.[18]

a. Use technology to estimate $q'(2)$.

b. Assume that it costs \$5 to transmit a million packets of data. What is the marginal cost $C'(q)$?

c. How fast was the cost increasing at the start of 1990?

Money Stock *Exercises 77–80 are based on the following demand function for money (taken from a question on the GRE economics test):*

$$M_d = 2 \times y^{0.6} \times r^{-0.3} \times p$$

where

M_d = demand for nominal money balances (money stock)
y = real income
r = an index of interest rates
p = an index of prices

These exercises also use the idea of ***percentage rate of growth:***

$$\text{Percentage Rate of Growth of } M = \frac{\text{Rate of Growth of } M}{M} = \frac{dM/dt}{M}$$

77. ◆ (From the GRE economics test) If the interest rate and price level are to remain constant while real income grows at 5 percent per year, the money stock must grow at what percent per year?

78. ◆ (From the GRE economics test) If real income and price level are to remain constant while the interest rate grows at 5 percent per year, the money stock must change by what percent per year?

79. ◆ (From the GRE economics test) If the interest rate is to remain constant while real income grows at 5 percent per year and the price level rises at 5 percent per year, the money stock must grow at what percent per year?

80. ◆ (From the GRE economics test) If real income grows by 5 percent per year, the interest rate grows by 2 percent per year, and the price level drops by 3 percent per year, the money stock must change by what percent per year?

Communication and Reasoning Exercises

81. ● Complete the following: The derivative of one over a glob is −1 over ___.

82. ● Complete the following: The derivative of the square root of a glob is 1 over ___.

83. ● Why was the following marked wrong?

$$\frac{d}{dx}[(3x^3 - x)^3] = 3(9x^2 - 1)^2 \qquad \text{✗ } \textit{WRONG!}$$

84. ● Why was the following marked wrong?

$$\frac{d}{dx}\left[\left(\frac{3x^2 - 1}{2x - 2}\right)^3\right] = 3\left(\frac{3x^2 - 1}{2x - 2}\right)^2\left(\frac{6x}{2}\right) \qquad \text{✗ } \textit{WRONG!}$$

85. Formulate a simple procedure for deciding whether to apply first the chain rule, the product rule, or the quotient rule when finding the derivative of a function.

86. Give an example of a function f with the property that calculating $f'(x)$ requires use of the following rules in the given order: (1) the chain rule, (2) the quotient rule, and (3) the chain rule.

87. ◆ Give an example of a function f with the property that calculating $f'(x)$ requires use of the chain rule five times in succession.

88. ◆ What can you say about composites of linear functions?

[18] This is the authors' model, based on figures published in *New York Times,* November 3, 1993.

4.3 Derivatives of Logarithmic and Exponential Functions

At this point, we know how to take the derivative of any algebraic expression in x (involving powers, radicals, and so on). We now turn to the derivatives of logarithmic and exponential functions.

Derivative of the Natural Logarithm

$$\frac{d}{dx}[\ln x] = \frac{1}{x}$$ Recall that $\ln x = \log_e x$

quick Examples

1. $\frac{d}{dx}[3\ln x] = 3 \cdot \frac{1}{x} = \frac{3}{x}$ Derivative of a constant times a function

2. $\frac{d}{dx}[x\ln x] = 1 \cdot \ln x + x \cdot \frac{1}{x}$ Product rule, because $x \ln x$ is a product

$= \ln x + 1$

The above simple formula works only for the natural logarithm (the logarithm with base e). For logarithms with bases other than e, we have the following:

Derivative of the Logarithm with Base *b*

$$\frac{d}{dx}[\log_b x] = \frac{1}{x\ln b}$$ Notice that, if $b = e$, we get the same formula as above

quick Examples

1. $\frac{d}{dx}[\log_3 x] = \frac{1}{x\ln 3} \approx \frac{1}{1.0986x}$

2. $\frac{d}{dx}[\log_2(x^4)] = \frac{d}{dx}(4\log_2 x)$ We used the logarithm identity $\log_b(x^r) = r\log_b x$

$= 4 \cdot \frac{1}{x\ln 2} \approx \frac{4}{0.6931x}$

Derivation of the Formulas $\frac{d}{dx}[\ln x] = \frac{1}{x}$ and $\frac{d}{dx}[\log_b x] = \frac{1}{x\ln b}$

To compute $\frac{d}{dx}[\ln x]$, we need to use the definition of the derivative. We also use properties of the logarithm to help evaluate the limit.

$$\frac{d}{dx}[\ln x] = \lim_{h\to 0} \frac{\ln(x+h) - \ln x}{h}$$ Definition of the derivative

$$= \lim_{h\to 0} \frac{1}{h}[\ln(x+h) - \ln x]$$ Algebra

$$= \lim_{h\to 0} \frac{1}{h}\ln\left(\frac{x+h}{x}\right)$$ Properties of the logarithm

$$= \lim_{h\to 0} \frac{1}{h} \ln\left(1 + \frac{h}{x}\right) \qquad \text{Algebra}$$

$$= \lim_{h\to 0} \ln\left(1 + \frac{h}{x}\right)^{1/h} \qquad \text{Properties of the logarithm}$$

which we rewrite as

$$\lim_{h\to 0} \ln\left[\left(1 + \frac{1}{(x/h)}\right)^{x/h}\right]^{1/x}$$

As $h \to 0^+$, the quantity x/h is getting large and positive, and so the quantity in brackets is approaching e (see the definition of e in Section 2.2), which leaves us with

$$\ln[e]^{1/x} = \frac{1}{x} \ln e = \frac{1}{x}$$

which is the derivative we are after.[19] What about the limit as $h \to 0^-$? We will glide over that case and leave it for the interested reader to pursue.[20]

The rule for the derivative of $\log_b x$ follows from the fact that $\log_b x = \ln x / \ln b$.

If we were to take the derivative of the natural logarithm of a *quantity* (a function of x), rather than just x, we would need to use the chain rule:

Derivatives of Logarithms of Functions

Original Rule	***Generalized Rule***	***In Words***
$\frac{d}{dx}[\ln x] = \frac{1}{x}$	$\frac{d}{dx}[\ln u] = \frac{1}{u}\frac{du}{dx}$	The derivative of the natural logarithm of a quantity is 1 over that quantity, times the derivative of that quantity.
$\frac{d}{dx}[\log_b x] = \frac{1}{x \ln b}$	$\frac{d}{dx}[\log_b u] = \frac{1}{u \ln b}\frac{du}{dx}$	The derivative of the log to base b of a quantity is 1 over the product of ln b and that quantity, times the derivative of that quantity.

quick **Examples**

1. $\frac{d}{dx} \ln[x^2 + 1] = \frac{1}{x^2+1}\frac{d}{dx}(x^2+1)$ $\qquad u = x^2 + 1$ (see the footnote*)

$$= \frac{1}{x^2+1}(2x) = \frac{2x}{x^2+1}$$

2. $\frac{d}{dx} \log_2[x^3 + x] = \frac{1}{(x^3+x)\ln 2}\frac{d}{dx}(x^3+x)$ $\qquad u = x^3 + x$

$$= \frac{1}{(x^3+x)\ln 2}(3x^2+1) = \frac{3x^2+1}{(x^3+x)\ln 2}$$

* If we were to evaluate $\ln(x^2 + 1)$, the last operation we would perform would be to take the natural logarithm of a quantity. Thus, the calculation thought experiment tells us that we are dealing with ln *of a quantity,* and so we need the generalized logarithm rule as stated above.

[19] We actually used the fact that the logarithm function is continuous when we took the limit.

[20] Here is an outline of the argument for negative h. Since x must be positive for $\ln x$ to be defined, we find that $x/h \to -\infty$ as $h \to 0^-$, and so we must consider the quantity $(1 + 1/m)^m$ for large *negative m*. It turns out the limit is still e (check it numerically!) and so the computation above still works.

Example 1 Derivative of Logarithmic Function

Find $\frac{d}{dx}[\ln\sqrt{x+1}]$

Solution The calculation thought experiment tells us that we have the natural logarithm of a quantity, so

$$\frac{d}{dx}[\ln\sqrt{x+1}] = \frac{1}{\sqrt{x+1}}\frac{d}{dx}\sqrt{x+1} \qquad \frac{d}{dx}\ln u = \frac{1}{u}\frac{du}{dx}$$

$$= \frac{1}{\sqrt{x+1}} \cdot \frac{1}{2\sqrt{x+1}} \qquad \frac{d}{dx}\sqrt{u} = \frac{1}{2\sqrt{u}}\frac{du}{dx}$$

$$= \frac{1}{2(x+1)}$$

+ *Before we go on...* What happened to the square root in Example 1? As with many problems involving logarithms, we could have done this one differently and with less bother if we had simplified the expression $\ln\sqrt{x+1}$ using the properties of logarithms *before* differentiating. Doing this, we get

$$\ln\sqrt{x+1} = \ln(x+1)^{1/2} = \frac{1}{2}\ln(x+1) \qquad \text{Simplify the logarithm first.}$$

Thus,

$$\frac{d}{dx}[\ln\sqrt{x+1}] = \frac{d}{dx}\left(\frac{1}{2}\ln(x+1)\right)$$

$$= \frac{1}{2}\left(\frac{1}{x+1}\right)\cdot 1 = \frac{1}{2(x+1)}$$

the same answer as above. ■

Example 2 Derivative of a Logarithmic Function

Find $\frac{d}{dx}[\ln[(1+x)(2-x)]]$.

Solution This time, we simplify the expression $\ln[(1+x)(2-x)]$ before taking the derivative.

$$\ln[(1+x)(2-x)] = \ln(1+x) + \ln(2-x) \qquad \text{Simplify the logarithm first.}$$

Thus,

$$\frac{d}{dx}[\ln[(1+x)(2-x)]] = \frac{d}{dx}[\ln(1+x)] + \frac{d}{dx}[\ln(2-x)]$$

$$= \frac{1}{1+x} - \frac{1}{2-x} \qquad \text{Because } \frac{d}{dx}\ln(2-x) = -\frac{1}{2-x}$$

$$= \frac{1-2x}{(1+x)(2-x)}$$

+*Before we go on...* For practice, try doing Example 2 without simplifying first. What other differentiation rule do you need to use? ■

Example 3 Logarithm of an Absolute Value

Find $\frac{d}{dx}[\ln|x|]$.

Solution Before we start, we note that $\ln x$ is defined only for positive values of x, so its domain is the set of positive real numbers. The domain of $\ln|x|$, on the other hand, is the set of *all* nonzero real numbers. For example, $\ln|-2| = \ln 2 \approx 0.6931$. For this reason, $\ln|x|$ often turns out to be more useful than the ordinary logarithm function.

Now we'll get to work. The calculation thought experiment tells us that $\ln|x|$ is the natural logarithm of a quantity, so we use the chain rule:

$$\frac{d}{dx}[\ln|x|] = \frac{1}{|x|}\frac{d}{dx}|x| \qquad u = |x|$$

$$= \frac{1}{|x|}\frac{|x|}{x} \qquad \text{Recall that } \frac{d}{dx}|x| = \frac{|x|}{x}$$

$$= \frac{1}{x}$$

+*Before we go on...* Figure 1a shows the graphs of $y = \ln|x|$ and $y = 1/x$. Figure 1b shows the graphs of $y = \ln|x|$ and $y = 1/|x|$. You should be able to see from these graphs why the derivative of $\ln|x|$ is $1/x$ and not $1/|x|$.

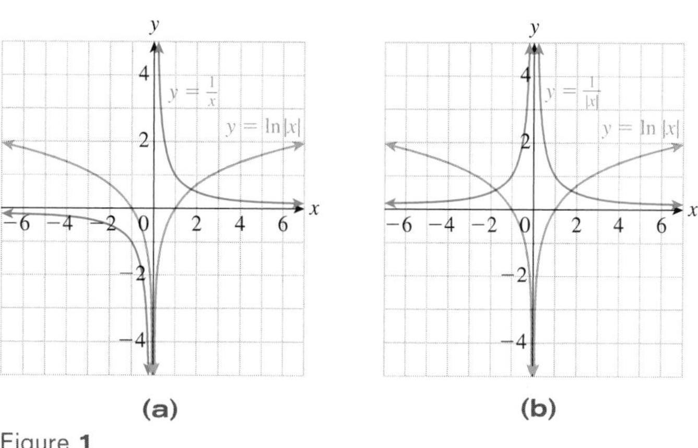

Figure 1 ■

This last example, in conjunction with the chain rule, gives us the following formulas.

Derivative of Logarithms of Absolute Values

Original Rule	*Generalized Rule*	*In Words*
$\frac{d}{dx}[\ln\|x\|] = \frac{1}{x}$	$\frac{d}{dx}[\ln\|u\|] = \frac{1}{u}\frac{du}{dx}$	The derivative of the natural logarithm of the absolute value of a quantity is 1 over that quantity, times the derivative of that quantity.
$\frac{d}{dx}[\log_b\|x\|] = \frac{1}{x\ln b}$	$\frac{d}{dx}[\log_b\|u\|] = \frac{1}{u\ln b}\frac{du}{dx}$	The derivative of the log to base b of the absolute value of a quantity is 1 over the product of ln b and that quantity, times the derivative of that quantity.

quick **Examples**

1. $\frac{d}{dx}[\ln|x^2+1|] = \frac{1}{x^2+1}\frac{d}{dx}(x^2+1)$ $\quad u = x^2+1$

$= \frac{1}{x^2+1}(2x) = \frac{2x}{x^2+1}$

2. $\frac{d}{dx}[\log_2|x^3+x|] = \frac{1}{(x^3+x)\ln 2}\frac{d}{dx}(x^3+x)$ $\quad u = x^3+x$

$= \frac{1}{(x^3+x)\ln 2}(3x^2+1) = \frac{3x^2+1}{(x^3+x)\ln 2}$

In other words, when taking the derivative of the logarithm of the absolute value of a quantity, we can simply ignore the absolute value!

We now turn to the derivatives of *exponential* functions—that is, functions of the form $f(x) = b^x$. We begin by showing how *not* to differentiate them.

Caution The derivative of b^x is *not* xb^{x-1}. The power rule applies only to *constant* exponents. In this case the exponent is decidedly *not* constant, and so the power rule does not apply.

The following shows the correct way of differentiating b^x.

Derivative of e^x

$$\frac{d}{dx}[e^x] = e^x$$

quick **Examples**

1. $\frac{d}{dx}[3e^x] = 3\frac{d}{dx}[e^x] = 3e^x$

2. $\frac{d}{dx}\left[\frac{e^x}{x}\right] = \frac{e^x x - e^x(1)}{x^2}$ $\quad$ Quotient rule

$= \frac{e^x(x-1)}{x^2}$

Thus, e^x has the amazing property that its derivative is itself![21] For bases other than e, we have the following generalization:

Derivative of b^x

If b is any positive number, then

$$\frac{d}{dx}[b^x] = b^x \ln b$$

Note that if $b = e$, we obtain the previous formula,

quick Example

$$\frac{d}{dx}[3^x] = 3^x \ln 3$$

Derivation of the Formula $\frac{d}{dx}[e^x] = e^x$

To find the derivative of e^x we use a shortcut.[22] Write $g(x) = e^x$. Then

$$\ln g(x) = x$$

Take the derivative of both sides of this equation to get

$$\frac{g'(x)}{g(x)} = 1$$

or

$$g'(x) = g(x) = e^x$$

In other words, the exponential function with base e is its own derivative. The rule for exponential functions with other bases follows from the equality $b^x = e^{x \ln b}$ (why?) and the chain rule. (Try it.)

If we were to take the derivative of e raised to a *quantity,* not just x, we would need to use the chain rule, as follows.

Derivatives of Exponentials of Functions

Original Rule	*Generalized Rule*	*In Words*
$\frac{d}{dx}[e^x] = e^x$	$\frac{d}{dx}[e^u] = e^u \frac{du}{dx}$	The derivative of e raised to a quantity is e raised to that quantity, times the derivative of that quantity.
$\frac{d}{dx}[b^x] = b^x \ln b$	$\frac{d}{dx}[b^u] = b^u \ln b \frac{du}{dx}$	The derivative of b raised to a quantity is b raised to that quantity, times $\ln b$, times the derivative of that quantity.

quick Examples

1. $\frac{d}{dx}[e^{x^2+1}] = e^{x^2+1}\frac{d}{dx}[x^2 + 1]$ $\qquad u = x^2 + 1$ (see note*)

$$= e^{x^2+1}(2x) = 2x\, e^{x^2+1}$$

* The calculation thought experiment tells us that we have e raised to a quantity.

---

[21] There is another—very simple—function that is its own derivative. What is it?

[22] This shortcut is an example of a technique called *logarithmic differentiation,* which is occasionally useful. We will see it again in the next section.

2. $\frac{d}{dx}[2^{3x}] = 2^{3x} \ln 2 \frac{d}{dx}[3x]$ $\quad u = 3x$

$$= 2^{3x}(\ln 2)(3) = (3 \ln 2)2^{3x}$$

3. If \$1000 is invested in an account earning 5% per year compounded continuously, then the rate of change of the account balance after t years is

$$\frac{d}{dt}[1000e^{0.05t}] = 1000(0.05)e^{0.05t} = 50e^{0.05t} \text{ dollars/year}$$

Applications

Example 4 Epidemics

In the early stages of the AIDS epidemic during the 1980s, the number of cases in the U.S. was increasing by about 50% every 6 months. By the start of 1983, there were approximately 1600 AIDS cases in the United States.* Had this trend continued, how many new cases per year would have been occurring by the start of 1993?

Solution To find the answer, we must first model this exponential growth using the methods of Chapter 2. Referring to Example 3 in Section 2.2, we find that t years after the start of 1983 the number of cases is

$$A = 1600(2.25^t)$$

We are asking for the number of new cases each year. In other words, we want the rate of change, dA/dt:

$$\frac{dA}{dt} = 1600(2.25)^t \ln 2.25 \text{ cases per year}$$

At the start of 1993, $t = 10$, so the number of new cases per year is

$$\left.\frac{dA}{dt}\right|_{t=10} = 1600(2.25)^{10} \ln 2.25 \approx 4{,}300{,}000 \text{ cases per year}$$

*Data based on regression of 1982–1986 figures. Source for data: Centers for Disease Control and Prevention. HIV/AIDS Surveillance Report, 2000;12 (No. 2).

+ *Before we go on...* In Example 4, the figure for the number of new cases per year is so large because we assumed that exponential growth—the 50% increase every six months—would continue. A more realistic model for the spread of a disease is the logistic model. (See Section 2.4, as well as the next example.) ■

Example 5 Sales Growth

The sales of the Cyberpunk II video game can be modeled by the logistic curve

$$q(t) = \frac{10{,}000}{1 + 0.5e^{-0.4t}}$$

where $q(t)$ is the total number of units sold t months after its introduction. How fast is the game selling two years after its introduction?

Solution We are asked for $q'(24)$. We can find the derivative of $q(t)$ using the quotient rule, or we can first write

$$q(t) = 10{,}000(1 + 0.5e^{-0.4t})^{-1}$$

and then use the generalized power rule:

$$q'(t) = -10{,}000(1 + 0.5e^{-0.4t})^{-2}(0.5e^{-0.4t})(-0.4)$$

$$= \frac{2000e^{-0.4t}}{(1 + 0.5e^{-0.4t})^2}$$

Thus,

$$q'(24) = \frac{2000e^{-0.4(24)}}{(1 + 0.5e^{-0.4(24)})^2} \approx 0.135 \text{ units per month}$$

So, after 2 years, sales are quite slow.

Before we go on... We can check the answer in Example 5 graphically. If we plot the total sales curve for $0 \le t \le 30$ and $6000 \le q \le 10{,}000$, on a TI-83/84, for example, we get the graph shown in Figure 2. Notice that total sales level off at about 10,000 units.[23] We computed $q'(24)$, which is the slope of the curve at the point with t-coordinate 24. If we zoom in to the portion of the curve near $t = 24$, we obtain the graph shown in Figure 3, with $23 \le t \le 25$ and $9999 \le q \le 10{,}000$. The curve is almost linear in this range. If we use the two endpoints of this segment of the curve, (23, 9999.4948) and (25, 9999.7730), we can approximate the derivative as

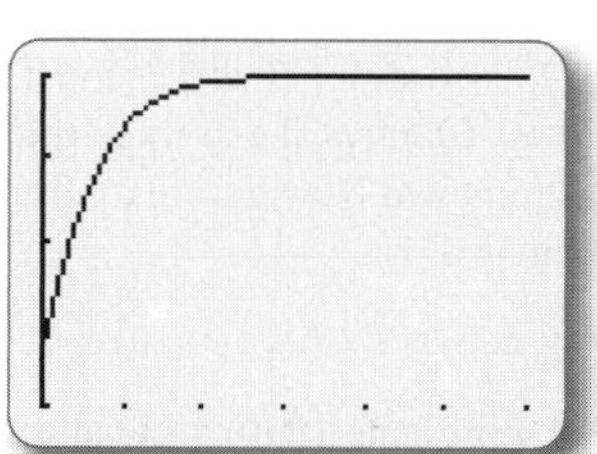

Figure **2**

$$\frac{9999.7730 - 9999.4948}{25 - 23} = 0.1391$$

which is accurate to two decimal places. ■

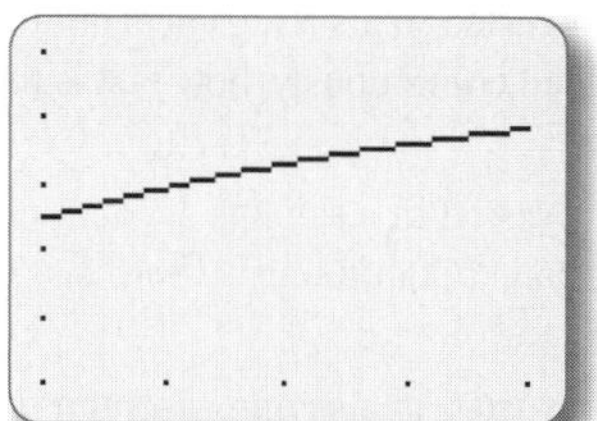

Figure **3**

[23] We can also say this using limits: $\lim_{t\to+\infty} q(t) = 10{,}000$.

4.3 EXERCISES

● denotes basic skills exercises

◆ denotes challenging exercises

tech Ex indicates exercises that should be solved using technology

Find the derivatives of the functions in Exercises 1–76.

1. ● $f(x) = \ln(x - 1)$ *hint* [see Quick Examples on p. 324]

2. ● $f(x) = \ln(x + 3)$

3. ● $f(x) = \log_2 x$

4. ● $f(x) = \log_3 x$

5. ● $g(x) = \ln|x^2 + 3|$

6. ● $g(x) = \ln|2x - 4|$

7. ● $h(x) = e^{x+3}$ *hint* [see Quick Examples on pp. 325, 326]

8. ● $h(x) = e^{x^2}$

9. ● $f(x) = e^{-x}$

10. ● $f(x) = e^{1-x}$

11. ● $g(x) = 4^x$

12. ● $g(x) = 5^x$

13. ● $h(x) = 2^{x^2-1}$

14. ● $h(x) = 3^{x^2-x}$

15. ● $f(x) = x\ln x$

16. ● $f(x) = 3\ln x$

17. ● $f(x) = (x^2 + 1)\ln x$

18. ● $f(x) = (4x^2 - x)\ln x$

19. ● $f(x) = (x^2 + 1)^5\ln x$

20. ● $f(x) = (x + 1)^{0.5}\ln x$

21. ● $g(x) = \ln|3x - 1|$

22. ● $g(x) = \ln|5 - 9x|$

23. ● $g(x) = \ln|2x^2 + 1|$

24. ● $g(x) = \ln|x^2 - x|$

25. ● $g(x) = \ln(x^2 - 2.1x^{0.3})$

26. ● $g(x) = \ln(x - 3.1x^{-1})$

27. ● $h(x) = \ln[(-2x + 1)(x + 1)]$

28. ● $h(x) = \ln[(3x + 1)(-x + 1)]$

29. ● $h(x) = \ln\left(\dfrac{3x + 1}{4x - 2}\right)$

30. ● $h(x) = \ln\left(\dfrac{9x}{4x - 2}\right)$

31. ● $r(x) = \ln\left|\dfrac{(x + 1)(x - 3)}{-2x - 9}\right|$

32. ● $r(x) = \ln\left|\dfrac{-x + 1}{(3x - 4)(x - 9)}\right|$

33. ● $s(x) = \ln(4x - 2)^{1.3}$

34. ● $s(x) = \ln(x - 8)^{-2}$

35. ● $s(x) = \ln\left|\dfrac{(x + 1)^2}{(3x - 4)^3(x - 9)}\right|$

36. ● $s(x) = \ln\left|\dfrac{(x + 1)^2(x - 3)^4}{2x + 9}\right|$

37. ● $h(x) = \log_2(x + 1)$

38. ● $h(x) = \log_3(x^2 + x)$

39. ● $r(t) = \log_3(t + 1/t)$

40. ● $r(t) = \log_3(t + \sqrt{t})$

41. ● $f(x) = (\ln|x|)^2$

42. ● $f(x) = \dfrac{1}{\ln|x|}$

43. ● $r(x) = \ln(x^2) - [\ln(x - 1)]^2$

44. ● $r(x) = (\ln(x^2))^2$

45. ● $f(x) = xe^x$

46. ● $f(x) = 2e^x - x^2e^x$

47. ● $r(x) = \ln(x + 1) + 3x^3e^x$

48. ● $r(x) = \ln|x + e^x|$

49. ● $f(x) = e^x \ln|x|$

50. ● $f(x) = e^x \log_2|x|$

51. ● $f(x) = e^{2x+1}$

52. ● $f(x) = e^{4x-5}$

53. ● $h(x) = e^{x^2-x+1}$

54. ● $h(x) = e^{2x^2-x+1/x}$

55. ● $s(x) = x^2e^{2x-1}$

56. ● $s(x) = \dfrac{e^{4x-1}}{x^3 - 1}$

57. ● $r(x) = (e^{2x-1})^2$

58. ● $r(x) = (e^{2x^2})^3$

59. ● $t(x) = 3^{2x-4}$

60. ● $t(x) = 4^{-x+5}$

61. ● $v(x) = 3^{2x+1} + e^{3x+1}$

62. ● $v(x) = e^{2x}4^{2x}$

63. ● $u(x) = \dfrac{3^{x^2}}{x^2 + 1}$

64. ● $u(x) = (x^2 + 1)4^{x^2-1}$

65. ● $g(x) = \dfrac{e^x + e^{-x}}{e^x - e^{-x}}$

66. ● $g(x) = \dfrac{1}{e^x + e^{-x}}$

67. $g(x) = e^{3x-1}e^{x-2}e^x$

68. $g(x) = e^{-x+3}e^{2x-1}e^{-x+11}$

69. $f(x) = \dfrac{1}{x \ln x}$

70. $f(x) = \dfrac{e^{-x}}{xe^x}$

71. $f(x) = [\ln(e^x)]^2 - \ln[(e^x)^2]$

72. $f(x) = e^{\ln x} - e^{2\ln(x^2)}$

73. $f(x) = \ln|\ln x|$

74. $f(x) = \ln|\ln|\ln x||$

75. $s(x) = \ln\sqrt{\ln x}$

76. $s(x) = \sqrt{\ln(\ln x)}$

Find the equations of the straight lines described in Exercises 77–82. Use graphing technology to check your answers by plotting the given curve together with the tangent line.

77. ● Tangent to $y = e^x \log_2 x$ at the point $(1, 0)$

78. ● Tangent to $y = e^x + e^{-x}$ at the point $(0, 2)$

79. ● Tangent to $y = \ln\sqrt{2x + 1}$ at the point where $x = 0$

80. ● Tangent to $y = \ln\sqrt{2x^2 + 1}$ at the point where $x = 1$

81. ● At right angles to $y = e^{x^2}$ at the point where $x = 1$

82. ● At right angles to $y = \log_2(3x + 1)$ at the point where $x = 1$

Applications

83. ● ***New York City Housing Costs: Downtown*** The average price of a two-bedroom apartment in downtown New York City from 1994 to 2004 could be approximated by

$$p(t) = 0.33e^{0.16t} \text{ million dollars} \quad (0 \le t \le 10)$$

where t is time in years ($t = 0$ represents 1994).[24] What was the average price of a two-bedroom apartment in downtown New York City in 2003, and how fast was it increasing? (Round your answers to two significant digits.) *hint* [see Example 4]

84. ● ***New York City Housing Costs: Uptown*** The average price of a two-bedroom apartment in uptown New York City from 1994 to 2004 could be approximated by

$$p(t) = 0.14e^{0.10t} \text{ million dollars} \quad (0 \le t \le 10)$$

where t is time in years ($t = 0$ represents 1994).[25] What was the average price of a two-bedroom apartment in uptown New York City in 2002, and how fast was it increasing? (Round your answers to two significant digits.)

85. ● ***Investments*** If \$10,000 is invested in a savings account offering 4% per year, compounded continuously, how fast is the balance growing after 3 years?

86. ● ***Investments*** If \$20,000 is invested in a savings account offering 3.5% per year, compounded continuously, how fast is the balance growing after 3 years?

87. ● ***Investments*** If \$10,000 is invested in a savings account offering 4% per year, compounded semiannually, how fast is the balance growing after 3 years?

88. ● ***Investments*** If \$20,000 is invested in a savings account offering 3.5% per year, compounded semiannually, how fast is the balance growing after 3 years?

89. ● ***Scientific Research*** The number of research articles in the research journal *Physics Review* that were written by researchers in Europe during 1983–2003 can be approximated by

$$A(t) = \frac{7.0}{1 + 5.4e^{-0.18t}} \text{ thousand articles} \quad (0 \le t \le 10)$$

[24] Model is based on a exponential regression. Source for data: Miller Samuel/*New York Times*, March 28, 2004, p. RE 11.

[25] Ibid.

($t = 0$ represents 1983).[26] How fast was this number increasing in 2000 ($t = 7$)? (Round your answer to two significant digits.) *hint* [see Example 5]

90. ● ***Personal Computers*** The percentage of U.S households with personal computers can be approximated by

$$P(t) = \frac{85}{1 + 2.6e^{0.26t}} \quad (0 \le t \le 9)$$

where t is time in years ($t = 0$ represents 1994).[27] How fast was this percentage increasing in 2000 ($t = 6$)? (Round your answer to two significant digits.)

91. ● ***Epidemics*** A flu epidemic described in Example 1 in Section 2.4 approximately followed the curve

$$P = \frac{150}{1 + 15{,}000e^{-0.35t}} \text{ million people}$$

where P is the number of people infected and t is the number of weeks after the start of the epidemic. How fast is the epidemic growing (that is, how many new cases are there each week) after 20 weeks? After 30 weeks? After 40 weeks? (Round your answers to two significant digits.)

92. ● ***Epidemics*** Another epidemic follows the curve

$$P = \frac{200}{1 + 20{,}000e^{-0.549t}} \text{ million people}$$

where t is in years. How fast is the epidemic growing after 10 years? After 20 years? After 30 years? (Round your answers to two significant digits.)

93. ● ***Scientific Research*** (Compare Exercise 89.) The number of research articles in the research journal *Physics Review* that were written by researchers in Europe during 1983–2003 can be approximated by

$$A(t) = \frac{7.0}{1 + 5.4(1.2)^{-t}} \text{ thousand articles}$$

($t = 0$ represents 1983).[28] How fast was this number increasing in 2000 ($t = 7$)? (Round your answer to two significant digits.)

94. ● ***Personal Computers*** (Compare Exercise 90.) The percentage of U.S households with personal computers can be approximated by

$$P(t) = \frac{85}{1 + 2.6(1.3)^{-t}} \quad (0 \le t \le 9)$$

where t is time in years ($t = 0$ represents 1994).[29] How fast was this percentage increasing in 2000 ($t = 6$)? (Round your answer to two significant digits.)

95. ***Population Growth*** The population of Lower Anchovia was 4,000,000 at the start of 1995 and was doubling every 10 years. How fast was it growing per year at the start of 1995? (Round your answer to 3 significant digits.)

96. ***Population Growth*** The population of Upper Anchovia was 3,000,000 at the start of 1996 and doubling every 7 years. How fast was it growing per year at the start of 1996? (Round your answer to 3 significant digits.)

97. ***Radioactive Decay*** Plutonium-239 has a half-life of 24,400 years. How fast is a lump of 10 grams decaying after 100 years?

98. ***Radioactive Decay*** Carbon-14 has a half-life of 5730 years. How fast is a lump of 20 grams decaying after 100 years?

99. ***SAT Scores by Income*** The following chart shows U.S. verbal SAT scores as a function of parents' income level:[30]

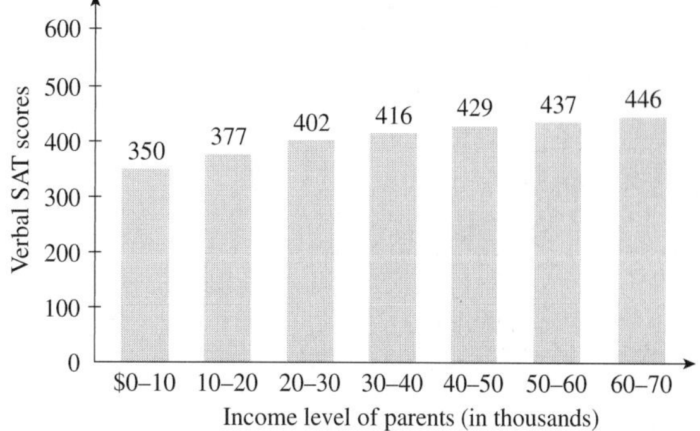

a. The data can best be modeled by which of the following?
(A) $S(x) = 470 - 136e^{-0.0000264x}$
(B) $S(x) = 136e^{-0.0000264x}$
(C) $S(x) = 355(1.000004^x)$
(D) $S(x) = 470 - 355(1.000004^x)$

($S(x)$ is the average verbal SAT score of students whose parents earn \$$x$ per year.)

b. Use $S'(x)$ to predict how a student's verbal SAT score is affected by a \$1000 increase in parents' income for a student whose parents earn \$45,000.

c. Does $S'(x)$ increase or decrease as x increases? Interpret your answer.

100. ***SAT Scores by Income*** The following chart shows U.S. average math SAT scores as a function of parents' income level:[31]

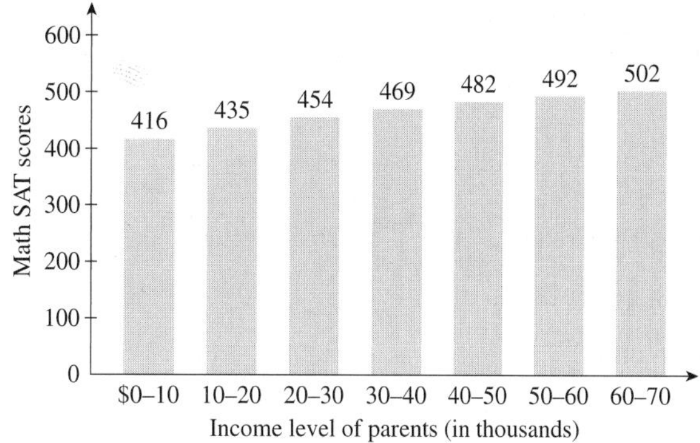

[26] SOURCE: The American Physical Society/*New York Times* May 3, 2003, p. A1.

[27] SOURCE: NTIA/Census Bureau/Pegasus Research International, LLC http://www.pegasusresearch.com/metrics/growthus.htm.

[28] SOURCE: The American Physical Society/*New York Times* May 3, 2003, p. A1.

[29] SOURCE: NTIA/Census Bureau/Pegasus Research International, LLC http://www.pegasusresearch.com/metrics/growthus.htm.

[30] SOURCE: The College Board/*New York Times*, March 5, 1995, p. E16.

[31] Ibid.

a. The data can best be modeled by which of the following?
(A) $S(x) = 535 - 415(1.000003^x)$
(B) $S(x) = 535 - 136e^{0.0000213x}$
(C) $S(x) = 535 - 136e^{-0.0000213x}$
(D) $S(x) = 415(1.000003^x)$

($S(x)$ is the average math SAT score of students whose parents earn \$$x$ per year.)

b. Use $S'(x)$ to predict how a student's math SAT score is affected by a \$1000 increase in parents' income for a student whose parents earn \$45,000.

c. Does $S'(x)$ increase or decrease as x increases? Interpret your answer.

101. ***Demographics: Average Age and Fertility*** The following graph shows a plot of average age of a population versus fertility rate (the average number of children each woman has in her lifetime) in the U.S. and Europe over the period 1950–2005.[32]

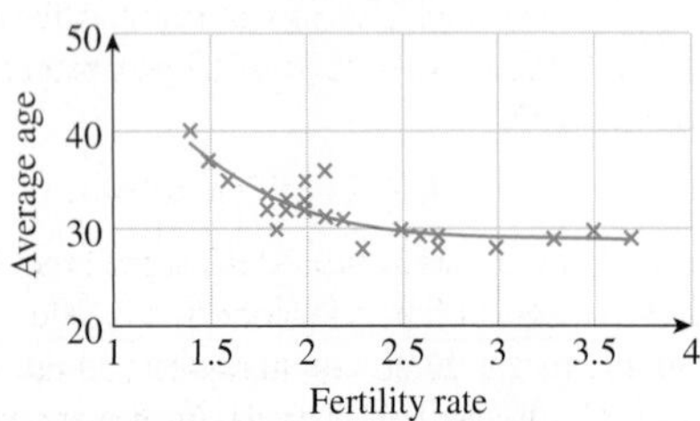

The equation of the accompanying curve is

$$a = 28.5 + 120(0.172)^x \qquad (1.4 \le x \le 3.7)$$

where a is the average age (in years) of the population and x is the fertility rate.

a. Compute $a'(2)$. What does the answer tell you about average age and fertility rates?

b. Use the answer to part (a) to estimate how much the fertility rate would need to increase from a level of 2 children per woman to lower the average age of a population by about 1 year.

102. ***Demographics: Average Age and Fertility*** The following graph shows a plot of average age of a population versus fertility rate (the average number of children each woman has in her lifetime) in Europe over the period 1950–2005.[33]

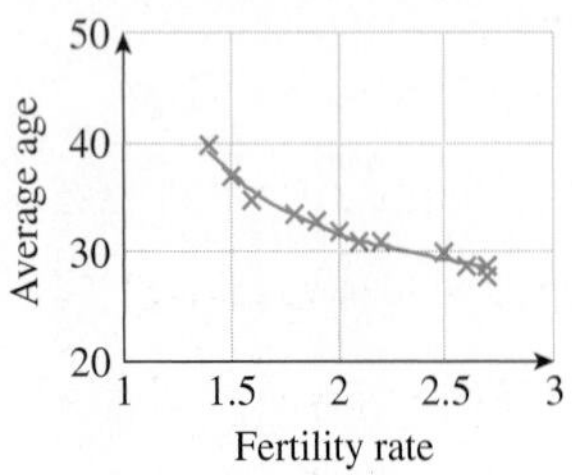

The equation of the accompanying curve is

$$g = 27.6 + 128(0.181)^x \qquad (1.4 \le x \le 3.7)$$

where g is the average age (in years) of the population and x is the fertility rate.

a. Compute $g'(2.5)$. What does the answer tell you about average age and fertility rates?

b. Referring to the model that combines the data for Europe and the U.S. in Exercise 101, which population's average age is affected more by a changing fertility rate at the level of 2.5 children per woman?

103. ***Big Brother*** The following chart shows the number of wiretaps authorized each year by U.S. courts from 1990 to 2000 ($t = 0$ represents 1990):[34]

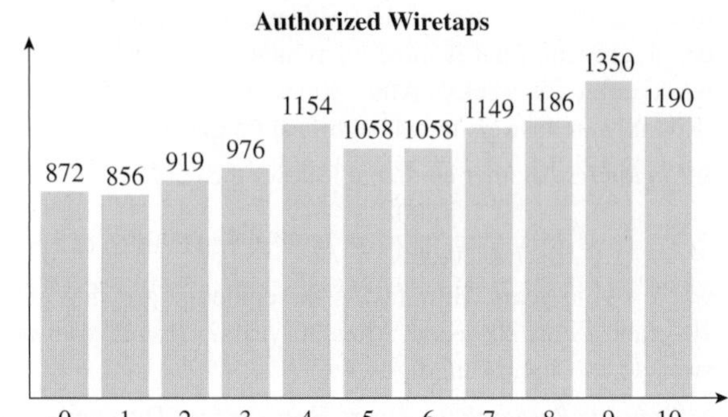

These data can be approximated with the logistic model

$$W(t) = \frac{1500}{1 + 0.77(1.16)^{-t}} \qquad (0 \le t \le 10)$$

where $W(t)$ is the number of authorized wiretaps in year $1990 + t$.

a. Calculate $W'(t)$ and use it to approximate $W'(6)$. To how many significant digits should we round the answer? Why? What does the answer tell you?

b. tech Ex Graph the function $W'(t)$. Based on the graph, the number of wiretaps authorized each year (choose one)
(A) increased at a decreasing rate
(B) decreased at an increasing rate
(C) increased at an increasing rate
(D) decreased at a decreasing rate

from 1990 to 2000.

104. ***Big Brother*** The following chart shows the number of wiretaps authorized each year by U.S. federal courts from 1990 to 2000 ($t = 0$ represents 1990):[35]

[32] The separate data for Europe and the U.S. are collected in the same graph. 2005 figures are estimates. Source: United Nations World Population Division/*New York Times,* June 29, 2003, p. 3.

[33] All European countries including the Russian Federation. 2005 figures are estimates. Source: United Nations World Population Division/New York Times, June 29, 2003, p. 3.

[34] Source: 2000 Wiretap Report, Administrative Office of the United States Courts www.epic.org/privacy/wiretap/stats/2000_report/default.html.

[35] Ibid.

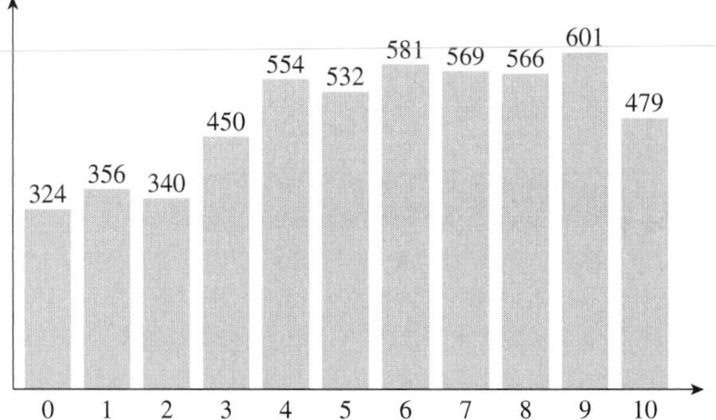

These data can be approximated with the logistic model

$$W(t) = \frac{600}{1 + 1.00(1.62)^{-t}} \qquad (0 \le t \le 10)$$

where $W(t)$ is the number of authorized wiretaps in year $1990 + t$.

a. Calculate $W'(t)$ and use it to approximate $W'(6)$. To how many significant digits should we round the answer? Why? What does the answer tell you?

b. tech Ex Graph the function $W'(t)$. Based on the graph, the number of wiretaps authorized each year (choose one)
(A) increased at an increasing rate
(B) decreased at a decreasing rate
(C) increased at a decreasing rate
(D) decreased at an increasing rate

from 1990 to 2000.

105. tech Ex ***Diffusion of New Technology*** Numeric control is a technology whereby the operation of machines is controlled by numerical instructions on disks, tapes, or cards. In a study, E. Mansfield et al[36] modeled the growth of this technology using the equation

$$p(t) = \frac{0.80}{1 + e^{4.46 - 0.477t}}$$

where $p(t)$ is the fraction of firms using numeric control in year t.

a. Graph this function for $0 \le t \le 20$ and estimate $p'(10)$ graphically. Interpret the result.

b. Use your graph to estimate $\lim_{t \to +\infty} p(t)$ and interpret the result.

c. Compute $p'(t)$, graph it, and again find $p'(10)$.

d. Use your graph to estimate $\lim_{t \to +\infty} p'(t)$ and interpret the result.

106. tech Ex ***Diffusion of New Technology*** Repeat Exercise 105 using the revised formula

$$p(t) = \frac{0.90e^{-0.1t}}{1 + e^{4.50 - 0.477t}}$$

which takes into account that in the long run this new technology will eventually become outmoded and will be replaced by a newer technology. Draw your graphs using the range $0 \le t \le 40$.

107. ◆ ***Cell Phone Revenues*** The number of cell phone subscribers in China for the period 2000–2005 was projected to follow the equation[37]

$$N(t) = 39t + 68 \text{ million subscribers}$$

in year t ($t = 0$ represents 2000). The average annual revenue per cell phone user was \$350 in 2000. Assuming that, due to competition, the revenue per cell phone user decreases continuously at an annual rate of 10%, give a formula for the annual revenue in year t. Hence, project the annual revenue and its rate of change in 2002. Round all answers to the nearest billion dollars or billion dollars per year.

108. ◆ ***Cell Phone Revenues*** The annual revenue for cell phone use in China for the period 2000–2005 was projected to follow the equation[38]

$$R(t) = 14t + 24 \text{ billion dollars}$$

in year t ($t = 0$ represents 2000). At the same time, there were approximately 68 million subscribers in 2000. Assuming that the number of subscribers increases continuously at an annual rate of 10%, give a formula for the annual revenue per subscriber in year t. Hence, project to the nearest dollar the annual revenue per subscriber and its rate of change in 2002. (Be careful with units!)

Communication and Reasoning Exercises

109. ● Complete the following: The derivative of e raised to a glob is ____.

110. ● Complete the following: The derivative of the natural logarithm of a glob is ____.

111. ● Complete the following: The derivative of 2 raised to a glob is ____.

112. ● Complete the following: The derivative of the base 2 logarithm of a glob is ____.

113. ● What is wrong with the following?

$$\frac{d}{dx}3^{2x} = (2x)3^{2x-1} \quad ✗ \quad \textit{WRONG!}$$

114. ● What is wrong with the following?

$$\frac{d}{dx}\ln(3x^2 - 1) = \frac{1}{6x} \quad ✗ \quad \textit{WRONG!}$$

115. The number N of music downloads on campus is growing exponentially with time. Can $N'(t)$ grow linearly with time? Explain.

[36] SOURCE: "The Diffusion of a Major Manufacturing Innovation," in *Research and Innovation in the Modern Corporation* (W.W. Norton and Company, Inc., New York, 1971, pp. 186–205).

[37] Based on a regression of projected figures (coefficients are rounded). SOURCE: Intrinsic Technology/*New York Times*, Nov. 24, 2000, p. C1.

[38] Not allowing for discounting due to increased competition. SOURCE: Ibid.

116. The number N of graphing calculators sold on campus is decaying exponentially with time. Can $N'(t)$ grow with time? Explain.

*The **percentage rate of change** or **fractional rate of change** of a function is defined to be the ratio $f'(x)/f(x)$. (It is customary to express this as a percentage when speaking about percentage rate of change.)*

117. ◆ Show that the fractional rate of change of the exponential function e^{kx} is equal to k, which is often called its **fractional growth rate.**

118. ◆ Show that the fractional rate of change of $f(x)$ is the rate of change of $\ln(f(x))$.

119. ◆ Let $A(t)$ represent a quantity growing exponentially. Show that the percentage rate of change, $A'(t)/A(t)$, is constant.

120. ◆ Let $A(t)$ be the amount of money in an account that pays interest which is compounded some number of times per year. Show that the percentage rate of growth, $A'(t)/A(t)$, is constant. What might this constant represent?

● basic skills ◆ challenging tech Ex technology exercise

4.4 Implicit Differentiation (OPTIONAL)

Consider the equation $y^5 + y + x = 0$, whose graph is shown in Figure 4.

How did we obtain this graph? We did not solve for y as a function of x; that is impossible. In fact, we solved for x in terms of y to find points to plot. Nonetheless, the graph in Figure 4 is the graph of a function because it passes the vertical line test: Every vertical line crosses the graph no more than once, so for each value of x there is no more than one corresponding value of y. Because we cannot solve for y explicitly in terms of x, we say that the equation $y^5 + y + x = 0$ determines y as an **implicit function** of x.

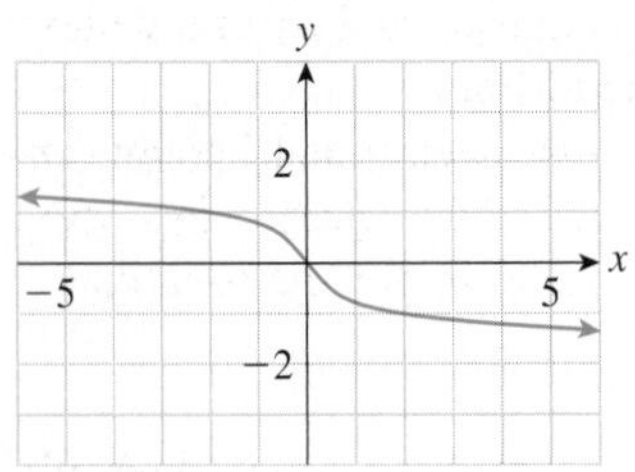

Figure **4**

Now, suppose we want to find the slope of the tangent line to this curve at, say, the point $(2, -1)$ (which, you should check, is a point on the curve). In the following example we find, surprisingly, that it is possible to obtain a formula for dy/dx without having to first solve the equation for y.

Example 1 Implicit Differentiation

Find $\dfrac{dy}{dx}$, given that $y^5 + y + x = 0$

Solution

We use the chain rule and a little cleverness. Think of y as a function of x and take the derivative with respect to x of both sides of the equation:

$$y^5 + y + x = 0 \qquad \text{Original equation}$$

$$\frac{d}{dx}[y^5 + y + x] = \frac{d}{dx}[0] \qquad \text{Derivative with respect to } x \text{ of both sides}$$

$$\frac{d}{dx}[y^5] + \frac{d}{dx}[y] + \frac{d}{dx}[x] = 0 \qquad \text{Derivative rules}$$

Now we must be careful. The derivative *with respect to x* of y^5 is *not* $5y^4$. Rather, because y is a function of x, we must use the chain rule, which tells us that

$$\frac{d}{dx}[y^5] = 5y^4\frac{dy}{dx}$$

Thus, we get

$$5y^4\frac{dy}{dx}+\frac{dy}{dx}+1=0$$

We want to find dy/dx, so we *solve for it:*

$$(5y^4+1)\frac{dy}{dx}=-1 \qquad \text{Isolate } dy/dx \text{ on one side.}$$

$$\frac{dy}{dx}=-\frac{1}{5y^4+1} \qquad \text{Divide both sides by } 5y^4+1.$$

+*Before we go on...* Note that we should not expect to obtain dy/dx as an explicit function of x if y was not an explicit function of x to begin with. For example, the formula we found in Example 1 for dy/dx is not a function of x because there is a y in it. However, the result is still useful because we can evaluate the derivative at any point on the graph. For instance, at the point $(2, -1)$ on the graph, we get

$$\frac{dy}{dx}=-\frac{1}{5y^4+1}=-\frac{1}{5(-1)^4+1}=-\frac{1}{6}$$

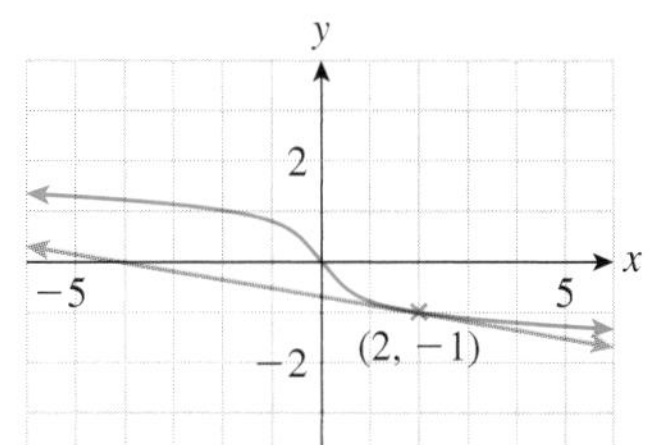

Figure **5**

Thus, the slope of the tangent line to the curve $y^5+y+x=0$ at the point $(2, -1)$ is $-1/6$. Figure 5 shows the graph and this tangent line. ■

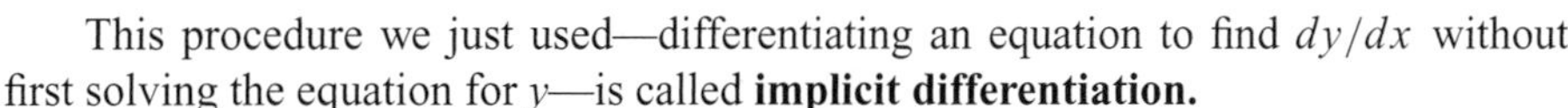

This procedure we just used—differentiating an equation to find dy/dx without first solving the equation for y—is called **implicit differentiation.**

In Example 1 we were given an equation in x and y that determined y as an (implicit) function of x, even though we could not solve for y. But an equation in x and y need not always determine y, as a function of x. Consider, for example, the equation

$$2x^2+y^2=2$$

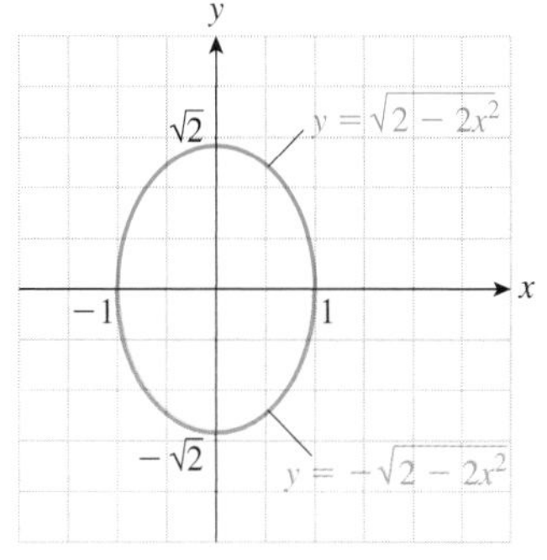

Figure **6**

Solving for y yields $y=\pm\sqrt{2-2x^2}$. The $\pm$ sign reminds us that for some values of x there are two corresponding values for y. We can graph this equation by superimposing the graphs of

$$y=\sqrt{2-2x^2} \quad \text{and } y=-\sqrt{2-2x^2}$$

The graph, an *ellipse,* is shown in Figure 6.

The graph of $y=\sqrt{2-2x^2}$ constitutes the top half of the ellipse, and the graph of $y=-\sqrt{2-2x^2}$ constitutes the bottom half.

Example **2** Slope of Tangent Line

Refer to Figure 6. Find she slope of the tangent line to the ellipse $2x^2+y^2=2$ at the point $(1/\sqrt{2}, 1)$.

Solution Because $(1/\sqrt{2}, 1)$ is on the top half of the ellipse in Figure 6, we *could* differentiate the function $y=\sqrt{2-2x^2}$, to obtain the result, but it is actually easier to apply implicit differentiation to the original equation.

$$2x^2+y^2=2 \qquad \text{Original equation}$$

$$\frac{d}{dx}[2x^2+y^2]=\frac{d}{dx}[2] \qquad \text{Derivative with respect to } x \text{ of both sides}$$

$$4x + 2y\frac{dy}{dx} = 0$$

$$2y\frac{dy}{dx} = -4x \qquad \text{Solve for } dy/dx$$

$$\frac{dy}{dx} = -\frac{4x}{2y} = -\frac{2x}{y}$$

To find the slope at $(1/\sqrt{2},\ 1)$ we now substitute for x and y:

$$\left.\frac{dy}{dx}\right|_{(1/\sqrt{2},1)} = -\frac{2/\sqrt{2}}{2} = -\sqrt{2}$$

Thus, the slope of the tangent to the ellipse at the point $(1/\sqrt{2},\ 1)$ is $-\sqrt{2} \approx -1.414$.

Example 3 Tangent Line for an Implicit Function

Find the equation of the tangent line to the curve $\ln y = xy$ at the point where $y = 1$.

Solution First, we use implicit differentiation to find dy/dx:

$$\frac{d}{dx}[\ln y] = \frac{d}{dx}[xy] \qquad \text{Take } d/dx \text{ of both sides}$$

$$\frac{1}{y}\frac{dy}{dx} = (1)y + x\frac{dy}{dx} \qquad \text{Chain rule on left, product rule on right}$$

To solve for dy/dx, we bring all the terms containing dy/dx to the left-hand side and all terms not containing it to the right-hand side:

$$\frac{1}{y}\frac{dy}{dx} - x\frac{dy}{dx} = y \qquad \text{Bring the terms with } dy/dx \text{ to the left.}$$

$$\frac{dy}{dx}\left(\frac{1}{y} - x\right) = y \qquad \text{Factor out } dy/dx.$$

$$\frac{dy}{dx}\left(\frac{1 - xy}{y}\right) = y$$

$$\frac{dy}{dx} = y\left(\frac{y}{1 - xy}\right) = \frac{y^2}{1 - xy} \qquad \text{Solve for } dy/dx.$$

The derivative gives the slope of the tangent line, so we want to evaluate the derivative at the point where $y = 1$. However, the formula for dy/dx requires values for both x and y. We get the value of x by substituting $y = 1$ in the original equation:

$$\ln y = xy$$

$$\ln(1) = x \cdot 1$$

But $\ln(1) = 0$, and so $x = 0$ for this point. Thus,

$$\left.\frac{dy}{dx}\right|_{(0,1)} = \frac{1^2}{1 - (0)(1)} = 1$$

Therefore, the tangent line is the line through $(x, y) = (0, 1)$ with slope 1, which is

$$y = x + 1$$

+*Before we go on...* Example 3 presents an instance of an implicit function in which it is simply not possible to solve for y. Try it. ■

Sometimes, it is easiest to differentiate a complicated function of x by first taking the logarithm and then using implicit differentiation—a technique called **logarithmic differentiation.**

Example 4 Logarithmic Differentiation

Find $\frac{d}{dx}\left[\frac{(x+1)^{10}(x^2+1)^{11}}{(x^3+1)^{12}}\right]$ without using the product or quotient rules.

Solution Write

$$y = \frac{(x+1)^{10}(x^2+1)^{11}}{(x^3+1)^{12}}$$

and then take the natural logarithm of both sides:

$$\ln y = \ln\left[\frac{(x+1)^{10}(x^2+1)^{11}}{(x^3+1)^{12}}\right]$$

We can use properties of the logarithm to simplify the right-hand side:

$$\begin{aligned}\ln y &= \ln(x+1)^{10} + \ln(x^2+1)^{11} - \ln(x^3+1)^{12} \\ &= 10\ln(x+1) + 11\ln(x^2+1) - 12\ln(x^3+1)\end{aligned}$$

Now we can find $\frac{dy}{dx}$ using implicit differentiation:

$$\frac{1}{y}\frac{dy}{dx} = \frac{10}{x+1} + \frac{22x}{x^2+1} - \frac{36x^2}{x^3+1} \qquad \text{Take } d/dx \text{ of both sides.}$$

$$\frac{dy}{dx} = y\left(\frac{10}{x+1} + \frac{22x}{x^2+1} - \frac{36x^2}{x^3+1}\right) \qquad \text{Solve for } dy/dx.$$

$$= \frac{(x+1)^{10}(x^2+1)^{11}}{(x^3+1)^{12}}\left(\frac{10}{x+1} + \frac{22x}{x^2+1} - \frac{36x^2}{x^3+1}\right) \qquad \text{Substitute for } y.$$

+*Before we go on...* Redo Example 4 using the product and quotient rules (and the chain rule) instead of logarithmic differentiation and compare the answers. Compare also the amount of work involved in both methods. ■

Application

Productivity usually depends on both labor and capital. Suppose, for example, you are managing a surfboard manufacturing company. You can measure its productivity by counting the number of surfboards the company makes each year. As a measure of labor, you can use the number of employees, and as a measure of capital you can use its operating budget. The so-called *Cobb-Douglas* model uses a function of the form:

$$P = Kx^a y^{1-a} \qquad \text{Cobb-Douglas model for productivity}$$

David Samuel Robbins/Corbis

where P stands for the number of surfboards made each year, x is the number of employees, and y is the operating budget. The numbers K and a are constants that depend on the particular situation studied, with a between 0 and 1.

Example 5 Cobb-Douglas Production Function

The surfboard company you own has the Cobb-Douglas production function

$$P = x^{0.3}y^{0.7}$$

where P is the number of surfboards it produces per year, x is the number of employees, and y is the daily operating budget (in dollars). Assume that the production level P is constant.

a. Find $\dfrac{dy}{dx}$.

b. Evaluate this derivative at $x = 30$ and $y = 10{,}000$, and interpret the answer.

Solution

a. We are given the equation $P = x^{0.3}y^{0.7}$, in which P is constant. We find $\dfrac{dy}{dx}$ by implicit differentiation

$$0 = \frac{d}{dx}[x^{0.3}y^{0.7}] \qquad d/dx \text{ of both sides}$$

$$0 = 0.3x^{-0.7}y^{0.7} + x^{0.3}(0.7)y^{-0.3}\frac{dy}{dx} \qquad \text{Product \& chain rules}$$

$$-0.7x^{0.3}y^{-0.3}\frac{dy}{dx} = 0.3x^{-0.7}y^{0.7} \qquad \text{Bring term with } dy/dx \text{ to left}$$

$$\frac{dy}{dx} = -\frac{0.3x^{-0.7}y^{0.7}}{0.7x^{0.3}y^{-0.3}} \qquad \text{Solve for } dy/dx$$

$$= -\frac{3y}{7x} \qquad \text{Simplify}$$

b. Evaluating this derivative at $x = 30$ and $y = 10{,}000$ gives

$$\left.\frac{dy}{dx}\right|_{x=30,\ y=10{,}000} = -\frac{3(10{,}000)}{7(30)} \approx -143$$

To interpret this result, first look at the units of the derivative: We recall that the units of dy/dx are units of y per unit of x. Because y is the daily budget, its units are dollars; because x is the number of employees, its units are employees. Thus,

$$\left.\frac{dy}{dx}\right|_{x=30,\ y=10{,}000} \approx -\$143 \text{ per employee}$$

Next, recall that dy/dx measures the rate of change of y as x changes. Because the answer is negative, the daily budget to maintain production at the fixed level is decreasing by approximately \$143 per additional employee at an employment level of 30 employees and a daily operating budget of \$10,000. In other words, increasing the workforce by one worker will result in a savings of approximately \$143 per day. Roughly speaking, *a new employee is worth \$143 per day* at the current levels of employment and production.

4.4 EXERCISES

● denotes basic skills exercises

◆ denotes challenging exercises

In Exercises 1–10, find dy/dx, using implicit differentiation. In each case, compare your answer with the result obtained by first solving for y as a function of x and then taking the derivative. hint [see Example 1]

1. ● $2x + 3y = 7$
2. ● $4x - 5y = 9$
3. ● $x^2 - 2y = 6$
5. ● $2x + 3y = xy$
7. ● $e^x y = 1$
9. ● $y \ln x + y = 2$

In Exercises 11–30, find the in… differentiation.

11. ● $x^2 + y^2 = 5; \frac{dy}{dx}$
13. ● $x^2 y - y^2 = 4; \frac{dy}{dx}$
15. ● $3xy - \frac{y}{3} = \frac{2}{x}; \frac{dy}{dx}$
17. ● $x^2 - 3y^2 = 8; \frac{dx}{dy}$
19. ● $p^2 - pq = 5p^2q^2; \frac{dp}{dq}$
21. ● $xe^y - ye^x = 1; \frac{dy}{dx}$
22. ● $x^2e^y - y^2 = e^x$…
23. $e^{st} = s^2; \frac{ds}{dt}$
24. $e^{s^2t} - st = 1; \frac{ds}{dt}$
25. $\frac{e^x}{y^2} = 1 + e^y; \frac{dy}{dx}$
26. $\frac{x}{e^y} + xy = 9y; \frac{dy}{dx}$
27. $\ln(y^2 - y) + x = y; \frac{dy}{dx}$
28. $\ln(xy) - x \ln y = y;$…
29. $\ln(xy + y^2) = e^y; \frac{dy}{dx}$
30. $\ln(1 + e^{xy}) = y; \frac{dy}{dx}$

*In Exercises 31–42, use implicit differentiation to find **(a)** th… slope of the tangent line, and **(b)** the equation of the tangent line at the indicated point on the graph. (Round answers to 4 decimal places as needed.) If only the x-coordinate is given, you must also find the y-coordinate.)* hint [see Examples 2, 3]

31. ● $4x^2 + 2y^2 = 12, (1, -2)$
32. ● $3x^2 - y^2 = 11, (-2, 1)$
33. ● $2x^2 - y^2 = xy, (-1, 2)$
34. ● $2x^2 + xy = 3y^2, (-1, -1)$
35. ● $x^2y - y^2 + x = 1, (1, 0)$
36. ● $(xy)^2 + xy - x = 8, (-8, 0)$
37. ● $xy - 2000 = y, x = 2$
38. ● $x^2 - 10xy = 200, x = 10$
39. $\ln(x + y) - x = 3x^2, x = 0$
40. $\ln(x - y) + 1 = 3x^2, x = 0$
41. $e^{xy} - x = 4x, x = 3$

…$= -1$

…*se logarithmic differentiation to find …fy the result.* hint [see Example 4]

44. ● $y = (3x + 2)(8x - 5)$
46. ● $y = \frac{x^2(3x + 1)^2}{(2x - 1)^3}$
48. ● $y = \frac{(3x + 2)^{2/3}}{3x - 1}$
50. ● $y = \sqrt{\frac{x - 1}{x^2 + 2}}$

… hour that Snappy …iven by

…lant and y is the …nstant, and com-

…terpret the result.

… accessory kits …r day that USA … plant in Cam-

… of workers at the plant and y is the monthly budget (in dollars). Assume P is constant, and compute $\frac{dy}{dx}$ when $x = 200$ and $y = 100{,}000$. Interpret the result.

55. ● ***Demand*** The demand equation for soccer tournament T-shirts is

$$xy - 2000 = y$$

where y is the number of T-shirts the Enormous State University soccer team can sell at a price of \$x per shirt. Find $\left.\frac{dy}{dx}\right|_{x=5}$, and interpret the result.

Please grade: 4.4 # 19, 29, 39, 53, 55

On # 19 & 29, there are multiple correct answers → they don't have to match the ans key as long as their work is correct.

56. ● ***Cost Equations*** The cost y (in cents) of producing x gallons of Ectoplasm hair gel is given by the cost equation

$$y^2 - 10xy = 200$$

Evaluate $\frac{dy}{dx}$ at $x = 1$ and interpret the result.

57. ● ***Housing Costs***[39] The cost C (in dollars) of building a house is related to the number k of carpenters used and the number e of electricians used by the formula

$$C = 15{,}000 + 50k^2 + 60e^2$$

If the cost of the house is fixed at \$200,000, find $\left.\frac{dk}{de}\right|_{e=15}$ and interpret your result.

58. ● ***Employment*** An employment research company estimates that the value of a recent MBA graduate to an accounting company is

$$V = 3e^2 + 5g^3$$

where V is the value of the graduate, e is the number of years of prior business experience, and g is the graduate school grade-point average. If V is fixed at 200, find $\frac{de}{dg}$ when $g = 3.0$ and interpret the result.

59. ***Grades***[40] A productivity formula for a student's performance on a difficult English examination is

$$g = 4tx - 0.2t^2 - 10x^2 \quad (t < 30)$$

where g is the score the student can expect to obtain, t is the number of hours of study for the examination, and x is the student's grade-point average.

a. For how long should a student with a 3.0 grade-point average study in order to score 80 on the examination?

b. Find $\frac{dt}{dx}$ for a student who earns a score of 80, evaluate it when $x = 3.0$, and interpret the result.

60. ***Grades*** Repeat the preceding exercise using the following productivity formula for a basket-weaving examination:

$$g = 10tx - 0.2t^2 - 10x^2 \quad (t < 10)$$

Comment on the result.

[39] Based on an Exercise in *Introduction to Mathematical Economics* by A. L. Ostrosky Jr., and J. V. Koch (Waveland Press, Springfield, Illinois, 1979).

[40] Ibid.

Exercises 61 and 62 are based on the following demand function for money (taken from a question on the GRE economics test):

$$M_d = (2) \times (y)^{0.6} \times (r)^{-0.3} \times (p)$$

where

M_d = demand for nominal money balances (money stock)
y = real income
r = an index of interest rates
p = an index of prices.

61. ◆ ***Money Stock*** If real income grows while the money stock and the price level remain constant, the interest rate must change at what rate? (First find dr/dy, then dr/dt; your answers will be expressed in terms of r, y, and $\frac{dy}{dt}$.)

62. ◆ ***Money Stock*** If real income grows while the money stock and the interest rate remain constant, the price level must change at what rate? (See hint for Exercise 61.)

Communication and Reasoning Exercises

63. ● Fill in the missing terms: The equation $x = y^3 + y - 3$ specifies ___ as a function of ___, and ___ as an implicit function of ___.

64. ● Fill in the missing terms: When $x \neq 0$ in the equation $xy = x^3 + 4$, it is possible to specify ___ as a function of ___. However, ___ is only an implicit function of ___.

65. Use logarithmic differentiation to give another proof of the product rule.

66. Use logarithmic differentiation to give a proof of the quotient rule.

67. If y is given explicitly as a function of x by an equation $y = f(x)$, compare finding dy/dx by implicit differentiation to finding it explicitly in the usual way.

68. Explain why one should not expect dy/dx to be a function of x if y is not a function of x.

69. ◆ If y is a function of x and $dy/dx \neq 0$ at some point, regard x as an implicit function of y and use implicit differentiation to obtain the equation

$$\frac{dx}{dy} = \frac{1}{dy/dx}$$

70. ◆ If you are given an equation in x and y such that dy/dx is a function of x only, what can you say about the graph of the equation?

Chapter 4 Review

KEY CONCEPTS

4.1 The Product and Quotient Rules

Product rule: $\frac{d}{dx}[f(x)g(x)] = f'(x)g(x) + f(x)g'(x)$ *p. 297*

Quotient rule: $\frac{d}{dx}\left(\frac{f(x)}{g(x)}\right) = \frac{f'(x)g(x) - f(x)g'(x)}{[g(x)]^2}$ *p. 297*

Using the product rule *p. 299*
Using the quotient rule *p. 300*
Calculation thought experiment *p. 301*
Application to revenue and average cost *p. 303*

4.2 The Chain Rule

Chain rule: $\frac{d}{dx}[f(u)] = f'(u)\frac{du}{dx}$ *p. 308*

Generalized power rule:

$\frac{d}{dx}[u^n] = nu^{n-1}\frac{du}{dx}$ *p. 309*

Using the chain rule *p. 310*
Application to marginal product *p. 313*
Chain rule in differential notation:

$\frac{dy}{dx} = \frac{dy}{du}\frac{du}{dx}$ *p. 314*

Manipulating derivatives in differential notation *p. 315*

4.3 Derivatives of Logarithmic and Exponential Functions

Derivative of the natural logarithm:

$\frac{d}{dx}[\ln x] = \frac{1}{x}$ *p. 320*

Derivative of logarithm with base b: $\frac{d}{dx}[\log_b x] = \frac{1}{x \ln b}$ *p. 320*

Derivatives of logarithms of functions:

$\frac{d}{dx}[\ln u] = \frac{1}{u}\frac{du}{dx}$

$\frac{d}{dx}[\log_b u] = \frac{1}{u \ln b}\frac{du}{dx}$ *p. 321*

Derivative of logarithms of absolute values:

$\frac{d}{dx}[\ln |x|] = \frac{1}{x}$

$\frac{d}{dx}[\ln |u|] = \frac{1}{u}\frac{du}{dx}$

$\frac{d}{dx}[\log_b |x|] = \frac{1}{x \ln b}$

$\frac{d}{dx}[\log_b |u|] = \frac{1}{u \ln b}\frac{du}{dx}$ *p. 323*

Derivative of e^x: $\frac{d}{dx}[e^x] = e^x$ *p. 324*

Derivative of b^x: $\frac{d}{dx}[b^x] = b^x \ln b$ *p. 325*

Derivatives of exponential functions *p. 325*
Application to epidemics *p. 326*
Application to sales growth (logistic function) *p. 326*

4.4 Implicit Differentiation

Implicit function of x *p. 332*
Implicit differentiation *p. 332*
Using implicit differentiation *p. 333*
Finding a tangent line *p. 334*
Logarithmic differentiation *p. 335*

REVIEW EXERCISES

In Exercises 1–12 find the derivative of the given function.

1. $f(x) = e^x(x^2 - 1)$

2. $f(x) = \frac{x^2 + 1}{x^2 - 1}$

3. $f(x) = (x^2 - 1)^{10}$

4. $f(x) = \frac{1}{(x^2 - 1)^{10}}$

5. $f(x) = e^x(x^2 + 1)^{10}$

6. $f(x) = \left[\frac{x - 1}{3x + 1}\right]^3$

7. $f(x) = \frac{3^x}{x - 1}$

8. $f(x) = 4^{-x}(x + 1)$

9. $f(x) = e^{x^2-1}$

10. $f(x) = (x^2 + 1)e^{x^2-1}$

11. $f(x) = \ln(x^2 - 1)$

12. $f(x) = \frac{\ln(x^2 - 1)}{x^2 - 1}$

In Exercises 13–16 find all values of x (if any) where the tangent line to the graph of the given equation is horizontal.

13. $y = x - e^{2x-1}$

14. $y = e^{x^2}$

15. $y = \frac{x}{x + 1}$

16. $y = \sqrt{x}(x - 1)$

In Exercises 17–22, find dy/dx for the given equation.

17. $x^2 - y^2 = x$

18. $2xy + y^2 = y$

19. $e^{xy} + xy = 1$

20. $\ln\left(\frac{y}{x}\right) = y$

21. $y = \frac{(2x - 1)^4(3x + 4)}{(x + 1)(3x - 1)^3}$

22. $y = x^{x-1}3^x$

In Exercises 23 and 24 find the equation of the tangent line to the graph of the given equation at the specified point.

23. $xy - y^2 = x^2 - 3$; $(-1, 1)$

24. $\ln(xy) + y^2 = 1$; $(-1, -1)$

Applications

25. ***Revenue*** At the moment, OHaganBooks.com is selling 1000 books per week and its sales are rising at a rate of 200 books per week. Also, it is now selling all its books for \$20 each, but its price is dropping at a rate of \$1 per week. At what rate is OHaganBooks.com's revenue rising or falling?

26. ***Revenue*** Refer to Exercise 25. John O'Hagan would like to see the company's revenue increase at a rate of \$5000 per week. At what rate would sales have to have been increasing to accomplish that goal, assuming all the other information is as given in Exercise 25?

27. ***Percentage Rate of Change of Revenue*** The percentage rate of change of a quantity Q is Q'/Q. Why is the percentage rate of change of revenue always equal to the sum of the percentage rates of change of unit price and weekly sales?

28. ***P/E Ratios*** At the beginning of last week, OHaganBooks.com stock was selling for \$100 per share, rising at a rate of \$50 per year. Its earnings amounted to \$1 per share, rising at a rate of \$0.10 per year. At what rate was its price-to-earnings (P/E) ratio, the ratio of its stock price to its earnings per share, rising or falling?

29. ***P/E Ratios*** Refer to Exercise 28. Curt Hinrichs, who recently invested in OHaganBooks.com stock, would have liked to see the P/E ratio increase at a rate of 100 points per year. How fast would the stock have to have been rising, assuming all the other information is as given in Exercise 28?

30. ***Percentage Rate of Change of P/E Ratios*** The percentage rate of change of a quantity Q is Q'/Q. Why is the percentage rate of change of P/E always equal to the percentage rate of change of unit price minus the percentage rate of change of earnings?

31. ***Sales*** OHaganBooks.com modeled its weekly sales over a period of time with the function

$$s(t) = 6053 + \frac{4474}{1 + e^{-0.55(t-4.8)}}$$

as shown in the following graph:

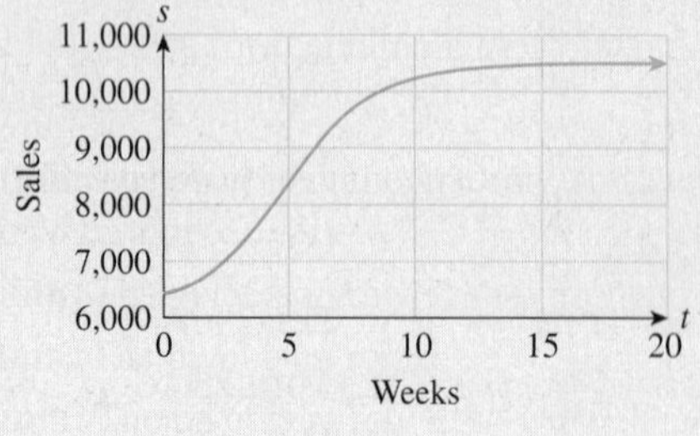

Compute $s'(t)$ and use the answer to compute the rate of increase of weekly sales at the beginning of the 7th week ($t = 6$). (Round your answer to the nearest unit.)

32. ***Sales*** refer to Exercise 31. Find the rate of increase of weekly sales at the beginning of the 15th week ($t = 14$).

33. ***Website Activity*** The number of "hits" on OHaganBooks .com's website was 1000 per day at the beginning of the year, growing at a rate of 5% per week. If this growth rate continued for the whole year (52 weeks), find the rate of increase (in hits per day per week) at the end of the year.

34. ***Demand and Revenue*** The price p that OHaganBooks.com charges for its latest leather-bound gift edition of *The Lord of the Rings* is related to the demand q in weekly sales by the equation

$$100pq + q^2 = 5{,}000{,}000$$

Suppose the price is set at \$40, which would make the demand 1000 copies per week.

a. Using implicit differentiation, compute the rate of change of demand with respect to price, and interpret the result. (Round the answer to two decimal places.)

b. Use the result of part (a) to compute the rate of change of revenue with respect to price. Should the price be raised or lowered to increase revenue?

CASE STUDY: Projecting Market Growth

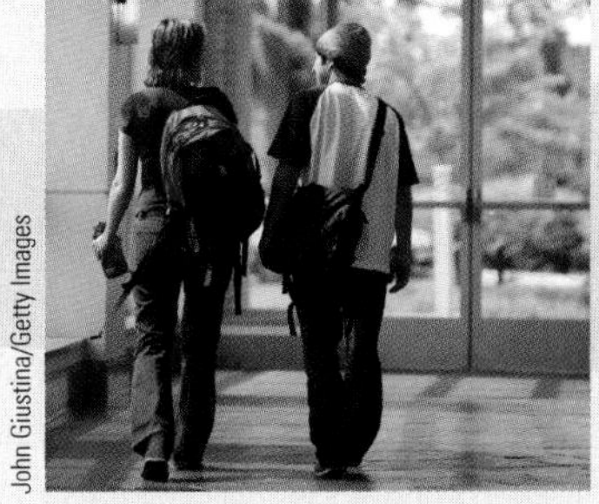

You are on the board of directors at Fullcourt Academic Press, and TJM, the sales director of the high school division, has just burst into your office with data showing the number of high school graduates each year over the past decade (Figure 7).[41]

TJM is pleased that the figures appear to support a basic premise of his recent proposal for a major expansion strategy: The number of high school seniors in the U.S. will be growing at a rate of at least 20,000 per year through the year 2005. The rate of increase, as he points out, has averaged around 50,000 per year since 1994, so it would not be overly optimistic to assume that the trend will continue—at least for the next 5 years.

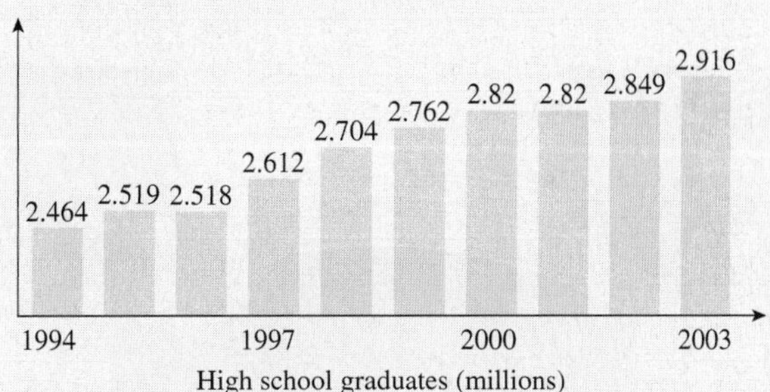

Figure **7**

Although you are tempted to support TJM's proposal at the next board meeting, you would like to estimate first whether the 20,000 figure is a realistic expectation, especially because the graph suggests that the number of graduates began to "level off" (in the language of calculus, the *derivative appears to be decreasing*) during the second half of the period. Moreover, you recall reading somewhere that the numbers of students in the lower grades have also begun to level off, so it is safe to predict that the slowing of growth in the senior class will continue over the next few years. You really need precise data about numbers in the lower grades in order to make a meaningful prediction, but TJM's report is scheduled to be presented tomorrow and you would like a quick and easy way of "extending the curve to the right" by then.

It would certainly be helpful if you had a mathematical model of the data in Figure 7 that you could use to project the current trend. But what kind of model should you use? A linear model would be no good because it would not show any change in the derivative (the derivative of a linear function is constant). In addition, best-fit polynomial and exponential functions do not accurately reflect the leveling off, as you realize after trying to fit a few of them (Figure 8).

You then recall that a logistic curve can model the leveling-off property you desire, and so you try fitting a curve of the form

$$y = \frac{N}{1 + Ab^{-t}}$$

[41] Data starting in 2000 are projections. SOURCE: U.S. Department of Education http://nces.ed.gov/pubs2001/proj01/tables/table23.asp.

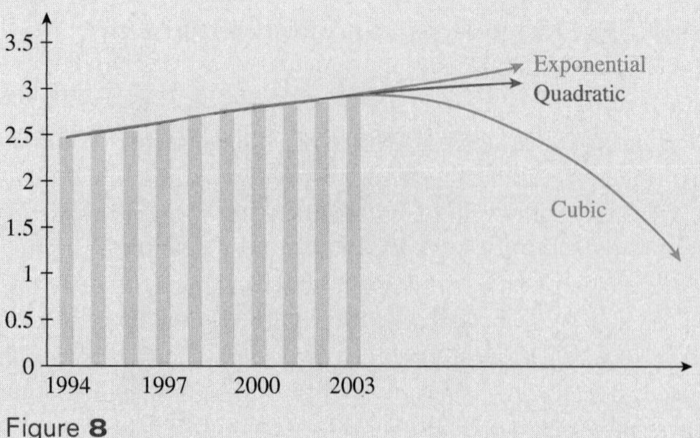

Figure 8

Figure 9 shows the best-fit logistic curve, which eventually levels off at around $N = 3.3$.

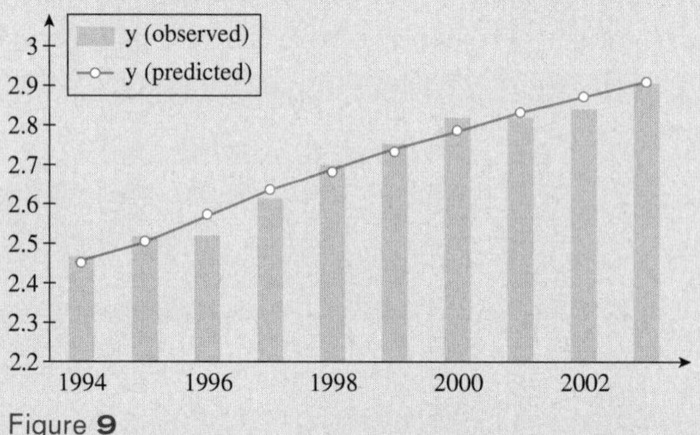

Figure 9

The leveling-off prediction certainly seems reasonable, but you are slightly troubled by the shape of the regression curve: It doesn't seem to "follow the s-shape" of the data very convincingly. Moreover, the curve doesn't appear to fit the data significantly more snugly than the quadratic or cubic models.[42] To reassure yourself, you decide to look for another kind of s-shaped model as a backup.

After flipping through a calculus book, you stumble across a function whose graph looks rather like the one you have (Figure 10).

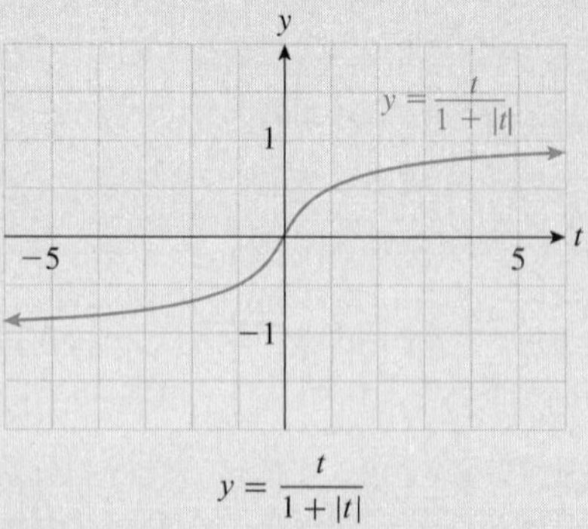

$$y = \frac{t}{1 + |t|}$$

Figure 10

[42] There is another, more mathematical, reason for not using logistic regression to predict long-term leveling off: The regression value of the long-term level N is extremely sensitive to the values of the other coefficients. As a result, there can be good fits to the same set of data with a wide variety of values of N.

Online, follow:
Chapter 1
→ New Functions from Old: Scaled and Shifted Functions
to find a detailed treatment of scaled and shifted functions.

Curves of this form are sometimes called predator satiation curves, and they are used to model the population of predators in an environment with limited prey. Although the curve does seem to have the proper shape, you realize that you will need to shift and scale the function in order to fit the actual data. The most general scaled and shifted version of this curve has the form

$$y = c + b\frac{a(t-m)}{1+a|t-m|} \qquad (a,\ b,\ c,\ m \text{ constant})$$

and you decide to try a model of this form, where y will represent the number of high school seniors (in millions), and t will represent years since 1994.

For the moment, you postpone the question of finding the best values for the constants a, b, c, and m, and decide first to calculate the derivative of the model in terms of the given constants. The derivative, dy/dt, will represent the rate of increase of high school graduates, which is exactly what you wish to estimate.

The main part of the function is a quotient, so you start with the quotient rule:

$$\frac{dy}{dt} = b\frac{a(1+a|t-m|) - a(t-m)\frac{d}{dt}(1+a|t-m|)}{(1+a|t-m|)^2}$$

You now recall the formula for the derivative of an absolute value:

$$\frac{d}{dt}[|t|] = \frac{|t|}{t} = \begin{cases} 1 & \text{if } t > 0 \\ -1 & \text{if } t \le 0 \end{cases}$$

which, you are disturbed to notice, is not defined at $t = 0$. Undaunted, you make a mental note and press on. Because you need the derivative of the absolute value of a quantity other than t, you use the chain rule, which tells you that

$$\frac{d}{dt}[|u|] = \frac{|u|}{u}\frac{du}{dt}$$

Thus,

$$\frac{d}{dt}[|t-m|] = \frac{|t-m|}{t-m} \cdot 1 \qquad u = t - m; \quad m = \text{constant}$$

(This is not defined when $t = m$.) Substituting into the formula for dy/dt, you find:

$$\begin{aligned} \frac{dy}{dt} &= b\frac{a(1+a|t-m|) - a(t-m)\cdot a\frac{|t-m|}{(t-m)}}{(1+a|t-m|)^2} \\ &= b\frac{a(1+a|t-m|) - a^2|t-m|}{(1+a|t-m|)^2} && \text{Cancel } (t-m) \\ &= \frac{ab}{(1+a|t-m|)^2} && a^2|t-m| - a^2|t-m| = 0 \end{aligned}$$

It is interesting that, although the derivative of $|t - m|$ is not defined when $t = m$, the offending term $t - m$ was canceled, so that dy/dt seems to be defined[43] at $t = m$.

Now you have a simple-looking expression for dy/dt, which will give you an estimate of the rate of change of the high school senior population. However, you still need

[43] In fact, it is defined and has the value given by the formula just derived: ab. To show this takes a bit more work. How might you do it?

values for the constants a, b, c, and m. (You don't really need the value of c to compute the derivative—where has it gone?—but it is a part of the model.) How do you find the values of a, b, c, and m that result in the curve that best fits the given data?

Turning once again to your calculus book (see the discussion of logistic regression in Section 2.4), you see that a best-fit curve is one that minimizes the sum-of-squares error. Here is an Excel spreadsheet showing the errors for $a = 1$, $b = 1$, $c = 1$, and $m = 1$.

Microsoft Excel - CS 4 High School Graduates in 1994.xls

File Edit View Insert Format Tools Data Window Help Adobe PDF

	A	B	C	D	E	F	G
1	t (year)	y (Observed)	y (Predicted)	Residue^2	Constants		
2	0	2.464	0.5	3.857296	a	1	
3	1	2.519	1	2.307361	b	1	
4	2	2.518	1.5	1.036324	c	1	
5	3	2.612	1.666666667	0.89365511	m	1	
6	4	2.704	1.75	0.910116			
7	5	2.762	1.8	0.925444	SSE:	13.8344343	
8	6	2.82	1.833333333	0.97351111			
9	7	2.82	1.857142857	0.92709388			
10	8	2.849	1.875	0.948676			
11	9	2.916	1.888888889	1.05495723			
12							
13							

The first two columns show the observed data (t = year since 1994, y = number of high school graduates in millions). The formula for y (Predicted) is our model

$$y = c + b\frac{a(t-m)}{1 + a|t-m|}$$

entered in cell C2 as

```
=$F$4 + $F$3*$F$2*(A2 - $F$5) / (1 + $F$2*ABS(A2 - $F$5))
  c   +  b  *  a  * (t − m)     / (1 +    a *   |t − m|)
```

and then copied into the cells below it. Since the square error (Residue^2) is defined as the square of the difference between y and y (Predicted), we enter

```
=(C2-B2)^2
```

in cell D2 and then copy into the cells below it. The sum-of-squares error, SSE (sum of the entries in D2–D11), is then placed in cell F7.

The values of a, b, c, and m shown are initial values and don't matter too much (but see below); you will have Excel change these values in order to improve your model. The smaller the SSE is, the better your model. (For a perfect fit, the `y (Observed)` column would equal the `y (Observed)` column, and SSE would be zero.) Hence, the goal is now to find values of a, b, c, and m that make the value of SSE as small as possible. (See the discussion in Section 1.4.) Finding these values analytically is an extremely difficult mathematical problem. However, there is software, such as Excel's built-in "Solver" routine,[44] that can be used to find *numerical* solutions.

Figure 11 shows how to set up Solver to find the best values for a, b, c, and m for the setup used in this spreadsheet.

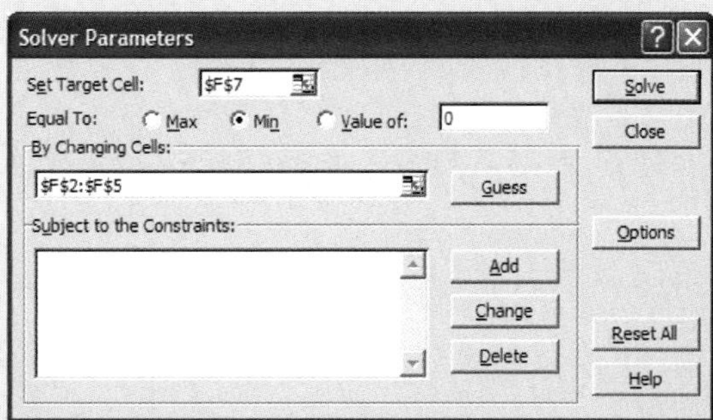

Figure 11

The Target Cell, $F$7, contains the value of SSE, which is to be minimized. The Changing Cells are the cells containing the values of the constants a, b, c, and m that we want to change. That's it.

Now press "Solve." After thinking about it for a few seconds, Excel gives the optimal values of a, b, c, and m in cells F2–F5, and the minimum value of SSE in cell D12.[45] You find

$$a = 0.24250175, \quad b = 0.4102711, \quad c = 2.65447873, \quad m = 3.5211956$$

with SSE ≈ 0.00288, which is a better fit than the logistic regression curve (SSE ≈ 0.00653)

Figure 12 shows that not only does this choice of model and constants give an excellent fit, but that the curve seems to follow the "s-shape" more convincingly than the logistic curve.

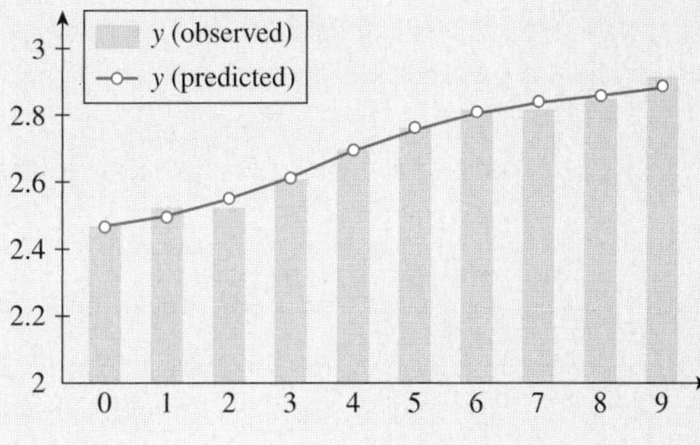

Figure 12

[44] See the similar discussion in Section 2.4. If "Solver" does not appear in the "Tools" menu, you should first install it using your Excel installation software. (Solver is one of the "Excel Add-Ins.")

[45] Depending on the settings in Solver, you may need to run the utility twice in succession to reach the minimum value of SSE.

Figure 13 shows how the model predicts the long-term leveling-off phenomenon you were looking for.

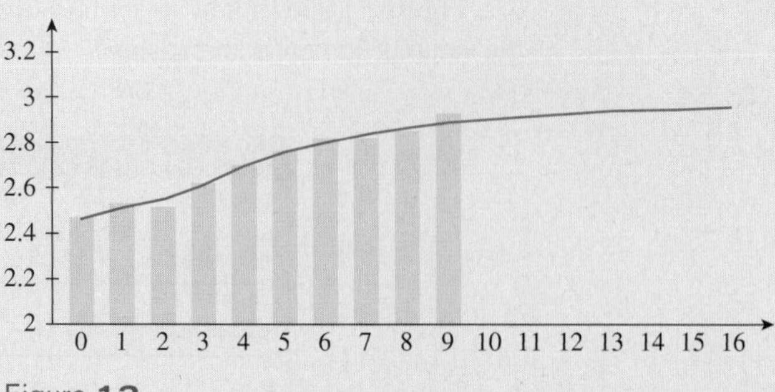

Figure **13**

You turn back to the problem at hand: projecting the rate of increase of the number of high school graduates in 2005. You have the formula

$$\frac{dy}{dt} = \frac{ab}{(1 + a|t - m|)^2}$$

and also values for the constants. So you compute:

$$\frac{dy}{dt} = \frac{(0.24250175)(0.4102711)}{(1 + 0.24250175[11 - 3.5211956])^2} \qquad t = 11 \text{ in } 2005$$

$$\approx 0.0126 \text{ million students per year}$$

or 12,600 students per year—far less than the optimistic estimate of 20,000 in the proposal!

You now conclude that TJM's prediction is suspect and that further research will have to be done before the board can support the proposal.

Q: *How accurately does the model predict the number of high school graduates?*

A: Using a regression curve-fitting model to make long-term predictions is always risky. A more accurate model would have to take into account such factors as the birth rate and current school populations at all levels. The U.S. Department of Education has used more sophisticated models to make the projections shown below, which we compare with those predicted by our model.

Year	*U.S. Dept. of Ed. Projections (Millions)*	*Model Predictions (Millions)*
2004	2.921	2.91
2005	2.929	2.92
2006	2.986	2.93
2007	3.054	2.94
2008	3.132	2.95
2009	3.127	2.96
2010	3.103	2.96
2011	3.063	2.97

■

Q: *Which values of the constants should I use as starting values when using Excel to find the best-fit curve?*

A: If the starting values of the constants are far from the optimal values, Solver may find a nonoptimal solution. Thus, you need to obtain some rough initial estimate of the constants by examining the graph. Figure 14 shows some important features of the curve that you can use to obtain estimates of *a*, *b*, *c*, and *m* by inspecting the graph.

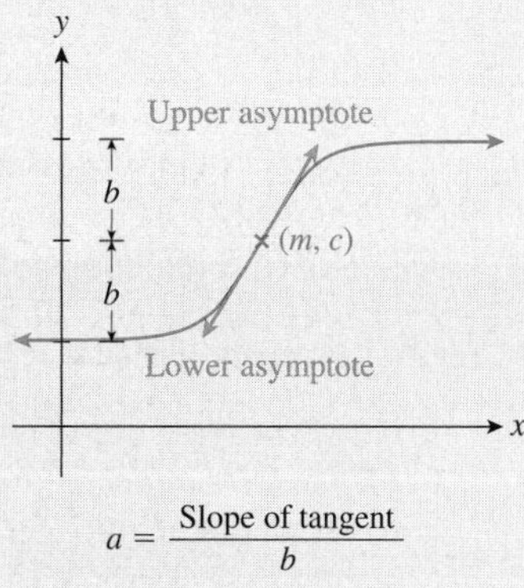

Figure **14**

From the graph, *m* and *c* are the coordinates of the point on the curve where it is steepest, and *b* is the vertical distance from that point to the upper or lower asymptote (where the curve "levels off"). To estimate *a*, first estimate the slope of the tangent at the point of steepest inclination, then divide by *b*. If *b* is negative (and *a* is positive), we obtain an "upside-down" version of the curve (Figure 15).

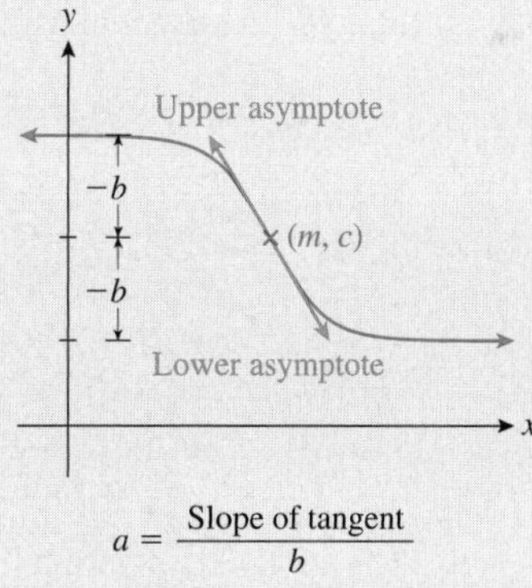

Figure **15**

■

Exercises

1. In 1993 there were 2.49 million high school graduates. What does the regression model "predict" for 1993? What is the residue ($y_{\text{predicted}} - y_{\text{observed}}$)? (Round answers to the nearest 0.01 million.)

2. What is the long-term prediction of the model?

3. Find $\lim_{t\to\infty} \dfrac{dy}{dt}$ and interpret the result.

4. tech Ex You receive a memo to the effect that the 1994 and 1995 figures are not accurate. Use Excel Solver to re-estimate the best-fit constants a, b, c, and m in the absence of this data and obtain new estimates for the 1994 and 1995 data. What does the new model predict the rate of change in the number of high school seniors will be in 2005?

5. tech Ex ***Shifted Logistic Model*** Using the original data, find the best-fit shifted logistic curve of the form

$$f(t) = c + \frac{N}{1 + Ab^{-t}}$$

(Start with the following values: $c = 0$, $N = 3$, and $A = b = 1$. You might have to run Solver twice in succession to minimize SSE.) Graph the data together with the model. What is SSE? Is the model as accurate a fit as the model used in the text? How do the long-term predictions of the two models compare with the U.S. Department of Education projections? What does this model predict will be the growth rate of the number of high school graduates in 2005? Round the coefficients in the model and all answers to four decimal places.

6. tech Ex ***Demand for Freon*** The demand for chlorofluorocarbon-12 (CFC-12)—the ozone-depleting refrigerant commonly known as freon[46]—has been declining significantly in response to regulation and concern about the ozone layer. The chart below shows the projected demand for CFC-12 for the period 1994–2005.[47]

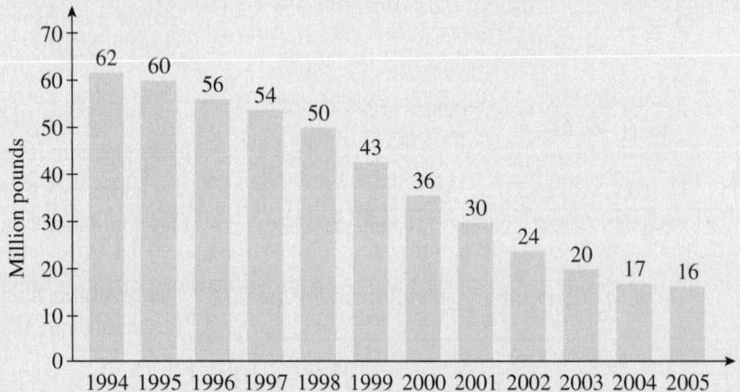

a. Use Excel Solver to obtain the best-fit equation of the form

$$f(t) = c + b\frac{a(t - m)}{1 + a|t - m|}$$

where t = years since 1990. Use your function to estimate the total demand for CFC-12 from the start of the year 2000 to the start of 2010. [Start with the following values: $a = 1$, $b = -25$, $c = 35$, and $m = 10$, and round your answers to four decimal places.]

b. According to your model, how fast is the demand for freon declining in 2000?

[46] The name given to it by Du Pont.

[47] SOURCE: The Automobile Consulting Group (*New York Times,* December 26, 1993, p. F23). The exact figures were not given, and the chart is a reasonable facsimile of the chart that appeared in the *New York Times*.

5 Applications of the Derivative

Get a better Grade!
www.thomsonedu.com/login

Logon to your Personalized Study plan to find:

- Section by section tutorials
- A detailed chapter summary
- Additional review exercises
- Graphers, Excel tutorials, and other resources

CASE STUDY Production Lot Size Management

Your publishing company is planning the production of its latest best seller, which it predicts will sell 100,000 copies each month over the coming year. The book will be printed in several batches of the same number, evenly spaced throughout the year. Each print run has a setup cost of \$5000, a single book costs \$1 to produce, and monthly storage costs for books awaiting shipment average 1¢ per book. To meet the anticipated demand at minimum total cost to your company, how many printing runs should you plan?

Jeff Greenberg/PhotoEdit

Introduction

In this chapter we begin to see the power of calculus as an optimization tool. In Chapter 2 we saw how to price an item in order to get the largest revenue when the demand function is linear. Using calculus, we can handle nonlinear functions, which are much more general. In Section 5.1 we show how calculus can be used to solve the problem of finding the values of a variable that lead to a maximum or minimum value of a given function. In Section 5.2 we show how this helps us in various real-world applications.

Another theme in this chapter is that calculus can help us to draw and understand the graph of a function. By the time you have completed the material in Section 5.1, you will be able to locate and sketch some of the important features of a graph. In Section 5.3 we discuss further how to explain what you see in a graph (drawn, for example, using graphing technology) and to locate its most important points.

We also include sections on related rates and elasticity of demand. The first of these (Section 5.4) examines further the concept of the derivative as a rate of change. The second (Section 5.5) returns to the problem of optimizing revenue based on the demand equation, looking at it in a new way that leads to an important idea in economics—elasticity.

algebra **Review**
For this chapter, you should be familiar with the algebra reviewed in Chapter 0, sections 5 and 6.

5.1 Maxima and Minima

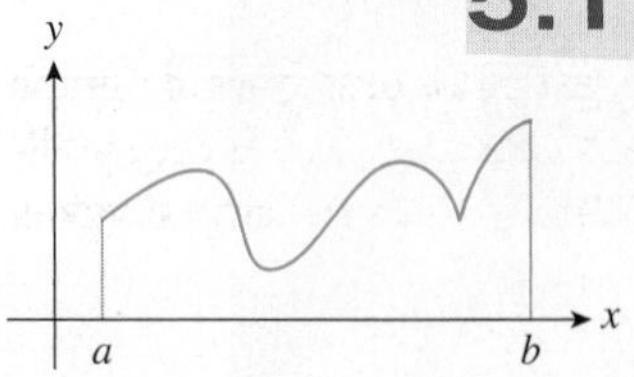

Figure **1**

Figure 1 shows the graph of a function f whose domain is the closed interval $[a, b]$. A mathematician sees lots of interesting things going on here. There are hills and valleys, and even a small chasm (called a *cusp*) toward the right. For many purposes, the important features of this curve are the highs and lows. Suppose, for example, you know that the price of the stock of a certain company will follow this graph during the course of a week. Although you would certainly make a handsome profit if you bought at time a and sold at time b, your best strategy would be to follow the old adage to "buy low and sell high," buying at all the lows and selling at all the highs.

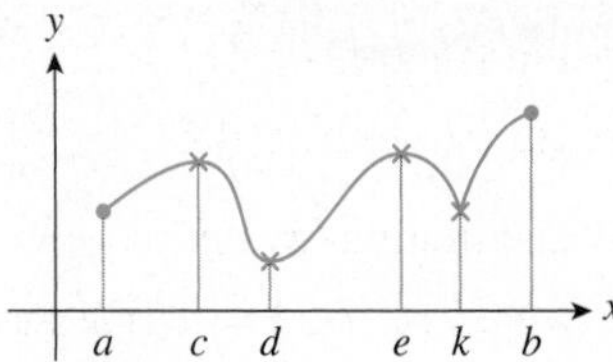

Figure **2**

Figure 2 shows the graph once again with the highs and lows marked. Mathematicians have names for these points: the highs (at the x-values c, e, and b) are referred to as **relative maxima,** and the lows (at the x-values a, d, and k) are referred to as **relative minima.** Collectively, these highs and lows are referred to as **relative extrema.** (A point of language: The singular forms of the plurals *minima, maxima,* and *extrema* are *minimum, maximum,* and *extremum.*)

Why do we refer to these points as relative extrema? Take a look at the point corresponding to $x = c$. It is the highest point of the graph *compared to other points nearby.* If you were an extremely nearsighted mountaineer standing at point c, you would *think* that you were at the highest point of the graph, not being able to see the distant peaks at $x = e$ and $x = b$.

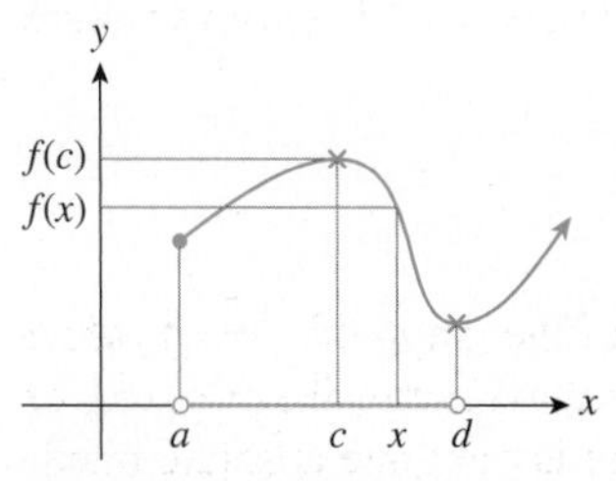

Figure **3**

Let's translate into mathematical terms. We are talking about the heights of various points on the curve. The height of the curve at $x = c$ is $f(c)$, so we are saying that $f(c)$ is greater than $f(x)$ for every x near c. For instance, *$f(c)$ is the greatest value that $f(x)$ has for all choices of x between a and d* (see Figure 3).

We can phrase the formal definition as follows.

Relative Extrema

f has a **relative maximum** at c if there is some interval (r, s) (even a very small one) containing c for which $f(c) \geq f(x)$ for all x between r and s for which $f(x)$ is defined.

f has a **relative minimum** at c if there is some interval (r, s) (even a very small one) containing c for which $f(c) \leq f(x)$ for all x between r and s for which $f(x)$ is defined.

quick Examples

In Figure 2, *f* has the following relative extrema:

1. A relative maximum at c, as shown by the interval (a, d)
2. A relative maximum at e, as shown by the interval (d, k)
3. A relative maximum at b, as shown by the interval $(k, b+1)$

   Note that $f(x)$ is not defined for $x > b$. However, $f(b) \geq f(x)$ for every x in the interval $(k, b+1)$ *for which $f(x)$ is defined*—that is, for every x in $(k, b]$.
4. A relative minimum at d, as shown by the interval (c, e)
5. A relative minimum at k, as shown by the interval (e, b)
6. A relative minimum at a, as shown by the interval $(a-1, c)$ (See Quick Example 3)

Note Our definition of relative extremum allows *f* to have a relative extremum at an endpoint of its domain; the definitions used in some books do not. In view of examples like our stock-market investing strategy, we find it very useful to count endpoints as extrema. ■

Looking carefully at Figure 2, we can see that the lowest point on the whole graph is where $x = d$ and the highest point is where $x = b$. This means that $f(d)$ is the smallest value of *f* on the whole domain of *f* (the interval $[a, b]$) and $f(b)$ is the largest value. We call these the *absolute* minimum and maximum.

Absolute Extrema

f has an **absolute maximum** at c if $f(c) \geq f(x)$ for every x in the domain of *f*.

f has an **absolute minimum** at c if $f(c) \leq f(x)$ for every x in the domain of *f*.

quick Examples

1. In Figure 2, *f* has an absolute maximum at b and an absolute minimum at d.
2. If $f(x) = x^2$ then $f(x) \geq f(0)$ for every real number x. Therefore, $f(x) = x^2$ has an absolute minimum at $x = 0$ (see the figure).
3. Generalizing (2), every quadratic function $f(x) = ax^2 + bx + c$ has an absolute extremum at its vertex $x = -b/(2a)$; it is an absolute minimum if $a > 0$ and an absolute maximum if $a < 0$.

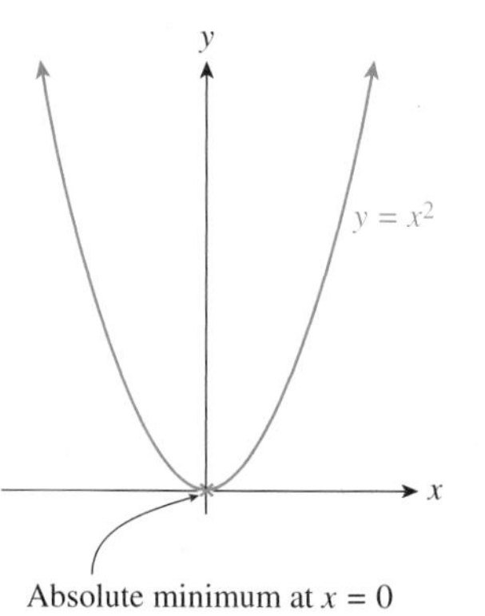

Absolute minimum at $x = 0$

Some graphs have no absolute extrema at all (think of the graph of $y = x$), while others might have an absolute minimum but no absolute maximum (like $y = x^2$), or vice versa. When *f* does have an absolute maximum, there is only one absolute maximum *value* of *f*, but this value may occur at different values of x. (see Figure 4).

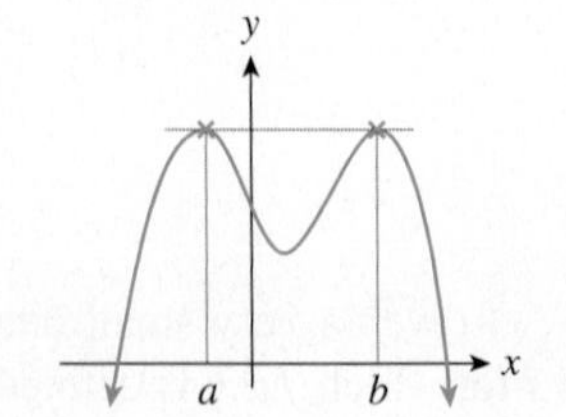

Absolute maxima at $x = a$ and $x = b$

Figure **4**

***Q:** At how many different values of x can f take on its absolute maximum value?*

A: An extreme case is that of a constant function; because we use $\geq$ in the definition of absolute maximum, a constant function has an absolute maximum (and minimum) at every point in its domain. ■

Now, how do we go about locating extrema? In many cases we can get a good idea by using graphing technology to zoom in on a maximum or minimum and approximate its coordinates. However, calculus gives us a way to find the exact locations of the extrema and at the same time to understand why the graph of a function behaves the way it does. In fact, it is often best to combine the powers of graphing technology with those of calculus, as we shall see.

In Figure 5 we see the graph from Figure 1 once more, but we have labeled each extreme point as one of three types.

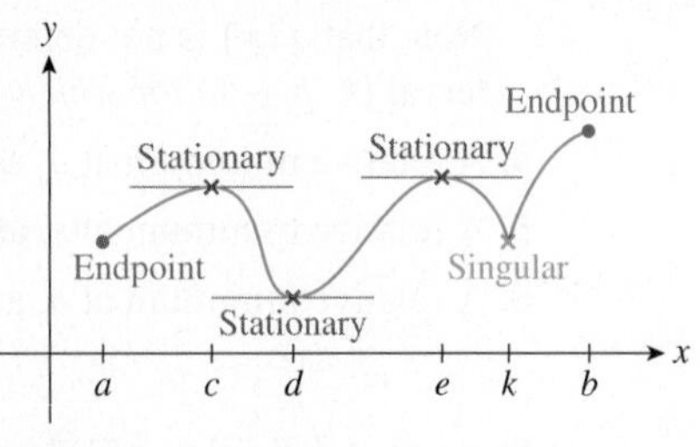

Figure **5**

At the points labeled "stationary," the tangent lines to the graph are horizontal, and so have slope 0, so f' (which gives the slope) is 0. Any time $f'(x) = 0$, we say that f has a **stationary point** at x because the rate of change of f is zero there. We call an *extremum* that occurs at a stationary point a **stationary extremum.** In general, to find the exact location of each stationary point, we need to solve the equation $f'(x) = 0$.

There is a relative minimum in Figure 5 at $x = k$, but there is no horizontal tangent there. In fact, there is no tangent line at all; $f'(k)$ is not defined. (Recall a similar situation with the graph of $f(x) = |x|$ at $x = 0$.) When $f'(x)$ does not exist, we say that f has a **singular point** at x. We shall call an extremum that occurs at a singular point a **singular extremum.** The points that are either stationary or singular we call collectively the **critical points** of f.

The remaining two extrema are at the **endpoints** of the domain.[1] As we see in the figure, they are (almost) always either relative maxima or relative minima.

***Q:** Are there any other types of relative extrema?*

A: No; relative extrema of a function always occur at critical points or endpoints (a rigorous proof is beyond the scope of this book).[2] ■

[1] Remember that we do allow relative extrema at endpoints.

[2] Here is an outline of the argument. Suppose f has a relative maximum, say, at $x = a$, at a point other than an endpoint of the domain. Then either f is differentiable there, or it is not. If it is not, then we have a singular point. If f is differentiable at $x = a$, then consider the slope of the secant line through the points where $x = a$ and $x = a + h$ for small positive h. Since f has a relative maximum at $x = a$, it is falling (or level) to the right of $x = a$, and so the slope of this secant line must be ≤ 0. Thus we must have $f'(a) \leq 0$ in the limit as $h \to 0$. On the other hand, if h is small and *negative,* then the corresponding secant line must have slope ≥ 0 because f is also falling (or level) as we move left from $x = a$, and so $f'(a) \geq 0$. Since $f'(a)$ is both ≥ 0 and ≤ 0, it must be zero, and so we have a stationary point at $x = a$.

Locating Candidates for Relative Extrema

If f is a real valued function, then its relative extrema occur among the following types of points:

1. **Stationary Points:** f has a stationary point at x if x is in the domain and $f'(x) = 0$. To locate stationary points, set $f'(x) = 0$ and solve for x.
2. **Singular Points:** f has a singular point at x if x is in the domain and $f'(x)$ is not defined. To locate singular points, find values of x where $f'(x)$ is *not* defined, but $f(x)$ *is* defined.
3. **Endpoints:** The x-coordinates of endpoints are endpoints of the domain, if any. Recall that closed intervals contain endpoints, but open intervals do not.

Once we have the x-coordinates of a candidate for a relative extremum, we find the corresponding y-coordinate using $y = f(x)$.

quick Examples

1. **Stationary Points:** Let $f(x) = x^3 - 12x$. Then to locate the stationary points, set $f'(x) = 0$ and solve for x. This gives $3x^2 - 12 = 0$, so f has stationary points at $x = \pm 2$. Thus, the stationary points are $(-2, f(-2)) = (-2, 16)$ and $(2, f(2)) = (2, -16)$.
2. **Singular points:** Let $f(x) = 3(x-1)^{1/3}$. Then $f'(x) = (x-1)^{-2/3} = 1/(x-1)^{2/3}$. $f'(1)$ is not defined, although $f(1)$ *is* defined. Thus, the (only) singular point occurs at $x = 1$. Its coordinates are $(1, f(1)) = (1, 0)$.
3. **Endpoints:** Let $f(x) = 1/x$, with domain $(-\infty, 0) \cup [1, +\infty)$. Then the only endpoint in the domain of f occurs when $x = 1$ and has coordinates $(1, 1)$. The natural domain of $1/x$ has no endpoints.

Remember, though, that these are only *candidates* for relative extrema. It is quite possible, as we shall see, to have a stationary point (or singular point) that is neither a relative maximum nor a relative minimum.

Now let's look at some examples of finding maxima and minima. In all of these examples, we will use the following procedure: First, we find the derivative, which we examine to find the stationary points and singular points. Next, we make a table listing the x-coordinates of the critical points and endpoints, together with their y-coordinates. We use this table to make a rough sketch of the graph. From the table and rough sketch, we usually have enough data to be able to say where the extreme points are and what kind they are.

Example 1 Maxima and Minima

Find the relative and absolute maxima and minima of

$$f(x) = x^2 - 2x$$

on the interval $[0, 4]$.

Solution We first calculate $f'(x) = 2x - 2$. We use this derivative to locate the stationary and singular points.

Stationary Points To locate the stationary points, we solve the equation $f'(x) = 0$, or

$$2x - 2 = 0,$$

getting $x = 1$. The domain of the function is $[0, 4]$, so $x = 1$ is in the domain. Thus, the only candidate for a stationary relative extremum occurs when $x = 1$.

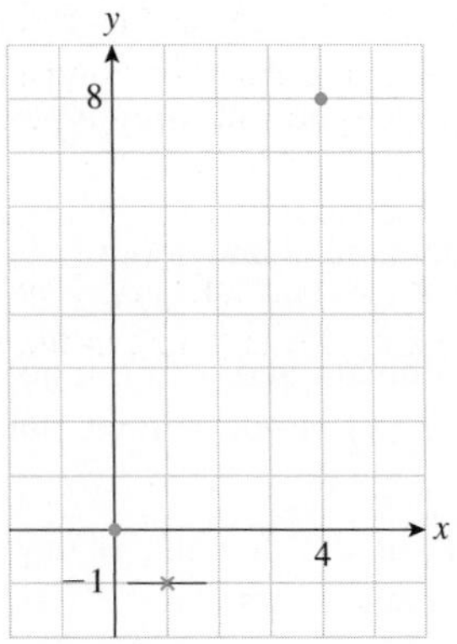

Figure 6

Singular Points We look for points where the derivative is not defined. However, the derivative is $2x - 2$, which is defined for every x. Thus, there are no singular points and hence no candidates for singular relative extrema.

Endpoints The domain is $[0, 4]$, so the endpoints occur when $x = 0$ and $x = 4$.

We record these values of x in a table, together with the corresponding y-coordinates (values of f):

x	0	1	4
$f(x) = x^2 - 2x$	0	−1	8

This gives us three points on the graph, (0, 0), (1, −1), and (4, 8), which we plot in Figure 6.

We remind ourselves that the point (1, −1) is a stationary point of the graph by drawing in a part of the horizontal tangent line. Connecting these points must give us a graph something like that in Figure 7.

Notice that the graph has a horizontal tangent line at $x = 1$ but not at either of the endpoints because the endpoints are not stationary points.

From Figure 7 we can see that f has the following extrema:

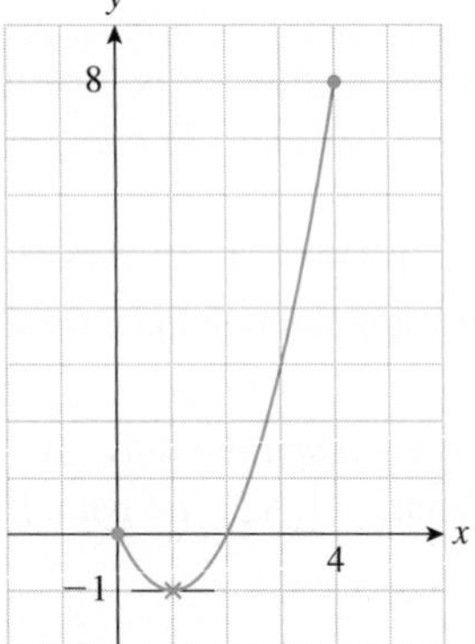

Figure 7

x	$y = x^2 - 2x$	*Classification*
0	0	Relative maximum (endpoint)
1	−1	Absolute minimum (stationary point)
4	8	Absolute maximum (endpoint)

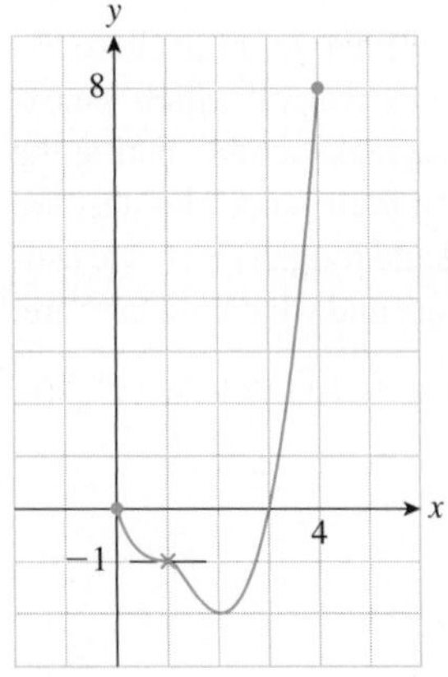

Figure 8

Q: *How can we be sure that the graph in Example 1 doesn't look like Figure 8?*

A: If it did, there would be another critical point somewhere between $x = 1$ and $x = 4$. But we already know that there aren't any other critical points. The table we made listed all of the possible extrema; there can be no more. ■

In Example 1 we found that $f'(1) = 0$; f has a stationary point at $x = 1$. It is also useful to consider values of $f'(x)$ to the left and right of the critical point. Here is a table with some values to the left and right of the critical point $x = 1$ in the above example:

		Critical Point	
x	0	1	2
$f'(x) = 2x - 2$	−2	0	2
Direction of Graph	↘	→	↗

At $x = 0$, $f'(0) = -2 < 0$, so the graph has negative slope and f is **decreasing;** its values are going down as x increases. We note this with the downward pointing arrow in the chart. At $x = 2$, $f'(2) = 2 > 0$, so the graph has positive slope and f is **increasing;** its values are going up as x increases. In fact, because $f'(x) = 0$ only at $x = 1$, we know that $f'(x) < 0$ for all x in $[0, 1)$, and we can say that f is decreasing on the interval $[0, 1]$.

Similarly, f is increasing on $[1, 4]$. So, starting at $x = 0$, the graph of f goes down until we reach $x = 1$ and then it goes back up. Notice that the arrows suggest exactly this type of graph. This is another way of checking that a critical point is a relative minimum and is known as the **first derivative test.**[3]

Note Here is some terminology: If the point (a, b) is a maximum (or minimum) of f, we sometimes say that ***f* has a maximum (or minimum) value of *b* at *x* = *a*.** Thus, in the above example, we could have said the following:

- f has a relative maximum value of 0 at $x = 0$.
- f has an absolute minimum value of -1 at $x = 1$.
- f has an absolute maximum value of 8 at $x = 4$. ■

Example 2 Unbounded Interval

Find all extrema of $f(x) = 3x^4 - 4x^3$ on $[-1, \infty)$.

Solution We first calculate $f'(x) = 12x^3 - 12x^2$.

Stationary points We solve the equation $f'(x) = 0$, which is

$$12x^3 - 12x^2 = 0 \quad \text{or}$$
$$12x^2(x - 1) = 0$$

There are two solutions, $x = 0$ and $x = 1$, and both are in the domain. These are our candidates for the x-coordinates of stationary relative extrema.

Singular points There are no points where $f'(x)$ is not defined, so there are no singular points.

Endpoints The domain is $[-1, \infty)$, so there is one endpoint, at $x = -1$.

We record these points in a table with the corresponding y-coordinates:

x	-1	0	1
$f(x) = 3x^4 - 4x^3$	7	0	-1

We will illustrate three methods we can use to determine which are minima, which are maxima, and which are neither:

1. Plot these points and sketch the graph by hand.

2. Use the First Derivative Test.

3. Use technology to help us.

Use the method you find most convenient.

Using a Hand Plot: If we plot these points by hand, we obtain Figure 9(a), which suggests Figure 9(b).

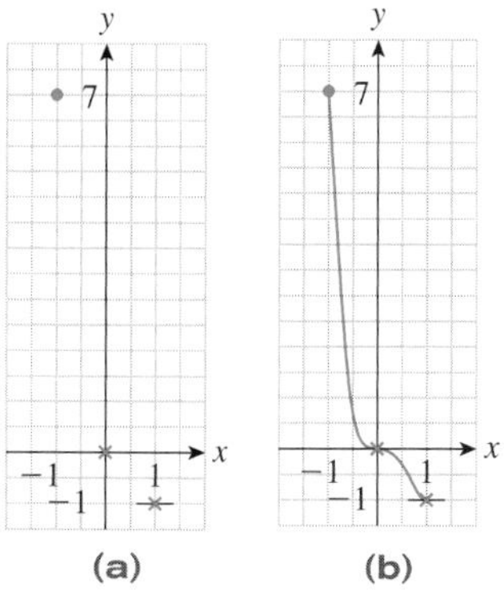

(a) (b)

Figure 9

[3] Why "first" derivative test? To distinguish it from a test based on the **second derivative** of a function, which we shall discuss in Section 5.3.

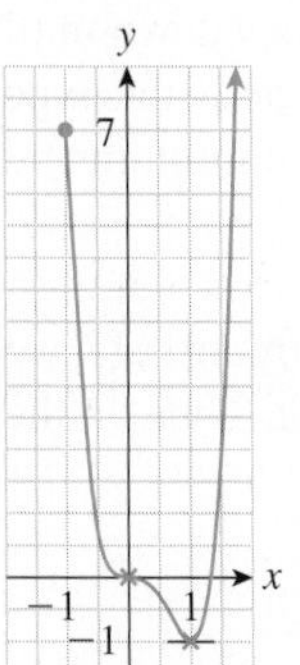

Figure 10

We can't be sure what happens to the right of $x = 1$. Does the curve go up, or does it go down? To find out, let's plot a "test point" to the right of $x = 1$. Choosing $x = 2$, we obtain $y = 3(2)^4 - 4(2)^3 = 16$, so (2, 16) is another point on the graph. Thus, it must turn upwards to the right of $x = 1$, as shown in Figure 10.

From the graph, we find that f has the following extrema:

A relative (endpoint) maximum at (−1, 7)

An absolute (stationary) minimum at (1, −1)

Using the First Derivative Test: List the critical and endpoints in a table, and add additional points as necessary so that each critical point has a noncritical point on either side. Then compute the derivative at each of these points, and draw an arrow to indicate the direction of the graph.

	Endpoint	Critical point		Critical point	
x	−1	0	0.5	1	2
$f'(x) = 12x^3 - 12x^2$	−24	0	−1.5	0	48
Direction of Graph	↘	→	↘	→	↗

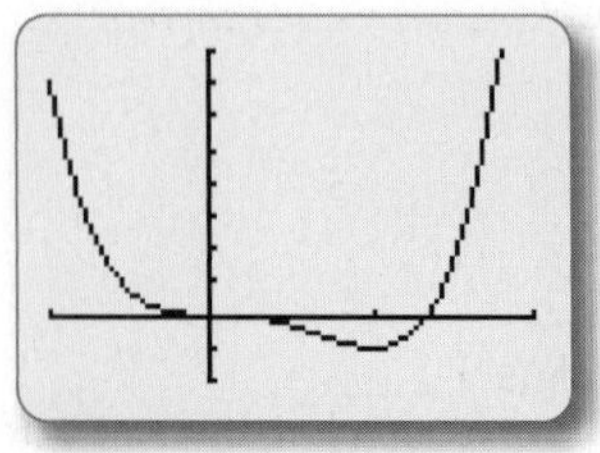

Figure 11

Notice that the arrows now suggest the shape of the curve in Figure 10, and hence permit us to determine that the function has a maximum at $x = -1$, neither a maximum nor a minimum at $x = 0$, and a minimum at $x = 1$. Deciding which of these extrema are absolute and which are relative requires us to compute y-coordinates and plot the corresponding points on the graph by hand, as we did in the first method.

using *Technology*

If we use technology to show the graph, we should choose the viewing window so that it contains the three interesting points we found: $x = -1$, $x = 0$, and $x = 1$. Again, we can't be sure yet what happens to the right of $x = 1$; does the graph go up or down from that point? If we set the viewing window to an interval of [−1, 2] for x and [−2, 8] for y, we will leave enough room to the right of $x = 1$ and below $y = -1$ to see what the graph will do. The result will be something like Figure 11.

Now we can tell what happens to the right of $x = 1$: the function increases. We know that it cannot later decrease again because if it did, there would have to be another critical point where it turns around, and we found that there are no other critical points. ■

+*Before we go on...* Notice that the stationary point at $x = 0$ in Example 2 is neither a relative maximum nor a relative minimum. It is simply a place where the graph of f flattens out for a moment before it continues to fall. Notice also that f has no absolute maximum because $f(x)$ increases without bound as x gets large. ■

Example 3 Singular Point

Find all extrema of $f(t) = t^{2/3}$ on [−1, 1].

Solution First, $f'(t) = \frac{2}{3}t^{-1/3}$

Stationary points We need to solve

$$\frac{2}{3}t^{-1/3} = 0$$

We can rewrite this equation without the negative exponent:

$$\frac{2}{3t^{1/3}} = 0$$

Now, the only way that a fraction can equal 0 is if the numerator is 0, so this fraction can never equal 0. Thus, there are no stationary points.

Singular points The derivative

$$f'(t) = \frac{2}{3t^{1/3}}$$

is not defined for $t = 0$. However, f itself *is* defined at $t = 0$, so 0 is in the domain. Thus, f has a singular point at $t = 0$.

Endpoints There are two endpoints, –1 and 1.

We now put these three points in a table with the corresponding y-coordinates:

t	-1	0	1
$f(t)$	1	0	1

Using a Hand Plot: The derivative, $f'(t) = 2/(3t^{1/3})$, is not defined at the singular point $t = 0$. To help us sketch the graph, let's use limits to investigate what happens to the derivative as we approach 0 from either side:

$$\lim_{t\to 0^-} f'(t) = \lim_{t\to 0^-} \frac{2}{3t^{1/3}} = -\infty$$

$$\lim_{t\to 0^+} f'(t) = \lim_{t\to 0^+} \frac{2}{3t^{1/3}} = +\infty$$

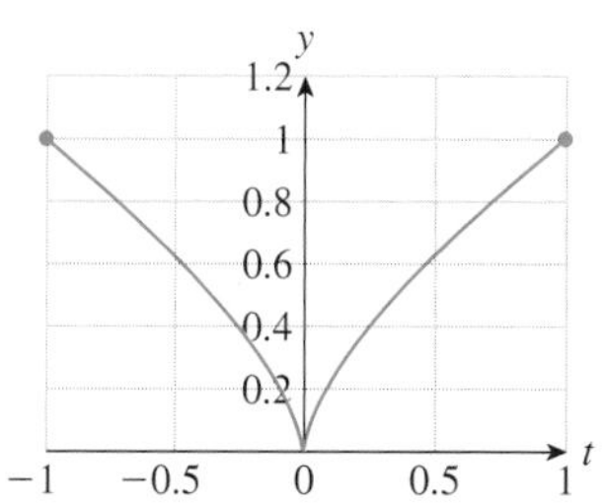

Figure **12**

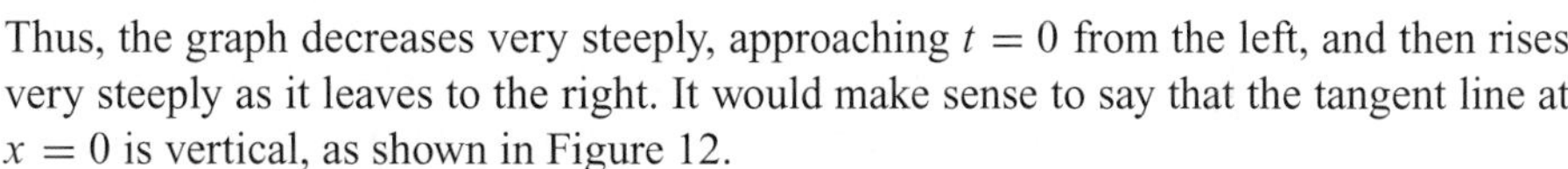

Thus, the graph decreases very steeply, approaching $t = 0$ from the left, and then rises very steeply as it leaves to the right. It would make sense to say that the tangent line at $x = 0$ is vertical, as shown in Figure 12.

From this graph, we find the following extrema for f:

An absolute (endpoint) maximum at (–1, 1)

An absolute (singular) minimum at (0, 0)

An absolute (endpoint) maximum at (1, 1)

Notice that the absolute maximum value of f is achieved at two values of t: $t = -1$ and $t = 1$.

First Derivative Test: Here is the corresponding table for the first derivative test.

t	-1	0	1
$f'(t) = \frac{2}{3t^{1/3}}$	$-\frac{2}{3}$	Undefined	$\frac{2}{3}$
Direction of graph	↘	↕	↗

We drew a vertical arrow at $t = 0$ to indicate a vertical tangent. Again, notice how the arrows suggest the shape of the curve in Figure 12.

Because there is only one critical point, at $t = 0$, it is clear from this table that f must decrease from $t = -1$ to $t = 0$ and then increase from $t = 0$ to $t = 1$. To graph f using technology, choose a viewing window with an interval of [–1, 1] for t and [0, 1] for y. The result will be something like Figure 12.*

* Many graphing calculators will give you only the right-hand half of the graph shown in Figure 12 because fractional powers of negative numbers are not, in general, real numbers. To obtain the whole curve, enter the formula as `Y=(x^2)^(1/3)`, a fractional power of the nonnegative function x^2.

In Examples 1 and 3, we could have found the absolute maxima and minima without doing any graphing. In Example 1, after finding the critical points and endpoints, we created the following table:

x	0	1	4
$f(x)$	0	-1	8

From this table we can see that f must decrease from its value of 0 at $x = 0$ to -1 at $x = 1$, and then increase to 8 at $x = 4$. The value of 8 must be the largest value it takes on, and the value of –1 must be the smallest, on the interval [0, 4]. Similarly, in Example 3 we created the following table:

t	-1	0	1
$f(t)$	1	0	1

From this table we can see that the largest value of f on the interval [–1, 1] is 1 and the smallest value is 0. We are taking advantage of the following fact, the proof of which uses some deep and beautiful mathematics (alas, beyond the scope of this book):

Absolute Extrema on a Closed Interval

If f is *continuous* on a closed interval $[a, b]$, then it will have an absolute maximum and an absolute minimum value on that interval. Each absolute extremum must occur either at an endpoint or a critical point. Therefore, the absolute maximum is the largest value in a table of the values of f at the endpoints and critical points, and the absolute minimum is the smallest value.

quick Example

The function $f(x) = 3x - x^3$ on the interval [0, 2], has one critical point, at $x = 1$. The values of f at the critical point and the endpoints of the interval are given in the following table:

	Endpoint	**Critical point**	**Endpoint**
x	0	1	2
$f(x)$	0	2	-2

From this table we can say that the absolute maximum value of f on [0, 2] is 2, which occurs at $x = 1$, and the absolute minimum value of f is –2, which occurs at $x = 2$.

As we can see in Example 2 and the following examples, if the domain is not a closed interval then f may not have an absolute maximum and minimum, and a table of values as above is of little help in determining whether it does.

Example 4 Domain Not a Closed Interval

Find all extrema of $f(x) = x + \dfrac{1}{x}$.

Solution Because no domain is specified, we take the domain to be as large as possible. The function is not defined at $x = 0$ but is at all other points, so we take its domain to be $(-\infty, 0) \cup (0, +\infty)$. We calculate

$$f'(x) = 1 - \frac{1}{x^2}$$

Stationary Points Setting $f'(x) = 0$, we solve

$$1 - \frac{1}{x^2} = 0$$

to find $x = \pm 1$. Calculating the corresponding values of f, we get the two stationary points $(1, 2)$ and $(-1, -2)$.

Singular Points The only value of x for which $f'(x)$ is not defined is $x = 0$, but then f is not defined there either, so there are no singular points in the domain.

Endpoints The domain, $(-\infty, 0) \cup (0, +\infty)$, has no endpoints.

From this scant information, it is hard to tell what f does. If we are sketching the graph by hand, or using the first derivative test, we will need to plot additional "test points" to the left and right of the stationary points $x = \pm 1$.

using *Technology*

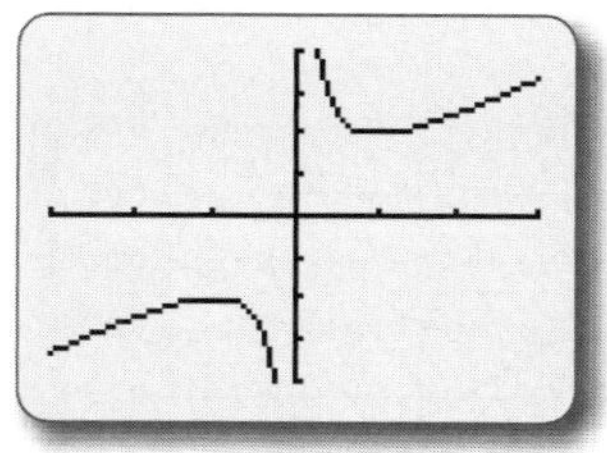

Figure **13**

For the technology approach, let's choose a viewing window with an interval of $[-3, 3]$ for x and $[-4, 4]$ for y, which should leave plenty of room to see how f behaves near the stationary points. The result is something like Figure 13.

From this graph we can see that f has

A relative (stationary) maximum at $(-1, -2)$

A relative (stationary) minimum at $(1, 2)$

Curiously, the relative maximum is lower than the relative minimum! Notice also that, because of the break in the graph at $x = 0$, the graph did not need to rise to get from $(-1, -2)$ to $(1, 2)$. ■

So far we have been solving the equation $f'(x) = 0$ to obtain our candidates for stationary extrema. However, it is often not easy—or even possible—to solve equations analytically. In the next example, we show a way around this problem by using graphing technology.

tech Ex

Example 5 Finding Approximate Extrema Using Technology

Graph the function $f(x) = (x - 1)^{2/3} - \dfrac{x^2}{2}$ with domain $[-2, +\infty)$. Also graph its derivative and hence locate and classify all extrema of f, with coordinates accurate to two decimal places.

Solution In Example 4 of Section 3.5, we saw how to draw the graphs of f and f' using technology. Note that the technology formula to use for the graph of f is

```
((x-1)^2)^(1/3)-0.5*x^2
```

instead of

```
(x-1)^(2/3)-0.5*x^2
```

(Why?)

Figure 14 shows the resulting graphs of f and f'.

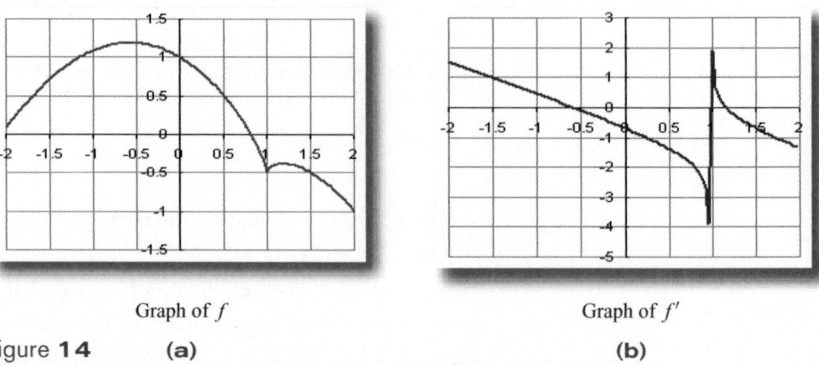

Graph of f Graph of f'

Figure **14** **(a)** **(b)**

If we extend Xmax beyond $x = 2$, we find that the graph continues downward, apparently without any further interesting behavior.

Stationary Points The graph of f shows two stationary points, both maxima, at around $x = -0.6$ and $x = 1.2$. Notice that the graph of f' is zero at precisely these points. Moreover, it is easier to locate these values accurately on the graph of f' because it is easier to pinpoint where a graph crosses the x-axis than to locate a stationary point. Zooming in to the stationary point at $x \approx -0.6$ results in Figure 15.

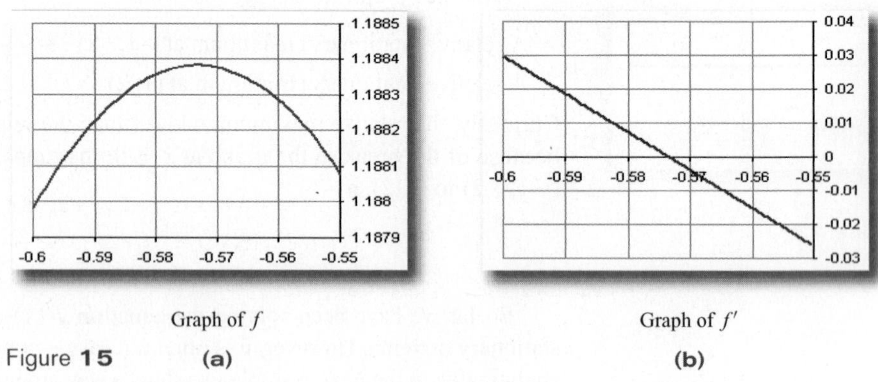

Graph of f Graph of f'

Figure **15** **(a)** **(b)**

From the graph of f, we can see that the stationary point is somewhere between –0.58 and –0.57. The graph of f' shows more clearly that the zero of f', hence the stationary point of f lies somewhat closer to –0.57 than to –0.58. Thus, the stationary point occurs at $x \approx -0.57$, rounded to two decimal places.

In a similar way, we find the second stationary point at $x \approx 1.18$.

Singular Points Going back to Figure 14, we notice what appears to be a cusp (singular point) at the relative minimum around $x = 1$, and this is confirmed by a glance at the graph of f', which seems to take a sudden jump at that value. Zooming in closer suggests that the singular point occurs at exactly $x = 1$. In fact, we can calculate

$$f'(x) = \frac{2}{3(x-1)^{1/3}} - x$$

From this formula we see clearly that $f'(x)$ is defined everywhere except at $x = 1$.

Endpoints The only endpoint in the domain is $x = -2$, which gives a relative minimum.

Thus, we have found the following approximate extrema for *f*:

A relative (endpoint) minimum at (–2, 0.08)
An absolute (stationary) maximum at (–0.57, 1.19)
A relative (singular) minimum at (1, −0.5)
A relative (stationary) maximum at (1.18, –0.38)

5.1 EXERCISES

● denotes basic skills exercises

tech Ex indicates exercises that should be solved using technology

In Exercises 1–12, locate and classify all extrema in each graph. (By classifying the extrema, we mean listing whether each extremum is a relative or absolute maximum or minimum.) Also, locate any stationary points or singular points that are not relative extrema.

1. ●
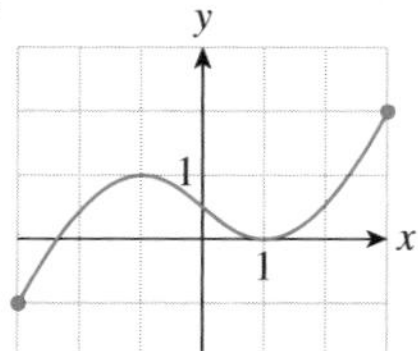

2. ●
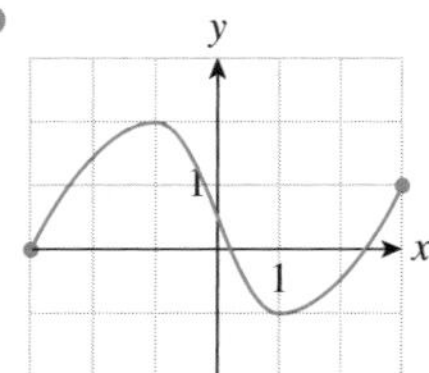

3. ●
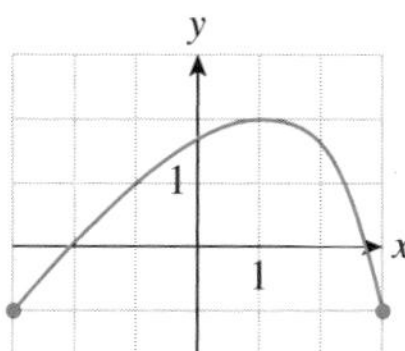

4. ●
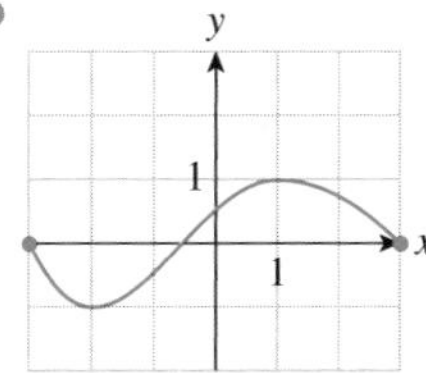

5. ●
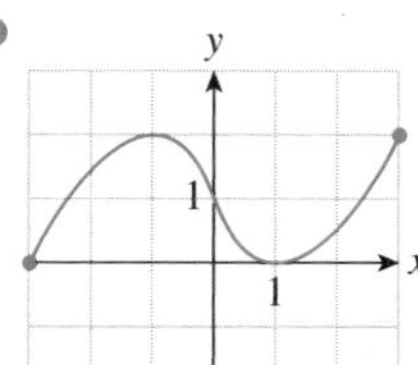

6. ●
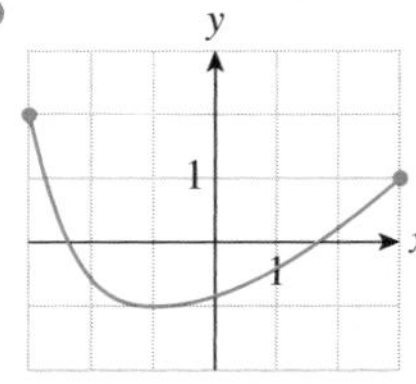

7. ●
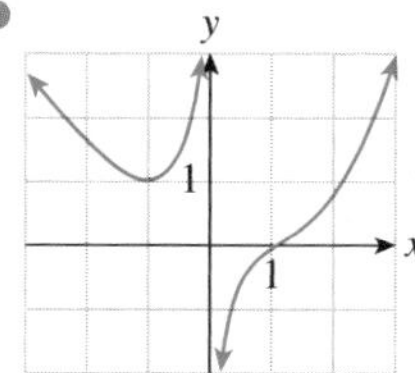

8. ●
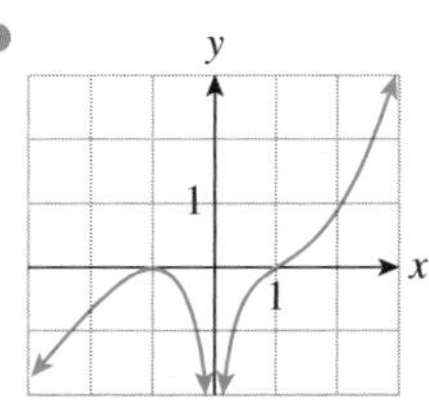

9. ●
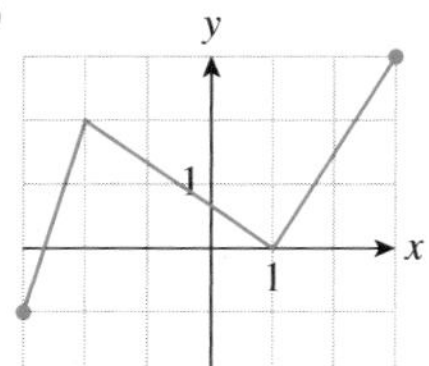

10. ●
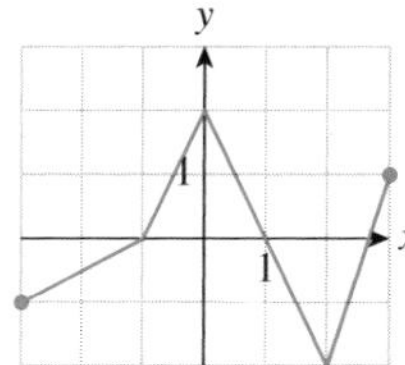

11. ●
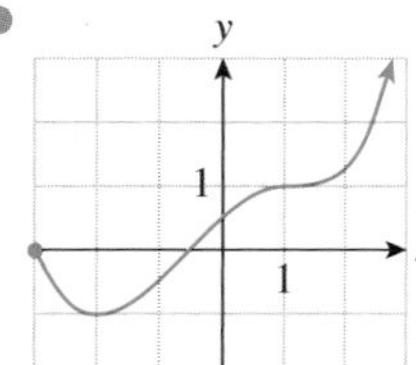

12. ●
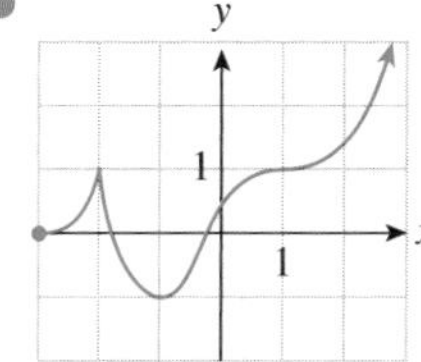

Find the exact location of all the relative and absolute extrema of each function in Exercises 13–44.

13. ● $f(x) = x^2 - 4x + 1$ with domain [0, 3] *hint* [see Example 1]

14. ● $f(x) = 2x^2 - 2x + 3$ with domain [0, 3]

15. ● $g(x) = x^3 - 12x$ with domain [–4, 4]

16. ● $g(x) = 2x^3 - 6x + 3$ with domain [–2, 2]

17. ● $f(t) = t^3 + t$ with domain [–2, 2]

18. ● $f(t) = -2t^3 - 3t$ with domain [–1, 1]

19. ● $h(t) = 2t^3 + 3t^2$ with domain $[-2, +\infty)$ *hint* [see Example 2]

20. ● $h(t) = t^3 - 3t^2$ with domain $[-1, +\infty)$

21. ● $f(x) = x^4 - 4x^3$ with domain $[-1, +\infty)$

22. ● $f(x) = 3x^4 - 2x^3$ with domain $[-1, +\infty)$

23. ● $g(t) = \frac{1}{4}t^4 - \frac{2}{3}t^3 + \frac{1}{2}t^2$ with domain $(-\infty, +\infty)$

24. ● $g(t) = 3t^4 - 16t^3 + 24t^2 + 1$ with domain $(-\infty, +\infty)$

25. ● $h(x) = (x-1)^{2/3}$ with domain [0, 2] *hint* [see Example 3]

26. ● $h(x) = (x+1)^{2/5}$ with domain $[-2, 0]$

27. ● $k(x) = \dfrac{2x}{3} + (x+1)^{2/3}$ with domain $(-\infty, 0]$

28. ● $k(x) = \dfrac{2x}{5} - (x-1)^{2/5}$ with domain $[0, +\infty)$

29. $f(t) = \dfrac{t^2+1}{t^2-1}$; $-2 \le t \le 2, t \ne \pm 1$

30. $f(t) = \dfrac{t^2-1}{t^2+1}$ with domain $[-2, 2]$

31. $f(x) = \sqrt{x}(x-1)$; $x \ge 0$

32. $f(x) = \sqrt{x}(x+1)$; $x \ge 0$

33. $g(x) = x^2 - 4\sqrt{x}$

34. $g(x) = \dfrac{1}{x} - \dfrac{1}{x^2}$

35. $g(x) = \dfrac{x^3}{x^2+3}$

36. $g(x) = \dfrac{x^3}{x^2-3}$

37. $f(x) = x - \ln x$ with domain $(0, +\infty)$

38. $f(x) = x - \ln x^2$ with domain $(0, +\infty)$

39. $g(t) = e^t - t$ with domain $[-1, 1]$

40. $g(t) = e^{-t^2}$ with domain $(-\infty, +\infty)$

41. $f(x) = \dfrac{2x^2-24}{x+4}$

42. $f(x) = \dfrac{x-4}{x^2+20}$

43. $f(x) = xe^{1-x^2}$

44. $f(x) = x \ln x$ with domain $(0, +\infty)$

In Exercises 45–48, use graphing technology and the method in Example 5 to find the x-coordinates of the critical points, accurate to two decimal places. Find all relative and absolute maxima and minima.

45. tech Ex $y = x^2 + \dfrac{1}{x-2}$ with domain $(-3, 2) \cup (2, 6)$

hint [see Example 5]

46. tech Ex $y = x^2 - 10(x-1)^{2/3}$ with domain $(-4, 4)$

47. tech Ex $f(x) = (x-5)^2(x+4)(x-2)$ with domain $[-5, 6]$

48. tech Ex $f(x) = (x+3)^2(x-2)^2$ with domain $[-5, 5]$

In Exercises 49–56, the graph of the derivative *of a function f is shown. Determine the x-coordinates of all stationary and singular points of f, and classify each as a relative maximum, relative minimum, or neither. (Assume that $f(x)$ is defined and continuous everywhere in $[-3, 3]$.)* hint [see Example 5]

49.

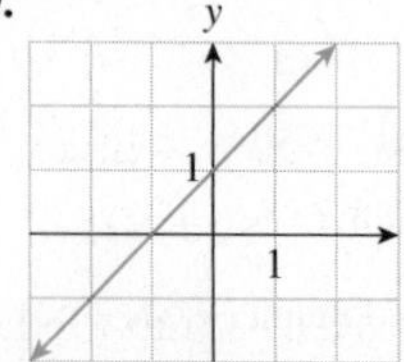

50.

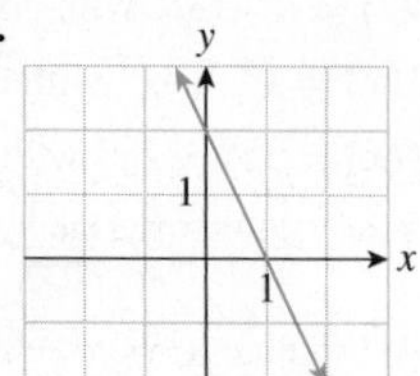

51.

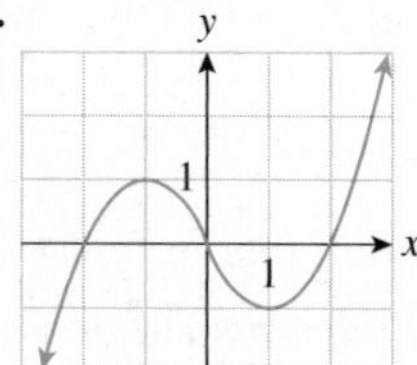

52.

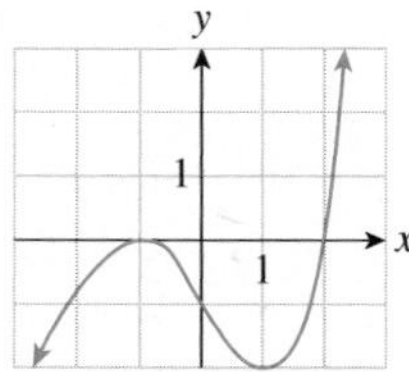

53.

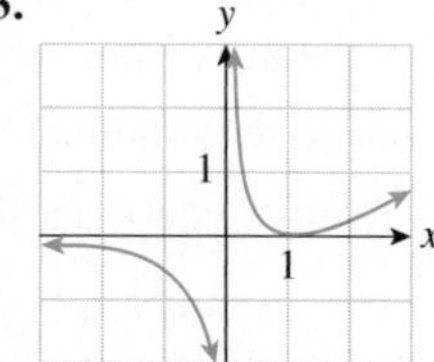

54.

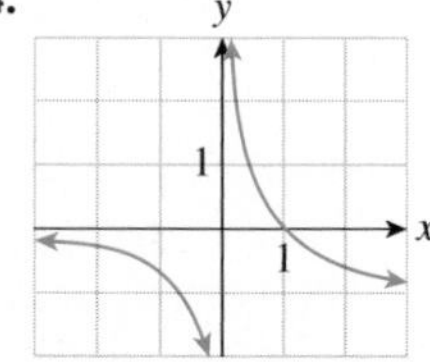

55.

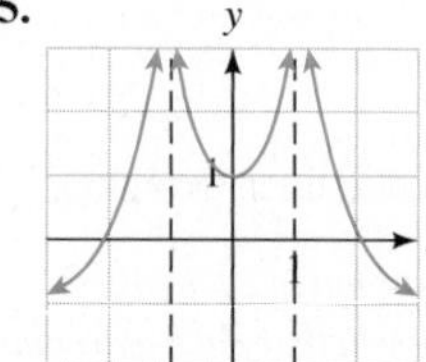

56.

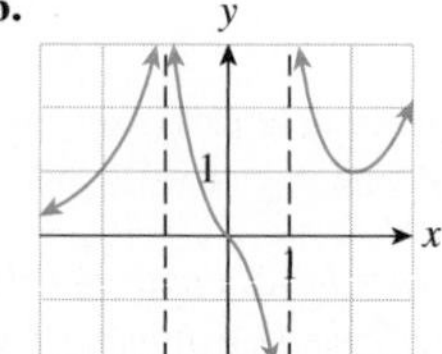

Communication and Reasoning Exercises

57. ● Draw the graph of a function f with domain the set of all real numbers, such that f is not linear and has no relative extrema.

58. ● Draw the graph of a function g with domain the set of all real numbers, such that g has a relative maximum and minimum but no absolute extrema.

59. ● Draw the graph of a function that has stationary and singular points but no relative extrema.

60. ● Draw the graph of a function that has relative, not absolute, maxima and minima, but has no stationary or singular points.

61. ● If a stationary point is not a relative maximum, then must it be a relative minimum? Explain your answer.

62. ● If one endpoint is a relative maximum, must the other be a relative minimum? Explain your answer.

63. We said that if f is continuous on a closed interval $[a, b]$, then it will have an absolute maximum and an absolute minimum. Draw the graph of a function with domain $[0, 1]$ having an absolute maximum but no absolute minimum.

64. Refer to Exercise 63. Draw the graph of a function with domain $[0, 1]$ having no absolute extrema.

5.2 Applications of Maxima and Minima

In many applications we would like to find the largest or smallest possible value of some quantity—for instance, the greatest possible profit or the lowest cost. We call this the *optimal* (best) value. In this section we consider several such examples and use calculus to find the optimal value in each.

In all applications the first step is to translate a written description into a mathematical problem. In the problems we look at in this section, there are *unknowns* that we are asked to find, there is an expression involving those unknowns that must be made as large or as small as possible—the **objective function**—and there may be **constraints**—equations or inequalities relating the variables.[4]

Example 1 Minimizing Average Cost

Gymnast Clothing manufactures expensive hockey jerseys for sale to college bookstores in runs of up to 500. Its cost (in dollars) for a run of x hockey jerseys is

$$C(x) = 2000 + 10x + 0.2x^2$$

How many jerseys should Gymnast produce per run in order to minimize average cost?*

Solution Here is the procedure we will follow to solve problems like this.

1. ***Identify the unknown(s).*** There is one unknown: x, the number of hockey jerseys Gymnast should produce per run. (We know this because the question is, How many jerseys. . . ?)
2. ***Identify the objective function.*** The objective function is the quantity that must be made as small (in this case) as possible. In this example it is the average cost, which is given by

$$\bar{C}(x) = \frac{C(x)}{x} = \frac{2000 + 10x + 0.2x^2}{x}$$
$$= \frac{2000}{x} + 10 + 0.2x \text{ dollars/jersey}$$

3. ***Identify the constraints (if any).*** At most 500 jerseys can be manufactured in a run. Also, $\bar{C}(0)$ is not defined. Thus, x is constrained by

$$0 < x \leq 500$$

Put another way, the domain of the objective function $\bar{C}(x)$ is $(0, 500]$.

4. ***State and solve the resulting optimization problem.*** Our optimization problem is:

$$\text{Minimize } \bar{C}(x) = \frac{2000}{x} + 10 + 0.2x \qquad \text{Objective function}$$
$$\text{subject to } 0 < x \leq 500 \qquad \text{Constraint}$$

* Why don't we seek to minimize total cost? The answer would be uninteresting; to minimize total cost, we would make *no* jerseys at all. Minimizing the average cost is a more practical objective.

[4] If you have studied linear programming, you will notice a similarity here, but unlike the situation in linear programming, neither the objective function nor the constraints need be linear.

We now solve this problem as in Section 5.1. We first calculate

$$\bar{C}'(x) = -\frac{2000}{x^2} + 0.2$$

We solve $\bar{C}'(x) = 0$ to find $x = \pm 100$. We reject $x = -100$ because -100 is not in the domain of $\bar{C}$ (and makes no sense), so we have one stationary point, at $x = 100$. There, the average cost is $\bar{C}(100) = \$50$ per jersey.

The only point at which the formula for $\bar{C}'$ is not defined is $x = 0$, but that is not in the domain of $\bar{C}$, so we have no singular points. We have one endpoint in the domain, at $x = 500$. There, the average cost is $\bar{C}(500) = \$114$.

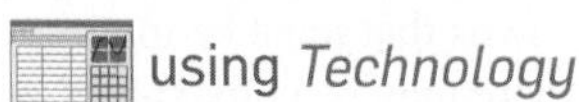
using *Technology*

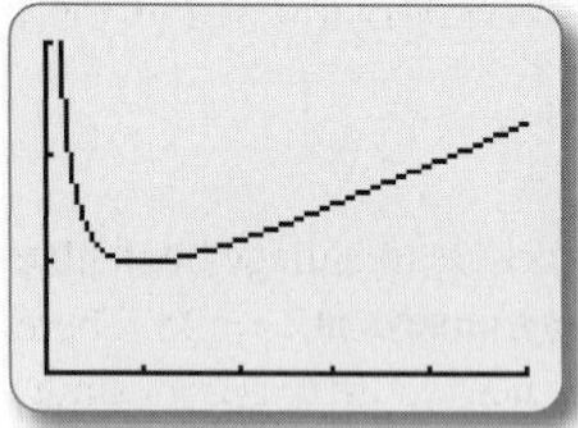

Figure **16**

Let's plot $\bar{C}$ in a viewing window with the intervals [0, 500] for x and [0, 150] for y, which will show the whole domain and the two interesting points we've found so far. The result is Figure 16.

From the graph of $\bar{C}$, we can see that the stationary point at $x = 100$ gives the absolute minimum. We can therefore say that Gymnast Clothing should produce 100 jerseys per run, for a lowest possible average cost of \$50 per jersey. ■

Example 2 Maximizing Area

Slim wants to build a rectangular enclosure for his pet rabbit, Killer, against the side of his house, as shown in Figure 17. He has bought 100 feet of fencing. What are the dimensions of the largest area that he can enclose?

Figure **17**

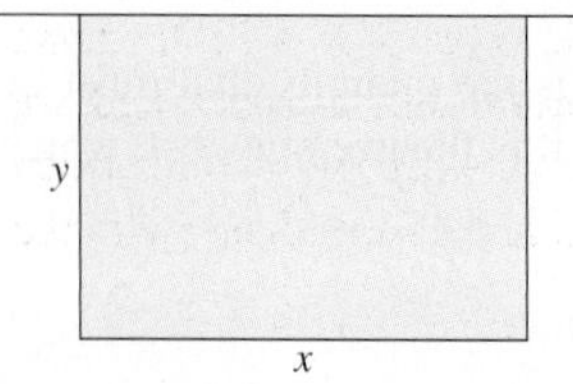

Figure **18**

Solution

1. ***Identify the unknown(s).*** To identify the unknown(s), we look at the question: What are the *dimensions* of the largest area he can enclose? Thus, the unknowns are the dimensions of the fence. We call these x and y, as shown in Figure 18.
2. ***Identify the objective function.*** We look for what it is that we are trying to maximize (or minimize). The phrase "largest area" tells us that our object is to *maximize the area,* which is the product of length and width, so our objective function is

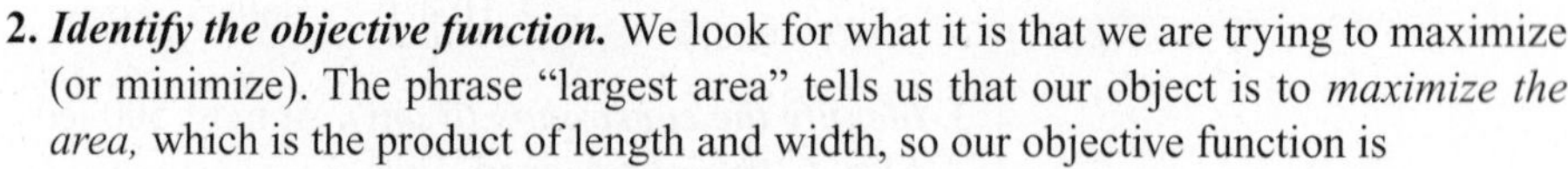

   $A = xy$ where A is the area of the enclosure

3. ***Identify the constraints (if any).*** What stops Slim from making the area as large as he wants? He has only 100 feet of fencing to work with. Looking again at Figure 18, we see that the sum of the lengths of the three sides must equal 100, so

   $$x + 2y = 100$$

   One more point: Because x and y represent the lengths of the sides of the enclosure, neither can be a negative number.
4. ***State and solve the resulting optimization problem.*** Our mathematical problem is:

   Maximize $A = xy$ — Objective function
   subject to $x + 2y = 100$, $x \geq 0$, and $y \geq 0$ — Constraints

We know how to find maxima and minima of a function of one variable, but A appears to depend on two variables. We can remedy this by using a constraint to express one variable in terms of the other. Let's take the constraint $x + 2y = 100$ and solve for x in terms of y:

$$x = 100 - 2y$$

Substituting into the objective function gives

$$A = xy = (100 - 2y)y = 100y - 2y^2$$

and we have eliminated x from the objective function. What about the inequalities? One says that $x \geq 0$, but we want to eliminate x from this as well. We substitute for x again, getting

$$100 - 2y \geq 0$$

Solving this inequality for y gives $y \leq 50$. The second inequality says that $y \geq 0$. Now, we can restate our problem with x eliminated:

$$\text{Maximize } A(y) = 100y - 2y^2 \text{ subject to } 0 \leq y \leq 50$$

We now proceed with our usual method of solving such problems. We calculate $A'(y) = 100 - 4y$. Solving $100 - 4y = 0$, we get one stationary point at $y = 25$. There, $A(25) = 1250$. There are no points at which $A'(y)$ is not defined, so there are no singular points. We have two endpoints, at $y = 0$ and $y = 50$. The corresponding areas are $A(0) = 0$ and $A(50) = 0$. We record the three points we found in a table:

y	0	25	50
$A(y)$	0	1250	0

It's clear now how A must behave: It increases from 0 at $y = 0$ to 1250 at $y = 25$ and then decreases back to 0 at $y = 50$. Thus, the largest possible value of A is 1250 square feet, which occurs when $y = 25$. To completely answer the question that was asked, we need to know the corresponding value of x. We have $x = 100 - 2y$, so $x = 50$ when $y = 25$. Thus, Slim should build his enclosure 50 feet across and 25 feet deep (with the "missing" 50-foot side being formed by part of the house).

+ *Before we go on...* Notice that the problem in Example 2 came down to finding the absolute maximum value of A on the closed and bounded interval [0, 50]. As we noted in the preceding section, the table of values of A at its critical points and the endpoints of the interval gives us enough information to find the absolute maximum. ■

Let's stop for a moment and summarize the steps we've taken in these two examples.

Solving an Optimization Problem

1. **Identify the unknown(s), possibly with the aid of a diagram.** These are usually the quantities asked for in the problem.
2. **Identify the objective function.** This is the quantity you are asked to maximize or minimize. You should name it explicitly, as in "Let S = surface area."
3. **Identify the constraint(s).** These can be equations relating variables or inequalities expressing limitations on the values of variables.

4. **State the optimization problem.** This will have the form "Maximize [minimize] the objective function subject to the constraint(s)."
5. **Eliminate extra variables.** If the objective function depends on several variables, solve the constraint equations to express all variables in terms of one particular variable. Substitute these expressions into the objective function to rewrite it as a function of a single variable. Substitute the expressions into any inequality constraints to help determine the domain of the objective function.
6. **Find the absolute maximum (or minimum) of the objective function.** Use the techniques of the preceding section.

Now for some further examples.

Example 3 Maximizing Revenue

Cozy Carriage Company builds baby strollers. Using market research, the company estimates that if it sets the price of a stroller at p dollars, then it can sell $q = 300{,}000 - 10p^2$ strollers per year. What price will bring in the greatest annual revenue?

Solution The question we are asked identifies our main unknown, the price p. However, there is another quantity that we do not know, q, the number of strollers the company will sell per year. The question also identifies the objective function, revenue, which is

$$R = pq$$

Including the equality constraint given to us, that $q = 300{,}000 - 10p^2$, and the "reality" inequality constraints $p \geq 0$ and $q \geq 0$, we can write our problem as

$$\text{Maximize } R = pq \text{ subject to } q = 300{,}000 - 10p^2,\ p \geq 0, \text{ and } q \geq 0$$

We are given q in terms of p, so let's substitute to eliminate q:

$$R = pq = p(300{,}000 - 10p^2) = 300{,}000p - 10p^3$$

Substituting in the inequality $q \geq 0$, we get

$$300{,}000 - 10p^2 \geq 0$$

Thus, $p^2 \leq 30{,}000$, which gives $-100\sqrt{3} \leq p \leq 100\sqrt{3}$. When we combine this with $p \geq 0$, we get the following restatement of our problem:

$$\text{Maximize } R(p) = 300{,}000p - 10p^3 \text{ such that } 0 \leq p \leq 100\sqrt{3}$$

We solve this problem in much the same way we did the preceding one. We calculate $R'(p) = 300{,}000 - 30p^2$. Setting $300{,}000 - 30p^2 = 0$, we find one stationary point at $p = 100$. There are no singular points and we have the endpoints $p = 0$ and $p = 100\sqrt{3}$. Putting these points in a table and computing the corresponding values of R, we get the following:

p	0	100	$100\sqrt{3}$
$R(p)$	0	20,000,000	0

Thus, Cozy Carriage should price its strollers at \$100 each, which will bring in the largest possible revenue of \$20,000,000.

Figure **19**

Example 4 Optimizing Resources

The Metal Can Company has an order to make cylindrical cans with a volume of 250 cubic centimeters. What should be the dimensions of the cans in order to use the least amount of metal in their production?

Solution We are asked to find the dimensions of the cans. It is traditional to take as the dimensions of a cylinder the height h and the radius of the base r, as in Figure 19.

We are also asked to minimize the amount of metal used in the can, which is the area of the surface of the cylinder. We can look up the formula or figure it out ourselves: Imagine removing the circular top and bottom and then cutting vertically and flattening out the hollow cylinder to get a rectangle, as shown in Figure 20.

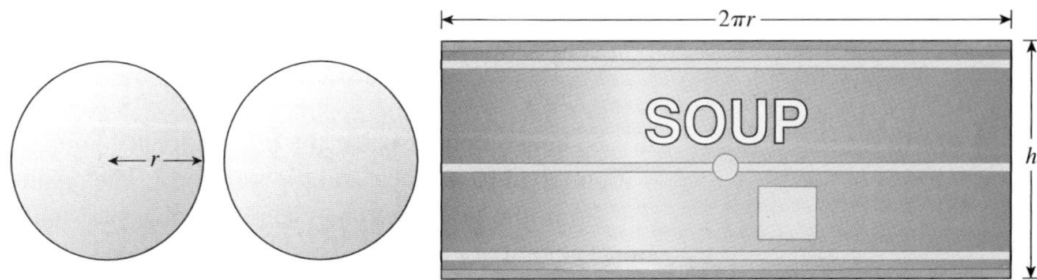

Figure **20**

Our objective function is the (total) surface area S of the can. The area of each disc is πr^2, while the area of the rectangular piece is $2\pi rh$. Thus, our objective function is

$$S = 2\pi r^2 + 2\pi rh$$

As usual, there is a constraint: The volume must be exactly 250 cubic centimeters. The formula for the volume of a cylinder is $V = \pi r^2 h$, so

$$\pi r^2 h = 250$$

It is easiest to solve this constraint for h in terms of r:

$$h = \frac{250}{\pi r^2}$$

Substituting in the objective function, we get

$$S = 2\pi r^2 + 2\pi r\frac{250}{\pi r^2} = 2\pi r^2 + \frac{500}{r}$$

Now r cannot be negative or 0, but it can become very large (a very wide but very short can could have the right volume). We therefore take the domain of $S(r)$ to be $(0, +\infty)$, so our mathematical problem is as follows:

$$\text{Minimize } S(r) = 2\pi r^2 + \frac{500}{r} \text{ subject to } r > 0$$

Now we calculate

$$S'(r) = 4\pi r - \frac{500}{r^2}$$

To find stationary points, we set this equal to 0 and solve:

$$4\pi r - \frac{500}{r^2} = 0$$

$$4\pi r = \frac{500}{r^2}$$

$$4\pi r^3 = 500$$

$$r^3 = \frac{125}{\pi}$$

So

$$r = \sqrt[3]{\frac{125}{\pi}} = \frac{5}{\sqrt[3]{\pi}} \approx 3.41$$

The corresponding surface area is approximately $S(3.41) \approx 220$. There are no singular points or endpoints in the domain.

using Technology

To see how S behaves near the one stationary point, let's graph it in a viewing window with interval [0, 5] for r and [0, 300] for S. The result is Figure 21.

From the graph we can clearly see that the smallest surface area occurs at the stationary point at $r \approx 3.41$. The height of the can will be

$$h = \frac{250}{\pi r^2} \approx 6.83$$ ■

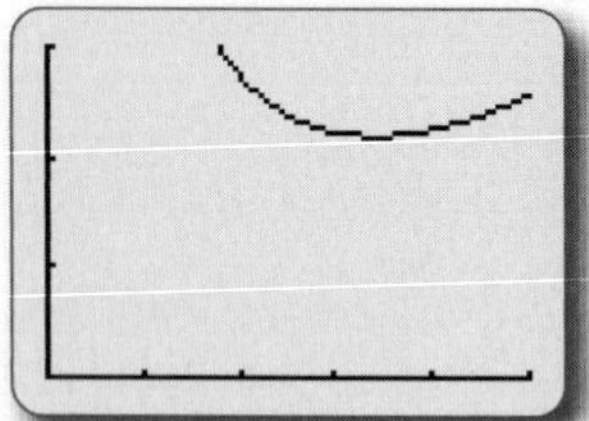

Figure **21**

Thus, the can that uses the least amount of metal has a height of approximately 6.83 centimeters and a radius of approximately 3.41 centimeters. Such a can will use approximately 220 square centimeters of metal.

+*Before we go on...* We obtained the value of r in Example 4 by solving the equation

$$4\pi r = \frac{500}{r^2}$$

This time, let us do things differently: divide both sides by 4π to obtain

$$r = \frac{500}{4\pi r^2} = \frac{125}{\pi r^2}$$

and compare what we got with the expression for h:

$$h = \frac{250}{\pi r^2}$$

which we see is exactly twice the expression for r. Put another way, the height is exactly equal to the diameter so that the can looks square when viewed from the side. Have you ever seen cans with that shape? Why do you think most cans do not have this shape? ■

Example 5 Allocation of Labor

The Gym Sock Company manufactures cotton athletic socks. Production is partially automated through the use of robots. Daily operating costs amount to \$50 per laborer and \$30 per robot. The number of pairs of socks the company can manufacture in a day is given by a Cobb-Douglas* production formula

$$q = 50n^{0.6}r^{0.4}$$

where q is the number of pairs of socks that can be manufactured by n laborers and r robots. Assuming that the company wishes to produce 1000 pairs of socks per day at a minimum cost, how many laborers and how many robots should it use?

Solution The unknowns are the number of laborers n and the number of robots r. The objective is to minimize the daily cost:

$$C = 50n + 30r$$

The constraints are given by the daily quota

$$1000 = 50n^{0.6}r^{0.4}$$

and the fact that n and r are nonnegative. We solve the constraint equation for one of the variables; let's solve for n:

$$n^{0.6} = \frac{1000}{50r^{0.4}} = \frac{20}{r^{0.4}}$$

Taking the $1/0.6$ power of both sides gives

$$n = \left(\frac{20}{r^{0.4}}\right)^{1/0.6} = \frac{20^{1/0.6}}{r^{0.4/0.6}} = \frac{20^{5/3}}{r^{2/3}} \approx \frac{147.36}{r^{2/3}}$$

Substituting in the objective equation gives us the cost as a function of r:

$$C(r) \approx 50\left(\frac{147.36}{r^{2/3}}\right) + 30r$$
$$= 7368r^{-2/3} + 30r$$

The only remaining constraint on r is that $r > 0$. To find the minimum value of $C(r)$, we first take the derivative:

$$C'(r) \approx -4912r^{-5/3} + 30$$

Setting this equal to zero, we solve for r:

$$r^{-5/3} \approx 0.006107$$
$$r \approx (0.006107)^{-3/5} \approx 21.3$$

The corresponding cost is $C(21.3) \approx \$1600$. There are no singular points or endpoints in the domain of C.

using *Technology*

To see how C behaves near its stationary point, let's draw its graph in a viewing window with an interval of [0, 40] for r and [0, 2000] for C. The result is Figure 22.

* Cobb-Douglas production formulas were discussed in Section 4.4.

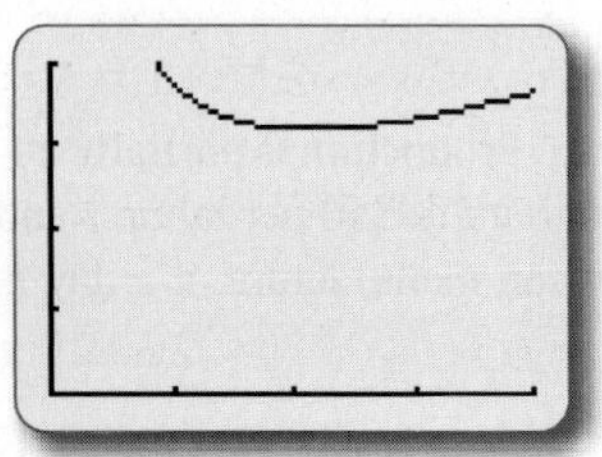
Figure **22**

From the graph we can see that C does have its minimum at the stationary point. The corresponding value of n is

$$n \approx \frac{147.36}{r^{2/3}} \approx 19.2$$

■

At this point, our solution appears to be this: Use (approximately) 19.2 laborers and (approximately) 21.3 robots to meet the manufacturing quota at a minimum cost. However, we are not interested in fractions of robots or people, so we need to find integer solutions for n and r. If we round these numbers, we get the solution $(n, r) = (19, 21)$. However, a quick calculation shows that

$$q = 50(19)^{0.6}(21)^{0.4} \approx 989 \text{ pairs of socks}$$

which fails to meet the quota of 1000. Thus we need to round at least one of the quantities n or r *upward* in order to meet the quota. The three possibilities, with corresponding values of q and C, are as follows:

$$(n, r) = (20, 21), \text{ with } q \approx 1020 \text{ and } C = \$1630$$
$$(n, r) = (19, 22), \text{ with } q \approx 1007 \text{ and } C = \$1610$$
$$(n, r) = (20, 22), \text{ with } q \approx 1039 \text{ and } C = \$1660$$

Of these, the solution that meets the quota at a minimum cost is $(n, r) = (19, 22)$. Thus, the Gym Sock Co. should use 19 laborers and 22 robots, at a cost of $50 \times 19 + 30 \times 22 = \$1610$, to manufacture $50 \times 19^{0.6} \times 22^{0.4} \approx 1007$ pairs of socks.

5.2 EXERCISES

● denotes basic skills exercises

◆ denotes challenging exercises

tech Ex indicates exercises that should be solved using technology

Solve the optimization problems in Exercises 1–8.

1. ● Maximize $P = xy$ with $x + y = 10$. *hint* [see Example 2]

2. ● Maximize $P = xy$ with $x + 2y = 40$.

3. ● Minimize $S = x + y$ with $xy = 9$ and both x and $y > 0$.

4. ● Minimize $S = x + 2y$ with $xy = 2$ and both x and $y > 0$.

5. ● Minimize $F = x^2 + y^2$ with $x + 2y = 10$.

6. ● Minimize $F = x^2 + y^2$ with $xy^2 = 16$.

7. ● Maximize $P = xyz$ with $x + y = 30$ and $y + z = 30$, and x, y, and $z \geq 0$.

8. ● Maximize $P = xyz$ with $x + z = 12$ and $y + z = 12$, and x, y, and $z \geq 0$.

9. ● For a rectangle with perimeter 20 to have the largest area, what dimensions should it have?

10. ● For a rectangle with area 100 to have the smallest perimeter, what dimensions should it have?

Applications

11. ● ***Average Cost*** The cost function for the manufacture of portable MP3 players is given by

$$C(x) = 25{,}000 + 20x + 0.001x^2 \text{ dollars}$$

where x is the number of MP3 players manufactured. How many MP3 players should be manufactured in order to minimize average cost? What is the resulting average cost of an MP3 player? (Give your answer to the nearest dollar.) *hint* [see Example 1]

12. ● ***Average Cost*** Repeat the preceding exercise using the revised cost function

$$C(x) = 6400 + 10x + 0.01x^2$$

13. ● ***Pollution Control*** The cost of controlling emissions at a firm rises rapidly as the amount of emissions reduced increases. Here is a possible model:

$$C(q) = 4000 + 100q^2$$

where q is the reduction in emissions (in pounds of pollutant per day) and C is the daily cost to the firm (in dollars) of this reduction. What level of reduction corresponds to the lowest average cost per pound of pollutant, and what would be the resulting average cost to the nearest dollar?

14. ● ***Pollution Control*** Repeat the preceding exercise using the following cost function:

$$C(q) = 2000 + 200q^2$$

15. ● ***Pollution Control*** (Compare Exercise 13.) The cost of controlling emissions at a firm is given by

$$C(q) = 4000 + 100q^2$$

where q is the reduction in emissions (in pounds of pollutant per day) and C is the daily cost to the firm (in dollars) of this reduction. Government clean-air subsidies amount to \$500 per pound of pollutant removed. How many pounds of pollutant should the firm remove each day in order to minimize *net* cost (cost minus subsidy)?

16. ● ***Pollution Control*** (Compare Exercise 14.) Repeat the preceding exercise, using the following cost function:

$$C(q) = 2000 + 200q^2$$

with government subsidies amounting to \$100 per pound of pollutant removed per day.

17. ● ***Fences*** I want to fence in a rectangular vegetable patch. The fencing for the east and west sides costs \$4 per foot, and the fencing for the north and south sides costs only \$2 per foot. I have a budget of \$80 for the project. What is the largest area I can enclose? hint [see Example 2]

18. ● ***Fences*** My orchid garden abuts my house so that the house itself forms the northern boundary. The fencing for the southern boundary costs \$4 per foot, and the fencing for the east and west sides costs \$2 per foot. If I have a budget of \$80 for the project, what is the largest area I can enclose?

19. ● ***Revenue*** Hercules Films is deciding on the price of the video release of its film *Son of Frankenstein.* Its marketing people estimate that at a price of p dollars, it can sell a total of $q = 200{,}000 - 10{,}000p$ copies. What price will bring in the greatest revenue? hint [see Example 3]

20. ● ***Profit*** Hercules Films is also deciding on the price of the video release of its film *Bride of the Son of Frankenstein.* Again, marketing estimates that at a price of p dollars, it can sell $q = 200{,}000 - 10{,}000p$ copies, but each copy costs \$4 to make. What price will give the greatest *profit*?

21. ● ***Revenue*** The demand for rubies at Royal Ruby Retailers (RRR) is given by the equation

$$q = -\frac{4}{3}p + 80$$

where p is the price RRR charges (in dollars) and q is the number of rubies RRR sells per week. At what price should RRR sell its rubies in order to maximize its weekly revenue?

22. ● ***Revenue*** The consumer demand curve for tissues is given by

$$q = (100 - p)^2 \qquad (0 \le p \le 100)$$

where p is the price per case of tissues and q is the demand in weekly sales. At what price should tissues be sold in order to maximize revenue?

23. ● ***Revenue*** Assume that the demand for tuna in a small coastal town is given by

$$p = \frac{500{,}000}{q^{1.5}}$$

where q is the number of pounds of tuna that can be sold in a month at p dollars per pound. Assume that the town's fishery wishes to sell at least 5000 pounds of tuna per month.

a. How much should the town's fishery charge for tuna in order to maximize monthly revenue?
b. How much tuna will it sell per month at that price?
c. What will be its resulting revenue?

24. ● ***Revenue*** Economist Henry Schultz devised the following demand function for corn:

$$p = \frac{6{,}570{,}000}{q^{1.3}}$$

where q is the number of bushels of corn that could be sold at p dollars per bushel in one year.[5] Assume that at least 10,000 bushels of corn per year must be sold.

a. How much should farmers charge per bushel of corn to maximize annual revenue?
b. How much corn can farmers sell per year at that price?
c. What will be the farmers' resulting revenue?

25. ● ***Revenue*** The wholesale price for chicken in the United States fell from 25¢ per pound to 14¢ per pound, while per capita chicken consumption rose from 22 pounds per year to 27.5 pounds per year.[6] Assuming that the demand for chicken depends linearly on the price, what wholesale price for chicken maximizes revenues for poultry farmers, and what does that revenue amount to?

26. ● ***Revenue*** Your underground used book business is booming. Your policy is to sell all used versions of *Calculus and You* at the same price (regardless of condition). When you set the price at \$10, sales amounted to 120 volumes during the first week of classes. The following semester, you set the price at \$30 and sold not a single book. Assuming that the demand for books depends linearly on the price, what price gives you the maximum revenue, and what does that revenue amount to?

27. ● ***Profit*** The demand for rubies at Royal Ruby Retailers (RRR) is given by the equation

$$q = -\frac{4}{3}p + 80$$

[5] Based on data for the period 1915–1929. SOURCE: Henry Schultz, *The Theory and Measurement of Demand,* (as cited in *Introduction to Mathematical Economics* by A. L. Ostrosky, Jr., and J. V. Koch (Waveland Press, Prospect Heights, Illinois, 1979).

[6] Data are provided for the years 1951–1958. SOURCE: U.S. Department of Agriculture, *Agricultural Statistics.*

where p is the price RRR charges (in dollars) and q is the number of rubies RRR sells per week. Assuming that due to extraordinary market conditions, RRR can obtain rubies for \$25 each, how much should it charge per ruby to make the greatest possible weekly profit, and what will that profit be?

28. ● ***Profit*** The consumer demand curve for tissues is given by

$$q = (100 - p)^2 \qquad (0 \le p \le 100)$$

where p is the price per case of tissues and q is the demand in weekly sales. If tissues cost \$30 per case to produce, at what price should tissues be sold for the largest possible weekly profit? What will that profit be?

29. ● ***Profit*** The demand equation for your company's virtual reality video headsets is

$$p = \frac{1000}{q^{0.3}}$$

where q is the total number of headsets that your company can sell in a week at a price of p dollars. The total manufacturing and shipping cost amounts to \$100 per headset.

a. What is the greatest profit your company can make in a week, and how many headsets will your company sell at this level of profit? (Give answers to the nearest whole number.)

b. How much, to the nearest \$1, should your company charge per headset for the maximum profit?

30. ● ***Profit*** Due to sales by a competing company, your company's sales of virtual reality video headsets have dropped, and your financial consultant revises the demand equation to

$$p = \frac{800}{q^{0.35}}$$

where q is the total number of headsets that your company can sell in a week at a price of p dollars. The total manufacturing and shipping cost still amounts to \$100 per headset.

a. What is the greatest profit your company can make in a week, and how many headsets will your company sell at this level of profit? (Give answers to the nearest whole number.)

b. How much, to the nearest \$1, should your company charge per headset for the maximum profit?

31. ***Box Design*** Chocolate Box Company is going to make open-topped boxes out of 6" × 16" rectangles of cardboard by cutting squares out of the corners and folding up the sides. What is the largest volume box it can make this way?

32. ***Box Design*** Vanilla Box Company is going to make open-topped boxes out of 12" × 12" rectangles of cardboard by cutting squares out of the corners and folding up the sides. What is the largest volume box it can make this way?

33. ***Box Design*** A packaging company is going to make closed boxes, with square bases, that hold 125 cubic centimeters. What are the dimensions of the box that can be built with the least material?

34. ***Box Design*** A packaging company is going to make open-topped boxes, with square bases, that hold 108 cubic centimeters. What are the dimensions of the box that can be built with the least material?

35. ***Luggage Dimensions*** American Airlines requires that the total outside dimensions (length + width + height) of a checked bag not exceed 62 inches.[7] Suppose you want to check a bag whose height equals its width. What is the largest volume bag of this shape that you can check on an American flight?

36. ***Luggage Dimensions*** American Airlines requires that the total outside dimensions (length + width + height) of a carry-on bag not exceed 45 inches.[8] Suppose you want to carry on a bag whose length is twice its height. What is the largest volume bag of this shape that you can carry on an American flight?

37. ***Luggage Dimensions*** Fly-by-Night Airlines has a peculiar rule about luggage: The length and width of a bag must add up to at most 45 inches, and the width and height must also add up to at most 45 inches. What are the dimensions of the bag with the largest volume that Fly-by-Night will accept?

38. ***Luggage Dimensions*** Fair Weather Airlines has a similar rule. It will accept only bags for which the sum of the length and width is at most 36 inches, while the sum of length, height, and twice the width is at most 72 inches. What are the dimensions of the bag with the largest volume that Fair Weather will accept?

39. ***Package Dimensions*** The U.S. Postal Service (USPS) will accept packages only if the length plus girth is no more than 108 inches.[9] (See the figure.)

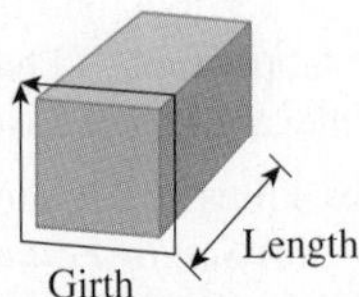

Assuming that the front face of the package (as shown in the figure) is square, what is the largest volume package that the USPS will accept?

40. ***Package Dimensions*** United Parcel Service (UPS) will only accept packages with a length of no more than 108 inches and length plus girth of no more than 165 inches.[10] (See figure for the preceding exercise.) Assuming that the front face of the package (as shown in the figure) is square, what is the largest volume package that UPS will accept?

[7] According to information on its website (http://www.aa.com) as of April, 2005.

[8] Ibid.

[9] The requirement for packages sent other than Parcel Post, as of April 2005 (www.usps.com).

[10] The requirement as of April, 2005 (www.ups.com).

41. ***Cell Phone Revenues*** The number of cell phone subscribers in China in the years 2000–2005 was projected to follow the equation $N(t) = 39t + 68$ million subscribers in year t ($t = 0$ represents January 2000). The average annual revenue per cell phone user was \$350 in 2000.[11] If we assume that due to competition the revenue per cell phone user decreases continuously at an annual rate of 30%, we can model the annual revenue as

$$R(t) = 350(39t + 68)e^{-0.3t} \text{ million dollars}$$

Determine **a.** when to the nearest 0.1 year the revenue is projected to peak and **b.** the revenue, to the nearest \$1 million, at that time.

42. ***Cell Phone Revenues*** Refer to Exercise 41. If we assume instead that the revenue per cell phone user decreases continuously at an annual rate of 20%, we obtain the revenue model

$$R(t) = 350(39t + 68)e^{-0.2t} \text{ million dollars}$$

Determine **a.** when to the nearest 0.1 year the revenue is projected to peak and **b.** the revenue, to the nearest \$1 million, at that time.

43. ***Research and Development*** Spending on research and development by drug companies in the U.S. t years after 1970 can be modeled by

$$S(t) = 2.5e^{0.08t} \text{ billion dollars} \qquad (0 \le t \le 31)$$

The number of new drugs approved by the FDA over the same period can be modeled by

$$D(t) = 10 + t \text{ drugs per year}^{12} \qquad (0 \le t \le 31)$$

When was the function $D(t)/S(t)$ at a maximum? What is the maximum value of $D(t)/S(t)$? What does the answer tell you about the cost of developing new drugs?

44. ***Research and Development*** Refer to Exercise 43. If the number of new drugs approved by the FDA had been $10 + 2t$ new drugs each year, when would the function $D(t)/S(t)$ have reached a maximum? What does the answer tell you about the cost of developing new drugs?

45. ***Asset Appreciation*** As the financial consultant to a classic auto dealership, you estimate that the total value (in dollars) of its collection of 1959 Chevrolets and Fords is given by the formula

$$v = 300{,}000 + 1000t^2 \quad (t \ge 5)$$

where t is the number of years from now. You anticipate a continuous inflation rate of 5% per year, so that the discounted (present) value of an item that will be worth \$$v$ in t years' time is

$$p = ve^{-0.05t}$$

When would you advise the dealership to sell the vehicles to maximize their discounted value?

46. ***Plantation Management*** The value of a fir tree in your plantation increases with the age of the tree according to the formula

$$v = \frac{20t}{1 + 0.05t}$$

where t is the age of the tree in years. Given a continuous inflation rate of 5% per year, the discounted (present) value of a newly planted seedling is

$$p = ve^{-0.05t}$$

At what age (to the nearest year) should you harvest your trees in order to ensure the greatest possible discounted value?

47. ***Marketing Strategy*** FeatureRich Software Company has a dilemma. Its new program, Doors-X 10.27, is almost ready to go on the market. However, the longer the company works on it, the better it can make the program and the more it can charge for it. The company's marketing analysts estimate that if it delays t days, it can set the price at $100 + 2t$ dollars. On the other hand, the longer it delays, the more market share they will lose to their main competitor (see the next exercise) so that if it delays t days it will be able to sell $400{,}000 - 2500t$ copies of the program. How many days should FeatureRich delay the release in order to get the greatest revenue?

48. ***Marketing Strategy*** FeatureRich Software's main competitor (see previous exercise) is Moon Systems, and Moon is in a similar predicament. Its product, Walls-Y 11.4, could be sold now for \$200, but for each day Moon delays, it could increase the price by \$4. On the other hand, it could sell 300,000 copies now, but each day it waits will cut sales by 1500. How many days should Moon delay the release in order to get the greatest revenue?

49. ***Average Profit*** The FeatureRich Software Company sells its graphing program, Dogwood, with a volume discount. If a customer buys x copies, then he pays[13] \$$500\sqrt{x}$. It cost the company \$10,000 to develop the program and \$2 to manufacture each copy. If a single customer were to buy all the copies of Dogwood, how many copies would the customer have to buy for FeatureRich Software's average profit per copy to be maximized? How are average profit and marginal profit related at this number of copies?

[11] Based on a regression of projected figures (coefficients are rounded). SOURCE: Intrinsic Technology/*New York Times*, Nov. 24, 2000, p. C1.

[12] The exponential model for R&D is based on the 1970 and 2001 spending in constant 2001 dollars, while the linear model for new drugs approved is based on the six-year moving average from data from 1970–2000. Source for data: Pharmaceutical Research and Manufacturers of America, FDA/*New York Times*, April 19, 2002, p. C1.

[13] This is similar to the way site licenses have been structured for the program Maple®.

50. ***Average Profit*** Repeat the preceding exercise with the charge to the customer $\$600\sqrt{x}$ and the cost to develop the program \$9000.

51. ***Prison Population*** The prison population of the U.S. followed the curve

$$N(t) = -145t^3 + 5300t^2 + 1300t + 350{,}000 \quad (0 \le t \le 23)$$

in the years 1980–2003. Here t is the number of years since 1980 and N is the number of prisoners.[14] When, to the nearest year, was the prison population increasing most rapidly? When was it increasing least rapidly?

52. ***Test Scores*** Combined SAT scores in the U.S. in the years 1985–2003 could be approximated by

$$T(t) = -0.015t^3 + 0.75t^2 - 10t + 1040 \quad (5 \le t \le 23)$$

where t is the number of years since 1980 and T is the combined SAT score average.[15] Based on this model, when (to the nearest year) was the average SAT score decreasing most rapidly? When was it increasing most rapidly?

53. ***Embryo Development*** The oxygen consumption of a bird embryo increases from the time the egg is laid through the time the chick hatches. In a typical galliform bird, the oxygen consumption can be approximated by

$$c(t) = -0.065t^3 + 3.4t^2 - 22t + 3.6 \text{ milliliters per day} \quad (8 \le t \le 30)$$

where t is the time (in days) since the egg was laid.[16] (An egg will typically hatch at around $t = 28$.) When, to the nearest day, is $c'(t)$ a maximum? What does the answer tell you?

54. ***Embryo Development*** The oxygen consumption of a turkey embryo increases from the time the egg is laid through the time the chick hatches. In a brush turkey, the oxygen consumption can be approximated by

$$c(t) = -0.028t^3 + 2.9t^2 - 44t + 95 \text{ milliliters per day} \quad (20 \le t \le 50)$$

where t is the time (in days) since the egg was laid.[17] (An egg will typically hatch at around $t = 50$.) When, to the nearest day, is $c'(t)$ a maximum? What does the answer tell you?

55. ***Minimizing Resources*** Basic Buckets, Inc., has an order for plastic buckets holding 5000 cubic centimeters. The buckets are open-topped cylinders, and the company want to know what dimensions will use the least plastic per bucket. (The volume of an open-topped cylinder with height h and radius r is $\pi r^2 h$, while the surface area is $\pi r^2 + 2\pi rh$.)

56. ***Optimizing Capacity*** Basic Buckets would like to build a bucket with a surface area of 1000 square centimeters. What is the volume of the largest bucket they can build? (See the preceding exercise.)

57. ◆ ***Agriculture*** The fruit yield per tree in an orchard containing 50 trees is 100 pounds per tree each year. Due to crowding, the yield decreases by 1 pound per season for every additional tree planted. How may additional trees should be planted for a maximum total annual yield?

58. ◆ ***Agriculture*** Two years ago your orange orchard contained 50 trees and the total yield was 75 bags of oranges. Last year you removed ten of the trees and noticed that the total yield increased to 80 bags. Assuming that the yield per tree depends linearly on the number of trees in the orchard, what should you do this year to maximize your total yield?

59. ● ***Resource Allocation*** Your automobile assembly plant has a Cobb-Douglas production function given by

$$q = x^{0.4}y^{0.6}$$

where q is the number of automobiles it produces per year, x is the number of employees, and y is the daily operating budget (in dollars). Annual operating costs amount to an average of \$20,000 per employee plus the operating budget of $\$365y$. Assume that you wish to produce 1000 automobiles per year at a minimum cost. How many employees should you hire? *hint* [see Example 5]

60. ● ***Resource Allocation*** Repeat the preceding exercise using the production formula

$$q = x^{0.5}y^{0.5}$$

The use of technology is recommended for Exercises 61–66.

61. tech Ex ***iPod Sales*** The quarterly sales of Apple iPods from the fourth quarter of 2002 through the third quarter of 2004 could be roughly approximated by the function

$$N(t) = \frac{1100}{1 + 9(1.8)^{-t}} \text{ thousand iPods} \quad (-1 \le t \le 6)$$

where t is time in quarters since the first quarter of 2003.[18] During which quarter were iPod sales increasing most rapidly? How fast, to the nearest 10 thousand iPods per quarter, were iPod sales increasing at that time?

62. tech Ex ***Grants*** The annual spending on grants by U.S. foundations in the period 1993 to 2003 was approximately

$$s(t) = 11 + \frac{20}{1 + 1800(2.5)^{-t}} \text{ billion dollars} \quad (3 \le t \le 13)$$

[14] The authors' model from data obtained from *Sourcebook of Criminal Justice Statistics Online*, http://www.albany.edu/sourcebook/, as of April, 2005.

[15] The model is the authors'. Source for data: *Digest of Educational Statistics, 2003*, National Center for Education Statistics, U.S. Dept. of Education, http://nces.ed.gov/programs/digest/.

[16] The model approximates graphical data published in the article "The Brush Turkey" by Roger S. Seymour, *Scientific American*, December, 1991, pp. 108–114.

[17] Ibid.

[18] Based on a logistic regression. Source for data: Apple Computer, Inc., quarterly earnings reports, available at www.apple.com.

where t is the number of years since 1990.[19] When, to the nearest year, was grant spending increasing most rapidly? How fast was it increasing at that time?

63. tech Ex ***Bottled Water Sales*** Annual sales of bottled water in the U.S. (including sparkling water) in the period 1993–2003 could be approximated by

$$R(t) = 17t^2 + 100t + 2300 \text{ million gallons} \quad (3 \le t \le 13)$$

where t is time in years since 1990.[20] Sales of sparkling water could be approximated by[21]

$$S(t) = -1.3t^2 + 4t + 160 \text{ million gallons} \quad (3 \le t \le 13)$$

Graph the derivative of $S(t)/R(t)$ for $3 \le t \le 13$. Determine when, to the nearest half year, this derivative had an absolute minimum and find its approximate value at that time. What does the answer tell you?

64. tech Ex ***Bottled Water versus Coffee*** Annual per capita consumption of bottled water in the U.S. for the period 1990–2003 could be approximated by

$$W(t) = 0.05t^2 + 0.4t + 9 \text{ gallons}^{22}$$

where t is the time in years since 1990. During the same period, annual per capita consumption of coffee could be approximated by

$$C(t) = -0.05t^2 - 0.03t + 26 \text{ gallons}^{23}$$

Graph the derivative of $W(t)/C(t)$ for $3 \le t \le 13$. Determine when, to the nearest half year, this derivative had an absolute maximum, and find its approximate value at that time. What does the answer tell you?

65. tech Ex ***Asset Appreciation*** You manage a small antique company that owns a collection of Louis XVI jewelry boxes. Their value v is increasing according to the formula

$$v = \frac{10{,}000}{1 + 500e^{-0.5t}}$$

where t is the number of years from now. You anticipate an inflation rate of 5% per year, so that the present value of an item that will be worth \$$v$ in t years' time is given by

$$p = v(1.05)^{-t}$$

When (to the nearest year) should you sell the jewelry boxes to maximize their present value? How much (to the nearest constant dollar) will they be worth at that time?

66. tech Ex ***Harvesting Forests*** The following equation models the approximate volume in cubic feet of a typical Douglas fir tree of age t years.[24]

$$V = \frac{22{,}514}{1 + 22{,}514t^{-2.55}}$$

The lumber will be sold at \$10 per cubic foot, and you do not expect the price of lumber to appreciate in the foreseeable future. On the other hand, you anticipate a general inflation rate of 5% per year, so that the present value of an item that will be worth \$$v$ in t years' time is given by

$$p = v(1.05)^{-t}$$

At what age (to the nearest year) should you harvest a Douglas fir tree in order to maximize its present value? How much (to the nearest constant dollar) will a Douglas fir tree be worth at that time?

67. ◆ ***Revenue (based on a question on the GRE economics test[25])*** If total revenue (TR) is specified by $TR = a + bQ - cQ^2$, where Q is quantity of output and a, b, and c are positive parameters, then TR is maximized for this firm when it produces Q equal to:
(A) $b/2ac$ **(B)** $b/4c$ **(C)** $(a+b)/c$ **(D)** $b/2c$ **(E)** $c/2b$

68. ◆ ***Revenue (based on a question on the GRE economics test)*** If total demand (Q) is specified by $Q = -aP + b$, where P is unit price and a and b are positive parameters, then total revenue is maximized for this firm when it charges P equal to:
(A) $b/2a$ **(B)** $b/4a$ **(C)** a/b **(D)** $a/2b$ **(E)** $-b/2a$

Communication and Reasoning Exercises

69. ● Explain why the following problem is uninteresting: A packaging company wishes to make cardboard boxes with open tops by cutting square pieces from the corners of a square sheet of cardboard and folding up the sides. What is the box with the least surface area it can make this way?

70. ● Explain why finding the production level that minimizes a cost function is frequently uninteresting. What would a more interesting objective be?

71. ● Your friend Margo claims that all you have to do to find the absolute maxima and minima in applications is set the

---

[19] Based on a logistic regression. Source for data: The Foundation Center, *Foundation Growth and Giving Estimates*, 2004, downloaded from the Center's website, http://fdncenter.org.

[20] Source: Beverage Marketing Corporation news release, "Bottled water now number-two commercial beverage in U.S., says Beverage Marketing Corporation," April 8, 2004, available at www.beveragemarketing.com.

[21] Source for data: Beverage Marketing Corporation of New York/*New York Times*, June 21, 2001, p. C1.

[22] Ibid.

[23] Extrapolated from data through 2000. Source for data: www.fas.usda.gov/htp/tropical/2002/06-02/coffusco.pdf

[24] The model is the authors' and is based on data in *Environmental and Natural Resource Economics* by Tom Tietenberg, Third Edition, (New York: HarperCollins, 1992), p. 282.

[25] Source: GRE Economics Test, by G. Gallagher, G. E. Pollock, W. J. Simeone, G. Yohe (Piscataway, NJ: Research and Education Association, 1989).

derivative equal to zero and solve. "All that other stuff about endpoints and so-on is a waste of time just to make life hard for us," according to Margo. Explain why she is wrong, and find at least one exercise in this exercise set to illustrate your point.

72. ● You are having a hard time persuading your friend Marco that maximizing revenue is not the same as maximizing profit. "How on earth can you expect to obtain the largest profit if you are not taking in the largest revenue?" Explain why he is wrong, and find at least one exercise in this exercise set to illustrate your point.

73. If demand q decreases as price p increases, what does the minimum value of dq/dp measure?

74. Explain how you would solve an optimization problem of the following form: Maximize $P = f(x, y, z)$ subject to $z = g(x, y)$ and $y = h(x)$.

● basic skills ◆ challenging *tech* Ex technology exercise

5.3 The Second Derivative and Analyzing Graphs

The **second derivative** is simply the derivative of the derivative function. To explain why we would be interested in such a thing, we start by discussing one of its interpretations.

Acceleration

Recall that if $s(t)$ represents the position of a car at time t, then its velocity is given by the derivative: $v(t) = s'(t)$. But one rarely drives a car at a constant speed; the velocity itself is changing. The rate at which the velocity is changing is the **acceleration.** Since the derivative measures the rate of change, acceleration is the derivative of velocity: $a(t) = v'(t)$. Because v is the derivative of s, we can express the acceleration in terms of s:

$$a(t) = v'(t) = (s')'(t) = s''(t)$$

That is, a is the derivative of the derivative of s, in other words, the second derivative of s which we write as s''. (In this context you will often hear the derivative s' referred to as the **first derivative.**)

Second Derivative, Acceleration

The **second derivative** of a function f is the derivative of the derivative of f, written as f''.

quick **Examples**

1. If $f(x) = x^3 - x$, then $f'(x) = 3x^2 - 1$, so $f''(x) = 6x$.
2. If $f(x) = 3x + 1$, then $f'(x) = 3$, so $f''(x) = 0$.

The **acceleration** of a moving object is the derivative of its velocity—that is, the second derivative of the position function.

quick **Example**

If t is time in hours and the position of a car at time t is $s(t) = t^3 + 2t^2$ miles, then the car's velocity is $v(t) = s'(t) = 3t^2 + 4t$ miles per hour and its acceleration is $a(t) = s''(t) = v'(t) = 6t + 4$ miles per hour per hour.

Differential Notation for the Second Derivative

We have written the second derivative of $f(x)$ as $f''(x)$. We could also use differential notation:

$$f''(x) = \frac{d^2f}{dx^2}$$

This notation comes from writing the second derivative as the derivative of the derivative in differential notation:

$$f''(x) = \frac{d}{dx}\left[\frac{df}{dx}\right] = \frac{d^2f}{dx^2}$$

Similarly, if $y = f(x)$, we write $f''(x)$ as $\frac{d}{dx}\left[\frac{dy}{dx}\right] = \frac{d^2y}{dx^2}$. For example, if $y = x^3$, then $\frac{d^2y}{dx^2} = 6x$.

An important example of acceleration is the acceleration due to gravity.

Example **1** Acceleration Due to Gravity

According to the laws of physics, the height of an object near the surface of the earth falling in a vacuum from an initial rest position 100 feet above the ground under the influence of gravity is approximately

$$s(t) = 100 - 16t^2 \text{ feet}$$

in t seconds. Find its acceleration.

Solution The velocity of the object is

$$v(t) = s'(t) = -32t \text{ ft/s}$$

Differential notation: $v = \frac{ds}{dt} = -32t$ ft/s

The reason for the negative sign is that the height of the object is decreasing with time, so its velocity is negative. Hence, the acceleration is

$$a(t) = s''(t) = -32 \text{ ft/s}^2$$

Differential notation: $a = \frac{d^2s}{dt^2} = -32$ ft/s^2

(We write ft/s^2 as an abbreviation for feet/second/second—that is, feet per second per second. It is often read "feet per second squared.") Thus, the *downward* velocity is increasing by 32 ft/s every second. We say that 32 ft/s^2 is the **acceleration due to gravity.** If we ignore air resistance, all falling bodies near the surface of the earth, no matter what their weight, will fall with this acceleration.*

* On other planets the acceleration due to gravity is different. For example, on Jupiter, it is about three times as large as on Earth.

+ *Before we go on...* In very careful experiments using balls rolling down inclined planes, Galileo made one of his most important discoveries—that the acceleration due to gravity is constant and does not depend on the weight or composition of the object falling.[26] A famous, though probably apocryphal, story has him dropping cannonballs of different weights off the Leaning Tower of Pisa to prove his point.[27] ■

Example 2 Acceleration of Sales

For the first 15 months after the introduction of a new video game, the total sales can be modeled by the curve

$$S(t) = 20e^{0.4t} \text{ units sold}$$

where t is the time in months since the game was introduced. After about 25 months total sales follow more closely the curve

$$S(t) = 100{,}000 - 20e^{17-0.4t}$$

How fast are total sales accelerating after 10 months? How fast are they accelerating after 30 months? What do these numbers mean?

Solution By acceleration we mean the rate of change of the rate of change, which is the second derivative. During the first 15 months, the first derivative of sales is

$$\frac{dS}{dt} = 8e^{0.4t}$$

and so the second derivative is

$$\frac{d^2S}{dt^2} = 3.2e^{0.4t}$$

Thus, after 10 months the acceleration of sales is

$$\left.\frac{d^2S}{dt^2}\right|_{t=10} = 3.2e^4 \approx 175 \text{ units/month/month, or units/month}^2$$

We can also compute total sales

$$S(10) = 20e^4 \approx 1092 \text{ units}$$

and the rate of change of sales

$$\left.\frac{dS}{dt}\right|_{t=10} = 8e^4 \approx 437 \text{ units/month}$$

What do these numbers mean? By the end of the tenth month, a total of 1092 video games have been sold. At that time the game is selling at the rate of 437 units per month. This rate of sales is increasing by 175 units per month per month. More games will be sold each month than the month before.

To analyze the sales after 30 months is similar, using the formula

$$S(t) = 100{,}000 - 20e^{17-0.4t}$$

[26] An interesting aside: Galileo's experiments depended on getting extremely accurate timings. Since the timepieces of his day were very inaccurate, he used the most accurate time measurement he could: He sang and used the beat as his stopwatch.

[27] A true story: The point was made again during the Apollo 15 mission to the moon (July, 1971) when astronaut David R. Scott dropped a feather and a hammer from the same height. The moon has no atmosphere, so the two hit the surface of the moon simultaneously.

The derivative is

$$\frac{dS}{dt} = 8e^{17-0.4t}$$

and the second derivative is

$$\frac{d^2S}{dt^2} = -3.2e^{17-0.4t}$$

After 30 months,

$$S(30) = 100{,}000 - 20e^{17-12} \approx 97{,}032 \text{ units}$$

$$\left.\frac{dS}{dt}\right|_{t=30} = 8e^{17-12} \approx 1187 \text{ units/month}$$

$$\left.\frac{d^2S}{dt^2}\right|_{t=30} = -3.2e^{17-12} \approx -475 \text{ units/month}^2$$

By the end of the 30th month, 97,032 video games have been sold, the game is selling at a rate of 1187 units per month, and the rate of sales is *decreasing* by 475 units per month per month. Fewer games are sold each month than the month before.

Concavity

The first derivative of f tells us where the graph of f is rising [where $f'(x) > 0$] and where it is falling [where $f'(x) < 0$]. The second derivative tells in what direction the graph of f *curves* or *bends.* Consider the graphs in Figures 23 and 24.

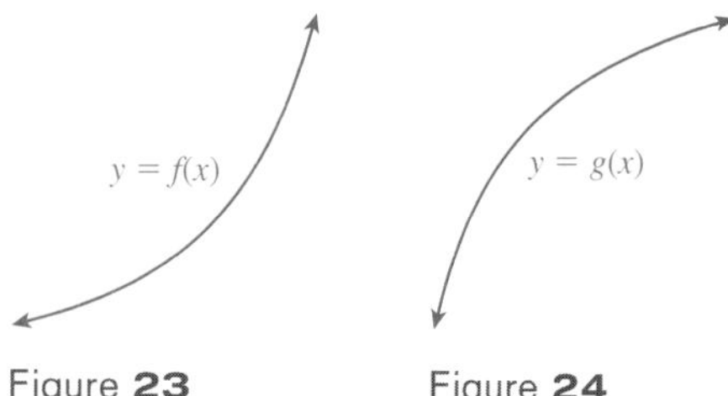

Figure **23** Figure **24**

Think of a car driving from left to right along each of the roads shown in the two figures. A car driving along the graph of f in Figure 23 will turn to the left (upward); a car driving along the graph of g in Figure 24 will turn to the right (downward). We say that the graph of f is **concave up** while the graph of g is **concave down.** Now think about the derivatives of f and g. The derivative $f'(x)$ starts small but *increases* as the graph gets steeper. Since $f'(x)$ is increasing, its derivative $f''(x)$ must be positive. On the other hand, $g'(x)$ *decreases* as we go to the right. Since $g'(x)$ is decreasing, its derivative $g''(x)$ must be negative. Summarizing, we have the following.

Concavity and the Second Derivative

A curve is **concave up** if its slope is increasing, in which case the second derivative is positive. A curve is **concave down** if its slope is decreasing, in which case the second derivative is negative. A point where the graph of f changes concavity, from concave up to concave down or vice versa, is called a **point of inflection.** At a point of inflection, the second derivative is either zero or undefined.

Locating Points of Inflection

To locate possible points of inflection, list points where $f''(x) = 0$ and also points where $f''(x)$ is not defined.

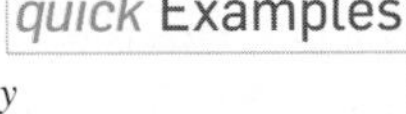

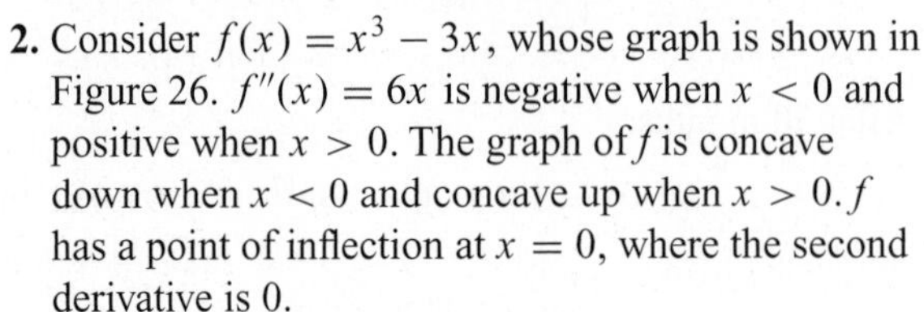

1. The function f whose graph is shown in Figure 25 has points of inflection at approximately $x = 1$ and $x = 3$.
2. Consider $f(x) = x^3 - 3x$, whose graph is shown in Figure 26. $f''(x) = 6x$ is negative when $x < 0$ and positive when $x > 0$. The graph of f is concave down when $x < 0$ and concave up when $x > 0$. f has a point of inflection at $x = 0$, where the second derivative is 0.

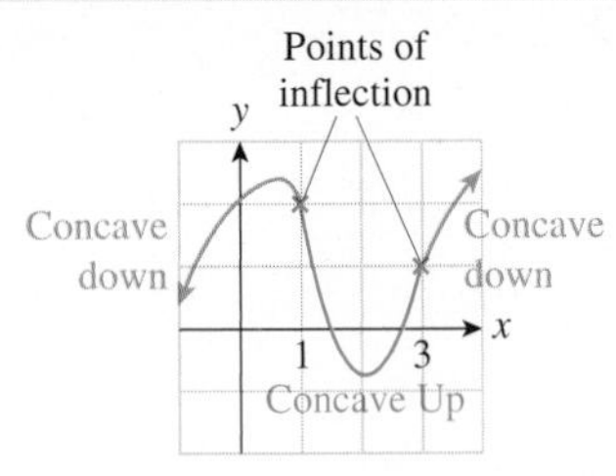

Figure **25**

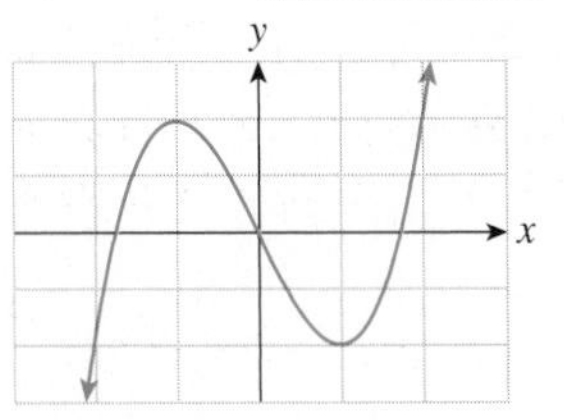

Figure **26**

The following example shows one of the reasons it's useful to look at concavity.

Example 3 The Point of Diminishing Returns

After the introduction of a new video game, the worldwide sales are modeled by the curve

$$S(t) = \frac{1}{1 + 50e^{-0.2t}} \text{ million units sold}$$

where t is the time in months since the game was introduced (compare Example 2). The graphs of $S(t)$, $S'(t)$ and $S''(t)$ are shown in Figure 27.

Where is the graph of S concave up, and where is it concave down? Where are any points of inflection? What does this all mean?

Solution Look at the graph of S. We see that the graph of S is concave up in the early months and then becomes concave down later. The point of inflection, where the concavity changes, is somewhere between 15 and 25 months.

Now look at the graph of S''. This graph crosses the t-axis very close to $t = 20$, is positive before that point, and negative after that point. Since positive values of S'' indicate S is concave up and negative values concave down, we conclude that the graph of S is concave up for about the first 20 months; that is, for $0 < t < 20$ and concave down for $20 < t < 40$. The concavity switches at the point of inflection which occurs at about $t = 20$ (when $S''(t) = 0$; a more accurate answer is $t \approx 19.56$).

What does this all mean? Look at the graph of S', which shows sales per unit time, or monthly sales. From this graph we see that monthly sales are increasing for $t < 20$: more units are being sold each month than the month before. Monthly sales reach a peak of 0.05 million $=$ 50,000 games per month at the point of inflection $t = 20$ and then begin to drop off. Thus, the point of inflection is the time when sales stop increasing and start to fall off. This is sometimes called the **point of diminishing returns.** Although the total sales figure continues to rise (see the graph of S: game units continue to be sold), the *rate* at which units are sold starts to drop.

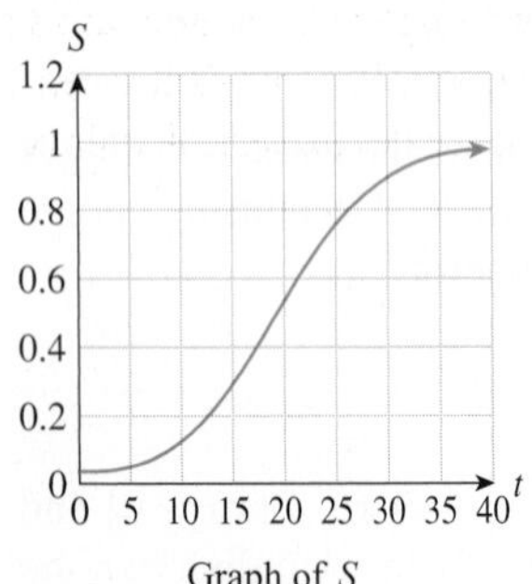

Graph of S

(a)

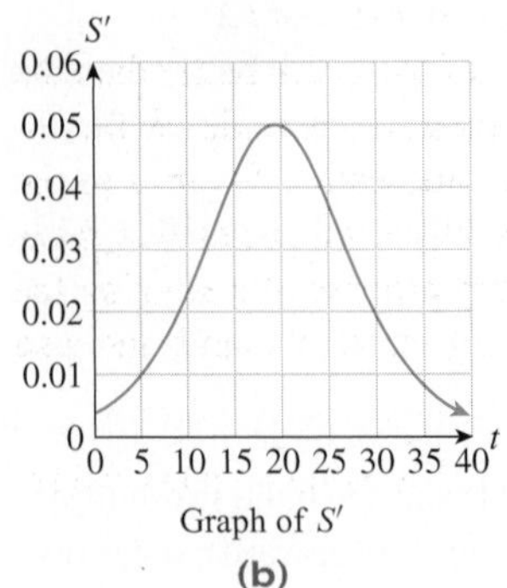

Graph of S'

(b)

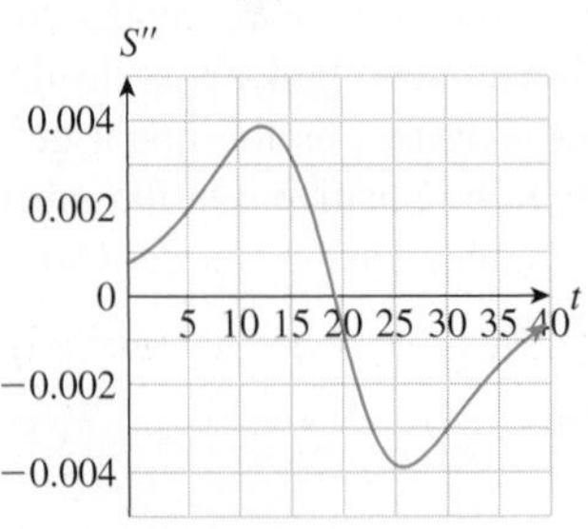

Graph of S''

(c)

Figure **27**

Analyzing Graphs

We now have the tools we need to find the most interesting points on the graph of a function. It is easy to use graphing technology to draw the graph, but we need to use calculus to understand what we are seeing. The most interesting features of a graph are the following.

Features of a Graph

1. ***The x- and y-intercepts:*** If $y = f(x)$, find the x-intercept(s) by setting $y = 0$ and solving for x; find the y-intercept by setting $x = 0$ and solving for y.
2. ***Relative extrema:*** Use the technique of Section 5.1 to locate the relative extrema.
3. ***Points of inflection:*** Use the technique of this section to find the points of inflection.
4. ***Behavior near points where the function is not defined:*** If $f(x)$ is not defined at $x = a$, consider $\lim_{x\to a^-} f(x)$ and $\lim_{x\to a^+} f(x)$ to see how the graph of f behaves as x approaches a.
5. ***Behavior at infinity:*** Consider $\lim_{x\to -\infty} f(x)$ and $\lim_{x\to +\infty} f(x)$ if appropriate, to see how the graph of f behaves far to the left and right.

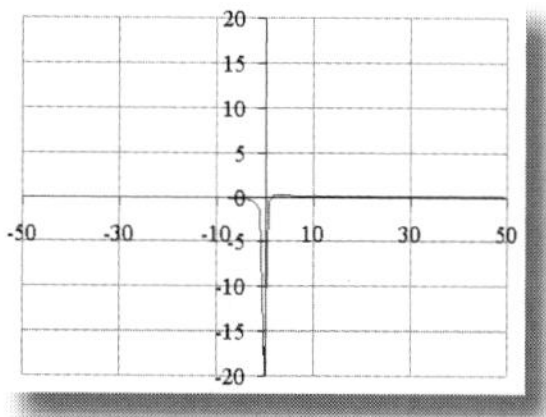

$-50 \le x \le 50,\ -20 \le y \le 20$

(a)

Note It is sometimes difficult or impossible to solve all of the equations that come up in Steps 1, 2, and 3 of the above analysis. As a consequence, we might not be able to say exactly where the x-intercept, extrema, or points of inflection are. When this happens, we will use graphing technology to assist us in determining accurate numerical approximations. ■

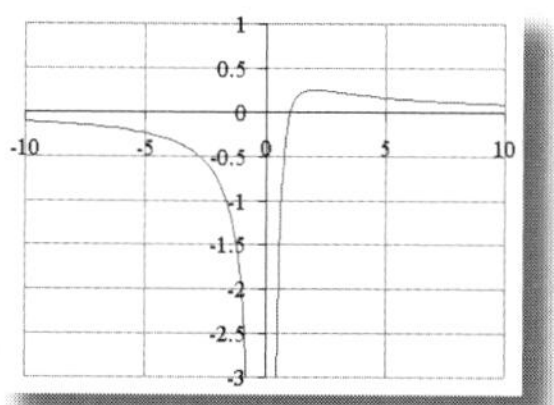

$-10 \le x \le 10,\ -3 \le y \le 1$

(b)

Figure **28**

Example 4 Analyzing a Graph

Analyze the graph of $f(x) = \dfrac{1}{x} - \dfrac{1}{x^2}$.

Solution The graph, as drawn using graphing technology, is shown in Figure 28, using two different viewing windows. (Note that $x = 0$ is not in the domain of f.)

The window in Figure 28(b) seems to show the features of the graph better than the window in Figure 28(a). Does the viewing window in Figure 28(b) include *all* the interesting features of the graph? Or are there perhaps some interesting features to the right of $x = 10$ or to the left of $x = -10$? Also, where exactly do features like maxima, minima, and points of inflection occur? In our five-step process of analyzing the interesting features of the graph, we will be able to sketch the curve by hand, and also answer these questions.

1. ***The x- and y-intercepts:*** We consider $y = \dfrac{1}{x} - \dfrac{1}{x^2}$. To find the x-intercept(s), we set $y = 0$ and solve for x:

$$0 = \frac{1}{x} - \frac{1}{x^2}$$

$$\frac{1}{x} = \frac{1}{x^2}$$

Multiplying both sides by x^2 (we know that x cannot be zero, so we are not multiplying both sides by 0) gives

$$x = 1$$

Thus, there is one x-intercept (which we can see in Figure 28) at $x = 1$.

For the y-intercept, we would substitute $x = 0$ and solve for y. However, we cannot substitute $x = 0$; because $f(0)$ is not defined, the graph does not meet the y-axis.

We add features to our freehand sketch as we go. Figure 29 shows what we have so far.

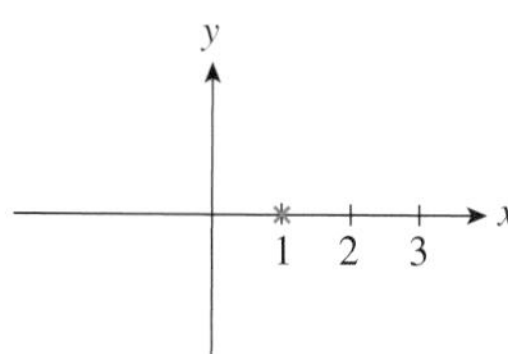

Figure **29**

2. *Relative extrema:* We calculate $f'(x) = -\dfrac{1}{x^2} + \dfrac{2}{x^3}$. To find any stationary points, we set the derivative equal to 0 and solve for x:

$$-\frac{1}{x^2} + \frac{2}{x^3} = 0$$

$$\frac{1}{x^2} = \frac{2}{x^3}$$

$$x = 2$$

Thus, there is one stationary point, at $x = 2$. We can use a test point to the right to determine that this stationary point is a relative maximum:

x	1 (Intercept)	2	3 (Test point)
$y = \dfrac{1}{x} - \dfrac{1}{x^2}$	0	$\dfrac{1}{4}$	$\dfrac{2}{9}$

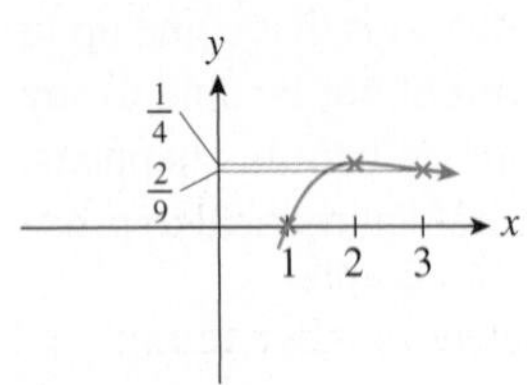

Figure 30

The only possible singular point is at $x = 0$ because $f'(0)$ is not defined. However, $f(0)$ is not defined either, so there are no singular points. Figure 30 shows our graph so far.

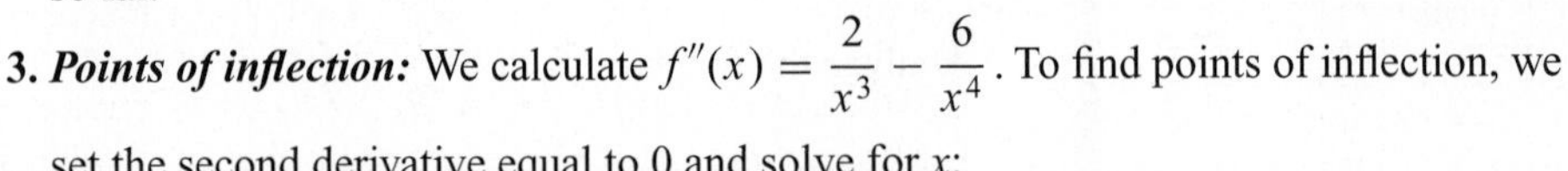

3. *Points of inflection:* We calculate $f''(x) = \dfrac{2}{x^3} - \dfrac{6}{x^4}$. To find points of inflection, we set the second derivative equal to 0 and solve for x:

$$\frac{2}{x^3} - \frac{6}{x^4} = 0$$

$$\frac{2}{x^3} = \frac{6}{x^4}$$

$$2x = 6$$

$$x = 3$$

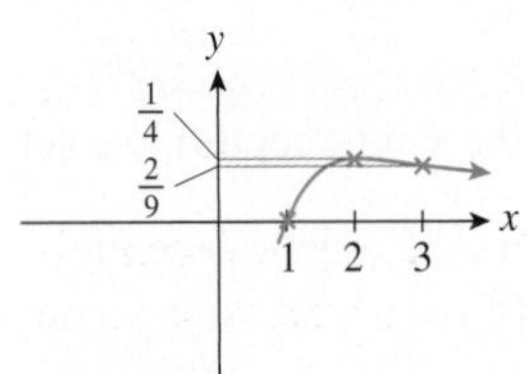

Figure 31

Figure 28 confirms that the graph of f changes from being concave down to being concave up at $x = 3$, so this is a point of inflection. $f''(x)$ is not defined at $x = 0$, but that is not in the domain, so there are no other points of inflection. For example, the graph must be concave down in the whole region $(-\infty, 0)$.

Figure 31 shows our graph so far (we extended the curve near $x = 3$ to suggest a point of inflection at $x = 3$).

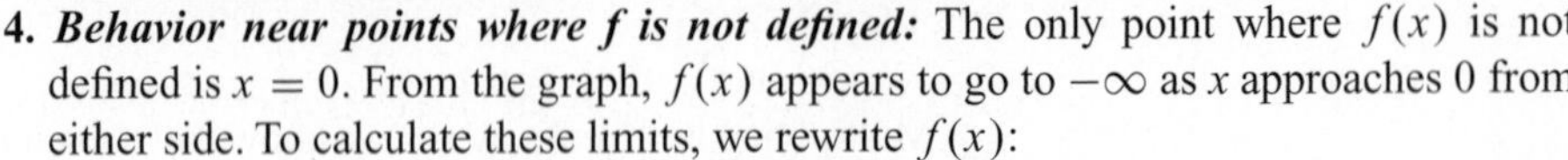

4. *Behavior near points where f is not defined:* The only point where $f(x)$ is not defined is $x = 0$. From the graph, $f(x)$ appears to go to $-\infty$ as x approaches 0 from either side. To calculate these limits, we rewrite $f(x)$:

$$f(x) = \frac{1}{x} - \frac{1}{x^2} = \frac{x-1}{x^2}$$

Now, if x is close to 0 (on either side), the numerator $x - 1$ is close to -1 and the denominator is a very small but positive number. The quotient is therefore a negative number of very large magnitude. Therefore,

$$\lim_{x \to 0^-} f(x) = -\infty$$

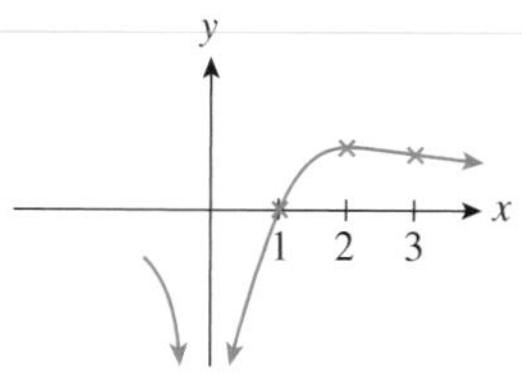

Figure **32**

and

$$\lim_{x\to 0^+} f(x) = -\infty$$

From these limits, we see the following:

(1) Immediately to the *left* of $x = 0$, the graph plunges down toward $-\infty$.

(2) Immediately to the *right* of $x = 0$, the graph also plunges down toward $-\infty$. Figure 32 shows our graph with these features added.

We say that f has a **vertical asymptote** at $x = 0$, meaning that the graph approaches the line $x = 0$ without touching it.

5. ***Behavior at infinity:*** Both $1/x$ and $1/x^2$ go to 0 as x goes to $-\infty$ or $+\infty$; that is,

$$\lim_{x\to -\infty} f(x) = 0$$

and

$$\lim_{x\to +\infty} f(x) = 0$$

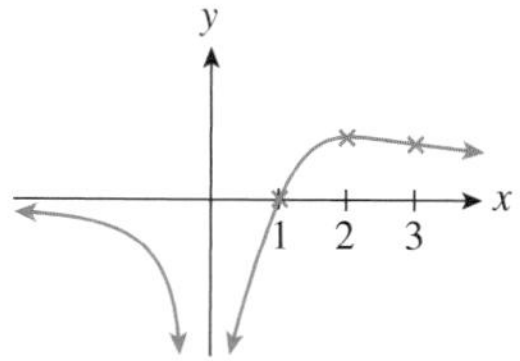

Figure **33**

Thus, on the extreme left and right of our picture, the height of the curve levels off toward zero. Figure 33 shows the completed freehand sketch of the graph.

We say that f has a **horizontal asymptote** at $y = 0$. (Notice another thing: we haven't plotted a single point to the left of the y-axis, and yet we have a pretty good idea of what the curve looks like there! Compare the technology-drawn curve in Figure 28).

In summary, there is one x-intercept at $x = 1$; there is one relative maximum (which, we can now see, is also an absolute maximum) at $x = 2$; there is one point of inflection at $x = 3$, where the graph changes from being concave down to concave up. There is a vertical asymptote at $x = 0$, on both sides of which the graph goes down toward $-\infty$, and a horizontal asymptote at $y = 0$.

Example **5** Analyzing a Graph

Analyze the graph of $f(x) = \dfrac{2x}{3} - (x - 2)^{2/3}$.

Solution

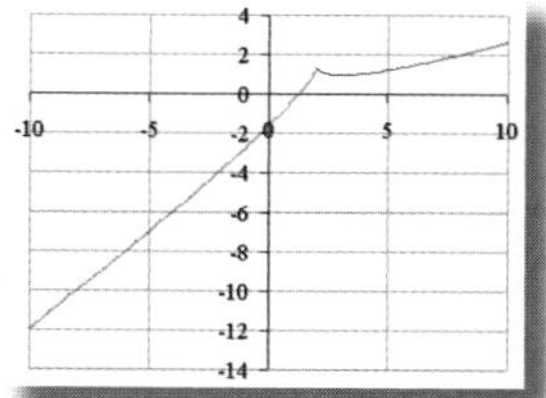

Technology:
`2*x/3-((x-2)^2)^(1/3)`
Figure **34**

Figure 34 shows a technology-generated version of the graph. (Note that in the technology formulation $(x - 2)^{2/3}$ is written as $[(x - 2)^2]^{1/3}$ to avoid problems with some graphing calculators and Excel.)

Let us now recreate this graph by hand, and in the process identify the features we see in Figure 34.

1. ***The x- and y-intercepts:*** We consider $y = \dfrac{2x}{3} - (x - 2)^{2/3}$. For the y-intercept, we set $x = 0$ and solve for y:

$$y = \frac{2(0)}{3} - (0 - 2)^{2/3} = -2^{2/3} \approx -1.59$$

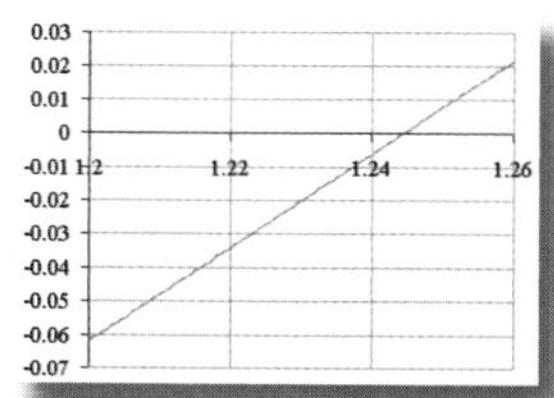

Figure **35**

To find the x-intercept(s), we set $y = 0$ and solve for x. However, if we attempt this, we will find ourselves with a cubic equation that is hard to solve. (Try it!) Following the advice in the note on p. 381, we use graphing technology to locate the x-intercept we see in Figure 34 by zooming in (Figure 35). From Figure 35, we find $x \approx 1.24$. We shall see in the discussion to follow that there can be no other x-intercepts.

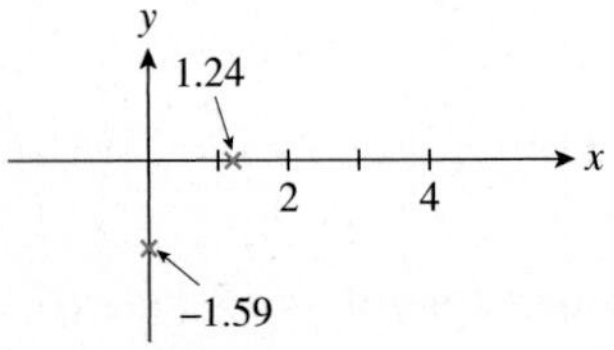

Figure **36**

Figure 36 shows our freehand sketch so far.

2. ***Relative extrema:*** We calculate

$$f'(x) = \frac{2}{3} - \frac{2}{3}(x-2)^{-1/3}$$
$$= \frac{2}{3} - \frac{2}{3(x-2)^{1/3}}$$

To find any stationary points, we set the derivative equal to 0 and solve for x:

$$\frac{2}{3} - \frac{2}{3(x-2)^{1/3}} = 0$$
$$(x-2)^{1/3} = 1$$
$$x - 2 = 1^3 = 1$$
$$x = 3$$

To check for singular points, look for points where $f(x)$ is defined and $f'(x)$ is not defined. The only such point is $x = 2$: $f'(x)$ is not defined at $x = 2$, whereas $f(x)$ is defined there, so we have a singular point at $x = 2$.

x	2 (Singular point)	3 (Stationary point)	4 (Test point)
$y = \frac{2x}{3} - (x-2)^{2/3}$	$\frac{4}{3}$	1	1.079

Figure 37 shows our graph so far.

We see that there is a singular relative maximum at $(2, 4/3)$ (we will confirm that the graph eventually gets higher on the right) and a stationary relative minimum at $x = 3$.

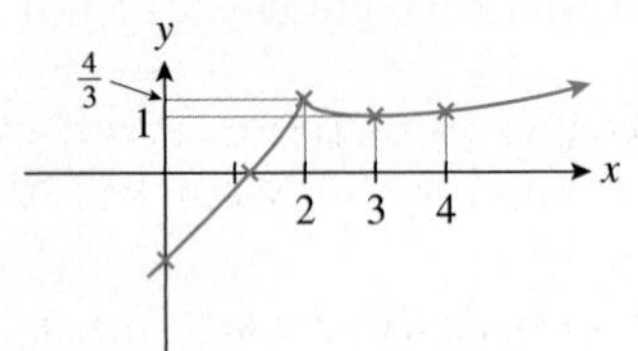

Figure **37**

3. ***Points of inflection:*** We calculate

$$f''(x) = \frac{2}{9(x-2)^{4/3}}$$

To find points of inflection, we set the second derivative equal to 0 and solve for x. But the equation

$$0 = \frac{2}{9(x-2)^{4/3}}$$

has no solution for x, so there are no points of inflection on the graph.

4. ***Behavior near points where f is not defined:*** Because $f(x)$ is defined everywhere, there are no such points to consider. In particular, there are no vertical asymptotes.

5. ***Behavior at infinity:*** We estimate the following limits numerically:

$$\lim_{x\to-\infty}\left[\frac{2x}{3} - (x-2)^{2/3}\right] = -\infty$$

and

$$\lim_{x\to+\infty}\left[\frac{2x}{3} - (x-2)^{2/3}\right] = +\infty$$

Thus, on the extreme left the curve goes down toward $-\infty$, and on the extreme right the curve rises toward $+\infty$. In particular, there are no horizontal asymptotes. (There can also be no other x-intercepts.)

Figure 38 shows the completed graph.

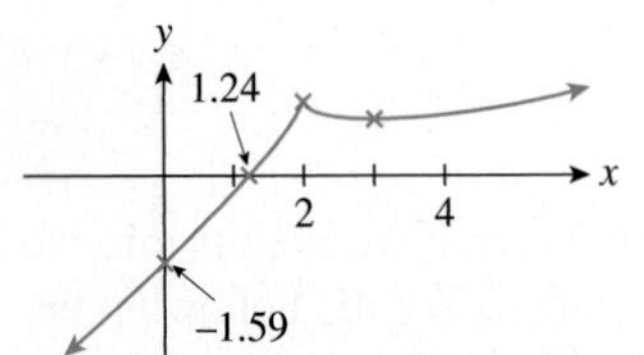

Figure **38**

5.3 EXERCISES

● denotes basic skills exercises

tech Ex indicates exercises that should be solved using technology

In Exercises 1–10, calculate $\dfrac{d^2y}{dx^2}$ hint [see Quick Examples on p. 376]

1. ● $y = 3x^2 - 6$
2. ● $y = -x^2 + x$
3. ● $y = \dfrac{2}{x}$
4. ● $y = -\dfrac{2}{x^2}$
5. ● $y = 4x^{0.4} - x$
6. ● $y = 0.2x^{-0.1}$
7. ● $y = e^{-(x-1)} - x$
8. ● $y = e^{-x} + e^x$
9. ● $y = \dfrac{1}{x} - \ln x$
10. ● $y = x^{-2} + \ln x$

In Exercises 11–16, the position s of a point (in feet) is given as a function of time t (in seconds). Find ***(a)*** *its acceleration as a function of t and* ***(b)*** *its acceleration at the specified time.*

11. ● $s = 12 + 3t - 16t^2;\ t = 2$
12. ● $s = -12 + t - 16t^2;\ t = 2$
13. ● $s = \dfrac{1}{t} + \dfrac{1}{t^2};\ t = 1$
14. ● $s = \dfrac{1}{t} - \dfrac{1}{t^2};\ t = 2$
15. ● $s = \sqrt{t} + t^2;\ t = 4$
16. ● $s = 2\sqrt{t} + t^3;\ t = 1$

In Exercises 17–24, the graph of a function is given. Find the approximate coordinates of all points of inflection of each function (if any). hint [see Quick Examples on p. 380]

17. ●

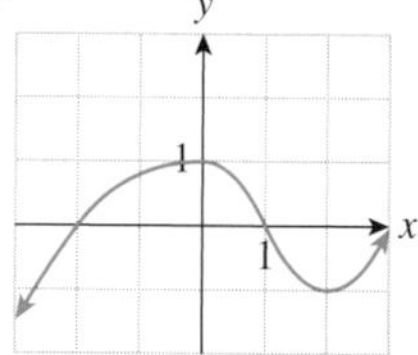

18. ●

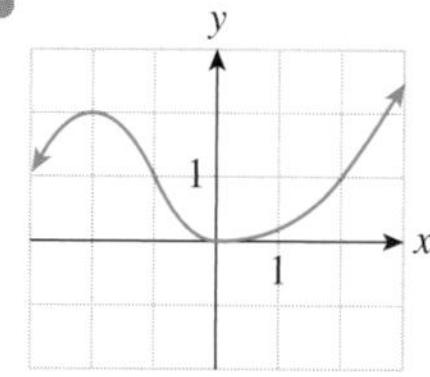

19. ●

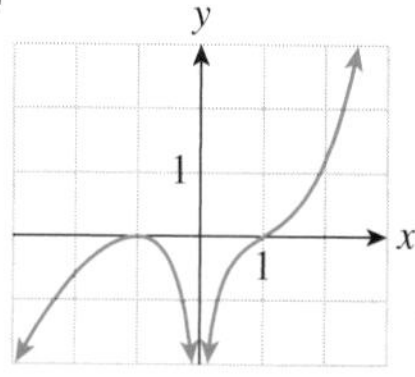

20. ●

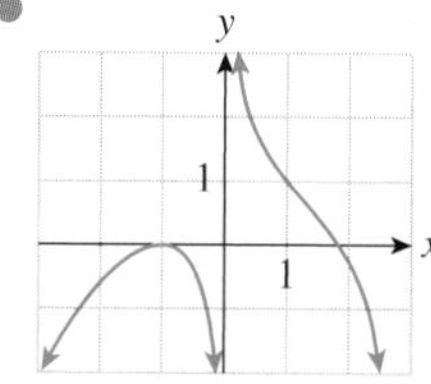

21. ●

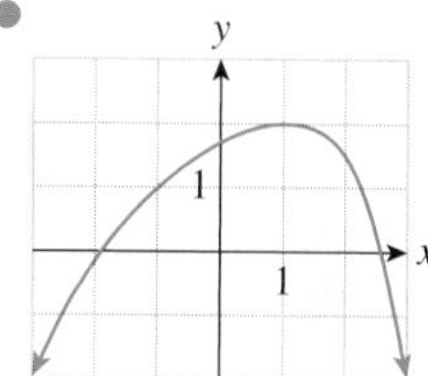

22. ●

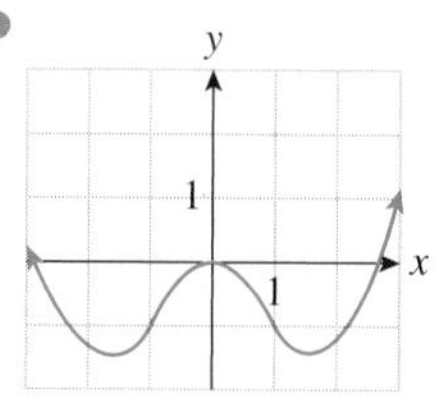

23. ●

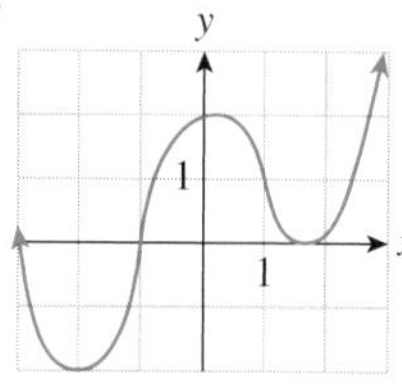

24. ●

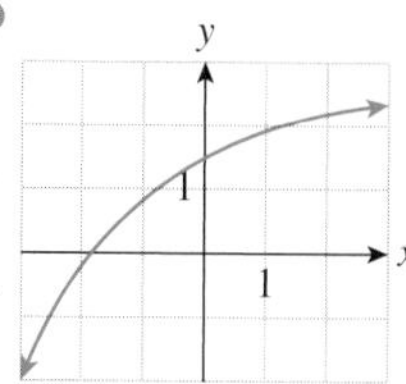

In Exercises 25–28, the graph of the derivative, *$f'(x)$, is given. Determine the x-coordinates of all points of inflection of $f(x)$, if any. (Assume that $f(x)$ is defined and continuous everywhere in $[-3, 3]$.)* hint [see *Before we go on* discussion in Example 3]

25. ●

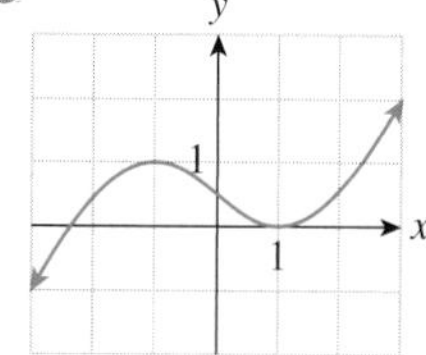

26. ●

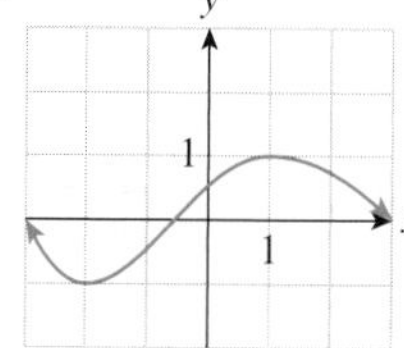

27. ●

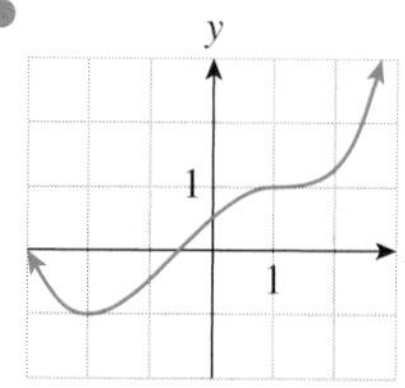

28. ●

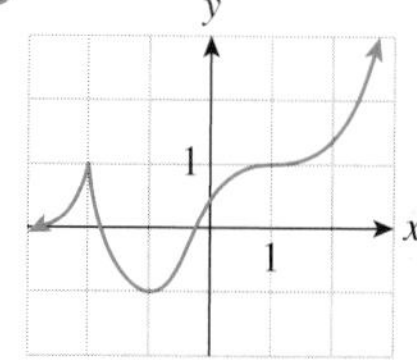

In Exercises 29–32, the graph of the second derivative, *$f''(x)$, is given. Determine the x-coordinates of all points of inflection of $f(x)$, if any. (Assume that $f(x)$ is defined and continuous everywhere in $[-3, 3]$.)*

29.

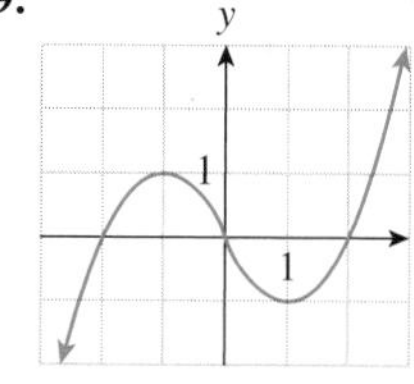

30.

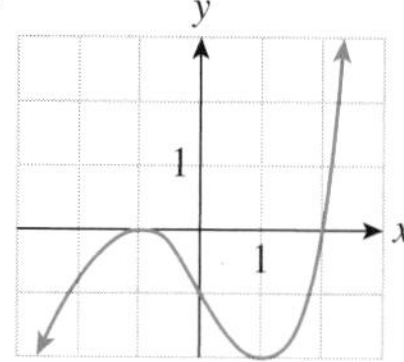

31.

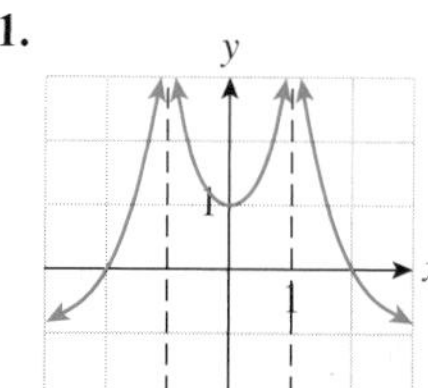

32.

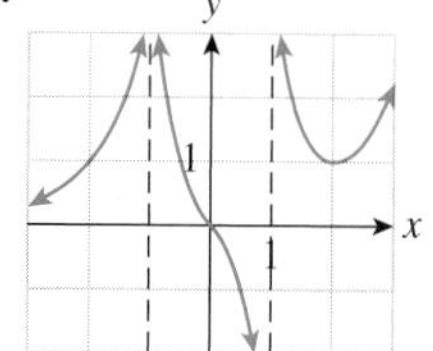

In Exercises 33–58, sketch the graph of the given function, labeling all relative and absolute extrema and points of inflection, and vertical and horizontal asymptotes. Check your graph using technology. In the marked exercises, use graphing technology to approximate the coordinates of the extrema and points of inflection to two decimal places.

33. ● $f(x) = x^2 + 2x + 1$ *hint* [see Example 4]

34. ● $f(x) = -x^2 - 2x - 1$

35. ● $f(x) = 2x^3 + 3x^2 - 12x + 1$

36. ● $f(x) = 4x^3 + 3x^2 + 2$

37. ● $g(x) = x^3 - 12x$, domain $[-4, 4]$

38. ● $g(x) = 2x^3 - 6x$, domain $[-4, 4]$

39. ● $g(t) = \frac{1}{4}t^4 - \frac{2}{3}t^3 + \frac{1}{2}t^2$

40. ● $g(t) = 3t^4 - 16t^3 + 24t^2 + 1$

41. ● $f(t) = \frac{t^2 + 1}{t^2 - 1}$, domain $[-2, 2]$, $t \neq \pm 1$

42. ● $f(t) = \frac{t^2 - 1}{t^2 + 1}$, domain $[-2, 2]$

43. ● $f(x) = x + \frac{1}{x}$

44. ● $f(x) = x^2 + \frac{1}{x^2}$

45. ● $k(x) = \frac{2x}{3} + (x + 1)^{2/3}$ *hint* [see Example 5]

46. ● $k(x) = \frac{2x}{5} - (x - 1)^{2/5}$

47. ● $g(x) = x^3/(x^2 + 3)$

48. ● $g(x) = x^3/(x^2 - 3)$

49. ● $f(x) = x - \ln x$, domain $(0, +\infty)$

50. ● $f(x) = x - \ln x^2$, domain $(0, +\infty)$

51. ● $f(x) = x^2 + \ln x^2$

52. ● $f(x) = 2x^2 + \ln x$

53. ● $g(t) = e^t - t$, domain $[-1, 1]$

54. ● $g(t) = e^{-t^2}$

55. tech Ex $f(x) = x^4 - 2x^3 + x^2 - 2x + 1$

56. tech Ex $f(x) = x^4 + x^3 + x^2 + x + 1$

57. tech Ex $f(x) = e^x - x^3$

58. tech Ex $f(x) = e^x - \frac{x^4}{4}$

Applications

59. ● ***Acceleration on Mars*** If a stone is dropped from a height of 40 meters above the Martian surface, its height in meters after t seconds is given by $s = 40 - 1.9t^2$. What is its acceleration? *hint* [see Example 1]

60. ● ***Acceleration on the Moon*** If a stone is thrown up at 10 m per second from a height of 100 meters above the surface of the Moon, its height in meters after t seconds is given by $s = 100 + 10t - 0.8t^2$. What is its acceleration?

61. ● ***Motion in a Straight Line*** The position of a particle moving in a straight line is given by $s = t^3 - t^2$ ft after t seconds. Find an expression for its acceleration after a time t. Is its velocity increasing or decreasing when $t = 1$?

62. ● ***Motion in a Straight Line*** The position of a particle moving in a straight line is given by $s = 3e^t - 8t^2$ ft after t seconds. Find an expression for its acceleration after a time t. Is its velocity increasing or decreasing when $t = 1$?

63. ● ***Bottled Water Sales*** Annual sales of bottled water in the U.S. in the period 1993–2003 could be approximated by

$$R(t) = 17t^2 + 100t + 2300 \text{ million gallons} \quad (3 \le t \le 13)$$

where t is time in years since 1990.[28] Were sales of bottled water accelerating or decelerating in 2000? How fast? *hint* [see Example 2]

64. ● ***Sparkling Water Sales*** Annual sales of sparkling water in the U.S. in the period 1993–2003 could be approximated by

$$S(t) = -1.3t^2 + 4t + 160 \text{ million gallons} \quad (3 \le t \le 13)$$

where t is time in years since 1990.[29] Were sales of sparkling water accelerating or decelerating in 2002? How fast?

65. ● ***Embryo Development*** The daily oxygen consumption of a bird embryo increases from the time the egg is laid through the time the chick hatches. In a typical galliform bird, the oxygen consumption can be approximated by

$$c(t) = -0.065t^3 + 3.4t^2 - 22t + 3.6 \text{ ml} \quad (8 \le t \le 30)$$

where t is the time (in days) since the egg was laid.[30] (An egg will typically hatch at around $t = 28$.) Use the model to estimate the following (give the units of measurement for each answer and round all answers to two significant digits):

a. The daily oxygen consumption 20 days after the egg was laid

b. The rate at which the oxygen consumption is changing 20 days after the egg was laid

c. The rate at which the oxygen consumption is accelerating 20 days after the egg was laid

66. ● ***Embryo Development*** The daily oxygen consumption of a turkey embryo increases from the time the egg is laid through the time the chick hatches. In a brush turkey, the oxygen consumption can be approximated by

$$c(t) = -0.028t^3 + 2.9t^2 - 44t + 95 \text{ ml} \quad (20 \le t \le 50)$$

where t is the time (in days) since the egg was laid.[31] (An egg will typically hatch at around $t = 50$.) Use the model to

---

[28] SOURCE: Beverage Marketing Corporation news release, "Bottled water now number-two commercial beverage in U.S., says Beverage Marketing Corporation," April 8, 2004, available at www.beveragemarketing.com.

[29] Source for data: Beverage Marketing Corporation of New York/*New York Times*, June 21, 2001, p. C1.

[30] The model approximates graphical data published in the article "The Brush Turkey" by Roger S. Seymour, *Scientific American*, December, 1991, pp. 108–114.

[31] Ibid.

estimate the following (give the units of measurement for each answer and round all answers to two significant digits):

a. The daily oxygen consumption 40 days after the egg was laid

b. The rate at which the oxygen consumption is changing 40 days after the egg was laid

c. The rate at which the oxygen consumption is accelerating 40 days after the egg was laid

67. ● ***Epidemics*** The following graph shows the total number n of people (in millions) infected in an epidemic as a function of time t (in years):

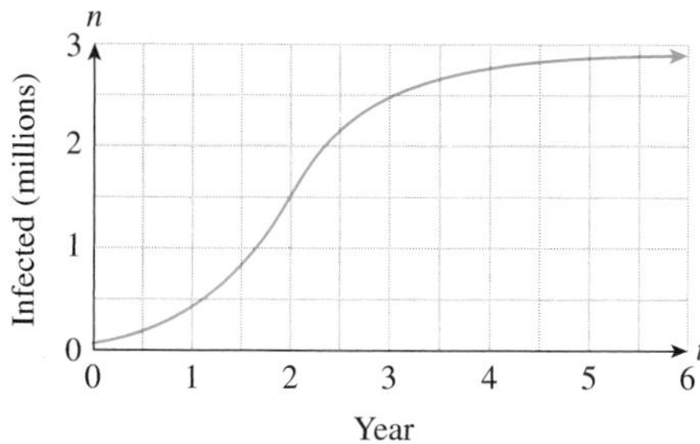

a. When to the nearest year was the rate of new infection largest?

b. When could the Centers for Disease Control and Prevention announce that the rate of new infection was beginning to drop?

68. ● ***Sales*** The following graph shows the total number of Pomegranate Q4 computers sold since their release (t is in years):

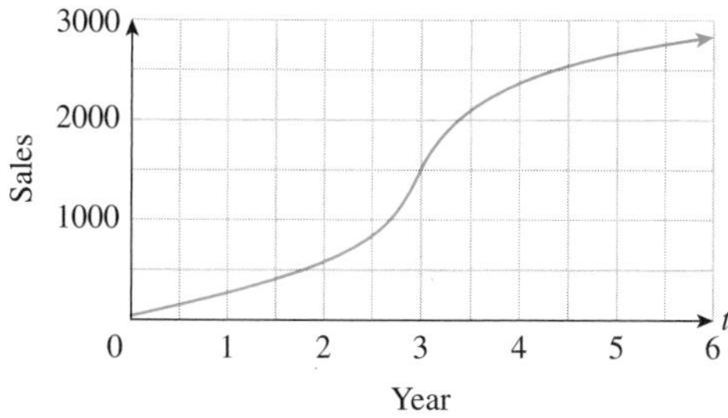

a. When were the computers selling fastest?

b. Explain why this graph might look as it does.

69. ● ***Industrial Output*** The following graph shows the yearly industrial output (measured in billions of dollars) of the Republic of Mars over a seven-year period:

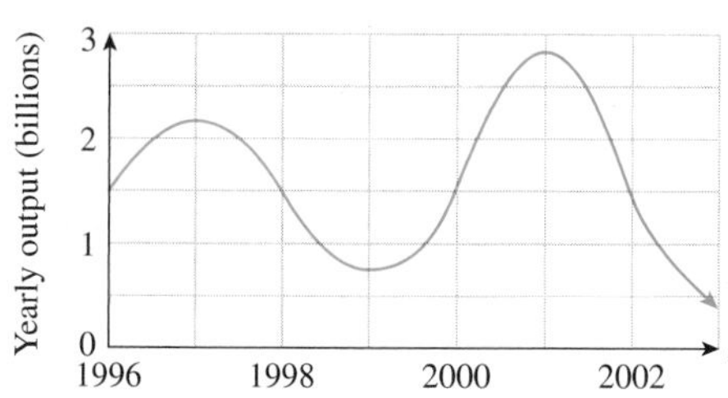

a. When to the nearest year did the rate of change of yearly industrial output reach a maximum?

b. When to the nearest year did the rate of change of yearly industrial output reach a minimum?

c. When to the nearest year did the rate of change of yearly industrial output first start to increase?

70. ● ***Profits*** The following graph shows the yearly profits of Gigantic Conglomerate, Inc. (GCI) from 1990 to 2005:

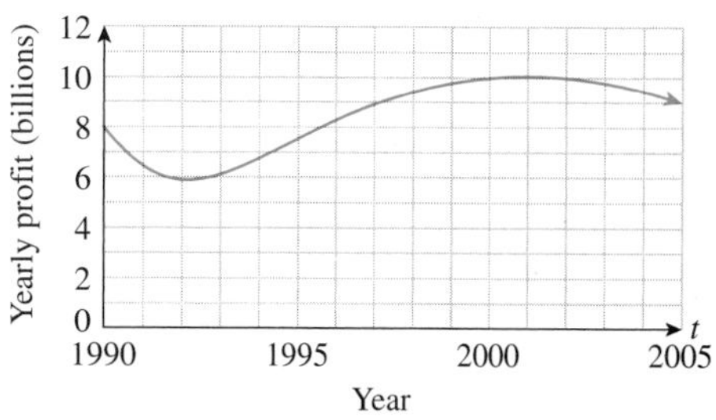

a. When were the profits rising most rapidly?

b. When were the profits falling most rapidly?

c. When could GCI's board of directors legitimately tell stockholders that they had "turned the company around"?

71. ● ***Scientific Research*** The percentage of research articles in the prominent journal *Physics Review* that were written by researchers in the U.S. during the years 1983–2003 can be modeled by

$$P(t) = 25 + \frac{36}{1 + 0.06(0.7)^{-t}}$$

where t is time in years since 1983.[32] The graphs of P, P' and P'' are shown here:

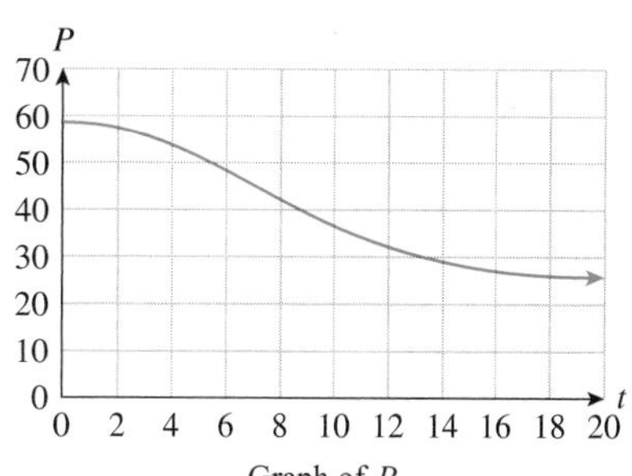

Graph of P

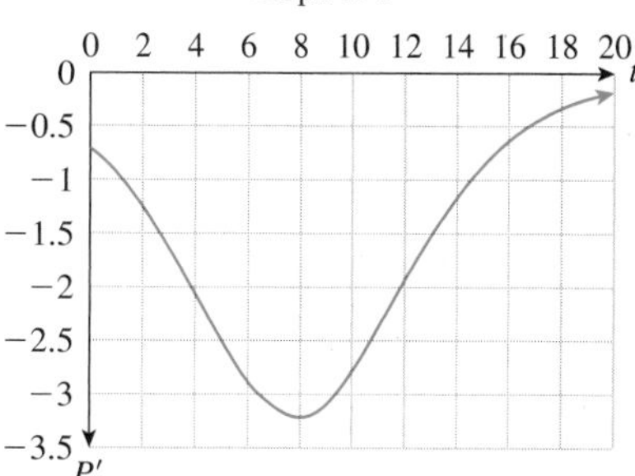

Graph of P'

[32] SOURCE: The American Physical Society/*New York Times,* May 3, 2003, p. A1.

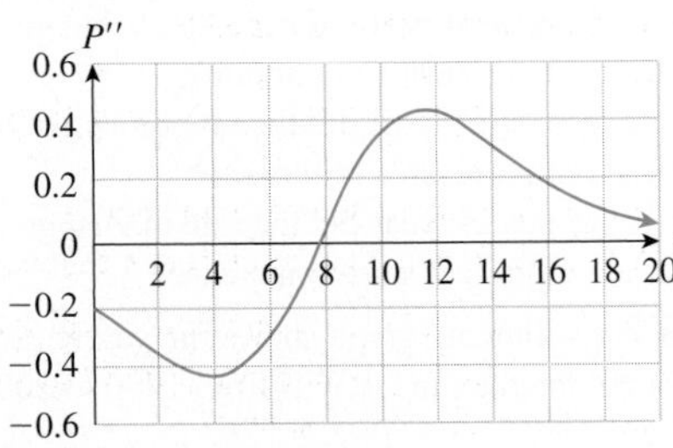

Graph of P''

Determine, to the nearest whole number, the values of t for which the graph of P is concave up, where it is concave down, and locate any points of inflection. What does the point of inflection tell you about science articles? *hint* [see Example 3]

72. ● ***Scientific Research*** The number of research articles in the prominent journal *Physics Review* that were written by researchers in Europe during the years 1983–2003 can be modeled by

$$P(t) = \frac{7.0}{1 + 5.4(1.2)^{-t}}$$

where t is time in years since 1983.[33] The graphs of P, P', and P'' are shown here:

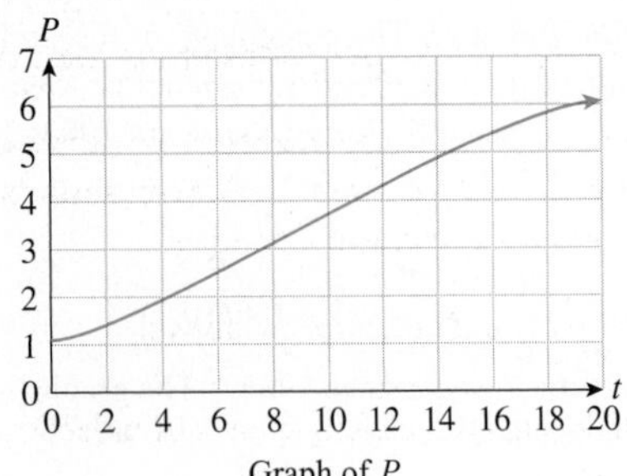

Graph of P

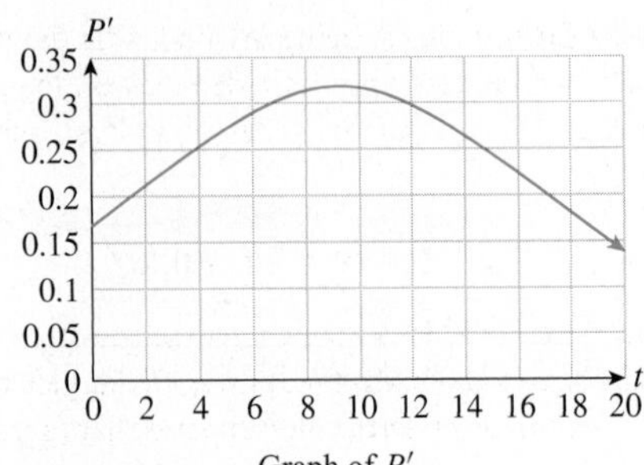

Graph of P'

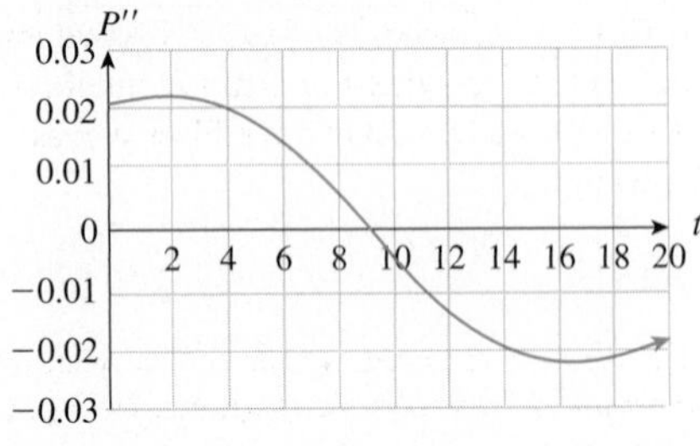

Graph of P''

Determine, to the nearest whole number, the values of t for which the graph of P is concave up, where it is concave down, and locate any points of inflection. What does the point of inflection tell you about science articles?

73. ● ***Embryo Development*** Here are sketches of the graphs of c, c', and c'' from Exercise 65:

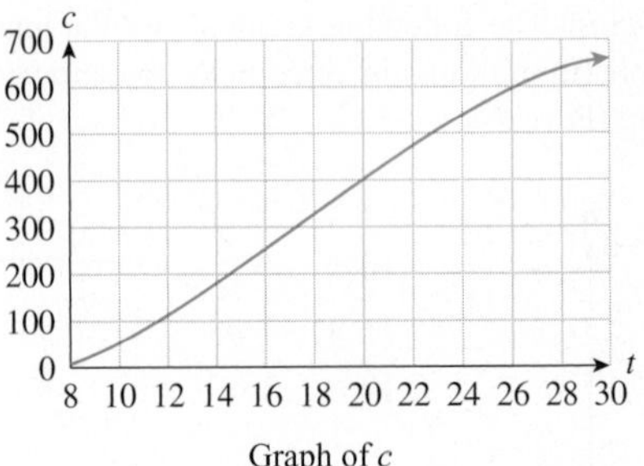

Graph of c

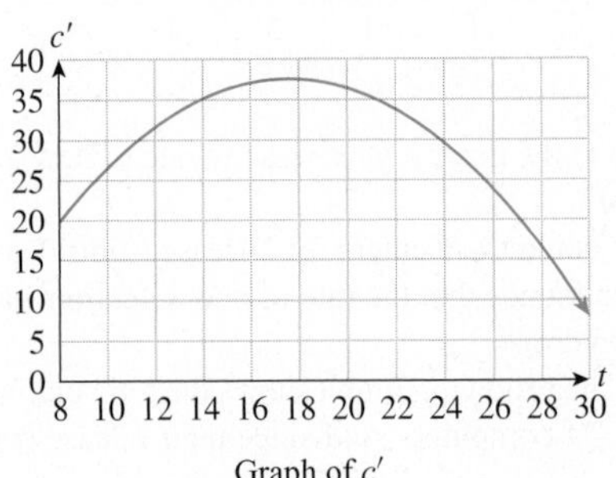

Graph of c'

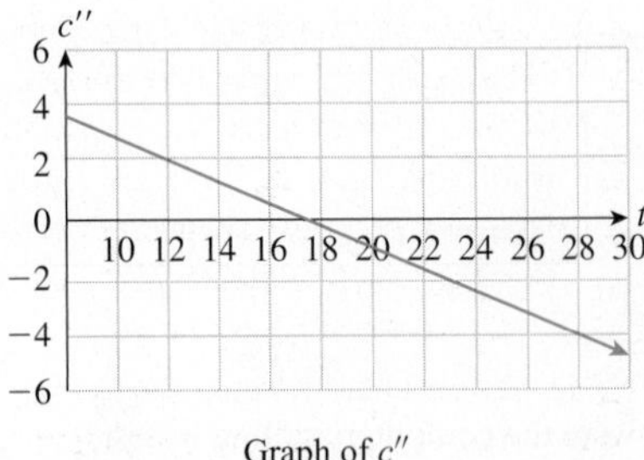

Graph of c''

Multiple choice:

a. The graph of c' **(A)** has a point of inflection. **(B)** has no points of inflection in the range shown.

b. At around 18 days after the egg is laid, daily oxygen consumption is **(A)** at a maximum. **(B)** increasing at a maximum rate. **(C)** just beginning to decrease.

c. For $t > 18$ days, the oxygen consumption is **(A)** increasing at a decreasing rate. **(B)** decreasing at an increasing rate. **(C)** increasing at an increasing rate.

74. ● ***Embryo Development*** Here are sketches of the graphs of c, c', and c'' from Exercise 66:

[33] SOURCE: The American Physical Society/*New York Times*, May 3, 2003, p. A1.

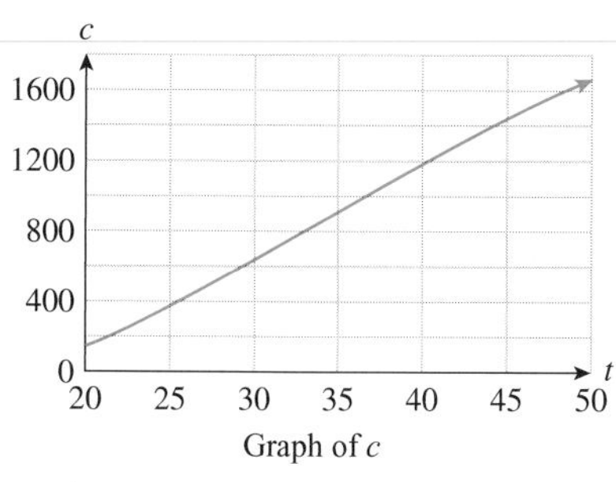

Graph of c

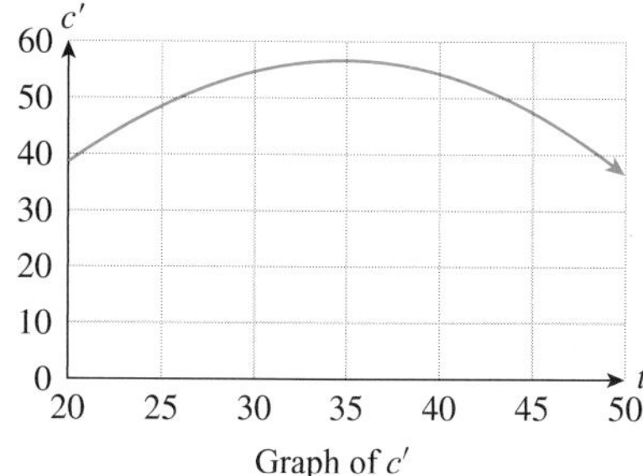

Graph of c'

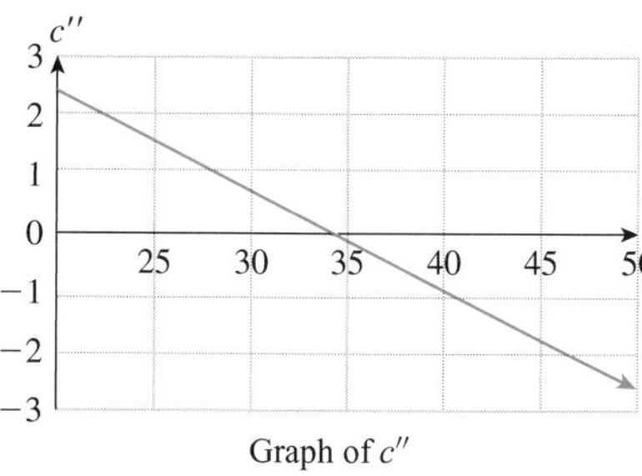

Graph of c''

Multiple choice:

a. The graph of c **(A)** has points of inflection. **(B)** has no points of inflection. **(C)** impossible to say from the graphs.

b. At around 35 days after the egg is laid, the rate of change of daily oxygen consumption is **(A)** at a maximum. **(B)** increasing at a maximum rate. **(C)** just becoming negative.

c. For $t < 35$ days, the oxygen consumption is **(A)** increasing at an increasing rate. **(B)** increasing at a decreasing rate. **(C)** decreasing at an increasing rate.

75. ***Education and Crime*** The following graph shows a striking relationship between the total prison population and the average combined SAT score in the U.S.:

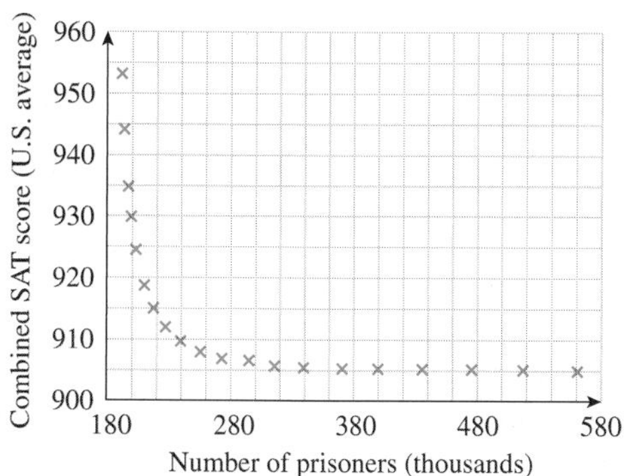

These data can be accurately modeled by

$$S(n) = 904 + \frac{1326}{(n-180)^{1.325}} \quad (192 \le n \le 563)$$

Here, $S(n)$ is the combined U.S. average SAT score at a time when the total U.S. prison population was n thousand.[34]

a. Are there any points of inflection on the graph of S?

b. What does the concavity of the graph of S tell you about prison populations and SAT scores?

76. ***Education and Crime*** Refer back to the model in the preceding exercise,

a. Are there any points of inflection on the graph of S'?

b. When is S'' a maximum? Interpret your answer in terms of prisoners and SAT scores.

77. ***Patents*** In 1965, the economist F.M. Scherer modeled the number, n, of patents produced by a firm as a function of the size, s, of the firm (measured in annual sales in millions of dollars). He came up with the following equation based on a study of 448 large firms:[35]

$$n = -3.79 + 144.42s - 23.86s^2 + 1.457s^3$$

a. Find $\left.\frac{d^2n}{ds^2}\right|_{s=3}$. Is the rate at which patents are produced as the size of a firm goes up increasing or decreasing with size when $s = 3$? Comment on Scherer's words, "... we find diminishing returns dominating."

b. Find $\left.\frac{d^2n}{ds^2}\right|_{s=7}$ and interpret the answer.

c. Find the s-coordinate of any points of inflection and interpret the result.

78. ***Returns on Investments*** A company finds that the number of new products it develops per year depends on the size of its annual R&D budget, x (in thousands of dollars), according to the formula

$$n(x) = -1 + 8x + 2x^2 - 0.4x^3$$

a. Find $n''(1)$ and $n''(3)$, and interpret the results.

b. Find the size of the budget that gives the largest rate of return as measured in new products per dollar (again, called the point of diminishing returns).

79. tech Ex ***Ecology*** Manatees are grazing sea mammals sometimes referred to as sea sirens. Increasing numbers of manatees have been killed by boats off the Florida coast, as shown in the following chart:

---

[34] The model is the authors' based on data for the years 1967–1989. SOURCES: *Sourcebook of Criminal Justice Statistics,* 1990, p. 604/Educational Testing Service.

[35] SOURCE: F. M. Scherer, "Firm Size, Market Structure, Opportunity, and the Output of Patented Inventions," *American Economic Review,* 55 (December 1965): pp. 1097–1125.

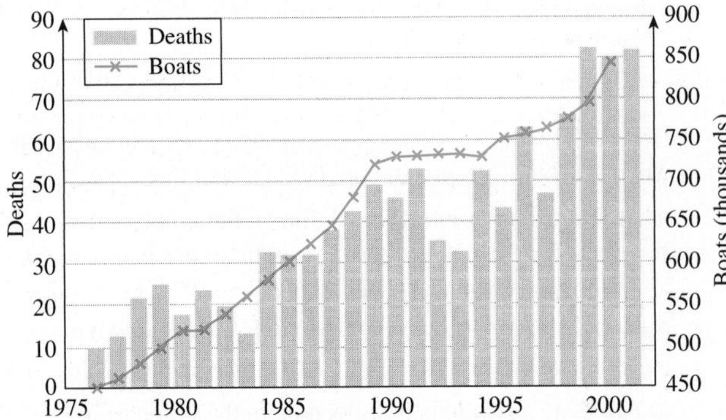

Let $M(t)$ be the number of manatees killed and let $B(t)$ be the number of boats registered in Florida in year t since 1975. These functions can be approximated by the following linear functions:[36]

$$M(t) = 2.48t + 6.87 \text{ manatees}$$
$$B(t) = 15{,}700t + 444{,}000 \text{ boats}$$

Graph the function $M(t)/B(t)$. Is the graph of $M(t)/B(t)$ concave up or concave down? The concavity of $M(t)/B(t)$ tells you that:

(A) Fewer manatees are killed per boat each year.
(B) More manatees are killed per boat each year.
(C) The number of manatees killed per boat is increasing at a decreasing rate.
(D) The number of manatees killed per boat is decreasing at an increasing rate.

80. tech Ex ***Saudi Oil Revenues*** The spot price of crude oil during the period 2000–2005 can be approximated by

$$P(t) = 5t + 25 \text{ dollars per barrel} \quad (0 \le t \le 5)$$

in year t, where $t = 0$ represents 2000. Saudi Arabia's crude oil production over the same period can be approximated by

$$Q(t) = 0.082t^2 - 0.22t + 8.2 \text{ million barrels per day}^{37} \quad (0 \le t \le 5)$$

Graph the revenue function $R(t) = P(t)Q(t)$. Is the graph of $R(t)$ concave up or concave down? The concavity of $R(t)$ tells you that:

(A) Saudi crude oil production was increasing at an accelerating rate.
(B) Revenues from Saudi crude oil production were increasing at an increasing rate.
(C) The acceleration of revenues from Saudi crude oil production was increasing.
(D) The rate of change of revenues from Saudi crude oil production was accelerating.

[36] Rounded regression model. Sources for data: Florida Department of Highway Safety & Motor Vehicles, Florida Marine Institute/*New York Times*, February 12, 2002, p. F4.

[37] Source for data: EIA/Saudi British Bank (www.sabb.com). 2004 figures are based on mid-year data, and 2005 data are estimates.

81. tech Ex ***Asset Appreciation*** You manage a small antique store that owns a collection of Louis XVI jewelry boxes. Their value v is increasing according to the formula

$$v = \frac{10{,}000}{1 + 500e^{-0.5t}}$$

where t is the number of years from now. You anticipate an inflation rate of 5% per year, so that the present value of an item that will be worth \$$v$ in t years' time is given by

$$p = v(1.05)^{-t}$$

What is the greatest rate of increase of the value of your antiques, and when is this rate attained?

82. tech Ex ***Harvesting Forests*** The following equation models the approximate volume in cubic feet of a typical Douglas fir tree of age t years.[38]

$$V = \frac{22{,}514}{1 + 22{,}514t^{-2.55}}$$

The lumber will be sold at \$10 per cubic foot, and you do not expect the price of lumber to appreciate in the foreseeable future. On the other hand, you anticipate a general inflation rate of 5% per year, so that the present value of an item that will be worth \$$v$ in t years time is given by

$$p = v(1.05)^{-t}$$

What is the largest rate of increase of the value of a fir tree, and when is this rate attained?

83. tech Ex ***Asset Appreciation*** As the financial consultant to a classic auto dealership, you estimate that the total value of its collection of 1959 Chevrolets and Fords is given by the formula

$$v = 300{,}000 + 1000t^2$$

where t is the number of years from now. You anticipate a continuous inflation rate of 5% per year, so that the discounted (present) value of an item that will be worth \$$v$ in t years' time is given by

$$p = ve^{-0.05t}$$

When is the value of the collection of classic cars increasing most rapidly? When is it decreasing most rapidly?

84. tech Ex ***Plantation Management*** The value of a fir tree in your plantation increases with the age of the tree according to the formula

$$v = \frac{20t}{1 + 0.05t}$$

[38] The model is the authors', and is based on data in *Environmental and Natural Resource Economics* by Tom Tietenberg, Third Edition, (New York: HarperCollins, 1992), p. 282.

where t is the age of the tree in years. Given a continuous inflation rate of 5% per year, the discounted (present) value of a newly planted seedling is

$$p = ve^{-0.05t}$$

When is the discounted value of a tree increasing most rapidly? Decreasing most rapidly?

Communication and Reasoning Exercises

85. ● Complete the following: If the graph of a function is concave up on its entire domain, then its second derivative is ______ on the domain.

86. ● Complete the following: If the graph of a function is concave up on its entire domain, then its first derivative is ______ on the domain.

87. ● Daily sales of Kent's Tents reached a maximum in January, 2002 and declined to a minimum in January, 2003 before starting to climb again. The graph of daily sales shows a point of inflection at June, 2002. What is the significance of the point of inflection?

88. ● The graph of daily sales of Luddington's Wellington boots is concave down, although sales continue to increase. What properties of the graph of daily sales versus time are reflected in the following behaviors: **a.** a point of inflection next year **b.** a horizontal asymptote?

89. ● Company A's profits satisfy $P(0) = \$1$ million, $P'(0) = \$1$ million per year, and $P''(0) = -\$1$ million per year per year. Company B's profits satisfy $P(0) = \$1$ million, $P'(0) = -\$1$ million per year, and $P''(0) = \$1$ million per year per year. There are no points of inflection in either company's profit curve. Sketch two pairs of profit curves: one in which Company A ultimately outperforms Company B and another in which Company B ultimately outperforms Company A.

90. ● Company C's profits satisfy $P(0) = \$1$ million, $P'(0) = \$1$ million per year, and $P''(0) = -\$1$ million per year per year. Company D's profits satisfy $P(0) = \$0$ million, $P'(0) = \$0$ million per year, and $P''(0) = \$1$ million per year per year. There are no points of inflection in either company's profit curve. Sketch two pairs of profit curves: one in which Company C ultimately outperforms Company D and another in which Company D ultimately outperforms Company C.

91. Explain geometrically why the derivative of a function has a relative extremum at a point of inflection, if it is defined there. Which points of inflection give rise to relative maxima in the derivative?

92. If we regard position, s, as a function of time, t, what is the significance of the *third* derivative, $s'''(t)$? Describe an everyday scenario in which this arises.

● basic skills   *tech* Ex technology exercise

5.4 Related Rates

We start by recalling some basic facts about the rate of change of a quantity:

Rate of Change of Q

If Q is a quantity changing over time t, then the derivative dQ/dt is the rate at which Q changes over time.

quick **Examples**

1. If A is the area of an expanding circle, then dA/dt is the rate at which the area is increasing.
2. *Words:* The radius r of a sphere is currently 3 cm and increasing at a rate of 2 cm/s.
   Symbols: $r = 3$ cm and $dr/dt = 2$ cm/s.

In this section we are concerned with what are called **related rates** problems. In such a problem we have two (sometimes more) related quantities, we know the rate at which one is changing, and we wish to find the rate at which another is changing. A typical example is the following.

Example 1 The Expanding Circle

The radius of a circle is increasing at a rate of 10 cm/s. How fast is the area increasing at the instant when the radius has reached 5 cm?

Solution We have two related quantities: the radius of the circle, r, and its area, A. The first sentence of the problem tells us that r is increasing at a certain rate. When we see a sentence referring to speed or change, it is very helpful to rephrase the sentence using the phrase "the rate of change of." Here, we can say

The rate of change of r is 10 cm/s.

Because the rate of change is the derivative, we can rewrite this sentence as the equation

$$\frac{dr}{dt} = 10$$

Similarly, the second sentence of the problem asks how A is changing. We can rewrite that question:

What is the rate of change of A when the radius is 5 *cm?*

Using mathematical notation, the question is:

$$\textit{What is } \frac{dA}{dt} \textit{ when } r = 5?$$

Thus, knowing one rate of change, dr/dt, we wish to find a related rate of change, dA/dt. To find exactly how these derivatives are related, we need the equation relating the variables, which is

$$A = \pi r^2$$

To find the relationship between the derivatives, we take the derivative of both sides of this equation *with respect to t*. On the left we get dA/dt. On the right we need to remember that r is a function of t and use the chain rule. We get

$$\frac{dA}{dt} = 2\pi r \frac{dr}{dt}$$

Now we substitute the given values $r = 5$ and $dr/dt = 10$. This gives

$$\left.\frac{dA}{dt}\right|_{r=5} = 2\pi(5)(10) = 100\pi \approx 314\,\text{cm}^2/\text{s}$$

Thus, the area is increasing at the rate of 314 cm^2/s when the radius is 5 cm.

We can organize our work as follows:

Solving a Related Rates Problem

A. The Problem

1. List the related, changing quantities.
2. Restate the problem in terms of rates of change. Rewrite the problem using mathematical notation for the changing quantities and their derivatives.

B. The Relationship

1. Draw a diagram, if appropriate, showing the changing quantities.
2. Find an equation or equations relating the changing quantities.
3. Take the derivative with respect to time of the equation(s) relating the quantities to get the **derived equation(s),** which relate the rates of change of the quantities.

C. The Solution

1. Substitute into the derived equation(s) the given values of the quantities and their derivatives.
2. Solve for the derivative required.

We can illustrate the procedure with the "ladder problem" found in almost every calculus textbook.

Example 2 The Falling Ladder

Jane is at the top of a 5-foot ladder when it starts to slide down the wall at a rate of 3 feet per minute. Jack is standing on the ground behind her. How fast is the base of the ladder moving when it hits him if Jane is 4 feet from the ground at that instant?

Solution The first sentence talks about (the top of) the ladder sliding down the wall. Thus, one of the changing quantities is the height of the top of the ladder. The question asked refers to the motion of the base of the ladder, so another changing quantity is the distance of the base of the ladder from the wall. Let's record these variables and follow the outline above to obtain the solution.

A. The Problem

1. The changing quantities are

   h = height of the top of the ladder
   b = distance of the base of the ladder from the wall

2. We rephrase the problem in words, using the phrase "rate of change":

   The rate of change of the height of the top of the ladder is -3 *feet per minute. What is the rate of change of the distance of the base from the wall when the top of the ladder is* 4 *feet from the ground?*

   We can now rewrite the problem mathematically:

$$\frac{dh}{dt} = -3.\text{ Find } \frac{db}{dt} \text{ when } h = 4$$

B. The Relationship

1. Figure 39 shows the ladder and the variables h and b. Notice that we put in the figure the fixed length, 5, of the ladder, but any changing quantities, like h and b, we leave as variables. We shall not use any specific values for h or b until the very end.
2. From the figure, we can see that h and b are related by the Pythagorean theorem:

$$h^2 + b^2 = 25$$

Figure 39

3. Taking the derivative with respect to time of the equation above gives us the derived equation:

$$2h\frac{dh}{dt} + 2b\frac{db}{dt} = 0$$

C. The Solution

1. We substitute the known values $dh/dt = -3$ and $h = 4$ into the derived equation:

$$2(4)(-3) + 2b\frac{db}{dt} = 0$$

We would like to solve for db/dt, but first we need the value of b, which we can determine from the equation $h^2 + b^2 = 25$, using the value $h = 4$:

$$\begin{aligned} 16 + b^2 &= 25 \\ b^2 &= 9 \\ b &= 3 \end{aligned}$$

Substituting into the derived equation, we get

$$-24 + 2(3)\frac{db}{dt} = 0$$

2. Solving for db/dt gives

$$\frac{db}{dt} = \frac{24}{6} = 4$$

Thus, the base of the ladder is sliding away from the wall at 4 ft/min when it hits Jack.

Example 3 Average Cost

AFP/Getty Images

The cost to manufacture x cell phones in a day is

$$C(x) = 10{,}000 + 20x + \frac{x^2}{10{,}000} \text{ dollars}$$

The daily production level is currently $x = 5000$ cell phones and is increasing at a rate of 100 units per day. How fast is the average cost changing?

Solution

A. The Problem

1. The changing quantities are the production level x and the average cost, $\bar{C}$.

2. We rephrase the problem as follows:

The daily production level is $x = 5000$ units and the rate of change of x is 100 units/day. What is the rate of change of the average cost, $\bar{C}$?

In mathematical notation,

$$x = 5000 \text{ and } \frac{dx}{dt} = 100. \text{ Find } \frac{d\bar{C}}{dt}$$

B. The Relationship

1. In this example the changing quantities cannot easily be depicted geometrically.

2. We are given a formula for the *total* cost. We get the *average* cost by dividing the total cost by x:

$$\bar{C} = \frac{C}{x}$$

So,

$$\bar{C} = \frac{10{,}000}{x} + 20 + \frac{x}{10{,}000}$$

3. Taking derivatives with respect to t of both sides, we get the derived equation:

$$\frac{d\bar{C}}{dt} = \left(-\frac{10{,}000}{x^2} + \frac{1}{10{,}000}\right)\frac{dx}{dt}$$

C. The Solution

Substituting the values from part A into the derived equation, we get

$$\begin{aligned}\frac{d\bar{C}}{dt} &= \left(-\frac{10{,}000}{5{,}000^2} + \frac{1}{10{,}000}\right)100 \\ &= -0.03 \text{ dollars/day}\end{aligned}$$

Thus, the average cost is decreasing by 3¢ per day.

The scenario in the following example is similar to Example 5 in Section 5.2.

Example 4 Allocation of Labor

The Gym Sock Company manufactures cotton athletic socks. Production is partially automated through the use of robots. The number of pairs of socks the company can manufacture in a day is given by a Cobb-Douglas production formula:

$$q = 50n^{0.6}r^{0.4}$$

where q is the number of pairs of socks that can be manufactured by n laborers and r robots. The company currently produces 1000 pairs of socks each day and employs 20 laborers. It is bringing one new robot on line every month. At what rate are laborers being laid off, assuming that the number of socks produced remains constant?

Solution

A. The Problem

1. The changing quantities are the number of laborers n and the number of robots r.

2. $\frac{dr}{dt} = 1$. Find $\frac{dn}{dt}$ when $n = 20$

B. The Relationship

1. No diagram is appropriate here.

2. The equation relating the changing quantities:

$$1000 = 50n^{0.6}r^{0.4}$$

or

$$20 = n^{0.6}r^{0.4}$$

(Productivity is constant at 1000 pairs of socks each day.)

3. The derived equation is

$$0 = 0.6n^{-0.4}\left(\frac{dn}{dt}\right)r^{0.4} + 0.4n^{0.6}r^{-0.6}\left(\frac{dr}{dt}\right)$$

$$= 0.6\left(\frac{r}{n}\right)^{0.4}\left(\frac{dn}{dt}\right) + 0.4\left(\frac{n}{r}\right)^{0.6}\left(\frac{dr}{dt}\right)$$

We solve this equation for dn/dt because we shall want to find dn/dt below and because the equation becomes simpler when we do this:

$$0.6\left(\frac{r}{n}\right)^{0.4}\left(\frac{dn}{dt}\right) = -0.4\left(\frac{n}{r}\right)^{0.6}\left(\frac{dr}{dt}\right)$$

$$\frac{dn}{dt} = -\frac{0.4}{0.6}\left(\frac{n}{r}\right)^{0.6}\left(\frac{n}{r}\right)^{0.4}\left(\frac{dr}{dt}\right)$$

$$= -\frac{2}{3}\left(\frac{n}{r}\right)\left(\frac{dr}{dt}\right)$$

C. The Solution

Substituting the numbers in A into the last equation in B, we get

$$\frac{dn}{dt} = -\frac{2}{3}\left(\frac{20}{r}\right)(1)$$

We need to compute r by substituting the known value of n in the original formula:

$$20 = n^{0.6}r^{0.4}$$

$$20 = 20^{0.6}r^{0.4}$$

$$r^{0.4} = \frac{20}{20^{0.6}} = 20^{0.4}$$

$$r = 20$$

Thus,

$$\frac{dn}{dt} = -\frac{2}{3}\left(\frac{20}{20}\right)(1) = -\frac{2}{3} \text{ laborers per month}$$

The company is laying off laborers at a rate of 2/3 per month, or two every three months.

We can interpret this result as saying that, at the current level of production and number of laborers, one robot is as productive as 2/3 of a laborer, or 3 robots are as productive as 2 laborers.

5.4 EXERCISES

● denotes basic skills exercises

◆ denotes challenging exercises

Rewrite the statements and questions in Exercises 1–8 in mathematical notation.

1. ● The population P is currently 10,000 and growing at a rate of 1000 per year. *hint* [see Quick Examples on p. 391]

2. ● There are presently 400 cases of Bangkok flu, and the number is growing by 30 new cases every month.

3. ● The annual revenue of your tie-dye T-shirt operation is currently \$7000 but is decreasing by \$700 each year. How fast are annual sales changing?

4. ● A ladder is sliding down a wall so that the distance between the top of the ladder and the floor is decreasing at a rate of

3 feet per second. How fast is the base of the ladder receding from the wall?

5. ● The price of shoes is rising \$5 per year. How fast is the demand changing?

6. ● Stock prices are rising \$1000 per year. How fast is the value of your portfolio increasing?

7. ● The average global temperature is 60°F and rising by 0.1°F per decade. How fast are annual sales of Bermuda shorts increasing?

8. ● The country's population is now 260,000,000 and is increasing by 1,000,000 people per year. How fast is the annual demand for diapers increasing?

Applications

9. ● ***Sun Spots*** The area of a circular sun spot is growing at a rate of 1200 km²/sec. *hint* [see Example 1]

   a. How fast is the radius growing at the instant when it equals 10,000 km?
   b. How fast is the radius growing at the instant when the sun spot has an area of 640,000 km²?

10. ● ***Puddles*** The radius of a circular puddle is growing at a rate of 5 cm/sec.

    a. How fast is its area growing at the instant when the radius is 10 cm?
    b. How fast is the area growing at the instant when it equals 36 cm²?

11. ● ***Balloons*** A spherical party balloon is being inflated with helium pumped in at a rate of 3 cubic feet per minute. How fast is the radius growing at the instant when the radius has reached 1 foot? (The volume of a sphere of radius r is $V = \frac{4}{3}\pi r^3$.)

12. ● ***More Balloons*** A rather flimsy spherical balloon is designed to pop at the instant its radius has reached 10 centimeters. Assuming the balloon is filled with helium at a rate of 10 cubic centimeters per second, calculate how fast the radius is growing at the instant it pops. (The volume of a sphere of radius r is $V = \frac{4}{3}\pi r^3$.)

13. ● ***Sliding Ladders*** The base of a 50-foot ladder is being pulled away from a wall at a rate of 10 feet per second. How fast is the top of the ladder sliding down the wall at the instant when the base of the ladder is 30 feet from the wall? *hint* [see Example 2]

14. ● ***Sliding Ladders*** The top of a 5-foot ladder is sliding down a wall at a rate of 10 feet per second. How fast is the base of the ladder sliding away from the wall at the instant when the top of the ladder is 3 feet from the ground?

15. ● ***Average Cost*** The average cost function for the weekly manufacture of portable CD players is given by

$$\bar{C}(x) = 150{,}000x^{-1} + 20 + 0.0001x \text{ dollars per player}$$

where x is the number of CD players manufactured that week. Weekly production is currently 3000 players and is increasing at a rate of 100 players per week. What is happening to the average cost? *hint* [see Example 3]

16. ● ***Average Cost*** Repeat the preceding exercise, using the revised average cost function

$$\bar{C}(x) = 150{,}000x^{-1} + 20 + 0.01x \text{ dollars per player}$$

17. ● ***Demand*** Demand for your tie-dyed T-shirts is given by the formula

$$q = 500 - 100p^{0.5}$$

where q is the number of T-shirts you can sell each month at a price of p dollars. If you currently sell T-shirts for \$15 each and you raise your price by \$2 per month, how fast will the demand drop? (Round your answer to the nearest whole number.)

18. ● ***Supply*** The number of portable CD players you are prepared to supply to a retail outlet every week is given by the formula

$$q = 0.1p^2 + 3p$$

where p is the price it offers you. The retail outlet is currently offering you \$40 per CD player. If the price it offers decreases at a rate of \$2 per week, how will this affect the number you supply?

19. ● ***Revenue*** You can now sell 50 cups of lemonade per week at 30¢ per cup, but demand is dropping at a rate of 5 cups per week each week. Assuming that raising the price does not affect demand, how fast do you have to raise your price if you want to keep your weekly revenue constant?

20. ● ***Revenue*** You can now sell 40 cars per month at \$20,000 per car, and demand is increasing at a rate of 3 cars per month each month. What is the fastest you could drop your price before your monthly revenue starts to drop?

21. ● ***Production*** The automobile assembly plant you manage has a Cobb-Douglas production function given by

$$P = 10x^{0.3}y^{0.7}$$

where P is the number of automobiles it produces per year, x is the number of employees, and y is the daily operating budget (in dollars). You maintain a production level of 1000 automobiles per year. If you currently employ 150 workers and are hiring new workers at a rate of 10 per year, how fast is your daily operating budget changing? *hint* [see Example 4]

22. ● ***Production*** Refer back to the Cobb-Douglas production formula in the preceding exercise. Assume that you maintain a constant work force of 200 workers and wish to increase production in order to meet a demand that is increasing by 100 automobiles per year. The current demand is 1000 automobiles per year. How fast should your daily operating budget be increasing?

23. ● ***Demand*** Assume that the demand equation for tuna in a small coastal town is

$$pq^{1.5} = 50{,}000$$

where q is the number of pounds of tuna that can be sold in one month at the price of p dollars per pound. The town's fishery finds that the demand for tuna is currently 900 pounds per month and is increasing at a rate of 100 pounds per month each month. How fast is the price changing?

24. ● ***Demand*** The demand equation for rubies at Royal Ruby Retailers is

$$q + \frac{4}{3}p = 80$$

where q is the number of rubies RRR can sell per week at p dollars per ruby. RRR finds that the demand for its rubies is currently 20 rubies per week and is dropping at a rate of one ruby per week. How fast is the price changing?

25. ***Ships Sailing Apart*** The H.M.S. Dreadnaught is 40 miles north of Montauk and steaming due north at 20 miles/hour, while the U.S.S. Mona Lisa is 50 miles east of Montauk and steaming due east at an even 30 miles/hour. How fast is their distance apart increasing?

26. ***Near Miss*** My aunt and I were approaching the same intersection, she from the south and I from the west. She was traveling at a steady speed of 10 miles/hour, while I was approaching the intersection at 60 miles/hour. At a certain instant in time, I was one-tenth of a mile from the intersection, while she was one-twentieth of a mile from it. How fast were we approaching each other at that instant?

27. ***Baseball*** A baseball diamond is a square with side 90 ft.

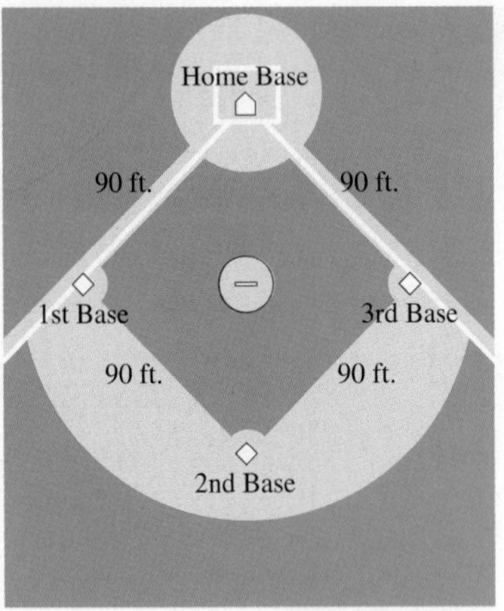

A batter at home base hits the ball and runs toward first base with a speed of 24 ft/sec. At what rate is his distance from third base increasing when he is halfway to first base?

28. ***Baseball*** Refer to Exercise 27. Another player is running from third base to home at 30 ft/sec. How fast is her distance from second base increasing when she is 60 feet from third base?

29. ***Movement along a Graph*** A point on the graph of $y = 1/x$ is moving along the curve in such a way that its x-coordinate is increasing at a rate of 4 units per second. What is happening to the y-coordinate at the instant the y-coordinate is equal to 2?

30. ***Motion around a Circle*** A point is moving along the circle $x^2 + (y - 1)^2 = 8$ in such a way that its x-coordinate is decreasing at a rate of 1 unit per second. What is happening to the y-coordinate at the instant when the point has reached $(-2, 3)$?

31. ***Education*** In 1991, the expected income of an individual depended on his or her educational level according to the following formula:

$$I(n) = 2928.8n^3 - 115{,}860n^2 + 1{,}532{,}900n - 6{,}760{,}800 \quad (12 \le n \le 15)$$

Here, n is the number of school years completed and $I(n)$ is the individual's expected income.[39] You have completed 13 years of school and are currently a part-time student. Your schedule is such that you will complete the equivalent of one year of college every three years. Assuming that your salary is linked to the above model, how fast is your income going up? (Round your answer to the nearest \$1.)

32. ***Education*** Refer back to the model in the preceding exercise. Assume that someone has completed 14 years of school and that her income is increasing by \$10,000 per year. How much schooling per year is this rate of increase equivalent to?

33. ***Employment*** An employment research company estimates that the value of a recent MBA graduate to an accounting company is

$$V = 3e^2 + 5g^3$$

where V is the value of the graduate, e is the number of years of prior business experience, and g is the graduate school grade point average. A company that currently employs graduates with a 3.0 average wishes to maintain a constant employee value of $V = 200$, but finds that the grade point average of its new employees is dropping at a rate of 0.2 per year. How fast must the experience of its new employees be growing in order to compensate for the decline in grade point average?

34. ***Grades***[40] A production formula for a student's performance on a difficult English examination is given by

$$g = 4hx - 0.2h^2 - 10x^2$$

where g is the grade the student can expect to obtain, h is the number of hours of study for the examination, and x is the student's grade point average. The instructor finds that students'

[39] The model is a best-fit cubic based on Table 358, U.S. Department of Education, *Digest of Education Statistics, 1991,* Washington, DC: Government Printing Office, 1991.

[40] Based on an Exercise in *Introduction to Mathematical Economics* by A.L. Ostrosky Jr. and J.V. Koch (Waveland Press, Illinois, 1979.)

grade point averages have remained constant at 3.0 over the years, and that students currently spend an average of 15 hours studying for the examination. However, scores on the examination are dropping at a rate of 10 points per year. At what rate is the average study time decreasing?

35. ***Cones*** A right circular conical vessel is being filled with green industrial waste at a rate of 100 cubic meters per second. How fast is the level rising after 200π cubic meters have been poured in? The cone has a height of 50 m and a radius 30 m at its brim. (The volume of a cone of height h and cross-sectional radius r at its brim is given by $V = \frac{1}{3}\pi r^2 h$.)

36. ***More Cones*** A circular conical vessel is being filled with ink at a rate of 10 cm^3/sec. How fast is the level rising after 20 cm^3 have been poured in? The cone has height 50 cm and radius 20 cm at its brim. (The volume of a cone of height h and cross-sectional radius r at its brim is given by $V = \frac{1}{3}\pi r^2 h$.)

37. ***Cylinders*** The volume of paint in a right cylindrical can is given by $V = 4t^2 - t$ where t is time in seconds and V is the volume in cm^3. How fast is the level rising when the height is 2 cm? The can has a height of 4 cm and a radius of 2 cm. [Hint: To get h as a function of t, first solve the volume $V = \pi r^2 h$ for h.]

38. ***Cylinders*** A cylindrical bucket is being filled with paint at a rate of 6 cm^3 per minute. How fast is the level rising when the bucket starts to overflow? The bucket has a radius of 30 cm and a height of 60 cm.

39. ***Computers vs. Income*** The demand for personal computers in the home goes up with household income. For a given community, we can approximate the average number of computers in a home as

$$q = 0.3454 \ln x - 3.047 \qquad 10{,}000 \le x \le 125{,}000$$

where x is mean household income.[41] Your community has a mean income of \$30,000, increasing at a rate of \$2,000 per year. How many computers per household are there, and how fast is the number of computers in a home increasing? (Round your answer to four decimal places.)

40. ***Computers vs. Income*** Refer back to the model in the preceding exercise. The average number of computers per household in your town is 0.5 and is increasing at a rate of 0.02 computers per household per year. What is the average household income in your town, and how fast is it increasing? (Round your answers to the nearest \$10).

Education and Crime *The following graph shows a striking relationship between the total prison population and the average combined SAT score in the U.S. Exercises 41 and 42 are based*

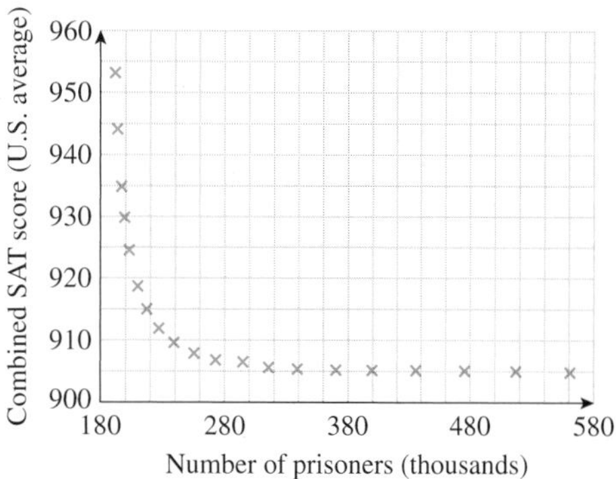

on the following model for these data:

$$S(n) = 904 + \frac{1326}{(n-180)^{1.325}} \qquad (192 \le n \le 563)$$

Here, $S(n)$ is the combined average SAT score at a time when the total prison population is n thousand.[42]

41. In 1985, the U.S. prison population was 475,000 and increasing at a rate of 35,000 per year. What was the average SAT score, and how fast, and in what direction, was it changing? (Round your answers to two decimal places.)

42. In 1970, the U.S. combined SAT average was 940 and dropping by 10 points per year. What was the U.S. prison population, and how fast, and in what direction, was it changing? (Round your answers to the nearest 100.)

Divorce Rates *A study found that the divorce rate d (given as a percentage) appears to depend on the ratio r of available men to available women.*[43] *This function can be approximated by*

$$d(r) = \begin{cases} -40r + 74 & \text{if } r \le 1.3 \\ \dfrac{130r}{3} - \dfrac{103}{3} & \text{if } r > 1.3 \end{cases}$$

Exercises 43 and 44 are based on this model.

43. ◆ There are currently 1.1 available men per available woman in Littleville, and this ratio is increasing by 0.05 per year. What is happening to the divorce rate?

44. ◆ There are currently 1.5 available men per available woman in Largeville, and this ratio is decreasing by 0.03 per year. What is happening to the divorce rate?

[41] The model is a regression model. Source for data: Income distribution: Luxenbourg Income Study/*New York Times,* August 14, 1995, p. A9. Computer data: Forrester Research/*The New York Times,* August 8, 1999, p. BU4.

[42] The model is the authors' based on data for the years 1967–1989. SOURCES: Sourcebook of Criminal Justice Statistics, 1990, p. 604/Educational Testing Service.

[43] The cited study, by Scott J. South and associates, appeared in the *American Sociological Review* (February, 1995). Figures are rounded. SOURCE: *The New York Times,* February 19, 1995, p. 40.

Communication and Reasoning Exercises

45. ● Why is this section titled "related rates"?

46. ● If you know how fast one quantity is changing and need to compute how fast a second quantity is changing, what kind of information do you need?

47. ● In a related rates problem, there is no limit to the number of changing quantities we can consider. Illustrate this by creating a related rates problem with four changing quantities.

48. ● If three quantities are related by a single equation, how would you go about computing how fast one of them is changing based on a knowledge of the other two?

49. The demand and unit price for your store's checkered T-shirts are changing with time. Show that the percentage rate of change of revenue equals the sum of the percentage rates of change of price and demand. (The percentage rate of change of a quantity Q is $Q'(t)/Q(t)$.)

50. The number N of employees and the total floor space S of your company are both changing with time. Show that the percentage rate of change of square footage per employee equals the percentage rate of change of S minus the percentage rate of change of N. (The percentage rate of change of a quantity Q is $Q'(t)/Q(t)$.)

51. In solving a related rates problem, a key step is solving the derived equation for the unknown rate of change (once we have substituted the other values into the equation). Call the unknown rate of change X. The derived equation is what kind of equation in X?

52. On a recent exam, you were given a related rates problem based on an algebraic equation relating two variables x and y. Your friend told you that the correct relationship between dx/dt and dy/dt was given by

$$\left(\frac{dx}{dt}\right) = \left(\frac{dy}{dt}\right)^2$$

Could he be correct?

53. Transform the following into a mathematical statement about derivatives: If my grades are improving at twice the speed of yours, then your grades are improving at half the speed of mine.

54. If two quantities x and y are related by a linear equation, how are their rates of change related?

● basic skills ◆ challenging

5.5 Elasticity

You manufacture an extremely popular brand of sneakers and want to know what will happen if you increase the selling price. Common sense tells you that demand will drop as you raise the price. But will the drop in demand be enough to cause your revenue to fall? Or will it be small enough that your revenue will rise because of the higher selling price? For example, if you raise the price by 1%, you might suffer only a 0.5% loss in sales. In this case, the loss in sales will be more than offset by the increase in price and your revenue will rise. In such a case, we say that the demand is **inelastic,** because it is not very sensitive to the increase in price. On the other hand, if your 1% price increase results in a 2% drop in demand, then raising the price will cause a drop in revenues. We then say that the demand is **elastic** because it reacts strongly to a price change.

We can use calculus to measure the response of demand to price changes if we have a demand equation for the item we are selling.[44] We need to know the *percentage drop in demand per percentage increase in price*. This ratio is called the **elasticity of demand,** or **price elasticity of demand,** and is usually denoted by E. Let's derive a formula for E in terms of the demand equation.

[44] Coming up with a good demand equation is not always easy. We saw in Chapter 1 that it is possible to find a linear demand equation if we know the sales figures at two different prices. However, such an equation is only a first approximation. To come up with a more accurate demand equation, we might need to gather data corresponding to sales at several different prices and use curve-fitting techniques like regression. Another approach would be an analytic one, based on mathematical modeling techniques that an economist might use.

Assume that we have a demand equation

$$q = f(p)$$

where q stands for the number of items we would sell (per week, per month, or what have you) if we set the price per item at p. Now suppose we increase the price p by a very small amount, Δp. Then our percentage increase in price is $(\Delta p/p) \times 100\%$. This increase in p will presumably result in a decrease in the demand q. Let's denote this corresponding decrease in q by $-\Delta q$ (we use the minus sign because, by convention, Δq stands for the *increase* in demand). Thus, the percentage decrease in demand is $(-\Delta q/q) \times 100\%$.

Now E is the ratio

$$E = \frac{\text{Percentage decrease in demand}}{\text{Percentage increase in price}}$$

so

$$E = \frac{-\frac{\Delta q}{q} \times 100\%}{\frac{\Delta p}{p} \times 100\%}$$

Canceling the 100%s and reorganizing, we get

$$E = -\frac{\Delta q}{\Delta p} \cdot \frac{p}{q}$$

Q: *What small change in price will we use for Δp?*

A: It should probably be pretty small. If, say, we increased the price of sneakers to \$1 million per pair, the sales would likely drop to zero. But knowing this tells us nothing about how the market would respond to a modest increase in price. In fact, we'll do the usual thing we do in calculus and let Δp approach 0. ■

In the expression for E, if we let Δp go to 0, then the ratio $\Delta q/\Delta p$ goes to the derivative dq/dp. This gives us our final and most useful definition of the elasticity.

Price Elasticity of Demand

The **price elasticity of demand E** is the percentage rate of decrease of demand per percentage increase in price. E is given by the formula

$$E = -\frac{dq}{dp} \cdot \frac{p}{q}$$

We say that the demand is **elastic** if $E > 1$, is **inelastic** if $E < 1$, and has **unit elasticity** if $E = 1$.

quick **Example**

Suppose that the demand equation is $q = 20{,}000 - 2p$ where p is the price in dollars. Then

$$E = -(-2)\frac{p}{20{,}000 - 2p} = \frac{p}{10{,}000 - p}$$

If $p = \$2000$, then $E = 1/4$, and demand is inelastic at this price.
If $p = \$8000$, then $E = 4$, and demand is elastic at this price.
If $p = \$5000$, then $E = 1$, and the demand has unit elasticity at this price.

mathematics At Work

Jeffery Olson

TITLE Network Manager, Clinical Network Services
INSTITUTION United Behavioral Health

Patrick Farace

As a Network Manager for United Behavioral Health (UBH), my objective is to enable UBH members to obtain high-quality, affordable behavioral health care by providing an outstanding panel of clinicians and facilities with sufficient availability to meet member needs.

To determine the adequacy of our clinical network we first determine a utilization rate. A utilization rate is the extent to which insured members utilize mental health/substance abuse services. We use this number to determine the number of clinicians and facilities needed to meet the needs of our membership. An analysis is completed to review the existing network against urban, suburban, and rural access standards. Clinician-to-member and facility-to-member ratios are assessed, along with the linguistic and cultural competency of the network as compared to U.S. Census data. If a network is found to be below standard on any of these measures, an action plan is developed to enhance the network via targeted recruitment in order to close any potential network gap as quickly as possible.

Clinicians who are contracted with a managed care organization agree to accept a negotiated rate for their services. This rate is an important factor when recruiting and contracting with clinicians. The managed care model is built on the principle that the managed care organization provides volume in exchange for a discounted fee. These negotiated rates are created using many factors. These factors consist of values based on human and financial resources consumed in the delivery of each procedure as well as the cost of malpractice insurance. This value is then multiplied by a conversion factor to take into account regional differences in service locations.

In addition to maintaining and recruiting clinicians for our insured members, I must also report many statistics required for state and federal regulatory bodies as well as other accrediting organizations.

Throughout my 13 year career in managed care I have worked with both medical and mental health providers and have also held positions in sales and accounting. All of these functions within managed care rely heavily on mathematics. As I progress in my field I realize more and more the important role that mathematics plays in not only managed care, but life.

We are generally interested in the price that maximizes revenue and, in ordinary cases, the price that maximizes revenue must give unit elasticity. One way of seeing this is as follows:[45] If the demand is inelastic (which ordinarily occurs at a low unit price) then raising the price by a small percentage—1% say—results in a smaller percentage drop in demand. For example, in the Quick Example above, if $p = \$2000$, then the demand would drop by only $\frac{1}{4}\%$ for every 1% increase in price. To see the effect on revenue, we use the fact[46] that, for small changes in price,

$$\begin{aligned}\text{Percentage change in revenue} &\approx \text{Percentage change in price} \\ &\quad + \text{Percentage change in demand} \\ &= 1 + \left(-\frac{1}{4}\right) = \frac{3}{4}\%\end{aligned}$$

Thus, the revenue will increase by about $3/4\%$. Put another way:

If the demand is inelastic, raising the price increases revenue.

On the other hand, if the price is elastic (which ordinarily occurs at a high unit price), then increasing the price slightly will lower the revenue, so:

If the demand is elastic, lowering the price increases revenue.

The price that results in the largest revenue must therefore be at unit elasticity.

---

[45] For another—more rigorous—argument, see Exercise 27.

[46] See, for example, Exercise 49 in Section 5.4.

Example 1 Price Elasticity of Demand: Dolls

Suppose that the demand equation for Bobby Dolls is given by $q = 216 - p^2$, where p is the price per doll in dollars and q is the number of dolls sold per week.

a. Compute the price elasticity of demand when $p = \$5$ and $p = \$10$, and interpret the results.

b. Find the ranges of prices for which the demand is elastic and the range for which the demand is inelastic.

c. Find the price at which the weekly revenue is maximized. What is the maximum weekly revenue?

Solution

a. The price elasticity of demand is

$$E = -\frac{dq}{dp} \cdot \frac{p}{q}$$

Taking the derivative and substituting for q gives

$$E = 2p \cdot \frac{p}{216 - p^2} = \frac{2p^2}{216 - p^2}$$

When $p = \$5$,

$$E = \frac{2(5)^2}{216 - 5^2} = \frac{50}{191} \approx 0.26$$

Thus, when the price is set at \$5, the demand is dropping at a rate of 0.26% per 1% increase in the price. Because $E < 1$, the demand is inelastic at this price, so raising the price will increase revenue.

When $p = \$10$,

$$E = \frac{2(10)^2}{216 - 10^2} = \frac{200}{116} \approx 1.72$$

Thus, when the price is set at \$10, the demand is dropping at a rate of 1.72% per 1% increase in the price. Because $E > 1$, demand is elastic at this price, so raising the price will decrease revenue; lowering the price will increase revenue.

b. and **c.** We answer part (c) first. Setting $E = 1$, we get

$$\frac{2p^2}{216 - p^2} = 1$$

$$p^2 = 72$$

using *Technology*

See the Technology Guide at the end of the chapter to find out how to automate computations such as those in part (a) using a TI-83/84 or Excel.

Thus, we conclude that the maximum revenue occurs when $p = \sqrt{72} \approx \$8.49$. We can now answer part (b): The demand is elastic when $p > \$8.49$ (the price is too high), and the demand is inelastic when $p < \$8.49$ (the price is too low). Finally, we calculate the maximum weekly revenue, which equals the revenue corresponding to the price of \$8.49:

$$R = qp = (216 - p^2)p = (216 - 72)\sqrt{72} = 144\sqrt{72} \approx \$1222$$

The concept of elasticity can be applied in other situations. In the following example we consider *income* elasticity of demand—the percentage increase in demand for a particular item per percentage increase in personal income.

Example 2 Income Elasticity of Demand: Porsches

You are the sales director at Suburban Porsche and have noticed that demand for Porsches depends on income according to

$$q = 0.005e^{-0.05x^2+x} \quad (1 \le x \le 10)$$

Here, x is the income of a potential customer in hundreds of thousands of dollars and q is the probability that the person will actually purchase a Porsche.* The **income elasticity of demand** is

$$E = \frac{dq}{dx}\frac{x}{q}$$

Compute and interpret E for $x = 2$ and 9.

Solution

Q: *Why is there no negative sign in the formula?*

A: Because we anticipate that the demand will increase as income increases, the ratio

$$\frac{\text{Percentage increase in demand}}{\text{Percentage increase in income}}$$

will be positive, so there is no need to introduce a negative sign. ■

Turning to the calculation, since $q = 0.005e^{-0.05x^2+x}$,

$$\frac{dq}{dx} = 0.005e^{-0.05x^2+x}(-0.1x + 1)$$

and so

$$\begin{aligned} E &= \frac{dq}{dx}\frac{x}{q} \\ &= 0.005e^{-0.05x^2+x}(-0.1x + 1)\frac{x}{0.005e^{-0.05x^2+x}} \\ &= x(-0.1x + 1) \end{aligned}$$

When $x = 2$, $E = 2[-0.1(2) + 1)] = 1.6$. Thus, at an income level of \$200,000, the probability that a customer will purchase a Porsche increases at a rate of 1.6% per 1% increase in income.

When $x = 9$, $E = 9[-0.1(9) + 1)] = 0.9$. Thus, at an income level of \$900,000, the probability that a customer will purchase a Porsche increases at a rate of 0.9% per 1% increase in income.

* In other words, q is the fraction of visitors to your showroom having income x who actually purchase a Porsche.

5.5 EXERCISES

● denotes basic skills exercises

◆ denotes challenging exercises

Applications

1. ● ***Demand for Oranges*** The weekly sales of Honolulu Red Oranges is given by $q = 1000 - 20p$. Calculate the price elasticity of demand when the price is \$30 per orange (yes, \$30 per orange[47]). Interpret your answer. Also, calculate the price that gives a maximum weekly revenue, and find this maximum revenue. hint [see Example 1]

2. ● ***Demand for Oranges*** Repeat the preceding exercise for weekly sales of $1000 - 10p$.

3. ● ***Tissues*** The consumer demand equation for tissues is given by $q = (100 - p)^2$, where p is the price per case of tissues and q is the demand in weekly sales.
   a. Determine the price elasticity of demand E when the price is set at \$30, and interpret your answer.
   b. At what price should tissues be sold in order to maximize the revenue?
   c. Approximately how many cases of tissues would be demanded at that price?

4. ● ***Bodybuilding*** The consumer demand curve for Professor Stefan Schwarzenegger dumbbells is given by $q = (100 - 2p)^2$, where p is the price per dumbbell, and q is the demand in weekly sales. Find the price Professor Schwarzenegger should charge for his dumbbells in order to maximize revenue.

5. ● ***T-Shirts*** The Physics Club sells $E = mc^2$ T-shirts at the local flea market. Unfortunately, the club's previous administration has been losing money for years, so you decide to do an analysis of the sales. A quadratic regression based on old sales data reveals the following demand equation for the T-shirts:

$$q = -2p^2 + 33p \qquad (9 \le p \le 15)$$

   Here, p is the price the club charges per T shirt, and q is the number it can sell each day at the flea market.
   a. Obtain a formula for the price elasticity of demand for $E = mc^2$ T-shirts.
   b. Compute the elasticity of demand if the price is set at \$10 per shirt. *Interpret the result.*
   c. How much should the Physics Club charge for the T-shirts in order to obtain the maximum daily revenue? What will this revenue be?

6. ● ***Comics*** The demand curve for original *Iguanawoman* comics is given by

$$q = \frac{(400 - p)^2}{100} \qquad (0 \le p \le 400)$$

   where q is the number of copies the publisher can sell per week if it sets the price at \$$p$.
   a. Find the price elasticity of demand when the price is set at \$40 per copy.
   b. Find the price at which the publisher should sell the books in order to maximize weekly revenue.
   c. What, to the nearest \$1, is the maximum weekly revenue the publisher can realize from sales of *Iguanawoman* comics?

7. ● ***College Tuition*** A study of about 1800 U.S. colleges and universities resulted in the demand equation $q = 9900 - 2.2p$, where q is the enrollment at a college or university, and p is the average annual tuition (plus fees) it charges.[48]
   a. The study also found that the average tuition charged by universities and colleges was \$2900. What is the corresponding price elasticity of demand? Is the price elastic or inelastic? Should colleges charge more or less on average to maximize revenue?
   b. Based on the study, what would you advise a college to charge its students in order to maximize total revenue, and what would the revenue be?

8. ● ***Demand for Fried Chicken*** A fried chicken franchise finds that the demand equation for its new roast chicken product, "Roasted Rooster," is given by

$$p = \frac{40}{q^{1.5}}$$

   where p is the price (in dollars) per quarter-chicken serving and q is the number of quarter-chicken servings that can be sold per hour at this price. Express q as a function of p and find the price elasticity of demand when the price is set at \$4 per serving. Interpret the result.

9. ● ***Paint-By-Number*** The estimated monthly sales of *Mona Lisa* paint-by-number sets is given by the formula $q = 100e^{-3p^2+p}$, where q is the demand in monthly sales and p is the retail price in yen.
   a. Determine the price elasticity of demand E when the retail price is set at ¥3 and interpret your answer.
   b. At what price will revenue be a maximum?
   c. Approximately how many paint-by-number sets will be sold per month at the price in part (b)?

[47] They are very hard to find, and their possession confers considerable social status.

[48] Based on a study by A.L. Ostrosky Jr. and J.V. Koch, as cited in their book, *Introduction to Mathematical Economics* (Waveland Press, Illinois, 1979) p. 133.

10. ● ***Paint-By-Number*** Repeat the previous exercise using the demand equation $q = 100e^{p-3p^2/2}$.

11. ***Linear Demand Functions*** A general linear demand function has the form $q = mp + b$ (m and b constants, $m \neq 0$).
 a. Obtain a formula for the price elasticity of demand at a unit price of p.
 b. Obtain a formula for the price that maximizes revenue.

12. ***Exponential Demand Functions*** A general exponential demand function has the form $q = Ae^{-bp}$ (A and b nonzero constants).
 a. Obtain a formula for the price elasticity of demand at a unit price of p.
 b. Obtain a formula for the price that maximizes revenue.

13. ***Hyperbolic Demand Functions*** A general hyperbolic demand function has the form $q = \dfrac{k}{p^r}$ (r and k nonzero constants).
 a. Obtain a formula for the price elasticity of demand at unit price p.
 b. How does E vary with p?
 c. What does the answer to part (b) say about the model?

14. ***Quadratic Demand Functions*** A general quadratic demand function has the form $q = ap^2 + bp + c$ (a, b, and c constants with $a \neq 0$).
 a. Obtain a formula for the price elasticity of demand at a unit price p.
 b. Obtain a formula for the price or prices that could maximize revenue.

15. ***Modeling Linear Demand*** You have been hired as a marketing consultant to Johannesburg Burger Supply, Inc., and you wish to come up with a unit price for its hamburgers in order to maximize its weekly revenue. To make life as simple as possible, you assume that the demand equation for Johannesburg hamburgers has the linear form $q = mp + b$, where p is the price per hamburger, q is the demand in weekly sales, and m and b are certain constants you must determine.
 a. Your market studies reveal the following sales figures: When the price is set at \$2.00 per hamburger, the sales amount to 3000 per week, but when the price is set at \$4.00 per hamburger, the sales drop to zero. Use these data to calculate the demand equation.
 b. Now estimate the unit price that maximizes weekly revenue and predict what the weekly revenue will be at that price.

16. ***Modeling Linear Demand*** You have been hired as a marketing consultant to Big Book Publishing, Inc., and you have been approached to determine the best selling price for the hit calculus text by Whiner and Istanbul entitled *Fun with Derivatives*. You decide to make life easy and assume that the demand equation for *Fun with Derivatives* has the linear form $q = mp + b$, where p is the price per book, q is the demand in annual sales, and m and b are certain constants you'll have to figure out.
 a. Your market studies reveal the following sales figures: when the price is set at \$50.00 per book, the sales amount to 10,000 per year; when the price is set at \$80.00 per book, the sales drop to 1000 per year. Use these data to calculate the demand equation.
 b. Now estimate the unit price that maximizes annual revenue and predict what Big Book Publishing, Inc.'s annual revenue will be at that price.

17. ● ***Income Elasticity of Demand: Live Drama*** The likelihood that a child will attend a live theatrical performance can be modeled by

$$q = 0.01(-0.0078x^2 + 1.5x + 4.1) \quad (15 \leq x \leq 100)$$

Here, q is the fraction of children with annual household income x thousand dollars who will attend a live dramatic performance at a theater during the year.[49] Compute the income elasticity of demand at an income level of \$20,000 and interpret the result. (Round your answer to two significant digits.) *hint* [see Example 2]

18. ● ***Income Elasticity of Demand: Live Concerts*** The likelihood that a child will attend a live musical performance can be modeled by

$$q = 0.01(0.0006x^2 + 0.38x + 35) \quad (15 \leq x \leq 100)$$

Here, q is the fraction of children with annual household income x who will attend a live musical performance during the year.[50] Compute the income elasticity of demand at an income level of \$30,000 and interpret the result.

19. ● ***Income Elasticity of Demand: Computer Usage*** The demand for personal computers in the home goes up with household income. The following graph shows some data on computer usage together with the logarithmic model $q = 0.3454\ \ln(x) - 3.047$, where q is the probability that a household with annual income x will have a computer.[51]

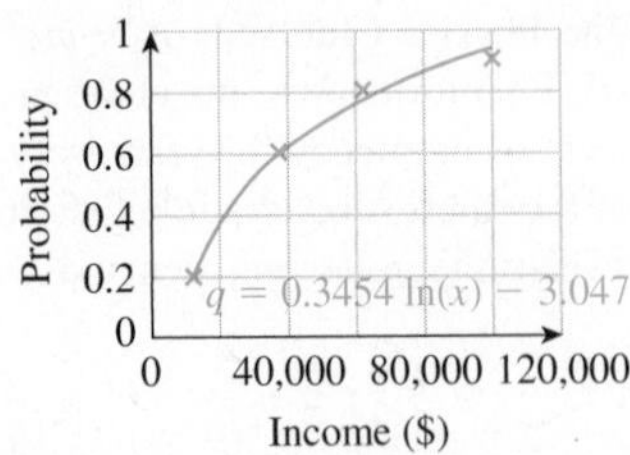

 a. Compute the income elasticity of demand for computers, to two decimal places, for a household income of \$60,000 and interpret the result.

[49] Based on a quadratic regression of data from a 2001 survey. Source for data: New York Foundation of the Arts; www.nyfa.org/culturalblueprint/.

[50] Ibid.

[51] All figures are approximate. The model is a regression model, and x measures the probability that a given household will have one or more computers. Source for data: Income distribution: Luxenbourg Income Study/*New York Times,* August 14, 1995, p. A9. Computer data: Forrester Research/ *The New York Times,* August 8, 1999, p. BU4.

b. As household income increases, how is income elasticity of demand affected?
c. How reliable is the given model of demand for incomes well above $120,000? Explain.
d. What can you say about E for incomes much larger than those shown?

20. ● ***Income Elasticity of Demand: Internet Usage*** The demand for Internet connectivity also goes up with household income. The following graph shows some data on Internet usage, together with the logarithmic model $q = 0.2802 \ln(x) - 2.505$, where q is the probability that a home with annual household income x will have an Internet connection.[52]

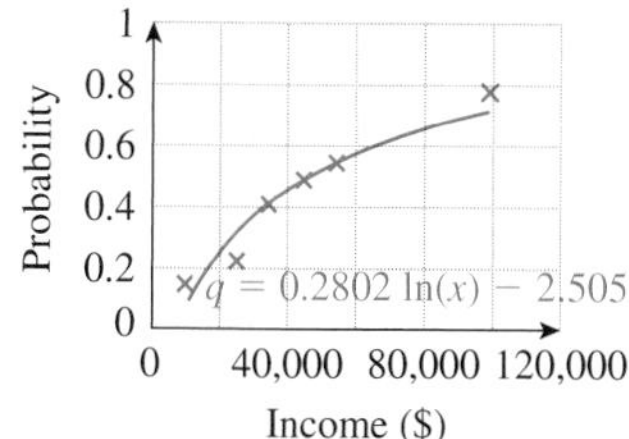

a. Compute the income elasticity of demand to two decimal places for a household income of $60,000 and interpret the result.
b. As household income increases, how is income elasticity of demand affected?
c. The logarithmic model shown above is not appropriate for incomes well above $100,000. Suggest a model that might be more appropriate.
d. In the model you propose, how does E behave for very large incomes?

21. ***Income Elasticity of Demand (Based on a question on the GRE economics test)*** If $Q = aP^{\alpha}Y^{\beta}$ is the individual's demand function for a commodity, where P is the (fixed) price of the commodity, Y is the individual's income, and a, α, and β are parameters, explain why β can be interpreted as the income elasticity of demand.

22. ***College Tuition (From the GRE economics test)*** A time-series study of the demand for higher education, using tuition charges as a price variable, yields the following result:

$$\frac{dq}{dp} \cdot \frac{p}{q} = -0.4$$

where p is tuition and q is the quantity of higher education. Which of the following is suggested by the result?

(A) As tuition rises, students want to buy a greater quantity of education.
(B) As a determinant of the demand for higher education, income is more important than price.
(C) If colleges lowered tuition slightly, their total tuition receipts would increase.
(D) If colleges raised tuition slightly, their total tuition receipts would increase.
(E) Colleges cannot increase enrollments by offering larger scholarships.

23. ***Modeling Exponential Demand*** As the new owner of a supermarket, you have inherited a large inventory of unsold imported Limburger cheese, and you would like to set the price so that your revenue from selling it is as large as possible. Previous sales figures of the cheese are shown in the following table:

Price per pound, p	$3.00	$4.00	$5.00
Monthly sales in pounds, q	407	287	223

a. Use the sales figures for the prices $3 and $5 per pound to construct a demand function of the form $q = Ae^{-bp}$, where A and b are constants you must determine. (Round A and b to two significant digits.)
b. Use your demand function to find the price elasticity of demand at each of the prices listed.
c. At what price should you sell the cheese in order to maximize monthly revenue?
d. If your total inventory of cheese amounts to only 200 pounds, and it will spoil one month from now, how should you price it in order to receive the greatest revenue? Is this the same answer you got in part (c)? If not, give a brief explanation.

24. ***Modeling Exponential Demand*** Repeat the preceding exercise, but this time use the sales figures for $4 and $5 per pound to construct the demand function.

Communication and Reasoning Exercises

25. ● Complete the following: When demand is inelastic, revenue will decrease if ___.

26. ● Complete the following: When demand has unit elasticity, revenue will decrease if ___.

27. Given that the demand q is a differentiable function of the unit price p, show that the revenue $R = pq$ has a stationary point when

$$q + p\frac{dq}{dp} = 0$$

Deduce that the stationary points of R are the same as the points of unit price elasticity of demand. (Ordinarily, there is only one such stationary point, corresponding to the

[52] All figures are approximate, and the model is a regression model. The Internet connection figures were actually quoted as "share of consumers who use the Internet, by household income." SOURCES: Luxembourg Income Study/*The New York Times*, August 14, 1995, p. A9, Commerce Department, Deloitte & Touche Survey/*The New York Times*, November 24, 1999, p. C1.

absolute maximum of R.) [Hint: Differentiate R with respect to p.]

28. Given that the demand q is a differentiable function of income x, show that the quantity $R = q/x$ has a stationary point when

$$q - x\frac{dq}{dx} = 0$$

Deduce that stationary points of R are the same as the points of unit income elasticity of demand. [Hint: Differentiate R with respect to x.]

29. ◆ Your calculus study group is discussing price elasticity of demand, and a member of the group asks the following question: "Since elasticity of demand measures the response of demand to change in unit price, what is the difference between elasticity of demand and the quantity $-dq/dp$?" How would you respond?

30. ◆ Another member of your study group claims that unit price elasticity of demand need not always correspond to maximum revenue. Is he correct? Explain your answer.

Chapter 5 Review

KEY CONCEPTS

5.1 Maxima and Minima

Relative maximum, relative minimum *p. 351*

Absolute maximum, absolute minimum *p. 351*

Stationary points, singular points, endpoints *p. 352*

Finding and classifying maxima and minima *p. 353*

Finding absolute extrema on a closed interval *p. 358*

Using technology to locate approximate extrema *p. 359*

5.2 Applications of Maxima and Minima

Minimizing average cost *p. 363*

Maximizing area *p. 364*

Steps in solving optimization problems *p. 365*

Maximizing revenue *p. 366*

Optimizing resources *p. 367*

Allocation of labor *p. 369*

5.3 The Second Derivative and Analyzing Graphs

The second derivative of a function f is the derivative of the derivative of f, written as f''. *p. 376*

The acceleration of a moving object is the second derivative of the position function. *p. 376*

Acceleration due to gravity *p. 377*

Acceleration of sales *p. 378*

Concave up, concave down, point of inflection *p. 379*

Locating points of inflection *p. 380*

The point of diminishing returns *p. 380*

Features of a graph: x- and y-intercepts, relative extrema, points of inflection; behavior near points where the function is not defined, behavior at infinity *p. 381*

Analyzing a graph *p. 381*

5.4 Related Rates

If Q is a quantity changing over time t, then the derivative dQ/dt is the rate at which Q changes over time. *p. 391*

The expanding circle *p. 392*

Steps in solving related rates problems *p. 392*

The falling ladder *p. 393*

Average cost *p. 394*

Allocation of labor *p. 395*

5.5 Elasticity

Price elasticity of demand

$E = -\frac{dq}{dp} \cdot \frac{p}{q}$; demand is elastic if $E > 1$, inelastic if $E < 1$, has unit elasticity if $E = 1$ *p. 401*

Computing and interpreting elasticity, and maximizing revenue *p. 402*

Using technology to compute elasticity *p. 403*

Income elasticity of demand *p. 404*

REVIEW EXERCISES

In Exercises 1–8, find all the relative and absolute extrema of the given functions on the given domain (if supplied) or on the largest possible domain (if no domain is supplied).

1. $f(x) = 2x^3 - 6x + 1$ on $[-2, +\infty)$

2. $f(x) = x^3 - x^2 - x - 1$ on $(-\infty, \infty)$

3. $g(x) = x^4 - 4x$ on $[-1, 1]$

4. $f(x) = \dfrac{x+1}{(x-1)^2}$ on $[-2, 1) \cup (1, 2]$

5. $g(x) = (x-1)^{2/3}$

6. $g(x) = x^2 + \ln x$ on $(0, +\infty)$

7. $h(x) = \dfrac{1}{x} + \dfrac{1}{x^2}$

8. $h(x) = e^{x^2} + 1$

In Exercises 9–12, the graph of the function f or its derivative is given. Find the approximate x-coordinates of all relative extrema and points of inflection of the original function f (if any).

9. Graph of f:

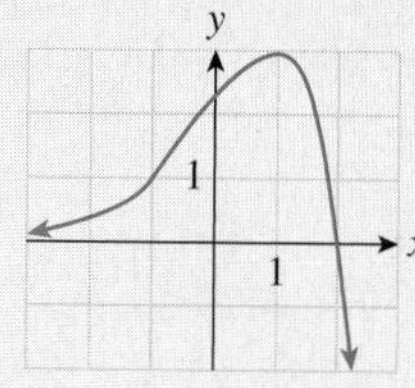

10. Graph of f:

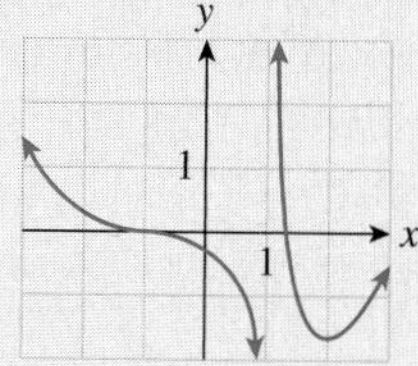

11. Graph of f':

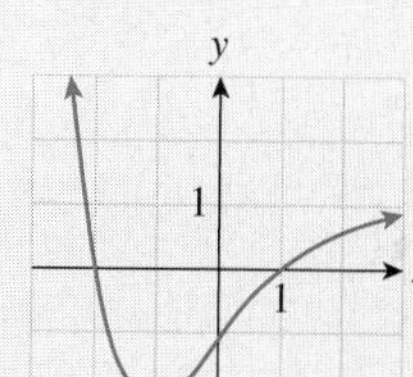

12. Graph of f':

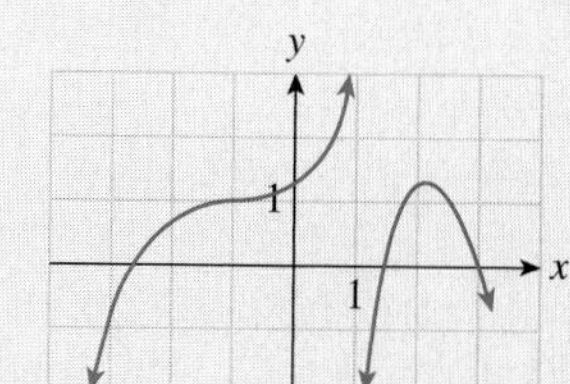

In Exercises 13 and 14, the graph of the second derivative of a function f is given. Find the approximate x-coordinates of all points of inflection of the original function f (if any).

13. Graph of f''

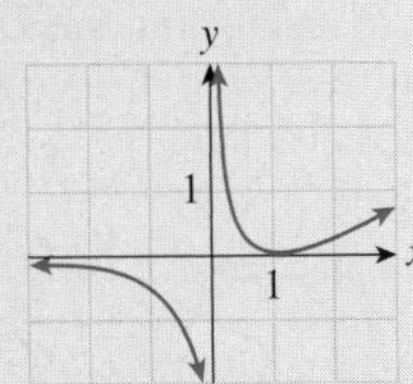

14. Graph of f''

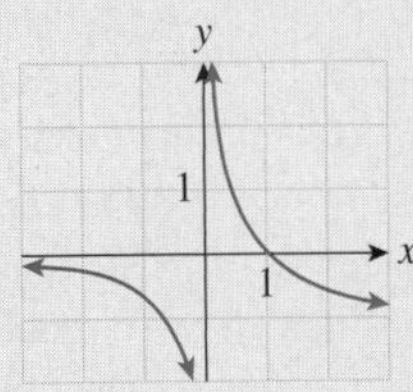

*In Exercises 15 and 16, the position s of a point (in meters) is given as a function of time t (in seconds). Find **(a)** its acceleration as a function of t and **(b)** its acceleration at the specified time.*

15. $s = \dfrac{2}{3t^2} - \dfrac{1}{t}; t = 1$

16. $s = \dfrac{4}{t^2} - \dfrac{3t}{4}; t = 2$

In Exercises 17–22, sketch the graph of the given function, indicating all relative and absolute extrema and points of inflection. Find the coordinates of these points exactly, where possible. Also indicate any horizontal and vertical asymptotes.

17. $f(x) = x^3 - 12x$ on $[-2, +\infty)$

18. $g(x) = x^4 - 4x$ on $[-1, 1]$

19. $f(x) = \dfrac{x^2 - 3}{x^3}$

20. $f(x) = (x - 1)^{2/3} + \dfrac{2x}{3}$

21. $g(x) = (x - 3)\sqrt{x}$

22. $g(x) = (x + 3)\sqrt{x}$

Applications

23. *Revenue* Demand for the latest best-seller at OHaganBooks.com, *A River Burns Through It,* is given by

$$q = -p^2 + 33p + 9 \qquad (18 \le p \le 28)$$

copies sold per week when the price is p dollars. What price should the company charge to obtain the largest revenue?

Profit *Taking into account storage and shipping, it costs OHaganBooks.com*

$$C = 9q + 100$$

dollars to sell q copies of A River Burns Through It *in a week.*

24. If demand is as in the preceding exercise, express the weekly profit earned by OHaganBooks.com from the sale of *A River Burns Through It* as a function of unit price p.

25. What price should the company charge to get the largest weekly profit?

26. What is the maximum possible weekly profit?

27. Compare your answer to Exercise 25 with the price the company should charge to obtain the largest revenue. Explain any difference.

28. *Box Design* The sales department at OHaganBooks.com, which has decided to send chocolate lobsters to each of its customers, is trying to design a shipping box with a square base. It has a roll of cardboard 36 inches wide from which to make the boxes. Each box will be obtained by cutting out corners from a rectangle of cardboard as shown in the following diagram:

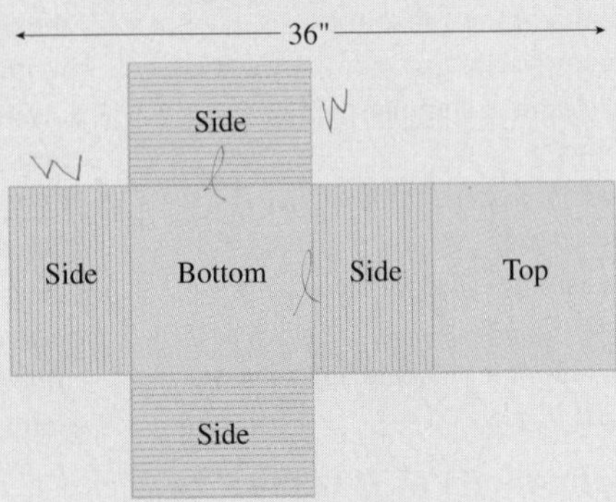

(Notice that the top and bottom of each box will be square, but the sides will not necessarily be square.) What are the dimensions of the boxes with the largest volume that can be made in this way? What is the maximum volume?

Elasticity of Demand *(Compare Exercise 23). Demand for the latest best-seller at OHaganBooks.com,* A River Burns Through It, *is given by*

$$q = -p^2 + 33p + 9 \qquad (18 \le p \le 28)$$

copies sold per week when the price is p dollars.

29. Find the price elasticity of demand as a function of p.

30. Find the elasticity of demand for this book at a price of \$20 and at a price of \$25. (Round your answers to two decimal places.) Interpret the answers.

31. What price should the company charge to obtain the largest revenue?

Elasticity of Demand *Last year OHaganBooks.com experimented with an online subscriber service, Red On Line (ROL) for its electronic book service. The consumer demand for ROL was modeled by the equation*

$$q = 1000e^{-p^2+p}$$

where p was the monthly access charge, and q is the number of subscribers.

32. Obtain a formula for the price elasticity of demand, E, for ROL services.

33. Compute the elasticity of demand if the monthly access charge is set at \$2 per month. Interpret the result.

34. How much should the company have charged in order to obtain the maximum monthly revenue? What would this revenue have been?

***Sales** OHaganBooks.com modeled its weekly sales over a period of time with the function*

$$s(t) = 6053 + \frac{4474}{1 + e^{-0.55(t-4.8)}}$$

where t is the time in weeks. Following are the graphs of s, s′, and s″:

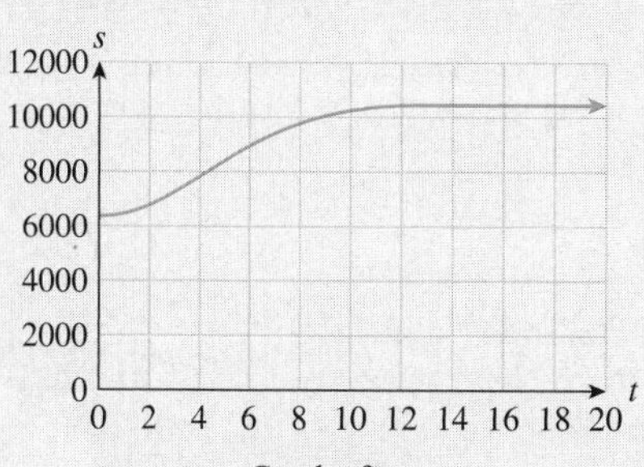

Graph of s

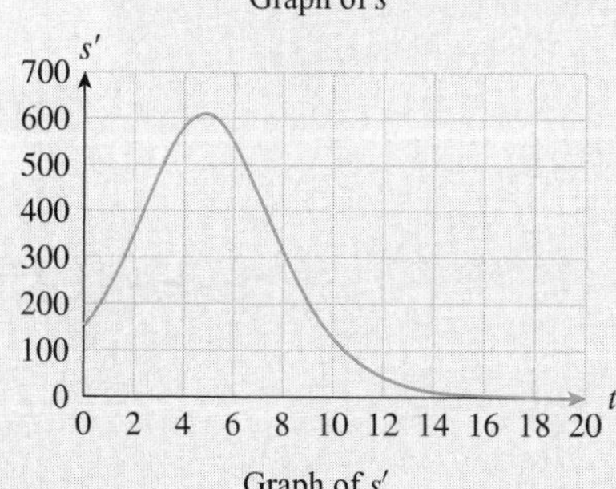

Graph of s'

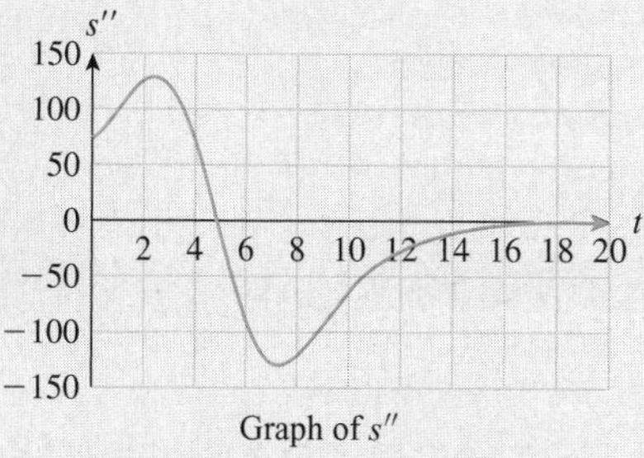

Graph of s''

35. Estimate when, to the nearest week, the weekly sales were growing fastest.

36. To what features on the graphs of s, s', and s'' does your answer to part (a) correspond?

37. The graph of s has a horizontal asymptote. What is the approximate value (s-coordinate) of this asymptote, and what is its significance in terms of weekly sales at OHaganBooks.com?

38. The graph of s' has a horizontal asymptote. What is the value (s'-coordinate) of this asymptote, and what is its significance in terms of weekly sales at OHaganBooks.com?

39. ***Chance Encounter*** Marjory Duffin is walking north towards the corner entrance of OHaganBooks.com company headquarters at 5 ft/sec, while John O'Hagan is walking west toward the same entrance, also at 5 ft/sec. How fast is their distance apart decreasing when:

a. Each of them is 2 ft from the corner?
b. Each of them is 1 ft. from the corner?
c. Each of them is h ft. from the corner?
d. They collide on the corner?

40. ***Company Logos*** OHaganBooks.com's website has an animated graphic with its name in a rectangle whose height and width change; on either side of the rectangle are semicircles, as in the figure, whose diameters are the same as the height of the rectangle.

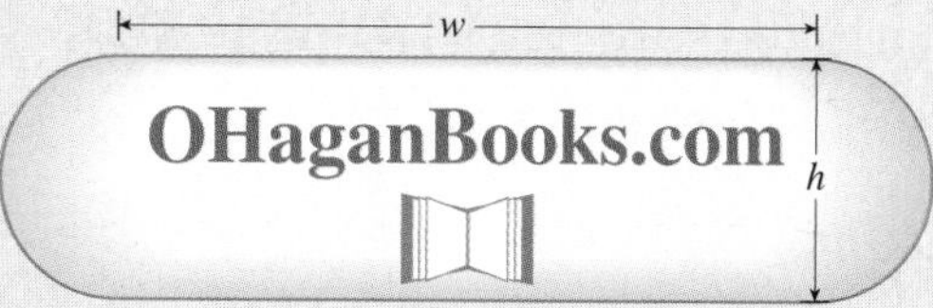

For reasons too complicated to explain, the designer wanted the combined area of the rectangle and semicircles to remain constant. At one point during the animation, the width of the rectangle is 1 inch, growing at a rate of 0.5 inches per second, while the height is 3 inches. How fast is the height changing?

CASE STUDY: Production Lot Size Management

Jeff Greenberg/PhotoEdit

Your publishing company, Knockem Dead Paperbacks, Inc., is about to release its next best-seller, *Henrietta's Heaving Heart* by Celestine A. Lafleur. The company expects to sell 100,000 books each month in the next year. You have been given the job of scheduling print runs to meet the anticipated demand and minimize total costs to the company. Each print run has a setup cost of $5000, each book costs $1 to produce, and monthly storage costs for books awaiting shipment average 1¢ per book. What will you do?

If you decide to print all 1,200,000 books (the total demand for the year, 100,000 books per month for 12 months) in a single run at the start of the year and sales run as predicted, then the number of books in stock would begin at 1,200,000 and decrease to zero by the end of the year, as shown in Figure 40.

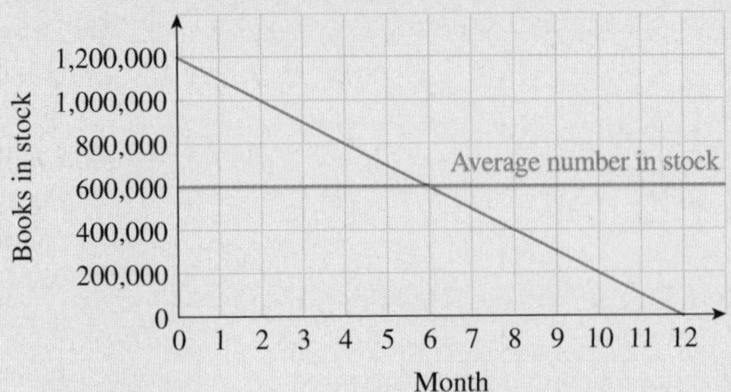

Figure **40**

On average, you would be storing 600,000 books for 12 months at 1¢ per book, giving a total storage cost of $600{,}000 \times 12 \times .01 = \$72{,}000$. The setup cost for the single print run would be \$5000. When you add to these the total cost of producing 1,200,000 books at \$1 per book, your total cost would be \$1,277,000.

If, on the other hand, you decide to cut down on storage costs by printing the books in two runs of 600,000 each, you would get the picture shown in Figure 41.

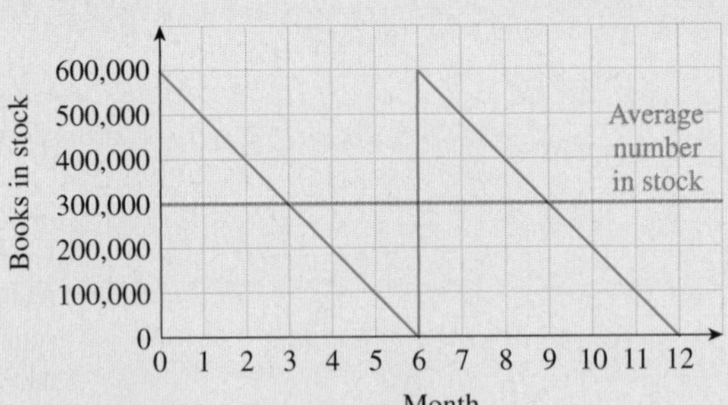

Figure **41**

Now, the storage cost would be cut in half because on average there would be only 300,000 books in stock. Thus, the total storage cost would be \$36,000, and the setup cost would double to \$10,000 (because there would now be two runs). The production costs would be the same: 1,200,000 books @ \$1 per book. The total cost would therefore be reduced to \$1,246,000, a savings of \$31,000 compared to your first scenario.

"Aha!" you say to yourself, after doing these calculations. "Why not drastically cut costs by setting up a run every month?" You calculate that the setup costs alone would be $12 \times \$5000 = \$60{,}000$, which is already more than the setup plus storage costs for two runs, so a run every month will cost too much. Perhaps, then, you should investigate three runs, four runs, and so on, until you find the lowest cost. This strikes you as too laborious a process, especially considering that you will have to do it all over again when planning for Lafleur's sequel, *Lorenzo's Lost Love,* due to be released next year. Realizing that this is an optimization problem, you decide to use some calculus to help you come up with a *formula* that you can use for all future plans. So you get to work.

Instead of working with the number 1,200,000, you use the letter N so that you can be as flexible as possible. (What if *Lorenzo's Lost Love* sells more copies?) Thus, you have a total of N books to be produced for the year. You now calculate the total cost of using x print runs per year. Because you are to produce a total of N books in x print runs, you will have to produce N/x books in each print run. N/x is called the **lot size.** As you can see from the diagrams above, the average number of books in storage will be half that amount, $N/(2x)$.

Now you can calculate the total cost for a year. Write P for the setup cost of a single print run ($P = \$5000$ in your case) and c for the *annual* cost of storing a book (to convert all of the time measurements to years; $c = \$0.12$ here). Finally, write b for the cost of producing a single book ($b = \$1$ here). The costs break down as follows.

Setup Costs: x print runs @ P dollars per run:	Px
Storage Costs: $N/(2x)$ books stored @ c dollars per year:	$cN/(2x)$
Production Costs: N books @ b dollars per book:	Nb
Total Cost:	$Px + \dfrac{cN}{2x} + Nb$

Remember that P, N, c, and b are all constants and x is the only variable. Thus, your cost function is

$$C(x) = Px + \frac{cN}{2x} + Nb$$

and you need to find the value of x that will minimize $C(x)$. But that's easy! All you need to do is find the relative extrema and select the absolute minimum (if any).

The domain of $C(x)$ is $(0, +\infty)$ because there is an x in the denominator and x can't be negative. To locate the extrema, you start by locating the critical points:

$$C'(x) = P - \frac{cN}{2x^2}$$

The only singular point would be at $x = 0$, but 0 is not in the domain. To find stationary points, you set $C'(x) = 0$ and solve for x:

$$P - \frac{cN}{2x^2} = 0$$

$$2x^2 = \frac{cN}{P}$$

so

$$x = \sqrt{\frac{cN}{2P}}$$

There is only one stationary point, and there are no singular points or endpoints. To graph the function you will need to put in numbers for the various constants. Substituting $N = 1{,}200{,}000$, $P = 5000$, $c = 0.12$, and $b = 1$, you get

$$C(x) = 5000x + \frac{72{,}000}{x} + 1{,}200{,}000$$

with the stationary point at

$$x = \sqrt{\frac{(0.12)(1{,}200{,}000)}{2(5000)}} \approx 3.79$$

The total cost at the stationary point is

$$C(3.79) \approx 1{,}240{,}000$$

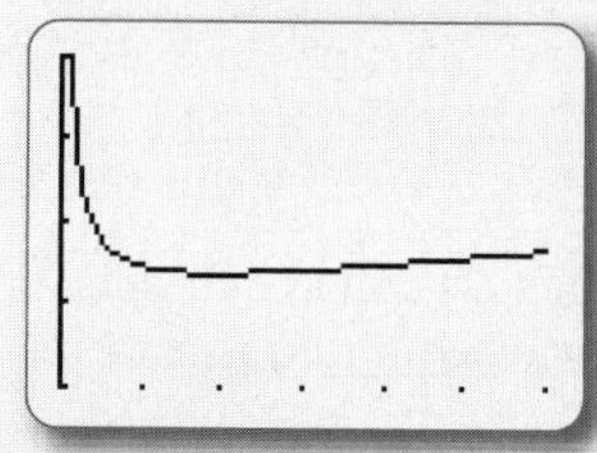

Figure **42**

You now graph $C(x)$ in a window that includes the stationary point, say, $0 \le x \le 12$ and $1{,}100{,}000 \le C \le 1{,}500{,}000$, getting Figure 42.

From the graph, you can see that the stationary point is an absolute minimum. In the graph it appears that the graph is always concave up, which also tells you that your stationary point is a minimum. You can check the concavity by computing the second derivative:

$$C''(x) = \frac{cN}{x^3} > 0$$

The second derivative is always positive because c, N, and x are all positive numbers, so indeed the graph is always concave up. Now you also know that it works regardless of the particular values of the constants.

So now you are practically done! You know that the absolute minimum cost occurs when you have $x \approx 3.79$ print runs per year. Don't be disappointed that the answer is not a whole number; whole number solutions are rarely found in real scenarios. What the answer (and the graph) do indicate is that either 3 or 4 print runs per year will cost the least money. If you take $x = 3$, you get a total cost of

$$C(3) = \$1{,}239{,}000$$

If you take $x = 4$, you get a total cost of

$$C(4) = \$1{,}238{,}000$$

So, four print runs per year will allow you to minimize your total costs.

Exercises

1. *Lorenzo's Lost Love* will sell 2,000,000 copies in a year. The remaining costs are the same. How many print runs should you use now?
2. In general, what happens to the number of runs that minimizes cost if both the setup cost and the total number of books are doubled?
3. In general, what happens to the number of runs that minimizes cost if the setup cost increases by a factor of 4?
4. Assuming that the total number of copies and storage costs are as originally stated, find the setup cost that would result in a single print run.
5. Assuming that the total number of copies and setup cost are as originally stated, find the storage cost that would result in a print run each month.
6. In Figure 41 we assumed that all the books in each run were manufactured in a very short time; otherwise the figure might have looked more like Figure 43, which shows the inventory, assuming a slower rate of production.

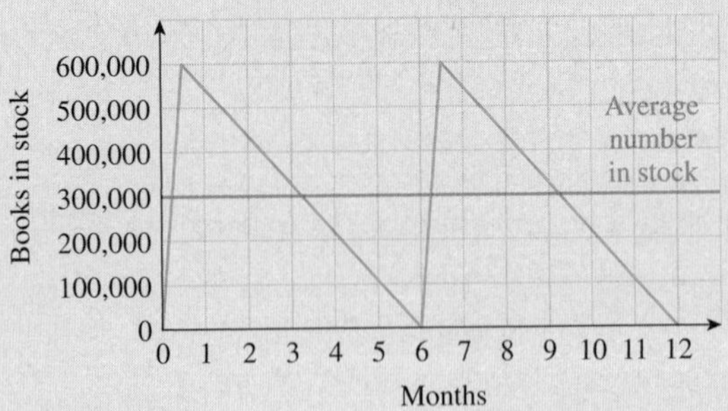

Figure **43**

How would this affect the answer?

7. Referring to the general situation discussed in the text, find the cost as a function of the total number of books produced, assuming that the number of runs is chosen to minimize total cost. Also find the average cost per book.
8. Let $\bar{C}$ be the average cost function found in the preceding exercise. Calculate $\lim_{N\to+\infty} \bar{C}(N)$ and interpret the result.

TI-83/84 Technology Guide

Section 5.5

Example 1 (a) Suppose that the demand equation for Bobby Dolls is given by $q = 216 - p^2$, where p is the price per doll in dollars and q is the number of dolls sold per week. Compute the price elasticity of demand when $p = \$5$ and $p = \$10$, and interpret the results.

Solution with Technology The TI-83/84 function `nDeriv` can be used to compute approximations of E at various prices.

1. Set

`Y1=216-X^2`	Demand equation
`Y2=-nDeriv(Y1,X,X)*X/Y1`	Formula for E

2. Use the table feature to list the values of elasticity for a range of prices, For part (a) we chose values of `X` close to 5:

X	Y1	Y2
4.7	193.91	.22784
4.8	192.96	.23881
4.9	191.99	.25012
5	191	[illegible]
5.1	189.99	.2738
5.2	188.96	.2862
5.3	187.91	.29897

Y2=.261780104712

EXCEL Technology Guide

Section 5.5

Example 1 (a) Suppose that the demand equation for Bobby Dolls is given by $q = 216 - p^2$, where p is the price per doll in dollars and q is the number of dolls sold per week. Compute the price elasticity of demand when $p = \$5$ and $p = \$10$, and interpret the results.

Solution with Technology To approximate E in Excel, we can use the following approximation of E.

$$E \approx \frac{\text{Percentage decrease in demand}}{\text{Percentage increase in price}} \approx -\frac{\left(\dfrac{\Delta q}{q}\right)}{\left(\dfrac{\Delta p}{p}\right)}$$

The smaller Δp is, the better the approximation. Let's use $\Delta p = 1¢$, or 0.01 (which is small compared with the typical prices we consider—around \$5 to \$10).

1. We start by setting up our worksheet to list a range of prices, in increments of Δp, on either side of a price in which we are interested, such as $p_0 = \$5$:

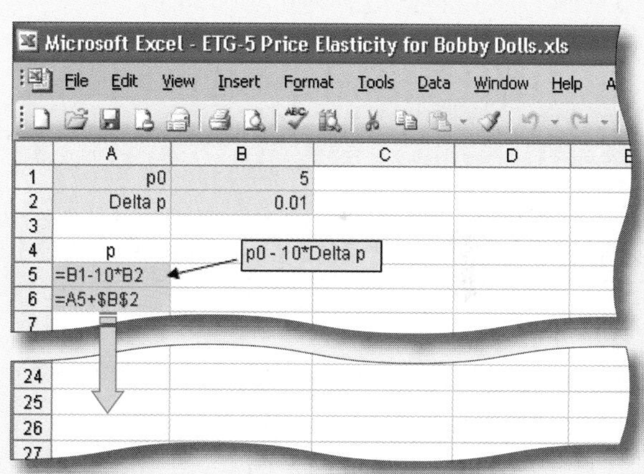

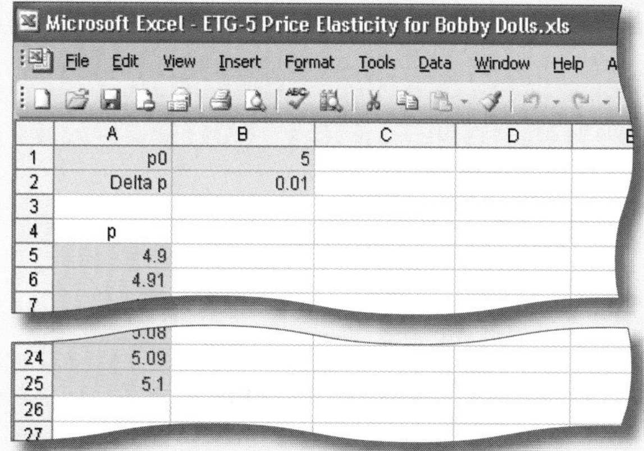

We start in cell A5 with the formula for $p_0 - 10\Delta p$ and then successively add Δp going down column A. You will find that the value $p_0 = 5$ appears midway down the list.

2. Next, we compute the corresponding values for the demand q in Column B.

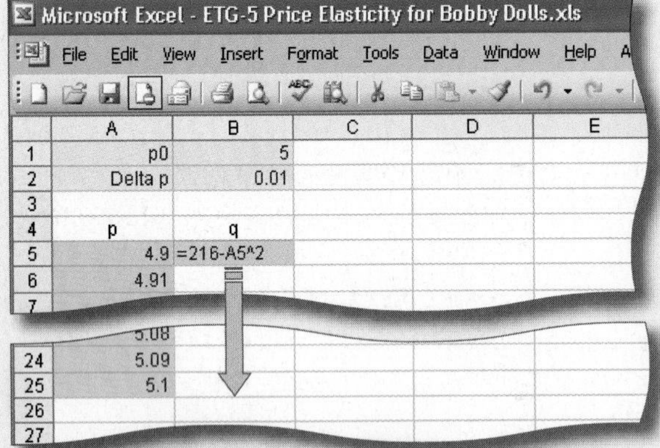

	A	B	C	D	E
1	p0	5			
2	Delta p	0.01			
3					
4	p	q			
5	4.9	=216-A5^2			
6	4.91				
7					
	5.08				
24	5.09				
25	5.1				
26					
27					

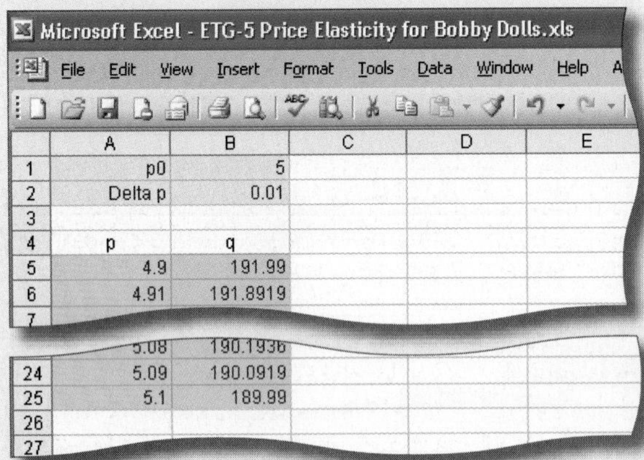

	A	B	C	D	E
1	p0	5			
2	Delta p	0.01			
3					
4	p	q			
5	4.9	191.99			
6	4.91	191.8919			
7					
	5.08	190.1936			
24	5.09	190.0919			
25	5.1	189.99			
26					
27					

3. We add two new columns for the percentage changes in p and q. The formula shown in cell C5 is copied down columns C and D, to Row 24. (Why not Row 25?)

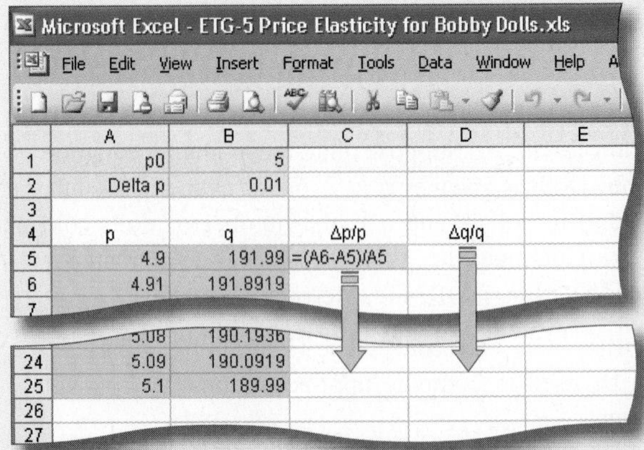

	A	B	C	D	E
1	p0	5			
2	Delta p	0.01			
3					
4	p	q	Δp/p	Δq/q	
5	4.9	191.99	=(A6-A5)/A5		
6	4.91	191.8919			
7					
	5.08	190.1936			
24	5.09	190.0919			
25	5.1	189.99			
26					
27					

4. The elasticity can now be computed in column E as shown:

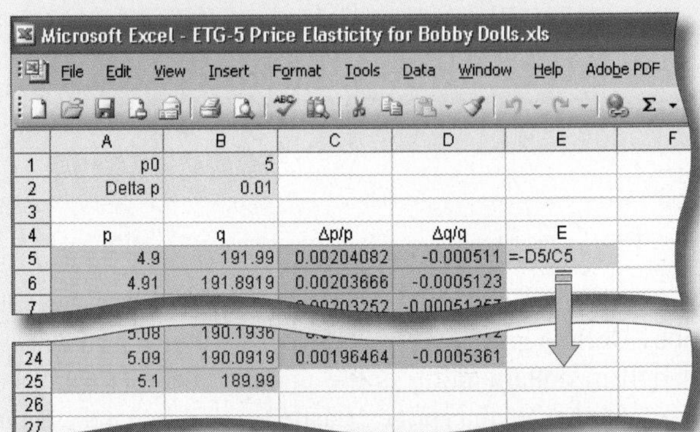

	A	B	C	D	E	F
1	p0	5				
2	Delta p	0.01				
3						
4	p	q	Δp/p	Δq/q	E	
5	4.9	191.99	0.00204082	-0.000511	=-D5/C5	
6	4.91	191.8919	0.00203666	-0.0005123		
7			0.00203252			
	5.08	190.1936				
24	5.09	190.0919	0.00196464	-0.0005361		
25	5.1	189.99				
26						
27						

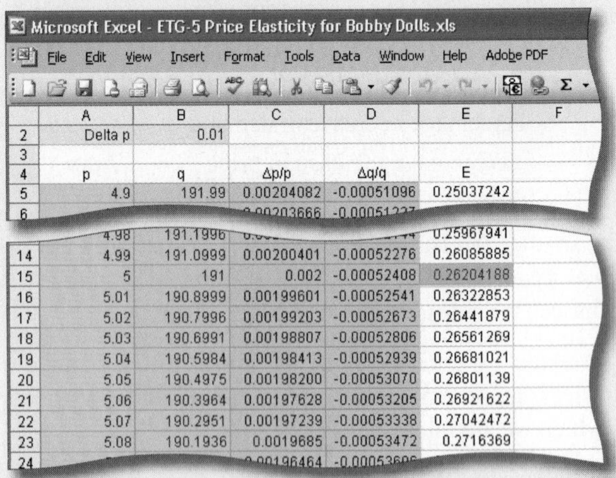

	A	B	C	D	E	F
2	Delta p	0.01				
3						
4	p	q	Δp/p	Δq/q	E	
5	4.9	191.99	0.00204082	-0.00051096	0.25037242	
6			0.00203666			
	4.98	191.1996			0.25967941	
14	4.99	191.0999	0.00200401	-0.00052276	0.26085885	
15	5	191	0.002	-0.00052408	0.26204188	
16	5.01	190.8999	0.00199601	-0.00052541	0.26322853	
17	5.02	190.7996	0.00199203	-0.00052673	0.26441879	
18	5.03	190.6991	0.00198807	-0.00052806	0.26561269	
19	5.04	190.5984	0.00198413	-0.00052939	0.26681021	
20	5.05	190.4975	0.00198200	-0.00053070	0.26801139	
21	5.06	190.3964	0.00197628	-0.00053205	0.26921622	
22	5.07	190.2951	0.00197239	-0.00053338	0.27042472	
23	5.08	190.1936	0.0019685	-0.00053472	0.2716369	
24			0.00196464			

TECHNOLOGY GUIDE

Math 30 Practice Set I

1. A. Your company makes a line of decorative clocks. In a typical week you expect to sell 2500 units at a price of \$20 and have a theory that you will lose 100 sales for each \$.80 increase in price. Find and sketch the demand function, **with the number of units sold as a function of price**. Find the price at which you would sell no clocks.
B. Find a function for the revenue you would take in as a function of price. Suppose that your weekly fixed costs of manufacturing the clocks are \$15,000 and that each clock costs \$15 to make. Find a formula for the week's profit, as a function of price. Using what you know about quadratic functions, find the price that would maximize the profit.

2. Alphabet soup: Solve the previous problem in an abstract setting, and thus solve it once and for all. Suppose the demand for a product is governed by the equation $q = a - b\,p$, where q is the number of units sold and p is the price. Suppose the cost of producing q units is $C(q) = f + v\,q$. Find a function that expresses profit **as a function of price**. Use what you know about quadratic functions to find the price that would maximize the profit. Prove that this price is the average of the variable cost figure, v, and the price at which you would sell no units.

3. The function $f(x)$ is defined in pieces. When x is less than 2, $f(x)$ is equal to $2x+1$; when x is greater than 2, $f(x)$ is $3 + x/2$; and $f(2)$ is 5. Sketch the graph of $f(x)$ on the interval [0,5].

4. An investment of \$1,000,000 grew to \$3,000,000 in 10 years, earning interest at a rate r, continuously compounded. Write a formula for r. Without a calculator, give a good estimate for this rate, based on your knowledge of logarithms.

5. A. I invested \$1000 at a spectacularly high interest rate (continuously compounded) and found that the money doubled in only $\ln(2^4)$ years (which is about 2.772... years, but don't use that approximation in your calculations—it's only an approximation!). What was the interest rate? How much would I have 4 years after the initial investment? Note that you can find all this out without using a calculator.
B. You made a very smart investment in the stock of a start-up company and found that your annual rate of return (as if this were continuously compounded interest) was exactly (ln 2)/3 . (This is about 23.1% but, again, **do not** use that in your computations.) If your original investment was \$1000, how much would it be worth after nine years?

6. A stone is dropped from the top of a 200 foot building. Its position, s , in feet above the ground, is given in terms of the time, t , in seconds from the start, by the formula:

$$s(t) = 200 - 16\,t^2$$

Find the average speed of the stone over the interval [2,3]. Find a formula for the average speed of this stone in the interval from $t = 2$ to $t = 2 + h$. What do you think was the exact speed when $t = 2$?

7. Suppose that $f(x) = \dfrac{5}{1+x}$. Find the average rate of change of f over the interval between $x = 2$ and $x = 2+h$. Simplify your answer. Use your answer to find the instantaneous rate of change of f at the point $x = 2$.

Math 30 Practice Set II

As a warm-up, do problems 1, 2, 3, 5, 9, and 11 from the Chapter 4 Review Exercises on p. 439. Those give plenty of practice with technical skills, so this set emphasizes word problems.

1. You run your own business scheduling tutoring sessions for calculus students. You do all the scheduling yourself, so there are no fixed costs. You hire expert tutors at $10 per hour and schedule sessions priced at $p per hour. Suppose that q is the number of hours of tutoring you sell per day, and that the demand for your service is modeled by

$$q = \sqrt{1600 - 40\,p}\ .$$

Find a formula for the daily profit you would make. What price would you charge in order to maximize this profit? How many hours of tutoring would you sell?

2. Essay: Write a formula that gives the definition of the derivative of a function $f(x)$. Write four sentences, one for each of the terms *average rate of change, instantaneous rate of change, secant line*, and *tangent line*, to tell how these terms apply to the various parts of the formula. Then show the steps in computing the derivative of the function $f(x) = 7/x$.

3. You found the following formula on a scrap of paper blowing across campus in the high winds.

$$\lim_{h \to 0} \frac{(5+h)^2 - 5^2}{h}$$

First, find the value of this limit. You realize that this was the starting point for someone who was computing the derivative of a certain function at a certain x-value. What was the function? What was the x-value?

4. A country has been suffering from rather high inflation, which is defined to be the instantaneous rate of change of the Consumer Price Index, or CPI. Its CPI is modeled by the equation

$$C(x) = x^3 - 6\,x^2 + 13\,x + 100\ ,$$

where x represents the number of years since 1995. Between 1995 and 2000, when was the **inflation** lowest and when was it highest? (Please read the words carefully here!)

5. A phone company is tracking the per-minute price it is charging a certain group of customers. This isn't easy, because there are so many rules for the cost of a particular call. In October, it collected $200,000 for 2,000,000 minutes of calls, which works out to ten cents a minute. Suppose the amount collected is increasing at a rate of $10,000 per month and the number of calls is increasing at a rate of 200,000 minutes per month. Use the quotient rule to find the rate of change in per-minute price. (Hints: Call the unit price p, the charges C, and the number of minutes M. Use powers of ten to keep track of all those zeroes! For the experts: Relate this to problem 30 on p. 340.)

6. Your Read-Anywhere electronic book sells q units in a month at price p. An eccentric analyst models monthly demand by the equation $p^2 + qp = 190{,}000$, so you realize that a price of $100 will stimulate 1,800 sales. First, find dp/dq by implicit differentiation. Use the result to find the marginal revenue; that is, predict how revenue would change if you sell one more unit.

Supplement: Problems for Extra Practice

Math 30 Practice Set III

1. Consider a web-design business with the following model of demand: if you charge your clients a price of $ p per hour, you would expect to sell q hours, where

$$q = \sqrt{3600 - 60\,p}\ .$$

A friend tells make the following claim: "At a price of $45 per hour, increasing the price by 20 % would decrease the sales by 30 %." Use the theory of elasticity to test your friend's remark. Also, find the range of prices for which demand is elastic. (For extra practice, suppose that your costs are $15 per hour for this business. Compute the price that would maximize your profit.)

2. You order blooming houseplants from a supplier and sell them in your store. They are expensive to store: it costs $120 to store one unit for a year (based on average inventory). Each order you place costs $100 (and the supplier will deliver up to 200 at a time). You expect to sell 6000 in a year. Form a function that gives the combined annual costs of storage and ordering as a function of the order size. Analyze the first and second derivatives of this function to determine the order size that would minimize your costs.

3. A country experienced a period of inflation, during which the Consumer Price Index (CPI) rose from a base level of 100 points at a substantial rate. The CPI is modeled by:

$$CPI(x) = 200 - 10\,x\,e^{-x/10} - 100\,e^{-x/10}, \text{ for } 0 \le x \le 30,$$

where x is the number of years from 1970. According to this model, what were the highest and lowest values of *inflation* during the given period? Be sure that you identify (and simplify) the inflation function correctly. For more practice, sketch the CPI function, showing the correct concavity.

4. A mathematical model for the advertising revenue brought in by a certain newspaper is

$$R(x) = \frac{x^2}{2} + 3\,x + 160$$

thousand dollars, when the circulation of the paper is x thousand daily sales. At a time when the circulation is 10,000, it is thought that circulation is increasing at a rate of 2000 sales per year. Based on this assumption, find the rate of change of advertising revenue, in thousand dollars per year.

5. "Ten becomes a million!" Thinking of generations to come, you invest the modest sum of $10 at a (continuously compounded) interest rate r. You leave instructions that the money should be withdrawn and given to SCU after 100 years, at which time it will be worth $1,000,000. Use what you know about interest and about logarithms to find an exact, calculator-ready formula for r. Then, find the two whole numbers that lie on either side of ln(10) and use them to find an estimate for r. (For instance, a person who knows the definition of natural logarithms would *not* say that $1 < \ln(10) < 2$.) Use your calculator to check.

Supplement: Problems for Extra Practice

Math 31 Practice Set I

1. Perform three of the indicated antidifferentiations, and explain why one is impossible to do. For the one that's impossible, alter the integrand to create an integral where u-substitution works. Evaluate the new integral.

$$\int \frac{3x}{2x^2+1}\,dx \qquad \int x^5 \ln(x)\,dx \qquad \int x^{2/3}\left(4+x^{5/3}\right)^{-4}dx \qquad \int \frac{x}{\sqrt{x^3+7}}\,dx$$

2. Find the value of each definite integral (the last one is very tricky!):

$$A.\ \int_1^3 \frac{1}{x^3}\,dx \qquad B.\ \int_0^2 \frac{8x^3}{\sqrt{x^4+9}}\,dx \qquad C.\ \int_0^{20} x\,e^{-x/10}\,dx \qquad D.\ \int_0^2 \frac{3x^7}{\sqrt{x^4+9}}\,dx$$

3. Essay: A) Write a brief explanation of the meaning of the symbol

$$\int_a^b f(x)\,dx$$

where $f(x)$ is a positive function. B) What are the two versions of the Fundamental Theorem of Calculus? Use a diagram to illustrate your explanations.

4. You run a small factory that assembles phones. You have a theory that the marginal revenue is given by

$$R'(x) = 9\sqrt{16+.03x}\,,$$

where x is the number of units assembled in a day. Find the revenue gained by assembling 300 phones in a day. For variety, solve this problem two ways: with indefinite and with definite integrals. (Note: As in the text examples, correctly determining the constant of integration can be a crucial step.)

5. A manufacturer of heavy machinery estimates marginal costs of

$$C'(x) = 7e^{-x/100}$$

for a week's production of x units (measured in thousands of dollars). The fixed costs for this period are three million dollars. Find the total cost of making 100 units. As in the previous problem, solve by two methods for more practice.

6. When you design a new microchip, profits are low on the first items produced, because you have to almost give them away in order to get manufacturers to build them into new products. Suppose your marginal profit, in dollars, for selling x crates of chips is modeled by

$$P'(x) = \frac{45e^{x/20}}{e^{x/20}+2}.$$

Suppose that you would lose \$1,500 if you sold none. Find the profit gained by selling the first 100 crates. Without using a calculator, estimate this value.

7. A computer game is estimated to have demand and supply functions:

$$p = D(q) = \frac{400}{1+0.02q}, \qquad p = S(q) = 0.4q.$$

Find the price at which supply equals demand; this requires solving a quadratic equation—use factoring or the quadratic formula. At this price level compute the suppliers' surplus and the consumers' surplus.

Math 31 Practice Set II

1. Find the present value of an annuity that would generate the continuous money flow $R(t) = 10 + t/2$ thousand dollars per year forever. Use a constant continuously compounded interest rate of $r = .05$. Explain why the total value of this income stream is infinite.

2. A finite-term annuity generates the continuous money flow $R(t) = 30 - 5\,t/4$ thousand dollars per year until R(t) becomes zero (**how long is that?**). Find the total value of this income stream as well as its present value. Assume a constant continuously compounded interest rate of $r = 1/24$ (which is a little more than 4%, but *use the exact figure* instead of this approximation). Without using a calculator, tell about how big the present value is.

3. Explain why each integral is improper. If the integral converges, tell its value.

$$\int_0^3 \frac{2x}{\sqrt{9-x^2}}\,dx \qquad \int_2^\infty \frac{6x}{(5+x^2)^{3/2}}\,dx$$

4. Lorentz curves in two societies are modeled by

$$f(x) = \frac{4}{5}x + \frac{1}{5}x^p \quad \text{and} \quad g(x) = \frac{1}{5}x + \frac{4}{5}x^p .$$

Compute the Gini index for each situation in terms of the unknown p. If you simplify and think carefully, you'll be able to see which one is larger. Given that the more equitable society has a Gini index of 1/10, determine p and find the Gini index for the less equitable society.

5. A cruise line sells tickets to two kinds of passengers, luxury and economy class. Economy passengers pay \$500 for the cruise, while luxury passengers pay \$800. The cost (in hundreds of dollars) of taking x economy passengers and y luxury passengers is thought to be:

$$C(x,y) = 3x + 5y + .01x^2 + .02xy + .02y^2 + 30$$

Find $P(x,y)$, the profit involved in taking x economy passengers and y luxury passengers. Find the combination of passengers that will maximize the profits. Use the second derivative test to verify that this is a maximum.

6. The function pictured to the right,

$$f(x,y) = 9y - 3y^3 - x^2 y$$

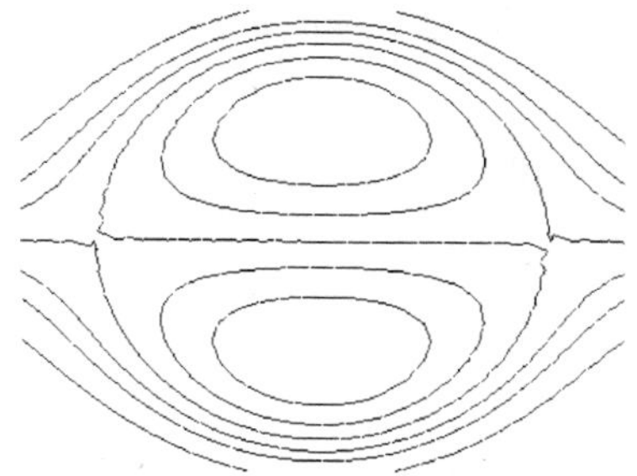

has four critical points. Use good logic to find all four.

Then use the second derivative test to classify them as saddles, maxima, or minima.

7. Find the indicated partial derivatives:

$$\frac{\partial^2}{\partial y \partial x}(x\,e^{2xy+1}) \qquad \frac{\partial^2}{\partial x \partial y}(x\,e^{2xy+1}) \qquad \frac{\partial^2}{\partial y^2}\left(\ln\left(\frac{1-xy}{1+xy}\right)\right)$$

8. A company sells x cheap DataFones at price p and y deluxe NetPhones at price q. Market research shows that the joint demand functions for these products are given by

$$p = 80 - 0.03x - 0.01y$$

$$q = 100 - 0.02x - 0.01y .$$

The cheap units cost \$32 to produce, and the deluxe models cost \$74. Fixed costs are \$9,600. Express the profit as a function of x and y. Find the number of each product that you should sell in order to maximize your profit. Determine the prices that would generate exactly this optimal demand.

Supplement: Problems for Extra Practice

Math 31 Practice Set III

1. The owner of a large farm with a known reservoir of gas beneath the ground sells the gas rights to a company for a guaranteed continuous money flow of $f(x) = 60\,e^{0.02\,x}$ thousand dollars per year *forever*, where x is the number of years from now. Find the present value of this perpetual income stream, assuming an interest rate of 7% compounded continuously.

2. Given that $f(x, y) = \sqrt{x^2 + 4\,x\,y + y^2}$, find the partial derivatives $f_x\,(2,0)$ and $f_{x\,y}\,(2,0)$. Simplify your answers.

3. You have 90 hours before you take the SAT. You theorize that your total score depends on how you balance your time use between sleeping and studying. You adopt a Cobb-Douglas model and assume that your score will be

$$f(y,z) = 30\; y^{\frac{7}{10}} z^{\frac{3}{10}}$$

where y is the number of hours you study and z is the number of hours you sleep. If you wanted to maximize your score, how many hours would you sleep and how many would you study?

4. A store sells x assembled computers and y do-it-yourself kits for the same machine. Their monthly profit (in dollars) is given by the model

$$P(x, y) = 480\;x + 400\;y - x^2 - x\;y - \frac{3}{2}\;y^2 - 30{,}000\;.$$

Suppose that the store can sell no more than 200 units in a month. Find the combination of sales that would maximize the profit in this situation. If there were a way to sell more than 200 units, would this lead to higher profit?

5.
   A. Determine the value of k so that $f(x) = k\;(\,10 - x\,)$ is a probability density function on the interval $[\,-10\;,\,10\,]$. Use this value in part B.
   B. The amount of time Professor Jetson will arrive before or after the start of class, is a continuous random variable with the probability density function in part A. What is the probability Professor Jetson arrives before the start of class (at $x = 0$) ?
   C. On the average, how many minutes, early or late, does Professor Jetson usually arrive, according to this model. Remember, the numerical answer can be negative and this would require interpretation.

6. The amount of water used (in thousands of gallons) at Terry's Classic Car Wash on a typical weekend day is thought to be a continuous random variable with the following density function:

$$f(x) = \begin{cases} \dfrac{1}{9}(x-1)^2 & 1 \le x \le 4, \\ 0 & \text{otherwise}. \end{cases}$$

Verify that this is a probability density function. They have to pay a fine if they are caught using more than 3 thousand gallons in a day. If the water inspector arrives on a typical Saturday, what are the chances Terry will have to pay the fine? Also, find the expected value of this random variable. (Hint: for this last computation, integration by parts is *by far* the simplest method.)

6 The Integral

CASE STUDY Wage Inflation

As assistant personnel manager for a large corporation, you have been asked to estimate the average annual wage earned by a worker in your company, from the time the worker is hired to the time the worker retires. You have data about wage increases. How will you estimate this average?

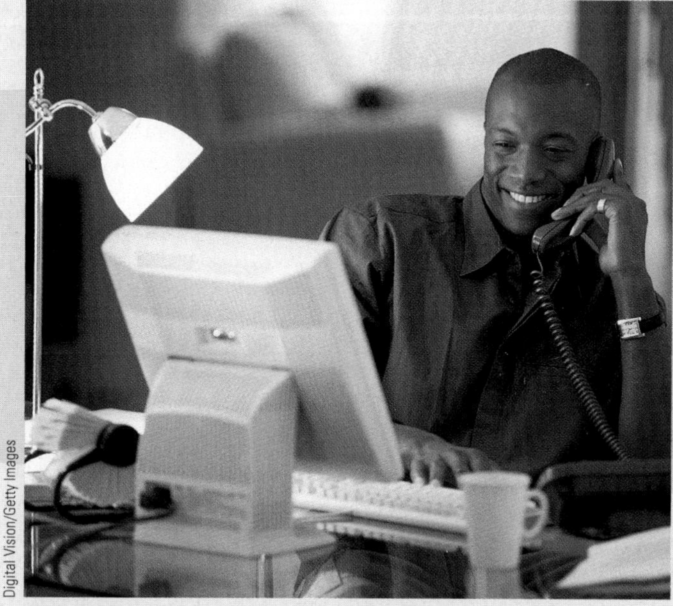

Digital Vision/Getty Images

Introduction

Roughly speaking, calculus is divided into two parts: **differential calculus** (the calculus of derivatives) and **integral calculus,** which is the subject of this chapter and the next. Integral calculus is concerned with problems that are in some sense the reverse of the problems seen in differential calculus. For example, where differential calculus shows how to compute the rate of change of a quantity, integral calculus shows how to find the quantity if we know its rate of change. This idea is made precise in the **Fundamental Theorem of Calculus.** Integral calculus and the Fundamental Theorem of Calculus allow us to solve many problems in economics, physics, and geometry, including one of the oldest problems in mathematics—computing areas of regions with curved boundaries.

6.1 The Indefinite Integral

Suppose that we knew the marginal cost to manufacture an item and we wanted to reconstruct the cost function. We would have to *reverse* the process of differentiation, to go from the derivative (the marginal cost function) back to the original function (the total cost). We'll first discuss how to do that and then look at some applications.

Here is an example: If the derivative of $F(x)$ is $4x^3$, what was $F(x)$? We recognize $4x^3$ as the derivative of x^4. So, we might have $F(x) = x^4$. However, $F(x) = x^4 + 7$ works just as well. In fact, $F(x) = x^4 + C$ works for any number C. Thus, there are *infinitely many* possible answers to this question.

In fact, we will see shortly that the formula $F(x) = x^4 + C$ covers *all* possible answers to the question. Let's give a name to what we are doing.

Antiderivative

An **antiderivative** of a function f is a function F such that $F' = f$.

quick **Examples**

1. An antiderivative of $4x^3$ is x^4. Because the derivative of x^4 is $4x^3$
2. Another antiderivative of $4x^3$ is $x^4 + 7$. Because the derivative of $x^4 + 7$ is $4x^3$
3. An antiderivative of $2x$ is $x^2 + 12$. Because the derivative of $x^2 + 12$ is $2x$

Thus,

If the derivative of $A(x)$ is $B(x)$, then an antiderivative of $B(x)$ is $A(x)$.

We call the set of *all* antiderivatives of a function the **indefinite integral** of the function.

Indefinite Integral

$$\int f(x)\,dx$$

is read "the **indefinite integral** of $f(x)$ with respect to x" and stands for the set of all antiderivatives of f. Thus, $\int f(x)\,dx$ is a *collection of functions;* it is not a single function, or a number. The function f that is being **integrated** is called the **integrand,** and the variable x is called the **variable of integration.**

quick **Examples**

1. $\int 4x^3\,dx = x^4 + C$ — Every possible antiderivative of $4x^3$ has the form $x^4 + C$.
2. $\int 2x\,dx = x^2 + C$ — Every possible antiderivative of $2x$ has the form $x^2 + C$.

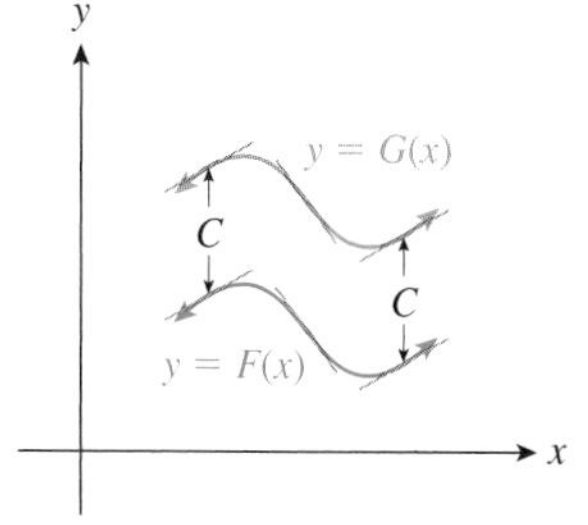

Figure 1

The **constant of integration** C reminds us that we can add any constant and get a different antiderivative.

Q: *If $F(x)$ is one antiderivative of $f(x)$, why must all other antiderivatives have the form $F(x) + C$?*

A: Suppose $F(x)$ and $G(x)$ are both antiderivatives of $f(x)$, so that $F'(x) = G'(x)$. Consider what this means by looking at Figure 1. ■

If $F'(x) = G'(x)$ for all x, then F and G have the *same slope* at each value of x. This means that their graphs must be *parallel* and hence remain exactly the same vertical distance apart. But that is the same as saying that the functions differ by a constant—that is, that $G(x) = F(x) + C$ for some constant C.[1]

Example 1 Indefinite Integral

Check that $\displaystyle\int x\,dx = \frac{x^2}{2} + C$.

Solution We check our answer by taking the derivative of the right-hand side:

$$\frac{d}{dx}\left(\frac{x^2}{2} + C\right) = \frac{2x}{2} + 0 = x \qquad ✔$$

Because the derivative of the right-hand side is the integrand x, we can conclude that $\displaystyle\int x\,dx = \frac{x^2}{2} + C$, as claimed.

Now, we would like to make the process of finding indefinite integrals (antiderivatives) more mechanical. For example, it would be nice to have a power rule for indefinite integrals similar to the one we already have for derivatives. Two cases suggested by the examples above are:

$$\int x\,dx = \frac{x^2}{2} + C \qquad \int x^3\,dx = \frac{x^4}{4} + C$$

You should check the last equation by taking the derivative of its right-hand side. These cases suggest the following general statement:

[1] This argument can be turned into a more rigorous proof—that is, a proof that does not rely on geometric concepts such as "parallel graphs." We should also say that the result requires that F and G have the same derivative *on an interval* $[a, b]$.

Power Rule for the Indefinite Integral, Part I

$$\int x^n\,dx = \frac{x^{n+1}}{n+1} + C \qquad (\text{if } n \neq -1)$$

In Words

To find the integral of x^n, add 1 to the exponent, and then divide by the new exponent. This rule works provided that n is not -1.

quick **Examples**

1. $\int x^{55}\,dx = \frac{x^{56}}{56} + C$

2. $\int \frac{1}{x^{55}}\,dx = \int x^{-55}\,dx$ Exponent form

$= \frac{x^{-54}}{-54} + C$ When we add 1 to -55, we get -54, *not* -56.

$= -\frac{1}{54x^{54}} + C$ See below*

3. $\int 1\,dx = x + C$ Because $1 = x^0$. This is an important special case.

* We are glossing over a subtlety here: The constant of integration C can be different for $x < 0$ and $x > 0$ because the graph breaks at $x = 0$. In general, our understanding will be that the constant of integration may be different on disconnected intervals of the domain.

Notes

1. The integral $\int 1\,dx$ is commonly written as $\int dx$. Similarly, the integral $\int \frac{1}{x^{55}}\,dx$ may be written as $\int \frac{dx}{x^{55}}$.

2. We can easily check the power rule formula by taking the derivative of the right-hand side:

$$\frac{d}{dx}\left(\frac{x^{n+1}}{n+1} + C\right) = \frac{(n+1)x^n}{n+1} = x^n \qquad ✔$$

■

Q: *What is the reason for the restriction $n \neq -1$?*

A: The right-hand side of the power rule formula has $n+1$ in the denominator, and thus makes no sense if $n = -1$. This leaves us not yet knowing how to compute

$$\int x^{-1}\,dx = \int \frac{1}{x}\,dx$$

Computing this derivative amounts to finding a function whose derivative is $1/x$. Prodding our memories a little, we recall that $\ln x$ has derivative $1/x$. In fact, as we pointed out when we first discussed it, $\ln|x|$ also has derivative $1/x$, but it has the advantage that its domain is the same as that of $1/x$. Thus, we can fill in the missing case as follows:

$$\int x^{-1}\,dx = \ln|x| + C$$

■

This and two other indefinite integrals that come from corresponding formulas for differentiation are summarized here:

Power Rule for the Indefinite Integral, Part II

$$\int x^{-1}\,dx = \ln|x| + C \qquad \text{Equivalently, } \int \frac{1}{x}\,dx = \ln|x| + C.$$

Indefinite Integral of e^x and b^x

$$\int e^x\,dx = e^x + C \qquad \text{Because } \frac{d}{dx}(e^x) = e^x$$

If b is any positive number other than 1, then

$$\int b^x\,dx = \frac{b^x}{\ln b} + C \qquad \text{Because } \frac{d}{dx}\left(\frac{b^x}{\ln b}\right) = \frac{b^x \ln b}{\ln b} = b^x$$

quick Example

$$\int 2^x\,dx = \frac{2^x}{\ln 2} + C$$

For more complicated functions, like $2x^3 + 6x^5 - 1$, we need the following rules for integrating sums, differences, and constant multiples.

Sums, Differences, and Constant Multiples

Sum and Difference Rules

$$\int [f(x) \pm g(x)]\,dx = \int f(x)\,dx \pm \int g(x)\,dx$$

In Words: The integral of a sum is the sum of the integrals, and the integral of a difference is the difference of the integrals.

Constant Multiple Rule

$$\int kf(x)\,dx = k\int f(x)\,dx \quad (k \text{ constant})$$

In Words: The integral of a constant times a function is the constant times the integral of the function. (In other words, the constant "goes along for the ride.")

quick Examples

Sum Rule: $\int (x^3 + 1)\,dx = \int x^3\,dx + \int 1\,dx = \frac{x^4}{4} + x + C$ $\quad f(x) = x^3;\ g(x) = 1$

Constant Multiple Rule: $\int 5x^3\,dx = 5\int x^3\,dx = 5\frac{x^4}{4} + C$ $\quad k = 5;\ f(x) = x^3$

Constant Multiple Rule: $\int 4\,dx = 4\int 1\,dx = 4x + C$ $\quad k = 4;\ f(x) = 1$

Constant Multiple Rule: $\int 4e^x\,dx = 4\int e^x\,dx = 4e^x + C$ $\quad k = 4;\ f(x) = e^x$

Proof of the Sum Rule

We saw above that if two functions have the same derivative, they differ by a (possibly zero) constant. Look at the rule for sums:

$$\int [f(x) + g(x)]\,dx = \int f(x)\,dx + \int g(x)\,dx$$

If we take the derivative of the left-hand side with respect to x, we get the integrand, $f(x) + g(x)$. If we take the derivative of the right-hand side, we get

$$\frac{d}{dx}\left[\int f(x)\,dx + \int g(x)\,dx\right] = \frac{d}{dx}\left[\int f(x)\,dx\right] + \frac{d}{dx}\left[\int g(x)\,dx\right]$$

Derivative of a sum = Sum of derivatives

$$= f(x) + g(x)$$

Because the left- and right-hand sides have the same derivative, they differ by a constant. But, because both expressions are indefinite integrals, adding a constant does not affect their value, so they are the same as indefinite integrals.

Notice that a key step in the proof was the fact that the derivative of a sum is the sum of the derivatives.

A similar proof works for the difference and constant multiple rule.

Example 2 Using the Sum and Difference Rules

Find the integrals

a. $\int (x^3 + x^5 - 1)\,dx$ **b.** $\int \left(x^{2.1} + \frac{1}{x^{1.1}} + \frac{1}{x} + e^x\right) dx$ **c.** $\int (e^x + 3^x - 1)\,dx$

Solution

a. $\int (x^3 + x^5 - 1)\,dx = \int x^3\,dx + \int x^5\,dx - \int 1\,dx$ Sum/difference rule

$= \frac{x^4}{4} + \frac{x^6}{6} - x + C$ Power rule

b. $\int \left(x^{2.1} + \frac{1}{x^{1.1}} + \frac{1}{x} + e^x\right) dx$

$= \int (x^{2.1} + x^{-1.1} + x^{-1} + e^x)\,dx$ Exponent form

$= \int x^{2.1}\,dx + \int x^{-1.1}\,dx + \int x^{-1}\,dx + \int e^x\,dx$ Sum rule

$= \frac{x^{3.1}}{3.1} + \frac{x^{-0.1}}{-0.1} + \ln|x| + e^x + C$ Power rule and exponential rule

$= \frac{x^{3.1}}{3.1} - \frac{10}{x^{0.1}} + \ln|x| + e^x + C$

c. $\int (e^x + 3^x - 1)\,dx = \int e^x\,dx + \int 3^x\,dx - \int 1\,dx$ Sum/difference rule

$= e^x + \frac{3^x}{\ln 3} - x + C$ Power rule and exponential rule

+ *Before we go on...* You should check each of the answers in Example 2 by differentiating.

Q: *Why is there only a single arbitrary constant C in each of the answers?*

A: We could have written the answer to part (a) as

$$\frac{x^4}{4} + D + \frac{x^6}{6} + E - x + F$$

where D, E, and F are all arbitrary constants. Now suppose, for example, we set $D = 1$, $E = -2$, and $F = 6$. Then the particular antiderivative we get is $x^4/4 + x^6/6 - x + 5$, which has the form $x^4/4 + x^6/6 - x + C$. Thus, we could have chosen the single constant C to be 5 and obtained the same answer. In other words, the answer $x^4/4 + x^6/6 - x + C$ is just as general as the answer $x^4/4 + D + x^6/6 + E - x + F$, but simpler. ■

In practice we do not explicitly write the integral of a sum as a sum of integrals but just "integrate term by term," much as we learned to differentiate term by term.

Example 3 Combining the Rules

Find the integrals

a. $\int (10x^4 + 2x^2 - 3e^x)\,dx$ **b.** $\int \left(\frac{2}{x^{0.1}} + \frac{x^{0.1}}{2} - \frac{3}{4x}\right) dx$ **c.** $\int [3e^x - 2(1.2^x)]\,dx$

Solution

a. We need to integrate separately each of the terms $10x^4$, $2x^2$, and $3e^x$. To integrate $10x^4$ we use the rules for constant multiples and powers:

$$\int 10x^4\,dx = 10\int x^4\,dx = 10\frac{x^5}{5} + C = 2x^5 + C$$

The other two terms are similar. We get

$$\int (10x^4 + 2x^2 - 3e^x)\,dx = 10\frac{x^5}{5} + 2\frac{x^3}{3} - 3e^x + C = 2x^5 + \frac{2}{3}x^3 - 3e^x + C$$

b. We first convert to exponent form and then integrate term by term:

$$\int \left(\frac{2}{x^{0.1}} + \frac{x^{0.1}}{2} - \frac{3}{4x}\right) dx = \int \left(2x^{-0.1} + \frac{1}{2}x^{0.1} - \frac{3}{4}x^{-1}\right) dx$$ Exponent form

$$= 2\frac{x^{0.9}}{0.9} + \frac{1}{2}\frac{x^{1.1}}{1.1} - \frac{3}{4}\ln|x| + C$$ Integrate term by term.

$$= \frac{20x^{0.9}}{9} + \frac{x^{1.1}}{2.2} - \frac{3}{4}\ln|x| + C$$ Back to rational form

c. $\int [3e^x - 2(1.2^x)]\,dx = 3e^x - 2\frac{1.2^x}{\ln(1.2)} + C$

Example 4 Different Variable Name

Find $\displaystyle\int \left(\frac{1}{u} + \frac{1}{u^2}\right) du$.

Solution

This integral may look a little strange because we are using the letter u instead of x, but there is really nothing special about x. Using u as the variable of integration, we get

$$\int \left(\frac{1}{u} + \frac{1}{u^2}\right) du = \int (u^{-1} + u^{-2})\, du \qquad \text{Exponent form.}$$

$$= \ln|u| + \frac{u^{-1}}{-1} + C \qquad \text{Integrate term by term.}$$

$$= \ln|u| - \frac{1}{u} + C \qquad \text{Simplify the result.}$$

+ *Before we go on...* When we compute an indefinite integral, we want the independent variable in the answer to be the same as the variable of integration. Thus, if the integral in Example 4 had been written in terms of x rather than u, we would have written

$$\int \left(\frac{1}{x} + \frac{1}{x^2}\right) dx = \ln|x| - \frac{1}{x} + C$$

■

Application: Cost and Marginal Cost

Example 5 Finding Cost from Marginal Cost

Rudi Von Briel/PhotoEdit

The marginal cost to produce baseball caps at a production level of x caps is $4 - 0.001x$ dollars per cap, and the cost of producing 100 caps is \$500. Find the cost function.

Solution We are asked to find the cost function $C(x)$, given that the *marginal* cost function is $4 - 0.001x$. Recalling that the marginal cost function is the derivative of the cost function, we can write

$$C'(x) = 4 - 0.001x$$

and must find $C(x)$. Now $C(x)$ must be an antiderivative of $C'(x)$, so

$$C(x) = \int (4 - 0.001x)\, dx$$

$$= 4x - 0.001\frac{x^2}{2} + K \qquad K \text{ is the constant of integration.}^*$$

$$= 4x - 0.0005x^2 + K$$

Now, unless we have a value for K, we don't really know what the cost function is. However, there is another piece of information we have ignored: The cost of producing 100 baseball caps is \$500. In symbols

$$C(100) = 500$$

* We used K and not C for the constant of integration because we are using C for cost.

Substituting in our formula for $C(x)$, we have

$$C(100) = 4(100) - 0.0005(100)^2 + K$$
$$500 = 395 + K$$
$$K = 105$$

Now that we know what K is, we can write down the cost function:

$$C(x) = 4x - 0.0005x^2 + 105$$

+ *Before we go on...* Let us consider the significance of the constant term 105 in Example 5. If we substitute $x = 0$ into the cost function, we get

$$C(0) = 4(0) - 0.0005(0)^2 + 105 = 105$$

Thus, \$105 is the cost of producing zero items; in other words, it is the **fixed cost.** ■

Application: Motion in a Straight Line

An important application of the indefinite integral is to the study of motion. The application of calculus to problems about motion is an example of the intertwining of mathematics and physics. We begin by bringing together some facts, scattered through the last several chapters, that have to do with an object moving in a straight line, and then restating them in terms of antiderivatives.

Position, Velocity, and Acceleration: Derivative Form

If $s = s(t)$ is the **position** of an object at time t, then its **velocity** is given by the derivative

$$v = \frac{ds}{dt}$$

In Words: Velocity is the derivative of position.

The **acceleration** of an object is given by the derivative

$$a = \frac{dv}{dt}$$

In Words: Acceleration is the derivative of velocity.

Position, Velocity, and Acceleration: Integral Form

$$s(t) = \int v(t)\,dt \qquad \text{Because } v = \frac{ds}{dt}$$

$$v(t) = \int a(t)\,dt \qquad \text{Because } a = \frac{dv}{dt}$$

quick Example

If the velocity of a particle moving in a straight line is given by $v(t) = 4t + 1$, then its position after t seconds is given by $s(t) = \int v(t)\,dt = \int (4t + 1)\,dt = 2t^2 + t + C$.

Example 6 Motion in a Straight Line

a. The velocity of a particle moving along in a straight line is given by $v(t) = 4t + 1$ m/sec. Given that the particle is at position $s = 2$ meters at time $t = 1$, find an expression for s in terms of t.

b. For a freely falling body experiencing no air resistance and zero initial velocity, find an expression for the velocity v in terms of t. [Note: On Earth, a freely falling body experiencing no air resistance accelerates downward at approximately 9.8 meters per second per second, or 9.8 m/s^2 (or 32 ft/s^2).]

Solution

a. As we saw in the Quick Example above, the position of the particle after t seconds is given by

$$s(t) = \int v(t)\,dt$$
$$= \int (4t + 1)\,dt = 2t^2 + t + C$$

But what is the value of C? Now, we are told that the particle is at position $s = 2$ at time $t = 1$. In other words, $s(1) = 2$. Substituting this into the expression for $s(t)$ gives

$$2 = 2(1)^2 + 1 + C$$

So $\quad C = -1$

Hence the position after t seconds is given by

$$s(t) = 2t^2 + t - 1 \text{ meters.}$$

b. Let's measure heights above the ground as positive, so that a rising object has positive velocity and the acceleration due to gravity is negative (it causes the upward velocity to decrease in value). Thus, the acceleration of the stone is given by

$$a(t) = -9.8 \text{ m/s}^2$$

We wish to know the velocity, which is an antiderivative of acceleration, so we compute

$$v(t) = \int a(t)\,dt = \int (-9.8)\,dt = -9.8t + C$$

To find the value of C, we use the given information that at time $t = 0$ the velocity is $0 : v(0) = 0$. Substituting this into the expression for $v(t)$ gives

$$0 = -9.8(0) + C$$

so $\quad C = 0$

Hence the velocity after t seconds is given by

$$v(t) = -9.8t \text{ m/s}$$

Example 7 Motion in a Straight Line Under Gravity

You are standing on the edge of a cliff and toss a stone upward at a speed of 30 feet per second.

a. Find the stone's velocity as a function of time. How fast and in what direction is it going after 5 seconds? (Neglect the effects of air resistance.)

b. Find the position of the stone as a function of time. Where will it be after 5 seconds?

c. When and where will the stone reach its zenith, its highest point?

Solution

a. This is similar to Example 6(b): Measuring height above the ground as positive, the acceleration of the stone is given by $a(t) = -32$ ft/s^2, and so

$$v(t) = \int (-32)\, dt = -32t + C$$

To obtain C, we use the fact that you tossed the stone upward at 30 ft/s; that is, when $t = 0$, $v = 30$, or $v(0) = 30$. Thus,

$$30 = v(0) = -32(0) + C$$

so $C = 30$ and the formula for velocity is $v(t) = -32t + 30$ ft/sec. In particular, after 5 seconds the velocity will be

$$v(5) = -32(5) + 30 = -130 \text{ ft/s}$$

After 5 seconds the stone is *falling* with a speed of 130 ft/s.

b. We wish to know the position, but position is an antiderivative of velocity. Thus,

$$s(t) = \int v(t)\, dt = \int (-32t + 30)\, dt = -16t^2 + 30t + C$$

Now to find C, we need to know the initial position $s(0)$. We are not told this, so let's measure heights so that the initial position is zero. Then

$$0 = s(0) = C$$

and $s(t) = -16t^2 + 30t$. In particular, after 5 seconds the stone has a height of

$$s(5) = -16(5)^2 + 30(5) = -250 \text{ ft}$$

In other words, the stone is now 250 ft *below* where it was when you first threw it, as shown in Figure 2.

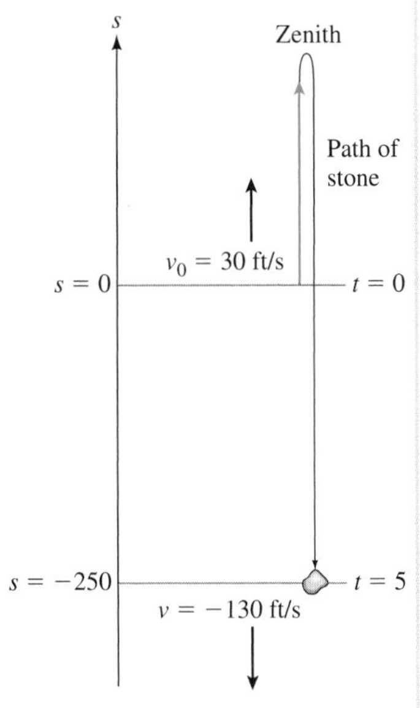

Figure 2

c. The stone reaches its zenith when its height $s(t)$ is at its maximum value, which occurs when $v(t) = s'(t)$ is zero. So we solve

$$v(t) = -32t + 30 = 0$$

getting $t = 30/32 = 15/16 = 0.9375$ s. This is the time when the stone reaches its zenith. The height of the stone at that time is

$$s(15/16) = -16(15/16)^2 + 30(15/16) = 14.0625 \text{ ft}$$

6.1 EXERCISES

● denotes basic skills exercises

Evaluate the integrals in Exercises 1–40.

1. ● $\int x^5\,dx$ *hint* [see Quick Examples p. 420]

2. ● $\int x^7\,dx$ **3.** ● $\int 6\,dx$ **4.** ● $\int (-5)\,dx$

5. ● $\int x\,dx$ **6.** ● $\int (-x)\,dx$

7. ● $\int (x^2 - x)\,dx$ *hint* [see Example 2]

8. ● $\int (x + x^3)\,dx$ **9.** ● $\int (1 + x)\,dx$

10. ● $\int (4 - x)\,dx$ **11.** ● $\int x^{-5}\,dx$

12. ● $\int x^{-7}\,dx$ **13.** ● $\int (x^{2.3} + x^{-1.3})\,dx$

14. ● $\int (x^{-0.2} - x^{0.2})\,dx$

15. ● $\int (u^2 - 1/u)\,du$ *hint* [see Example 4]

16. ● $\int (1/v^2 + 2/v)\,dv$

17. ● $\int \sqrt{x}\,dx$ **18.** ● $\int \sqrt[3]{x}\,dx$

19. ● $\int (3x^4 - 2x^{-2} + x^{-5} + 4)\,dx$ *hint* [see Example 3]

20. ● $\int (4x^7 - x^{-3} + 1)\,dx$

21. ● $\int \left(\frac{2}{u} + \frac{u}{4}\right) du$ **22.** ● $\int \left(\frac{2}{u^2} + \frac{u^2}{4}\right) du$

23. ● $\int \left(\frac{1}{x} + \frac{2}{x^2} - \frac{1}{x^3}\right) dx$ **24.** ● $\int \left(\frac{3}{x} - \frac{1}{x^5} + \frac{1}{x^7}\right) dx$

25. ● $\int (3x^{0.1} - x^{4.3} - 4.1)\,dx$ **26.** ● $\int \left(\frac{x^{2.1}}{2} - 2.3\right) dx$

27. ● $\int \left(\frac{3}{x^{0.1}} - \frac{4}{x^{1.1}}\right) dx$ **28.** ● $\int \left(\frac{1}{x^{1.1}} - \frac{1}{x}\right) dx$

29. ● $\int \left(5.1t - \frac{1.2}{t} + \frac{3}{t^{1.2}}\right) dt$

30. ● $\int \left(3.2 + \frac{1}{t^{0.9}} + \frac{t^{1.2}}{3}\right) dt$

31. ● $\int (2e^x + 5/x + 1/4)\,dx$

32. ● $\int (-e^x + x^{-2} - 1/8)\,dx$

33. ● $\int \left(\frac{6.1}{x^{0.5}} + \frac{x^{0.5}}{6} - e^x\right) dx$

34. ● $\int \left(\frac{4.2}{x^{0.4}} + \frac{x^{0.4}}{3} - 2e^x\right) dx$

35. ● $\int (2^x - 3^x)\,dx$ **36.** ● $\int (1.1^x + 2^x)\,dx$

37. ● $\int 100(1.1^x)\,dx$ **38.** ● $\int 1000(0.9^x)\,dx$

39. $\int \frac{x+2}{x^3} dx$ **40.** $\int \frac{x^2-2}{x} dx$

41. ● Find $f(x)$ if $f(0) = 1$ and the tangent line at $(x, f(x))$ has slope x. *hint* [see Example 5]

42. ● Find $f(x)$ if $f(1) = 1$ and the tangent line at $(x, f(x))$ has slope $\frac{1}{x}$.

43. ● Find $f(x)$ if $f(0) = 0$ and the tangent line at $(x, f(x))$ has slope $e^x - 1$.

44. ● Find $f(x)$ if $f(1) = -1$ and the tangent line at $(x, f(x))$ has slope $2e^x + 1$.

Applications

45. ● ***Marginal Cost*** The marginal cost of producing the xth box of light bulbs is $5 - \frac{x}{10{,}000}$ and the fixed cost is \$20,000. Find the cost function $C(x)$. *hint* [see Example 5]

46. ● ***Marginal Cost*** The marginal cost of producing the xth box of Zip disks is $10 + \frac{x^2}{100{,}000}$ and the fixed cost is \$100,000. Find the cost function $C(x)$.

47. ● ***Marginal Cost*** The marginal cost of producing the xth roll of film is $5 + 2x + \frac{1}{x}$. The total cost to produce one roll is \$1000. Find the cost function $C(x)$.

48. ● ***Marginal Cost*** The marginal cost of producing the xth box of CDs is $10 + x + \frac{1}{x^2}$. The total cost to produce 100 boxes is \$10,000. Find the cost function $C(x)$.

49. ● ***Motion in a Straight Line*** The velocity of a particle moving in a straight line is given by $v(t) = t^2 + 1$.

a. Find an expression for the position s after a time t.

b. Given that $s = 1$ at time $t = 0$, find the constant of integration C, and hence find an expression for s in terms of t without any unknown constants. *hint* [see Example 6]

50. ● ***Motion in a Straight Line*** The velocity of a particle moving in a straight line is given by $v = 3e^t + t$.

a. Find an expression for the position s after a time t.
b. Given that $s = 3$ at time $t = 0$, find the constant of integration C, and hence find an expression for s in terms of t without any unknown constants.

51. ● ***Motion in a Straight Line*** If a stone is dropped from a rest position above the ground, how fast (in feet per second) and in what direction will it be traveling after 10 seconds? (Neglect the effects of air resistance.)

52. ● ***Motion in a Straight Line*** If a stone is thrown upward at 10 feet per second, how fast (in feet per second) and in what direction will it be traveling after 10 seconds? (Neglect the effects of air resistance.)

53. ● ***Motion in a Straight Line*** Your name is Galileo Galilei and you toss a weight upward at 16 feet per second from the top of the Leaning Tower of Pisa (height 185 ft).

a. Neglecting air resistance, find the weight's velocity as a function of time t in seconds.
b. Find the height of the weight above the ground as a function of time. Where and when will it reach its zenith? hint [see Example 7]

54. ● ***Motion in a Straight Line*** Your name is Francesca Dragonetti (an assistant of Galileo Galilei) and, to impress your boss, you toss a weight upward at 24 feet per second from the top of the Leaning Tower of Pisa (height 185 ft).

a. Neglecting air resistance, find the weight's velocity as a function of time t in seconds.
b. Find the height of the weight above the ground as a function of time. Where and when will it reach its zenith?

Vertical Motion *In Exercises 55–62, neglect the effects of air resistance.*

55. Show that if a projectile is thrown upward with a velocity of v_0 ft/s, then it will reach its highest point after $v_0/32$ ds.

56. Use the result of the preceding exercise to show that if a projectile is thrown upward with a velocity of v_0 ft/s, its highest point will be $v_0^2/64$ feet above the starting point.

Exercises 57–62 use the results in the preceding two exercises.

57. I threw a ball up in the air to a height of 20 feet. How fast was the ball traveling when it left my hand?

58. I threw a ball up in the air to a height of 40 feet. How fast was the ball traveling when it left my hand?

59. A piece of chalk is tossed vertically upward by Prof. Schwarzenegger and hits the ceiling 100 feet above with a *BANG*.

a. What is the minimum speed the piece of chalk must have been traveling to enable it to hit the ceiling?
b. Assuming that Prof. Schwarzenegger in fact tossed the piece of chalk up at 100 ft/sec, how fast was it moving when it struck the ceiling?
c. Assuming that Prof. Schwarzenegger tossed the chalk up at 100 ft/sec, and that it recoils from the ceiling with the same speed it had at the instant it hit, how long will it take the chalk to make the return journey and hit the ground?

60. A projectile is fired vertically upward from ground level at 16,000 feet per second.

a. How high does the projectile go?
b. How long does it take to reach its zenith (highest point)?
c. How fast is it traveling when it hits the ground?

61. ***Strength*** Prof. Strong can throw a 10-pound dumbbell twice as high as Professor Weak can. How much faster can Prof. Strong throw it?

62. ***Weakness*** Prof. Weak can throw a computer disk three times as high as Professor Strong can. How much faster can Prof. Weak throw it?

63. ***Household Income*** From 1990 to 2003, median household income in the U.S. rose by an average of approximately \$1000 per year.[2] Given that the median household income in 1990 was approximately \$30,000, use an indefinite integral to find a formula for median household income I as a function of time t since 1990 ($t = 0$ represents 1990), and use your formula to find the median household income in 2003.

64. ***Household Income*** From 1990 to 2003, mean household income in the U.S. rose by an average of approximately \$1700 per year.[3] Given that the mean household income in 2003 was approximately \$59,000, find a formula for mean household income A as a function of time t since 1990 ($t = 0$ represents 1990), and use your formula to find the mean household income in 2000.

65. ***Health Care Spending*** Write $H(t)$ for the amount spent in the U.S. on health care in year t, where t is measured in years since 1990. The rate of increase of $H(t)$was approximately \$65 billion per year in 1990 and rose to \$100 billion per year in 2000.[4]

a. Find a linear model for the rate of change $H'(t)$.
b. Given that \$700 billion was spent on health care in the U.S. in 1990, find the function $H(t)$.

66. ***Health Care Spending*** Write $H(t)$ for the amount spent in the U.S. on health care in year t, where t is measured in years since 2000. The rate of increase of $H(t)$ was projected to rise from \$100 billion per year in 2000 to approximately \$190 billion per year in 2010.[5]

a. Find a linear model for the rate of change $H'(t)$.
b. Given that \$1300 billion was spent on health care in the U.S. in 2000, and using your model from (a), find the function $H(t)$.

---

[2] In current dollars, unadjusted for inflation. SOURCE: U.S. Census Bureau; "Table H-5. Race and Hispanic Origin of Householder—Households by Median and Mean Income: 1967 to 2003;" published August 27, 2004; www.census.gov/hhes/income.

[3] Ibid.

[4] SOURCE: Centers for Medicare and Medicaid Services, "National Health Expenditures," 2002 version, released January 2004; www.cms.hhs.gov/statistics/nhe/.

[5] SOURCE: Centers for Medicare and Medicaid Services, "National Health Expenditures 1965–2013, History and Projections," www.cms.hhs.gov/statistics/nhe/.

67. ***Bottled-Water Sales*** The rate of U.S. sales of bottled water for the period 1993–2003 could be approximated by

$$R(t) = 17t^2 + 100t + 2300 \text{ million gallons per year} \quad (3 \le t \le 13)$$

where t is time in years since 1990.[6] Use an indefinite integral to approximate the total sales $S(t)$ of bottled water since 1993. Approximately how much bottled water was sold from 1993 to 2003?

68. ***Bottled-Water Sales*** The rate of U.S. per capita sales of bottled water for the period 1993–2003 could be approximated by

$$Q(t) = 0.05t^2 + 0.4t + 9 \text{ gallons per year} \quad (3 \le t \le 13)$$

where t is the time in years since 1990.[7] Use an indefinite integral to approximate the total per capita sales $P(t)$ of bottled water since 1993. Approximately how much bottled water was sold, per capita, from 1993 to 2003?

Communication and Reasoning Exercises

69. ● If $F(x)$ and $G(x)$ are both antiderivatives of $f(x)$, how are $F(x)$ and $G(x)$ related?

70. ● Your friend Marco claims that once you have one antiderivative of $f(x)$, you have all of them. Explain what he means.

71. ● Complete the following: The total cost function is an _____ of the _____ cost function.

72. ● Complete the following: The distance covered is an antiderivative of the _____ function, and the velocity is an antiderivative of the _____ function.

73. ● If x represents the number of items manufactured and $f(x)$ represents dollars per item, what does $\int f(x)\,dx$ represent? In general, how are the units of $f(x)$ and the units of $\int f(x)\,dx$ related?

74. ● Complete the following: $-\frac{1}{x}$ is an _____ of $\frac{1}{x^2}$, whereas $\ln x^2$ is not. Also, $-\frac{1}{x} + C$ is the _____ of $\frac{1}{x^2}$, because the _____ of $-\frac{1}{x} + C$ is _____.

75. Give an argument for the rule that the integral of a sum is the sum of the integrals.

76. Is it true that $\int \frac{1}{x^3}\,dx = \ln(x^3) + C$? Give a reason for your answer.

77. Give an example to show that the integral of a product is not the product of the integrals.

78. Give an example to show that the integral of a quotient is not the quotient of the integrals.

79. Complete the following: If you take the _____ of the _____ of $f(x)$, you obtain $f(x)$ back. On the other hand, if you take the _____ of the _____ of $f(x)$, you obtain $f(x) + C$.

80. If a Martian told you that the Institute of Alien Mathematics, after a long and difficult search, has announced the discovery of a new antiderivative of $x - 1$ called $M(x)$ [the formula for $M(x)$ is classified information and cannot be revealed here], how would you respond?

[6] The authors' regression model, based on data in the Beverage Marketing Corporation news release, "Bottled water now number-two commercial beverage in U.S., says Beverage Marketing Corporation," April 8, 2004, available at www.beveragemarketing.com.

[7] Ibid.

● basic skills

6.2 Substitution

The chain rule for derivatives gives us an extremely useful technique for finding antiderivatives. This technique is called **change of variables** or **substitution.**

Recall that to differentiate a function like $(x^2 + 1)^6$, we first think of the function as $g(u)$ where $u = x^2 + 1$ and $g(u) = u^6$. We then compute the derivative, using the chain rule, as

$$\frac{d}{dx}g(u) = g'(u)\frac{du}{dx}$$

Any rule for derivatives can be turned into a technique for finding antiderivatives. The chain rule turns into the following formula:

$$\int g'(u)\frac{du}{dx}dx = g(u) + C$$

But, if we write $g(u) + C = \int g'(u)du$, we get the following interesting equation:

$$\int g'(u)\frac{du}{dx}dx = \int g'(u)du$$

This equation is the one usually called the change of variables formula. We can turn it into a more useful integration technique as follows. Let $f = g'(u)(du/dx)$. We can rewrite the above change of variables formula using *f*:

$$\int f\,dx = \int \left(\frac{f}{du/dx}\right) du$$

In essence, we are making the formal substitution

$$dx = \frac{1}{du/dx}du$$

Here's the technique:

Substitution Rule

If u is a function of x, then we can use the following formula to evaluate an integral:

$$\int f\,dx = \int \left(\frac{f}{du/dx}\right) du$$

Rather than use the formula directly, we use the following step-by-step procedure:

1. Write u as a function of x.

2. Take the derivative du/dx and solve for the quantity dx in terms of du.

3. Use the expression you obtain in Step 2 to substitute for dx in the given integral and substitute u for its defining expression.

Now let's see how this procedure works in practice.

Example 1 Substitution

Find $\int 4x(x^2 + 1)^6 dx$.

Solution To use substitution we need to choose an expression to be u. There is no hard and fast rule, but here is one hint that often works:

Take u to be an expression that is being raised to a power.

In this case, let's set $u = x^2 + 1$. Continuing the procedure above, we place the calculations for step (2) in a box.

$u = x^2 + 1$	Write u as a function of x.
$\frac{du}{dx} = 2x$	Take the derivative of u with respect to x.
$dx = \frac{1}{2x}du$	Solve for dx: $dx = \frac{1}{du/dx}du$.

Now we *substitute u for its defining expression, and substitute for dx* in the original integral:

$$\int 4x(x^2+1)^6\,dx = \int 4xu^6\frac{1}{2x}du \qquad \text{Substitute}^* \text{ for } u \text{ and } dx.$$

$$= \int 2u^6 du \qquad \text{Cancel the } x\text{s and simplify.}$$

We have boiled the given integral down to the much simpler integral $\int 2u^6 du$, and we can now write down the solution:

$$2\frac{u^7}{7} + C = \frac{2(x^2+1)^7}{7} + C \qquad \text{Substitute } (x^2+1) \text{ for } u \text{ in the answer.}$$

---

* This step is equivalent to using the formula stated in the Substitution Rule box. If it should bother you that the integral contains both x and u, note that x is now a function of u.

+ *Before we go on...* There are two points to notice in Example 1. First, before we can actually integrate with respect to u, *we must eliminate all xs from the integrand*. If we cannot, we may have chosen the wrong expression for u. Second, after integrating, we must substitute back to obtain an expression involving x.

It is easy to check our answer. We differentiate:

$$\frac{d}{dx}\left[\frac{2(x^2+1)^7}{7}\right] = \frac{2(7)(x^2+1)^6(2x)}{7} = 4x(x^2+1)^6 \quad ✔$$

Notice how we used the chain rule to check the result obtained by substitution. ■

When we use substitution, the first step is always to decide what to take as u. Again, there are no set rules, but we see some common cases in the examples.

Example 2 More Substitution

Calculate $\int x^2(x^3+1)^2 dx$.

Solution

As we said in Example 1, it often works to take u to be an expression that is being raised to a power. We usually also want to see the derivative of u as a factor in the integrand so that we can cancel terms involving x. In this case, x^3+1 is being raised to a power, so let's set $u = x^3+1$. Its derivative is $3x^2$; in the integrand is x^2, which is missing the factor 3, but missing or incorrect constant factors are not a problem.

$$u = x^3 + 1 \qquad \text{Write } u \text{ as a function of } x.$$

$$\frac{du}{dx} = 3x^2 \qquad \text{Take the derivative of } u \text{ with respect to } x.$$

$$dx = \frac{1}{3x^2}du \qquad \text{Solve for } dx\text{: } dx = \frac{1}{du/dx}du.$$

$$\begin{aligned}\int x^2(x^3+1)^2dx &= \int x^2u^2\frac{1}{3x^2}du && \text{Substitute for } u \text{ and } dx.\\ &= \int \frac{1}{3}u^2du && \text{Cancel the terms with } x.\\ &= \frac{1}{9}u^3+C && \text{Take the antiderivative.}\\ &= \frac{1}{9}(x^3+1)^3+C && \text{Substitute for } u \text{ in the answer.}\end{aligned}$$

Example 3 An Expression in the Exponent

Evaluate $\int 3xe^{x^2}\,dx$.

Solution When we have an exponential with an expression in the exponent, it often works to substitute u for that expression. In this case, let's set $u = x^2$.

$$u = x^2 \qquad \frac{du}{dx} = 2x \qquad dx = \frac{1}{2x}du$$

Substituting into the integral, we have

$$\int 3xe^{x^2}dx = \int 3xe^u\frac{1}{2x}du = \int \frac{3}{2}e^u du$$
$$= \frac{3}{2}e^u + C = \frac{3}{2}e^{x^2} + C$$

Example 4 A Special Power

Evaluate $\int \frac{1}{2x+5}dx$.

Solution We begin by rewriting the integrand as a power.

$$\int \frac{1}{2x+5}dx = \int (2x+5)^{-1}dx$$

Now we take our earlier advice and set u equal to the expression that is being raised to a power:

$$u = 2x+5 \qquad \frac{du}{dx} = 2 \qquad dx = \frac{1}{2}du$$

Substituting into the integral, we have

$$\int \frac{1}{2x+5}dx = \int \frac{1}{2}u^{-1}du = \frac{1}{2}\ln|u| + C$$
$$= \frac{1}{2}\ln|2x+5| + C$$

Example 5 Choosing *u*

Evaluate $\int (x+3)\sqrt{x^2+6x}\,dx$.

Solution There are two parenthetical expressions. Notice however, that the derivative of the expression (x^2+6x) is $2x+6$, which is twice the term $(x+3)$ in front of the radical. Recall that we would like the derivative of u to appear as a factor. Thus, let's take $u = x^2+6x$.

$$u = x^2 + 6x$$
$$\frac{du}{dx} = 2x + 6 = 2(x+3)$$
$$dx = \frac{1}{2(x+3)}du$$

Substituting into the integral, we have

$$\int (x+3)\sqrt{x^2+6x}\,dx = \int (x+3)\sqrt{u}\left(\frac{1}{2(x+3)}\right)du$$
$$= \int \frac{1}{2}\sqrt{u}\,du = \frac{1}{2}\int u^{1/2}du$$
$$= \frac{1}{2}\frac{2}{3}u^{3/2} + C = \frac{1}{3}(x^2+6x)^{3/2} + C$$

Some cases require a little more work.

Example 6 When the *x* Terms Do Not Cancel

Evaluate $\int \frac{2x}{(x-5)^2}dx$.

Solution We first rewrite

$$\int \frac{2x}{(x-5)^2}dx = \int 2x(x-5)^{-2}dx$$

This suggests that we should set $u = x - 5$.

$$u = x - 5$$
$$\frac{du}{dx} = 1$$
$$dx = du$$

Substituting, we have

$$\int \frac{2x}{(x-5)^2}dx = \int 2xu^{-2}du$$

Now, there is nothing in the integrand to cancel the x that appears. If, as here, there is still an x in the integrand after substituting, we go back to the expression for u, solve for x, and substitute the expression we obtain for x in the integrand. So, we take $u = x - 5$ and solve for $x = u + 5$. Substituting, we get

$$\int 2xu^{-2}du = \int 2(u+5)u^{-2}du$$
$$= 2\int (u^{-1} + 5u^{-2})du$$
$$= 2\ln|u| - \frac{10}{u} + C$$
$$= 2\ln|x-5| - \frac{10}{x-5} + C$$

Example 7 Application: iPod Sales

The rate of sales of Apple iPods from the fourth quarter of 2002 through the third quarter of 2004 could be roughly approximated by the logistic function

$$r(t) = \frac{1100e^{0.6t}}{9 + e^{0.6t}} \text{ thousand iPods per quarter} \quad (-1 \le t \le 6)$$

where t is time in quarters since the first quarter of 2003.*

a. Find an expression for the total number of iPods sold since the first quarter of 2003 $(t = 0)$.

b. Roughly how many iPods were sold in 2003?

Solution

a. If we write the total number of iPods sold from the first quarter of 2003 to time t as $N(t)$, then the information we are given says that

$$N'(t) = r(t) = \frac{1100e^{0.6t}}{9 + e^{0.6t}}$$

Thus, $$N(t) = \int \frac{1100e^{0.6t}}{9 + e^{0.6t}}\,dt$$

is the function we are after. To integrate the expression, take u to be the denominator of the integrand:

$$u = 9 + e^{0.6t}$$
$$\frac{du}{dt} = 0.6e^{0.6t}$$
$$dt = \frac{1}{0.6e^{0.6t}}du$$

$$\begin{aligned} N(t) &= \int \frac{1100e^{0.6t}}{9 + e^{0.6t}}\,dt \\ &= \int \frac{1100e^{0.6t}}{u} \cdot \frac{1}{0.6e^{0.6t}}\,du \\ &= \frac{1100}{0.6}\int \frac{1}{u}\,du \\ &\approx 1800 \ln|u| + C = 1800\ln(9 + e^{0.6t}) + C \end{aligned}$$

(Why could we drop the absolute value in the last step?)

Now what is C? Because $N(t)$ represents the total number of iPods sold *since time t* $= 0$, we have $N(0) = 0$ (because that is when we started counting). Thus,

$$\begin{aligned} 0 &= 1800 \ln(9 + e^{0.6(0)}) + C \\ &= 1800 \ln(10) + C \\ C &= -1800 \ln(10) \approx -4100 \end{aligned}$$

Therefore, the total number of iPods sold since the first quarter of 2003 is approximately

$$N(t) = 1800 \ln(9 + e^{0.6t}) - 4100 \text{ thousand iPods}$$

b. Since the last quarter of 2003 ended when $t = 4$, the total number of iPods sold in 2003 was approximately

$$N(4) = 1800 \ln(9 + e^{0.6(4)}) - 4100 \approx 1300 \text{ thousand iPods}^{\dagger}$$

* Based on a logistic regression. Source for data: Apple Computer, Inc., quarterly earnings reports, available at www.apple.com.

† The actual number of iPods sold in 2003 was 939 thousand. This discrepancy results from a less than perfect fit of the logistic model to the actual data.

+ *Before we go on...* You might wonder why we are writing a logistic function in the form we used in Example 7 rather than in one of the "standard" forms $\frac{N}{1 + Ab^{-t}}$ or $\frac{N}{1 + Ae^{-kt}}$. Our only reason for doing this is to make the substitution work. To convert from the second "standard" form to the form we used in the example, multiply top and bottom by e^{kt}. (See Exercises 67 and 68 in Section 6.4 for further discussion.) ■

Shortcuts

The following shortcuts allow us to simply write down the antiderivative in cases where we would otherwise need the substitution $u = ax + b$, as in Example 4. (a and b are constants with $a \neq 0$.) All of the shortcuts can be obtained using the substitution $u = ax + b$. Their derivation will appear in the exercises.

Shortcuts: Integrals of Expressions Involving $(ax + b)$

Rule	*quick* **Example**
$\int (ax+b)^n\,dx = \frac{(ax+b)^{n+1}}{a(n+1)} + C$ (if $n \neq -1$)	$\int (3x-1)^2\,dx = \frac{(3x-1)^3}{3(3)} + C = \frac{(3x-1)^3}{9} + C$
$\int (ax+b)^{-1}dx = \frac{1}{a}\ln\lvert ax+b\rvert + C$	$\int (3-2x)^{-1}dx = \frac{1}{(-2)}\ln\lvert 3-2x\rvert + C = -\frac{1}{2}\ln\lvert 3-2x\rvert + C$
$\int e^{ax+b}dx = \frac{1}{a}e^{ax+b} + C$	$\int e^{-x+4}dx = \frac{1}{(-1)}e^{-x+4} + C = -e^{-x+4} + C$
$\int c^{ax+b}\,dx = \frac{1}{a\ln c}c^{ax+b} + C$	$\int 2^{-3x+4}\,dx = \frac{1}{(-3\ln 2)}2^{-3x+4} + C = -\frac{1}{3\ln 2}2^{-3x+4} + C$

FAQs When to Use Substitution and What to Use for u

Q: *If I am asked to calculate an antiderivative, how do I know when to use a substitution and when not to use one?*

A: Do *not* use substitution when integrating sums, differences, and/or constant multiples of powers of x and exponential functions, such as $2x^3 - \frac{4}{x^2} + \frac{1}{2x} + 3^x + \frac{2^x}{3}$.

To recognize when you should try a substitution, pretend that you are *differentiating* the given expression instead of integrating it. If differentiating the expression would require use of the chain rule, then integrating that expression may well require a substitution, as in, say, $x(3x^2-4)^3$ or $(x+1)e^{x^2+2x-1}$. (In the first we have a *quantity* cubed, and in the second we have e raised to a *quantity*.) ■

Q: *If an integral seems to call for a substitution, what should I use for u?*

A: There are no set rules for deciding what to use for *u*, but the preceding examples show some common patterns:

- If you see a linear expression raised to a power, try setting *u* equal to that linear expression. For example, in $(3x-2)^{-3}$, set $u = 3x - 2$. (Alternatively, try using the shortcuts above.)
- If you see a constant raised to a linear expression, try setting *u* equal to that linear expression. For example, in $3^{(2x+1)}$, set $u = 2x + 1$. (Alternatively, try a shortcut.)
- If you see an expression raised to a power multiplied by the derivative of that expression (or a constant multiple of the derivative), try setting *u* equal to that expression. For example, in $x^2(3x^3-4)^{-1}$, set $u = 3x^3 - 4$.
- If you see a constant raised to an expression, multiplied by the derivative of that expression (or a constant multiple of its derivative), try setting *u* equal to that expression. For example, in $5(x+1)e^{x^2+2x-1}$, set $u = x^2 + 2x - 1$.
- If you see an expression in the denominator and its derivative (or a constant multiple of its derivative) in the numerator, try setting *u* equal to that expression. For example, in $\frac{2^{3x}}{3-2^{3x}}$, set $u = 3 - 2^{3x}$.

Persistence often pays off: if a certain substitution does not work, try another approach or a different substitution. ■

6.2 EXERCISES

● denotes basic skills exercises

In Exercises 1–10, evaluate the given integral using the substitution (or method) indicated.

1. ● $\int (3x-5)^3\,dx;\ u = 3x - 5$

2. ● $\int (2x+5)^{-2}\,dx;\ u = 2x + 5$

3. ● $\int (3x-5)^3\,dx$; Shortcut p. 436

4. ● $\int (2x+5)^{-2}\,dx$; Shortcut p. 436

5. ● $\int e^{-x}\,dx;\ u = -x$

6. ● $\int e^{x/2}\,dx;\ u = x/2$

7. ● $\int e^{-x}\,dx$; Shortcut p. 436

8. ● $\int e^{x/2}\,dx$; Shortcut p. 436

9. ● $\int (x+1)e^{(x+1)^2}\,dx;\ u = (x+1)^2$

10. ● $\int (x-1)^2 e^{(x-1)^3}\,dx;\ u = (x-1)^3$

In Exercises 11–48, decide on what substitution to use, and then evaluate the given integral using a substitution.

11. ● $\int (3x+1)^5\,dx$ hint [see Example 1]

12. ● $\int (-x-1)^7\,dx$

13. ● $\int (-2x+2)^{-2}\,dx$

14. ● $\int (2x)^{-1}\,dx$

15. ● $\int 7.2\sqrt{3x-4}\,dx$

16. ● $\int 4.4e^{(-3x+4)}\,dx$

17. ● $\int 1.2e^{(0.6x+2)}\,dx$

18. ● $\int 8.1\sqrt{-3x+4}\,dx$

19. ● $\int x(3x^2+3)^3\,dx$

20. ● $\int x(-x^2-1)^3\,dx$

21. ● $\int x(x^2+1)^{1.3}\,dx$

22. ● $\int \frac{x}{(3x^2-1)^{0.4}}\,dx$

23. ● $\int (1+9.3e^{3.1x-2})\,dx$

24. ● $\int (3.2-4e^{1.2x-3})\,dx$

25. ● $\int 2x\sqrt{3x^2-1}\,dx$

26. ● $\int 3x\sqrt{-x^2+1}\,dx$ **27.** ● $\int xe^{-x^2+1}\,dx$

28. ● $\int xe^{2x^2-1}\,dx$

29. ● $\int (x+1)e^{-(x^2+2x)}\,dx$ *hint* [see Example 5]

30. ● $\int (2x-1)e^{2x^2-2x}\,dx$

31. ● $\int \frac{-2x-1}{(x^2+x+1)^3}\,dx$ **32.** ● $\int \frac{x^3-x^2}{3x^4-4x^3}\,dx$

33. ● $\int \frac{x^2+x^5}{\sqrt{2x^3+x^6-5}}\,dx$ **34.** ● $\int \frac{2(x^3-x^4)}{(5x^4-4x^5)^5}\,dx$

35. ● $\int x(x-2)^5\,dx$ *hint* [see Example 6]

36. ● $\int x(x-2)^{1/3}\,dx$ **37.** ● $\int 2x\sqrt{x+1}\,dx$

38. ● $\int \frac{x}{\sqrt{x+1}}\,dx$

39. ● $\int \frac{e^{-0.05x}}{1-e^{-0.05x}}\,dx$ *hint* [see Example 7]

40. ● $\int \frac{3e^{1.2x}}{2+e^{1.2x}}\,dx$ **41.** $\int \frac{3e^{-1/x}}{x^2}\,dx$

42. $\int \frac{2e^{2/x}}{x^2}\,dx$ **43.** $\int \frac{e^x+e^{-x}}{2}\,dx$

44. $\int e^{x/2}+e^{-x/2}\,dx$ **45.** $\int \frac{e^x-e^{-x}}{e^x+e^{-x}}\,dx$

46. $\int \frac{e^{x/2}+e^{-x/2}}{e^{x/2}-e^{-x/2}}\,dx$

47. $\int \left((2x-1)e^{2x^2-2x}+xe^{x^2}\right)dx$

48. $\int \left(xe^{-x^2+1}+e^{2x}\right)dx$

In Exercises 49–52, derive the given equation, where a and b are constants with $a \neq 0$.

49. ● $\int (ax+b)^n\,dx = \frac{(ax+b)^{n+1}}{a(n+1)}+C \quad (\text{if } n \neq -1)$

50. ● $\int (ax+b)^{-1}\,dx = \frac{1}{a}\ln|ax+b|+C$

51. ● $\int \sqrt{ax+b}\,dx = \frac{2}{3a}(ax+b)^{3/2}+C$

52. ● $\int e^{ax+b}\,dx = \frac{1}{a}e^{ax+b}+C$

In Exercises 53–66, use the shortcut formulas on p. 436 and Exercises 49–52 to calculate the given integral.

53. ● $\int e^{-x}\,dx$ **54.** ● $\int e^{x-1}\,dx$

55. ● $\int e^{2x-1}\,dx$ **56.** ● $\int e^{-3x}\,dx$

57. ● $\int (2x+4)^2\,dx$ **58.** ● $\int (3x-2)^4\,dx$

59. ● $\int \frac{1}{5x-1}\,dx$ **60.** ● $\int (x-1)^{-1}\,dx$

61. ● $\int (1.5x)^3\,dx$ **62.** ● $\int e^{2.1x}\,dx$

63. ● $\int 1.5^{3x}\,dx$ **64.** ● $\int 4^{-2x}\,dx$

65. ● $\int (2^{3x+4}+2^{-3x+4})\,dx$ **66.** ● $\int (1.1^{-x+4}+1.1^{x+4})\,dx$

67. ● Find $f(x)$ if $f(0)=0$ and the tangent line at $(x, f(x))$ has slope $x(x^2+1)^3$.

68. ● Find $f(x)$ if $f(1)=0$ and the tangent line at $(x, f(x))$ has slope $\frac{x}{x^2+1}$.

69. ● Find $f(x)$ if $f(1)=1/2$ and the tangent line at $(x, f(x))$ has slope xe^{x^2-1}.

70. ● Find $f(x)$ if $f(2)=1$ and the tangent line at x has slope $(x-1)e^{x^2-2x}$.

Applications

71. ● ***Cost*** The marginal cost of producing the xth roll of film is given by $5+1/(x+1)^2$. The total cost to produce one roll is \$1000. Find the total cost function $C(x)$.

72. ● ***Cost*** The marginal cost of producing the xth box of CDs is given by $10-x/(x^2+1)^2$. The total cost to produce 2 boxes is \$1000. Find the total cost function $C(x)$.

73. ● ***Scientific Research*** The number of research articles in the prominent journal *Physics Review* written by researchers in Europe can be approximated by

$$E(t) = \frac{7e^{0.2t}}{5+e^{0.2t}} \text{ thousand articles per year} \quad (t \geq 0)$$

where t is time in years ($t=0$ represents 1983).[8]

a. Find an (approximate) expression for the total number of articles written by researchers in Europe since 1983 ($t=0$).

b. Roughly how many articles were written by researchers in Europe from 1983 to 2003? *hint* [see Example 7]

74. ● ***Scientific Research*** The number of research articles in the prominent journal *Physics Review* written by researchers in the U.S. can be approximated by

$$U(t) = \frac{4.6e^{0.6t}}{0.4+e^{0.6t}} \text{ thousand articles per year} \quad (t \geq 0)$$

where t is time in years ($t=0$ represents 1983).[9]

[8] Based on data from 1983 to 2003. SOURCE: The American Physical Society/*New York Times*, May 3, 2003, p. A1.

[9] Ibid.

a. Find an (approximate) expression for the total number of articles written by researchers in the U.S. since 1983 ($t = 0$).
b. Roughly how many articles were written by researchers in the U.S. from 1983 to 2003?

75. ● ***Motion in a Straight Line*** The velocity of a particle moving in a straight line is given by $v = t(t^2 + 1)^4 + t$.

a. Find an expression for the position s after a time t.
b. Given that $s = 1$ at time $t = 0$, find the constant of integration C and hence an expression for s in terms of t without any unknown constants.

76. ● ***Motion in a Straight Line*** The velocity of a particle moving in a straight line is given by $v = 3te^{t^2} + t$.

a. Find an expression for the position s after a time t.
b. Given that $s = 3$ at time $t = 0$, find the constant of integration C and hence an expression for s in terms of t without any unknown constants.

77. ● ***Bottled-Water Sales*** The rate of U.S. sales of bottled water for the period 1993–2003 could be approximated by

$$R(t) = 17(t - 1990)^2 + 100(t - 1990) + 2300$$
million gallons per year $\quad (1993 \le t \le 2003)$

where t is the year.[10] Use an indefinite integral to approximate the total sales $S(t)$ of bottled water since 1993 ($t = 1993$). Approximately how much bottled water was sold from 1993 to 2003?

78. ● ***Bottled-Water Sales*** The rate of U.S. per capita sales of bottled water for the period 1993–2003 could be approximated by

$$Q(t) = 0.05(t - 1990)^2 + 0.4(t - 1990) + 9$$
gallons per year $\quad (1993 \le t \le 2003)$

where t is the year.[11] Use an indefinite integral to approximate the total per capita sales $P(t)$ of bottled water since 1993. Approximately how much bottled water was sold, per capita, from 1993 to 2003?

Communication and Reasoning Exercises

79. ● Are there any circumstances in which you should use the substitution $u = x$? Illustrate your answer by giving an example that shows the effect of this substitution.

80. ● At what stage of a calculation using a u substitution should you substitute back for u in terms of x: before or after taking the antiderivative?

81. ● You are asked to calculate $\int \frac{u}{u^2+1}\,du$. What is wrong with the substitution $u = u^2 + 1$?

82. ● What is wrong with the following "calculation" of $\int \frac{1}{x^2 - 1}\,dx$?

$$\int \frac{1}{x^2-1} = \int \frac{1}{u} \qquad \text{Using the substitution } u = x^2 - 1$$
$$= \ln|u| + C$$
$$= \ln|x^2 - 1| + C$$

83. ● Give an example of an integral that can be calculated by using the substitution $u = x^2 + 1$, and then carry out the calculation.

84. Give an example of an integral that can be calculated either by using the power rule for antiderivatives or by using the substitution $u = x^2 + x$, and then carry out the calculations.

85. Show that *none* of the following substitutions work for $\int e^{-x^2}\,dx$: $u = -x$, $u = x^2$, $u = -x^2$. (The antiderivative of e^{-x^2} involves the *error function* erf(x).)

86. Show that *none* of the following substitutions work for $\int \sqrt{1 - x^2}\,dx$: $u = 1 - x^2$, $u = x^2$, and $u = -x^2$. (The antiderivative of $\sqrt{1-x^2}$ involves inverse trigonometric functions, discussion of which is beyond the scope of this book.)

[10] The authors' regression model, based on data in the Beverage Marketing Corporation news release, "Bottled water now number-two commercial beverage in U.S., says Beverage Marketing Corporation," April 8, 2004, available at www.beveragemarketing.com.

[11] Ibid.

● basic skills

6.3 The Definite Integral: Numerical and Graphical Approaches

In Sections 6.1 and 6.2, we discussed the indefinite integral. There is an older, related concept called the **definite integral.** Let's introduce this new idea with an example. (We'll drop hints now and then about how the two types of integral are related. In Section 6.4 we discuss the exact relationship, which is one of the most important results in calculus.)

In Section 6.1, we used antiderivatives to answer questions of the form "Given the marginal cost, compute the total cost" (see Example 5 in Section 6.1). In this section we approach such questions more directly, and we will forget about antiderivatives for now.

Royalty Free/Corbis

Example 1 Total Cost

Your cell phone company offers you an innovative pricing scheme. When you make a call, the *marginal* cost is

$$c(t) = \frac{5}{10t + 1} \text{ dollars per hour}$$

Use a numerical calculation to estimate the total cost of a two-hour phone call.

Solution The graph of $c(t)$ is shown in Figure 3.

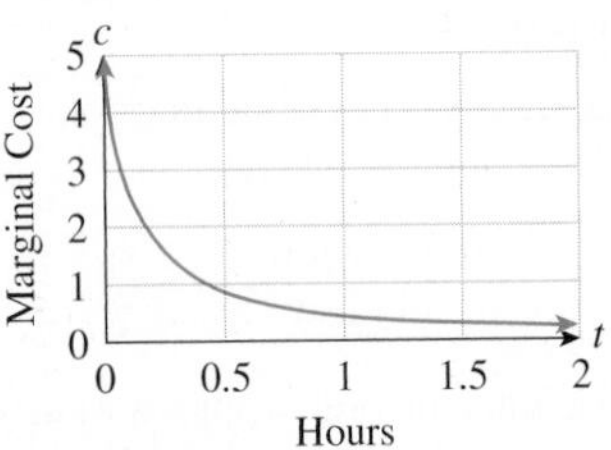

Figure 3

Let's start with a very crude estimate of the total cost, using the graph as a guide. The marginal cost at the beginning of your call is $c(0) = 5/(0 + 1) = \$5$ per hour. If this cost were to remain constant for the length of your call, the total cost of the call would be

$$\text{Cost of Call} = \text{Cost per hour} \times \text{Number of hours} = 5 \times 2 = \$10$$

Figure 4 shows how we can represent this calculation on the graph of $c(t)$.

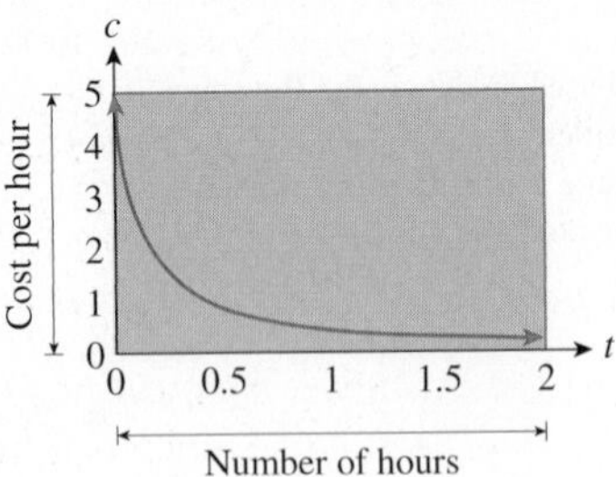

Figure 4

The cost per hour based on $c(0) = 5$ is represented by the y-coordinate of the graph at its left edge, while the number of hours is represented by the width of the interval $[0, 2]$ on the x-axis. Therefore, computing the area of the shaded rectangle in the figure gives the same calculation:

$$\begin{aligned} \text{Area of rectangle} &= \text{Cost per hour} \times \text{Number of hours} \\ &= 5 \times 2 = \$10 = \text{Cost of Call} \end{aligned}$$

But, as we see in the graph, the marginal cost does not remain constant, but goes down quite dramatically over the course of the call. We can obtain a somewhat more accurate estimate of the total cost by looking at the call hour by hour—that is, by dividing the length of the call into two equal intervals, or subdivisions. We estimate the cost of each one-hour subdivision, using the marginal cost at the beginning of that hour.

$$\begin{aligned}\text{Cost of first hour} &= \text{Cost per hour} \times \text{Number of hours}\\ &= c(0) \times 1 = 5 \times 1 = \$5\\ \text{Cost of second hour} &= \text{Cost per hour} \times \text{Number of hours}\\ &= c(1) \times 1 = 5/11 \times 1 \approx \$0.45\end{aligned}$$

Adding these costs gives us the more accurate estimate

$$c(0) \times 1 + c(1) \times 1 = \$5.45 \qquad \text{Calculation using 2 subdivisions}$$

In Figure 5 we see that we are computing the combined area of two rectangles, each of whose heights is determined by the height of the graph at its left edge:

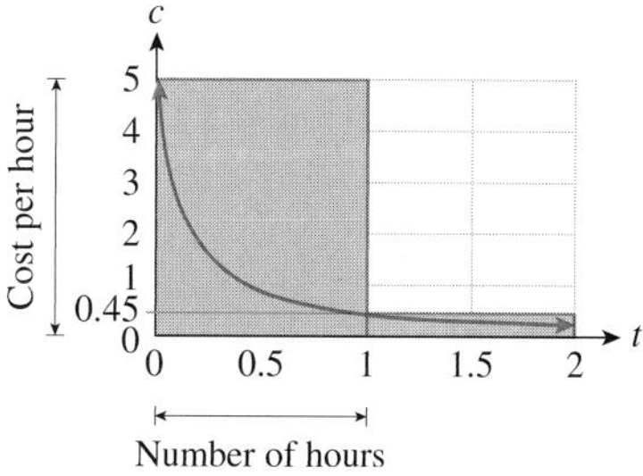

The areas of the rectangles are estimates of the costs for successive one-hour periods.

Figure **5**

$$\begin{aligned}\text{Area of first rectangle} &= \text{Cost per hour} \times \text{Number of hours}\\ &= c(0) \times 1 = \$5 = \text{Cost of first hour}\\ \text{Area of second rectangle} &= \text{Cost per hour} \times \text{Number of hours}\\ &= c(1) \times 1 \approx \$0.45 = \text{Cost of second hour}\end{aligned}$$

If we assume that the phone company is honest about $c(t)$ being the marginal cost and is actually calculating your cost more than once an hour, we get an even better estimate of the cost by looking at the call by using four divisions of a half-hour each. The calculation for this estimate is

$$\begin{aligned}&c(0) \times 0.5 + c(0.5) \times 0.5 + c(1) \times 0.5 + c(1.5) \times 0.5\\ &\approx 2.500 + 0.417 + 0.227 + 0.156 = \$3.30 \qquad \text{Calculation using 4 subdivisions}\end{aligned}$$

As we see in Figure 6, we have now computed the combined area of *four* rectangles each of whose heights is again determined by the height of the graph at its left edge.

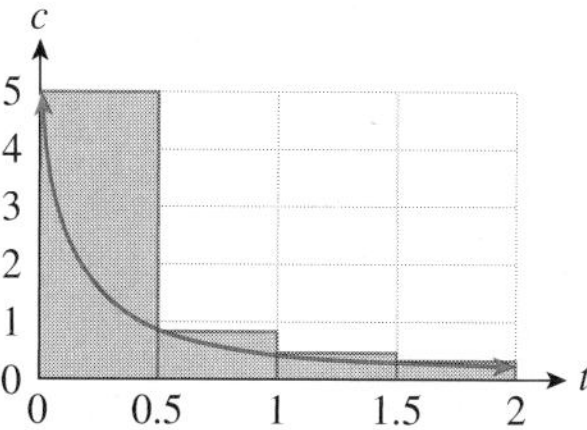

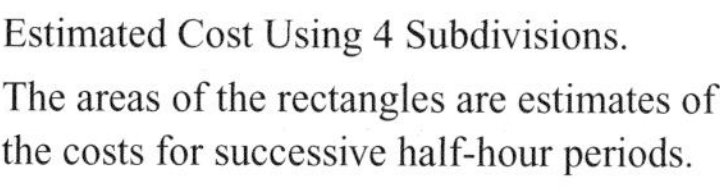
Estimated Cost Using 4 Subdivisions.

The areas of the rectangles are estimates of the costs for successive half-hour periods.

Figure **6**

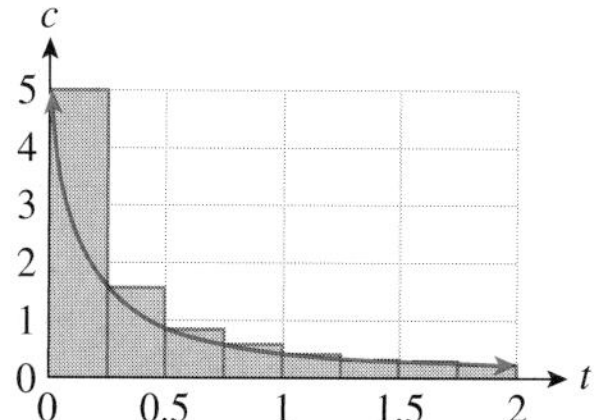

Estimated Cost Using 8 Subdivisions.

The areas of the rectangles are estimates of the costs for successive quarter-hour periods.

Figure **7**

Notice how the cost seems to be decreasing as we use more subdivisions. More importantly, total cost seems to be getting closer to the area under the graph. Figure 7 illustrates the calculation for 8 equal subdivisions. The approximate total cost using 8 subdivisions is the total area of the shaded region in Figure 7:

$$c(0) \times 0.25 + c(0.25) \times 0.25 + c(0.5) \times 0.25 + \cdots + c(1.75) \times 0.25 \approx \$2.31$$

Calculation using 8 subdivisions

Looking at Figure 7, one still gets the impression that we are being overcharged, especially for the first period. If the phone company wants to be *really* honest about $c(t)$ being the marginal cost, it should really be calculating your cost *continuously,* minute by minute or, better yet, second-by-second, as illustrated in Figure 8.

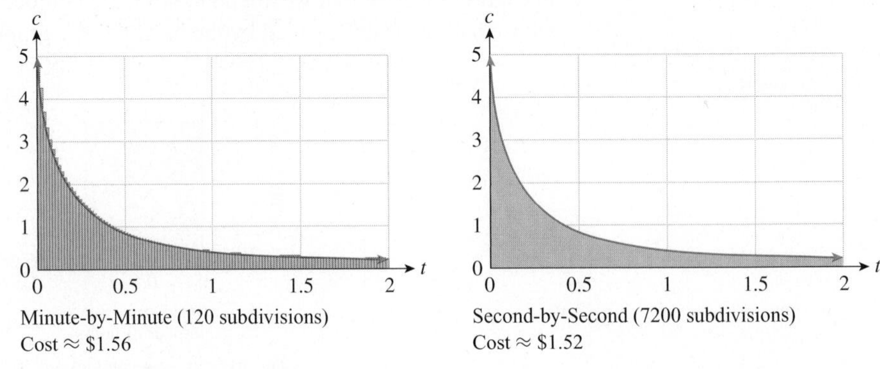

Minute-by-Minute (120 subdivisions)
Cost ≈ \$1.56

Second-by-Second (7200 subdivisions)
Cost ≈ \$1.52

Figure **8**

Figure 8 strongly suggests that the more accurately we calculate the total cost, the closer the answer gets to the exact area under the portion of the graph of $c(t)$ with $0 \le t \le 2$, and leads us to the conclusion that the *exact* total cost is the exact area under the marginal cost curve for $0 \le t \le 2$. In other words, we have made the following remarkable discovery:

Total cost is the area under the marginal cost curve!

+ *Before we go on...* The minute-by-minute calculation in Example 1 is tedious to do by hand, and no one in their right mind would even *attempt* to do the second-by-second calculation by hand! Below we discuss ways of doing these calculations with the aid of technology. ■

The type of calculation done in Example 1 is useful in many applications. Let's look at the general case and give the result a name.

In general, we have a function f (such as the function c in the example) and we consider an interval $[a, b]$ of possible values of the independent variable x. We subdivide the interval $[a, b]$ into some number of segments of equal length. Write n for the number of segments, or **subdivisions.**

Next, we label the endpoints of these subdivisions x_0 for a, x_1 for the end of the first subdivision, x_2 for the end of the second subdivision, and so on until we get to x_n, the end of the nth subdivision, so that $x_n = b$. Thus,

$$a = x_0 < x_1 < \cdots < x_n = b$$

The first subdivision is the interval $[x_0, x_1]$, the second subdivision is $[x_1, x_2]$, and so on until we get to the last subdivision, which is $[x_{n-1}, x_n]$. We are dividing the interval

$[a, b]$ into n subdivisions of equal length, so each segment has length $(b-a)/n$. We write Δx for $(b-a)/n$ (Figure 9).

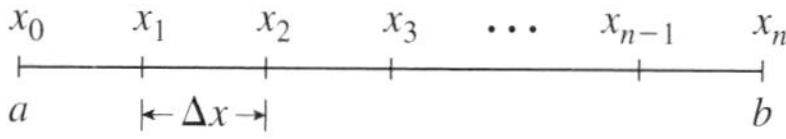

Figure 9

Having established this notation, we can write the calculation that we want to do as follows: For each subdivision $[x_{k-1}, x_k]$, compute $f(x_{k-1})$, the value of the function f at the left endpoint. Multiply this value by the length of the interval, which is Δx. Then add together all n of these products to get the number

$$f(x_0)\Delta x + f(x_1)\Delta x + \cdots + f(x_{n-1})\Delta x$$

This sum is called a **(left) Riemann[12] sum** for f. In Example 1 we computed several different Riemann sums. Here is the computation for $n = 4$ we used in the cell phone example (see Figure 10):

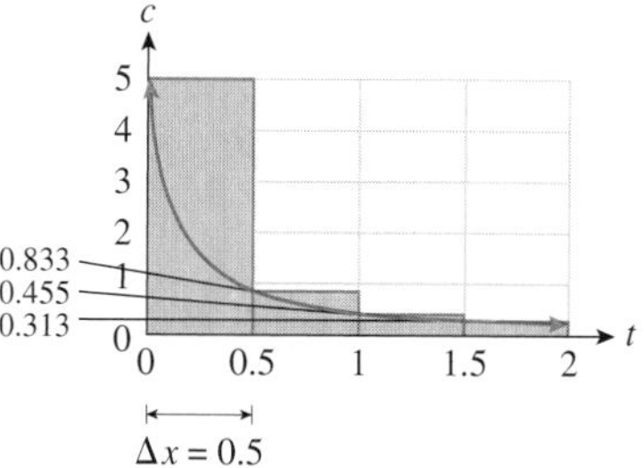

Figure 10

$$\begin{aligned}\text{Left Riemann Sum} &= f(x_0)\Delta x + f(x_1)\Delta x + \cdots + f(x_{n-1})\Delta x \\ &= f(0)(0.5) + f(0.5)(0.5) + f(1)(0.5) + f(1.5)(0.5) \\ &\approx (5)(0.5) + (0.833)(0.5) + (0.455)(0.5) + (0.313)(0.5) \approx 3.30\end{aligned}$$

Because sums are often used in mathematics, mathematicians have developed a shorthand notation for them. We write

$$f(x_0)\Delta x + f(x_1)\Delta x + \cdots + f(x_{n-1})\Delta x \text{ as } \sum_{k=0}^{n-1} f(x_k)\Delta x$$

The symbol $\sum$ is the Greek letter sigma and stands for **summation.** The letter k here is called the index of summation, and we can think of it as counting off the segments. We read the notation as "the sum from $k = 0$ to $n - 1$ of the quantities $f(x_k)\Delta x$." Think of it as a set of instructions:

Set $k = 0$, and calculate $f(x_0)\Delta x$. — $f(0)(0.5)$ in the above calculation

Set $k = 1$, and calculate $f(x_1)\Delta x$. — $f(0.5)(0.5)$ in the above calculation

...

Set $k = n - 1$, and calculate $f(x_{n-1})\Delta x$. — $f(1.5)(0.5)$ in the above calculation

Then sum all the quantities so calculated.

[12] After Georg Friedrich Bernhard Riemann (1826–1866).

Riemann Sum

If f is a continuous function, the **left Riemann sum** with n equal subdivisions for f over the interval $[a, b]$ is defined to be

$$\begin{aligned}\text{Left Riemann sum} &= \sum_{k=0}^{n-1} f(x_k)\Delta x \\ &= f(x_0)\Delta x + f(x_1)\Delta x + \cdots + f(x_{n-1})\Delta x \\ &= [f(x_0) + f(x_1) + \cdots + f(x_{n-1})]\Delta x\end{aligned}$$

where $a = x_0 < x_1 < \cdots < x_n = b$ are the subdivisions, and $\Delta x = (b - a)/n$.

Interpretation of the Riemann Sum

If f is the rate of change of a quantity F (that is, $f = F'$), then the Riemann sum of f approximates the total change of F from $x = a$ to $x = b$. The approximation improves as the number of subdivisions increases toward infinity.

quick **Example**

If $f(t)$ is the rate of change in the number of bats in a bell tower and $[a, b] = [2, 3]$, then the Riemann sum approximates the total change in the number of bats in the tower from time $t = 2$ to time $t = 3$.

Visualizing a Left Riemann Sum (Nonnegative Function)

Graphically, we can represent a left Riemann sum of a nonnegative function as an approximation of the area under a curve:

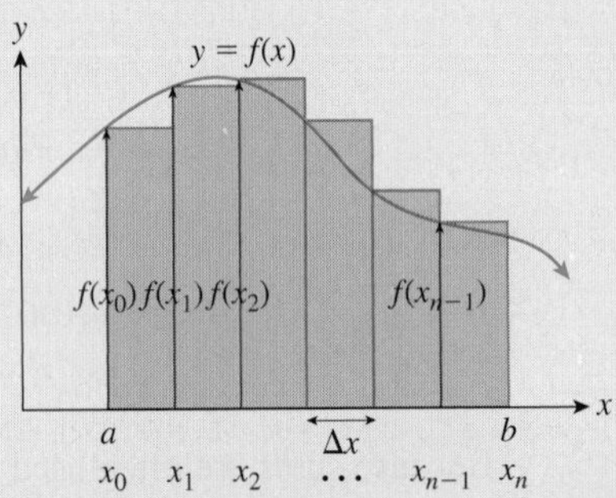

Riemann Sum = Shaded Area = Area of first rectangle + Area of second rectangle + ⋯ + Area of nth rectangle $= f(x_0)\Delta x + f(x_1)\Delta x + f(x_2)\Delta x + \cdots + f(x_{n-1})\Delta x$

quick **Example**

In Example 1 we computed several Riemann sums, including these:

$n = 1$: Riemann sum $= c(0)\Delta t = 5 \times 2 = \$10$

$n = 2$: Riemann sum $= [c(t_0) + c(t_1)]\Delta t$
$= [c(0) + c(1)] \cdot (1) \approx \$5.45$

$n = 4$: Riemann sum $= [c(t_0) + c(t_1) + c(t_2) + c(t_3)]\Delta t$
$= [c(0) + c(0.5) + c(1) + c(1.5)] \cdot (0.5) \approx \$3.30$

$n = 8$: Riemann sum $= [c(t_0) + c(t_1) + \cdots + c(t_7)]\Delta t$
$= [c(0) + c(0.25) + \cdots + c(1.75)] \cdot (0.25) \approx \$2.31$

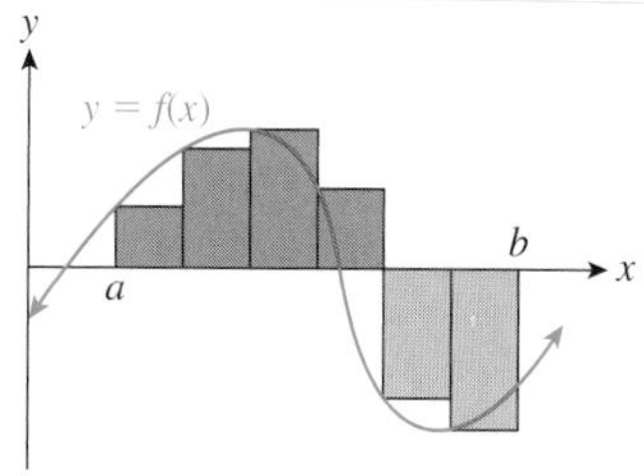

Riemann sum = Area above x-axis − Area below x-axis

Figure 11

Note To visualize the Riemann sum of a function that is negative, look again at the formula $f(x_0)\Delta x + f(x_1)\Delta x + f(x_2)\Delta x + \cdots + f(x_{n-1})\Delta x$ for the Riemann sum. Each term $f(x_i)\Delta x_i$ represents the area of one rectangle in the figure above. So, the areas of the rectangles with negative values of $f(x_i)$ are automatically counted as negative. They appear as gold rectangles in Figure 11. ■

Example 2 Computing a Riemann Sum From a Graph

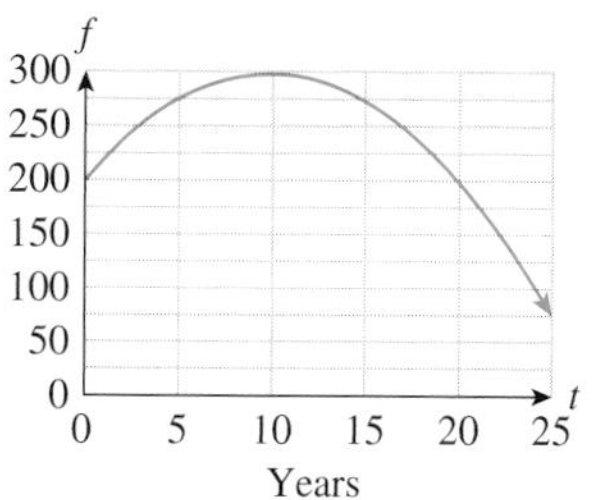

Figure 12

Figure 12 shows the approximate rate f at which convicts have been given the death sentence in the U.S. since 1980 (t is time in years since 1980.)*

Use a left Riemann sum with 4 subdivisions to estimate the total number of death sentences handed down from 1985 to 2005.

Solution Let us represent the total number of death sentences handed down since the institution of the death sentence up to time t by $F(t)$. The total number of death sentences handed down from 1985 to 2005 is then the total change in F over the interval [5, 25]. In view of the above discussion, we can approximate the total change in F using a Riemann sum of its rate of change f. Because $n = 4$ subdivisions are specified, the width of each subdivision is

$$\Delta x = \frac{b-a}{n} = \frac{25-5}{4} = 5$$

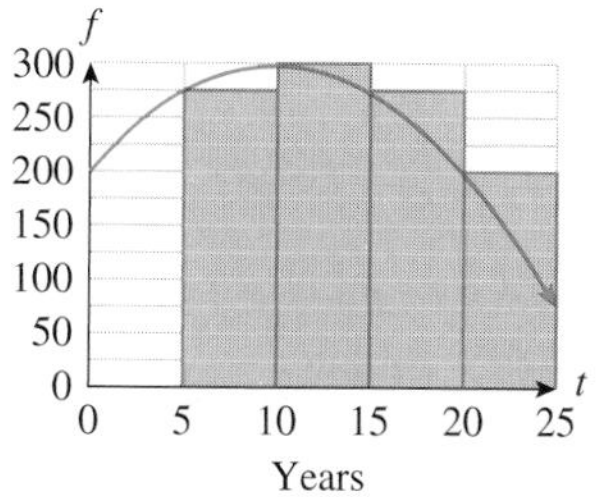

Figure 13

We can therefore represent the left Riemann sum by the shaded area shown in Figure 13. From the graph,

$$\begin{aligned}\text{Left Sum} &= f(5)\Delta t + f(10)\Delta t + f(15)\Delta t + f(20)\Delta t \\ &= (275)(5) + (300)(5) + (275)(5) + (200)(5) = 5250\end{aligned}$$

So, we estimate that a total of 5250 death sentences were handed down during the given period.

* The death penalty was reinstated by the U.S. Supreme Court in 1976. Source for data through 2003: Bureau of Justice Statistics, NAACP Defense Fund Inc./*New York Times,* September 15, 2004, p. A16.

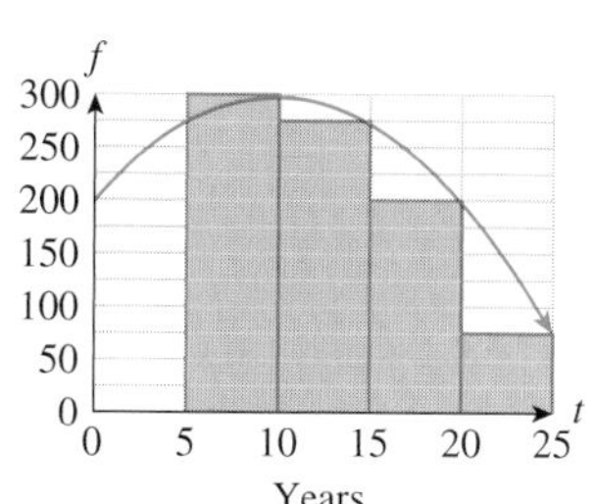

Right Riemann Sum = (300)(5) + (275)(5) + (200)(5) + (75)(5) = 4250

Height of each rectangle is determined by height of graph at right edge.

Figure 14

+ *Before we go on...* Although in this section we focus primarily on left Riemann sums, we could also approximate the total in Example 2 using a **right Riemann sum,** as shown Figure 14.

For continuous functions, the distinction between these two types of Riemann sums approaches zero as the number of subdivisions approaches infinity (see below). ■

Example 3 Computing a Riemann Sum From a Formula

Compute the left Riemann sum for $f(x) = x^2 + 1$ over the interval $[-1, 1]$, using $n = 5$ subdivisions.

Solution Because the interval is $[a, b] = [-1, 1]$ and $n = 5$, we have

$$\Delta x = \frac{b-a}{n} = \frac{1-(-1)}{5} = 0.4 \qquad \text{Width of subdivisions}$$

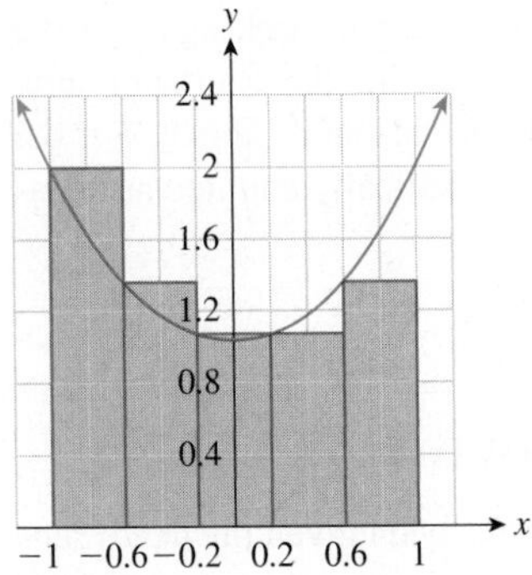

Figure **15**

Thus, the subdivisions of $[-1, 1]$ are given by

$$-1 < -0.6 < -0.2 < 0.2 < 0.6 < 1 \quad \text{Start with } -1 \text{ and keep adding } \Delta x = 0.4.$$

Figure 15 shows the graph with a representation of the Riemann sum.

The Riemann sum we want is

$$[f(x_0) + f(x_1) + \cdots + f(x_4)]\Delta x$$
$$= [f(-1) + f(-0.6) + f(-0.2) + f(0.2) + f(0.6)]0.4$$

We can conveniently organize this calculation in a table as follows:

x	-1	-0.6	-0.2	0.2	0.6	**Total**
$f(x) = x^2 + 1$	2	1.36	1.04	1.04	1.36	6.8

The Riemann sum is therefore

$$6.8\Delta x = 6.8 \times 0.4 = 2.72$$

As in Example 1, we're most interested in what happens to the Riemann sum when we let n get very large. When f is continuous,[13] its Riemann sums will always approach a limit as n goes to infinity. (This is not meant to be obvious. Proofs may be found in advanced calculus texts.) We give the limit a name.

The Definite Integral

If f is a continuous function, the **definite integral of f from a to b** is defined to be the limit of the Riemann sums as the number of partitions approaches infinity:

$$\int_a^b f(x)\,dx = \lim_{n\to\infty} \sum_{k=0}^{n-1} f(x_k)\,\Delta x$$

In Words: The integral, from a to b, of $f(x)\,dx$ equals the limit, as $n \to \infty$, of the Riemann Sum with a partition of n subdivisions.

The function f is called the **integrand,** the numbers a and b are the **limits of integration,** and the variable x is the **variable of integration.** A Riemann sum with a large number of subdivisions may be used to approximate the definite integral.

Interpretation of the Definite Integral

If f is the rate of change of a quantity F (that is, $f = F'$), then $\int_a^b f(x)\,dx$ is the (exact) total change of F from $x = a$ to $x = b$.

quick **Examples**

1. If $f(t)$ is the rate of change in the number of bats in a bell tower and $[a, b] = [2, 3]$, then $\int_2^3 f(t)\,dt$ is the total change in the number of bats in the tower from time $t = 2$ to time $t = 3$.

2. If, at time t hours, you are selling wall posters at a rate of $s(t)$ posters per hour, then

$$\text{Total number of posters sold from hour 3 to hour 5} = \int_3^5 s(t)\,dt$$

[13] And for some other functions as well.

Visualizing the Definite Integral

Nonnegative Functions: If $f(x) \geq 0$ for all x in $[a, b]$, then $\int_a^b f(x)\,dx$ is the area under the graph of f over the interval $[a, b]$, as shaded in the figure.

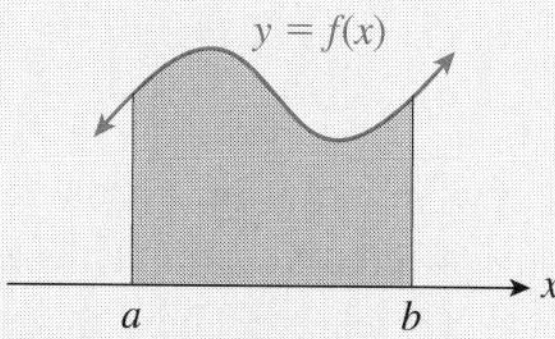

General Functions: $\int_a^b f(x)\,dx$ is the area between $x = a$ and $x = b$ that is above the x-axis and below the graph of f, minus the area that is below the x-axis and above the graph of f:

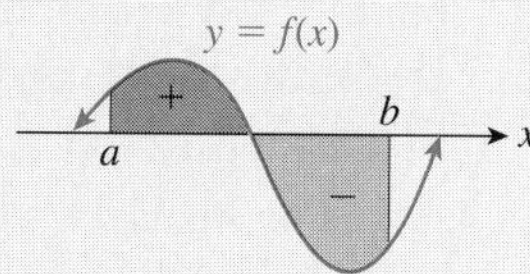

$$\int_a^b f(x)\,dx = \text{Area above } x\text{-axis} - \text{Area below } x\text{-axis}$$

quick Examples

1.

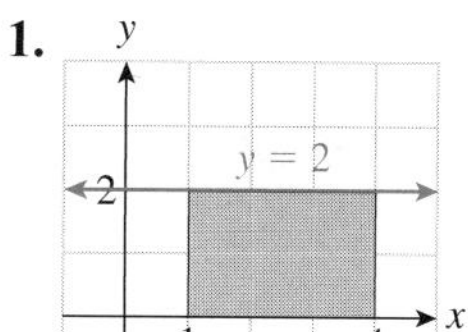

$$\int_1^4 2\,dx = \text{Area of rectangle} = 6$$

2.

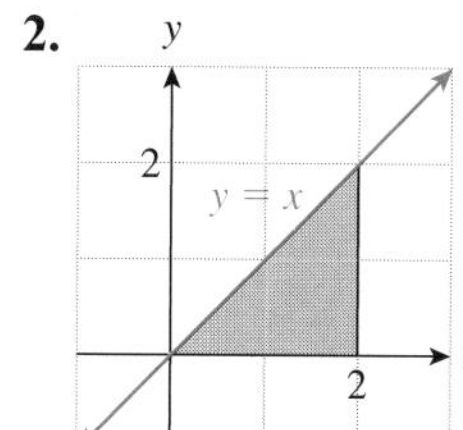

$$\int_0^2 x\,dx = \text{Area of triangle} = \frac{1}{2}\text{ base} \times \text{height} = 2$$

3.

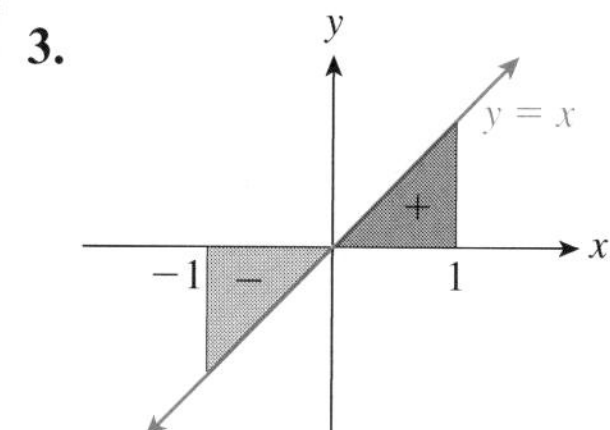

$$\int_{-1}^1 x\,dx = 0$$ The areas above and below the x-axis are equal

Notes

1. Remember that $\int_a^b f(x)\,dx$ stands for a number that depends on f, a, and b. The variable x that appears is called a **dummy variable** because it has no effect on the answer. In other words,

$$\int_a^b f(x)\,dx = \int_a^b f(t)\,dt \qquad x \text{ or } t \text{ is just a name we give the variable.}$$

2. The notation for the definite integral (due to Leibniz) comes from the notation for the Riemann sum. The integral sign $\int$ is an elongated S, the Roman equivalent of the Greek $\sum$. The d in dx is the lowercase Roman equivalent of the Greek Δ.
3. The definition above is adequate for continuous functions, but more complicated definitions are needed to handle other functions. For example, we broke the interval $[a, b]$ into n subdivisions of equal length, but other definitions allow a **partition** of the interval into subdivisions of possibly unequal lengths. We have evaluated f at the left endpoint of each subdivision, but we could equally well have used the right endpoint or any other point in the subdivision. All of these variations lead to the same answer when f is continuous.
4. The similarity between the notations for the definite integral and the indefinite integral is no mistake. We will discuss the exact connection in the next section. ■

Computing Definite Integrals

In some cases, we can compute the definite integral directly from the graph (see the quick examples above and the next example below). In general, the only method of computing definite integrals we have discussed so far is numerical estimation: compute the Riemann sums for larger and larger values of n and then estimate the number it seems to be approaching as we did in Example 1. (In the next section we will discuss an algebraic method for computing them.)

Example 4 Estimating a Definite Integral From a Graph

Figure 16 shows the graph of the (approximate) rate $f'(t)$, in billions of barrels per year, at which the U.S. has been consuming oil from 1995 through 2004. (t is time in years since 1995).*

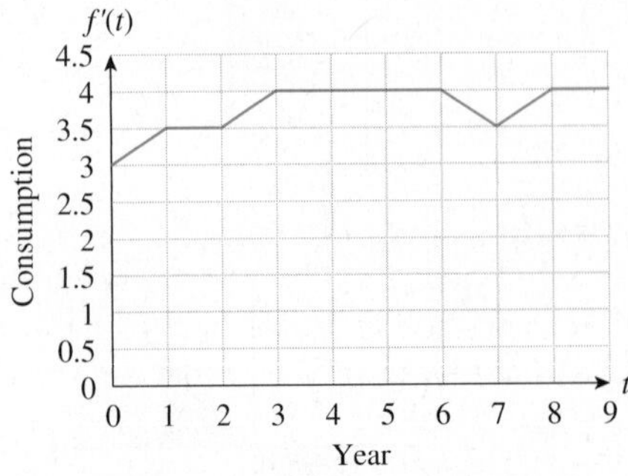

Figure **16**

* SOURCE: Energy Information Administration: Standard & Poors/*New York Times,* April 23, 2005, p. C3.

Use the graph to estimate the total U.S. consumption of oil over the period shown.

Solution The derivative $f'(t)$ represents the rate of change of the U.S. consumption of oil, and so the total U.S. consumption of oil over the given period [0, 9] is given by the definite integral:

$$\text{Total U.S. consumption of oil} = \text{Total change in } f'(t) = \int_0^9 f'(t)\,dt$$

and is given by the area under the graph (Figure 17).

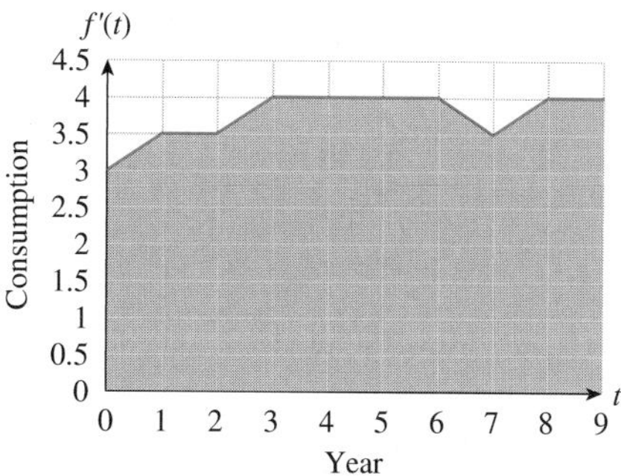

Figure **17**

One way to determine the area is to count the number of filled rectangles as defined by the grid. Each rectangle has an area of $1 \times 0.5 = 0.5$ units (so that the half-rectangles determined by diagonal portions of the graph have half that area). Counting rectangles, we find a total of 68 complete rectangles, so

$$\text{Total area} = 34$$

Because $f'(t)$ is in billions of barrels per year, we conclude that the total U.S. consumption of oil over the given period was about 34 billion barrels.

While counting rectangles might seem easy, it becomes awkward in cases involving large numbers of rectangles or partial rectangles whose area is not easy to determine. Rather than counting rectangles, we can get the area by averaging the left and right Riemann sums whose subdivisions are determined by the grid:

$$\text{Left Sum} = (3 + 3.5 + 3.5 + 4 + 4 + 4 + 4 + 3.5 + 4)(1) = 33.5$$

$$\text{Right Sum} = (3.5 + 3.5 + 4 + 4 + 4 + 4 + 3.5 + 4 + 4)(1) = 34.5$$

$$\text{Average} = \frac{33.5 + 34.5}{2} = 34$$

To see why this works, look at the single interval [0,1]. The left sum contributes $3 \times 1 = 3$ and the right sum contributes $3.5 \times 1 = 3.5$. The exact area is their average, 3.25 (Figure 18).

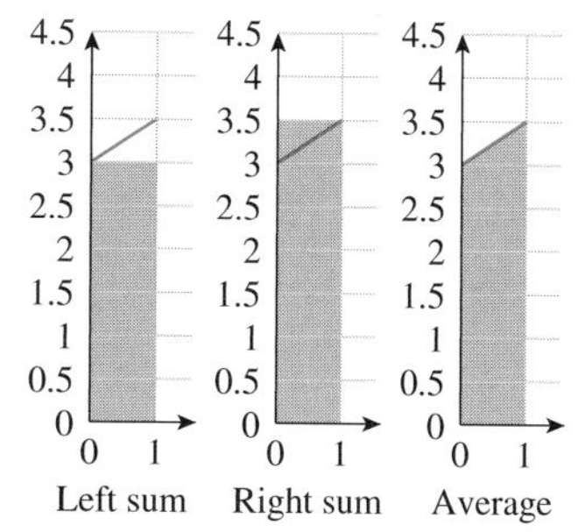

Figure **18**

+ *Before we go on...* It is important to check that the units we are using in Example 4 match up correctly: t is given in *years* and $f'(t)$ is given in billions of barrels per *year.* The integral is then given in

$$\text{Years} \times \frac{\text{Billions of barrels}}{\text{Year}} = \text{Billions of barrels}$$

If we had specified $f'(t)$ in, say, billions of barrels per *day* but t in years, then we would have needed to convert either t or $f'(t)$ so that the units of time match. ■

The next example illustrates the use of technology in estimating definite integrals using Riemann sums.

Example 5 Using Technology to Approximate the Definite Integral

Use technology to estimate the area under the graph of $f(x) = 1 - x^2$ over the interval $[0, 1]$ using $n = 100$, $n = 200$, and $n = 500$ partitions.

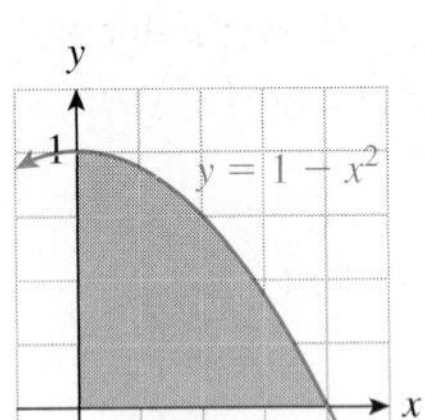

Figure **19**

Solution We need to estimate the area under the parabola shown in Figure 19.

From the discussion above,

$$\text{Area} = \int_0^1 (1 - x^2)\, dx$$

The Riemann sum with $n = 100$ has $\Delta x = (b - a)/n = (1 - 0)/100 = 0.01$ and is given by

$$\sum_{k=0}^{99} f(x_k)\Delta x = [f(0) + f(0.01) + \cdots + f(0.99)](0.01)$$

Similarly, the Riemann sum with $n = 200$ has $\Delta x = (b - a)/n = (1 - 0)/200 = 0.005$ and is given by

$$\sum_{k=0}^{199} f(x_k)\Delta x = [f(0) + f(0.005) + \cdots + f(0.995)](0.005)$$

For $n = 500$, $x = (b - a)/n = (1 - 0)/500 = 0.002$ and the Riemann sum is

$$\sum_{k=0}^{499} f(x_k)\Delta x = [f(0) + f(0.002) + \cdots + f(0.998)](0.002)$$

See the Technology Guides at the end of the chapter to find out how to compute these sums on a TI-83/84 and Excel.

From the numerical results, we find the following Riemann sums:

Online, follow:
Chapter 6
→ Tools
→ Numerical Integration Utility
to obtain a utility that computes left and right Riemann sums. In the utilities, there is also a downloadable Excel spreadsheet that computes and also graphs Riemann sums (Riemann Sum Grapher).

$$n = 100: \sum_{k=0}^{99} f(x_k)\Delta x = 0.67165$$

$$n = 200: \sum_{k=0}^{199} f(x_k)\Delta x = 0.6691625$$

$$n = 500: \sum_{k=0}^{499} f(x_k)\Delta x = 0.667666$$

so we estimate that the area under the curve is about 0.667. (The exact answer is $2/3$, as we will be able to verify using the techniques in the next section.)

Example 6 Motion

A fast car has velocity $v(t) = 6t^2 + 10t$ ft/s after t seconds (as measured by a radar gun). Use several values of n to find the distance covered by the car from time $t = 3$ seconds to time $t = 4$ seconds.

Solution Because the velocity $v(t)$ is rate of change of position, the total change in position over the interval [3, 4] is

$$\text{Distance covered} = \text{Total change in position} = \int_3^4 v(t)\,dt = \int_3^4 (6t^2 + 10t)\,dt$$

As in Examples 1 and 5, we can subdivide the one-second interval [3, 4] into smaller and smaller pieces to get more and more accurate approximations of the integral. By computing Riemann sums for various values of n, we get the following results.

$$n = 10: \sum_{k=0}^{9} v(t_k)\Delta t = 106.41 \qquad n = 100: \sum_{k=0}^{99} v(t_k)\Delta t \approx 108.740$$

$$n = 1000: \sum_{k=0}^{999} v(t_k)\Delta t \approx 108.974 \quad n = 10{,}000: \sum_{k=0}^{9999} v(t_k)\Delta t \approx 108.997$$

These calculations suggest that the total distance covered by the car, the value of the definite integral, is approximately 109 feet.

+*Before we go on...* Do Example 6 using antiderivatives instead of Riemann sums, as in Section 6.1. Do you notice a relationship between antiderivatives and definite integrals? This will be explored in the next section. ■

Online, find optional section: Numerical Integration

6.3 EXERCISES

● denotes basic skills exercises

tech Ex indicates exercises that should be solved using technology

In Exercises 1–8, use the given graph to estimate the left Riemann sum for the given interval with the stated number of subdivisions. hint [see Example 2]

1. ● [0, 5], $n = 5$

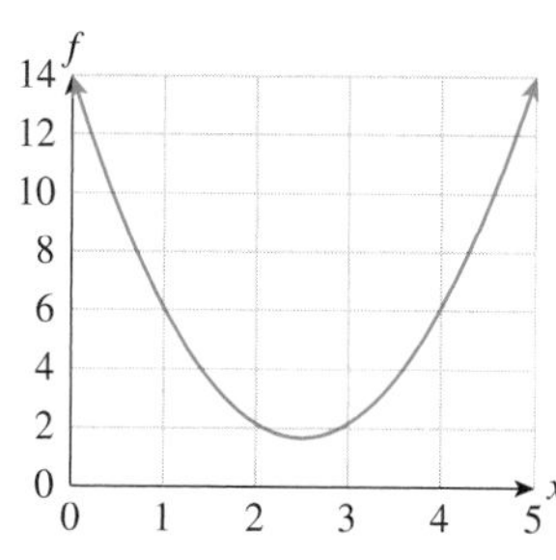

2. ● [0, 8], $n = 4$

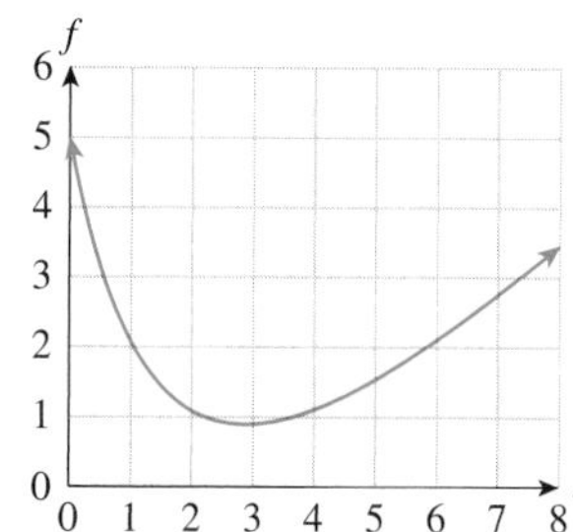

3. ● [1, 9], $n = 4$

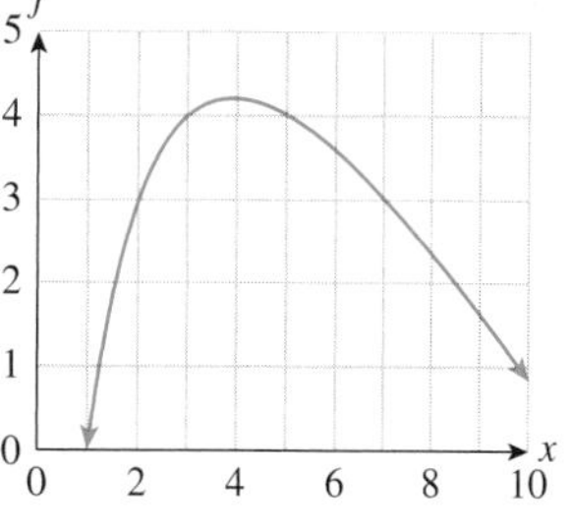

4. ● [0.5, 2.5], $n = 4$

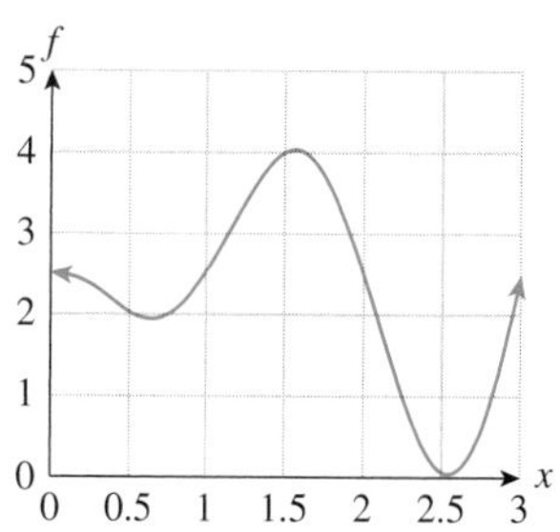

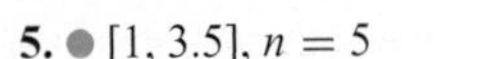
5. ● $[1, 3.5]$, $n = 5$

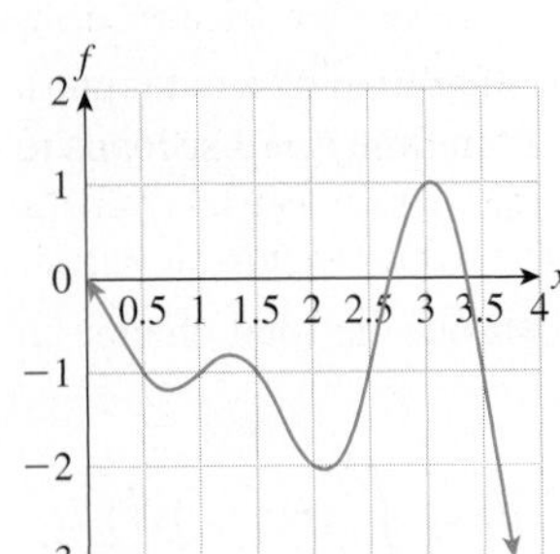

6. ● $[0.5, 3.5]$, $n = 3$

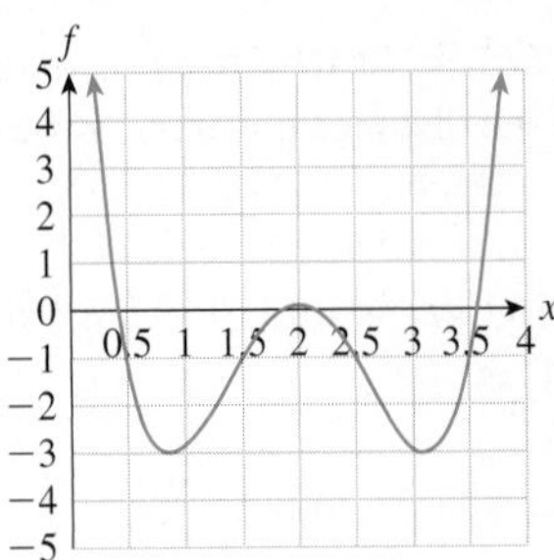

7. ● $[0, 3]$; $n = 3$

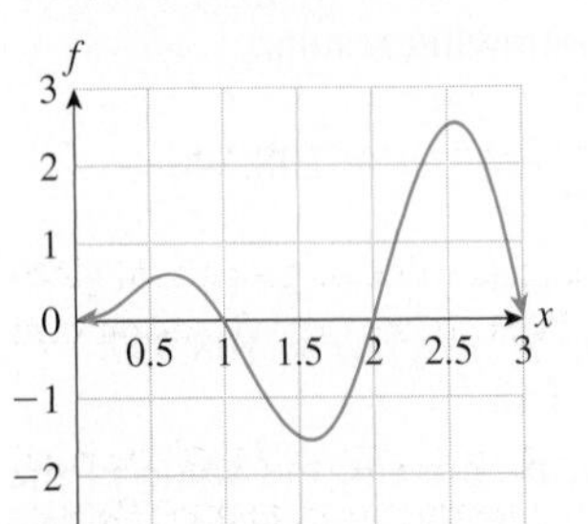

8. ● $[0.5, 3]$; $n = 5$

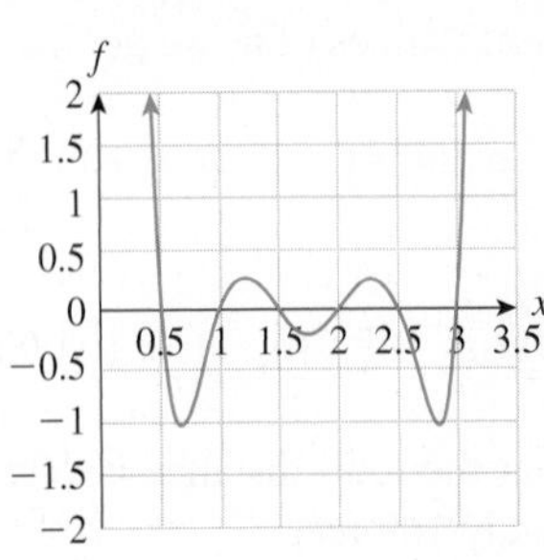

Calculate the left Riemann sums for the given functions over the given interval in Exercises 9–18, using the given values of n. (When rounding, round answers to four decimal places.) hint [see Example 3]

9. ● $f(x) = 4x - 1$ over $[0, 2]$, $n = 4$
10. ● $f(x) = 1 - 3x$ over $[-1, 1]$, $n = 4$
11. ● $f(x) = x^2$ over $[-2, 2]$, $n = 4$
12. ● $f(x) = x^2$ over $[1, 5]$, $n = 4$
13. ● $f(x) = \dfrac{1}{1+x}$ over $[0, 1]$, $n = 5$
14. ● $f(x) = \dfrac{x}{1+x^2}$ over $[0, 1]$, $n = 5$
15. ● $f(x) = e^{-x}$ over $[0, 10]$, $n = 5$
16. ● $f(x) = e^{-x}$ over $[-5, 5]$, $n = 5$
17. ● $f(x) = e^{-x^2}$ over $[0, 10]$, $n = 4$
18. ● $f(x) = e^{-x^2}$ over $[0, 100]$, $n = 4$

Use geometry (not Riemann sums) to compute the integrals in Exercises 19–28. hint [see Quick Examples p. 447]

19. ● $\int_0^1 1\,dx$
20. ● $\int_0^2 5\,dx$
21. ● $\int_0^1 x\,dx$
22. ● $\int_1^2 x\,dx$
23. ● $\int_0^1 \frac{x}{2}\,dx$
24. ● $\int_1^2 \frac{x}{2}\,dx$
25. ● $\int_2^4 (x-2)\,dx$
26. ● $\int_3^6 (x-3)\,dx$
27. ● $\int_{-1}^1 x^3\,dx$
28. ● $\int_{-2}^2 \frac{x}{2}\,dx$

In Exercises 29–34, the graph of the derivative $f'(t)$ of $f(t)$ is shown. Compute the total change of $f(t)$ over the given interval. hint [see Example 4]

29. ● $[1, 5]$

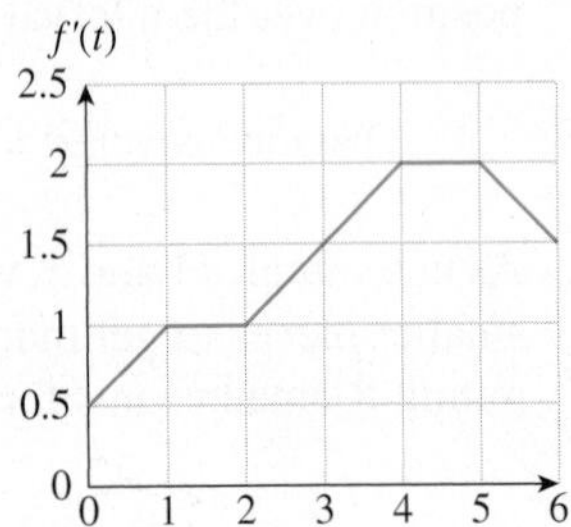

30. ● $[2, 6]$

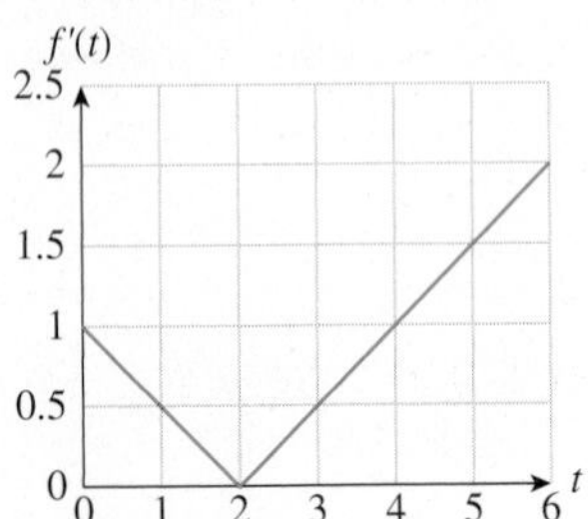

31. ● $[2, 6]$

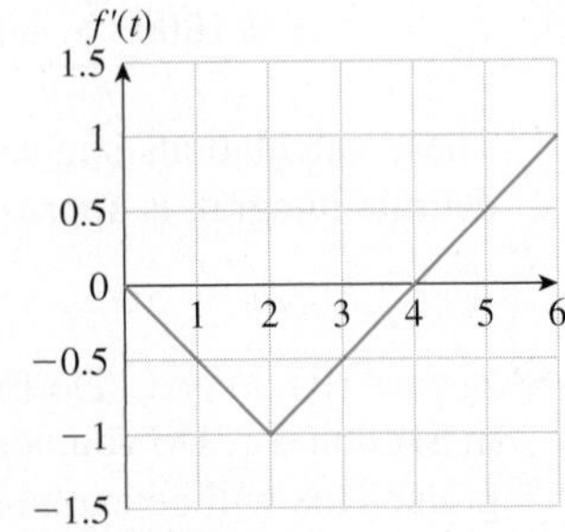

32. ● $[0, 5]$

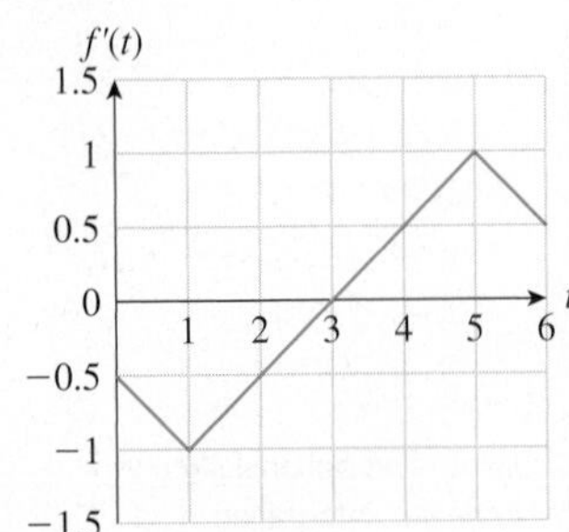

33. ● $[-1, 2]$

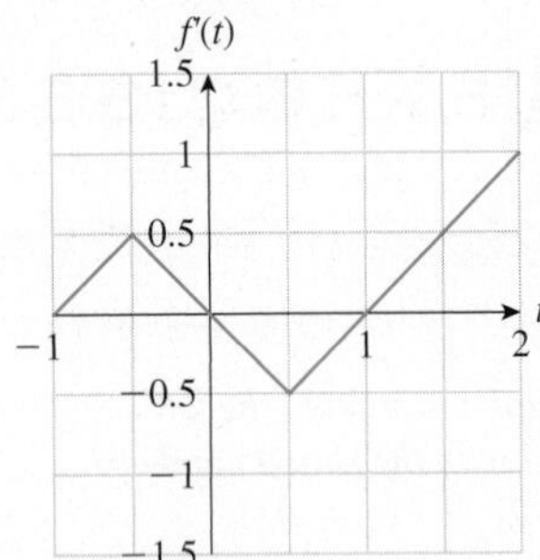

34. ● $[-1, 2]$

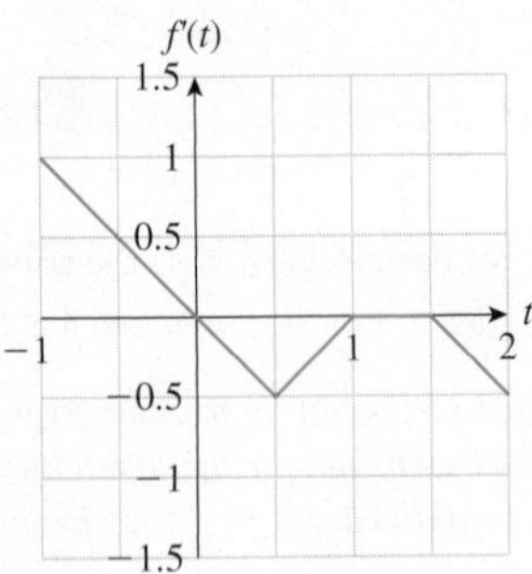

tech Ex *In Exercises 35–38, use technology to approximate the given integrals with Riemann sums, using **(a)** n = 10, **(b)** n = 100, and **(c)** n = 1000. Round all answers to four decimal places.* hint [see Example 5]

35. **tech Ex** $\int_0^1 4\sqrt{1-x^2}\,dx$
36. **tech Ex** $\int_0^1 \frac{4}{1+x^2}\,dx$
37. **tech Ex** $\int_2^3 \frac{2x^{1.2}}{1+3.5x^{4.7}}\,dx$
38. **tech Ex** $\int_3^4 3xe^{1.3x}\,dx$

Applications

39. ● ***Cost*** The marginal cost function for the manufacture of portable MP3 players is given by

$$C'(x) = 20 - \frac{x}{200}$$

where x is the number of MP3 players manufactured. Use a Riemann sum with $n = 5$ to estimate the cost of producing the first 5 MP3 players. hint [see Example 1]

40. ● ***Cost*** Repeat the preceding exercise using the marginal cost function

$$C'(x) = 25 - \frac{x}{50}$$

41. ● ***Bottled-Water Sales*** The rate of U.S. sales of bottled water for the period 1993–2003 could be approximated by

$$R(t) = 17t^2 + 100t + 2300 \text{ million gallons per year} \quad (3 \le t \le 13)$$

where t is time in years since 1990.[14] Use a Riemann sum with $n = 5$ to estimate the total U.S. sales of bottled water from 1995 to 2000. (Round your answer to the nearest billion gallons.)

42. ● ***Bottled-Water Sales*** The rate of U.S. per capita sales of bottled water for the period 1993–2003 could be approximated by

$$Q(t) = 0.05t^2 + 0.4t + 9 \text{ gallons per year} \quad (3 \le t \le 13)$$

where t is the time in years since 1990.[15] Use a Riemann sum with $n = 5$ to estimate the total U.S. per capita sales of bottled water from 1995 to 2000. (Round your answer to the nearest gallon.)

43. ● ***Online Auctions: U.S.*** The following graph shows the approximate rate of change $s(t)$ of the total value, in billions of dollars, of goods sold in the U.S. through eBay. (t is time in years since 1998)

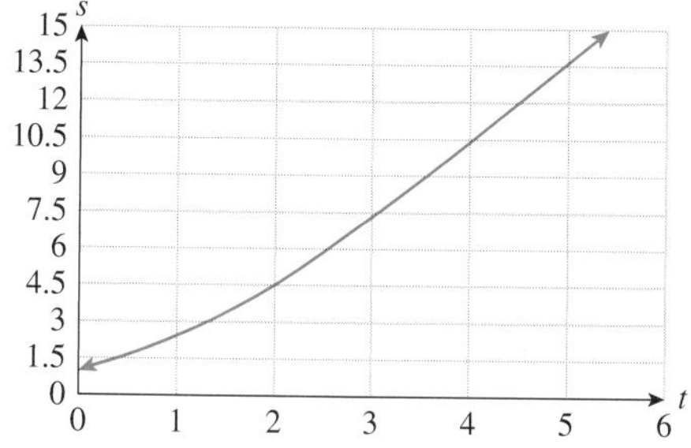

Use the graph to estimate the total value of goods sold in the U.S. through eBay for 2000–2003. (Use a left Riemann sum with 3 subdivisions).[16] hint [see Example 2]

44. ● ***Online Auctions: Global*** The following graph shows the approximate rate of change $s(t)$ of the total value, in billions of dollars, of goods sold through eBay throughout the world. (t is time in years since 1998).

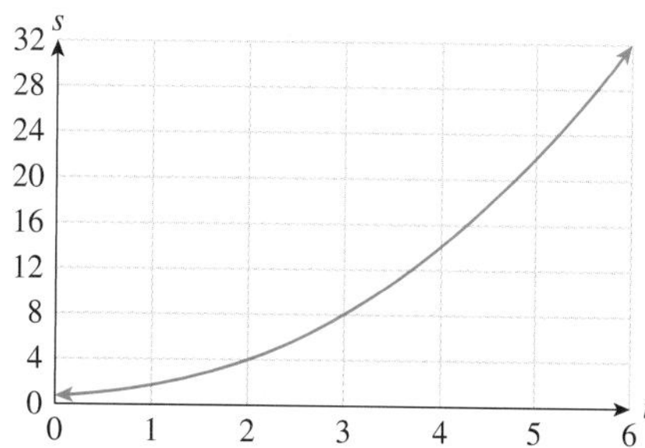

Use the graph to estimate the total value of goods sold globally through eBay for 1999–2004. (Use a left Riemann sum with 5 subdivisions).[17]

45. ● ***Scientific Research*** The rate of change $r(t)$ of the total number of research articles in the prominent journal *Physics Review* written by researchers in Europe is shown in the following graph:

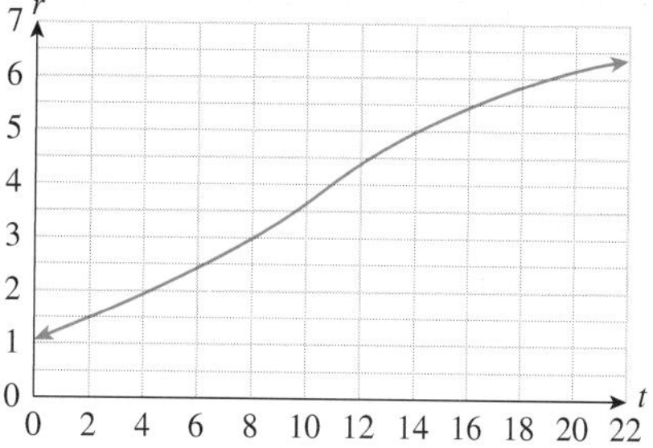

Here, t is time in years ($t = 0$ represents the start of 1983).[18]

a. Use both left and right Riemann sums with 8 subdivisions to estimate the total number of articles in *Physics Review* written by researchers in Europe during the 16-year period beginning at the start of 1983. (Estimate each value of $r(t)$ to the nearest 0.5.)

b. Use the answers from part (a) to obtain an estimate of $\int_0^{16} r(t)\,dt$. (See the "Before we go on" discussion at the end of Example 4.) Interpret the result.

[14] The authors' regression model, based on data in the Beverage Marketing Corporation news release, "Bottled water now number-two commercial beverage in U.S., says Beverage Marketing Corporation," April 8, 2004, available at www.beveragemarketing.com.

[15] Ibid.

[16] SOURCE: Company Reports/Bloomberg Financial Market/*New York Times,* March 6, 2005, p. BU4.

[17] Ibid.

[18] Based on data from 1983 to 2003. SOURCE: The American Physical Society/*New York Times,* May 3, 2003, p. A1.

46. ● ***Scientific Research*** The rate of change $r(t)$ of the total number of research articles in the prominent journal *Physics Review* written by researchers in the U.S. is shown in the following graph:

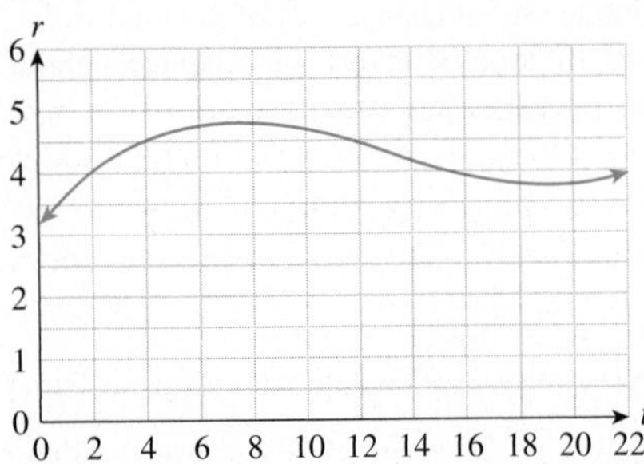

Here, t is time in years ($t = 0$ represents the start of 1983).[19]

a. Use both left and right Riemann sums with 6 subdivisions to estimate the total number of articles in *Physics Review* written by researchers in Europe during the 12-year period beginning at the start of 1993. (Estimate each value of $r(t)$ to the nearest 0.25.)

b. Use the answers from part (a) to obtain an estimate of $\int_{10}^{22} r(t)\,dt$. (See the "Before we go on" discussion at the end of Example 4.) Interpret the result.

47. ● ***Visiting Students*** The following graph shows the approximate rate of change $c'(t)$ in the number of students from China who have taken the GRE exam required for admission to U.S. universities (t is time in years since 2000):[20]

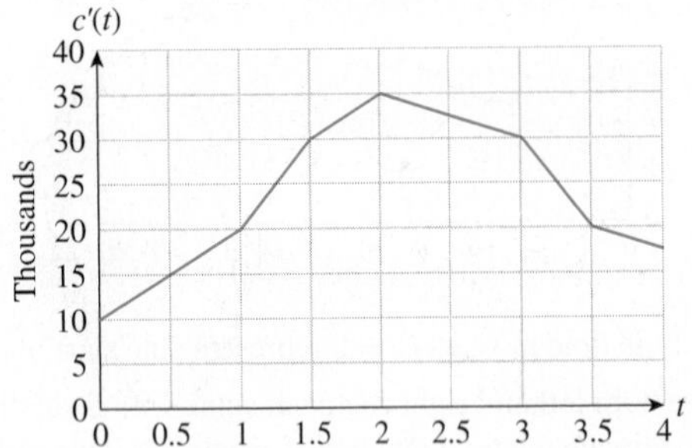

Use the graph to estimate, to the nearest 1000, the total number of students from China who took the GRE exams during the period 2002–2004. *hint* [see Example 4]

48. ● ***Visiting Students*** Repeat Exercise 47, using the following graph for students from India:[21]

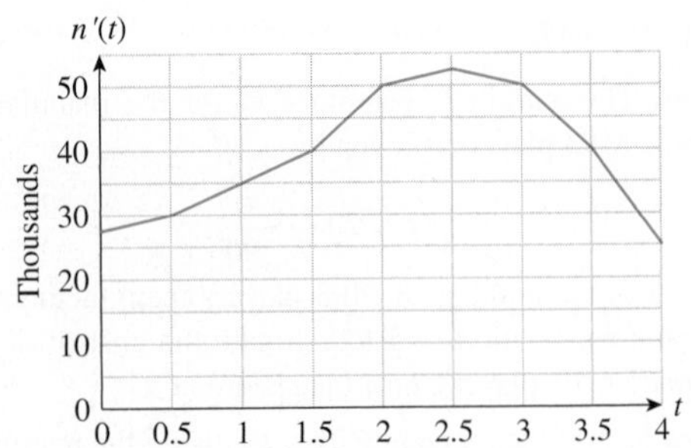

49. ● ***Downsizing*** The following graph shows the approximate rate of change $p'(t)$ in the total General Motors payroll for hourly employees in 2000–2004. t is time in years since 2000, and $p'(t)$ is in billions of dollars per year.[22]

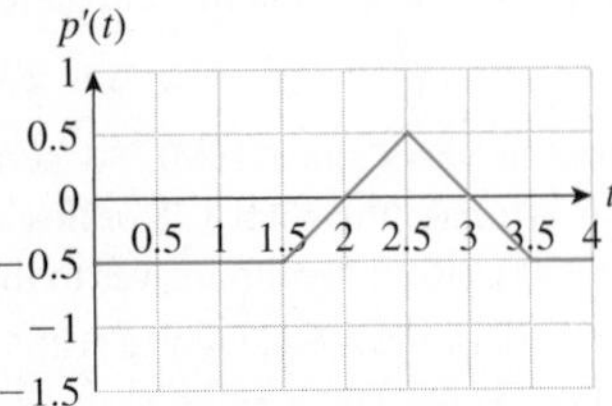

Use the graph to estimate the total change in the General Motors payroll for hourly employees for the given period.

50. ● ***Downsizing*** The following graph shows the approximate rate of change $n'(t)$ in the total number of General Motors employees in the U.S. in 2000–2004; t is time in years since 2000, and $n'(t)$ is thousands of employees per year.[23]

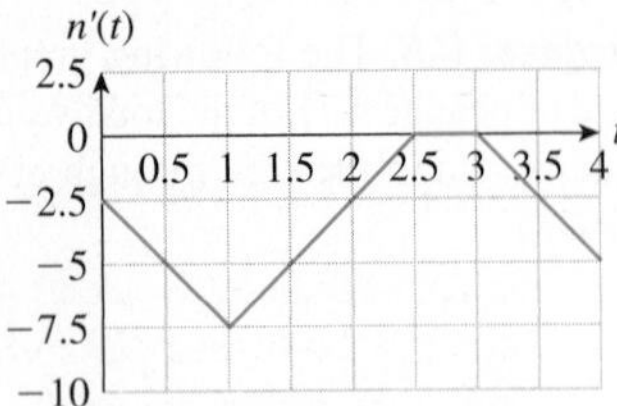

Use the graph to estimate the total change in the total number of General Motors employees in the U.S for the given period.

51. ***Big Brother*** The following chart shows the number of wiretaps authorized by U.S. courts in 1990–2003 (t is the number of years since 1990):[24]

[19] Based on data from 1983 to 2003. Source: The American Physical Society/*New York Times,* May 3, 2003, p. A1.

[20] Source: Educational Testing Services/Shanghai and Jiao Tong University/*New York Times,* December 21, 2004, p. A25.

[21] Ibid.

[22] Source: G.M./Automotive News/*New York Times,* June 8, 2005, p, C1.

[23] Ibid.

[24] Source: 2000 & 2003 Wiretap Reports, Administrative Office of the United States Courts, www.uscourts.gov/library/wiretap.

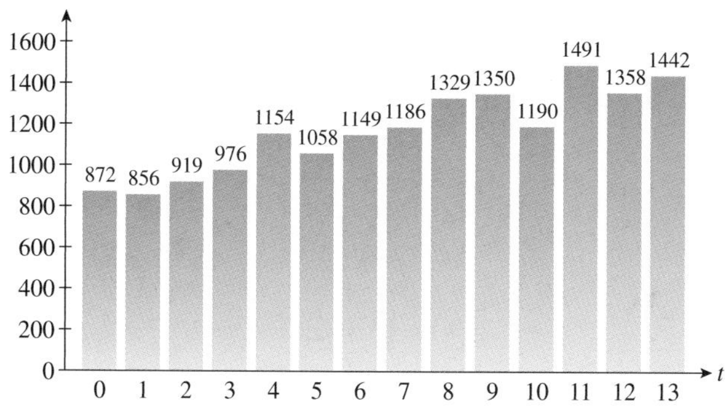

Let $W(t)$ be the number of wiretaps in year t. Estimate $\int_8^{14} W(t)\,dt$ using a Riemann sum with $n = 6$. What does this number represent?

52. ***Profit*** The following chart shows the annual profits of SABMiller, in millions of dollars, for the fiscal years ending March 31, 1997 through 2004:[25]

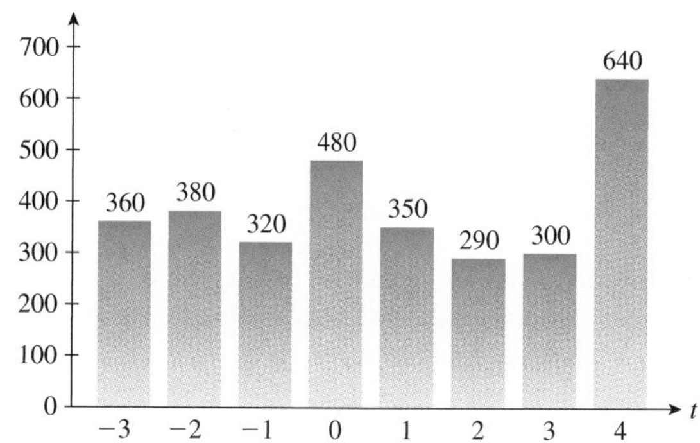

Let $p(t)$ be the annual profit of SABMiller in the year beginning at time t, where $t = 0$ represents March 31, 1999. Estimate $\int_1^5 p(t)\,dt$ using a Riemann sum with $n = 4$. What does this number represent?

53. ● ***Motion*** A model rocket has upward velocity $v(t) = 40t^2$ ft/s, t seconds after launch. Use a Riemann sum with $n = 10$ to estimate how high the rocket is 2 seconds after launch. hint [see Example 6]

54. ● ***Motion*** A race car has a velocity of $v(t) = 600(1 - e^{-0.5t})$ ft/s, t seconds after starting. Use a Riemann sum with $n = 10$ to estimate how far the car travels in the first 4 seconds. (Round your answer to the nearest whole number.)

[25] SOURCE: 2004 Annual Report, obtained from www.SABMiller.com/. In 2002 South African Breweries acquired Miller Brewing and changed its name to SABMiller.

55. tech Ex ***Household Income*** In the period 1967 to 2003, median household income in the U.S. increased at a rate of approximately

$$R(t) = -1.5t^2 - 0.9t + 1200 \text{ dollars per year}$$

where t is the number of years since 1990.[26] Estimate $\int_{-10}^{10} R(t)\,dt$ using a Riemann sum with $n = 100$. (Round your answer to the nearest \$1000.) Interpret the answer.

56. tech Ex ***Health-Care Spending*** In the period 1965 to 2003, the rate of increase of health-care spending in the U.S. was approximately

$$K(t) = 17t^2 + 2600t + 55{,}000 \text{ million dollars per year}$$

where t is the number of years since 1990.[27] Estimate $\int_{-10}^{10} K(t)\,dt$ using a Riemann sum with $n = 100$. (Round your answer to the nearest \$100 billion.) Interpret the answer.

57. ***Surveying*** My uncle intends to build a kidney-shaped swimming pool in his small yard, and the town zoning board will approve the project only if the total area of the pool does not exceed 500 square feet. The accompanying figure shows a diagram of the planned swimming pool, with measurements of its width at the indicated points. Will my uncle's plans be approved? Use a (left) Riemann sum to approximate the area.

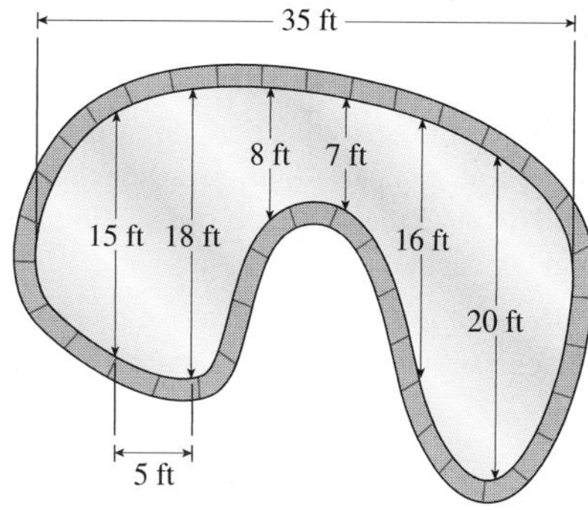

58. ***Pollution*** An aerial photograph of an ocean oil spill shows the pattern in the accompanying diagram. Assuming that the oil slick has a uniform depth of 0.01 m, how many cubic meters of oil would you estimate to be in the spill? (Volume = Area × Thickness. Use a (left) Riemann sum to approximate the area.)

[26] In current dollars, unadjusted for inflation. SOURCE: U.S. Census Bureau; "Table H-5. Race and Hispanic Origin of Householder—Households by Median and Mean Income: 1967 to 2003;" published August 27, 2004; www.census.gov/hhes/income.

[27] SOURCE: Centers for Medicare and Medicaid Services, "National Health Expenditures," 2002 version, released January 2004; www.cms.hhs.gov/statistics/nhe/.

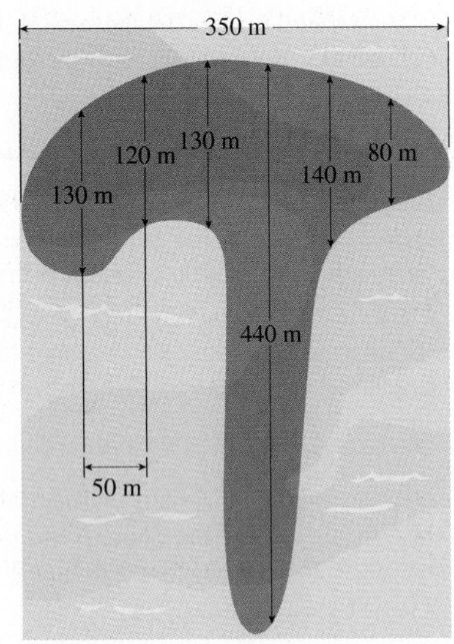

59. tech Ex ***Household Income*** In the period 1967 to 2003, mean annual household income in the U.S. could be approximated by

$$I(t) = -0.6t^3 + 9t^2 + 1800t + 37{,}000 \text{ dollars per household}$$

where t is the number of years since 1990.[28] Over the same period, the number of households could be approximated by

$$P(t) = 1.4t + 94 \text{ million households}$$

a. Graph the annual household income function $A(t) = I(t)P(t)$ for $0 \le t \le 14$, indicating the area that represents $\int_{10}^{14} A(t)\,dt$. What does this area mean?
b. Estimate the area in part (a) using a Riemann sum with $n = 200$. (Round the answer to two significant digits.) Interpret the answer.

60. tech Ex ***Household Income*** Repeat the preceding exercise, using the constant dollar median annual household income function

$$I(t) = 0.1t^3 + 10t^2 + 680t + 51{,}000 \text{ dollars per household}^{29}$$

The Normal Curve The *normal distribution* curve, which models the distributions of data in a wide range of applications, is given by the function

$$p(x) = \frac{1}{\sqrt{2\pi}\sigma}e^{-(x-\mu)^2/2\sigma^2}$$

where $\pi = 3.14159265\ldots$ and σ and μ are constants called the **standard deviation** and the **mean,** respectively. Its graph (when $\sigma = 1$ and $\mu = 2$) is shown in the figure. Exercises 61 and 62 illustrate its use.

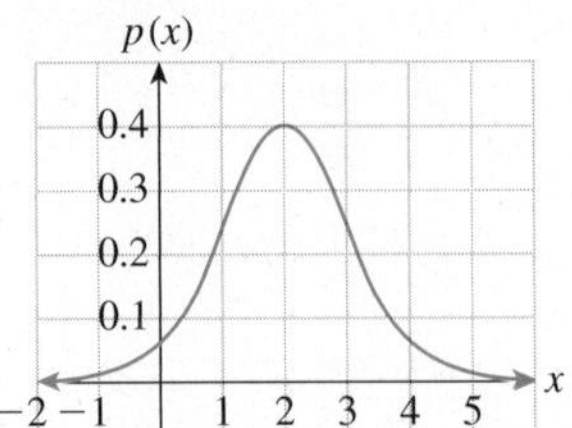

61. tech Ex ***Test Scores*** Enormous State University's Calculus I test scores are modeled by a normal distribution with $\mu = 72.6$ and $\sigma = 5.2$. The percentage of students who obtained scores between a and b on the test is given by

$$\int_a^b p(x)\,dx$$

a. Use a Riemann sum with $n = 40$ to estimate the percentage of students who obtained between 60 and 100 on the test.
b. What percentage of students scored less than 30?

62. tech Ex ***Consumer Satisfaction*** In a survey, consumers were asked to rate a new toothpaste on a scale of 1–10. The resulting data are modeled by a normal distribution with $\mu = 4.5$ and $\sigma = 1.0$. The percentage of consumers who rated the toothpaste with a score between a and b on the test is given by

$$\int_a^b p(x)\,dx$$

a. Use a Riemann sum with $n = 10$ to estimate the percentage of customers who rated the toothpaste 5 or above. (Use the range 4.5 to 10.5.)
b. What percentage of customers rated the toothpaste 0 or 1? (Use the range –0.5 to 1.5.)

Communication and Reasoning Exercises

63. ● If $f(x) = 6$, then the left Riemann sum _______ (increases/decreases/stays the same) as n increases.

64. ● If $f(x) = -1$, then the left Riemann sum _______ (increases/decreases/stays the same) as n increases.

65. ● If f is an increasing function of x, then the left Riemann sum _______ (increases/decreases/stays the same) as n increases.

66. ● If f is a decreasing function of x, then the left Riemann sum _______ (increases/decreases/stays the same) as n increases.

67. ● If $\int_a^b f(x)\,dx = 0$, what can you say about the graph of f?

68. ● Sketch the graphs of two (different) functions $f(x)$ and $g(x)$ such that $\int_a^b f(x)\,dx = \int_a^b g(x)\,dx$.

69. ● The definite integral counts the area under the x-axis as negative. Give an example that shows how this can be useful in applications.

[28] In current dollars, unadjusted for inflation. SOURCE: U.S. Census Bureau; "Table H-5. Race and Hispanic Origin of Householder—Households by Median and Mean Income: 1967 to 2003;" published August 27, 2004; www.census.gov/hhes/income.

[29] In constant 2003 dollars. SOURCE: U.S. Census Bureau; "Table H-5. Race and Hispanic Origin of Householder—Households by Median and Mean Income: 1967 to 2003;" published August 27, 2004; www.census.gov/hhes/income.

70. Sketch the graph of a nonconstant function whose Riemann sum with $n = 1$ gives the exact value of the definite integral.

71. Sketch the graph of a nonconstant function whose Riemann sums with $n = 1, 5$, and 10 are all zero.

72. Besides left and right Riemann sums, another approximation of the integral is the **midpoint** approximation, in which we compute the sum

$$\sum_{k=1}^{n} f(\bar{x}_k)\,\Delta x$$

where $\bar{x}_k = (x_{k-1} + x_k)/2$ is the point midway between the left and right endpoints of the interval $[x_{k-1}, x_k]$. Why is it true that the midpoint approximation is exact if f is linear? (Draw a picture.)

73. Your cell phone company charges you $c(t) = \dfrac{20}{t+100}$ dollars for the tth minute. You make a 60-minute phone call. What kind of (left) Riemann sum represents the total cost of the call? Explain.

74. Your friend's cell phone company charges her $c(t) = \dfrac{20}{t+100}$ dollars for the $(t+1)$st minute. Your friend makes a 60-minute phone call. What kind of (left) Riemann sum represents the total cost of the call? Explain.

75. Give a formula for the **right Riemann Sum** with n equal subdivisions $a = x_0 < x_1 < \cdots < x_n = b$ for f over the interval $[a, b]$.

76. Refer to Exercise 75. If f is continuous, what happens to the difference between the left and right Riemann sums as $n \to \infty$? Explain.

77. When approximating a definite integral by computing Riemann sums, how might you judge whether you have chosen n large enough to get your answer accurate to, say, three decimal places?

● basic skills   tech Ex technology exercise

6.4 The Definite Integral: Algebraic Approach and the Fundamental Theorem of Calculus

In Section 6.3 we saw that the definite integral of the marginal cost function gives the total cost. However, in Section 6.1 we used antiderivatives to recover the cost function from the marginal cost function, so we *could* use antiderivatives to compute total cost. The following example, based on Example 5 in Section 6.1, compares these two approaches.

Example 1 Finding Cost from Marginal Cost

The marginal cost of producing baseball caps at a production level of x caps is $4 - 0.001x$ dollars per cap. Find the total change of cost if production is increased from 100 to 200 caps.

Solution

Method 1: Using an Antiderivative (based on Example 5 in Section 6.1): Let $C(x)$ be the cost function. Because the marginal cost function is the derivative of the cost function, we have $C'(x) = 4 - 0.001x$ and so

$$C(x) = \int (4 - 0.001x)\,dx$$

$$= 4x - 0.001\frac{x^2}{2} + K \qquad K \text{ is the constant of integration.}$$

$$= 4x - 0.0005x^2 + K$$

Although we do not know what to use for the value of the constant K, we can say:

$$\begin{aligned}\text{Cost at production level of 100 caps} &= C(100)\\ &= 4(100) - 0.0005(100)^2 + K = \$395 + K\\ \text{Cost at production level of 200 caps} &= C(200)\\ &= 4(200) - 0.0005(200)^2 + K = \$780 + K\end{aligned}$$

Therefore,

$$\begin{aligned}\text{Total change in cost} &= C(200) - C(100)\\ &= (\$780 + K) - (\$395 + K) = \$385\end{aligned}$$

Notice how the constant of integration simply canceled out! So, we could choose any value for K that we wanted (such as $K = 0$) and still come out with the correct total change. Put another way, we could use *any antiderivative* of $C'(x)$, such as

$$F(x) = 4x - 0.0005x^2$$

or

$$F(x) = 4x - 0.0005x^2 + 4$$

$F(x)$ is *any* antiderivative of $C'(x)$ whereas $C(x)$ is the actual cost function

compute $F(200) - F(100)$, and obtain the total change, \$385.

Summarizing this method: To compute the total change of $C(x)$ over the interval [100, 200], use any antiderivative $F(x)$ of $C'(x)$, and compute $F(200) - F(100)$.

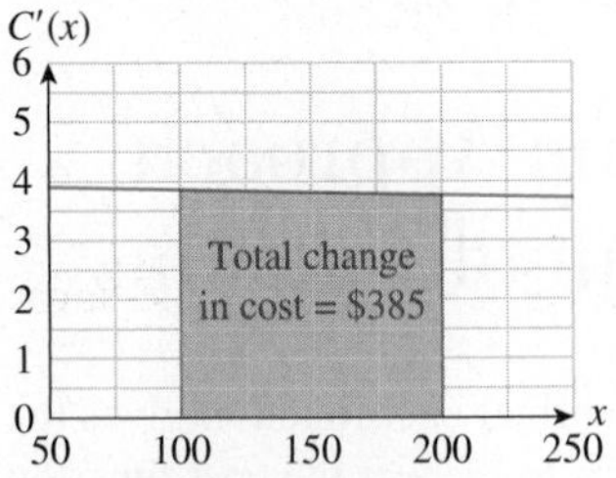

Method 2: Using a Definite Integral (based on Example 1 in Section 6.3): Because the marginal cost $C(x)$ is the rate of change of the total cost function $C(x)$, the total change in $C(x)$ over the interval [100, 200] is given by

$$\begin{aligned}\text{Total change in cost} &= \text{Area under the marginal cost function curve}\\ &= \int_{100}^{200} C'(x)\,dx\\ &= \int_{100}^{200} (4 - 0.001x)\,dx \qquad \text{See Figure 20.}\\ &= \$385 \qquad \text{Using geometry or Riemann sums}\end{aligned}$$

Figure **20**

Putting these two methods together gives us the following surprising result:

$$\int_{100}^{200} C'(x)\,dx = F(200) - F(100)$$

where $F(x)$ is any antiderivative of $C'(x)$.

Now, there is nothing special in Example 1 about the specific function $C'(x)$ or the choice of endpoints of integration. So if we replace $C'(x)$ by a general continuous function $f(x)$, we can write

$$\int_a^b f(x)\,dx = F(b) - F(a)$$

where $F(x)$ is any antiderivative of $f(x)$. This result is known as the **Fundamental Theorem of Calculus.**

The Fundamental Theorem of Calculus (FTC)

Let f be a continuous function defined on the interval $[a, b]$ and if F is *any* antiderivative of f and is defined on $[a, b]$, we have

$$\int_a^b f(x)\,dx = F(b) - F(a)$$

Moreover, such an antiderivative is guaranteed to exist.

In Words

Every continuous function has an antiderivative. To compute the definite integral of $f(x)$ over $[a, b]$, first find an antiderivative $F(x)$, then evaluate it at $x = b$, evaluate it at $x = a$, and subtract the two answers.

quick **Example** Because $F(x) = x^2$ is an antiderivative of $f(x) = 2x$,

$$\int_0^1 2x\,dx = F(1) - F(0) = 1^2 - 0^2 = 1$$

Example 2 Using the FTC to Calculate a Definite Integral

Calculate $\displaystyle\int_0^1 (1 - x^2)\,dx$

Solution To use the FTC, we need to find an antiderivative of $1 - x^2$. But we know that

$$\int (1 - x^2)\,dx = x - \frac{x^3}{3} + C$$

We need only one antiderivative, so let's take $F(x) = x - x^3/3$. The FTC tells us that

$$\int_0^1 (1 - x^2)\,dx = F(1) - F(0) = \left(1 - \frac{1}{3}\right) - (0) = \frac{2}{3}$$

which is the value we estimated in Section 6.4.

+ *Before we go on...* A useful piece of notation is often used here. We write[30]

$$[F(x)]_a^b = F(b) - F(a)$$

Thus, we can rewrite the computation in Example 2 as

$$\int_0^1 (1 - x^2)\,dx = \left[x - \frac{x^3}{3}\right]_0^1 = \left(1 - \frac{1}{3}\right) - (0) = \frac{2}{3}$$

■

[30] There seem to be several notations in use, actually. Another common notation is $F(x)\Big|_a^b$.

Example 3 More Use of the FTC

Compute the following definite integrals.

a. $\displaystyle\int_0^1 (2x^3 + 10x + 1)\,dx$ **b.** $\displaystyle\int_1^5 \left(\frac{1}{x^2} + \frac{1}{x}\right) dx$

Solution

a.
$$\begin{aligned}\int_0^1 (2x^3 + 10x + 1)\,dx &= \left[\frac{1}{2}x^4 + 5x^2 + x\right]_0^1\\ &= \left(\frac{1}{2} + 5 + 1\right) - (0)\\ &= \frac{13}{2}\end{aligned}$$

b.
$$\begin{aligned}\int_1^5 \left(\frac{1}{x^2} + \frac{1}{x}\right) dx &= \int_1^5 (x^{-2} + x^{-1})\,dx\\ &= \left[-x^{-1} + \ln|x|\right]_1^5\\ &= \left(-\frac{1}{5} + \ln 5\right) - (-1 + \ln 1)\\ &= \frac{4}{5} + \ln 5\end{aligned}$$

When calculating a definite integral, we may have to use substitution to find the necessary antiderivative. We could substitute, evaluate the indefinite integral with respect to u, express the answer in terms of x, and then evaluate at the limits of integration. However, there is a shortcut, as we shall see in the next example.

Example 4 Using the FTC with Substitution

Evaluate $\displaystyle\int_1^2 (2x - 1)e^{2x^2-2x}\,dx.$

Solution The shortcut we promised is to put *everything* in terms of u, including the limits of integration.

$$u = 2x^2 - 2x$$

$$\frac{du}{dx} = 4x - 2$$

$$dx = \frac{1}{4x - 2}\,du$$

When $x = 1$, $u = 0$ Substitute $x = 1$ in the formula for u

When $x = 2$, $u = 4$ Substitute $x = 2$ in the formula for u

We get the value $u = 0$, for example, by substituting $x = 1$ in the equation $u = 2x^2 - 2x$. We can now rewrite the integral.

$$\int_1^2 (2x-1)e^{2x^2-2x}\,dx = \int_0^4 (2x-1)e^u \frac{1}{4x-2}\,du$$

$$= \int_0^4 \frac{1}{2} e^u\,du$$

$$= \left[\frac{1}{2}e^u\right]_0^4 = \frac{1}{2}e^4 - \frac{1}{2}$$

+ *Before we go on...* The alternative, longer calculation in Example 4 is first to calculate the indefinite integral:

$$\int (2x-1)e^{2x^2-2x}\,dx = \int \frac{1}{2}e^u\,du$$

$$= \frac{1}{2}e^u + C = \frac{1}{2}e^{2x^2-2x} + C$$

Then we can say that

$$\int_1^2 (2x-1)e^{2x^2-2x}\,dx = \left[\frac{1}{2}e^{2x^2-2x}\right]_1^2 = \frac{1}{2}e^4 - \frac{1}{2}$$

■

Applications

Example 5 Total Cost

In Section 6.3 we considered the following example. Your cell phone company offers you an innovative pricing scheme. When you make a call, the marginal cost is

$$c(t) = \frac{5}{10t+1} \text{ dollars per hour}$$

Compute the total cost of a two-hour phone call.

Solution We calculate

$$\text{Total Cost} = \int_0^2 \frac{5}{10t+1}\,dt = 5\int_0^2 \frac{1}{10t+1}\,dt$$

$$= 5\left[\frac{1}{10}\ln(10t+1)\right]_0^2$$

See the shortcuts on p. 436

$$= \frac{5}{10}[\ln(21) - \ln(1)]$$

$$= \frac{1}{2}\ln 21 \approx \$1.52$$

Compare this with Example 1 of Section 6.3, where we found the same answer by approximating with Riemann sums.

mathematics At Work

Drew Taylor

TITLE Geographic Information Systems Analyst
INSTITUTION RECON Environmental

Patrick Farace

As a Geographic Information Systems (GIS) Analyst for an environmental consulting firm in San Diego, I'm helping to create a higher quality of life for Southern Californians. My company, RECON Environmental, Inc. is dedicated to balancing the demands of industry and a growing population with the hope of preserving our cultural landscape and protecting our environment. My job is a combination of cartography and information systems; I provide spatial statistics and geographic resources to archeologists and biologists. The data I provide are presented both as hard numbers and graphically as maps and figures. These are presented in documents such as Environmental Impact Reports.

GIS is a powerful tool used to answer spatial questions that help manage our environment. Even though I'm not solving equations day to day, it is my responsibility to input the correct variables and to know what to "tell" the GIS software to do with the data. Without a background in calculus I would not be able evaluate the computer's output. My background in applied mathematics allows me to understand the methodology and to review my work by making sure the final data are in fact realistic and accurate. This ensures a quality product to my clients.

GIS can quickly calculate the area of a site and determine the distance to other geographic features such as bodies of water, developed/urban areas, or competing habitats. Like other information systems, GIS organizes and manipulates information, but what makes GIS different is that all the data it works with are spatially referenced—either by *X*- or *Y*- (and sometimes *Z*-elevation) coordinates or in some cases a street address. By assigning each record of a GIS database a coordinate value—essentially representing everything in space with numbers, analysts can then input these data into software such as ArcGIS or ArcView that is capable of running rigorous algorithms in order to calculate area and distance. This allows us to understand the relationship of geographic features in a less abstract, and more quantitative way, resulting in more informed decisions about the way we manage our world.

In the end, my work—with the help of understanding applied mathematics—allows policy makers, city and regional planners, and environmentally conscious individuals the ability to make intelligent and informed land use decisions that increase the quality of life for all of us.

Example 6 Computing Area

Find the total area of the region enclosed by the graph of $y = xe^{x^2}$, the x-axis, and the vertical lines $x = -1$ and $x = 1$.

Solution The region whose area we want is shown in Figure 21. Notice the symmetry of the graph. Also, half the region we are interested in is above the x-axis, while the other half is below. If we calculated the integral $\int_{-1}^{1} xe^{x^2}\,dx$, the result would be

$$\text{Area above } x\text{-axis} - \text{Area below } x\text{-axis} = 0$$

which does not give us the total area. To prevent the area below the x-axis from being combined with the area above the axis, we do the calculation in two parts, as illustrated in Figure 22.

(In Figure 22 we broke the integral at $x = 0$ because that is where the graph crosses the x-axis.) These integrals can be calculated using the substitution $u = x^2$:

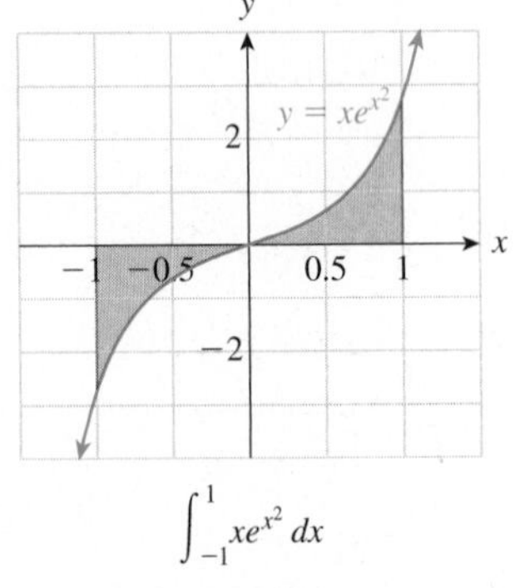

$\int_{-1}^{1} xe^{x^2}\,dx$

Figure **21**

$$\int_{-1}^{0} xe^{x^2}\,dx = \frac{1}{2}\left[e^{x^2}\right]_{-1}^{0} = \frac{1}{2}(1 - e) \approx -0.85914$$

Why is it negative?

$$\int_{0}^{1} xe^{x^2}\,dx = \frac{1}{2}\left[e^{x^2}\right]_{0}^{1} = \frac{1}{2}(e - 1) \approx 0.85914$$

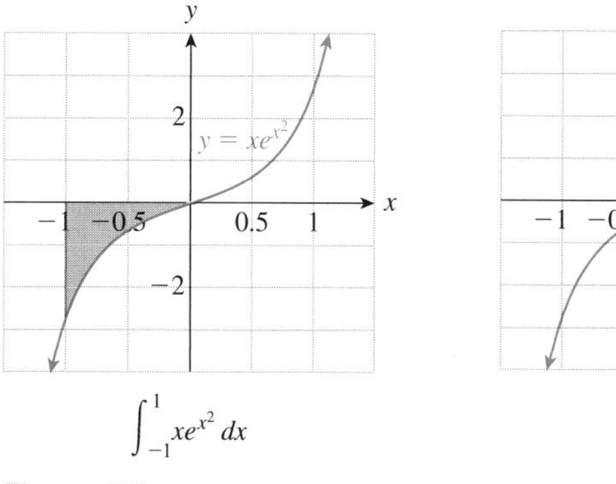

$$\int_{-1}^{1} xe^{x^2}\,dx \qquad \int_{0}^{1} xe^{x^2}\,dx$$

Figure **22**

To obtain the total area, we should add the *absolute* values of these answers because we don't wish to count any area as negative. Thus,

$$\text{Total area} \approx 0.85914 + 0.85914 = 1.71828.$$

6.4 EXERCISES

● denotes basic skills exercises

◆ denotes challenging exercises

tech Ex indicates exercises that should be solved using technology

Evaluate the integrals in Exercises 1–42.

1. ● $\int_{-1}^{1} (x^2 + 2)\,dx$ hint [see Example 2]

2. ● $\int_{-2}^{1} (x - 2)\,dx$

3. ● $\int_{0}^{1} (12x^5 + 5x^4 - 6x^2 + 4)\,dx$

4. ● $\int_{0}^{1} (4x^3 - 3x^2 + 4x - 1)\,dx$

5. ● $\int_{-2}^{2} (x^3 - 2x)\,dx$

6. ● $\int_{-1}^{1} (2x^3 + x)\,dx$

7. ● $\int_{1}^{3} \left(\frac{2}{x^2} + 3x\right) dx$

8. ● $\int_{2}^{3} \left(x + \frac{1}{x}\right) dx$

9. ● $\int_{0}^{1} (2.1x - 4.3x^{1.2})\,dx$

10. ● $\int_{-1}^{0} (4.3x^2 - 1)\,dx$

11. ● $\int_{0}^{1} 2e^x\,dx$

12. ● $\int_{-1}^{0} 3e^x\,dx$

13. ● $\int_{0}^{1} \sqrt{x}\,dx$

14. ● $\int_{-1}^{1} \sqrt[3]{x}\,dx$

15. ● $\int_{0}^{1} 2^x\,dx$

16. ● $\int_{0}^{1} 3^x\,dx$

17. ● $\int_{0}^{1} 18(3x + 1)^5\,dx$

18. ● $\int_{0}^{1} 8(-x + 1)^7\,dx$

19. ● $\int_{-1}^{1} e^{2x-1}\,dx$ hint [see Example 4]

20. ● $\int_{0}^{2} e^{-x+1}\,dx$

21. ● $\int_{0}^{2} 2^{-x+1}\,dx$

22. ● $\int_{-1}^{1} 3^{2x-1}\,dx$

23. ● $\int_{0}^{50} e^{-0.02x-1}\,dx$

24. ● $\int_{-20}^{0} 3e^{2.2x}\,dx$

25. ● $\int_{-1.1}^{1.1} e^{x+1}\,dx$

26. ● $\int_{0}^{\sqrt{2}} x\sqrt{2x^2 + 1}\,dx$

27. ● $\int_{-\sqrt{2}}^{\sqrt{2}} 3x\sqrt{2x^2 + 1}\,dx$

28. $\int_{-1.2}^{1.2} e^{-x-1}\,dx$

29. ● $\int_{0}^{1} 5xe^{x^2+2}\,dx$

30. ● $\int_{0}^{2} \frac{3x}{x^2 + 2}\,dx$

31. ● $\int_{2}^{3} \frac{x^2}{x^3 - 1}\,dx$

32. ● $\int_{2}^{3} \frac{x}{2x^2 - 5}\,dx$

33. ● $\int_{0}^{1} x(1.1)^{-x^2}\,dx$

34. ● $\int_{0}^{1} x^2(2.1)^{x^3}\,dx$

35. $\int_{1}^{2} \frac{e^{1/x}}{x^2}\,dx$

36. $\int_{1}^{2} \frac{\sqrt{\ln x}}{x}\,dx$

37. $\int_{0}^{2} \frac{x}{x + 1}\,dx$

38. $\int_{-1}^{1} \frac{2x}{x + 2}\,dx$

39. $\int_{1}^{2} x(x - 2)^5\,dx$

40. $\int_{1}^{2} x(x - 2)^{1/3}\,dx$

41. $\int_{0}^{1} x\sqrt{2x + 1}\,dx$

42. $\int_{-1}^{0} 2x\sqrt{x + 1}\,dx$

Calculate the total area of the regions described in Exercises 43–50. Do not count area beneath the x-axis as negative.

43. ● Bounded by the line $y = x$, the x-axis, and the lines $x = 0$ and $x = 1$ *hint* [see Example 6]

44. ● Bounded by the line $y = 2x$, the x-axis, and the lines $x = 1$ and $x = 2$

45. ● Bounded by the curve $y = \sqrt{x}$, the x-axis, and the lines $x = 0$ and $x = 4$

46. ● Bounded by the curve $y = 2\sqrt{x}$, the x-axis, and the lines $x = 0$ and $x = 16$

47. Bounded by the curve $y = x^2 - 1$, the x-axis, and the lines $x = 0$ and $x = 4$

48. Bounded by the curve $y = 1 - x^2$, the x-axis, and the lines $x = -1$ and $x = 2$

49. Bounded by the x-axis, the curve $y = xe^{x^2}$, and the lines $x = 0$ and $x = (\ln 2)^{1/2}$

50. Bounded by the x-axis, the curve $y = xe^{x^2-1}$ and the lines $x = 0$ and $x = 1$

Applications

51. ● ***Cost*** The marginal cost of producing the xth box of light bulbs is $5 + x^2/1000$ dollars. Determine how much is added to the total cost by a change in production from $x = 10$ to $x = 100$ boxes. *hint* [see Example 5]

52. ● ***Revenue*** The marginal revenue of the xth box of zip disks sold is $100e^{-0.001x}$ dollars. Find the revenue generated by selling items 101 through 1000.

53. ● ***Displacement*** A car traveling down a road has a velocity of $v(t) = 60 - e^{-t/10}$ mph at time t hours. Find the total distance it travels from time $t = 1$ hour to time $t = 6$. (Round your answer to the nearest mile.)

54. ● ***Displacement*** A ball thrown in the air has a velocity of $v(t) = 100 - 32t$ ft/s at time t seconds. Find the total displacement of the ball between times $t = 1$ second and $t = 7$ seconds, and interpret your answer.

55. ● ***Bottled-Water Sales*** The rate of U.S. sales of bottled water for the period 1993–2003 could be approximated by

$$R(t) = 17t^2 + 100t + 2300 \text{ million gallons per year} \quad (3 \le t \le 13)$$

where t is time in years since 1990.[31] Use the FTC to estimate the total U.S. sales of bottled water from 1995 to 2000. (Round your answer to the nearest billion gallons.)

56. ● ***Bottled-Water Sales*** The rate of U.S. per capita sales of bottled water for the period 1993–2003 could be approximated by

$$Q(t) = 0.05t^2 + 0.4t + 9 \text{ gallons per year} \quad (3 \le t \le 13)$$

where t is the time in years since 1990.[32] Use the FTC to estimate the total U.S. per capita sales of bottled water from 1995 to 2000. (Round your answer to the nearest gallon.)

57. ● ***Household Income*** In the period 1967 to 2003, median household income in the U.S. increased at a rate of approximately

$$R(t) = -1.5t^2 - 0.9t + 1200 \text{ dollars per year}$$

where t is the number of years since 1990.[33] Use a definite integral to estimate the total change in median household income from 1980 to 2000. (Round your answer to the nearest \$1000.)

58. ● ***Health-Care Spending*** In the period 1965 to 2003, the rate of increase of health-care spending in the U.S. was approximately

$$K(t) = 17t^2 + 2600t + 55{,}000 \text{ million dollars per year}$$

where t is the number of years since 1990.[34] Use a definite integral to estimate the total change in health-care spending from 1980 to 2000. (Round your answer to two significant digits.)

59. ***Embryo Development*** The oxygen consumption of a bird embryo increases from the time the egg is laid through the time the chick hatches. In a typical galliform bird, the oxygen consumption can be approximated by

$$c(t) = -0.065t^3 + 3.4t^2 - 22t + 3.6 \text{ milliliters per day} \quad (8 \le t \le 30)$$

where t is the time (in days) since the egg was laid.[35] (An egg will typically hatch at around $t = 28$.) Find the total amount of oxygen consumed during the ninth and tenth days ($t = 8$ to $t = 10$). Round your answer to the nearest milliliter.

60. ***Embryo Development*** The oxygen consumption of a turkey embryo increases from the time the egg is laid through the time the chick hatches. In a brush turkey, the oxygen consumption can be approximated by

$$c(t) = -0.028t^3 + 2.9t^2 - 44t + 95 \text{ milliliters per day} \quad (20 \le t \le 50)$$

where t is the time (in days) since the egg was laid[36] (An egg will typically hatch at around $t = 50$.) Find the total amount of oxygen consumed during the 21st and 22nd days ($t = 20$ to $t = 22$). Round your answer to the nearest 10 milliliters.

---

[31] The authors' regression model, based on data in the Beverage Marketing Corporation news release, "Bottled water now number-two commercial beverage in U.S., says Beverage Marketing Corporation," April 8, 2004, available at www.beveragemarketing.com.

[32] Ibid.

[33] In current dollars, unadjusted for inflation. SOURCE: U.S. Census Bureau; "Table H-5. Race and Hispanic Origin of Householder—Households by Median and Mean Income: 1967 to 2003;" published August 27, 2004; www.census.gov/hhes/income.

[34] SOURCE: Centers for Medicare and Medicaid Services, "National Health Expenditures," 2002 version, released January 2004; www.cms.hhs.gov/statistics/nhe/.

[35] The model approximates graphical data published in the article "The Brush Turkey" by Roger S. Seymour, *Scientific American,* December, 1991, pp. 108–114.

[36] Ibid.

61. ***Sales*** Weekly sales of your *Lord of the Rings* T-shirts have been falling by 5% per week. Assuming you are now selling 50 T-shirts per week, how many shirts will you sell during the coming year? (Round your answer to the nearest shirt.)

62. ***Sales*** Annual sales of fountain pens in Littleville are presently 4000 per year and are increasing by 10% per year. How many fountain pens will be sold over the next five years?

63. ***Fuel Consumption*** The way Professor Waner drives, he burns gas at the rate of $1 - e^{-t}$ gallons each hour, t hours after a fill-up. Find the number of gallons of gas he burns in the first 10 hours after a fill-up.

64. ***Fuel Consumption*** The way Professor Costenoble drives, he burns gas at the rate of $1/(t+1)$ gallons each hour, t hours after a fill-up. Find the number of gallons of gas he burns in the first 10 hours after a fill-up.

65. ***Total Cost*** Use the Fundamental Theorem of Calculus to show that if $m(x)$ is the marginal cost at a production level of x items, then the cost function $C(x)$ is given by

$$C(x) = C(0) + \int_0^x m(t)\,dt$$

What term do we use for $C(0)$?

66. ***Total Sales*** The total cost of producing x items is given by

$$C(x) = 246.76 + \int_0^x 5t\,dt$$

Find the fixed cost and the marginal cost of producing the 10th item.

67. ◆ ***The Logistic Function and iPod Sales***

a. Show that the logistic function $f(x) = \dfrac{N}{1 + Ab^{-x}}$ can be written in the form

$$f(x) = \frac{Nb^x}{A + b^x}$$

b. Use the result of part (a) and a suitable substitution to show that

$$\int \frac{N}{1 + Ab^{-x}}\,dx = \frac{N\ln(A + b^x)}{\ln b} + C$$

c. The rate of sales of Apple iPods from the fourth quarter of 2002 through the third quarter of 2004 could be roughly approximated by the function

$$R(t) = \frac{1100}{1 + 18(1.9)^{-t}} \text{ thousand iPods per quarter} \quad (0 \le t \le 7)$$

where t is time in quarters since the start of 2003.[37] Use the result of part (b) to estimate, to the nearest hundred thousand, the total number of iPods sold from the start of 2003 to the middle of 2004.

[37] Based on a logistic regression. Source for data: Apple Computer, Inc., quarterly earnings reports, available at www.apple.com.

68. ◆ ***The Logistic Function and Grants***

a. Show that the logistic function $f(x) = \dfrac{N}{1 + Ae^{-kx}}$ can be written in the form

$$f(x) = \frac{Ne^{kx}}{A + e^{kx}}$$

b. Use the result of part (a) and a suitable substitution to show that

$$\int \frac{N}{1 + Ae^{-kx}}\,dx = \frac{N\ln(A + e^{kx})}{k} + C$$

c. The rate of spending on grants by U.S. foundations in the period 1993 to 2003 was approximately

$$s(t) = 11 + \frac{20}{1 + 1800e^{-0.9t}} \text{ billion dollars per year} \quad (3 \le t \le 13)$$

where t is the number of years since 1990.[38] Use the result of part (b) to estimate, to the nearest \$10 billion, the total spending on grants from 1998 to 2003.

69. ◆ ***Big Brother*** The number of wiretaps authorized each year by U.S. courts from 1990 to 2003 can be approximated by

$$W(t) = 620 + \frac{900e^{0.25t}}{3 + e^{0.25t}} \quad (0 \le t \le 14)$$

where t is the number of years since the start of 1990.[39]

a. Use a definite integral to estimate the total number of wiretaps from the start of 1998 to the end of 2003. (Round the answer to two significant digits.)

b. The following graph shows the actual number of authorized wiretaps.

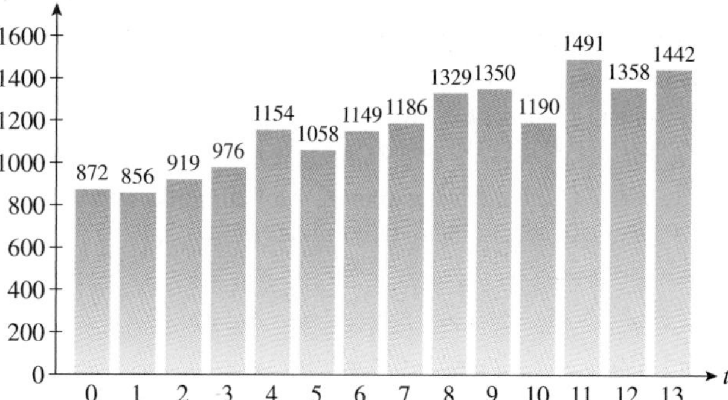

Does the integral in part (a) give an accurate estimate of the actual number to two significant digits? Explain.

[38] Based on a logistic regression. Source for data: The Foundation Center, *Foundation Growth and Giving Estimates,* 2004, downloaded from the Center's website, http://fdncenter.org.

[39] SOURCE: 2000 & 2003 Wiretap Reports, Administrative Office of the United States Courts, www.uscourts.gov/library/wiretap.

70. ◆ ***Big Brother*** The total number of wiretaps authorized each year by U.S. federal courts from 1990 to 2003 can be approximated by

$$W(t) = 340 + \frac{200e^{5t}}{3{,}000{,}000 + e^{5t}} \quad 0 \le t \le 13$$

where t is the number of years since the start of 1990.[40]

a. Use a definite integral to estimate the total number of federal wiretaps from the start of 1998 to the end of 2003. (Round the answer to two significant digits.)

b. The following graph shows the actual number of authorized wiretaps.

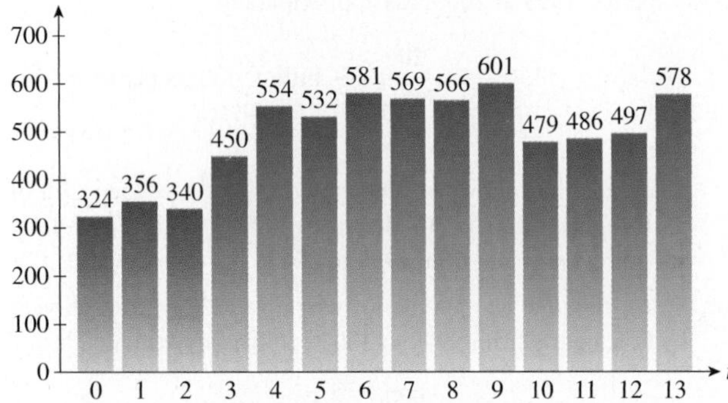

Does the integral in part (a) give an accurate estimate of the actual number to two significant digits? Explain.

71. ◆ ***Kinetic Energy*** The work done in accelerating an object from velocity v_0 to velocity v_1 is given by

$$W = \int_{v_0}^{v_1} v\frac{dp}{dv}\,dv$$

where p is its momentum, given by $p = mv$ (m = mass). Assuming that m is a constant, show that

$$W = \frac{1}{2}mv_1^2 - \frac{1}{2}mv_0^2$$

The quantity $\frac{1}{2}mv^2$ is referred to as the **kinetic energy** of the object, so the work required to accelerate an object is given by its change in kinetic energy.

72. ◆ ***Einstein's Energy Equation*** According to the special theory of relativity, the apparent mass of an object depends on its velocity according to the formula

$$m = \frac{m_0}{\left(1 - \frac{v^2}{c^2}\right)^{1/2}}$$

where v is its velocity, m_0 is the "rest mass" of the object (that is, its mass when $v = 0$), and c is the velocity of light: approximately 3×10^8 meters per second.

a. Show that, if $p = mv$ is the momentum,

$$\frac{dp}{dv} = \frac{m_0}{\left(1 - \frac{v^2}{c^2}\right)^{3/2}}$$

b. Use the integral formula for W in the preceding exercise, together with the result in part (a), to show that the work required to accelerate an object from a velocity of v_0 to v_1 is given by

$$W = \frac{m_0c^2}{\sqrt{1 - \frac{v_1^2}{c^2}}} - \frac{m_0c^2}{\sqrt{1 - \frac{v_0^2}{c^2}}}$$

We call the quantity $\frac{m_0c^2}{\sqrt{1 - \frac{v^2}{c^2}}}$ the **total relativistic energy** of an object moving at velocity v. Thus, the work to accelerate an object from one velocity to another is given by the change in its total relativistic energy.

c. Deduce (as Albert Einstein did) that the total relativistic energy E of a body at rest with rest mass m is given by the famous equation

$$E = mc^2$$

Communication and Reasoning Exercises

73. ● Explain how the indefinite integral and the definite integral are related.

74. ● What is "definite" about the definite integral?

75. ● Complete the following: The total sales from time a to time b are obtained from the marginal sales by taking its _____ _____ from _____ to _____.

76. ● What does the Fundamental Theorem of Calculus permit one to do?

77. Give an example of a nonzero velocity function that will produce a displacement of 0 from time $t = 0$ to time $t = 10$.

78. Give an example of a nonzero function whose definite integral over the interval [4, 6] is zero.

79. Give an example of a decreasing function $f(x)$ with the property that $\int_a^b f(x)\,dx$ is positive for every choice of a and $b > a$.

80. Explain why, in computing the total change of a quantity from its rate of change, it is useful to have the definite integral subtract area below the x-axis.

81. ◆ If $f(x)$ is a continuous function defined for $x \ge a$, define a new function $F(x)$ by the formula

$$F(x) = \int_a^x f(t)\,dt$$

Use the Fundamental Theorem of Calculus to deduce that $F'(x) = f(x)$. What, if anything, is interesting about this result?

82. ◆ tech Ex Use the result of Exercise 81 and technology to compute a table of values for $x = 1, 2, 3$ for an antiderivative of e^{-x^2} with the property that $A(0) = 0$. (Round answers to two decimal places.)

[40] Ibid.

Chapter 6 Review

KEY CONCEPTS

6.1 The Indefinite Integral

An antiderivative of a function f is a function F such that $F' = f$. *p. 418*

Indefinite integral $\int f(x)\,dx$ *p. 418*

Power rule for the indefinite integral:

$$\int x^n dx = \frac{x^{n+1}}{n+1} + C \quad (\text{if } n \neq -1) \quad p.\ 420$$

$$\int x^{-1} dx = \ln|x| + C \quad p.\ 420$$

Indefinite Integral of e^x and b^x:

$$\int e^x dx = e^x + C$$

$$\int b^x dx = \frac{b^x}{\ln b} + C \quad p.\ 421$$

Sums, differences, and constant multiples:

$$\int [f(x) \pm g(x)]\,dx = \int f(x)\,dx \pm \int g(x)\,dx$$

$$\int kf(x)\,dx = k\int f(x)\,dx \quad (k \text{ constant}) \quad p.\ 421$$

Combining the rules *p. 423*

Position, velocity, and acceleration:

$$v = \frac{ds}{dt} \qquad s(t) = \int v(t)\,dt$$

$$a = \frac{dv}{dt} \qquad v(t) = \int a(t)\,dt \quad p.\ 425$$

Motion in a straight line *p. 426*

Motion in a straight line under gravity *p. 427*

6.2 Substitution

Substitution rule: $\int f\,dx = \int \left(\frac{f}{du/dx}\right) du$ *p. 431*

Using the substitution rule *p. 431–432*

Shortcuts: integrals of expressions involving $(ax + b)$:

$$\int (ax+b)^n dx = \frac{(ax+b)^{n+1}}{a(n+1)} + C \quad (\text{if } n \neq -1)$$

$$\int (ax+b)^{-1} dx = \frac{1}{a}\ln|ax+b| + C$$

$$\int e^{ax+b} dx = \frac{1}{a}e^{ax+b} + C$$

$$\int c^{ax+b} dx = \frac{1}{a\ln c}c^{ax+b} + C \quad p.\ 436$$

6.3 The Definite Integral: Numerical and Graphical Approaches

Left Riemann sum:

$$\sum_{k=0}^{n-1} f(x_k)\Delta x = [f(x_0) + f(x_1) + \cdots + f(x_{n-1})]\Delta x$$

p. 444

Computing the Riemann sum from a graph *p. 445*

Computing the Riemann sum from a formula *p. 445*

Definite integral of f from a to b:

$$\int_a^b f(x)\,dx = \lim_{n\to\infty}\sum_{k=0}^{n-1} f(x_k)\Delta x \quad p.\ 446$$

Estimating the definite integral from a graph *p. 448*

Estimating the definite integral using technology *p. 450*

Application to motion in a straight line *p. 451*

6.4 The Definite Integral: An Algebraic Approach and The Fundamental Theorem of Calculus

The Fundamental Theorem of Calculus (FTC) *p. 459*

Using the FTC to compute definite integrals *p. 459–460*

Computing total cost from marginal cost *p. 461*

Computing area *p. 462*

REVIEW EXERCISES

Evaluate the indefinite integrals in Exercises 1–12.

1. $\int (x^2 - 10x + 2)\,dx$

2. $\int (e^x + \sqrt{x})\,dx$

3. $\int \left(\frac{4x^2}{5} - \frac{4}{5x^2}\right) dx$

4. $\int \left(\frac{3x}{5} - \frac{3}{5x}\right) dx$

5. $\int e^{-2x+11}\,dx$

6. $\int \frac{dx}{(4x-3)^2}$

7. $\int x(x^2+4)^{10}\,dx$

8. $\int \frac{x^2+1}{(x^3+3x+2)^2}\,dx$

9. $\int 5e^{-2x}\,dx$

10. $\int xe^{-x^2/2}\,dx$

11. $\int \frac{x+1}{x+2}\,dx$

12. $\int x\sqrt{x-1}\,dx$

In Exercises 13 and 14, use the given graph to estimate the left Riemann sum for the given interval with the stated number of subdivisions.

13. $[0, 3]$, $n = 6$

14. $[1, 3]$, $n = 4$

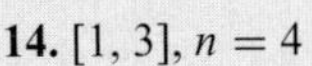

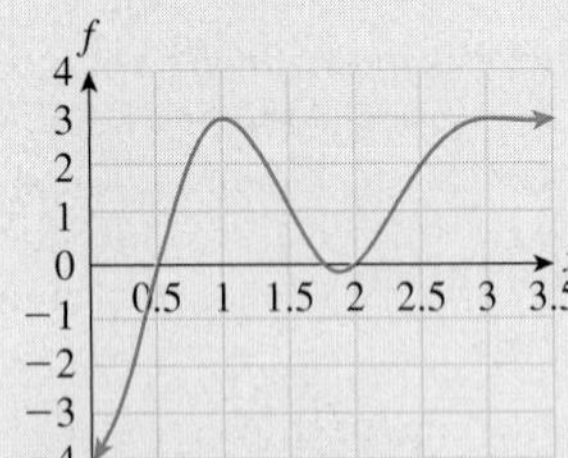

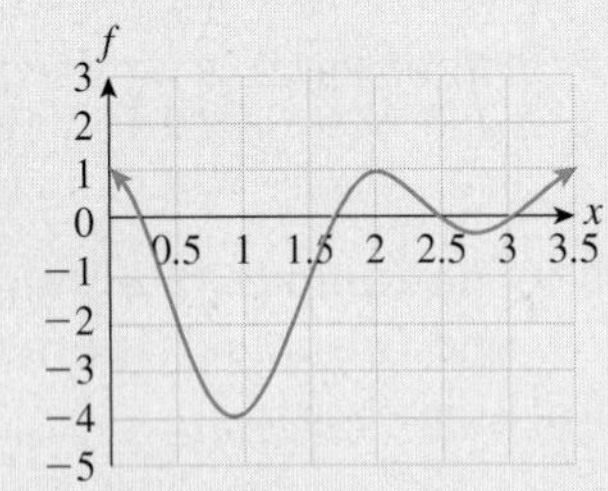

Calculate the left Riemann sums for the given functions over the given interval in Exercises 15–18, using the given values of n. (When rounding, round answers to four decimal places.)

15. $f(x) = x^2 + 1$ over $[-1, 1]$, $n = 4$

16. $f(x) = (x-1)(x-2) - 2$ over $[0, 4]$, $n = 4$

17. $f(x) = x(x^2 - 1)$ over $[0, 1]$, $n = 5$

18. $f(x) = \frac{x-1}{x-2}$ over $[0, 1.5]$, $n = 3$

tech Ex *In Exercises 19 and 20, use technology to approximate the given definite integrals using left Riemann sums with $n = 10, 100,$ and 1000. (Round answers to four decimal places.)*

19. $\int_0^1 e^{-x^2}\,dx$

20. $\int_1^3 x^{-x}\,dx$

In Exercises 21 and 22 the graph of the derivative $f'(x)$ of $f(x)$ is shown. Compute the total change of $f(x)$ over the given interval.

21. $[-1, 2]$

22. $[0, 2]$

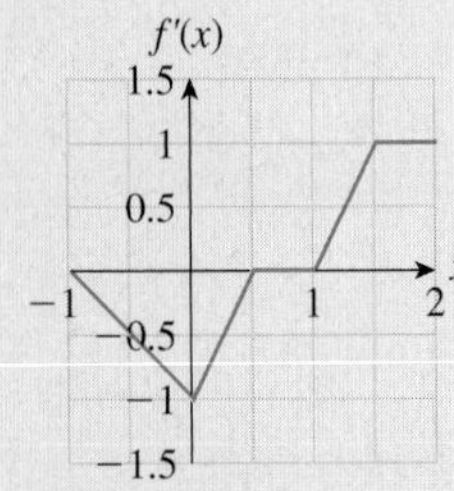

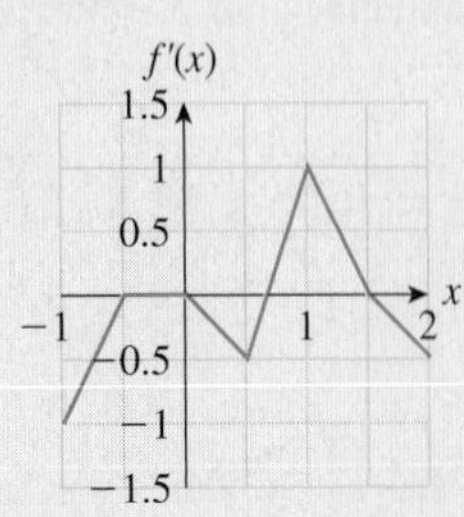

Evaluate the definite integrals in Exercises 23–30, using the Fundamental Theorem of Calculus.

23. $\int_0^1 (x - x^3)\,dx$

24. $\int_0^9 \frac{1}{x+1}\,dx$

25. $\int_{-1}^1 (1 + e^x)\,dx$

26. $\int_0^9 (x + \sqrt{x})\,dx$

27. $\int_0^2 x^2\sqrt{x^3+1}\,dx$

28. $\int_{-1}^1 3^{2x-2}\,dx$

29. $\int_0^{\ln 2} \frac{e^{-2x}}{1+4e^{-2x}}\,dx$

30. $\int_0^1 3xe^{-x^2}\,dx$

In Exercises 31–34, find the areas of the specified regions. (Do not count area below the x-axis as negative.)

31. The area bounded by $y = 4 - x^2$, the x-axis, and the lines $x = -2$ and $x = 2$.

32. The area bounded by $y = 4 - x^2$, the x-axis, and the lines $x = 0$ and $x = 5$.

33. The area bounded by $y = xe^{-x^2}$, the x-axis, and the lines $x = 0$ and $x = 5$.

34. The area bounded by $y = |2x|$, the x-axis, and the lines $x = -1$ and $x = 1$.

Applications

35. *Demand* If OHaganBooks.com were to give away its latest bestseller, *A River Burns Through* It, the demand would be 100,000 books. The marginal demand for the book is $-20p$ at a price of p dollars.

a. What is the demand function for this book?

b. At what price does demand drop to zero?

36. *Motion Under Gravity* An overworked employee at OHaganBooks.com goes to the top of the company's 100 foot tall headquarters building and flings a book up into the air at a speed of 60 feet per second.

a. When will the book hit the ground 100 feet below? (Neglect air resistance.)

b. How fast will it be traveling when it hits the ground?

c. How high will the book go?

37. *Sales* Sales at the OHaganBooks.com website of *Larry Potter Episode V: Return of the Headmasters* fluctuated rather wildly in first 5 months of last year as the following graph shows:

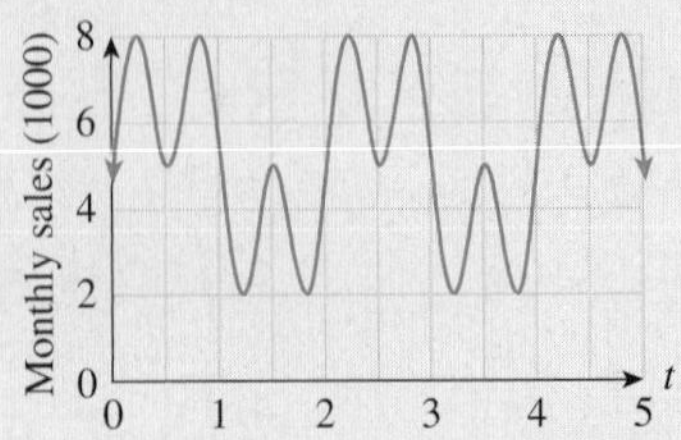

Puzzled by the graph, CEO John O'Hagan asks Jimmy Duffin[41] to estimate the total sales over the entire 5-month period shown. Jimmy decides to use a left Riemann sum with 10 partitions to estimate the total sales. What does he find?

38. ***Promotions*** Unlike *Larry Potter and the Riemann Sum,* sales at OHaganBooks.com of the special leather-bound gift editions of *Lord of the Rings* have been suffering lately, as shown in the following graph (negative sales indicate returns by dissatisfied customers; t is time in months since January 1 of this year):

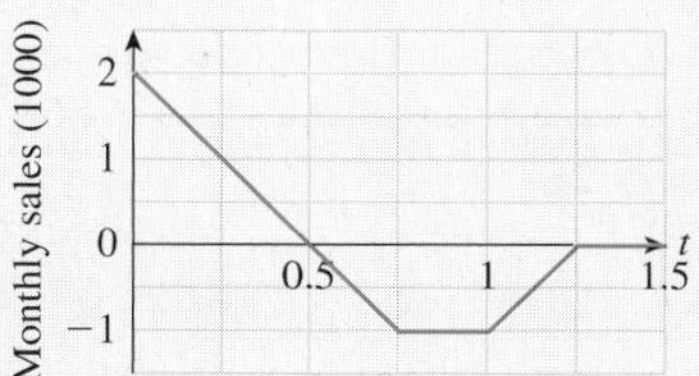

Use the graph to compute the total (net) sales over the period shown.

39. ***Website Activity*** The number of "hits" on the OHaganBooks.com website has been steadily increasing over the past month in response to recent publicity over a software glitch that caused the company to pay customers for buying books online. The activity can be modeled by

$$n(t) = 1000t - 10t^2 + t^3 \text{ hits per day}$$

where t is time in days since news about the software glitch was first publicized on GrungeReport.com. Use a left Riemann sum with 5 partitions to estimate the total number of hits during the first 10 days of the period.

[41] Marjory Duffin's nephew, currently at OHaganBooks.com on a summer internship.

40. ***Legal Costs*** The legal team maintained by OHaganBooks.com to handle the numerous lawsuits brought against the company by disgruntled clients may have to be expanded. The marginal monthly cost to maintain a team of x lawyers is estimated (by a method too complicated to explain) as

$$c(x) = (x-2)^2[8-(x-2)^3]^{3/2} \text{ thousand dollars per additional lawyer}$$

Compute, to the nearest $1000, the total monthly cost if O'HaganBooks goes ahead with a proposal to increase the size of the legal team from 2 to 4.

41. ***Projected Sales*** When OHaganBooks.com was about to go online, it estimated that its weekly sales would begin at about 6400 books per week, with sales increasing at such a rate that weekly sales would double about every 2 weeks. If these estimates had been correct, how many books would the company have sold in the first 5 weeks?

42. ***Actual Sales*** In fact, OHaganBooks.com modeled its weekly sales over a period of time after it went online with the function

$$s(t) = 6053 + \frac{4474e^{0.55t}}{e^{0.55t} + 14.01}$$

where t is the time in weeks after it went online. According to this model, how many books did it actually sell in the first five weeks?

vMentor Do you need a live tutor for homework problems? Access vMentor on the ThomsonNOW! website at **www.thomsonedu.com** for one-on-one tutoring from a mathematics expert.

CASE STUDY: Wage Inflation

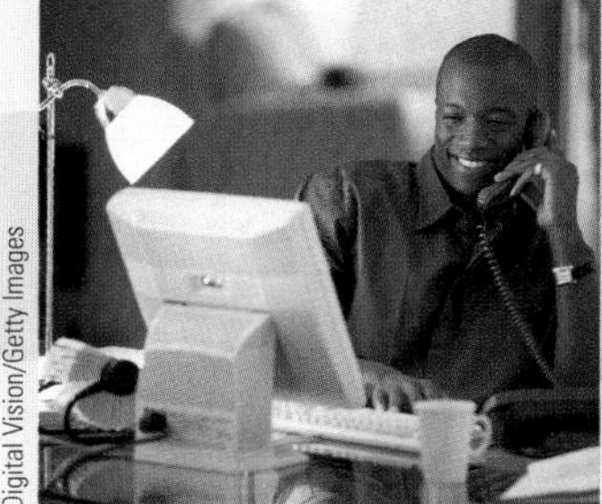
Digital Vision/Getty Images

You are the assistant personnel manager at ABC Development Enterprises, a large corporation, and yesterday you received the following memo from the Personnel Manager.

TO: SW
FROM: SC
SUBJECT: Cost of labor

Yesterday, the CEO asked me to find some mathematical formulas to estimate (1) the trend in annual wage increases and (2) the average annual wage of assembly line workers from the time they join the company to the time they retire. (She needs the information for next week's stockholder meeting.) So far, I have had very little luck: All I have been able to find is a table giving annual percentage wage increases (attached). Also, I know that the average wage for an assembly-line worker in 1981 was \$25,000 per year. Do you have any ideas?

ATTACHMENT*

Date	'81	'82	'83	'84	'85	'86	'87	'88
Annual Change (%)	9.3	8.0	5.3	5.0	4.2	4.0	3.2	3.4

Date	'89	'90	'91	'92	'93	'94	'95
Annual Change (%)	4.2	4.2	4.0	3.4	2.8	3.0	2.8

*The data show approximate year-to-year percentage change in U.S. wages.
SOURCE: DataStream/*The New York Times,* August 13, 1995, p. 26.

(So, for example, the wages increased 9.3% from 1981 to 1982.)

Getting to work, you decide that the first thing to do is fit these data to a mathematical curve that you can use to project future changes in wages. You graph the data to get a sense of what mathematical models might be appropriate (Figure 1).

Figure 1

The graph suggests a decreasing trend, leveling off at about 3%. You recall that there are a variety of curves that behave this way. One of the simplest is the curve

$$y = \frac{a}{t} + b \qquad (t \geq 1)$$

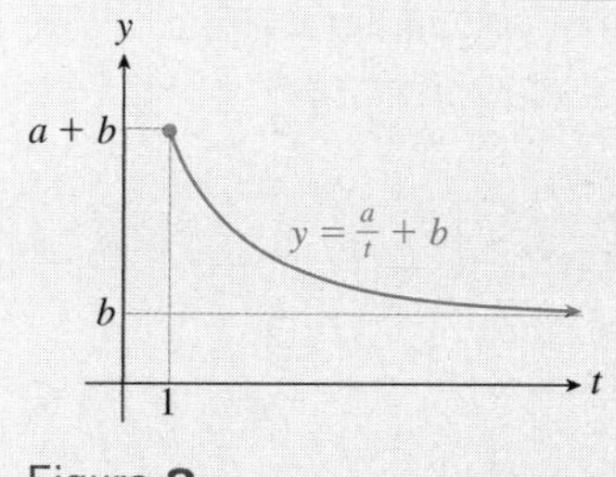

Figure 2

where a and b are constants (Figure 2).[42]

You let $t = 1$ correspond to the time of the first data point, 1981, and convert all the percentages to decimals, giving the following table of data:

t	1	2	3	4	5	6	7	8
y	0.093	0.080	0.053	0.050	0.042	0.040	0.032	0.034
t	9	10	11	12	13	14	15	
y	0.042	0.042	0.040	0.034	0.028	0.030	0.028	

You then find the values of a and b that best fit the given data.[43] This gives you the following model for wage inflation (with figures rounded to five significant digits):

$$y = \frac{0.071813}{t} + 0.028647$$

(It is interesting that the model predicts wage inflation leveling off to about 2.86%.) Figure 2 shows the graph of y superimposed on the data.

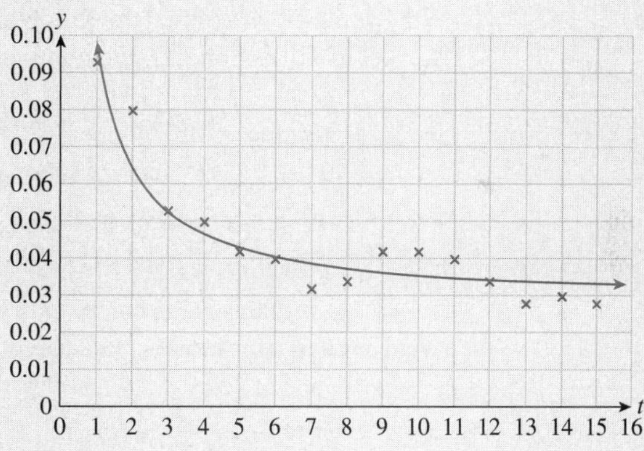

Figure 3

Now that you have a model for wage inflation, you must use it to find the annual wage. First, you realize that the model gives the *fractional rate of increase* of wages (because it is specified as a percentage, or fraction, of the total wage). In other words, if $w(t)$ represents a worker's annual wage at time t, Then

$$y = \frac{dw/dt}{w} = \frac{d}{dt}(\ln w) \qquad \text{By the chain rule for derivatives.}$$

[42] There is a good mathematical reason for choosing a curve of this form: it is a first approximation (for $t \geq 1$) to a general rational function that approaches a constant as $t \to +\infty$.

[43] To do this, you note that y is a linear function of $1/t$, namely, $y = a(1/t) + b$. Then you run a linear regression on the data $(1/t,\ y)$.

You find an equation for a worker's annual wage at time t by solving for w:

$$\begin{aligned}\ln w &= \int y\,dt \\ &= \int \left(\frac{a}{t} + b\right) dt \\ &= a \ln t + bt + C\end{aligned}$$

where a and b are as above and C is the constant of integration, so

$$w = e^{a \ln t + bt + C}$$

To compute C, you substitute the initial data from the memo: $w(1) = 25{,}000$. Thus,

$$25{,}000 = e^{a \ln 1 + b + C} = e^{b+C} = e^{0.028647 + C}$$

Thus,

$$\ln(25{,}000) = 0.028647 + C$$

which gives

$$C = \ln(25{,}000) - 0.028647 \approx 10.098 \qquad \text{(to 5 significant digits).}$$

Now you can write down the following formula for the annual wage of an assembly-line worker as a function of t, the number of years since 1980:

$$\begin{aligned}w(t) &= e^{a \ln t + bt + C} = e^{0.071813 \ln t + 0.028647t + 10.098} \\ &= e^{0.071813 \ln t} e^{0.028647t} e^{10.098} \\ &= t^{0.071813} e^{0.028647t} e^{10.098}\end{aligned}$$

What remains is the calculation of the average annual wage. The average is the total wage earned over the worker's career divided by the number of years worked:

$$\bar{w} = \frac{1}{s-r} \int_r^s w(t)\,dt$$

where r is the time an employee begins working at the company and s is the time he or she retires. Substituting the formula for $w(t)$ gives

$$\begin{aligned}\bar{w} &= \frac{1}{s-r} \int_r^s t^{0.071813} e^{0.028647t} e^{10.098}\,dt \\ &= \frac{e^{10.098}}{s-r} \int_r^s t^{0.071813} e^{0.028647t}\,dt\end{aligned}$$

You cannot find an explicit antiderivative for the integrand, so you decide that the only way to compute it is numerically. You send the following memo to SC.

TO: SC
FROM: SW
SUBJECT: The formula you wanted

The average annual salary of an assembly-line worker here at ABC Development Enterprises is given by the formula

$$\bar{w} = \frac{e^{10.098}}{s-r}\int_r^s t^{0.071813}e^{0.028647t}\,dt$$

where r is the time in years after 1980 that a worker joins ABC and s is the time (in years after 1980) the worker retires. (The formula is valid only from 1981 on.) To calculate it easily (and impress the board members), I suggest you enter the following on your graphing calculator:

```
Y1=(e^(10.098)/(S-R))fnInt(T^0.071813e^(0.028647T),T,R,S)
```

Then suppose, for example, that a worker joined the company in 1983 ($r = 3$) and retired in 2001 ($s = 21$). All you do is enter

```
3→R
21→S
Y1
```

and your calculator will give you the result: The average salary of the worker is $41,307.16.

Have a nice day.
SW

Exercises

1. Use the model developed above to compute the average annual income of a worker who joined the company in 1998 and left 3 years later.

2. What was the total amount paid by ABC Enterprises to the worker in Exercise 1?

3. What (if any) advantages are there to using a model for the annual wage inflation rate when the actual annual wage inflation rates are available?

4. The formula in the model was based on a 1981 salary of $25,000. Change the model to allow for an arbitrary 1981 salary of $\$w_0$.

5. tech Ex If we had used exponential regression to model the wage inflation data, we would have obtained

$$y = 0.07142e^{-0.067135t}$$

Graph this equation along with the actual wage data and the earlier model for y. Is this a better model or a worse model?

6. Use the actual data in the table to calculate the average salary of an assembly-line worker for the 6-year period from 1981 through the end of 1986, and compare it with the figure predicted by the model in the text.

TI-83/84 Technology Guide

Section 6.3

Example 5 Estimate the area under the graph of $f(x) = 1 - x^2$ over the interval [0, 1] using $n = 100$, $n = 200$, and $n = 500$ partitions.

Solution with Technology There are several ways to compute Riemann sums with a graphing calculator. We illustrate one method. For $n = 100$, we need to compute the sum

$$\sum_{k=0}^{99} f(x_k)\Delta x = [f(0) + f(0.01) + \cdots + f(0.99)](0.01)$$ See discussion in Example 5

Thus, we first need to calculate the numbers $f(0)$, $f(0.01)$, and so on, and add them up. The TI-83/84 has a built-in `sum` function (available in the LIST MATH menu), which, like the SUM function in a spreadsheet, sums the entries in a list.

1. To generate a list that contains the numbers we want to add together, use the `seq` function (available in the LIST OPS menu). If we enter

   `seq(1-X^2,X,0,0.99,0.01)` seq: [2ND] [LIST] OPS [5]

   the calculator will calculate a list by evaluating `1-X^2` for values of `X` from 0 to 0.99 in steps of 0.01.

2. To take the sum of all these numbers, we wrap the `seq` function in a call to `sum`:

   `sum(seq(1-X^2,X,0,0.99,0.01))` sum: [2ND] [LIST] MATH [5]

   This gives the sum

   $$f(0) + f(0.01) + \cdots + f(0.99) = 67.165$$

3. To obtain the Riemann sum, we need to multiply this sum by $\Delta x = 0.01$, and we obtain the estimate of $67.165 \approx 0.67165$ for the Riemann sum:

```
sum(seq(1-X^2,X,
0,0.99,0.01))
           67.165
```

We obtain the other Riemann sums similarly, as shown here:

```
sum(seq(1-X^2,X,
0,0.995,0.005)*0
.005
        .6691625
```

$n = 200$

```
sum(seq(1-X^2,X,
0,0.998,0.002)*0
.002
         .667666
```

$n = 500$

One disadvantage of this method is that the TI-83/84 can generate and sum a list of at most 999 entries. The TI-83/84 also has a built-in function `fnInt`, which finds a very accurate approximation of a definite integral, but it uses a more sophisticated technique than the one we are discussing here.

The LEFTSUM Program for the TI-83/84

The following program calculates (left) Riemann sums for any n. The latest version of this program (and others) is available at the website.

Program	Comments
`PROGRAM: LEFTSUM`	
`:Input "LEFT ENDPOINT? ",A`	Prompts for the left end-point a
`:Input "RIGHT ENDPOINT? ",B`	Prompts for the right end-point b
`:Input "N? ",N`	Prompts for the number of rectangles
`:(B-A)/N→D`	D is $\Delta x = (b-a)/n$
`:Ø→L`	L will eventually be the left sum
`:A→X`	X is the current x-coordinate
`:For(I,1,N)`	Start of a loop—recall the sigma notation
`:L+Y1→L`	Add $f(x_{i-1})$ to L
`:A+I*D→X`	Uses formula $x_i = a + i\Delta x$
`:End`	End of loop
`:L*D→L`	Multiply by Δx
`:Disp "LEFT SUM IS ",L`	
`:Stop`	

EXCEL Technology Guide

Section 6.3

Example 5 Estimate the area under the graph of $f(x) = 1 - x^2$ over the interval [0, 1] using $n = 100$, $n = 200$, and $n = 500$ partitions.

Solution with Technology We need to compute various sums

$$\sum_{k=0}^{99} f(x_k)\Delta x = [f(0) + f(0.01) + \cdots + f(0.99)](0.01)$$

See discussion in Example 5

$$\sum_{k=0}^{199} f(x_k)\Delta x = [f(0) + f(0.005) + \cdots + f(0.995)](0.005)$$

$$\sum_{k=0}^{499} f(x_k)\Delta x = [f(0) + f(0.002) + \cdots + f(0.998)](0.002)$$

TECHNOLOGY GUIDE

Here is how you can compute them all on same spreadsheet.

1. Enter the values for the endpoints a and b, the number of subdivisions n, and the formula $\Delta x = (b - a)/n$:

Microsoft Excel - ETG 6 Estimating Area Under the Graph.xls

	A	B	C	D	E
1	x	f(x)	a	0	
2			b	1	
3			n	100	
4			Delta x	=(D2-D1)/D3	
5					
6					

2. Next, we compute all the x-values we might need in column A. Because the largest value of n that we will be using is 500, we will need a total of 501 values of x. Note that the value in each cell below A3 is obtained from the one above by adding Δx.

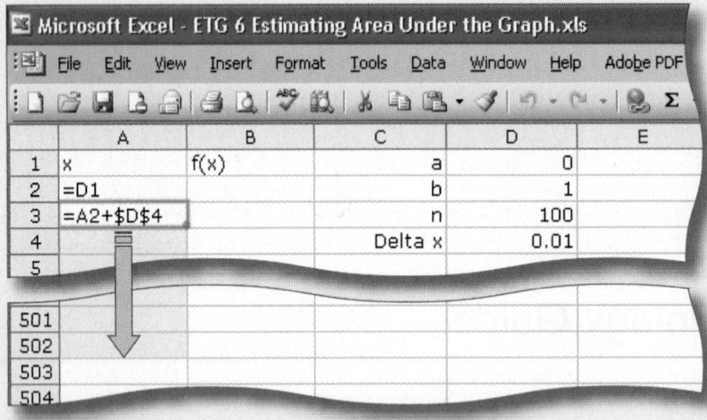

Microsoft Excel - ETG 6 Estimating Area Under the Graph.xls

	A	B	C	D	E
1	x	f(x)	a	0	
2	=D1		b	1	
3	=A2+$D$4		n	100	
4			Delta x	0.01	
5					
501					
502					
503					
504					

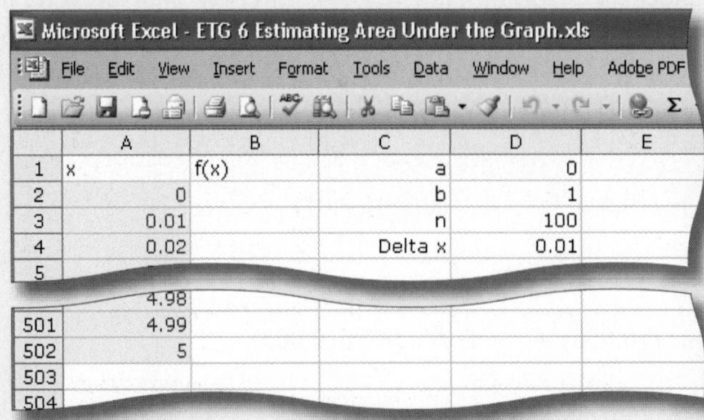

Microsoft Excel - ETG 6 Estimating Area Under the Graph.xls

	A	B	C	D	E
1	x	f(x)	a	0	
2	0		b	1	
3	0.01		n	100	
4	0.02		Delta x	0.01	
5					
	4.98				
501	4.99				
502	5				
503					
504					

(The fact that the values of x presently go too far will be corrected in the next step.)

3. We need to calculate the numbers $f(0)$, $f(0.01)$, and so on, but only those for which the corresponding x-value is less than b. To do this, we use a logical formula as we did with piecewise-defined functions in Chapter 1:

Microsoft Excel - ETG 6 Estimating Area Under the Graph.xls

	A	B	C	D	E
1	x	f(x)	a	0	
2	0	=(1-A2^2)*(A2<$D$2)	b	1	
3	0.01		n	100	
4	0.02		Delta x	0.01	
5					
	4.98				
501	4.99				
502	5				
503					
504					

When the value of x is b or above, the function will evaluate to zero, because we do not want to count it.

4. Finally, we compute the Riemann sum by adding up everything in Column B and multiplying by Δx:

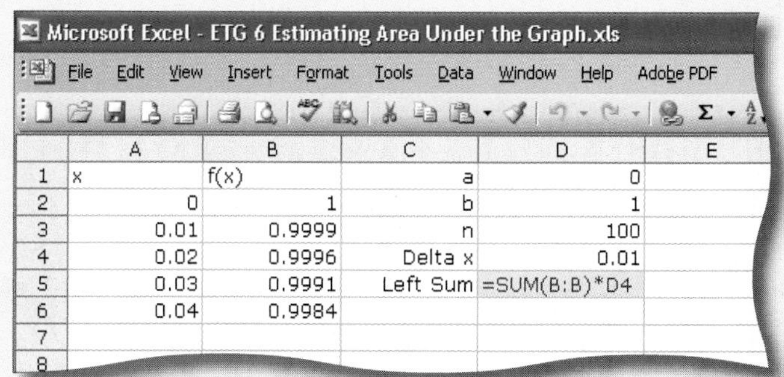

Microsoft Excel - ETG 6 Estimating Area Under the Graph.xls

	A	B	C	D	E
1	x	f(x)	a	0	
2	0	1	b	1	
3	0.01	0.9999	n	100	
4	0.02	0.9996	Delta x	0.01	
5	0.03	0.9991	Left Sum	=SUM(B:B)*D4	
6	0.04	0.9984			
7					
8					

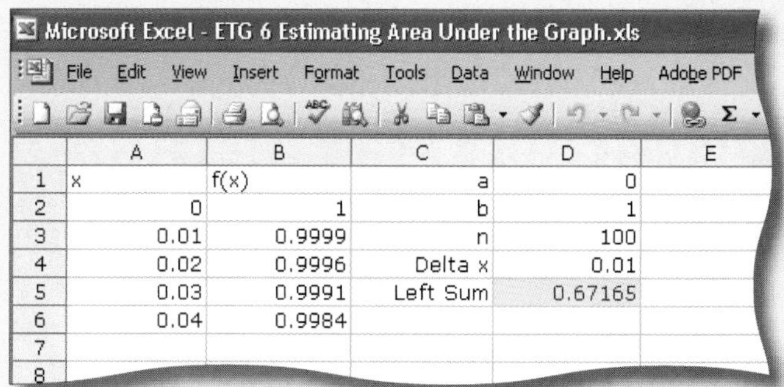

Microsoft Excel - ETG 6 Estimating Area Under the Graph.xls

	A	B	C	D	E
1	x	f(x)	a	0	
2	0	1	b	1	
3	0.01	0.9999	n	100	
4	0.02	0.9996	Delta x	0.01	
5	0.03	0.9991	Left Sum	0.67165	
6	0.04	0.9984			
7					
8					

Now it is easy to obtain the sums for $n = 200$ and $n = 500$: Simply change the value of n in cell D3:

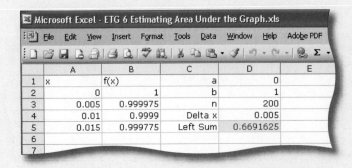

Microsoft Excel - ETG 6 Estimating Area Under the Graph.xls

	A	B	C	D	E
1	x	f(x)	a	0	
2	0	1	b	1	
3	0.005	0.999975	n	200	
4	0.01	0.9999	Delta x	0.005	
5	0.015	0.999775	Left Sum	0.6691625	
6					
7					

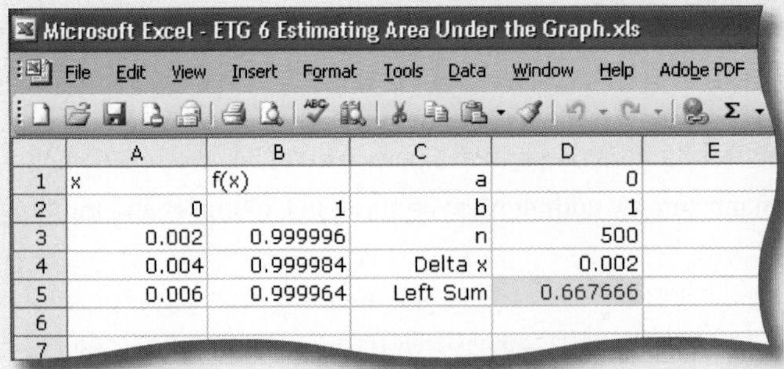

Microsoft Excel - ETG 6 Estimating Area Under the Graph.xls

	A	B	C	D	E
1	x	f(x)	a	0	
2	0	1	b	1	
3	0.002	0.999996	n	500	
4	0.004	0.999984	Delta x	0.002	
5	0.006	0.999964	Left Sum	0.667666	
6					
7					

Chapter 7: Further Techniques of Integration and Applications of the Integral

7.1 Integration by Parts

7.2 Area between Two Curves & Appications

7.3 Averages and Moving Averages

7.4 Applications to Business and Economics

7.5 Improper Integrals and Applications

7.6 Differential Equations (optional)

7.7 Special topics for SCU

Key Concepts
Review Exercises
Case Study Exercises
Technology Guides

In Chapter 6, you learned basic strategies for finding antiderivatives, as well as a few specific rules. The rules included the Power Rule and special antiderivatives for exponential and logarithmic functions. The strategies involve breaking up sums, allowing multiplicative constants to be carried along, and the technique of substitution. Substitution is the most difficult of these, and you need to be well grounded in that method before you proceed to Chapter 7.

In Chapter 7, we introduce a powerful new technique of integration and apply all of our techniques to diverse applications: financial computations with continuous income streams and applications from economics (Consumers'/Producers' Surplus and the Gini Index). We will see how to extend the definition of the definite integral to infinite intervals, in order to consider income streams that go on forever.

You should realize that you will be called upon to decide for yourself which technique of integration to use in a given situation. This requires a lot of independent thinking. The correct technique is usually evident if you can correctly answer the question, "What type of function do I see?" For instance, the Power Rule is for situations where you asked, "Can this expression be written as a sum of powers of the variable?" and realized, "Yes, with a little work, I can turn this one into powers of x." Substitution is for integrals where you can detect a composite function.

Throughout our course, it is vital for you to become the decision-maker who can correctly select the right mathematical idea to apply. In Chapter 7, it is up to you to choose the right tool from your "integration toolkit."

Section 7.1 Integration by Parts

Almost every rule you learned for taking derivatives has its mirror image as an integration rule (the exception being the quotient rule). Integration by parts is the mirror image of the product rule. Let's recall the product rule. If u and v are functions of x, then

$$\frac{d}{dx}(u \cdot v) = \frac{du}{dx} \cdot v + u \cdot \frac{dv}{dx} .$$

We antidifferentiate both sides and then rearrange the whole formula to get:

$$\int u \cdot \frac{dv}{dx} \, dx = \int \frac{d}{dx}(u \cdot v) \, dx - \int \frac{du}{dx} \cdot v \, dx .$$

Look at the second term. It asks us to antidifferentiate the derivative of $u \cdot v$. Of course this gives us just $u \cdot v$ (except possibly for a constant of integration, which can be absorbed into the adjacent term). Our rewritten version of the product rule becomes

$$\int u \cdot \frac{dv}{dx} \, dx = u \cdot v - \int \frac{du}{dx} \cdot v \, dx .$$

Examine this formula closely. Think of the left-hand side as some particular integral we wish to evaluate. The right-hand side gives the solution in two terms, $u \cdot v$ and a new integral, which we may or may not be able to evaluate.

The formula looks simple when we use differential notation, just as in Section 6.2, so that $du = \frac{du}{dx} dx$ and $dv = \frac{dv}{dx} dx$. In this notation, the **integration by parts formula** is:

$$\int u \, dv = u \cdot v - \int v \, du .$$

Let's work through an example before we summarize the method.

Example 1. Find $\int (4x + 6) \, e^{2x} \, dx$.

Solution: First, observe that none of our Chapter 6 ideas will work on this integral. Go through your mental checklist and observe that this integrand cannot be written as the sum of powers of x; a moment's thought shows that no progress can be made with substitution. Therefore we resolve to try our new formula. Our formula works to evaluate an integral called

$$\int u \cdot \frac{dv}{dx} \, dx .$$

Nobody has told us how to interpret this particular integral in terms of us and vs, so it is up to us to decide. Let's pick $u = 4x + 6$, because then du / dx becomes simpler than u. This forces us to choose

$$\frac{dv}{dx} \, dx = dv = e^{2x} \, dx,$$

because that's what's left over in the integral and the parts *must* fit together to make the given integrand. Part of the choice was up to us, and part was forced on us.

To apply the formula, we need to know du / dx and v. Finding these quantities amounts to learning the consequences of our choices. Notice that we need to *differentiate* u and *antidifferentiate* dv/ dx. If you have been having trouble telling the difference between differentiation and antidifferentiation, now is a good time to have a talk with yourself and stabilize your knowledge. To help you keep things in order, it is convenient to gather this data in a table, like this:

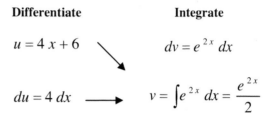

Differentiate		**Integrate**
$u = 4x + 6$	↘	$dv = e^{2x}\, dx$
$du = 4\, dx$	⟶	$v = \int e^{2x}\, dx = \dfrac{e^{2x}}{2}$

We move down the left column by differentiating and move down the right column by integrating. In many examples, you will be able to do the integration in your head. Note that we didn't worry about adding a constant of integration in v. If we did add any particular constant here, it would cancel out later, so it is simplest not to add any constant.

We assemble the parts by looking at the formula above. The formula has two terms,

$$u \cdot v \text{ and } \quad -\int \frac{du}{dx} \cdot v \; dx \; .$$

The first term is the product of the functions on the diagonal marked with a slanted arrow; the second is the *negative* of the integral of the product of the functions in the bottom row. When you say it in words, it sounds complicated, but when you look at the table above, it's easy to remember that it is telling you to

- multiply the terms on the main diagonal and
- subtract the integral of the product of the terms in the bottom row.

When we do these activities in our example, we get

$$\int (4x+6)\, e^{2x}\, dx = (4x+6)\, e^{2x} / 2 - \int 4\; e^{2x} / 2\, dx$$
$$= (2x+3)\, e^{2x} - e^{2x} + C = (2x+2)\, e^{2x} + C.$$

You should check that the derivative of $(2x+2)\, e^{2x}$ really is $(4x+6)\, e^{2x}$. It's like magic!

Note that this time, we *did* have to add a constant of integration, to express the idea that our answer is only defined up to an additive constant. However, this would *not* be necessary if our goal were to evaluate a definite integral, as shown in Example 3. Before thinking about definite integrals, let's summarize what we learned from this example and solidify our understanding of Integration by Parts.

Summary of the Integration by Parts formula

To evaluate an integral where the integrand is the product of dissimilar functions, you should:

- Name two parts, u and dv / dx whose product is the integrand.
- Integrate one and differentiate the other.
- Assemble the pieces according to the formula below, using spatial locations to assist you. Once you get used to the spatial locations, you may not need to memorize this formula.

$$\int u\,dv = u \cdot v - \int v\,du .$$

You may be asking, "How do I choose the parts?" This is a famous question. To gain insight, let us try Example 1 again, with a different choice of parts.

Example 1 revisited. Find $\int (4x+6)\,e^{2x}\,dx$.

Solution (attempt): This time, suppose that we choose $u = e^{2x}$ and $dv = 4x+6\ dx$. Since multiplication can be done in any order, these parts can indeed be multiplied together to make our integrand. They are a *legal* choice of parts. Let's see how they work out.

Differentiate		**Integrate**
$u = e^{2x}$	↘	$dv = 4x+6\ dx$
$du = 2\ e^{2x}\ dx$	→	$v = \int 4x+6\ dx$
		$= 2x^2 + 6x$

According to the formula,

$$\int (4x+6)\,e^{2x}\,dx = \left(2x^2+6x\right)e^{2x} - \int 2\left(2x^2+6x\right)e^{2x}\,dx .$$

This equation is *true*, but is it useful? Is the new integral on the right-hand side simpler that the original? No. In contrast to our first try, where we traded a tough integral for some stuff and a *simpler* integral, here we have traded a tough integral for an even tougher integral. We went the wrong way.

This may happen to you, especially when you are new to this technique. All you have to do is go back and change your choice. Still, you may appreciate the guide provided on page 484.

A comment on Section 7.1 as originally written: Although we at SCU very much admire the work of Waner and Costenoble, we think they got this section wrong. They use a nonstandard notation that they think students will find easier. We disagree and have decided to offer you the most commonly used notation. If you look at the Student Solutions Manual, try to ignore the letters, but do notice the spatial locations of the quantities, because this will help you.

It can sometimes happen that you need to apply this technique twice. If you truly know the method, this is not very difficult. Here is a simple example to illustrate.

Example 2. Evaluate $\int x^2 e^{3x}\, dx$.

Solution. We choose $u = x^2$ and $dv = e^{3x}\, dx$. On your own paper, write these down in the suggested tabular format. Then compute that $du = 2x\, dx$ and $v = e^{3x}/3$. Try assembling the parts according to the formula and you will find that

$$\int x^2 e^{3x}\, dx = \frac{1}{3} x^2 e^{3x} - \int \frac{2}{3} x e^{3x}\, dx.$$

We have made progress, because the new integral is simpler than the original, having a lower power of x. On your own, apply the technique to the second integral on the right. You should get

$$\int x^2 e^{3x}\, dx = \frac{1}{3} x^2 e^{3x} - \int \frac{2}{3} x e^{3x}\, dx$$
$$= \frac{1}{3} x^2 e^{3x} - \frac{2}{9} x e^{3x} + \frac{2}{27} e^{3x} + C = \frac{1}{27}\left(9x^2 - 6x + 2\right) e^{3x} + C.$$

Now let's think about using this formula in *definite* integrals, where we must *find* an antiderivative and *evaluate* it at the limits of integration. The integration by parts formula delivers our antiderivate in two separate terms. All we have to remember is to evaluate each term. Keep in mind that definite integrals always simplify to give a specific number, never a function of x.

We follow this idea through an example.

Example 3. Find $\int_0^3 4xe^{-2x}\, dx$.

Solution: The choice of parts is easy; just as in Example 1, we target the power function, $4x$, for differentiation, which leaves the exponential function in the integration column. Please write the parts in a table of your own, and check that you can assemble the parts, as follows:

$$\int_0^3 4xe^{-2x}\, dx = -2xe^{-2x}\,\Big|_0^3 + \int_0^3 2e^{-2x}\, dx.$$

Let's notice a few things before we go on. The first term on the right, $-2xe^{-2x}$, is one term in the antiderivate, which we must eventually evaluate, so we put a vertical bar to indicate that evaluation. (If you leave this out, your formula is not accurate.) In the second term, the + sign is due to two negatives canceling each other. Finally, notice that we still have to perform one more integration. (It's easy, because there's a simple rule for these exponential functions, but we still have to remember to do it.) Our solution continues:

$$\int_0^3 4xe^{-2x}\, dx = -2xe^{-2x}\,\Big|_0^3 - e^{-2x}\,\Big|_0^3 = -(2x+1)e^{-2x}\,\Big|_0^3 = -7e^{-6} + 1.$$

This is the exact calculator-ready answer. Those who know a little about the exponential function do not need a calculator to know that this is very close to 1. In fact, it works out to be about .9826. Notice how factoring the antiderivative made evaluation easier. This often happens.

Some common applications involve one quantity that changes exponentially and another quantity with linear change. This can lead to integrals where integration by parts is necessary, as follows:

Example 4. You offer mathematics consulting for the CEO of a start-up company, using *Excel* and elementary modeling to display data for potential investors. You charge \$20 per hour, but raise your rate by 5%, continuously compounded, annually. At first, you work only 50 hours per year, but as your skills grow and your work is more in demand, you increase linearly to 300 hours per year over a five-year period. How much would you earn at this job?

Solution: The first step is to find a function that expresses your salary, in thousands of dollars per year. We need to know how many hours you work each year and how many dollars you gain for each hour. According to the specifications, the number of hours is $50 + 50\,t$. (The slope of this linear function is just 250 hrs/5 years.) Your hourly fee is computed from the "Pert" formula: $\$\,20\,e^{.05\,t}$ per hour. Thus, your salary after t years is

$$20\,e^{.05\,t}\,\frac{\$}{\text{hr.}}\,(\,50+50\,t\,)\,\frac{\text{hr.}}{\text{yr.}} = 1000\,(\,1+t\,)\,e^{t/20}\,\frac{\$}{\text{yr.}}\,.$$

Using integration by parts, the total amount you earn works out to be (in thousands of dollars)

$$\int_0^5 (1+t)\,e^{t/20}\;dt = 20\,(1+t)\,e^{t/20}\,\Big|_0^5 - \int_0^5 20\,e^{t/20}\;dt$$

$$= 20\,(\,1+t\,)\,e^{t/20}\,\Big|_0^5 - 400\,e^{t/20}\,\Big|_0^5 = 120\,e^{1/4} - 20 - (400\,e^{1/4} - 400)$$

and that simplifies to $380 - 280\;e^{1/4} \approx 20.47$, which is about \$20,470. Not bad for a little part-time mathematics!

Continue to digest integration by parts by doing lots of exercises.

Choosing the parts: When choosing u, look for something that becomes simpler when you differentiate; powers of the variable often, but not always, go in the u column. When choosing the quantity to play the role of dv/dx, make sure that quantity is one you know how to integrate. A famous error is putting $\ln x$ in that right-hand column. Never do that. We know how to differentiate $\ln x$, but not how to antidifferentiate it. In fact, this concept suggests a nice last example.

Example 5. Find $\int \ln x\;dx$.

Solution: The trick here is to see the integrand $\ln x$ as $\ln x \cdot 1$. Think for a moment about where to put $\ln x$. Since we *do* know how to differentiate $\ln x$, but *not* how to antidifferentiate it (after all, this is our problem!), we put $\ln x$ in the left-hand column:

Differentiate		**Integrate**
$u = \ln x$	↘	$dv = 1\;dx$
$du = \frac{1}{x}\;dx$	→	$v = x$

Use the spatial locations to guide you in assembling the parts. We now rejoin Waner and Costenoble, who have this same example in progress. Be sure to check their answer and make sure that it works.

We notice that the product of $1/x$ and x is just 1, which we know how to integrate, so we can stop here:

$$\begin{aligned}\int \ln x\,dx &= x\ln x - \int\left(\frac{1}{x}\right)x\,dx\\ &= x\ln x - \int 1\,dx\\ &= x\ln x - x + C\end{aligned}$$

FAQs Whether to Use Integration by Parts, and What Goes in the *D* and *I* Columns

Q: *Will integration by parts always work to integrate a product?*

A: No. While integration by parts often works for products in which one factor is a polynomial, it will almost *never* work in the examples of products we saw when discussing substitution in Section 6.2. For example, although integration by parts can be used to compute $\int(x^2-x)e^{2x-1}\,dx$ (put x^2-x in the *D* column and e^{2x-1} in the *I* column), it *cannot* be used to compute $\int(2x-1)e^{x^2-x}\,dx$ (put $u=x^2-x$). Recognizing when to use integration by parts is best learned by experience. ■

Q: *When using integration by parts, which expression goes in the D column, and which in the I column?*

A: Although there is no general rule, the following guidelines are useful:

- To integrate a product in which one factor is a polynomial and the other can be integrated several times, put the polynomial in the *D* column and the other factor in the *I* column. Then differentiate the polynomial until you get zero.
- If one of the factors is a polynomial but the other factor cannot be integrated easily, put the polynomial in the *I* column and the other factor in the *D* column. Stop when the product of the functions in the bottom row can be integrated.
- If neither factor is a polynomial, put the factor that seems easier to integrate in the *I* column and the other factor in the *D* column. Again, stop the table as soon as the product of the functions in the bottom row can be integrated.
- If your method doesn't work, try switching the functions in the *D* and *I* columns or try breaking the integrand into a product in a different way. If none of this works, maybe integration by parts isn't the technique to use on this problem. ■

7.1 EXERCISES

● denotes basic skills exercises

◆ denotes challenging exercises

Evaluate the integrals in Exercises 1–38.

1. ● $\int 2xe^x\,dx$ *hint* [see Example 1]

2. ● $\int 3xe^{-x}\,dx$

3. ● $\int(3x-1)e^{-x}\,dx$

4. ● $\int(1-x)e^x\,dx$

5. ● $\int(x^2-1)e^{2x}\,dx$

6. ● $\int(x^2+1)e^{-2x}\,dx$

7. ● $\int(x^2+1)e^{-2x+4}\,dx$

8. ● $\int(x^2+1)e^{3x+1}\,dx$

9. ● $\int(2-x)2^x\,dx$

10. ● $\int(3x-2)4^x\,dx$

11. ● $\int(x^2-1)3^{-x}\,dx$

12. ● $\int(1-x^2)2^{-x}\,dx$

13. $\int \frac{x^2 - x}{e^x} dx$ **14.** $\int \frac{2x+1}{e^{3x}} dx$

15. ● $\int x(x+2)^6 dx$ **16.** ● $\int x^2(x-1)^6 dx$

17. $\int \frac{x}{(x-2)^3} dx$ **18.** $\int \frac{x}{(x-1)^2} dx$

19. ● $\int x^3 \ln x\, dx$ *hint* [see Example 3]

20. ● $\int x^2 \ln x\, dx$

21. ● $\int (t^2+1)\ln(2t)\, dt$ **22.** ● $\int (t^2 - t)\ln(-t)\, dt$

23. ● $\int t^{1/3} \ln t\, dt$ **24.** ● $\int t^{-1/2} \ln t\, dt$

25. ● $\int \log_3 x\, dx$ **26.** ● $\int x \log_2 x\, dx$

27. $\int (xe^{2x} - 4e^{3x})\, dx$ **28.** $\int (x^2 e^{-x} + 2e^{-x+1})\, dx$

29. $\int (x^2 e^x - xe^{x^2})\, dx$ **30.** $\int [(2x+1)\, e^{x^2+x} - x^2 e^{2x+1}]\, dx$

31. ● $\int_0^1 (x+1)e^x\, dx$ **32.** ● $\int_{-1}^1 (x^2+x)e^{-x}\, dx$

33. ● $\int_0^1 x^2(x+1)^{10}\, dx$ **34.** ● $\int_0^1 x^3(x+1)^{10}\, dx$

35. ● $\int_1^2 x\ln(2x)\, dx$ **36.** ● $\int_1^2 x^2 \ln(3x)\, dx$

37. ● $\int_0^1 x\ln(x+1)\, dx$ **38.** ● $\int_0^1 x^2 \ln(x+1)\, dx$

39. ● Find the area bounded by the curve $y = xe^{-x}$, the x-axis, and the lines $x = 0$ and $x = 10$.

40. ● Find the area bounded by the curve $y = x\ln x$, the x-axis, and the lines $x = 1$ and $x = e$.

41. ● Find the area bounded by the curve $y = (x+1)\ln x$, the x-axis, and the lines $x = 1$ and $x = 2$.

42. ● Find the area bounded by the curve $y = (x-1)e^x$, the x-axis, and the lines $x = 0$ and $x = 2$.

Applications

43. ● ***Displacement*** A rocket rising from the ground has a velocity of $2000te^{-t/120}$ ft/s, after t seconds. How far does it rise in the first two minutes?

44. ● ***Sales*** Weekly sales of graphing calculators can be modeled by the equation

$$s(t) = 10 - te^{-t/20}$$

where s is the number of calculators sold per week after t weeks. How many graphing calculators (to the nearest unit) will be sold in the first 20 weeks?

45. ● ***Total Cost*** The marginal cost of the xth box of light bulbs is $10 + [\ln(x+1)]/(x+1)^2$, and the fixed cost is \$5000. Find the total cost to make x boxes of bulbs.

46. ● ***Total Revenue*** The marginal revenue for selling the xth box of light bulbs is $10 + 0.001x^2 e^{-x/100}$. Find the total revenue generated by selling 200 boxes of bulbs.

47. ***Revenue*** You have been raising the price of your *Lord of the Rings*® T-shirts by 50¢ per week, and sales have been falling continuously at a rate of 2% per week. Assuming you are now selling 50 T-shirts per week and charging \$10 per T-shirt, how much revenue will you generate during the coming year? (Round your answer to the nearest dollar.) [Hint: Weekly revenue = weekly sales × price per T-shirt.]

48. ***Revenue*** Luckily, sales of your *Star Wars*® T-shirts are now 50 T-shirts per week and increasing continuously at a rate of 5% per week. You are now charging \$10 per T-shirt and are decreasing the price by 50¢ per week. How much revenue will you generate during the next six weeks?

49. ***Bottled-Water Revenue*** U.S. sales of bottled water for the period 1993–2003 could be approximated by

$$q(t) = 17t^2 + 100t + 2300 \text{ million gallons per year} \quad (3 \le t \le 13)$$

where t is time in years since 1990.[2] Assume that the average price of a gallon of bottled water was \$3.00 in 1990 and that this price rose continuously at 3% per year. How much revenue was generated by sales of bottled water in the U.S. in the period 1993 to 2003? (Give your answer to the nearest \$10,000 million.)

50. ***Bottled-Water Revenue*** U.S. per capita sales of bottled water for the period 1993–2003 could be approximated by

$$Q(t) = 0.05t^2 + 0.4t + 9 \text{ gallons}$$

where t is the time in years since 1990.[3] Assume that the average price of a gallon of bottled water was \$3.00 in 1990 and that this price rose continuously at 3% per year. How much total revenue was generated per capita in the period 1993 to 2003? (Give your answer to the nearest \$100.)

Communication and Reasoning Exercises

51. ● Your friend Janice claims that integration by parts allows one to integrate any product of two functions. Prove her wrong by giving an example of a product of two functions that cannot be integrated using integration by parts.

52. ● Complete the following sentence in words: The integral of $u\, v$ is the first times the integral of the second minus the integral of _____.

[2] The authors' regression model, based on data in the Beverage Marketing Corporation news release, "Bottled water now number-two commercial beverage in U.S., says Beverage Marketing Corporation," April 8, 2004, available at www.beveragemarketing.com.

[3] Ibid.

53. If $p(x)$ is a polynomial of degree n and $f(x)$ is some function of x, how many times do we generally have to integrate $f(x)$ to compute $\int p(x)f(x)\,dx$?

54. Use integration by parts to show that $\int(\ln x)^2\,dx = x(\ln x)^2 - 2x\ln x + 2x + C$.

55. ◆ ***Hermite's Identity*** If $f(x)$ is a polynomial of degree n, show that

$$\int_0^b f(x)e^{-x}\,dx = F(0) - F(b)e^{-b}$$

where $F(x) = f(x) + f'(x) + f''(x) + \cdots + f^{(n)}(x)$ (this is the sum of f and all of its derivatives).

56. ◆ Write down a formula similar to Hermite's identity for $\int_0^b f(x)e^x\,dx$ when $f(x)$ is a polynomial of degree n.

● basic skills ◆ challenging

7.2 Area Between Two Curves and Applications

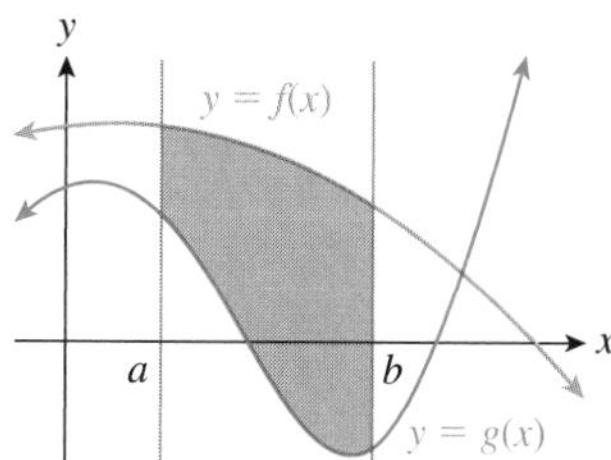

Figure **1**

As we saw in the preceding chapter, we can use the definite integral to calculate the area between the graph of a function and the x-axis. With only a little more work, we can use it to calculate the area between two graphs. Figure 1 shows the graphs of two functions, $f(x)$ and $g(x)$, with $f(x) \geq g(x)$ for every x in the interval $[a, b]$.

To find the shaded area between the graphs of the two functions, we use the following formula:

Area Between Two Graphs

If $f(x) \geq g(x)$ for all x in $[a, b]$, then the area of the region between the graphs of f and g and between $x = a$ and $x = b$ is given by

$$A = \int_a^b [f(x) - g(x)]\,dx$$

Let's look at an example and then discuss why the formula works.

Example 1 The Area Between Two Curves

Find the area of the region between $f(x) = -x^2 - 3x + 4$ and $g(x) = x^2 - 3x - 4$ and between $x = -1$ and $x = 1$.

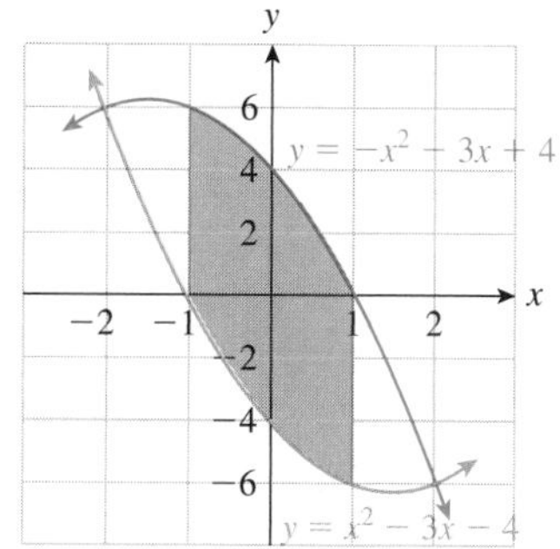

Figure **2**

Solution The area in question is shown in Figure 2. Because the graph of f lies above the graph of g in the interval $[-1, 1]$, we have $f(x) \geq g(x)$ for all x in $[-1, 1]$. Therefore, we can use the formula given above and calculate the area as follows:

$$\begin{aligned} A &= \int_{-1}^{1} [f(x) - g(x)]\,dx \\ &= \int_{-1}^{1} [(-x^2 - 3x + 4) - (x^2 - 3x - 4)]\,dx \\ &= \int_{-1}^{1} (8 - 2x^2)\,dx \\ &= \left[8x - \frac{2}{3}x^3\right]_{-1}^{1} \\ &= \frac{44}{3} \end{aligned}$$

Q: *Why does the formula for the area between two curves work?*

A: Let's go back once again to the general case illustrated in Figure 1, where we were given two functions f and g with $f(x) \geq g(x)$ for every x in the interval $[a, b]$. To avoid complicating the argument by the fact that the graph of g, or f, or both, may dip below the x-axis in the interval $[a, b]$ (as occurs in Figure 1 and also in Example 1), we shift both graphs vertically upward by adding a big enough constant M to lift them both above the x-axis in the interval $[a, b]$, as shown in Figure 3.

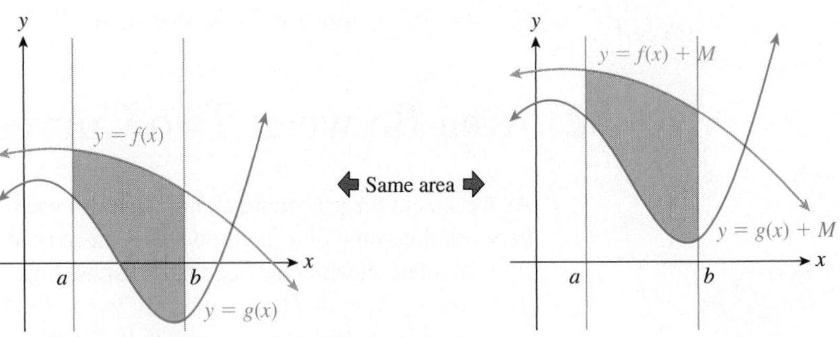

Figure **3**

As the figure illustrates, the area of the region between the graphs is not affected, so we will calculate the area of the region shown on the right of Figure 3. That calculation is shown in Figure 4.

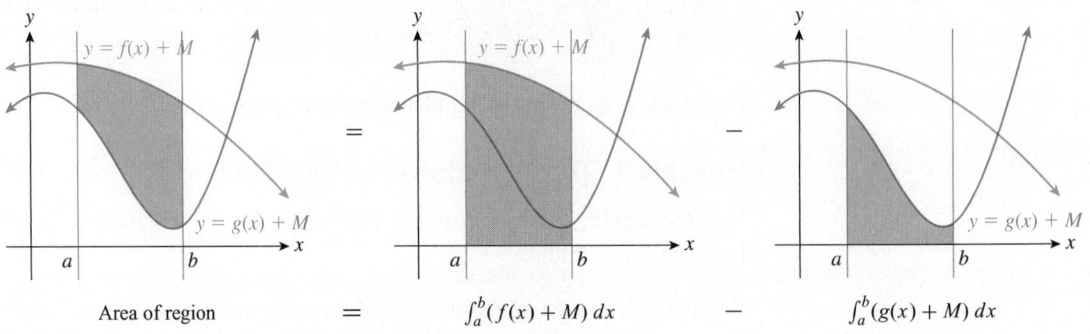

Figure **4**

From the figure, the area we want is

$$\int_a^b (f(x) + M)dx - \int_a^b (g(x) + M)dx = \int_a^b [(f(x) + M) - (g(x) + M)]dx$$

$$= \int_a^b [f(x) - g(x)]dx$$

which is the formula we gave originally. ■

So far, we've been assuming that $f(x) \geq g(x)$, so that the graph of f never dips below the graph of g and so the graphs cannot cross (although they can touch). Example 2 shows what happens when the two graphs *do* cross.

Example 2 Regions Enclosed by Crossing Curves

Find the area of the region between $y = 3x^2$ and $y = 1 - x^2$ and between $x = 0$ and $x = 1$.

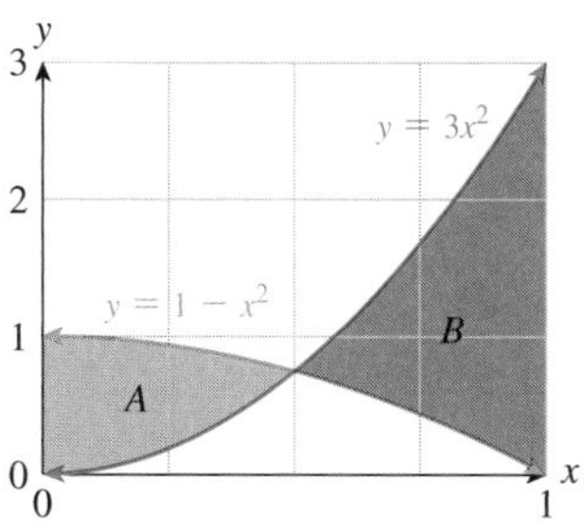

Figure 5

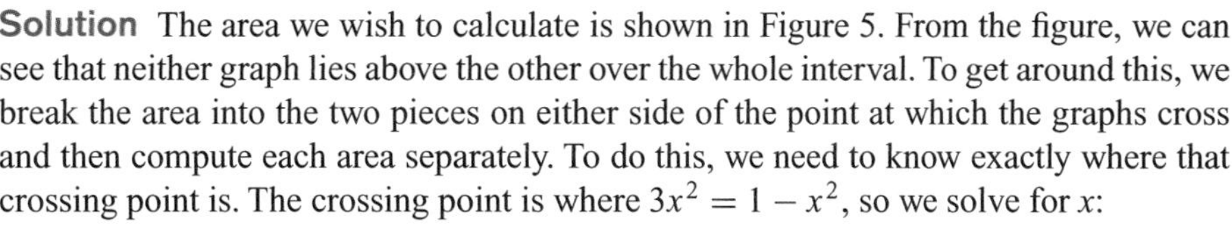

Solution The area we wish to calculate is shown in Figure 5. From the figure, we can see that neither graph lies above the other over the whole interval. To get around this, we break the area into the two pieces on either side of the point at which the graphs cross and then compute each area separately. To do this, we need to know exactly where that crossing point is. The crossing point is where $3x^2 = 1 - x^2$, so we solve for x:

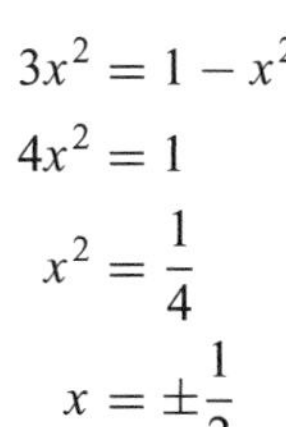

$$\begin{aligned} 3x^2 &= 1 - x^2 \\ 4x^2 &= 1 \\ x^2 &= \frac{1}{4} \\ x &= \pm\frac{1}{2} \end{aligned}$$

Because we are interested only in the interval [0, 1], the crossing point we're interested in is at $x = 1/2$.

Now, to compute the areas A and B, we need to know which graph is on top in each of these areas. We can see that from the figure, but what if the functions were more complicated and we could not easily draw the graphs? To be sure, we can test the values of the two functions at some point in each region. But we really need not worry. If we make the wrong choice for the top function, the integral will yield the negative of the area (why?), so we can simply take the absolute value of the integral to get the area of the region in question. For this example, we have

$$\begin{aligned} A &= \int_0^{1/2} [(1 - x^2) - 3x^2]\,dx = \int_0^{1/2} (1 - 4x^2)\,dx \\ &= \left[x - \frac{4x^3}{3}\right]_0^{1/2} \\ &= \left(\frac{1}{2} - \frac{1}{6}\right) - (0 - 0) = \frac{1}{3} \end{aligned}$$

and

$$\begin{aligned} B &= \int_{1/2}^{1} [3x^2 - (1 - x^2)]\,dx = \int_{1/2}^{1} (4x^2 - 1)\,dx \\ &= \left[\frac{4x^3}{3} - x\right]_{1/2}^{1} \\ &= \left(\frac{4}{3} - 1\right) - \left(\frac{1}{6} - \frac{1}{2}\right) = \frac{2}{3} \end{aligned}$$

This gives a total area of $A + B = \dfrac{1}{3} + \dfrac{2}{3} = 1$.

+ *Before we go on...* What would have happened in Example 2 if we had not broken the area into two pieces but had just calculated the integral of the difference of the two functions? We would have calculated

$$\int_0^1 [(1 - x^2) - 3x^2]\, dx = \int_0^1 [1 - 4x^2]\, dx = \left[x - \frac{4x^3}{3}\right]_0^1 = -\frac{1}{3}$$

which is not even close to the right answer. What this integral calculated was actually $A - B$ rather than $A + B$. Why? ■

Example 3 The Area Enclosed by Two Curves

Find the area enclosed by $y = x^2$ and $y = x^3$.

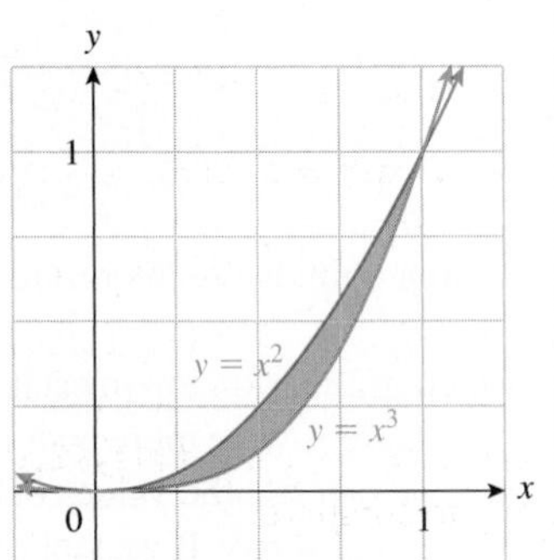

Figure 6

Solution This example has a new wrinkle: we are not told what interval to use for x. However, if we look at the graph in Figure 6, we see that the question can have only one meaning.

We are being asked to find the area of the shaded sliver, which is the only region that is actually *enclosed* by the two graphs. This sliver is bounded on either side by the two points where the graphs cross, so our first task is to find those points. They are the points where $x^2 = x^3$, so we solve for x:

$$x^2 = x^3$$
$$x^3 - x^2 = 0$$
$$x^2(x - 1) = 0$$
$$x = 0 \quad \text{or} \quad x = 1$$

Thus, we must integrate over the interval [0, 1]. Although we see from the diagram (or by substituting $x = 1/2$) that the graph of $y = x^2$ is above that of $y = x^3$, if we didn't notice that we might calculate

$$\int_0^1 (x^3 - x^2)\, dx = \left[\frac{x^4}{4} - \frac{x^3}{3}\right]_0^1 = -\frac{1}{12}$$

This tells us that the required area is $1/12$ square units and also that we had our integral reversed. Had we calculated $\int_0^1 (x^2 - x^3)\, dx$ instead, we would have found the correct answer, $1/12$, directly.

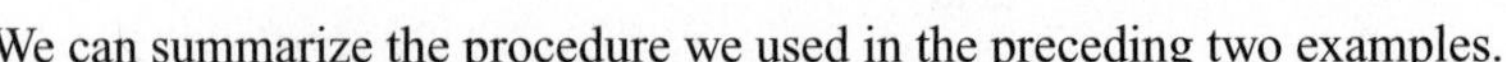

We can summarize the procedure we used in the preceding two examples.

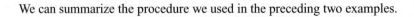

Finding the Area Between the Graphs of *f*(*x*) and *g*(*x*)

1. Find all points of intersection by solving $f(x) = g(x)$ for x. This either determines the interval over which you will integrate or breaks up a given interval into regions between the intersection points.
2. Determine the area of each region you found by integrating the difference of the larger and the smaller function. (If you accidentally take the smaller minus the larger, the integral will give the negative of the area, so just take the absolute value.)
3. Add together the areas you found in Step 2 to get the total area.

Q: Is there any quick and easy method to find the area between two graphs without having to find all points of intersection? What if it is hard or impossible to find out where the curves intersect?

A: We *can* use technology to give the approximate area between two graphs. First recall that, if $f(x) \geq g(x)$ for all x in $[a, b]$, then the area between their graphs over $[a, b]$ is given by $\int_a^b [f(x) - g(x)]dx$, whereas if $g(x) \geq f(x)$, the area is given by $\int_a^b [g(x) - f(x)]dx$. Notice that both expressions are equal to

$$\int_a^b |f(x) - g(x)|\,dx$$

telling us that we can use the same formula in both cases:

tech Ex

Area Between Two Graphs: Approximation using Technology

The area of the region between the graphs of f and g and between $x = a$ and $x = b$ is given by

$$A = \int_a^b |f(x) - g(x)|\,dx$$

quick **Example**

To approximate the area of the region between $y = 3x^2$ and $y = 1 - x^2$ and between $x = 0$ and $x = 1$ we calculated in Example 2, use technology to compute

$$\int_a^b |3x^2 - (1 - x^2)|\,dx = 1$$ TI-83/84: `fnInt(abs(3x^2-(1-x^2)),X,0,1)`

7.2 EXERCISES

● denotes basic skills exercises

tech Ex indicates exercises that should be solved using technology

Find the areas of the indicated regions in Exercises 1–24. (We suggest you use technology to check your answers.)

1. ● Between $y = x^2$ and $y = -1$ for x in $[-1, 1]$ *hint* [see Example 1]
2. ● Between $y = x^3$ and $y = -1$ for x in $[-1, 1]$
3. ● Between $y = -x$ and $y = x$ for x in $[0, 2]$
4. ● Between $y = -x$ and $y = x/2$ for x in $[0, 2]$
5. ● Between $y = x$ and $y = x^2$ for x in $[-1, 1]$ *hint* [see Example 2]
6. ● Between $y = x$ and $y = x^3$ for x in $[-1, 1]$
7. ● Between $y = e^x$ and $y = x$ for x in $[0, 1]$
8. ● Between $y = e^{-x}$ and $y = -x$ for x in $[0, 1]$
9. ● Between $y = (x - 1)^2$ and $y = -(x - 1)^2$ for x in $[0, 1]$
10. ● Between $y = x^2(x^3+1)^{10}$ and $y = -x(x^2 + 1)^{10}$ for x in $[0, 1]$
11. ● Enclosed by $y = x$ and $y = x^4$ *hint* [see Example 3]
12. ● Enclosed by $y = x$ and $y = -x^4$
13. ● Enclosed by $y = x^3$ and $y = x^4$
14. ● Enclosed by $y = x$ and $y = x^3$
15. ● Enclosed by $y = x^2$ and $y = x^4$
16. ● Enclosed by $y = x^4 - x^2$ and $y = x^2 - x^4$
17. ● Enclosed by $y = e^x$, $y = 2$, and the y-axis
18. ● Enclosed by $y = e^{-x}$, $y = 3$, and the y-axis
19. ● Enclosed by $y = \ln x$, $y = 2 - \ln x$, and $x = 4$

20. ● Enclosed by $y = \ln x$, $y = 1 - \ln x$, and $x = 4$

21. tech Ex Enclosed by $y = e^x$, $y = 2x + 1$, $x = -1$, and $x = 1$ (Round answer to four significant digits.) *hint* [see Quick Example p. 491]

22. tech Ex Enclosed by $y = 2^x$, $y = x + 2$, $x = -2$, and $x = 2$ (Round answer to four significant digits.)

23. tech Ex Enclosed by $y = \ln x$ and $y = \frac{x}{2} - \frac{1}{2}$ (Round answer to four significant digits.) [First use technology to determine approximately where the graphs cross.]

24. tech Ex Enclosed by $y = \ln x$ and $y = x - 2$ (Round answer to four significant digits.) [First use technology to determine approximately where the graphs cross.]

Applications

25. ● ***Revenue and Cost*** Suppose your daily revenue from selling used DVDs is

$$R(t) = 100 + 10t \qquad (0 \le t \le 5)$$

dollars per day, where t represents days from the beginning of the week, while your daily costs are

$$C(t) = 90 + 5t \qquad (0 \le t \le 5)$$

dollars per day. Find the area between the graphs of $R(t)$ and $C(t)$ for $0 \le t \le 5$. What does your answer represent?

26. ● ***Income and Expenses*** Suppose your annual income is

$$I(t) = 50{,}000 + 2000t \qquad (0 \le t \le 3)$$

dollars per year, where t represents the number of years since you began your job, while your annual expenses are

$$E(t) = 45{,}000 + 1500t \qquad (0 \le t \le 3)$$

dollars per year. Find the area between the graphs of $I(t)$ and $E(t)$ for $0 \le t \le 3$. What does your answer represent?

27. ***Foreign Trade*** Annual U.S. imports from China in the years 1996–2004 could be approximated by

$$I = t^2 + 3.5t + 50 \qquad (1 \le t \le 9)$$

billion dollars per year, where t represents time in years since the start of 1995. During the same period, annual U.S. exports to China could be approximated by

$$E = 0.4t^2 - 1.6t + 14 \qquad (1 \le t \le 9)$$

billion dollars per year.[4]

a. What does the area between the graphs of I and E over the interval [1, 9] represent?

b. Compute the area in part (a), and interpret your answer. (Round your answer to the nearest \$10 billion.)

28. ● ***Revenue*** Apple Computer, Inc.'s total revenue from the fourth quarter of 2002 through the third quarter of 2004 was flowing in at a rate of approximately

$$R_t = 5t^2 + 70t + 1500 \qquad (-1 \le t \le 6)$$

million dollars per quarter, where t is time in quarters since the first quarter of 2003. During the same period, revenue from sales of iPods alone flowed in at a rate of approximately

$$R_i = 2.6t^2 + 22t + 60 \qquad (-1 \le t \le 6)$$

million dollars per quarter.[5]

a. What does the area between the graphs of R_t and R_i over the interval [0, 6] represent?

b. Compute the area in part (a) and interpret your answer. (Round your answer to the nearest \$100 million.)

29. ***Health-Care Spending*** The rate of private spending (including from insurance) on health care in the U.S. from 1965 through 2002 was approximately

$$P(t) = 20t^3 + 1000t^2 + 28{,}000t + 360{,}000 \qquad (-25 \le t \le 12)$$

million dollars per year, where t is the number of years since 1990. The rate of spending on health care in the U.S. from 1965 through 2002 by private insurance only was approximately

$$I(t) = 15t^3 + 800t^2 + 19{,}000t + 200{,}000 \qquad (-25 \le t \le 12)$$

million dollars per year.[6] Take these functions as projections of spending rates through 2010.

a. Use these models to project the total spent on health care from private funds other than insurance from 2000 to 2010. (Round your answer to the nearest \$100 billion.)

b. How does your answer to part (a) relate to the area between two curves?

30. ***Health-Care Spending*** The rate of public spending (including by the federal government) on health care in the U.S. from 1965 through 2002 was approximately

$$G(t) = 17t^3 + 900t^2 + 24{,}000t + 270{,}000 \qquad (-25 \le t \le 12)$$

million dollars per year, where t is the number of years since 1990. The rate of spending on health care by the federal government only was approximately

$$F(t) = 11t^3 + 600t^2 + 17{,}000t + 190{,}000 \qquad (-25 \le t \le 12)$$

[4] The models are based on quadratic regression using data from the U.S. Census Bureau Foreign Trade Division website www.census.gov/foreign-trade/sitcl as of December 2004.

[5] Based on a quadratic regression. Source for data: Apple Computer, Inc., quarterly earnings reports, available at www.apple.com.

[6] SOURCE: Centers for Medicare and Medicaid Services, "National Health Expenditures," 2002 version, released January 2004; www.cms.hhs.gov/statistics/nhe.

million dollars per year.[7] Take these functions as projections of spending rates through 2010.

a. Use these models to project the total public spending on health care, excluding spending by the federal government, from 2000 to 2010. (Round your answer to the nearest \$100 billion.)

b. How does your answer to part (a) relate to the area between two curves?

Communication and Reasoning Exercises

31. ● The following graph shows Canada's annual exports and imports for the period 1997–2001.[8]

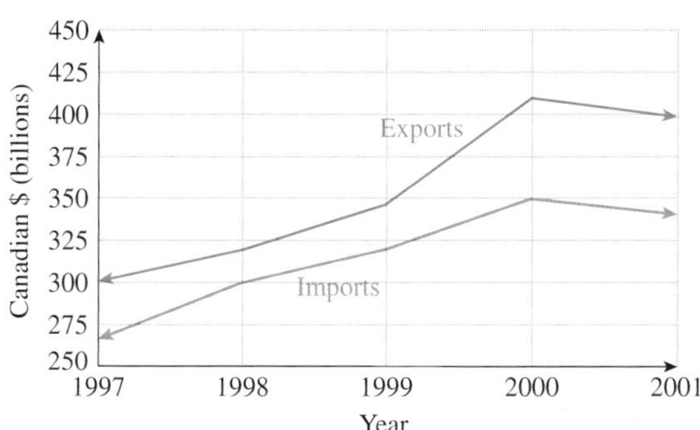

What does the area between the export and import curves represent?

32. ● The following graph shows a fictitious country's monthly exports and imports for the period 1997–2001.

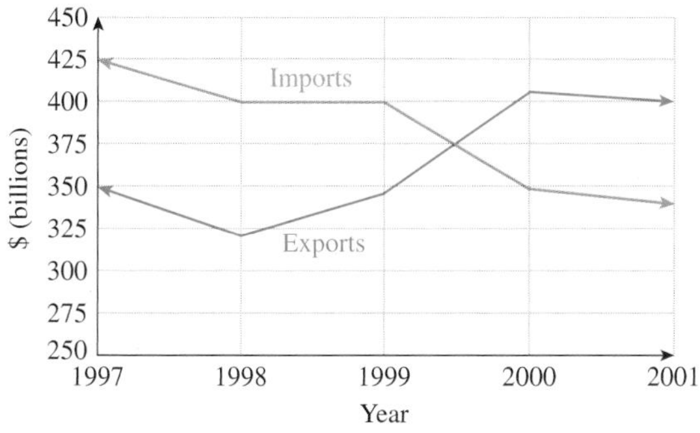

What does the total area enclosed by the export and import curves represent, and what does the definite integral of the difference, Exports – Imports, represent?

33. The following graph shows the daily revenue and cost in your Adopt-a-Chia operation t days from its inception:

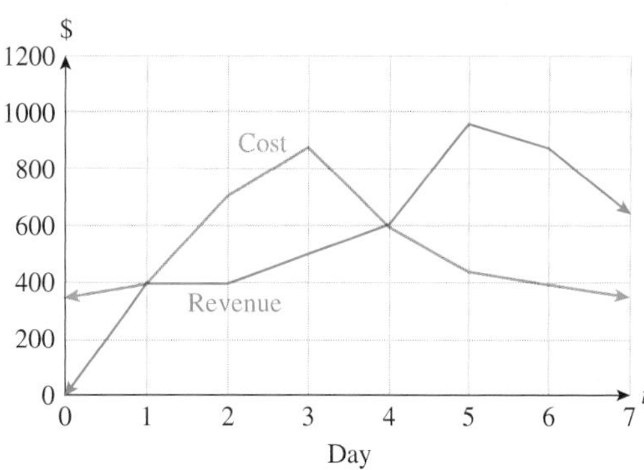

Multiple Choice: The area between the cost and revenue curves represents:

(A) The accumulated loss through day 4 plus the accumulated profit for days 5 through 7

(B) The accumulated profit for the week

(C) The accumulated loss for the week

(D) The accumulated cost through day 4 plus the accumulated revenue for days 5 through 7

34. The following graph shows daily orders and inventory (stock on hand) for your Mona Lisa paint-by-number sets t days into last week.

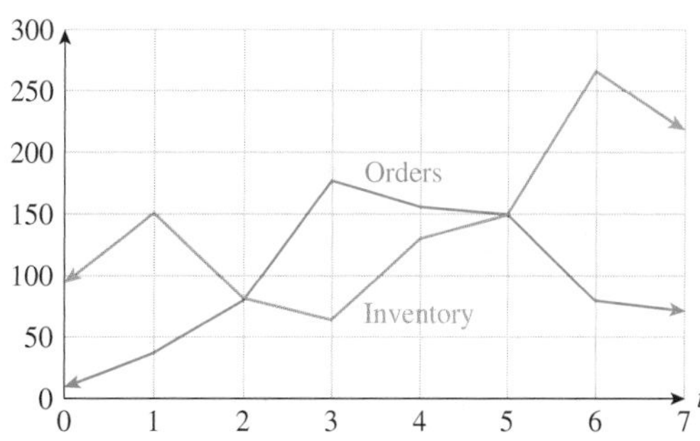

a. Multiple Choice: Which is greatest:

(A) $\int_0^7 (\text{Orders} - \text{Inventory})\, dt$

(B) $\int_0^7 (\text{Inventory} - \text{Orders})\, dt$

(C) The area between the Orders and Inventory curves.

b. Multiple Choice: The answer to part (a) measures

(A) The accumulated gap between orders and inventory

(B) The accumulated surplus through day 3 minus the accumulated shortage for days 3 through 5 plus the accumulated surplus through days 6 through 7

(C) The total net surplus

(D) The total net loss

[7] SOURCE: Centers for Medicare and Medicaid Services, "National Health Expenditures," 2002 version, released January 2004; www.cms.hhs.gov/statistics/nhe.

[8] SOURCE: http://strategis.ic.gc.ca, August, 2002.

35. What is wrong with the following claim: "I purchased Consolidated Edison shares for \$40 at the beginning of January, 2002. My total profit per share from this investment from January through July is represented by the area between the stock price curve and the purchase price curve as shown on the following graph."[9]

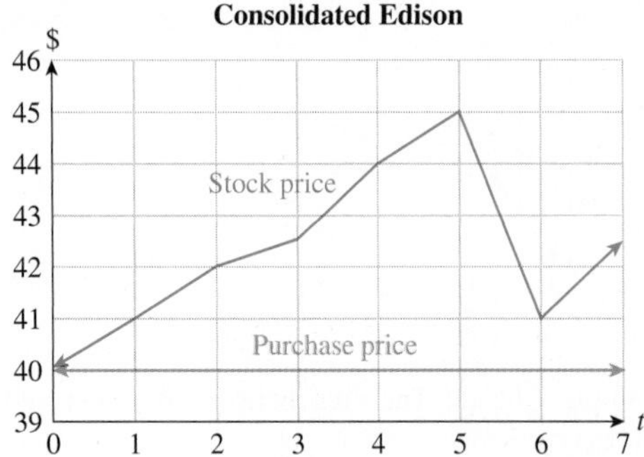

[9] Source: http://money.excite.com, August 5, 2002.

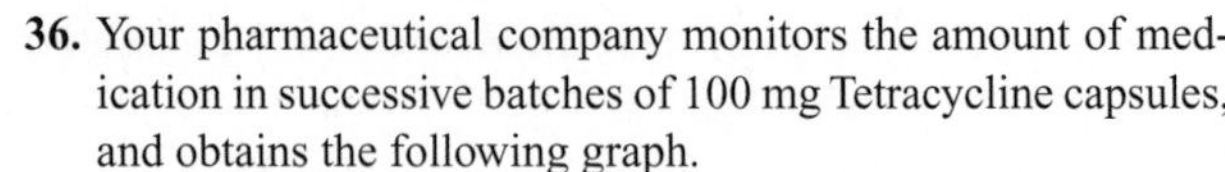

36. Your pharmaceutical company monitors the amount of medication in successive batches of 100 mg Tetracycline capsules, and obtains the following graph.

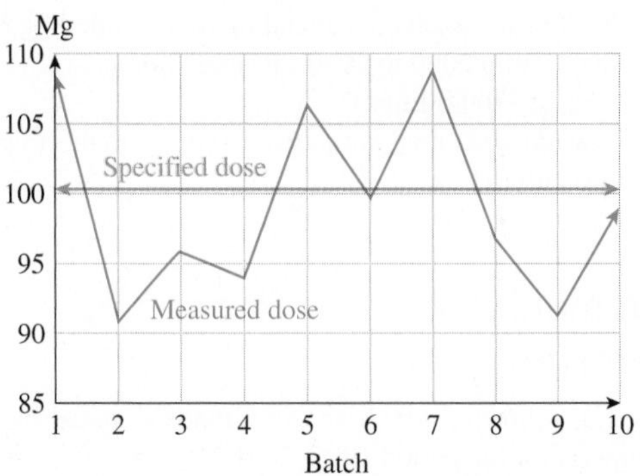

Your production manager claims that the batches of tetracycline conform to the exact dosage requirement because half of the area between the graphs is above the Specified Dose line and half is below it. Comment on this reasoning.

● basic skills **tech Ex** technology exercise

7.3 Averages and Moving Averages

Averages

To find the average of, say, 20 numbers, we simply add them up and divide by 20. More generally, if we want to find the **average,** or **mean,** of the n numbers $y_1, y_2, y_3, \ldots, y_n$, we add them up and divide by n. We write this average as $\bar{y}$ ("y-bar").

Average, or Mean, of a Collection of Values

$$\bar{y} = \frac{y_1 + y_2 + \cdots + y_n}{n}$$

quick Example

The average of $\{0, 2, -1, 5\}$ is $\bar{y} = \frac{0+2-1+5}{4} = \frac{6}{4} = 1.5$

But, we also use the word *average* in other senses. For example, we speak of the average speed of a car during a trip.

Example 1 Average Speed

Over the course of 2 hours, my speed varied from 50 miles per hour to 60 miles per hour, following the function $v(t) = 50 + 2.5t^2$, $0 \le t \le 2$. What was my average speed over those two hours?

Solution Recall that average speed is simply the total distance traveled divided by the time it took. Recall, also, that we can find the distance traveled by integrating the speed:

$$\begin{aligned}\text{Distance traveled} &= \int_0^2 v(t)\,dt \\ &= \int_0^2 (50 + 2.5t^2)\,dt \\ &= \left[50t + \frac{2.5}{3}t^3\right]_0^2 \\ &= 100 + \frac{20}{3} \\ &\approx 106.67 \text{ miles}\end{aligned}$$

It took 2 hours to travel this distance, so the average speed was

$$\text{Average speed} \approx \frac{106.67}{2} \approx 53.3 \text{ mph}$$

In general, if we travel with velocity $v(t)$ from time $t = a$ to time $t = b$, we will travel a distance of $\int_a^b v(t)\,dt$ in time $b - a$, which gives an average velocity of

$$\text{Average velocity} = \frac{1}{b-a}\int_a^b v(t)\,dt$$

Thinking of this calculation as finding the average value of the velocity function, we generalize and make the following definition:

Average Value of a Function

The **average,** or **mean,** of a function $f(x)$ on an interval $[a, b]$ is

$$\bar{f} = \frac{1}{b-a}\int_a^b f(x)\,dx$$

quick **Example** The average of $f(x) = x$ on $[1, 5]$ is

$$\begin{aligned}\bar{f} &= \frac{1}{b-a}\int_a^b f(x)\,dx \\ &= \frac{1}{5-1}\int_1^5 x\,dx \\ &= \frac{1}{4}\left[\frac{x^2}{2}\right]_1^5 = \frac{1}{4}\left(\frac{25}{2} - \frac{1}{2}\right) = 3\end{aligned}$$

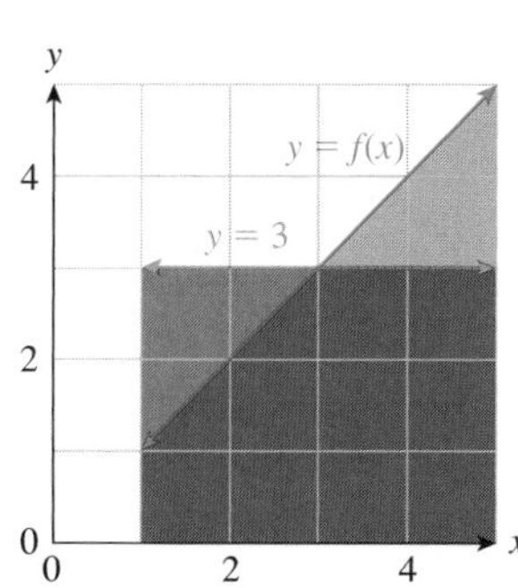

Figure 7

Interpreting the Average of a Function Geometrically

The average of a function has a geometric interpretation. Referring to the Quick Example above, we can compare the graph of $y = f(x)$ with the graph of $y = 3$, both over the interval $[1, 5]$ (Figure 7).

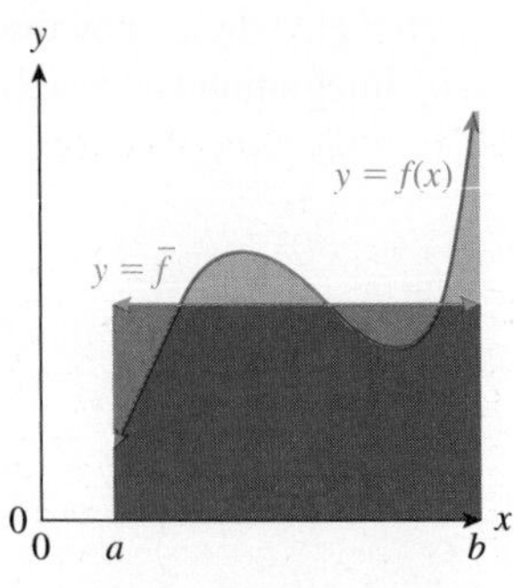

Figure **8**

We can find the area under the graph of $f(x) = x$ by geometry or by calculus; it is 12. The area in the rectangle under $y = 3$ is also 12.

In general, the average $\bar{f}$ of a positive function over the interval $[a, b]$ gives the height of the rectangle over the interval $[a, b]$ that has the same area as the area under the graph of $f(x)$ as illustrated in Figure 8. The equality of these areas follows from the equation

$$(b-a)\bar{f} = \int_a^b f(x)\,dx$$

Example **2** Average Balance

A savings account at the People's Credit Union pays 3% interest, compounded continuously, and at the end of the year you get a bonus of 1% of the average balance in the account during the year. If you deposit \$10,000 at the beginning of the year, how much interest and how large a bonus will you get?

Solution We can use the continuous compound interest formula to calculate the amount of money you have in the account at time t:

$$A(t) = 10{,}000e^{0.03t}$$

where t is measured in years. At the end of 1 year, the account will have

$$A(1) = \$10{,}304.55$$

so you will have earned \$304.55 interest. To compute the bonus, we need to find the average amount in the account, which is the average of $A(t)$ over the interval $[0, 1]$. Thus,

$$\begin{aligned}\bar{A} &= \frac{1}{b-a}\int_a^b A(t)\,dt \\ &= \frac{1}{1-0}\int_0^1 10{,}000e^{0.03t}\,dt = \frac{10{,}000}{0.03}\left[e^{0.03t}\right]_0^1 \\ &\approx \$10{,}151.51\end{aligned}$$

The bonus is 1% of this, or \$101.52.

+*Before we go on...* The 1% bonus in Example 2 was one-third of the total interest. Why did this happen? What fraction of the total interest would the bonus be if the interest rate was 4%, 5%, or 10%? ■

Moving Averages

Suppose you follow the performance of a company's stock by recording the daily closing prices. The graph of these prices may seem jagged or "jittery" due to random day-to-day fluctuations. To see any trends, you would like a way to "smooth out" these data. The **moving average** is one common way to do that.

Example 3 Stock Prices

The following table shows Colossal Conglomerate's closing stock prices for 20 consecutive trading days:

Day	1	2	3	4	5	6	7	8	9	10
Price	20	22	21	24	24	23	25	26	20	24
Day	11	12	13	14	15	16	17	18	19	20
Price	26	26	25	27	28	27	29	27	25	24

Plot these prices and the 5-day moving average.

Solution The 5-day moving average is the average of each day's price together with the prices of the preceding 4 days. We can compute the 5-day moving averages starting on the fifth day. We get these numbers:

Day	1	2	3	4	5	6	7	8	9	10
Moving Average					22.2	22.8	23.4	24.4	23.6	23.6
Day	11	12	13	14	15	16	17	18	19	20
Moving Average	24.2	24.4	24.2	25.6	26.4	26.6	27.2	27.6	27.2	26.4

The closing stock prices and moving averages are plotted in Figure 9.

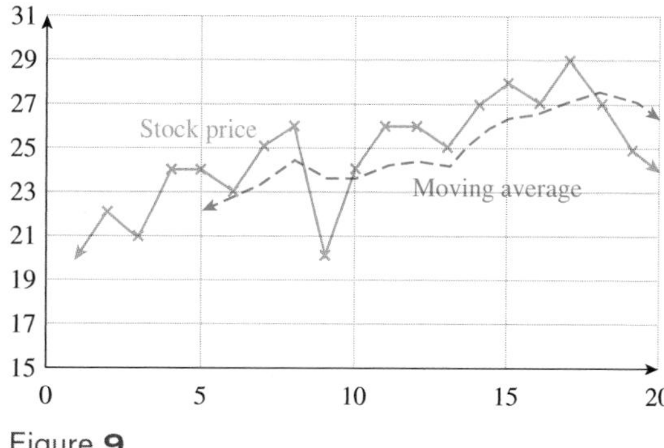

Figure 9

We can automate these computations using a graphing calculator or Excel. See the Technology Guides at the end of the chapter to find out how to tabulate and graph moving averages.

As you can see, the moving average is less volatile than the closing price. Because the moving average incorporates the stock's performance over 5 days at a time, a single day's fluctuation is smoothed out. Look at day 9 in particular. The moving average also tends to lag behind the actual performance because it takes past history into account. Look at the downturns at days 6 and 18 in particular.

The period of 5 days for a moving average, as used in Example 3, is arbitrary. Using a longer period of time would smooth the data more but increase the lag. For data used as economic indicators, such as housing prices or retail sales, it is common to compute the 4-quarter moving average to smooth out seasonal variations.

It is also sometimes useful to compute moving averages of continuous functions. We may want to do this if we use a mathematical model of a large collection of data. Also, some physical systems have the effect of converting an input function (an electrical signal, for example) into its moving average. By an **n-unit moving average** of a function $f(x)$ we mean the function $\bar{f}$ for which $\bar{f}(x)$ is the average of the value of $f(x)$ on $[x-n, x]$. Using the formula for the average of a function, we get the following formula.

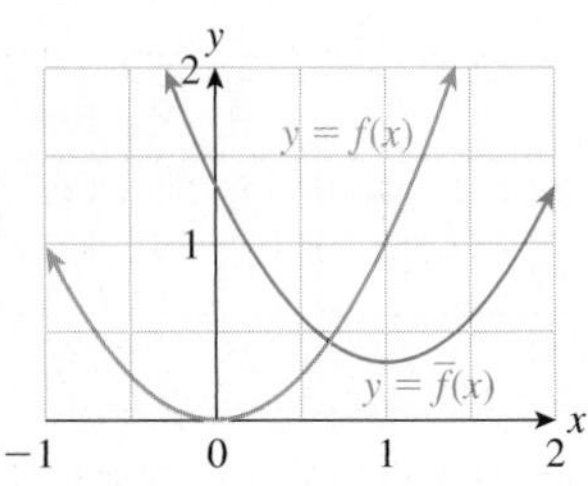

Figure **10**

n-Unit Moving Average of a Function

The n-unit moving average of a function f is

$$\bar{f}(x) = \frac{1}{n}\int_{x-n}^{x} f(t)\, dt$$

quick Example

The 2-unit moving average of $f(x) = x^2$ is

$$\bar{f}(x) = \frac{1}{2}\int_{x-2}^{x} t^2\, dt = \frac{1}{6}[t^3]_{x-2}^{x} = x^2 - 2x + \frac{4}{3}$$

The graphs of $f(x)$ and $\bar{f}(x)$ are shown in Figure 10.

tech Ex

Example 4 Moving Average via Technology

Use technology to plot the 3-unit moving average of

$$f(x) = \frac{x}{1+|x|} \qquad (-5 \le x \le 5)$$

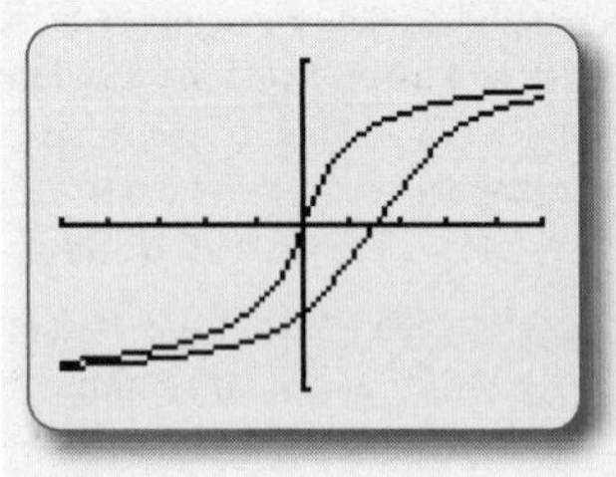
Figure **11**

Solution This function is a little tricky to integrate analytically because $|x|$ is defined differently for positive and negative values of x, so instead we use technology to approximate the integral. Figure 11 shows the output we can obtain using a TI-83/84 graphing calculator (the lower curve is the moving average). See the TI 83/84 Technology Guide at the end of the chapter to find out how to obtain this output.

7.3 EXERCISES

● denotes basic skills exercises

tech Ex indicates exercises that should be solved using technology

Find the averages of the functions in Exercises 1–6 over the given intervals. Plot each function and its average on the same graph (as in Figure 7). *hint* [see Quick Example p. 495]

1. ● $f(x) = x^3$ over $[0, 2]$

2. ● $f(x) = x^3$ over $[-1, 1]$

3. ● $f(x) = x^3 - x$ over $[0, 2]$

4. ● $f(x) = x^3 - x$ over $[0, 1]$

5. ● $f(x) = e^{-x}$ over $[0, 2]$

6. ● $f(x) = e^x$ over $[-1, 1]$

In Exercises 7 and 8, complete the given table with the values of the 3-unit moving average of the given function. *hint* [see Example 3]

7. ●

x	0	1	2	3	4	5	6	7
$r(x)$	3	5	10	3	2	5	6	7
$\bar{r}(x)$								

8. ●

x	0	1	2	3	4	5	6	7
$s(x)$	2	9	7	3	2	5	7	1
$\bar{s}(x)$								

In Exercises 9 and 10, some values of a function and its 3-unit moving average are given. Supply the missing information.

9. ●

x	0	1	2	3	4	5	6	7
$r(x)$	1	2			11		10	2
$\bar{r}(x)$			3	5		11		

10. ●

x	0	1	2	3	4	5	6	7
$s(x)$	1	5		1				
$\bar{s}(x)$			5		5	2	3	2

Calculate the 5-unit moving average of each function in Exercises 11–18. Plot each function and its moving average on the same graph, as in Example 4. (You may use graphing technology for these plots, but you should compute the moving averages analytically.) hint [see Quick Example p. 498]

11. ● $f(x) = x^3$
12. ● $f(x) = x^3 - x$
13. ● $f(x) = x^{2/3}$
14. ● $f(x) = x^{2/3} + x$
15. ● $f(x) = e^{0.5x}$
16. ● $f(x) = e^{-0.02x}$
17. ● $f(x) = \sqrt{x}$
18. ● $f(x) = x^{1/3}$

In Exercises 19–22, use graphing technology to plot the given functions together with their 3-unit moving averages. hint [see Example 4]

19. tech Ex $f(x) = \dfrac{10x}{1+5|x|}$
20. tech Ex $f(x) = \dfrac{1}{1+e^x}$
21. tech Ex $f(x) = \ln(1+x^2)$
22. tech Ex $f(x) = e^{1-x^2}$

Applications

23. ● ***Employment*** The following table shows the approximate number of people employed each year in the U.S. during the period 1995–2004[10]:

Year t	1995	1996	1997	1998	1999	2000	2001	2002	2003	2004
Employment (millions)	117	120	123	126	129	132	132	130	130	131

What was the average number of people employed in the U.S. for the years 1995 through 2004? hint [see Quick Example p. 494]

24. ● ***Cell Phone Sales*** The following table shows the net sales (revenue) of the Finnish cell phone company Nokia for each year in the period 1999–2003[11]:

Year t	1999	2000	2001	2002	2003
Nokia net sales (billions of euros)	20	30	31	30	29

What were Nokia's average net sales for the years 1999 through 2003?

25. ● ***Television Advertising*** The cost, in millions of dollars, of a 30-second television ad during the Super Bowl in the years 1998 to 2001 can be approximated by

$$C(t) = 0.355t - 1.6 \text{ million dollars} \quad (8 \le t \le 11)$$

($t = 8$ represents 1998).[12] What was the average cost of a Super Bowl ad during the given period? hint [see Example 1]

26. ● ***Television Advertising*** The cost, in millions of dollars, of a 30-second television ad during the Super Bowl in the years 1990 to 1998 can be approximated by

$$C(t) = 0.08t + 0.6 \text{ million dollars} \quad (0 \le t \le 8)$$

($t = 0$ represents 1990).[13] What was the average cost of a Super Bowl ad during the given period?

27. ● ***Investments*** If you invest \$10,000 at 8% interest compounded continuously, what is the average amount in your account over one year? hint [see Example 2]

28. ● ***Investments*** If you invest \$10,000 at 12% interest compounded continuously, what is the average amount in your account over one year?

29. ● ***Average Balance*** Suppose you have an account (paying no interest) into which you deposit \$3000 at the beginning of each month. You withdraw money continuously so that the amount in the account decreases linearly to 0 by the end of the month. Find the average amount in the account over a period of several months. (Assume that the account starts at \$0 at $t = 0$ months.)

30. ● ***Average Balance*** Suppose you have an account (paying no interest) into which you deposit \$4000 at the beginning of each month. You withdraw \$3000 during the course of each month, in such a way that the amount decreases linearly. Find the average amount in the account in the first two months. (Assume that the account starts at \$0 at $t = 0$ months.)

31. ● ***Employment*** Refer back to Exercise 23. Complete the following table by computing the 4-year moving average of employment in the U.S. Round each average to the nearest whole number.

Year t	1995	1996	1997	1998	1999	2000	2001	2002	2003	2004
Employment (millions)	117	120	123	126	129	132	132	130	130	131
Moving average (millions)										

How do the year-by-year changes in the moving average compare with those in the employment figures? hint [see Example 3]

[10] The values represent nonfarm employment. SOURCE: U.S. Bureau of Labor Statistics, Division of Current Employment Statistics, http://bls.gov/ces, January 13, 2005.

[11] SOURCE: Nokia financial statements downloaded from www.nokia.com, January 13, 2005.

[12] SOURCE: *New York Times*, January 26, 2001, p. C1.

[13] Ibid.

32. ● ***Cell Phone Sales*** Refer back to Exercise 24. Complete the following table by computing the 3-year moving average of Nokia's net sales. Round each average to the nearest whole number.

Year t	1999	2000	2001	2002	2003
Nokia net sales (billions of euros)	20	30	31	30	29
Moving Average (billions of euros)					

Is the average of the moving averages the same as the overall average? Explain.

33. tech Ex ***Health-Care Spending*** The following table shows approximate public spending on health care in the U.S. in the years 1981–2000, in billions of dollars.[14]

1981	**1982**	**1983**	**1984**	**1985**	**1986**	**1987**	**1988**	**1989**	**1990**
121	134	147	161	175	190	209	226	252	282
1991	**1992**	**1993**	**1994**	**1995**	**1996**	**1997**	**1998**	**1999**	**2000**
321	359	390	427	457	482	504	521	553	595

a. Use technology to compute and plot the 5-year moving average of these data.

b. The graph of the moving average will appear almost linear over the range 1991–1997. Use the 1991 and 1997 moving average figures to give an estimate (to the nearest billion dollars per year) of the rate of change of public spending on health care in the U.S. for the period 1991–1997. Interpret the result.

34. tech Ex ***Health-Care Spending*** The following table shows approximate private spending on health care in the U.S. in the years 1981–2000, in billions of dollars.[15]

1981	**1982**	**1983**	**1984**	**1985**	**1986**	**1987**	**1988**	**1989**	**1990**
160	190	210	230	250	270	290	330	370	410
1991	**1992**	**1993**	**1994**	**1995**	**1996**	**1997**	**1998**	**1999**	**2000**
440	470	500	510	530	560	590	630	670	710

a. Use technology to compute and plot the 5-year moving average of these data.

b. The graph of the moving average will appear almost linear over the range 1993–2000. Use the 1993 and 2000 moving average figures to give an estimate (to the nearest 10 billion dollars per year) of the rate of change of private spending on health care in the U.S. for the period 1993–2000. Interpret the result.

35. ● ***Bottled-Water Sales*** The rate of U.S. sales of bottled water for the period 1993–2003 could be approximated by

$$R(t) = 17t^2 + 100t + 2300 \text{ million gallons per year} \quad (3 \le t \le 13)$$

where t is time in years since 1990.[16]

a. Compute the average annual sales of bottled water over the period 1993–2003, to the nearest 100 million gallons per year.

b. Compute the two-year moving average of R. (You need not simplify the answer.)

c. Without simplifying the answer in part (b), say what kind of function the moving average is.

hint [see Quick Examples p. 495, 498]

36. ● ***Bottled-Water Sales*** The rate of U.S. per capita sales of bottled water for the period 1993–2003 could be approximated by

$$Q(t) = 0.05t^2 + 0.4t + 9 \text{ gallons per year}$$

where t is the time in years since 1990.[17] Repeat the preceding exercise as applied to per capita sales. (Give your answer to (a) to the nearest gallon per year.)

37. ● ***Medicare Spending*** Annual federal spending on Medicare (in constant 2000 dollars) was projected to increase from \$240 billion in 2000 to \$600 billion in 2025.[18]

a. Use this information to express s, the annual spending on Medicare (in billions of dollars), as a linear function of t, the number of years since 2000.

b. Find the 4-year moving average of your model.

c. What can you say about the slope of the moving average?

38. ● ***Pasta Imports*** In 1990, the United States imported 290 million pounds of pasta. From 1990 to 2001 imports increased by an average of 40 million pounds per year.[19]

a. Use these data to express q, the annual U.S. imports of pasta (in millions of pounds), as a linear function of t, the number of years since 1990.

[14] SOURCE: Centers for Medicare and Medicaid Services, "National Health Expenditures," 2002 version, released January 2004; www.cms.hhs.gov/statistics/nhe.

[15] Ibid.

[16] The authors' regression model, based on data in the Beverage Marketing Corporation news release, "Bottled water now number-two commercial beverage in U.S., says Beverage Marketing Corporation," April 8, 2004, available at www.beveragemarketing.com.

[17] Ibid.

[18] Data are rounded. SOURCE: The Urban Institute's Analysis of the 1999 Trustee's Report www.urban.org.

[19] Data are rounded. SOURCES: Department of Commerce/*New York Times*, September 5, 1995, p. D4, International Trade Administration (www.ita.doc.gov) March 31, 2002.

b. Find the 4-year moving average of your model.

c. What can you say about the slope of the moving average?

39. ***Moving Average of a Linear Function*** Find a formula for the a-unit moving average of a general linear function $f(x) = mx + b$.

40. ***Moving Average of an Exponential Function*** Find a formula for the a-unit moving average of a general exponential function $f(x) = Ae^{kx}$.

41. ***Fair Weather***[20] The Cancun Royal Hotel's advertising brochure features the following chart, showing the year-round temperature:

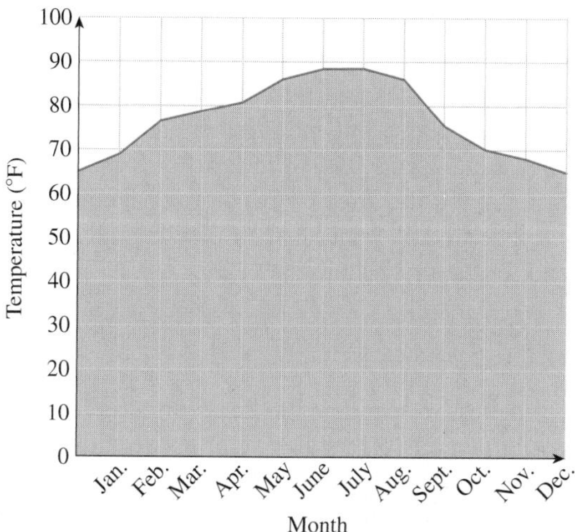

a. Estimate and plot the two- and three-month moving averages. (Use graphing technology, if available.)

b. What can you say about the 24-month moving average?

c. Comment on the limitations of a quadratic model for these data.

42. ***Foul Weather*** Repeat the preceding exercise, using the following data from the Tough Traveler Lodge in Frigidville:

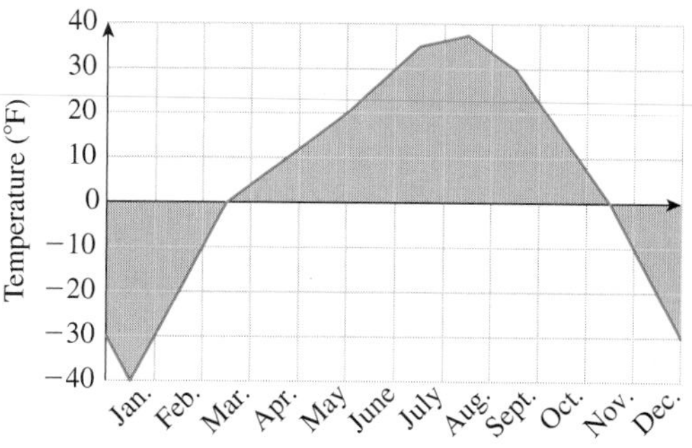

[20] Inspired by an exercise in the Harvard Consortium Calculus project.

Communication and Reasoning Exercises

43. ● Explain why it is sometimes more useful to consider the moving average of a stock price rather than the stock price itself.

44. ● Your monthly salary has been increasing steadily for the past year, and your average monthly salary over the past year was x dollars. Would you have earned more money if you had been paid x dollars per month? Explain your answer.

45. What property does a (nonconstant) function have if its average value over an interval is zero? Sketch a graph of such a function.

46. Can the average value of a function f on an interval be greater than its value at every point in that interval? Explain.

47. Criticize the following claim: The average value of a function on an interval is midway between its highest and lowest value.

48. Your manager tells you that 12-month moving averages gives at least as much information as shorter-term moving averages and very often more. How would you argue that he is wrong?

49. Which of the following most closely approximates the original function, (A) its 10-unit moving average, (B) its 1-unit moving average, or (C) its 0.8-unit moving average? Explain your answer.

50. Is an increasing function larger or smaller than its 1-unit moving average? Explain.

● basic skills   tech Ex technology exercise

7.4 Applications to Business and Economics: Consumers' and Producers' Surplus and Continuous Income Streams (OPTIONAL)

Consumers' Surplus

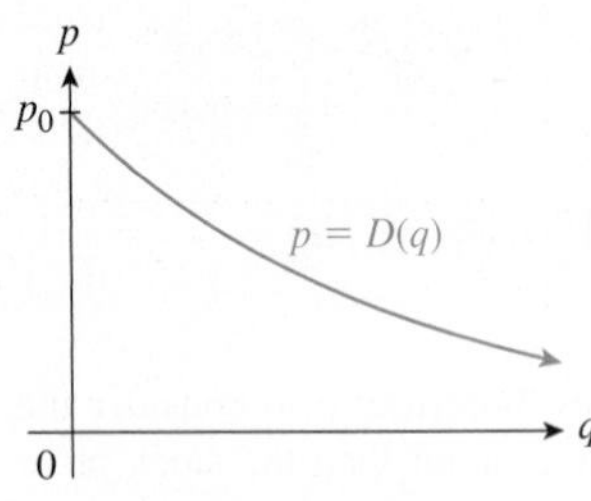

Figure **12**

Consider a general demand curve presented, as is traditional in economics, as $p = D(q)$, where p is unit price and q is demand measured, say, in annual sales (Figure 12). Thus, $D(q)$ is the price at which the demand will be q units per year. The price p_0 shown on the graph is the highest price that customers are willing to pay.

Suppose, for example, that the graph is the demand curve for a particular new model of computer. When the computer first comes out and supplies are low (q is small), "early adopters" will be willing to pay a high price. This is the part of the graph on the left, near the p axis. As supplies increase and the price drops, more consumers will be willing to pay and more computers will be sold. We can ask the following question: How much are consumers willing to spend for the first $\bar{q}$ units?

Consumers' Willingness to Spend

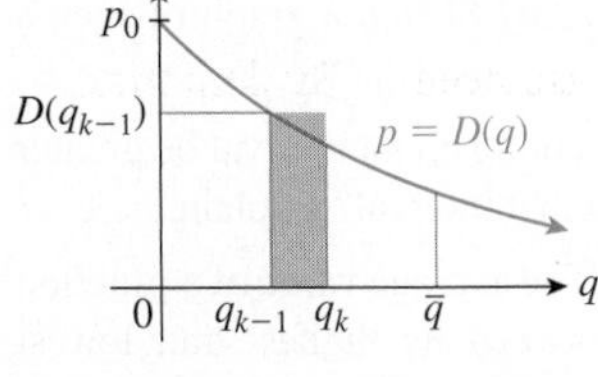

Figure **13**

We can approximate consumers' willingness to spend on the first $\bar{q}$ units as follows. We partition the interval $[0, \bar{q}\,]$ into n subintervals of equal length, as we did when discussing Riemann sums. Figure 13 shows a typical subinterval, $[q_{k-1}, q_k]$.

The price consumers are willing to pay for each of units q_{k-1} through q_k is approximately $D(q_{k-1})$, so the total that consumers are willing to spend for these units is approximately $D(q_{k-1})(q_k - q_{k-1}) = D(q_{k-1})\Delta q$, the area of the shaded region in Figure 13. Thus, the total amount that consumers are willing to spend for items 0 through $\bar{q}$ is

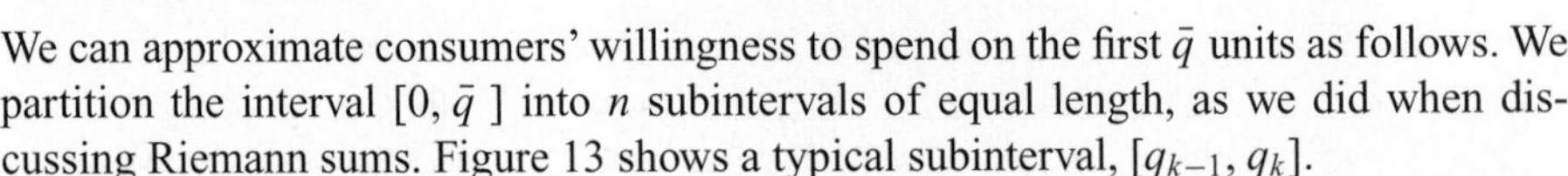

$$W \approx D(q_0)\Delta q + D(q_1)\Delta q + \cdots + D(q_{n-1})\Delta q = \sum_{k=0}^{n-1} D(q_k)\Delta q$$

which is a Riemann sum. The approximation becomes better the larger n becomes, and in the limit the Riemann sums converge to the integral

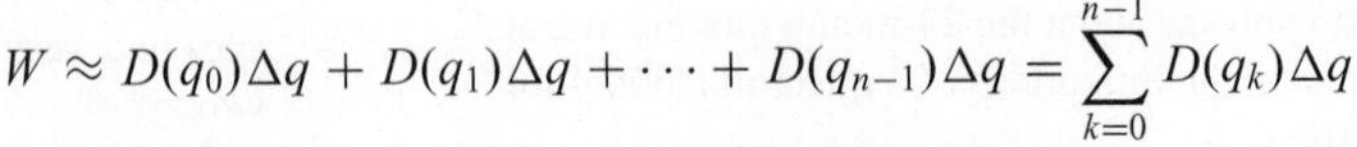

$$W = \int_0^{\bar{q}} D(q)\,dq$$

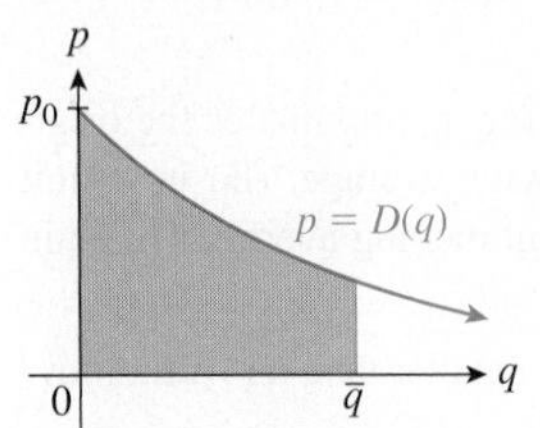

Figure **14**

This quantity, the area shaded in Figure 14, is the total consumers' willingness to spend to buy the first $\bar{q}$ units.

Consumers' Expenditure

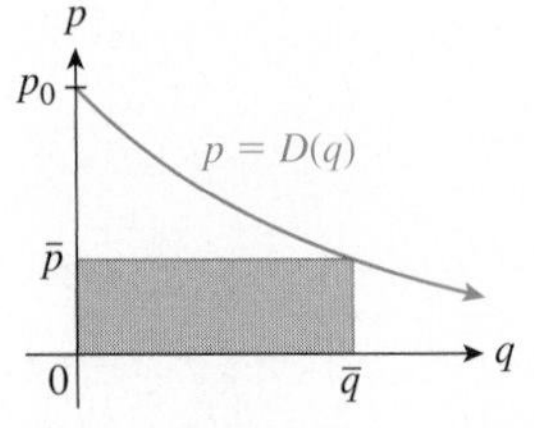

Figure **15**

Now suppose that the manufacturer simply sets the price at $\bar{p}$, with a corresponding demand of $\bar{q}$, so $D(\bar{q}) = \bar{p}$. Then the amount that consumers will actually spend to buy these $\bar{q}$ is $\bar{p}\bar{q}$, the product of the unit price and the quantity sold. This is the area of the rectangle shown in Figure 15. Notice that we can write $\bar{p}\bar{q} = \int_0^{\bar{q}} \bar{p}\,dq$, as suggested by the figure.

The difference between what consumers are willing to pay and what they actually pay is money in their pockets and is called the **consumers' surplus.**

Consumers' Surplus

If demand for an item is given by $p = D(q)$, the selling price is $\bar{p}$, and $\bar{q}$ is the corresponding demand [so that $D(\bar{q}) = \bar{p}$], then the **consumers' surplus** is the difference between their willingness to spend and their actual expenditure:

$$CS = \int_0^{\bar{q}} D(q)\,dq - \bar{p}\bar{q} = \int_0^{\bar{q}} (D(q) - \bar{p})\,dq$$

Graphically, it is the area between the graphs of $p = D(q)$ and $p = \bar{p}$, as shown in the figure.

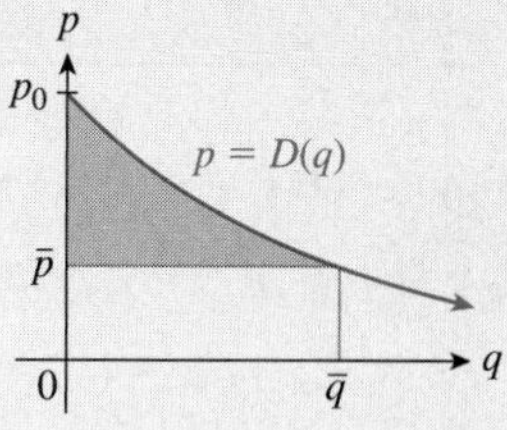

Example 1 Consumers' Surplus

Your used-CD store has an exponential demand equation of the form

$$p = 15e^{-0.01q}$$

where q represents daily sales of used CDs and p is the price you charge per CD. Calculate the daily consumers' surplus if you sell your used CDs at \$5 each.

Solution We are given $D(q) = 15e^{-0.01q}$ and $\bar{p} = 5$. We also need $\bar{q}$. By definition,

$$D(\bar{q}) = \bar{p}$$

or $\quad 15e^{-0.01\bar{q}} = 5$

which we must solve for $\bar{q}$:

$$e^{-0.01\bar{q}} = \frac{1}{3}$$

$$-0.01\bar{q} = \ln\left(\frac{1}{3}\right) = -\ln 3$$

$$\bar{q} = \frac{\ln 3}{0.01} \approx 109.8612$$

We now have

$$CS = \int_0^{\bar{q}} (D(q) - \bar{p})\,dq$$

$$= \int_0^{109.8612} (15e^{-0.01q} - 5)\,dq$$

$$= \left[\frac{15}{-0.01}e^{-0.01q} - 5q\right]_0^{109.8612}$$

$$\approx (-500 - 549.31) - (-1500 - 0)$$

$$= \$450.69 \text{ per day}$$

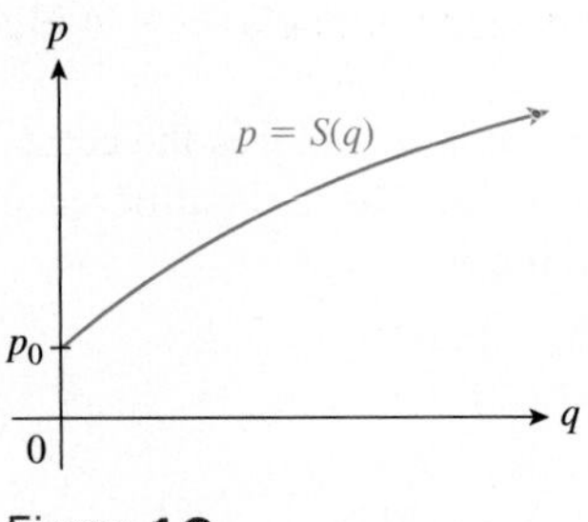

Figure **16**

Producers' Surplus

We can also calculate extra income earned by producers. Consider a supply equation of the form $p = S(q)$, where $S(q)$ is the price at which a supplier is willing to supply q items (per time period). Because a producer is generally willing to supply more units at a higher price per unit, a supply curve usually has a positive slope, as shown in Figure 16. The price p_0 is the lowest price that a producer is willing to charge.

Arguing as before, we see that the minimum amount of money producers are willing to receive in exchange for $\bar{q}$ items is $\int_0^{\bar{q}} S(q)\,dq$. On the other hand, if the producers charge $\bar{p}$ per item for $\bar{q}$ items, their actual revenue is $\bar{p}\bar{q} = \int_0^{\bar{q}} \bar{p}\,dq$.

The difference between the producers' actual revenue and the minimum they would have been willing to receive is the **producers' surplus.**

Producers' Surplus

The **producers' surplus** is the extra amount earned by producers who were willing to charge less than the selling price of $\bar{p}$ per unit and is given by

$$PS = \int_0^{\bar{q}} [\bar{p} - S(q)]\,dq$$

where $S(\bar{q}) = \bar{p}$. Graphically, it is the area of the region between the graphs of $p = \bar{p}$ and $p = S(q)$ for $0 \le q \le \bar{q}$, as in the figure.

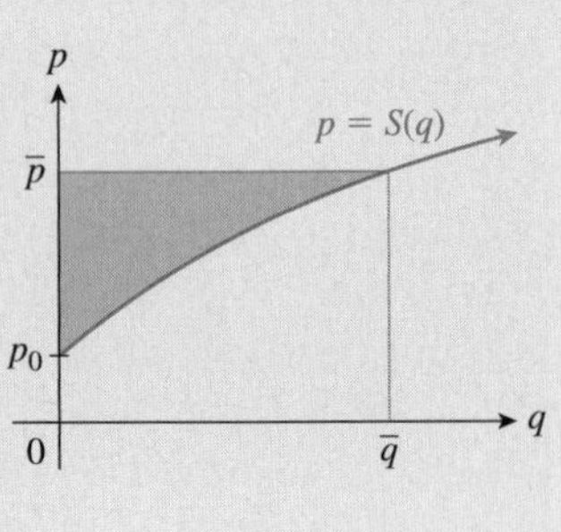

Example **2** **Producers' Surplus**

My tie-dye T-shirt enterprise has grown to the extent that I am now able to produce T-shirts in bulk, and several campus groups have begun placing orders. I have informed one group that I am prepared to supply $20\sqrt{p-4}$ T-shirts at a price of p dollars per shirt. What is my total surplus if I sell T-shirts to the group at \$8 each?

Solution We need to calculate the producers' surplus when $\bar{p} = 8$. The supply equation is

$$q = 20\sqrt{p-4}$$

but in order to use the formula for producers' surplus, we need to express p as a function of q. First, we square both sides to remove the radical sign:

$$q^2 = 400(p-4)$$

so

$$p - 4 = \frac{q^2}{400}$$

giving

$$p = S(q) = \frac{q^2}{400} + 4$$

We now need the value of $\bar{q}$ corresponding to $\bar{p} = 8$. Substituting $p = 8$ in the original equation, gives

$$\bar{q} = 20\sqrt{8-4} = 20\sqrt{4} = 40$$

Thus,

$$\begin{aligned} PS &= \int_0^{\bar{q}} (\bar{p} - S(q))\,dq \\ &= \int_0^{40} \left[8 - \left(\frac{q^2}{400} + 4\right)\right] dq \\ &= \int_0^{40} \left(4 - \frac{q^2}{400}\right) dq \\ &= \left[4q - \frac{q^3}{1200}\right]_0^{40} \approx \$106.67 \end{aligned}$$

Thus, I earn a surplus of \$106.67 if I sell T-shirts to the group at \$8 each.

Example 3 Equilibrium

To continue the preceding example: A representative informs me that the campus group is prepared to order only $\sqrt{200(16-p)}$ T-shirts at p dollars each. I would like to produce as many T-shirts for them as possible but avoid being left with unsold T-shirts. Given the supply curve from the preceding example, what price should I charge per T-shirt, and what are the consumers' and producers' surpluses at that price?

Solution The price that guarantees neither a shortage nor a surplus of T-shirts is the **equilibrium price,** the price where supply equals demand. We have

$$\begin{aligned} &\text{Supply:} && q = 20\sqrt{p-4} \\ &\text{Demand:} && q = \sqrt{200(16-p)} \end{aligned}$$

Equating these gives

$$\begin{aligned} 20\sqrt{p-4} &= \sqrt{200(16-p)} \\ 400(p-4) &= 200(16-p) \\ 400p - 1600 &= 3200 - 200p \\ 600p &= 4800 \\ p &= \$8 \text{ per T-shirt} \end{aligned}$$

We therefore take $\bar{p} = 8$ (which happens to be the price we used in the preceding example). We get the corresponding value for q by substituting $p = 8$ into either the demand or supply equation:

$$\bar{q} = 20\sqrt{8-4} = 40$$

Thus, $\bar{p} = 8$ and $\bar{q} = 40$.

We must now calculate the consumers' surplus and the producers' surplus. We calculated the producers' surplus for $\bar{p} = 8$ in the preceding example:

$$PS = \$106.67$$

For the consumers' surplus, we must first express p as a function of q for the demand equation. Thus, we solve the demand equation for p as we did for the supply equation and we obtain

$$\text{Demand:}\quad D(q) = 16 - \frac{q^2}{200}$$

Therefore,

$$\begin{aligned} CS &= \int_0^{\bar{q}} (D(q) - \bar{p})\, dq \\ &= \int_0^{40} \left[\left(16 - \frac{q^2}{200}\right) - 8\right] dq \\ &= \int_0^{40} \left(8 - \frac{q^2}{200}\right) dq \\ &= \left[8q - \frac{q^3}{600}\right]_0^{40} \approx \$213.33 \end{aligned}$$

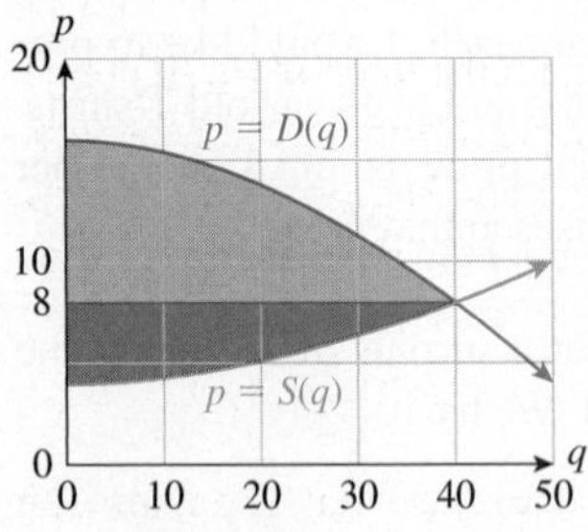

Figure **17**

+*Before we go on...* Figure 17 shows both the consumers' surplus (top portion) and the producers' surplus (bottom portion) from Example 3. Because extra money in people's pockets is a Good Thing, the total of the consumers' and the producers' surpluses is called the **total social gain.** In this case it is

$$\text{Social gain} = CS + PS = 213.33 + 106.67 = \$320.00$$

As you can see from the figure, the total social gain is also the area between two curves and equals

$$\int_0^{40} (D(q) - S(q))\, dq$$

■

Continuous Income Streams

For purposes of calculation, it is often convenient to assume that a company with a high sales volume receives money continuously. In such a case, we have a function $R(t)$ that represents the rate at which money is being received by the company at time t.

Photodisc/Getty Images

Example 4 Continuous Income

An ice cream store's business peaks in late summer; the store's summer revenue is approximated by

$$R(t) = 300 + 4.5t - 0.05t^2 \text{ dollars per day} \quad (0 \le t \le 92)$$

where t is measured in days after June 1. What is its total revenue for the months of June, July, and August?

mathematics At Work

Richard Mizak

TITLE Director
INSTITUTION Kroll Zolfo Cooper

Kroll Zolfo Cooper is one of the world's leading restructuring firms and works with companies experiencing critical financial or operational problems. We are retained as interim management or advisors to assist in stabilizing, rehabilitating and reorganizing the business, whether through performance improvement changes or Chapter 11 (bankruptcy) reorganization. We then make recommendations based on the financial analysis to the company's senior management team and use the analysis to develop concrete action plans to help get the company back on track. As a Director at Kroll Zolfo Cooper, I use mathematics when I perform financial analysis on companies in financial distress and/or bankruptcy.

At a large merchant power company we built a highly complex mathematical model to analyze the financial capabilities of the corporation and to project the company's financial performance into the future. The model was used by the company to forecast performance and by the lenders, investors and other key stakeholders to determine whether or not to lend money, invest and/or partner with the company.

At a major jewelry manufacturer, we determined that the company was losing money on most of its smaller orders. We used our mathematical analysis to work with the company to eliminate a series of costly activities that were unimportant to the smaller customers, determined the true cost of handling smaller orders, revised their computer pricing models, improved the company's pricing, and created incentives for customers to place larger orders. Almost immediately our financial analysis resulted in higher profitability for the department and higher overall sales results.

While these are just a few examples, the bulk of the work performed in the financial world has its basis in the same mathematical principals taught in your college coursework.

Solution Let's approximate the total revenue by breaking up the interval [0, 92] representing the three months into n subintervals $[t_{k-1}, t_k]$, each with length Δt. In the interval $[t_{k-1}, t_k]$ the store receives money at a rate of approximately $R(t_{k-1})$ dollars per day for Δt days, so it will receive a total of $R(t_{k-1})\Delta t$ dollars. Over the whole summer, then, the store will receive approximately

$$R(t_0)\Delta t + R(t_1)\Delta t + \cdots + R(t_{n-1})\Delta t \text{ dollars}$$

As we let n become large to better approximate the total revenue, this Riemann sum approaches the integral

$$\text{Total revenue} = \int_0^{92} R(t)\,dt$$

Substituting the function we were given, we get

$$\begin{aligned}\text{Total revenue} &= \int_0^{92} (300 + 4.5t - 0.05t^2)\,dt \\ &= \left[300t + 2.25t^2 - \frac{0.05}{3}t^3\right]_0^{92} \\ &\approx \$33{,}666\end{aligned}$$

+ *Before we go on...* We could approach the calculation in Example 4 another way: $R(t) = S'(t)$ where $S(t)$ is the total revenue earned up to day t. By the Fundamental Theorem of Calculus,

$$\text{Total revenue} = S(92) - S(0) = \int_0^{92} R(t)\,dt$$

We did the calculation using Riemann sums mainly as practice for the next example. ■

Generalizing Example 4, we can say the following:

Total Value of a Continuous Income Stream

If the rate of receipt of income is $R(t)$ dollars per unit of time, then the total income received from time $t = a$ to $t = b$ is

$$\text{Total value} = TV = \int_a^b R(t)\,dt$$

Example 5 Future Value

Suppose the ice cream store in the preceding example deposits its receipts in an account paying 5% interest per year compounded continuously. How much money will it have in its account at the end of August?

Solution Now we have to take into account not only the revenue but also the interest it earns in the account. Again, we break the interval [0, 92] into n subintervals. During the interval $[t_{k-1}, t_k]$, approximately $R(t_{k-1})\Delta t$ dollars are deposited in the account. That money will earn interest until the end of August, a period of $92 - t_{k-1}$ days, or $(92 - t_{k-1})/365$ years. The formula for continuous compounding tells us that by the end of August, those $R(t_{k-1})\Delta t$ dollars will have turned into

$$R(t_{k-1})\Delta t e^{0.05(92-t_{k-1})/365} = R(t_{k-1})e^{0.05(92-t_{k-1})/365}\Delta t \text{ dollars}$$

(Recall that 5% is the *annual* interest rate.) Adding up the contributions from each subinterval, we see that the total in the account at the end of August will be approximately

$$R(t_0)e^{0.05(92-t_0)/365}\Delta t + R(t_1)e^{0.05(92-t_1)/365}\Delta t + \cdots + R(t_{n-1})e^{0.05(92-t_{n-1})/365}\Delta t$$

This is a Riemann sum; as n gets large the sum approaches the integral

$$\text{Future value} = FV = \int_0^{92} R(t)e^{0.05(92-t)/365}\,dt$$

Substituting $R(t) = 300 + 4.5t - 0.05t^2$, we obtain

$$FV = \int_0^{92} (300 + 4.5t - 0.05t^2)e^{0.05(92-t)/365}\,dt$$

$$\approx \$33{,}880 \qquad \text{Using technology or integration by parts}$$

+*Before we go on...* The interest earned in the account in Example 5 was fairly small (compare this answer to that in Example 4). Not only was the money in the account for only three months, but much of it was put in the account towards the end of that period, so had very little time to earn interest. ■

Generalizing again, we have the following:

Future Value of a Continuous Income Stream

If the rate of receipt of income from time $t = a$ to $t = b$ is $R(t)$ dollars per unit of time and the income is deposited as it is received in an account paying interest at rate r per unit of time, compounded continuously, then the amount of money in the account at time $t = b$ is

$$\text{Future value} = FV = \int_a^b R(t)e^{r(b-t)}\,dt$$

Example 6 Present Value

You are thinking of buying the ice cream store discussed in the preceding two examples. What is its income stream worth to you on June 1? Assume that you have access to the same account paying 5% per year compounded continuously.

Solution The value of the income stream on June 1 is the amount of money that, if deposited June 1, would give you the same future value as the income stream will. If we let PV denote this "present value," its value after 92 days will be

$$PVe^{0.05\times 92/365}$$

We equate this with the future value of the income stream to get

$$PVe^{0.05\times 92/365} = \int_0^{92} R(t)e^{0.05(92-t)/365}\,dt$$

so

$$PV = \int_0^{92} R(t)e^{-0.05t/365}\,dt$$

Substituting the formula for $R(t)$ and integrating using technology or integration by parts, we get

$$PV \approx \$33{,}455$$

The general formula is the following:

Present Value of a Continuous Income Stream

If the rate of receipt of income from time $t = a$ to $t = b$ is $R(t)$ dollars per unit of time and the income is deposited as it is received in an account paying interest at rate r per unit of time, compounded continuously, then the value of the income stream at time $t = a$ is

$$\text{Present value} = PV = \int_a^b R(t)e^{r(a-t)}\,dt$$

We can derive this formula from the relation

$$FV = PVe^{r(b-a)}$$

because the present value is the amount that would have to be deposited at time $t = a$ to give a future value of FV at time $t = b$.

Note These formulas are more general than we've said. They still work when $R(t) < 0$ if we interpret negative values as money flowing *out* rather than in. That is, we can use these formulas for income we receive or for payments that we make, or for situations where we sometimes receive money and sometimes pay it out. These formulas can also be used for flows of quantities other than money. For example, if we use an exponential model for population growth and we let $R(t)$ represent the rate of immigration $[R(t) > 0]$ or emigration $[R(t) < 0]$, then the future value formula gives the future population. ■

7.4 EXERCISES

● denotes basic skills exercises

Calculate the consumers' surplus at the indicated unit price $\bar{p}$ for each of the demand equations in Exercises 1–12. hint [see Example 1]

1. ● $p = 10 - 2q$; $\bar{p} = 5$
2. ● $p = 100 - q$; $\bar{p} = 20$
3. ● $p = 100 - 3\sqrt{q}$; $\bar{p} = 76$
4. ● $p = 10 - 2q^{1/3}$; $\bar{p} = 6$
5. ● $p = 500e^{-2q}$; $\bar{p} = 100$
6. ● $p = 100 - e^{0.1q}$; $\bar{p} = 50$
7. ● $q = 100 - 2p$; $\bar{p} = 20$
8. ● $q = 50 - 3p$; $\bar{p} = 10$
9. ● $q = 100 - 0.25p^2$; $\bar{p} = 10$
10. ● $q = 20 - 0.05p^2$; $\bar{p} = 5$
11. ● $q = 500e^{-0.5p} - 50$; $\bar{p} = 1$
12. ● $q = 100 - e^{0.1p}$; $\bar{p} = 20$

Calculate the producers' surplus for each of the supply equations in Exercises 13–24 at the indicated unit price $\bar{p}$. hint [see Example 2]

13. ● $p = 10 + 2q$; $\bar{p} = 20$
14. ● $p = 100 + q$; $\bar{p} = 200$
15. ● $p = 10 + 2q^{1/3}$; $\bar{p} = 12$
16. ● $p = 100 + 3\sqrt{q}$; $\bar{p} = 124$
17. ● $p = 500e^{0.5q}$; $\bar{p} = 1000$
18. ● $p = 100 + e^{0.01q}$; $\bar{p} = 120$
19. ● $q = 2p - 50$; $\bar{p} = 40$
20. ● $q = 4p - 1000$; $\bar{p} = 1000$
21. ● $q = 0.25p^2 - 10$; $\bar{p} = 10$
22. ● $q = 0.05p^2 - 20$; $\bar{p} = 50$
23. ● $q = 500e^{0.05p} - 50$; $\bar{p} = 10$
24. ● $q = 10(e^{0.1p} - 1)$; $\bar{p} = 5$

In Exercises 25–30, find the total value of the given income stream and also find its future value (at the end of the given interval) using the given interest rate. hint [see Examples 4 & 5]

25. ● $R(t) = 30{,}000$, $0 \le t \le 10$, at 7%
26. ● $R(t) = 40{,}000$, $0 \le t \le 5$, at 10%
27. ● $R(t) = 30{,}000 + 1000t$, $0 \le t \le 10$, at 7%
28. ● $R(t) = 40{,}000 + 2000t$, $0 \le t \le 5$, at 10%
29. ● $R(t) = 30{,}000e^{0.05t}$, $0 \le t \le 10$, at 7%
30. ● $R(t) = 40{,}000e^{0.04t}$, $0 \le t \le 5$, at 10%

In Exercises 31–36, find the total value of the given income stream and also find its present value (at the beginning of the given interval) using the given interest rate. hint [see Examples 4 & 6]

31. ● $R(t) = 20{,}000$, $0 \le t \le 5$, at 8%
32. ● $R(t) = 50{,}000$, $0 \le t \le 10$, at 5%
33. ● $R(t) = 20{,}000 + 1000t$, $0 \le t \le 5$, at 8%
34. ● $R(t) = 50{,}000 + 2000t$, $0 \le t \le 10$, at 5%
35. ● $R(t) = 20{,}000e^{0.03t}$, $0 \le t \le 5$, at 8%
36. ● $R(t) = 50{,}000e^{0.06t}$, $0 \le t \le 10$, at 5%

Applications

37. ● ***College Tuition*** A study of U.S. colleges and universities resulted in the demand equation $q = 20{,}000 - 2p$, where q is the enrollment at a public college or university and p is the average annual tuition (plus fees) it charges.[21] Officials at Enormous State University have developed a policy whereby the number of students it will accept per year at a tuition level of p dollars is given by $q = 7500 + 0.5p$. Find the equilibrium tuition price $\bar{p}$ and the consumers' and producers' surpluses at this tuition level. What is the total social gain at the equilibrium price? hint [see Example 3]

38. ● ***Fast Food*** A fast-food outlet finds that the demand equation for its new side dish, "Sweetdough Tidbit," is given by

$$p = \frac{128}{(q+1)^2}$$

where p is the price (in cents) per serving and q is the number of servings that can be sold per hour at this price. At the same time, the franchise is prepared to sell $q = 0.5p - 1$ servings per hour at a price of p cents. Find the equilibrium price $\bar{p}$ and

[21] Idea based on a study by A. L. Ostrosky Jr. and J. V. Koch, as cited in their book, *Introduction to Mathematical Economics* (Waveland Press, Illinois, 1979. p. 133). The data used here are fictitious, however.

the consumers' and producers' surpluses at this price level. What is the total social gain at the equilibrium price?

39. ***Linear Demand*** Given a linear demand equation of the form $q = -mp + b\ (m > 0)$, find a formula for the consumers' surplus at a price level of $\bar{p}$ per unit.

40. ***Linear Supply*** Given a linear supply equation of the form $q = mp + b\ (m > 0)$, find a formula for the producers' surplus at a price level of $\bar{p}$ per unit.

41. ● ***Revenue*** The annual net sales (revenue) earned by the Finnish cell phone company Nokia from January 1999 to January 2004 can be approximated by

$$R(t) = -1.7t^2 + 5t + 28 \text{ billion euros per year} \quad (-1 \le t \le 4)$$

where t is time in years ($t = 0$ represents January 2000).[22] Estimate, to the nearest €10 billion, Nokia's total revenue from January 1999 through December 2003. *hint* [see Example 4]

42. ● ***Revenue*** The annual net sales (revenue) earned by Nintendo Co., Ltd., in the fiscal years ending March 31, 1995 to March 31, 2004, can be approximated by

$$R(t) = -4t^2 + 10t + 530 \text{ billion yen per year} \quad (-6 \le t \le 4)$$

where t is time in years ($t = 0$ represents March 31, 2000).[23] Estimate, to the nearest ¥100 billion, Nintendo's total revenue from April 1, 1994, through March 31, 2004.

43. ***Revenues*** The annual revenue earned by Wal-Mart in the fiscal years ending January 31, 1994 to January 31, 2004 can be approximated by

$$R(t) = 150e^{0.14t} \text{ billion dollars per year} \quad (-7 \le t \le 4)$$

where t is time in years ($t = 0$ represents January 31, 2000).[24] Estimate, to the nearest \$10 billion, Wal-Mart's total revenue from January 31, 1999 through January 31, 2004.

44. ***Revenues*** The annual revenue earned by Target for fiscal years 1998 through 2003 can be approximated by

$$R(t) = 37e^{0.09t} \text{ billion dollars per year} \quad (-2 \le t \le 4)$$

where t is time in years ($t = 0$ represents the beginning of fiscal year 2000).[25] Estimate, to the nearest \$10 billion, Target's total revenue in fiscal years 1998 through 2003.

45. ***Revenue*** Refer back to Exercise 41. Suppose that, from January 1999 on, Nokia invested its revenue in an investment yielding 4% compounded continuously. What, to the nearest €10 billion, would the total value of Nokia's revenues have been at the end of 2003? *hint* [see Example 5]

46. ***Revenue*** Refer back to Exercise 42. Suppose that, from April 1994 on, Nintendo invested its revenue in an investment yielding 5% compounded continuously. What, to the nearest ¥100 billion, would the total value of Nintendo's revenue have been by the end of March 2004?

47. ***Revenue*** Refer back to Exercise 43. Suppose that, from January 1999 on, Wal-Mart invested its revenue in an investment that depreciated continuously at a rate of 5% per year. What, to the nearest \$10 billion, would the total value of Wal-Mart's revenues have been by the end of January 2004?

48. ***Revenue*** Refer back to Exercise 44. Suppose that, from fiscal year 1998 on, Target invested its revenue in an investment that depreciated continuously at a rate of 3% per year. What, to the nearest \$10 billion, would the total value of Target's revenue have been by the end of fiscal year 2003?

49. ***Saving for Retirement*** You are saving for your retirement by investing \$700 per month in an annuity with a guaranteed interest rate of 6% per year. With a continuous stream of investment and continuous compounding, how much will you have accumulated in the annuity by the time you retire in 45 years?

50. ***Saving for College*** When your first child is born, you begin to save for college by depositing \$400 per month in an account paying 12% interest per year. With a continuous stream of investment and continuous compounding, how much will you have accumulated in the account by the time your child enters college 18 years later?

51. ***Saving for Retirement*** You begin saving for your retirement by investing \$700 per month in an annuity with a guaranteed interest rate of 6% per year. You increase the amount you invest at the rate of 3% per year. With continuous investment and compounding, how much will you have accumulated in the annuity by the time you retire in 45 years?

52. ***Saving for College*** When your first child is born, you begin to save for college by depositing \$400 per month in an account paying 12% interest per year. You increase the amount you save by 2% per year. With continuous investment and compounding, how much will have accumulated in the account by the time your child enters college 18 years later?

53. ***Bonds*** The U.S. Treasury issued a 30-year bond on October 15, 2001, paying 3.375% interest.[26] Thus, if you bought \$100,000 worth of these bonds you would receive \$3375 per year in interest for 30 years. An investor wishes to buy the

[22] SOURCE: Nokia financial statements downloaded from www.nokia.com, January 13, 2005.

[23] The model is based on a quadratic regression. Source for data: Nintendo Co., Ltd. annual reports, downloaded from www.nintendo.com, January 23, 2005.

[24] The model is based on an exponential regression. Source for data: WalMart 2004 annual report, downloaded from www.walmartstores.com.

[25] The model is based on an exponential regression. Source for data: Target 2003 annual report, downloaded from www.targetcorp.com.

[26] The U.S. Treasury suspended selling Treasury Bonds after October 2001 but resumed selling them in February 2006. SOURCE: The Bureau of the Public Debt's website: www.publicdebt.treas.gov.

rights to receive the interest on \$100,000 worth of these bonds. The amount the investor is willing to pay is the present value of the interest payments, assuming a 4% rate of return. Assuming (incorrectly, but approximately) that the interest payments are made continuously, what will the investor pay? *hint* [see Example 6]

54. ***Bonds*** The Megabucks Corporation is issuing a 20-year bond paying 7% interest (see the preceding exercise). An investor wishes to buy the rights to receive the interest on \$50,000 worth of these bonds, and seeks a 6% rate of return. Assuming that the interest payments are made continuously, what will the investor pay?

55. ***Valuing Future Income*** Inga was injured and can no longer work. As a result of a lawsuit, she is to be awarded the present value of the income she would have received over the next 20 years. Her income at the time she was injured was \$100,000 per year, increasing by \$5000 per year. What will be the amount of her award, assuming continuous income and a 5% interest rate?

56. ***Valuing Future Income*** Max was injured and can no longer work. As a result of a lawsuit, he is to be awarded the present value of the income he would have received over the next 30 years. His income at the time he was injured was \$30,000 per year, increasing by \$1500 per year. What will be the amount of his award, assuming continuous income and a 6% interest rate?

Communication and Reasoning Exercises

57. ● Complete the following: The future value of a continuous income stream earning 0% interest is the same as the _____ value.

58. ● Complete the following: The present value of a continuous income stream earning 0% interest is the same as the _____ value.

59. Your study group friend says that the future value of a continuous stream of income is always greater than the total value, assuming a positive rate of return. Is she correct? Why?

60. Your other study group friend says that the present value of a continuous stream of income can sometimes be greater than the total value, depending on the (positive) interest rate. Is he correct? Explain.

61. Arrange from smallest to largest: Total Value, Future Value, Present Value of a continuous stream of income (assuming a positive income and positive rate of return).

62. a. Arrange the following functions from smallest to largest: $R(t)$, $R(t)e^{r(b-t)}$, $R(t)e^{r(a-t)}$, where $a \le t \le b$, and r and $R(t)$ are positive.

b. Use the result from part (a) to justify your answers in Exercises 59–61.

● basic skills

7.5 Improper Integrals and Applications

All the definite integrals we have seen so far have had the form $\int_a^b f(x)\,dx$, with a and b finite and $f(x)$ piecewise continuous on the closed interval $[a, b]$. If we relax one or both of these requirements somewhat, we obtain what are called **improper integrals.** There are various types of improper integrals.

Integrals in Which a Limit of Integration is Infinite

Integrals in which one or more limits of integration are infinite can be written as

$$\int_a^{+\infty} f(x)\,dx, \quad \int_{-\infty}^{b} f(x)\,dx, \quad \text{or} \quad \int_{-\infty}^{+\infty} f(x)\,dx$$

Let's concentrate for a moment on the first form, $\int_a^{+\infty} f(x)\,dx$. What does the $+\infty$ mean here? As it often does, it means that we are to take a limit as something gets large. Specifically, it means the limit as the upper bound of integration gets large.

Improper Integral with an Infinite Limit of Integration

We define

$$\int_a^{+\infty} f(x)\,dx = \lim_{M\to+\infty}\int_a^M f(x)\,dx$$

provided the limit exists. If the limit exists, we say that $\int_a^{+\infty} f(x)\,dx$ **converges.** Otherwise, we say that $\int_a^{+\infty} f(x)\,dx$ **diverges.** Similarly, we define

$$\int_{-\infty}^b f(x)\,dx = \lim_{M\to-\infty}\int_M^b f(x)\,dx$$

provided the limit exists. Finally, we define

$$\int_{-\infty}^{+\infty} f(x)\,dx = \int_{-\infty}^a f(x)\,dx + \int_a^{+\infty} f(x)\,dx$$

for some convenient a, provided *both* integrals on the right converge.

quick Examples

1. $\displaystyle\int_1^{+\infty}\frac{dx}{x^2} = \lim_{M\to+\infty}\int_1^M\frac{dx}{x^2} = \lim_{M\to+\infty}\left[-\frac{1}{x}\right]_1^M = \lim_{M\to+\infty}\left(-\frac{1}{M}+1\right) = 1$ Converges

2. $\displaystyle\int_1^{+\infty}\frac{dx}{x} = \lim_{M\to+\infty}\int_1^M\frac{dx}{x} = \lim_{M\to+\infty}[\ln|x|]_1^M = \lim_{M\to+\infty}(\ln M - \ln 1) = +\infty$ Diverges

3. $\displaystyle\int_{-\infty}^{-1}\frac{dx}{x^2} = \lim_{M\to-\infty}\int_M^{-1}\frac{dx}{x^2} = \lim_{M\to-\infty}\left[-\frac{1}{x}\right]_M^{-1} = \lim_{M\to-\infty}\left(1+\frac{1}{M}\right) = 1$ Converges

4.
$$\begin{aligned}\int_{-\infty}^{+\infty} e^{-x}\,dx &= \int_{-\infty}^0 e^{-x}\,dx + \int_0^{+\infty} e^{-x}\,dx\\ &= \lim_{M\to-\infty}\int_M^0 e^{-x}\,dx + \lim_{M\to+\infty}\int_0^M e^{-x}\,dx\\ &= \lim_{M\to-\infty} -[e^{-x}]_M^0 + \lim_{M\to+\infty} -[e^{-x}]_0^M\\ &= \lim_{M\to-\infty}(e^{-M}-1) + \lim_{M\to+\infty}(1-e^{-M})\\ &= +\infty + 1\end{aligned}$$
Diverges

5.
$$\begin{aligned}\int_{-\infty}^{+\infty} xe^{-x^2}\,dx &= \int_{-\infty}^0 xe^{-x^2}\,dx + \int_0^{+\infty} xe^{-x^2}\,dx\\ &= \lim_{M\to-\infty}\int_M^0 xe^{-x^2}\,dx + \lim_{M\to+\infty}\int_0^M xe^{-x^2}\,dx\\ &= \lim_{M\to-\infty}\left[-\frac{1}{2}e^{-x^2}\right]_M^0 + \lim_{M\to+\infty}\left[-\frac{1}{2}e^{-x^2}\right]_0^M\\ &= \lim_{M\to-\infty}\left(-\frac{1}{2}+\frac{1}{2}e^{-M^2}\right) + \lim_{M\to+\infty}\left(-\frac{1}{2}e^{-M^2}+\frac{1}{2}\right)\\ &= -\frac{1}{2}+\frac{1}{2} = 0\end{aligned}$$
Converges

Q: We learned that the integral can be interpreted as the area under the curve. Is this still true for improper integrals?

A: Yes. Figure 18 illustrates how we can represent an improper integral as the area of an infinite region.

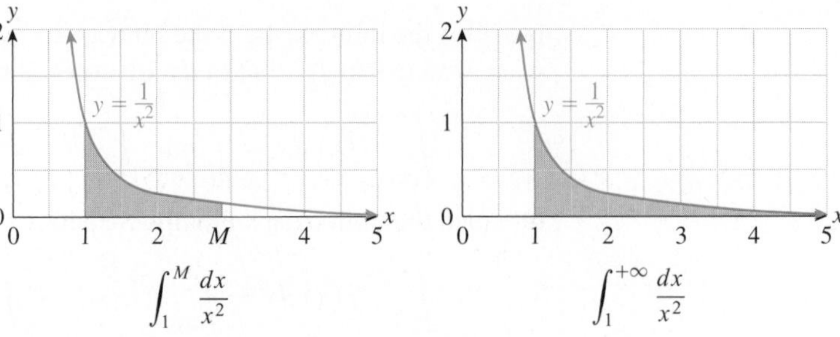

Figure **18**

On the left we see the area represented by $\int_1^M dx/x^2$. As M gets larger, the integral approaches $\int_1^{+\infty} dx/x^2$. In the picture, think of M being moved farther and farther along the x-axis in the direction of increasing x, resulting in the region shown on the right. ■

Q: Wait! We calculated $\int_1^{+\infty} dx/x^2 = 1$. Does this mean that the infinitely long area in Figure 18 has an area of only 1 square unit?

A: That is exactly what it means. If you had enough paint to cover 1 square unit, you would never run out of paint while painting the region in Figure 18. This is one of the places where mathematics seems to contradict common sense. But common sense is notoriously unreliable when dealing with infinities. ■

George B. Diebold/Corbis

Example 1 **Future Sales of VCRs**

In 2001, sales of DVD players were starting to make inroads into the sales of VCRs, but VCRs were still selling well.* Approximately 15 million VCRs were expected to be sold in 2001. Suppose that sales of VCRs decrease by 15% per year from 2001 on. How many VCRs, total, will be sold from 2001 on?

Solution Recall that the total sales between two dates can be computed as the definite integral of annual sales. So, if we wanted the sales between the year 2001 and a year far in the future, we would compute $\int_0^M s(t)\,dt$ with a large M, where $s(t)$ is the annual sales t years after 2001. Because we want to know the *total* number of VCRs sold from 2001 on, we let $M \to +\infty$; that is, we compute $\int_0^{+\infty} s(t)\,dt$.

Because sales of VCRs are decreasing by 15% per year, we can model $s(t)$ by

$$s(t) = 15(0.85)^t \text{ million VCRs}$$

where t is the number of years since 2001.

$$\text{Total sales from 2001 on} = \int_0^{+\infty} 15(0.85)^t\,dt$$

$$= \lim_{M\to+\infty} \int_0^M 15(0.85)^t\,dt$$

* SOURCE: "VCRs outsell DVD players over holidays," *USA Today*, Jan. 24, 2001.

$$= \frac{15}{\ln 0.85} \lim_{M \to +\infty} [0.85^t]_0^M$$

$$= \frac{15}{\ln 0.85} \lim_{M \to +\infty} (0.85^M - 0.85^0)$$

$$= \frac{15}{\ln 0.85}(-1) \approx 92.3 \text{ million VCRs}$$

Integrals in Which the Integrand Becomes Infinite

We can sometimes compute integrals $\int_a^b f(x)\,dx$ in which $f(x)$ becomes infinite. As we'll see in Example 4, the Fundamental Theorem of Calculus does not work for such integrals. The first case to consider is when $f(x)$ approaches $\pm\infty$ at either a or b.

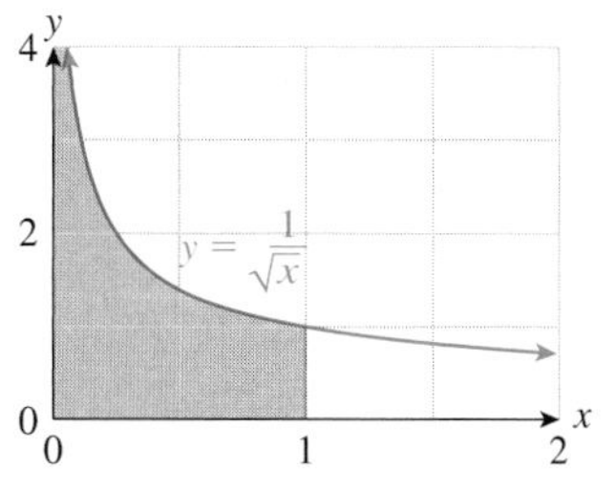

Figure **19**

Example **2** Integrand Infinite at One Endpoint

Calculate $\displaystyle\int_0^1 \frac{1}{\sqrt{x}}\,dx$.

Solution Notice that the integrand approaches $+\infty$ as x approaches 0 from the right and is not defined at 0. This makes the integral an improper integral. Figure 19 shows the region whose area we are trying to calculate; it extends infinitely vertically rather than horizontally.

Now, if $0 < r < 1$, the integral $\int_r^1 (1/\sqrt{x})\,dx$ is a proper integral because we avoid the bad behavior at 0. This integral gives the area shown in Figure 20. If we let r approach 0 from the right, the area in Figure 20 will approach the area in Figure 19. So, we calculate

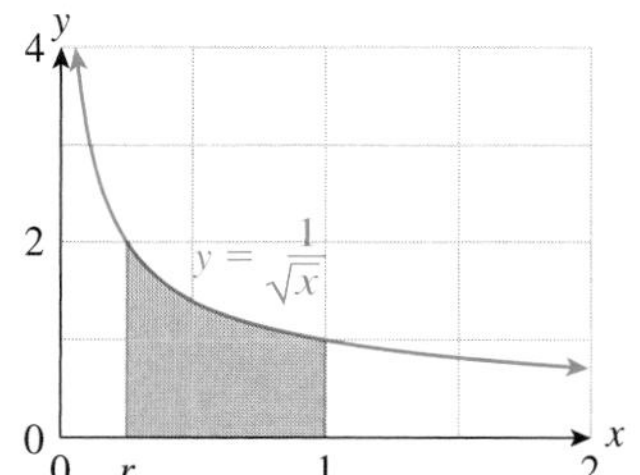

Figure **20**

$$\int_0^1 \frac{1}{\sqrt{x}}\,dx = \lim_{r \to 0^+} \int_r^1 \frac{1}{\sqrt{x}}\,dx$$

$$= \lim_{r \to 0^+} [2\sqrt{x}]_r^1$$

$$= \lim_{r \to 0^+} (2 - 2\sqrt{r})$$

$$= 2$$

Thus, we again have an infinitely long region with finite area.

Generalizing, we make the following definition.

Improper Integral in Which the Integrand Becomes Infinite

If $f(x)$ is defined for all x with $a < x \le b$ but approaches $\pm\infty$ as x approaches a, we define

$$\int_a^b f(x)\,dx = \lim_{r \to a^+} \int_r^b f(x)\,dx$$

provided the limit exists. Similarly, if $f(x)$ is defined for all x with $a \le x < b$ but approaches $\pm\infty$ as x approaches b, we define

$$\int_a^b f(x)\,dx = \lim_{r \to b^-} \int_a^r f(x)\,dx$$

provided the limit exists. In either case, if the limit exists, we say that $\int_a^b f(x)\,dx$ **converges.** Otherwise, we say that $\int_a^b f(x)\,dx$ **diverges.**

Example 3 Testing for Convergence

Does $\int_{-1}^{3} \frac{x}{x^2-9}\,dx$ converge? If so, to what?

Solution We first check to see where, if anywhere, the integrand approaches $\pm\infty$. That will happen where the denominator becomes 0, so we solve $x^2 - 9 = 0$.

$$\begin{aligned} x^2 - 9 &= 0 \\ x^2 &= 9 \\ x &= \pm 3 \end{aligned}$$

The solution $x = -3$ is outside of the range of integration, so we ignore it. The solution $x = 3$ is, however, the right endpoint of the range of integration, so the integral is improper. We need to investigate the following limit:

$$\int_{-1}^{3} \frac{x}{x^2-9}\,dx = \lim_{r\to 3^-} \int_{-1}^{r} \frac{x}{x^2-9}\,dx$$

Now, to calculate the integral we use a substitution:

$$\begin{aligned} u &= x^2 - 9 \\ \frac{du}{dx} &= 2x \\ dx &= \frac{1}{2x}\,du \end{aligned}$$

when $x = r$, $u = r^2 - 9$
when $x = -1$, $u = (-1)^2 - 9 = -8$

Thus,

$$\begin{aligned} \int_{-1}^{r} \frac{x}{x^2-9}\,dx &= \int_{-8}^{r^2-9} \frac{1}{2u}\,du \\ &= \frac{1}{2}[\ln|u|]_{-8}^{r^2-9} \\ &= \frac{1}{2}(\ln|r^2-9| - \ln 8) \end{aligned}$$

Now we take the limit:

$$\begin{aligned} \int_{-1}^{3} \frac{x}{x^2-9}\,dx &= \lim_{r\to 3^-} \int_{-1}^{r} \frac{x}{x^2-9}\,dx \\ &= \lim_{r\to 3^-} \frac{1}{2}(\ln|r^2-9| - \ln 8) \\ &= -\infty \end{aligned}$$

because, as $r \to 3$, $r^2 - 9 \to 0$, and so $\ln|r^2 - 9| \to -\infty$. Thus, this integral diverges.

Example 4 Integrand Infinite Between the Endpoints

Does $\int_{-2}^{3} \frac{1}{x^2}\, dx$ converge? If so, to what?

Solution Again we check to see if there are any points at which the integrand approaches $\pm\infty$. There is such a point, at $x = 0$. This is between the endpoints of the range of integration. To deal with this we break the integral into two integrals:

$$\int_{-2}^{3} \frac{1}{x^2}\, dx = \int_{-2}^{0} \frac{1}{x^2}\, dx + \int_{0}^{3} \frac{1}{x^2}\, dx$$

Each integral on the right is an improper integral with the integrand approaching $\pm\infty$ at an endpoint. If both of the integrals on the right converge, we take the sum as the value of the integral on the left. So now we compute

$$\begin{aligned}\int_{-2}^{0} \frac{1}{x^2}\, dx &= \lim_{r\to 0^-} \int_{-2}^{r} \frac{1}{x^2}\, dx \\ &= \lim_{r\to 0^-} \left[-\frac{1}{x}\right]_{-2}^{r} \\ &= \lim_{r\to 0^-} \left(-\frac{1}{r} - \frac{1}{2}\right)\end{aligned}$$

which diverges to $+\infty$. There is no need now to check $\int_0^3 (1/x^2)\, dx$; because one of the two pieces of the integral diverges, we simply say that $\int_{-2}^{3} (1/x^2)\, dx$ diverges.

+ *Before we go on...* What if we had been sloppy in Example 4 and had not checked first whether the integrand approached $\pm\infty$ somewhere? Then we probably would have applied the Fundamental Theorem of Calculus and done the following:

$$\int_{-2}^{3} \frac{1}{x^2}\, dx = \left[-\frac{1}{x}\right]_{-2}^{3} = \left(-\frac{1}{3} - \frac{1}{2}\right) = -\frac{5}{6} \quad \text{✗ } \textit{WRONG!}$$

Notice that the answer this "calculation" gives is patently ridiculous. Because $1/x^2 > 0$ for all x for which it is defined, any definite integral of $1/x^2$ must give a positive answer. *Moral:* Always check to see whether the integrand blows up anywhere in the range of integration. If it does, the FTC does not apply, and we must use the methods of this example. ■

We end with an example of what to do if an integral is improper for more than one reason.

Example 5 An Integral Improper in Two Ways

Does $\int_{0}^{+\infty} \frac{1}{\sqrt{x}}\, dx$ converge? If so, to what?

Solution This integral is improper for two reasons. First, the range of integration is infinite. Second, the integrand blows up at the endpoint 0. In order to separate these two problems, we break up the integral at some convenient point:

$$\int_0^{+\infty} \frac{1}{\sqrt{x}}\,dx = \int_0^1 \frac{1}{\sqrt{x}}\,dx + \int_1^{+\infty} \frac{1}{\sqrt{x}}\,dx$$

We chose to break the integral at 1. Any positive number would have sufficed, but 1 is generally easier to use in calculations.

The first piece, $\int_0^1 (1/\sqrt{x})\,dx$, we discussed in Example 2; it converges to 2. For the second piece we have:

$$\begin{aligned}\int_1^{+\infty} \frac{1}{\sqrt{x}}\,dx &= \lim_{M\to+\infty} \int_1^M \frac{1}{\sqrt{x}}\,dx \\ &= \lim_{M\to+\infty} [2\sqrt{x}]_1^M \\ &= \lim_{M\to+\infty} (2\sqrt{M} - 2)\end{aligned}$$

which diverges to $+\infty$. Because the second piece of the integral diverges, we conclude that $\int_0^{+\infty} (1/\sqrt{x})\,dx$ diverges.

7.5 EXERCISES

● denotes basic skills exercises

◆ denotes challenging exercises

tech Ex indicates exercises that should be solved using technology

For some of the exercises in this section you need to assume the fact that $\lim_{M\to+\infty} M^n e^{-M} = 0$ *for all n.*

Decide whether each integral in Exercises 1–26 converges. If the integral converges, compute its value.

1. ● $\int_1^{+\infty} x\,dx$ *hint* [see Quick Examples p. 513]

2. ● $\int_0^{+\infty} e^{-x}\,dx$

3. ● $\int_{-2}^{+\infty} e^{-0.5x}\,dx$

4. ● $\int_1^{+\infty} \frac{1}{x^{1.5}}\,dx$

5. ● $\int_{-\infty}^{2} e^x\,dx$

6. ● $\int_{-\infty}^{-1} \frac{1}{x^{1/3}}\,dx$

7. ● $\int_{-\infty}^{-2} \frac{1}{x^2}\,dx$

8. ● $\int_{-\infty}^{0} e^{-x}\,dx$

9. ● $\int_0^{+\infty} x^2 e^{-6x}\,dx$

10. ● $\int_0^{+\infty} (2x-4)e^{-x}\,dx$

11. ● $\int_0^5 \frac{2}{x^{1/3}}\,dx$ *hint* [see Example 2]

12. ● $\int_0^2 \frac{1}{x^2}\,dx$

13. ● $\int_{-1}^{2} \frac{3}{(x+1)^2}\,dx$ *hint* [see Example 3]

14. ● $\int_{-1}^{2} \frac{3}{(x+1)^{1/2}}\,dx$

15. ● $\int_{-1}^{2} \frac{3x}{x^2-1}\,dx$ *hint* [see Example 4]

16. ● $\int_{-1}^{2} \frac{3}{x^{1/3}}\,dx$

17. ● $\int_{-2}^{2} \frac{1}{(x+1)^{1/5}}\,dx$

18. ● $\int_{-2}^{2} \frac{2x}{\sqrt{4-x^2}}\,dx$

19. ● $\int_{-1}^{1} \frac{2x}{x^2-1}\,dx$

20. ● $\int_{-1}^{2} \frac{2x}{x^2-1}\,dx$

21. ● $\int_{-\infty}^{+\infty} xe^{-x^2}\,dx$

22. ● $\int_{-\infty}^{\infty} xe^{1-x^2}\,dx$

23. ● $\int_0^{+\infty} \frac{1}{x\ln x}\,dx$ *hint* [see Example 5]

24. ● $\int_0^{+\infty} \ln x\,dx$

25. $\int_0^{+\infty} \frac{2x}{x^2-1}\,dx$

26. $\int_{-\infty}^{0} \frac{2x}{x^2-1}\,dx$

Applications

27. ● ***Advertising Revenue*** From June 2001 to June 2002, *GQ Magazine's* advertising revenues could be approximated by

$$R(t) = 91.7(0.90)^t \text{ million dollars per year} \quad (0 \le t \le 1)$$

where t is time in years since June 2001.[27] By extrapolating this model into the indefinite future, project *GQ's* total advertising revenue from June 2001 on. (Round your answer to the nearest $1 million.) hint [see Example 1]

28. ● ***Advertising Revenue*** From June 2001 to June 2002, *Esquire Magazine*'s advertising revenues could be approximated by

$$R(t) = 57.0(0.927)^t \text{ million dollars per year} \quad (0 \le t \le 1)$$

where t is time in years since June 2001.[28] By extrapolating this model into the indefinite future, project *Esquire's* total advertising revenue from June 2001 on. (Round your answer to the nearest $1 million.)

29. ***Cigarette Sales*** According to the Federal Trade Commission, the number of cigarettes sold domestically in 2002 decreased by 5.5% from the 2001 total of approximately 400 billion cigarettes.[29] Use an exponential model to forecast the total number of cigarettes sold from 2001 on. (Round your answer to the nearest 100 billion cigarettes.)

30. ***Sales*** Sales of the text *Calculus and You* have been declining continuously at a rate of 5% per year. Assuming that *Calculus and You* currently sells 5000 copies per year and that sales will continue this pattern of decline, calculate total future sales of the text.

31. ***Sales*** My financial adviser has predicted that annual sales of Frodo T-shirts will continue to decline by 10% each year. At the moment, I have 3200 of the shirts in stock and am selling them at a rate of 200 per year. Will I ever sell them all?

32. ***Revenue*** Alarmed about the sales prospects for my Frodo T-shirts (see the preceding exercise), I will try to make up lost revenues by increasing the price by $1 each year. I now charge $10 per shirt. What is the total amount of revenue I can expect to earn from sales of my T-shirts, assuming the sales levels described in the previous exercise? (Give your answer to the nearest $1000.)

33. ***Education*** Let $N(t)$ be the number of high school students graduated in the U.S. in year t. This number is projected to change at a rate of about

$$N'(t) = 0.214t^{-0.91} \text{ million graduates per year} \quad (0 \le t \le 21)$$

where t is time in years since 1990.[30] In 1991, there were about 2.5 million high school students graduated. By extrapolating the model, what can you say about the number of high school students graduated in a year far in the future?

34. ***Education, Martian*** Let $M(t)$ be the number of high school students graduated in the Republic of Mars in year t. This number is projected to change at a rate of about

$$M'(t) = 0.321t^{-1.10} \text{ thousand graduates per year} \quad (0 \le t \le 50)$$

where t is time in years since 2020. In 2021, there were about 1300 high school students graduated. By extrapolating the model, what can you say about the number of high school students graduated in a year far in the future?

35. ***Cell Phone Revenues*** The number of cell phone subscribers in China for the period 2000–2005 was projected to follow the equation[31]

$$N(t) = 39t + 68 \text{ million subscribers}$$

in year t ($t = 0$ represents 2000). The average annual revenue per cell phone user was $350 in 2000.

a. Assuming that, due to competition, the revenue per cell phone user decreases continuously at an annual rate of 10%, give a formula for the annual revenue in year t.

b. Using the model you obtained in part (a) as an estimate of the rate of change of total revenue, estimate the total revenue from 2000 into the indefinite future.

36. ***Vid Phone Revenues*** The number of vid phone subscribers in the Republic of Mars for the period 2200–2300 was projected to follow the equation

$$N(t) = 18t - 10 \text{ thousand subscribers}$$

in year t ($t = 0$ represents 2200). The average annual revenue per vid phone user was Z̿40 in 2200.[32]

a. Assuming that, due to competition, the revenue per vid phone user decreases continuously at an annual rate of 20%, give a formula for the annual revenue in year t.

b. Using the model you obtained in part (a) as an estimate of the rate of change of total revenue, estimate the total revenue from 2200 into the indefinite future.

37. ***Foreign Investments*** According to data published by the World Bank, foreign direct investment in low income countries from 1999 through 2002 was approximately

$$q(t) = 1.7t^2 - 0.5t + 8 \text{ billion dollars per year}$$

where t is time in years since 2000.[33] Assuming a worldwide inflation rate of 5% per year, find the value of all foreign direct investment in low income countries from 2000 on in constant dollars. (The constant dollar value of $q(t)$ dollars t years from now is given by $q(t)e^{-rt}$, where r is the fractional

[27] Based on six-month advertising revenue figures for June, 2001 and June, 2002. SOURCE: *New York Times*, July, 29, 2002, p. C1.

[28] Ibid.

[29] SOURCE: Federal Trade Commission Cigarette Report for 2002, issued 2004, available at www.ftc.gov/reports/cigarette/041022cigaretterpt.pdf.

[30] Based on a regression model. Source for data: U.S. Department of Education, 2002; http://nces.ed.gov.

[31] Based on a regression of projected figures (coefficients are rounded). SOURCE: Intrinsic Technology/*New York Times*, Nov. 24, 2000, p. C1.

[32] Z̿ designates Zonars, the designated currency for the city-state of Utarek, Mars. SOURCE: www.marsnext.com/comm/zonars.html.

[33] The authors' approximation, based on data from the World Bank, obtained from www.worldbank.org.

rate of inflation. Give your answer to the nearest \$1000 billion.)

38. ***Foreign Aid*** Repeat the preceding exercise, using the following model for per capita aid to the least developed countries.[34] (Give your answer to the nearest \$1000.)

$$q(t) = t^2 + 0.7t + 19 \text{ dollars per year}$$

39. ***Online Book Sales*** The number of books per year sold online in the U.S. in the period 1997–2000 can be approximated by

$$N(t) = \frac{82.8(7.14)^t}{21.8 + (7.14)^t} \text{ million books per year}$$

($t = 0$ represents 1997).[35] Investigate the integrals $\int_0^{+\infty} N(t)\,dt$ and $\int_{-\infty}^0 N(t)\,dt$ and interpret your answers.

40. ***Mousse Sales*** The weekly demand for your company's Lo-Cal Mousse is modeled by the equation

$$q(t) = \frac{50e^{2t-1}}{1 + e^{2t-1}}$$

where t is time from now in weeks and $q(t)$ is the number of gallons sold per week. Investigate the integrals $\int_0^{+\infty} q(t)\,dt$ and $\int_{-\infty}^0 q(t)\,dt$ and interpret your answers.

tech Ex ***The Normal Curve*** *Exercises 41–44 require the use of a graphing calculator or computer programmed to do numerical integration. The* normal distribution curve, *which models the distributions of data in a wide range of applications, is given by the function*

$$p(x) = \frac{1}{\sqrt{2\pi}\sigma} e^{-(x-\mu)^2/2\sigma^2}$$

where $\pi = 3.14159265\ldots$ *and* σ *and* μ *are constants called the standard deviation and the mean, respectively. Its graph (for* $\sigma = 1$ *and* $\mu = 2$*) is shown in the figure.*

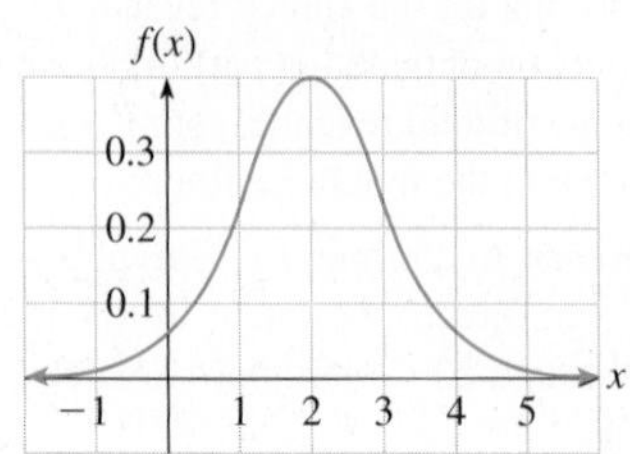

41. tech Ex With $\sigma = 4$ and $\mu = 1$, approximate $\int_{-\infty}^{+\infty} p(x)\,dx$.

42. tech Ex With $\sigma = 1$ and $\mu = 0$, approximate $\int_0^{+\infty} p(x)\,dx$.

43. tech Ex With $\sigma = 1$ and $\mu = 0$, approximate $\int_1^{+\infty} p(x)\,dx$.

44. tech Ex With $\sigma = 1$ and $\mu = 0$, approximate $\int_{-\infty}^1 p(x)\,dx$.

45. ◆ ***Variable Sales*** The value of your Chateau Petit Mont Blanc 1963 vintage burgundy is increasing continuously at an annual rate of 40%, and you have a supply of 1000 bottles worth \$85 each at today's prices. In order to ensure a steady income, you have decided to sell your wine at a diminishing rate—starting at 500 bottles per year, and then decreasing this figure continuously at a fractional rate of 100% per year. How much income (to the nearest dollar) can you expect to generate by this scheme? [*Hint:* Use the formula for continuously compounded interest.]

46. ◆ ***Panic Sales*** Unfortunately, your large supply of Chateau Petit Mont Blanc is continuously turning to vinegar at a fractional rate of 60% per year! You have thus decided to sell off your Petit Mont Blanc at \$50 per bottle, but the market is a little thin, and you can only sell 400 bottles per year. Because you have no way of knowing which bottles now contain vinegar until they are opened, you shall have to give refunds for all the bottles of vinegar. What will your net income be before all the wine turns to vinegar?

47. ◆ ***Meteor Impacts*** The frequency of meteor impacts on earth can be modeled by

$$n(k) = \frac{1}{5.6997k^{1.081}}$$

where $n(k) = N'(k)$, and $N(k)$ is the average number of meteors of energy less than or equal to k megatons that will hit the earth in one year.[36] (A small nuclear bomb releases on the order of one megaton of energy.)

a. How many meteors of energy at least $k = 0.2$ hit the earth each year?

b. Investigate and interpret the integral $\int_0^1 n(k)\,dk$.

48. ◆ ***Meteor Impacts*** (continuing the previous exercise)

a. Explain why the integral

$$\int_a^b k \cdot n(k)\,dk$$

computes the total energy released each year by meteors with energies between a and b megatons.

b. Compute and interpret

$$\int_0^1 k \cdot n(k)\,dk$$

c. Compute and interpret

$$\int_1^{+\infty} k \cdot n(k)\,dk$$

49. ◆ ***The Gamma Function*** The gamma function is defined by the formula

$$\Gamma(x) = \int_0^{+\infty} t^{x-1}e^{-t}\,dt$$

[34] Ibid.

[35] The model is a logistic regression. Source for data: Ipsos-NPD Book Trends/*New York Times,* April 16, 2001, p. C1.

[36] The authors' model, based on data published by NASA International Near-Earth-Object Detection Workshop (*The New York Times,* Jan. 25, 1994, p. C1).

a. Find $\Gamma(1)$ and $\Gamma(2)$.
b. Use integration by parts to show that for every positive integer n, $\Gamma(n+1) = n\Gamma(n)$.
c. Deduce that $\Gamma(n) = (n-1)!\ [= (n-1)(n-2)\dots 2 \cdot 1]$ for every positive integer n.

50. ◆ ***Laplace Transforms*** The Laplace Transform $F(x)$ of a function $f(t)$ is given by the formula

$$F(x) = \int_0^{+\infty} f(t)e^{-xt}\,dt \quad (x > 0)$$

a. Find $F(x)$ for $f(t) = 1$ and for $f(t) = t$.
b. Find a formula for $F(x)$ if $f(t) = t^n$ $(n = 1, 2, 3, \dots)$.
c. Find a formula for $F(x)$ if $f(t) = e^{at}$ (a constant).

Communication and Reasoning Exercises

51. ● Why can't the Fundamental Theorem of Calculus be used to evaluate $\displaystyle\int_{-1}^{1} \frac{1}{x}\,dx$?

52. ● Why can't the Fundamental Theorem of Calculus be used to evaluate $\displaystyle\int_{1}^{+\infty} \frac{1}{x^2}\,dx$?

53. ● It sometimes happens that the Fundamental Theorem of Calculus gives the correct answer for an improper integral. Does the FTC give the correct answer for improper integrals of the form

$$\int_{-a}^{a} \frac{1}{x^{1/r}}\,dx$$

if $r = 3, 5, 7, \dots$?

54. ● Does the FTC give the correct answer for improper integrals of the form

$$\int_{-a}^{a} \frac{1}{x^r}\,dx$$

if $r = 3, 5, 7, \dots$?

55. tech Ex How could you use technology to approximate improper integrals? (Your discussion should refer to each type of improper integral.)

56. tech Ex Use technology to approximate the integrals $\int_0^M e^{-(x-10)^2}\,dx$ for larger and larger values of M, using Riemann sums with 500 subdivisions. What do you find? Comment on the answer.

57. Make up an interesting application whose solution is $\int_{10}^{+\infty} 100te^{-0.2t}\,dt = \$1{,}015.01$.

58. Make up an interesting application whose solution is $\displaystyle\int_{100}^{+\infty} \frac{1}{r^2}\,dr = 0.01$.

● basic skills ◆ challenging tech Ex technology exercise

7.6 Differential Equations and Applications

A **differential equation** is an equation that involves a derivative of an unknown function. A **first-order differential equation** involves only the first derivative of the unknown function. A **second-order differential equation** involves the second derivative of the unknown function (and possibly the first derivative). Higher-order differential equations are defined similarly. In this book, we will deal only with first-order differential equations.

To **solve** a differential equation means to find the unknown function. Many of the laws of science and other fields describe how things change. When expressed mathematically, these laws take the form of equations involving derivatives—that is, differential equations. The field of differential equations is a large and very active area of study in mathematics, and we shall see only a small part of it in this section.

Example 1 Motion

A dragster accelerates from a stop so that its speed t seconds after starting is $40t$ ft/s. How far will the car go in 8 seconds?

Solution We wish to find the car's position function $s(t)$. We are told about its speed, which is ds/dt. Precisely, we are told that

$$\frac{ds}{dt} = 40t$$

This is the differential equation we have to solve to find $s(t)$. But we already know how to solve this kind of differential equation; we integrate:

$$s(t) = \int 40t\ dt = 20t^2 + C$$

We now have the **general solution** to the differential equation. By letting C take on different values, we get all the possible solutions. We can specify the one **particular solution** that gives the answer to our problem by imposing the **initial condition** that $s(0) = 0$. Substituting into $s(t) = 20t^2 + C$, we get

$$0 = s(0) = 20(0)^2 + C = C$$

so $C = 0$ and $s(t) = 20t^2$. To answer the question, the car travels $20(8)^2 = 1280$ feet in 8 seconds.

We did not have to work hard to solve the differential equation in Example 1. In fact, any differential equation of the form $dy/dx = f(x)$ can (in theory) be solved by integrating. (Whether we can actually carry out the integration is another matter!)

Simple Differential Equations

A **simple** differential equation has the form

$$\frac{dy}{dx} = f(x)$$

Its general solution is

$$y = \int f(x)\ dx$$

quick **Example**

The differential equation

$$\frac{dy}{dx} = 2x^2 - 4x^3$$

is simple and has general solution

$$y = \int f(x)\ dx = \frac{2x^3}{3} - x^4 + C$$

Not all differential equations are simple, as the next example shows.

Example 2 Separable Differential Equation

Consider the differential equation $\dfrac{dy}{dx} = \dfrac{x}{y^2}$.

a. Find the general solution.

b. Find the particular solution that satisfies the initial condition $y(0) = 2$.

Solution

a. This is not a simple differential equation because the right-hand side is a function of both x and y. We cannot solve this equation by just integrating; the solution to this problem is to "separate" the variables.

Step 1 ***Separate the variables algebraically.*** We rewrite the equation as

$$y^2\,dy = x\,dx$$

Step 2 ***Integrate both sides.***

$$\int y^2\,dy = \int x\,dx$$

giving

$$\frac{y^3}{3} = \frac{x^2}{2} + C$$

Step 3 ***Solve for the dependent variable.*** We solve for y:

$$y^3 = \frac{3}{2}x^2 + 3C = \frac{3}{2}x^2 + D$$

(rewriting $3C$ as D, an equally arbitrary constant), so

$$y = \left(\frac{3}{2}x^2 + D\right)^{1/3}$$

This is the general solution of the differential equation.

b. We now need to find the value for D that will give us the solution satisfying the condition $y(0) = 2$. Substituting 0 for x and 2 for y in the general solution, we get

$$2 = \left(\frac{3}{2}(0)^2 + D\right)^{1/3} = D^{1/3}$$

so

$$D = 2^3 = 8$$

Thus, the particular solution we are looking for is

$$y = \left(\frac{3}{2}x^2 + 8\right)^{1/3}$$

+ *Before we go on...* We can check the general solution in Example 2 by calculating both sides of the differential equation and comparing.

$$\frac{dy}{dx} = \frac{d}{dx}\left(\frac{3}{2}x^2 + D\right)^{1/3} = x\left(\frac{3}{2}x^2 + D\right)^{-2/3}$$

$$\frac{x}{y^2} = \frac{x}{\left(\frac{3}{2}x^2 + 8\right)^{2/3}} = x\left(\frac{3}{2}x^2 + D\right)^{-2/3} \quad ✔$$

■

Q: *In Example 2, we wrote $y^2\,dy$ and $x\,dx$. What do they mean?*

A: Although it is possible to give meaning to these symbols, for us they are just a notational convenience. We could have done the following instead:

$$y^2\frac{dy}{dx} = x$$

Now we integrate both sides with respect to x.

$$\int y^2\frac{dy}{dx}\,dx = \int x\,dx$$

We can use substitution to rewrite the left-hand side:

$$\int y^2\frac{dy}{dx}\,dx = \int y^2\,dy$$

which brings us back to the equation

$$\int y^2\,dy = \int x\,dx$$

■

We were able to separate the variables in the preceding example because the right-hand side, x/y^2, was a *product* of a function of x and a function of y—namely,

$$\frac{x}{y^2} = x\left(\frac{1}{y^2}\right)$$

In general, we can say the following:

Separable Differential Equation

A **separable** differential equation has the form

$$\frac{dy}{dx} = f(x)g(y)$$

We solve a separable differential equation by separating the xs and the ys algebraically, writing

$$\frac{1}{g(y)}\,dy = f(x)\,dx$$

and then integrating:

$$\int \frac{1}{g(y)}\,dy = \int f(x)\,dx$$

Example 3 Rising Medical Costs

Spending on Medicare from 2000 to 2025 was projected to rise continuously at an instantaneous rate of 3.7% per year.* Find a formula for Medicare spending y as a function of time t in years since 2000.

Solution When we say that Medicare spending y was going up continuously at an instantaneous rate of 3.7% per year, we mean that

the instantaneous rate of increase of y was 3.7% of its value

* Spending is in constant 2000 dollars. Source for projected data: The Urban Institute's Analysis of the 1999 Trustee's Report; www.urban.org.

or $\dfrac{dy}{dt} = 0.037y$

This is a separable differential equation. Separating the variables gives

$$\frac{1}{y}dy = 0.037\,dt$$

Integrating both sides, we get

$$\int \frac{1}{y}dy = \int 0.037\,dt$$

so $\ln y = 0.037t + C$

(We should write $\ln|y|$, but we know that the medical costs are positive.) We now solve for y.

$$y = e^{0.037t+C} = e^C e^{0.037t} = Ae^{0.037t}$$

where A is a positive constant. This is the formula we used before for continuous percentage growth.

+ *Before we go on...* To determine A in Example 3 we need to know, for example, Medicare spending at time $t = 0$. The source cited estimates Medicare spending as \$239.6 billion in 2000. Substituting $t = 0$ in the equation above gives

$$239.6 = Ae^0 = A$$

Thus, projected Medicare spending is

$$y = 239.6e^{0.037t} \text{ billion dollars}$$

t years after 2000. ■

Example **4** **Newton's Law of Cooling**

Newton's Law of Cooling states that a hot object cools at a rate proportional to the difference between its temperature and the temperature of the surrounding environment (the **ambient temperature**). If a hot cup of coffee, at 170°F, is left to sit in a room at 70°F, how will the temperature of the coffee change over time?

Solution We let $H(t)$ denote the temperature of the coffee at time t. Newton's Law of Cooling tells us that $H(t)$ *decreases* at a rate proportional to the difference between $H(t)$ and 70°F, the ambient temperature. In other words,

$$\frac{dH}{dt} = -k(H - 70)$$

where k is some positive constant.* Note that $H \geq 70$: The coffee will never cool to less than the ambient temperature.

---

* When we say that a quantity Q is *proportional* to a quantity R, we mean that $Q = kR$ for some constant k. The constant k is referred to as the **constant of proportionality.**

The variables here are H and t, which we can separate as follows:

$$\frac{dH}{H-70} = -k\,dt$$

Integrating, we get

$$\int \frac{dH}{H-70} = \int (-k)\,dt$$

so $\quad \ln(H-70) = -kt + C$

(Note that $H - 70$ is positive, so we don't need absolute values.) We now solve for H:

$$\begin{aligned} H - 70 &= e^{-kt+C} \\ &= e^C e^{-kt} \\ &= Ae^{-kt} \end{aligned}$$

so

$$H(t) = 70 + Ae^{-kt}$$

where A is some positive constant. We can determine the constant A using the initial condition $H(0) = 170$:

$$170 = 70 + Ae^0 = 70 + A$$

so $\quad A = 100$

Therefore,

$$H(t) = 70 + 100e^{-kt}$$

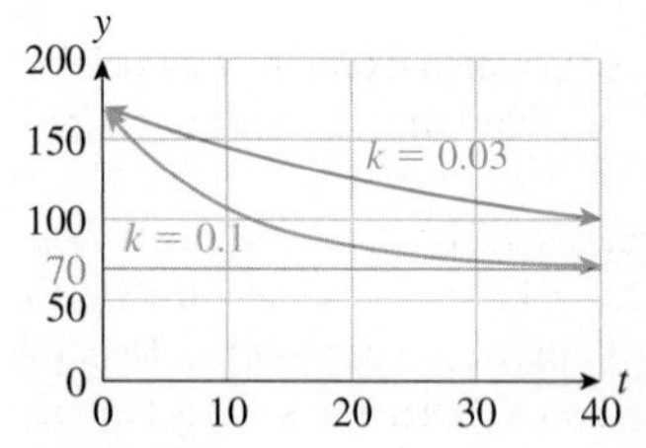

Figure 21

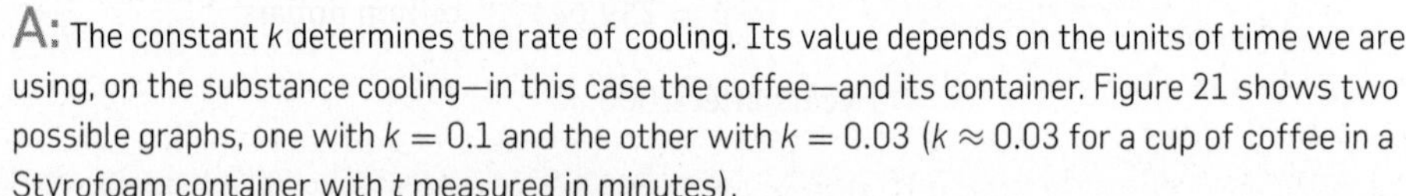

Q: But what is k?

A: The constant k determines the rate of cooling. Its value depends on the units of time we are using, on the substance cooling—in this case the coffee—and its container. Figure 21 shows two possible graphs, one with $k = 0.1$ and the other with $k = 0.03$ ($k \approx 0.03$ for a cup of coffee in a Styrofoam container with t measured in minutes).

In any case, we can see from the graph or the formula for $H(t)$ that the temperature of the coffee will approach the ambient temperature exponentially. ■

7.6 EXERCISES

● denotes basic skills exercises

tech Ex indicates exercises that should be solved using technology

Find the general solution of each differential equation in Exercises 1–10. Where possible, solve for y as a function of x. hint [see Quick Examples p. 522]

1. ● $\dfrac{dy}{dx} = x^2 + \sqrt{x}$

2. ● $\dfrac{dy}{dx} = \dfrac{1}{x} + 3$

3. ● $\dfrac{dy}{dx} = \dfrac{x}{y}$ hint [see Example 2a]

4. ● $\dfrac{dy}{dx} = \dfrac{y}{x}$

5. ● $\dfrac{dy}{dx} = xy$

6. ● $\dfrac{dy}{dx} = x^2 y$

7. ● $\dfrac{dy}{dx} = (x+1)y^2$

8. ● $\dfrac{dy}{dx} = \dfrac{1}{(x+1)y^2}$

9. ● $x\dfrac{dy}{dx} = \dfrac{1}{y}\ln x$

10. ● $\dfrac{1}{x}\dfrac{dy}{dx} = \dfrac{1}{y}\ln x$

For each differential equation in Exercises 11–20, find the particular solution indicated. hint [see Example 2b]

11. ● $\dfrac{dy}{dx} = x^3 - 2x;\ y = 1$ when $x = 0$

12. ● $\frac{dy}{dx} = 2 - e^{-x}$; $y = 0$ when $x = 0$

13. ● $\frac{dy}{dx} = \frac{x^2}{y^2}$; $y = 2$ when $x = 0$

14. ● $\frac{dy}{dx} = \frac{y^2}{x^2}$; $y = \frac{1}{2}$ when $x = 1$

15. ● $x\frac{dy}{dx} = y$; $y(1) = 2$

16. ● $x^2\frac{dy}{dx} = y$; $y(1) = 1$

17. ● $\frac{dy}{dx} = x(y+1)$; $y(0) = 0$

18. ● $\frac{dy}{dx} = \frac{y+1}{x}$; $y(1) = 2$

19. ● $\frac{dy}{dx} = \frac{xy^2}{x^2+1}$; $y(0) = -1$

20. ● $\frac{dy}{dx} = \frac{xy}{(x^2+1)^2}$; $y(0) = 1$

Applications

21. ● ***Sales*** Your monthly sales of Green Tea Ice Cream are falling at an instantaneous rate of 5% per month. If you currently sell 1000 quarts per month, find the differential equation describing your change in sales, and then solve it to predict your monthly sales. *hint* [see Example 3]

22. ● ***Profit*** Your monthly profit on sales of Avocado Ice Cream is rising at an instantaneous rate of 10% per month. If you currently make a profit of $15,000 per month, find the differential equation describing your change in profit, and solve it to predict your monthly profits.

23. ● ***Cooling*** A bowl of clam chowder at 190°F is placed in a room whose air temperature is 75°F. After 10 minutes, the soup has cooled to 150°F. Find the temperature of the chowder as a function of time. (Refer to Example 4 for Newton's Law of Cooling.)

24. ● ***Heating*** Newton's Law of Heating is just the same as his Law of Cooling: The rate of change of temperature is proportional to the difference between the temperature of an object and its surroundings, whether the object is hotter or colder than its surroundings. Suppose that a pie, at 20°F, is put in an oven at 350°F. After 15 minutes, its temperature has risen to 80°F. Find the temperature of the pie as a function of time.

25. ● ***Market Saturation*** You have just introduced a new flatscreen monitor to the market. You predict that you will eventually sell 100,000 monitors and that your monthly rate of sales will be 10% of the difference between the saturation value and the total number you have sold up to that point. Find a differential equation for your total sales (as a function of the month) and solve. (What are your total sales at the moment when you first introduce the monitor?)

26. ● ***Market Saturation*** Repeat the preceding exercise, assuming that monthly sales will be 5% of the difference between the saturation value (of 100,000 monitors) and the total sales to that point, and assuming that you sell 5000 monitors to corporate customers before placing the monitor on the open market.

27. ***Approach to Equilibrium*** The Extrasoft Toy Co. has just released its latest creation, a plush platypus named "Eggbert." The demand function for Eggbert dolls is $D(p) = 50{,}000 - 500p$ dolls per month when the price is p dollars. The supply function is $S(p) = 30{,}000 + 500p$ dolls per month when the price is p dollars. This makes the equilibrium price $20. The Evans price adjustment model assumes that if the price is set at a value other than the equilibrium price, it will change over time in such a way that its rate of change is proportional to the shortage $D(p) - S(p)$.

  a. Write the differential equation given by the Evans price adjustment model for the price p as a function of time.

  b. Find the general solution of the differential equation you wrote in (a). (You will have two unknown constants, one being the constant of proportionality.)

  c. Find the particular solution in which Eggbert dolls are initially priced at $10 and the price rises to $12 after one month.

28. ***Approach to Equilibrium*** Spacely Sprockets has just released its latest model, the Dominator. The demand function is $D(p) = 10{,}000 - 1000p$ sprockets per year when the price is p dollars. The supply function is $S(p) = 8000 + 1000p$ sprockets per year when the price is p dollars.

  a. Using the Evans price adjustment model described in the preceding exercise, write the differential equation for the price $p(t)$ as a function of time.

  b. Find the general solution of the differential equation you wrote in (a).

  c. Find the particular solution in which Dominator sprockets are initially priced at $5 each but fall to $3 each after one year.

29. ***Determining Demand*** Nancy's Chocolates estimates that the elasticity of demand for its dark chocolate truffles is $E = 0.05p - 1.5$ where p is the price per pound. Nancy's sells 20 pounds of truffles per week when the price is $20 per pound. Find the formula expressing the demand q as a function of p. Recall that the elasticity of demand is given by

$$E = -\frac{dq}{dp} \times \frac{p}{q}$$

30. ***Determining Demand*** Nancy's Chocolates estimates that the elasticity of demand for its chocolate strawberries is $E = 0.02p - 0.5$ where p is the price per pound. It sells 30 pounds of chocolate strawberries per week when the price is $30 per pound. Find the formula expressing the demand q as a function of p. Recall that the elasticity of demand is given by

$$E = -\frac{dq}{dp} \times \frac{p}{q}$$

31. ***Logistic Equation*** There are many examples of growth in which the rate of growth is slow at first, becomes faster, and then slows again as a limit is reached. This pattern can be described by the differential equation

$$\frac{dy}{dt} = ay(L - y)$$

where a is a constant and L is the limit of y. Show by substitution that

$$y = \frac{CL}{e^{-aLt} + C}$$

is a solution of this equation, where C is an arbitrary constant.

32. ***Logistic Equation*** Using separation of variables and integration with a table of integrals or a symbolic algebra program, solve the differential equation in the preceding exercise to derive the solution given there.

tech Ex *Exercises 33–36 require the use of technology.*

33. tech Ex ***Market Saturation*** You have just introduced a new model of DVD player. You predict that the market will saturate at 2,000,000 DVD players and that your total sales will be governed by the equation

$$\frac{dS}{dt} = \frac{1}{4}S(2 - S)$$

where S is the total sales in millions of DVD players and t is measured in months. If you give away 1000 DVD players when you first introduce them, what will S be? Sketch the graph of S as a function of t. About how long will it take to saturate the market? (See Exercise 31.)

34. tech Ex ***Epidemics*** A certain epidemic of influenza is predicted to follow the function defined by

$$\frac{dA}{dt} = \frac{1}{10}A(20 - A)$$

where A is the number of people infected in millions and t is the number of months after the epidemic starts. If 20,000 cases are reported initially, find $A(t)$ and sketch its graph. When is A growing fastest? How many people will eventually be affected? (See Exercise 31.)

35. tech Ex ***Growth of Tumors*** The growth of tumors in animals can be modeled by the Gompertz equation:

$$\frac{dy}{dt} = -ay \ln\left(\frac{y}{b}\right)$$

where y is the size of a tumor, t is time, and a and b are constants that depend on the type of tumor and the units of measurement.

a. Solve for y as a function of t.

b. If $a = 1$, $b = 10$, and $y(0) = 5$ cm^3 (with t measured in days), find the specific solution and graph it.

36. tech Ex ***Growth of Tumors*** Refer back to the preceding exercise. Suppose that $a = 1$, $b = 10$, and $y(0) = 15$ cm^3. Find the specific solution and graph it. Comparing its graph to the one obtained in the preceding exercise, what can you say about tumor growth in these instances?

Communication and Reasoning Exercises

37. ● What is the difference between a particular solution and the general solution of a differential equation? How do we get a particular solution from the general solution?

38. ● Why is there always an arbitrary constant in the general solution of a differential equation? Why are there not two or more arbitrary constants in a first-order differential equation?

39. Show by example that a **second-order** differential equation, one involving the second derivative y'', usually has two arbitrary constants in its general solution.

40. Find a differential equation that is not separable.

41. Find a differential equation whose general solution is $y = 4e^{-x} + 3x + C$.

42. Explain how, knowing the elasticity of demand as a function of either price or demand, you may find the demand equation (see Exercise 29).

The Gini Index—a measure of social equity

In Section 7.2, you learned about the area between two curves. The Gini index applies that mathematical concept to give a single number that tells how equally a resource is distributed in a population. The resource could be income, wealth, food, land, health care, or any other resource you can quantify. The Gini index lets us summarize the fairness of the distribution. We compare different societies or see how a society has changed over time.

Lorentz curves

Lorentz curves give a detailed picture of the distribution of a resource in a population. For instance, let's talk about wealth in America. On the left is a table from the U.S. Census Bureau that gives facts about the positive net worth of families, in thousands of dollars. The 77,418,000 families in the country are grouped by percentile. Let's examine the census data before looking at the table on the right.

Census data

0 to 25%	0
25% to 49.9%	47.1
50% to 74.9%	185.4
75% to 90%	526.7
90% to 100%	3,114.2

Lorentz data

0	0
0.25	0
0.5	0.026272
0.75	0.129685
0.9	0.305957
1	1.0

The first row on the left means that the poorest 25% of families—about 19 million families—have zero positive net worth. (In fact, the average wealth of these families is -1.4 thousand dollars, meaning that they owe that much, on average. For simplicity, we count this as having zero wealth.) The last row means that the wealthiest 10% of the families have an average wealth of $3,114,200. When you take the known figure of about 77.4 million families, take percentages, and add up all the wealth, it works out to be about 34 *trillion* dollars.

On the right, the first column holds the *percentile* variable, which we call x. The last column shows what fraction of the wealth is owned by the poorest fraction x of the population. Thus, the third row in the Lorentz data table means that the poorest 50% of the population owned about 2.6% of the wealth. This data illustrates what we call a Lorentz curve:

> When a resource is distributed in a population, the Lorentz curve contains the point $(x, f(x))$ when the poorest fraction x of the population owns the fraction $f(x)$ of that resource.

You don't need to know how to compute values of the Lorentz curve, you just need to know the definition. But in case you are curious, here is how we computed that $f(.5) = 0.026272$: The poorest quarter have nothing and the fraction owned by the next quarter is

$$19{,}354.5\text{ K families}\cdot \$47.1\ \frac{\text{K}}{\text{family}}\ /\ \$\,34{,}698{,}747{,}600\text{ K total} = 0.026271754\,.$$

As usual, K stands for thousands, so that figure for total wealth is over \$34 trillion. Notice that $f(0) = 0$ and $f(1) = 1$ for every Lorentz curve, because 0% of the people have 0% of the resource and 100% have 100%.

The Gini Index

In 1921, Italian statistician Corrado Gini proposed a quantity that summarizes the information in a Lorentz curve. This is now called the Gini Index. It is a number between 0 and 1 that gives an overall picture of how equitably (or inequitably) the resource is distributed.

To understand the Gini Index, look at the figure, which shows the Lorentz data from the table above. The lower curve is the Lorentz curve, $y = f(x)$ while the upper curve is simply the graph $y = x$. The upper curve is called the "curve of perfect equity," because it represents a situation where the poorest 20% of the people have 20% of the resource, and so on.

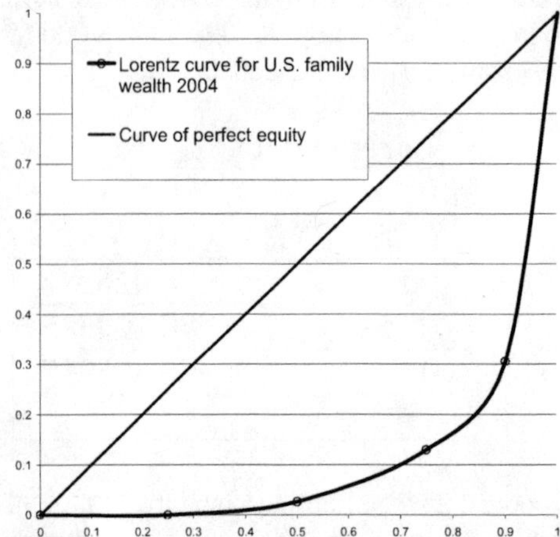

In Section 7.2, you studied Area between Two Curves. Do you see how this might be useful here? If the Lorentz curve is very close to the curve of perfect equity, there is very little deviation from a perfectly equal distribution and there is not much area between the two curves. In the figure, there looks like a lot of area.

We define the *Gini Index* for a given Lorentz curve $f(x)$ to be

$$G = 2 \int_0^1 x - f(x)\, dx .$$

Except for the scaling factor of 2, this is just the area between the two curves. The 2 is introduced to force the index to be a number between 0 and 1. (To see this, ask yourself how much total possible area there could be under the curve $y = x$.)

One insight can be gained from imagining that everyone had an equal share. The Lorentz curve and the curve of perfect equity would be the same and the area would work out to be 0. Thus, a Gini index of 0 indicates perfect equity. On the other hand, a Gini index of 1 indicates that the distribution is as inequitable as it can be: It is as if one person has everything and everyone else has nothing.

Even though we introduced this idea using the idea of wealth, it is most common to use the Gini Index to talk about income, specifically family income. You can look up Gini indices for countries that interest you at the CIA World Fact Book. They list .45 as the Gini for U.S. family income, somewhere in between perfect equity and perfect inequity. Brazil's is listed as .567 and many other similar countries have Gini indices around there. At the other end of the world spectrum are countries like Denmark, whose Gini is given as .24 . Does this fit with what you know about these countries?

It is also instructive to see how the U.S. income Gini has changed over time. During the 20th century, the Gini was lowest at about .34 in 1967 and has risen rather steadily to its current value. Does this fit with your knowledge of recent history?

Of course, we do not mean to suggest that a low Gini index for income always indicates a good society. Poor people in a rich country can be better off than middle-class people in a poor country. Also, many argue that policies to redistribute income incur serious costs in economic productivity.

Example 1. The function $f(x) = x^{22/3}$ gives a fairly good model for the Lorentz curve for U.S. Wealth. Compute the Gini index associated with this Lorentz curve.

Solution:

$$G = 2\int_0^1 x - x^{22/3}\,dx = 2\left(\frac{x^2}{2} - \frac{x^{25/3}}{25/3}\right)\Bigg|_0^1$$

$$= 1 - 6/25 = 19/25 = .76$$

Example 2. While walking to class one day in the mid-90s, I saw this statement chalked onto the sidewalk: "In California, 87% of the private land is owned by 5% of the population." Assume a Lorentz cuve of the form $f(x) = x^p$ and determine *p* from the given statement. Then find the Gini index.

Solution: The given sentence must be translated, but a bit of thought gives one point on the Lorentz curve: $f(.95) = .13$. Perhaps after reviewing something about logarithms, we find that $p = \ln(.13)/\ln(.95) \approx 39.77$. The Gini index for private land ownership in California, according to this model, is

$$G = 2\int_0^1 x - x^{39.77}\,dx = 1 - \frac{2}{40.77} \approx .95\ .$$

Exercises

1. Find the Gini index corresponding to the Lorentz curve $f(x) = x^3$.

2. Find the Gini index corresponding to the Lorentz curve $f(x) = \frac{x}{4} + \frac{3}{4}x^3$.

3. Working backwards: In 2001, the CIA website reported that the Gini index for the distribution of family income in the US was .408 .
   - A) Determine the number *p* so that gives this value for the Gini, if the Lorentz curve has the form of a power function $f(x) = x^p$.
   - B) According to this model, how much of the family income is earned by the top 5% of families?

4. One type of function often used to model Lorentz curves is $f(x) = a\,x + (1-a)\,x^p$. Suppose that $a = 1/4$ and that the Gini index for the distribution of wealth in a country is known to be 9/16.

A) Find the value of p that fits this situation.
B) According to this model, how much of the wealth is owned by the wealthiest 5% of the population?

5. Two-class societies: In theory, it could happen that one portion of the total resources is distributed equitably among one class, with the rest being shared equally by another class. Here are two functions that represent **two different** two-class societies:

$$f(x) = \begin{cases} x/2 & 0 \le x \le 1/2 \\ 3x/2 - 1/2 & 1/2 < x \le 1 \end{cases}, \quad g(x) = \begin{cases} x/2 & 0 \le x \le 3/4 \\ 5x/2 - 3/2 & 3/4 < x \le 1 \end{cases}.$$

Compute the Gini index for each and decide which is the more equitable society. In each case, what fraction of the total resources is owned by the richest half of the population?

6. Beyond the Gini: In two of the problems 1 through 5 above, the Gini index turns out to be the same. Which two? These are not identical societies. Which is the more equitable? It will help to graph both Lorentz curves on the same axis. This shows that the Gini index is only a summary statistic; economists often look beyond it to see more detail about equality.

Perpetuities—income streams that last forever

Your wealthy Aunt Grace was pleased to hear that you were studying the present value of future income in Math 31. She has been meaning to talk with you about setting up an annuity to help you get started in life. She wants to set up a fund that will pay you about $30,000 a year for about 25 years, at which time you should be able to take care of yourself. She realizes that you might need a little more money each year, so she decides to increase the amount of your payment by about $500 a year. A continuous model for this income stream is

$$R(t) = 30 + t/2, \text{ in thousands of dollars per year.}$$

Suppose that Aunt Grace has a banker who can ensure her a continuously compounded interest rate of 5 %. She computes, and you should check, that the present value of this income stream (in other words, the amount that Aunt Grace should expect to pay into the fund at the start) is

$$\int_0^{25} \left(30 + \frac{t}{2}\right) e^{-.05t}\, dt = 800 - 1{,}050e^{-5/4} \approx \$\,499.169\text{ K}.$$

You are grateful to Aunt Grace. It would be very nice to have this income stream. After all, the rate of payment will be 42.5 thousand dollars a year at the time this income stream runs out.

However, you do some computations, and tell Aunt Grace that funding this same income stream for 40 years would cost only $637.597 K. Since she is already willing to devote half a million dollars to this worthy cause, why not pay an extra $140 K or so to insure that her great-nieces and nephews will be well provided for? After all, the rate of payment when the annuity runs out would be $50 K per year. Aunt Grace agrees and prepares to write the check.

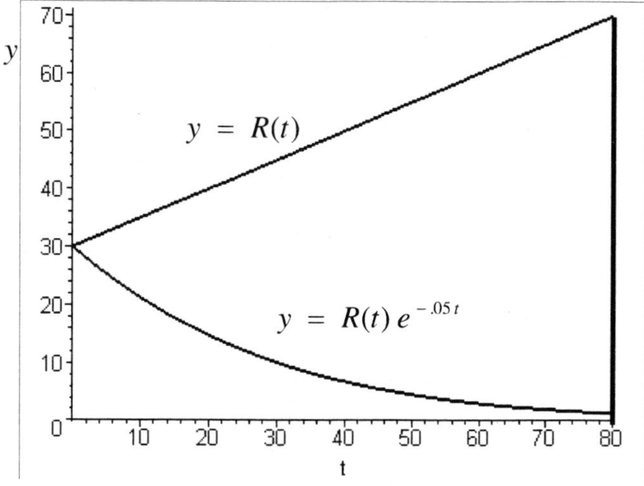

Figure: The area under the higher curve gives the total amount of income paid from the fund over 80 years. Area under the lower curve gives the present value of that income.

You quickly sharpen your pencil and compute that the price tag on the same income stream for 80 years is only $770.695 K. Another payment of less than $140 K would double the time period of her generous gift! And when the endowment ends, the rate of payment would be a comfortable $70 K per year. You tell this to Aunt Grace and show her the diagram on the previous page. She is impressed with your ability to integrate by parts and expresses her willingness to fund this new annuity.

You ask your aunt, "Why stop there?" The price for a 120-year endowment is $ 795 K. For 150 years, it's just short of $ 799 K. In fact, if she could spare $ 800 K, the income stream would go on forever! Aunt Grace is suspicious of the word *forever*, but you prove to her with computations that the value of this annuity (now called a *perpetuity* because it has no stop-date and is thus perpetual) can be written as an improper integral:

$$\int_0^{\infty} (30 + \frac{t}{2})\, e^{-.05t}\, dt\, .$$

You give convincing arguments that the improper integral converges to $800 K and Aunt Grace writes the check, happy that her descendents will benefit from your knowledge of calculus for many years to come.

Exercises:

1. Suppose Aunt Grace wanted to give annual increases of $1000 per year. How would this change the computations above? Give values for the amount Aunt Grace would have to pay to fund the income stream for 25 years, 80 years, 120 years, 150 years, and forever. (Hint: You need only integrate by parts *once*.)

2. You decide to give SCU an endowment that will pay out $50 K per year forever, with a continuously compounded annual increase of 4 %. Assuming that you can lock in an interest rate of 6%, figure out how much this endowment would cost.

3. You take all the information about Aunt Grace's gift to your not-quite-so-wealthy Aunt Margaret. In addition to the $800K already deposited there by Aunt Grace, how much would Aunt Margaret have to add to the fund to enable it to pay out an income stream of

$$R(t) = 50 + t$$

forever?

Chapter 7 Review

KEY CONCEPTS

7.1 Integration by Parts

Integration by parts formula:

$$\int u \cdot v\,dx = u \cdot I(v) - \int D(u)I(v)\,dx$$
p. 480

Tabular method for integration by parts *p. 481*

Integrating a polynomial times a logarithm *p. 484*

7.2 Area Between Two Curves and Applications

If $f(x) \geq g(x)$ for all x in $[a, b]$, then the area of the region between the graphs of f and g and between $x = a$ and $x = b$ is given by

$$A = \int_a^b [f(x) - g(x)]\,dx \quad p.\ 487$$

Regions enclosed by crossing curves *p. 489*

Area enclosed by two curves *p. 490*

General instructions for finding the area between the graphs of $f(x)$ and $g(x)$ *p. 490*

Approximating the area between two curves using technology:

$$A = \int_a^b |f(x) - g(x)|\,dx \quad p.\ 490$$

7.3 Averages and Moving Averages

Average, or mean, of a collection of values

$$\bar{y} = \frac{y_1 + y_2 + \cdots + y_n}{n} \quad p.\ 494$$

The ***average,** or* ***mean,*** of a function $f(x)$ on an interval $[a, b]$ is

$$\bar{f} = \frac{1}{b-a}\int_a^b f(x)\,dx \quad p.\ 495$$

Average balance *p. 496*

Computing the moving average of a set of data *p. 496*

n-Unit moving average of a function:

$$\bar{f}(x) = \frac{1}{n}\int_{x-n}^{x} f(t)\,dt \quad p.\ 498$$

Computing moving average using technology *p. 498*

7.4 Applications to Business and Economics: Consumers' and Producers' Surplus and Continuous Income Streams

Consumers' surplus:

$$CS = \int_0^{\bar{q}} (D(q) - \bar{p})\,dq \quad p.\ 502$$

Producers' surplus:

$$PS = \int_0^{\bar{q}} [\bar{p} - S(q)]\,dq \quad p.\ 504$$

Equilibrium price *p. 505*

Social gain $= CS + PS$ *p. 506*

Total value of a continuous income stream: $TV = \int_a^b R(t)\,dt$ *p. 508*

Future value of a continuous income stream: $FV = \int_a^b R(t)e^{r(b-t)}\,dt$ *p. 508*

Present value of a continuous income stream:

$$PV = \int_a^b R(t)e^{r(a-t)}\,dt \quad p.\ 509$$

7.5 Improper Integrals and Applications

Improper integral with an infinite limit of integration:

$$\int_a^{+\infty} f(x)\,dx,\ \int_{-\infty}^{b} f(x)\,dx,\ \int_{-\infty}^{+\infty} f(x)\,dx \quad p.\ 512$$

Improper integral in which the integrand becomes infinite *p. 512*

Testing for convergence *p. 516*

Integrand infinite between the endpoints *p. 517*

Integral improper in two ways *p. 517*

7.6 Differential Equations and Applications

Simple differential equations:

$$\frac{dy}{dx} = f(x) \quad p.\ 522$$

Separable differential equations:

$$\frac{dy}{dx} = f(x)g(y) \quad p.\ 522$$

Newton's Law of Cooling *p. 525*

REVIEW EXERCISES

Evaluate the integrals in Exercises 1–10 that converge. (Some of the integrals are improper and may diverge.)

1. $\int (x^2 + 2)e^x\,dx$

2. $\int (x^2 - x)e^{-3x+1}\,dx$

3. $\int x^2 \ln(2x)\,dx$

4. $\int \log_5 x\,dx$

5. $\int_{-2}^{2} (x^3 + 1)e^{-x}\,dx$

6. $\int_1^e x^2 \ln x\,dx$

7. $\int_1^{\infty} \frac{1}{x^5}\,dx$

8. $\int_0^1 \frac{1}{x^5}\,dx$

9. $\int_{-2}^{2} \frac{1}{(x+1)^{1/3}}\,dx$

10. $\int_0^1 \frac{1}{\sqrt{1-x}}\,dx$

In Exercises 11–14, find the areas of the given regions.

11. Between $y = x^3$ and $y = 1 - x^3$ for x in $[0, 1]$

12. Between $y = e^x$ and $y = e^{-x}$ for x in $[0, 2]$

13. Enclosed by $y = 1 - x^2$ and $y = x^2$

14. Between $y = x$ and $y = xe^{-x}$ for x in $[0, 2]$

In Exercises 15–18, find the average value of the given function over the indicated interval.

15. $f(x) = x^3 - 1$ over $[-2, 2]$

16. $f(x) = \frac{x}{x^2+1}$ over $[0, 1]$

17. $f(x) = x^2e^x$ over $[0, 1]$

18. $f(x) = (x + 1)\ln x$ over $[1, 2e]$

In Exercises 19–22, find the 2-unit moving averages of the given function.

19. $f(x) = 3x + 1$

20. $f(x) = 6x^2 + 12$

21. $f(x) = x^{4/3}$

22. $f(x) = \ln x$

In Exercises 23 and 24, calculate the consumers' surplus at the indicated unit price $\bar{p}$ for the given demand equation.

23. $p = 50 - \frac{1}{2}q;\ \bar{p} = 10$

24. $p = 10 - q^{1/2};\ \bar{p} = 4$

In Exercises 25 and 26, calculate the producers' surplus at the indicated unit price $\bar{p}$ for the given supply equation.

25. $p = 50 + \frac{1}{2}q;\ \bar{p} = 100$

26. $p = 10 + q^{1/2};\ \bar{p} = 40$

Solve the differential equations in Exercises 27–30.

27. $\frac{dy}{dx} = x^2y^2$

28. $\frac{dy}{dx} = xy + 2x$

29. $xy\frac{dy}{dx} = 1;\ y(1) = 1$

30. $y(x^2 + 1)\frac{dy}{dx} = xy^2;\ y(0) = 2$

Applications

31. ***Investments*** OHaganBooks.com keeps its cash reserves in a bank account paying 6% compounded continuously. It starts a year with \$1 million in reserves and does not withdraw or deposit any money.

a. What is the average amount it will have in the account over the course of two years?

b. Find the one-month moving average of the amount it has in the account.

32. ***Consumers' and Producers' Surplus*** OHaganBooks.com is about to start selling a new coffee table book, *Computer Designs of the Late Twentieth Century*. It estimates the demand curve to be $q = 1000\sqrt{200 - 2p}$, and its willingness to order books from the publisher is given by the supply curve $q = 1000\sqrt{10p - 400}$.

a. Find the equilibrium price and demand.

b. Find the consumers' and producers' surpluses at the equilibrium price.

33. ***Revenue*** Sales of the bestseller *A River Burns Through It* are dropping at OHaganBooks.com. To try to bolster sales, the company is dropping the price of the book, now \$40, at a rate of \$2 per week. As a result, this week OHaganBooks.com will sell 5000 copies, and it estimates that sales will fall continuously at a rate of 10% per week. How much revenue will it earn on sales of this book over the next 8 weeks?

34. ***Investments*** OHaganBooks.com CEO John O'Hagan has started a gift account for the Marjory Duffin Foundation. The account pays 6% compounded continuously and is initially empty. OHaganBooks.com deposits money continuously into it, starting at the rate of \$100,000 per month and increasing continuously by \$10,000 per month.

a. How much money will the company have in the account at the end of two years?

b. How much of the amount you found in part (a) was principal deposited and how much was interest earned?

35. ***Acquisitions*** The Megabucks Corporation is considering buying OHaganBooks.com. They estimate OHaganBooks.com's revenue stream at \$50 million per year, growing continuously at a 10% rate. Assuming interest rates of 6%, how much is OHaganBooks.com's revenue for the next year worth now?

36. ***Incompetence*** OHaganBooks.com is shopping around for a new bank. A junior executive at one bank offers them the following interesting deal: The bank will pay them interest continuously at a rate equal to 0.01% of the square of the amount of money they have in the account at any time. By considering what would happen if \$10,000 was deposited in such an account, explain why the junior executive was fired shortly after this offer was made.

CASE STUDY: Estimating Tax Revenues

Bob Daemmrich/The Image Works

You have just been hired by the incoming administration of your country as chief consultant for national tax policy, and you have been getting conflicting advice from the finance experts on your staff. Several of them have come up with plausible suggestions for new tax structures, and your job is to choose the plan that results in more revenue for the government.

Before you can evaluate their plans, you realize that it is essential to know your country's income distribution—that is, how many people earn how much money.[37] One might think that the most useful way of specifying income distribution would be to use a function that gives the exact number $f(x)$ of people who earn a given salary x. This would necessarily be a discrete function—it only makes sense if x happens to be a whole number of cents. There is, after all, no one earning a salary of exactly \$22,000.142567! Furthermore, this function would behave rather erratically, because there are, for example, probably many more people making a salary of exactly \$30,000 than exactly \$30,000.01. Given these problems, it is far more convenient to start with the function defined by

$$N(x) = \textit{the total number of people earning between } 0 \textit{ and } x \textit{ dollars}$$

Actually, you would want a "smoothed" version of this function. The graph of $N(x)$ might look like the one shown in Figure 22.

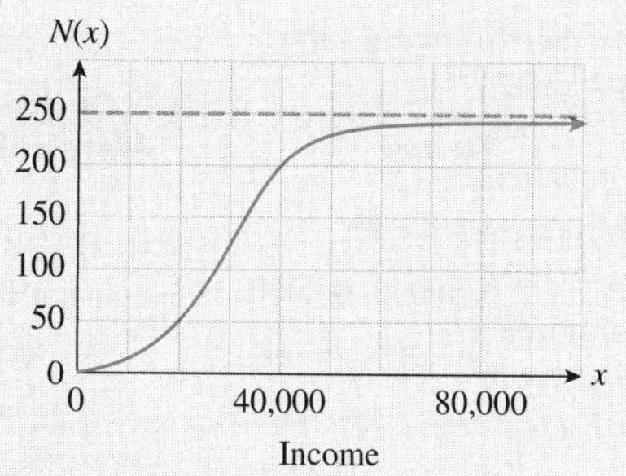

Figure **22**

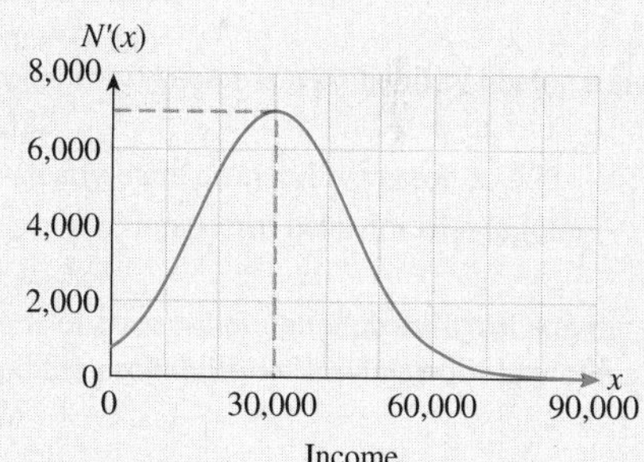

Figure **23**

If we take the *derivative* of $N(x)$, we get an income distribution function. Its graph might look like the one shown in Figure 23. Because the derivative measures the rate of change, its value at x is the additional number of taxpayers per \$1 increase in salary. Thus, the fact that $N'(20{,}000) \approx 5500$ tells us that approximately 5500 people are earning a salary of between \$20,000 and \$20,001. In other words, N' shows the distribution of incomes among the population—hence, the name "distribution function."[38]

You thus send a memo to your experts requesting the income distribution function for the nation. After much collection of data, they tell you that the income distribution

[37] To simplify our discussion, we are assuming that (1) all tax revenues are based on earned income and that (2) everyone in the population we consider earns some income.

[38] A very similar idea is used in probability. See the optional chapter on Calculus Applied to Probability and Statistics at the website.

function is

$$N'(x) = 7000e^{-(x-30,000)^2/400,000,000}$$

This is in fact the function whose graph is shown in Figure 23 and is an example of a **normal distribution.** Notice that the curve is symmetric around the median income of \$30,000 and that about 7000 people are earning between \$30,000 and \$30,001 annually.[39]

Given this income distribution, your financial experts have come up with the two possible tax policies illustrated in Figures 24 and 25.

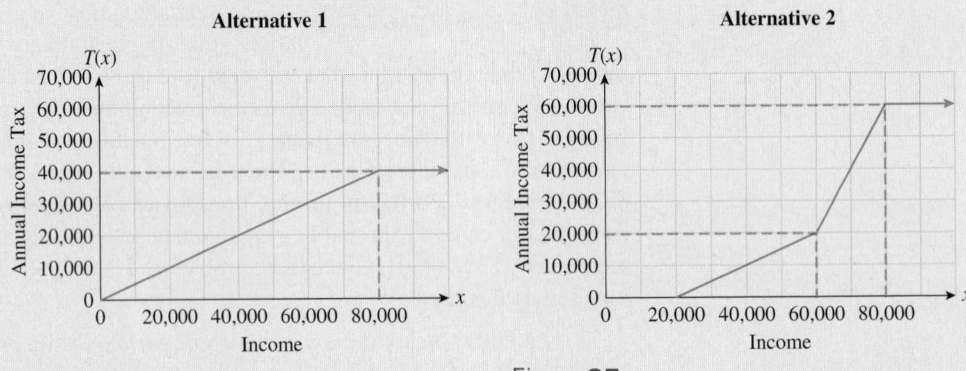

Figure **24**

Figure **25**

In the first alternative, all taxpayers pay half of their income in taxes, except that no one pays more than \$40,000 in taxes. In the second alternative, there are four tax brackets, described by the following table:

Income	*Marginal tax rate*
\$0–20,000	0%
\$20,000–60,000	50%
\$60,000–80,000	200%
Above \$80,000	0%

Now you must determine which alternative will generate more annual tax revenue.

Each of Figures 24 and 25 is the graph of a function, T. Rather than using the formulas for these particular functions, you begin by working with the general situation. You have an income distribution function N' and a tax function T, both functions of annual income. You need to find a formula for total tax revenues. First you decide to use a cutoff so that you need to work only with incomes in some finite bracket $[0, M]$; you might use, for example, $M = \$10$ million (later you will let M approach $+\infty$). Next you subdivide the interval $[0, M]$ into a large number of intervals of small width, Δx. If $[x_{k-1}, x_k]$ is a typical such interval, you wish to calculate the approximate tax revenue from people whose total incomes lie between x_{k-1} and x_k. You will then sum over k to get the total revenue.

You need to know how many people are making incomes between x_{k-1} and x_k. Because $N(x_k)$ people are making incomes *up to* x_k and $N(x_{k-1})$ people are making

[39] You might find it odd that you weren't given the original function N, but it will turn out that you don't need it. How would you compute it?

incomes up to x_{k-1}, the number of people making incomes between x_{k-1} and x_k is $N(x_k) - N(x_{k-1})$. Because x_k is very close to x_{k-1}, the incomes of these people are all approximately equal to x_{k-1} dollars, so each of these taxpayers is paying an annual tax of about $T(x_{k-1})$. This gives a tax revenue of

$$[N(x_k) - N(x_{k-1})]T(x_{k-1})$$

Now you do a clever thing. You write $x_k - x_{k-1} = \Delta x$ and replace $N(x_k) - N(x_{k-1})$ by

$$\frac{N(x_k) - N(x_{k-1})}{\Delta x}\Delta x$$

This gives you a tax revenue of about

$$\frac{N(x_k) - N(x_{k-1})}{\Delta x}T(x_{k-1})\Delta x$$

from wage-earners in the bracket $[x_{k-1}, x_k]$. Summing over k gives an approximate total revenue of

$$\sum_{k=1}^{n} \frac{N(x_k) - N(x_{k-1})}{\Delta x}T(x_{k-1})\Delta x$$

where n is the number of subintervals. The larger n is, the more accurate your estimate will be, so you take the limit of the sum as $n \to \infty$. When you do this, two things happen. First, the quantity

$$\frac{N(x_k) - N(x_{k-1})}{\Delta x}$$

approaches the derivative, $N'(x_{k-1})$. Second, the sum, which you recognize as a Riemann sum, approaches the integral

$$\int_0^M N'(x)T(x)\,dx$$

You now take the limit as $M \to +\infty$ to get

$$\text{Total tax revenue} = \int_0^{+\infty} N'(x)T(x)\,dx$$

This improper integral is fine in theory, but the actual calculation will have to be done numerically, so you stick with the upper limit of \$10 million for now. You will have to check that it is reasonable at the end (notice that, by the graph of N', it appears that extremely few, if any, people earn that much). Now you already have a formula for $N'(x)$, but you still need to write formulas for the tax functions $T(x)$ for both alternatives.

Alternative 1 The graph in Figure 24 rises linearly from 0 to 40,000 as x ranges from 0 to 80,000, and then stays constant at 40,000. The slope of the first part is 40,000/80,000 = 1/2. The taxation function is therefore

$$T(x) = \begin{cases} \frac{x}{2} & \text{if } 0 \le x \le 80{,}000 \\ 40{,}000 & \text{if } x \ge 80{,}000 \end{cases}$$

To perform the integration, you will therefore need to break the integral into two pieces, the first from 0 to 80,000 and the second from 80,000 to 10,000,000. In other words,

$$R_1 = \int_0^{80,000} (7000\, e^{-(x-30,000)^2/400,000,000})\frac{x}{2}\, dx$$
$$+ \int_{80,000}^{10,000,000} (7000\, e^{-(x-30,000)^2/400,000,000})40,000\, dx$$

You decide not to attempt this by hand![40] You use numerical integration software to obtain a grand total of $R_1 = \$3{,}732{,}760{,}000{,}000$, or \$3.73276 trillion (rounded to six significant digits).

Alternative 2 The graph in Figure 25 rises linearly from 0 to 20,000 as x ranges from 20,000 to 60,000, then rises from 20,000 to 60,000 as x ranges from 60,000 to 80,000, and then stays constant at 60,000. The slope of the first incline is 1/2 and the slope of the second incline is 2 (this is why the *marginal* tax rates are 50% and 200% respectively). The taxation function is therefore

$$T(x) = \begin{cases} 0 & \text{if } 0 \le x \le 20,000 \\ \dfrac{x - 20,000}{2} & \text{if } 20,000 \le x \le 60,000 \\ 20,000 + 2(x - 60,000) & \text{if } 60,000 \le x \le 80,000 \\ 60,000 & \text{if } x \ge 80,000 \end{cases}$$

Values of x between 0 and 20,000 do not contribute to the integral, so

$$R_2 = \int_{20,000}^{60,000} (7000\, e^{-(x-30,000)^2/400,000,000}) \left(\frac{x - 20,000}{2}\right) dx$$
$$+ \int_{60,000}^{80,000} (7000\, e^{-(x-30,000)^2/400,000,000})\, [20,000 + 2(x - 60,000)]\, dx$$
$$+ \int_{80,000}^{10,000,000} (7000\, e^{-(x-30,000)^2/400,000,000})60,000\, dx$$

Numerical integration software gives $R_2 = \$1.52016$ trillion—considerably less than Alternative 1. Thus, even though Alternative 2 taxes the wealthy more heavily, it yields less total revenue.

Now what about the cutoff at \$10 million annual income? If you try either integral again with an upper limit of \$100 million, you will see no change in either result to six significant digits. There simply are not enough taxpayers earning an income above \$10,000,000 to make a difference. You conclude that your answers are sufficiently accurate and that the first alternative provides more tax revenue.

Exercises

In Exercises 1–6, calculate the total tax revenue for a country with the given income distribution and tax policies (all currency in dollars).

1. tech Ex $N'(x) = 3000e^{-(x-10,000)^2/10,000}$; 25% tax on all income

2. tech Ex $N'(x) = 3000e^{-(x-10,000)^2/10,000}$; 45% tax on all income

[40] In fact, these integrals cannot be done in elementary terms at all.

3. tech Ex $N'(x) = 5000e^{-(x-30,000)^2/100,000}$; no tax on an income below \$30,000, \$10,000 tax on any income of \$30,000 or above

4. tech Ex $N'(x) = 5000e^{-(x-30,000)^2/100,000}$; no tax on an income below \$50,000, \$20,000 tax on any income of \$50,000 or above

5. tech Ex $N'(x) = 7000\,e^{-(x-30,000)^2/400,000,000}$; $T(x)$ with the following graph:

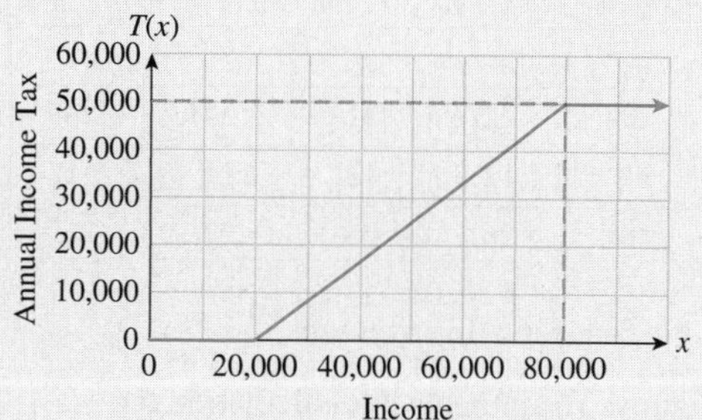

6. tech Ex $N'(x) = 7000\,e^{-(x-30,000)^2/400,000,000}$; $T(x)$ with the following graph:

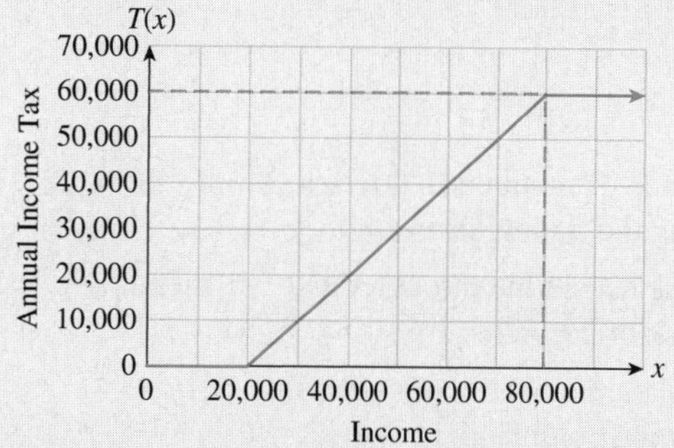

7. Let $P(x)$ be the number of people earning more than x dollars.

a. What is $N(x) + P(x)$?

b. Show that $P'(x) = -N'(x)$.

c. Use integration by parts to show that, if $T(0) = 0$, then the total tax revenue is

$$\int_0^{+\infty} P(x)T'(x)\,dx$$

[Note: You may assume that $T'(x)$ is continuous, but the result is still true if we assume only that $T(x)$ is continuous and piecewise continuously differentiable.]

8. Income tax functions T are most often described, as in the text, by tax brackets and marginal tax rates.

a. If one tax bracket is $a < x \le b$, show that $\int_a^b P(x)\,dx$ is the total income earned in the country that falls into that bracket (P as in the preceding exercise).

b. Use (a) to explain directly why $\int_0^{+\infty} P(x)T'(x)\,dx$ gives the total tax revenue in the case where T is described by tax brackets and constant marginal tax rates in each bracket.

Section 7.3

Example 3 The following table shows Colossal Conglomerate's closing stock prices for 20 consecutive trading days:

Day	1	2	3	4	5	6	7	8	9	10
Price	20	22	21	24	24	23	25	26	20	24
Day	11	12	13	14	15	16	17	18	19	20
Price	26	26	25	27	28	27	29	27	25	24

Plot these prices and the 5-day moving average.

Solution with Technology To automate this calculation on a TI-83/84:

1. Use

```
seq(X,X,1,20)→L1
```
2ND STAT → OPS → 5
STO 2ND STAT → L_1

to enter the sequence of numbers 1 through 20 into the list L_1, representing the trading days.

2. Using the list editor accessible through the STAT menu, enter the daily stock prices in list L_2.
3. You can now calculate the list of 5-day moving averages by using the following command:

```
seq((L2(X)+L2(X-1)+L2(X-2)+L2
  (X-3)+L2(X-4))/5,X,5,20)→L3
```

This has the effect of putting the moving averages into elements 1 through 15 of list L_3.

4. If you wish to plot the moving average on the same graph as the daily prices, you will want the averages in L_3 to match up with the prices in L_2. One way to do this is to put four more entries at the beginning of L_3—say, copies of the first four entries of L_2. The following command accomplishes this:

```
augment(seq(L2(X),X,1,4),L3)→L3
```
2ND STAT → OPS → 9

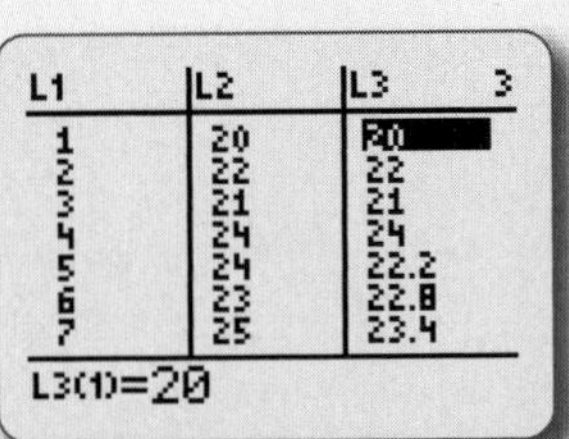

5. You can now graph the prices and moving averages by creating an xyLine scatter plot through the STAT PLOT menu, with L_1 being the Xlist and L_2 being the Ylist for Plot1, and L_1 being the Xlist and L_3 the Ylist for Plot2:

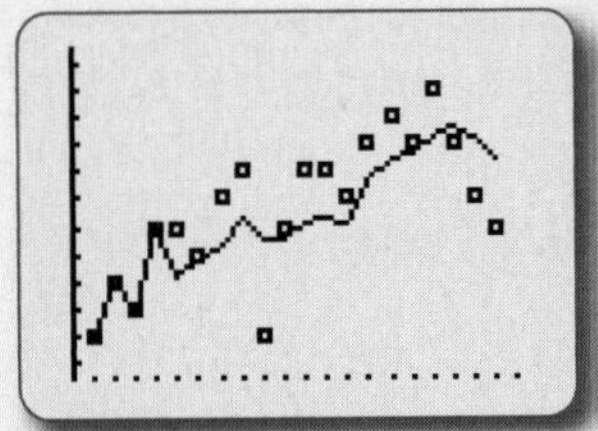

Example 4 Use technology to plot the 3-unit moving average of

$$f(x) = \frac{x}{1+|x|} \qquad (-5 \le x \le 5)$$

Solution with Technology

1. We enter the following:

```
Y1 = X/(1+abs(X))
Y2 = (1/3)fnInt(Y1(T),T,X-3,X)
```

The Y_1 entry is $f(x)$, and the Y_2 entry is a numerical approximation of the 3-unit moving average of $f(x)$:

$$\bar{f}(x) = \frac{1}{3}\int_{x-3}^{x} \frac{t}{1+|t|}\,dt$$

2. We set the viewing window ranges to $-5 \le x \le 5$ and $-1 \le y \le 1$, and plot these curves. (Be patient—the calculator has to do a numerical integration to obtain each point on the graph of the moving average.) The result is shown here (the lower curve is the moving average):

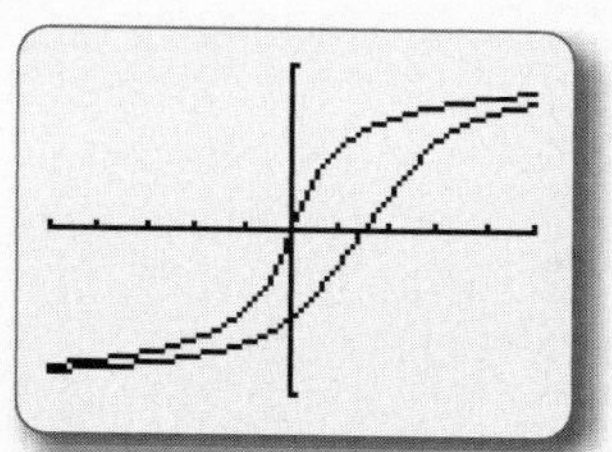

3. Of course, once we've entered `Y1` and `Y2` as above, we can use the calculator to evaluate the moving average at any value of x. For instance, to calculate $\bar{f}(1.2)$ we enter `Y2(1.2)` on the home screen and find

$$\bar{f}(1.2) \approx -0.1196$$

EXCEL Technology Guide

Section 7.3

Example 3 The following table shows Colossal Conglomerate's closing stock prices for 20 consecutive trading days:

Day	1	2	3	4	5	6	7	8	9	10
Price	20	22	21	24	24	23	25	26	20	24
Day	11	12	13	14	15	16	17	18	19	20
Price	26	26	25	27	28	27	29	27	25	24

Plot these prices and the 5-day moving average.

Solution with Technology

1. Compute the moving averages in a column next to the daily prices, as shown here:

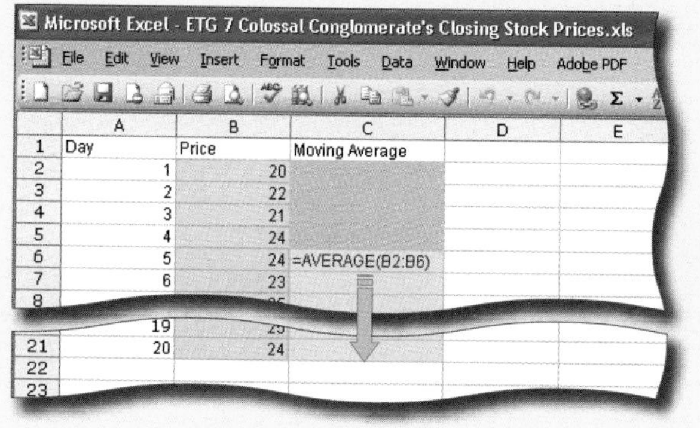

→

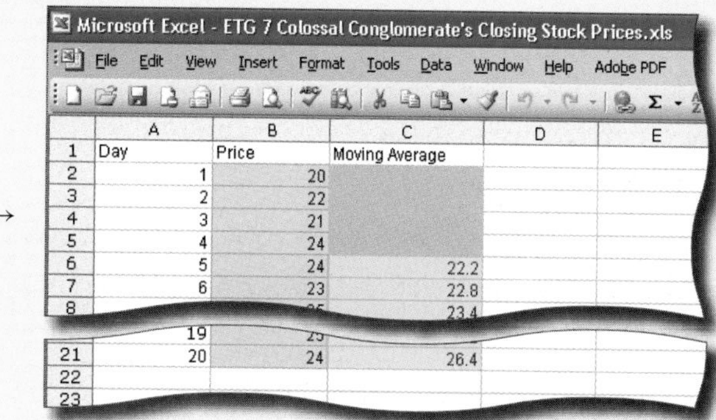

2. You can then graph the average and moving average using a scatter plot.

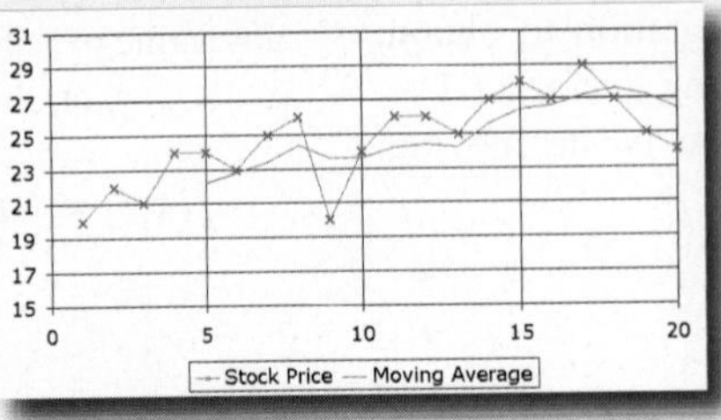

8 Functions of Several Variables

CASE STUDY Modeling Household Income

The Millennium Real Estate Development Corporation is interested in developing housing projects for medium-sized families that have high household incomes. To decide which income bracket to target, the company has asked you, a paid consultant, for an analysis of the relationship of household size to household income and the effect of increasing household size on household income. How can you analyze the relevant data?

Bill Varie/Corbis

Introduction

We have studied functions of a single variable extensively. But not every useful function is a function of only one variable. In fact, most are not. For example, if you operate an online bookstore in competition with Amazon.com, BN.com, and Booksamillion.com, your sales may depend on those of your competitors. Your company's daily revenue might be modeled by a function such as

$$R(x, y, z) = 10{,}000 - 0.01x - 0.02y - 0.01z + 0.00001yz$$

where x, y, and z are the online daily revenues of Amazon.com, BN.com, and Booksamillion.com, respectively. Here, R is a function of three variables because it *depends on* x, y, and z. As we shall see, the techniques of calculus extend readily to such functions. Among the applications we shall look at is optimization: finding, where possible, the maximum or minimum of a function of two or more variables.

8.1 Functions of Several Variables from the Numerical and Algebraic Viewpoints

Recall that a function of one variable is a rule for manufacturing a new number $f(x)$ from a single independent variable x. A function of two or more variables is similar, but the new number now depends on more than one independent variable.

Function of Several Variables

A **real-valued function, f, of** $x, y, z, \ldots$ is a rule for manufacturing a new number, written $f(x, y, z, \ldots)$, from the values of a sequence of independent variables $x, y, z, \ldots$. The function f is called a **real-valued function of two variables** if there are two independent variables, a **real-valued function of three variables** if there are three independent variables, and so on.

quick **Examples**

1. $f(x, y) = x - y$ — Function of two variables
   $f(1, 2) = 1 - 2 = -1$ — Substitute 1 for x and 2 for y.
   $f(2, -1) = 2 - (-1) = 3$ — Substitute 2 for x and -1 for y.
   $f(y, x) = y - x$ — Substitute y for x and x for y.
2. $g(x, y) = x^2 + y^2$ — Function of two variables
   $g(-1, 3) = (-1)^2 + 3^2 = 10$ — Substitute -1 for x and 3 for y.
3. $h(x, y, z) = x + y + xz$ — Function of three variables
   $h(2, 2, -2) = 2 + 2 + 2(-2) = 0$ — Substitute 2 for x, 2 for y, and -2 for z.

Figure 1 illustrates the concept of a function of two variables: In goes a pair of numbers and out comes a single number.

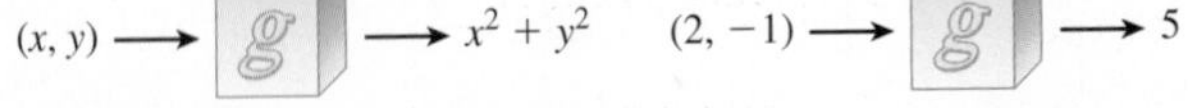

$(x, y) \longrightarrow$ [g] $\longrightarrow x^2 + y^2$ $\quad$ $(2, -1) \longrightarrow$ [g] $\longrightarrow 5$

Figure 1

As with functions of one variable, functions of several variables can be represented numerically (using a table of values), algebraically (using a formula as in the above examples), and sometimes graphically[1] (using a graph).

Let's now look at a number of examples of interesting functions of several variables.

Roy Mehta/Getty Images

Example 1 Cost Function

You own a company that makes two models of speakers: the Ultra Mini and the Big Stack. Your total monthly cost (in dollars) to make x Ultra Minis and y Big Stacks is given by

$$C(x, y) = 10{,}000 + 20x + 40y$$

What is the significance of each term in this formula?

Solution The terms have meanings similar to those we saw for linear cost functions of a single variable. Let us look at the terms one at a time.

Constant Term Consider the monthly cost of making no speakers at all ($x = y = 0$). We find

$$C(0, 0) = 10{,}000 \qquad \text{Cost of making no speakers is \$10,000.}$$

Thus, the constant term 10,000 is the **fixed cost,** the amount you have to pay each month even if you make no speakers.

Coefficients of x and y Suppose you make a certain number of Ultra Minis and Big Stacks one month and the next month you increase production by one Ultra Mini. The costs are

$$\begin{aligned} C(x, y) &= 10{,}000 + 20x + 40y && \text{First Month} \\ C(x + 1, y) &= 10{,}000 + 20(x + 1) + 40y && \text{Second Month} \\ &= 10{,}000 + 20x + 20 + 40y \\ &= C(x, y) + 20 \end{aligned}$$

Thus, each Ultra Mini adds \$20 to the total cost. We say that \$20 is the **marginal cost** of each Ultra Mini. Similarly, because of the term $40y$, each Big Stack adds \$40 to the total cost. The marginal cost of each Big Stack is \$40.

using *Technology*

See the Technology Guides at the end of the chapter to find out how you can use a TI-83/84 and Excel to display various values of $C(x, y)$.

This is an example of a linear function of two variables. The coefficients of x and y play roles similar to that of the slope of a line. In particular, they give the rates of change of the function as each variable increases while the other stays constant (think about it). We shall say more about linear functions below.

+ *Before we go on...* In Example 1, which values of x and y may we substitute into $C(x, y)$? Certainly we must have $x \geq 0$ and $y \geq 0$ because it makes no sense to speak of manufacturing a negative number of speakers. Also, there is certainly some upper bound to the number of speakers that can be made in a month. The bound might take one of several forms. The number of each model may be bounded—say $x \leq 100$ and $y \leq 75$. The inequalities $0 \leq x \leq 100$ and $0 \leq y \leq 75$ describe the region in the plane shaded in Figure 2.

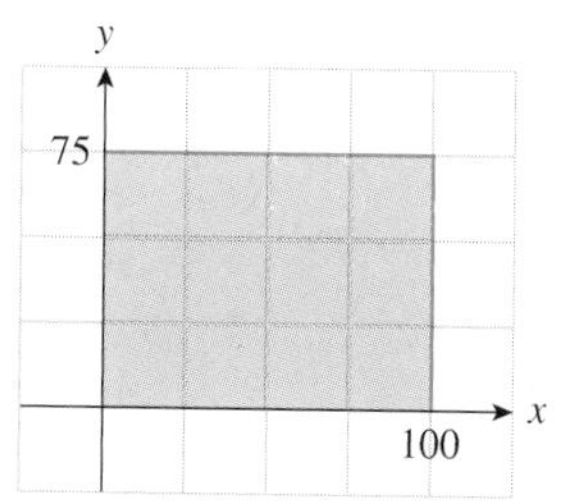

Figure **2**

[1] See the next section.

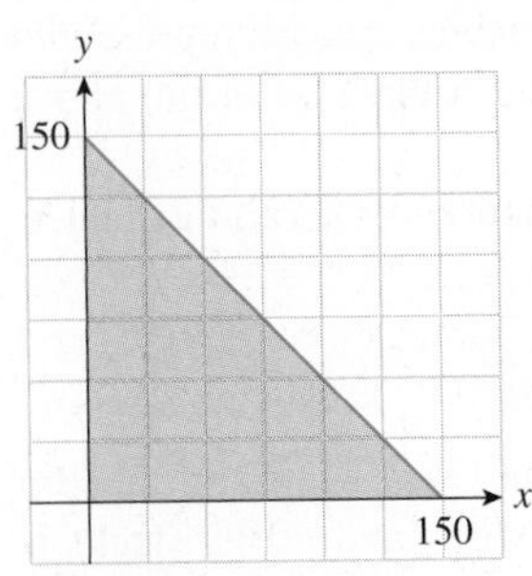

Figure **3**

Another possibility is that the *total* number of speakers is bounded—say, $x + y \le 150$. This, together with $x \ge 0$ and $y \ge 0$, describes the region shaded in Figure 3.

In either case, the region shown represents the pairs (x, y) for which $C(x, y)$ is defined. Just as with a function of one variable, we call this region the **domain** of the function. As before, when the domain is not given explicitly, we agree to take the largest domain possible. ■

Example **2** Faculty Salaries

David Katz came up with the following function for the salary of a professor with 10 years of teaching experience in a large university.

$$S(x, y, z) = 13{,}005 + 230x + 18y + 102z$$

Here, S is the salary in 1969–1970 in dollars per year, x is the number of books the professor has published, y is the number of articles published, and z is the number of "excellent" articles published.* What salary do you expect that a professor with 10 years' experience earned in 1969–1970 if she published two books, 20 articles, and 3 "excellent" articles?

Solution All we need to do is calculate

$$\begin{aligned} S(2, 20, 3) &= 13{,}005 + 230(2) + 18(20) + 102(3) \\ &= \$14{,}131 \end{aligned}$$

* David A. Katz, "Faculty Salaries, Promotions and Productivity at a Large University," *American Economic Review,* June 1973, pp. 469–477. Prof. Katz's equation actually included other variables, such as the number of dissertations supervised; our equation assumes that all of these are zero.

+ *Before we go on...* In Example 1, we gave a linear function of two variables. In Example 2 we have a linear function of three variables. Katz came up with his model by surveying a large number of faculty members and then finding the linear function "best" fitting the data. Such models are called **multiple linear regression** models. In the Case Study at the end of this chapter, we shall see a spreadsheet method of finding the coefficients of a multiple regression model from a set of observed data.

What does this model say about the value of a single book or a single article? If a book takes 15 times as long to write as an article, how would you recommend that a professor spend her writing time? ■

Here are two simple kinds of functions of several variables.

Linear Function

A **linear function of the variables** $x_1, x_2, \ldots, x_n$ is a function of the form

$$f(x_1, x_2, \ldots, x_n) = a_0 + a_1x_1 + \cdots + a_nx_n \qquad (a_0, a_1, a_2, \ldots, a_n \text{ constants})$$

quick **Examples**

1. $f(x, y) = 3x - 5y$ — Linear function of x and y

2. $C(x, y) = 10{,}000 + 20x + 40y$ — Example 1

3. $S(x, y, z) = 13{,}005 + 230x + 18y + 102z$ — Example 2

mathematics At Work

Deb Farace

TITLE Sr. National Accounts Manager
INSTITUTION PepsiCo Beverages & Foods

Working for the national accounts division for PepsiCo Beverages & Foods, I need to understand applied mathematics in order to control the variables associated with making profit, manufacturing, production, and most importantly selling our products to mass club channels. Examples of these large, "quality product at great value" outlets are Wal*Mart, Costco and Target. The types of products I handle include Gatorade, Tropicana, and Quaker foods.

Our studies show that the grocery store channels' sales are flattening or declining as a whole in lieu of large, national outlets like the above. So in order to maximize growth in this segment of our business, I meet with regional buying offices of these chains and discuss various packaging, pricing, product, promotional and shipping options so that we can successfully compete in the market.

A number of factors must be taken into consideration in order to meet my company's financial forecasts. Precision using mathematical models is key here, since so many variables can impact last-minute decision-making. Extended variables of supply-and-demand include time of year, competitive landscape, special coupon distribution and other promotions, selling cycles and holidays, size of the outlets, and yes—even the weather.

For example, it's natural to assume that when it's hot outside people will buy more thirst-quenching products like Gatorade. But since our business is so precise, we need to understand mathematically how the weather affects sales. A mathematical model developed by Gatorade analyzes long-term data that impacts sales by geographic market due to the weather. Its findings include exponentially increased sales of Gatorade for each degree above the 90 degrees. I share our mathematical analysis like this study with buyers and negotiate larger orders based on up-to-the-minute weather forecasts. The result: increased sales of product based on math.

Interaction Function

If we add to a linear function one or more terms of the form bx_ix_j (b a nonzero constant and $i \neq j$), we get a **second-order interaction function.**

quick Examples

1. $C(x, y) = 10{,}000 + 20x + 40y + 0.1xy$

2. $R(x, y, z) = 10{,}000 - 0.01x - 0.02y - 0.01z + 0.00001yz$

So far, we have been specifying functions of several variables **algebraically**—by using algebraic formulas. If you have ever studied statistics, you are probably familiar with statistical tables. These tables may also be viewed as representing functions **numerically,** as the next example shows.

Example 3 Function Represented Numerically: Body Mass Index

The following table lists some values of the "body mass index," which gives a measure of the massiveness of your body, taking height into account.* The variable w represents

*It is interesting that weight-lifting competitions are usually based on weight, rather than body mass index. As a consequence, taller people are at a significant disadvantage in weight-lifting competitions because they must compete with shorter, stockier people of the same weight. (An extremely thin, very tall person can weigh as much as a muscular short person, although his body mass index would be significantly lower.) SOURCES: *Shape Up America*/National Institute of Health/*The New York Times,* May 2, 1999, p. WK3.

your weight in pounds, and h represents your height in inches. An individual with a body mass index of 25 or above is generally considered overweight.

$w \rightarrow$

$h \downarrow$	130	140	150	160	170	180	190	200	210
60	25.2	27.1	29.1	31.0	32.9	34.9	36.8	38.8	40.7
61	24.4	26.2	28.1	30.0	31.9	33.7	35.6	37.5	39.4
62	23.6	25.4	27.2	29.0	30.8	32.7	34.5	36.3	38.1
63	22.8	24.6	26.4	28.1	29.9	31.6	33.4	35.1	36.9
64	22.1	23.8	25.5	27.2	28.9	30.7	32.4	34.1	35.8
65	21.5	23.1	24.8	26.4	28.1	29.7	31.4	33.0	34.7
66	20.8	22.4	24.0	25.6	27.2	28.8	30.4	32.0	33.6
67	20.2	21.8	23.3	24.9	26.4	28.0	29.5	31.1	32.6
68	19.6	21.1	22.6	24.1	25.6	27.2	28.7	30.2	31.7
69	19.0	20.5	22.0	23.4	24.9	26.4	27.8	29.3	30.8
70	18.5	19.9	21.4	22.8	24.2	25.6	27.0	28.5	29.9
71	18.0	19.4	20.8	22.1	23.5	24.9	26.3	27.7	29.1
72	17.5	18.8	20.2	21.5	22.9	24.2	25.6	26.9	28.3
73	17.0	18.3	19.6	20.9	22.3	23.6	24.9	26.2	27.5
74	16.6	17.8	19.1	20.4	21.7	22.9	24.2	25.5	26.7
75	16.1	17.4	18.6	19.8	21.1	22.3	23.6	24.8	26.0
76	15.7	16.9	18.1	19.3	20.5	21.7	22.9	24.2	25.4

As the table shows, the value of the body mass index depends on two quantities: w and h. Let us write $M(w, h)$ for the body mass index function. What are $M(140, 62)$ and $M(210, 63)$?

Solution We can read the answers from the table:

$$M(140, 62) = 25.4 \qquad w = 140 \text{ lb}, h = 62 \text{ in.}$$

and

$$M(210, 63) = 36.9 \qquad w = 210 \text{ lb}, h = 63 \text{ in.}$$

The function $M(w, h)$ is actually given by the formula

$$M(w, h) = \frac{0.45w}{(0.0254h)^2}$$

[The factor 0.45 converts the weight to kilograms, and 0.0254 converts the height to meters. If w is in kilograms and h is in meters, the formula is simpler: $M(w, h) = w/h^2$.]

using *Technology*

See the Technology Guides at the end of the chapter to find out how you can use Excel to create the table in this example.

Distance and Related Functions

Newton's Law of Gravity states that the gravitational force exerted by one particle on another depends on their masses and the distance between them. The distance between two particles in the xy-plane can be expressed as a function of their coordinates, as follows:

Distance Formula

The distance between the points $P(x_1, y_1)$ and $Q(x_2, y_2)$ is

$$d = \sqrt{(x_2 - x_1)^2 + (y_2 - y_1)^2} = \sqrt{(\Delta x)^2 + (\Delta y)^2}$$

Derivation

The distance d is shown in the figure below.

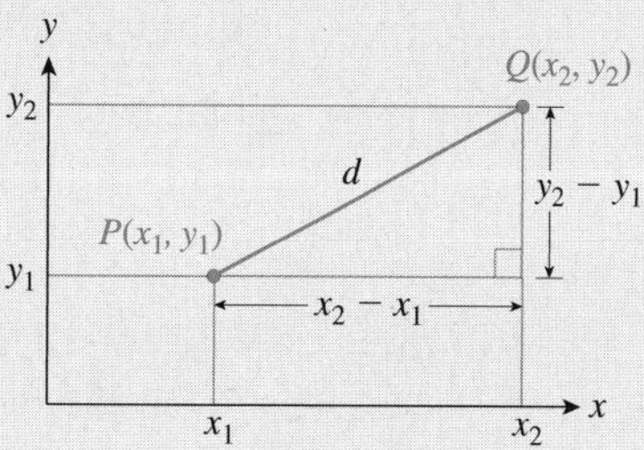

By the Pythagorean theorem applied to the right triangle shown, we get

$$d^2 = (x_2 - x_1)^2 + (y_2 - y_1)^2$$

Taking square roots (d is a distance, so we take the positive square root), we get the distance formula. Notice that if we switch x_1 with x_2 or y_1 with y_2, we get the same result.

quick **Examples**

1. The distance between the points $(3, -2)$ and $(-1, 1)$ is

$$d = \sqrt{(-1 - 3)^2 + (1 + 2)^2} = \sqrt{25} = 5$$

2. The distance from (x, y) to the origin $(0, 0)$ is

$$d = \sqrt{(x - 0)^2 + (y - 0)^2} = \sqrt{x^2 + y^2} \qquad \text{Distance to the origin}$$

The set of all points (x, y) whose distance from the origin $(0, 0)$ is a fixed quantity r is a circle centered at the origin with radius r. From the second Quick Example, we get the following equation for the circle centered at the origin with radius r:

$$\sqrt{x^2 + y^2} = r \qquad \text{Distance from the origin} = r$$

Squaring both sides gives the following equation, which we use in later sections:

Equation of the Circle of Radius *r* Centered at the Origin

$$x^2 + y^2 = r^2$$

quick **Examples**

1. The circle of radius 1 centered at the origin has equation $x^2 + y^2 = 1$.

2. The circle of radius 2 centered at the origin has equation $x^2 + y^2 = 4$.

3. The circle of radius 3 centered at the origin has equation $x^2 + y^2 = 9$.

Now, let's return to Newton's Law of Gravity. According to Newton's Law, the gravitational force exerted on a particle with mass m by another particle with mass M is given by the following function of distance:

$$F(r) = G\frac{Mm}{r^2}$$

Here, r is the distance in meters between the two particles, the masses M and m are given in kilograms, $G \approx 6.67 \times 10^{-11}$, and the resulting force is measured in newtons.[2]

Example 4 Newton's Law of Gravity

Find the gravitational force exerted on a particle with mass m situated at the point (x, y) by another particle with mass M situated at the point (a, b). Express the answer as a function F of the coordinates of the particle with mass m.

Solution The formula above for gravitational force is expressed as a function of the distance, r, between the two particles. Because we are given the coordinates of the two particles, we can express r in terms of these coordinates using the formula for distance:

$$r = \sqrt{(x-a)^2 + (y-b)^2}$$

Substituting for r, we get

$$F(x, y) = G\frac{Mm}{(x-a)^2 + (y-b)^2}$$

+*Before we go on...* In Example 4, notice that $F(a, b)$ is not defined because substituting $x = a$ and $y = b$ makes the denominator equal 0. Thus, the largest possible domain of F excludes the point (a, b). Because (a, b) is the only value of (x, y) for which F is not defined, we deduce that *the domain of F consists of all points (x, y) except for (a, b)*. In other words, the domain of F is the whole xy-plane with the single point (a, b) missing.[3] ■

Q: *Why have we expressed F as a function of x and y only, and not also as a function of a and b?*

A: It's a matter of interpretation. When we write F as a function of x and y, we are thinking of a and b as *constants*. For example, (a, b) could be the coordinates of the sun—which we often assume to be fixed in space—while (x, y) could be the coordinates of the earth—which is moving around the sun. In that case it is most natural to think of x and y as variables and a and b as constants. In another context we may indeed want to consider F as a function of four variables, x, y, a, and b. ■

[2] A newton is the force that will cause a 1-kilogram mass to accelerate at 1 m/sec^2.

[3] Mathematicians often refer to this as a "punctured plane."

8.1 EXERCISES

● denotes basic skills exercises

tech Ex indicates exercises that should be solved using technology

For each function in Exercises 1–4, evaluate ***(a)*** $f(0, 0)$; ***(b)*** $f(1, 0)$; ***(c)*** $f(0, -1)$; ***(d)*** $f(a, 2)$; ***(e)*** $f(y, x)$; ***(f)*** $f(x+h, y+k)$ hint [see Quick Examples p. 540]

1. ● $f(x, y) = x^2 + y^2 - x + 1$

2. ● $f(x, y) = x^2 - y - xy + 1$

3. ● $f(x, y) = 0.2x + 0.1y - 0.01xy$

4. ● $f(x, y) = 0.4x - 0.5y - 0.05xy$

For each function in Exercises 5–8, evaluate ***(a)*** $g(0, 0, 0)$; ***(b)*** $g(1, 0, 0)$; ***(c)*** $g(0, 1, 0)$; ***(d)*** $g(z, x, y)$; ***(e)*** $g(x+h, y+k, z+l)$, *provided such a value exists.*

5. ● $g(x, y, z) = e^{x+y+z}$ **6.** ● $g(x, y, z) = \ln(x + y + z)$

7. ● $g(x, y, z) = \dfrac{xyz}{x^2 + y^2 + z^2}$

8. ● $g(x, y, z) = \dfrac{e^{xyz}}{x + y + z}$

9. ● Let $f(x, y, z) = 1.5 + 2.3x - 1.4y - 2.5z$. Complete the following sentences.

a. f ___ by ___ units for every 1 unit of increase in x.

b. f ___ by ___ units for every 1 unit of increase in y.

c. ______ by 2.5 units for every ______.

hint [see Example 1]

10. ● Let $g(x, y, z) = 0.01x + 0.02y - 0.03z - 0.05$. Complete the following sentences.

a. g ___ by ___ units for every 1 unit of increase in z.

b. g ___ by ___ units for every 1 unit of increase in x.

c. ______ by 0.02 units for every ______.

In Exercises 11–18, classify each function as linear, interaction, or neither. hint [see Quick Examples pp. 542, 543]

11. ● $L(x, y) = 3x - 2y + 6xy - 4y^2$

12. ● $L(x, y, z) = 3x - 2y + 6xz$

13. ● $P(x_1, x_2, x_3) = 0.4 + 2x_1 - x_3$

14. ● $Q(x_1, x_2) = 4x_2 - 0.5x_1 - x_1^2$

15. ● $f(x, y, z) = \dfrac{x + y - z}{3}$

16. ● $g(x, y, z) = \dfrac{xz - 3yz + z^2}{4z} \quad (z \neq 0)$

17. ● $g(x, y, z) = \dfrac{xz - 3yz + z^2 y}{4z} \quad (z \neq 0)$

18. ● $f(x, y) = x + y + xy + x^2 y$

In Exercises 19 and 20, use the given tabular representation of the function f to compute the quantities asked for. hint [see Example 3]

19. ●

$y \downarrow$ \ $x \rightarrow$	10	20	30	40
10	−1	107	162	−3
20	−6	194	294	−14
30	−11	281	426	−25
40	−16	368	558	−36

a. $f(20, 10)$ **b.** $f(40, 20)$

c. $f(10, 20) - f(20, 10)$

20. ●

$y \downarrow$ \ $x \rightarrow$	10	20	30	40
10	162	107	−5	−7
20	294	194	−22	−30
30	426	281	−39	−53
40	558	368	−56	−76

a. $f(10, 30)$ **b.** $f(20, 10)$

c. $f(10, 40) + f(10, 20)$

tech Ex *In Exercises 21 and 22, use a spreadsheet or some other method to complete the given tables.*

21. ● $P(x, y) = x - 0.3y + 0.45xy$

$y \downarrow$ \ $x \rightarrow$	10	20	30	40
10				
20				
30				
40				

22. ● $Q(x, y) = 0.4x + 0.1y - 0.06xy$

$y \downarrow$ \ $x \rightarrow$	10	20	30	40
10				
20				
30				
40				

23. tech Ex The following statistical table lists some values of the "Inverse F distribution" ($\alpha = 0.5$):

$n \rightarrow$, $d \downarrow$

	1	2	3	4	5	6	7	8	9	10
1	161.4	199.5	215.7	224.6	230.2	234.0	236.8	238.9	240.5	241.9
2	18.51	19.00	19.16	19.25	19.30	19.33	19.35	19.37	19.39	19.40
3	10.13	9.552	9.277	9.117	9.013	8.941	8.887	8.812	8.812	8.785
4	7.709	6.944	6.591	6.388	6.256	6.163	6.094	5.999	5.999	5.964
5	6.608	5.786	5.409	5.192	5.050	4.950	4.876	4.772	4.772	4.735
6	5.987	5.143	4.757	4.534	4.387	4.284	4.207	4.099	4.099	4.060
7	5.591	4.737	4.347	4.120	3.972	3.866	3.787	3.677	3.677	3.637
8	5.318	4.459	4.066	3.838	3.688	3.581	3.500	3.388	3.388	3.347
9	5.117	4.256	3.863	3.633	3.482	3.374	3.293	3.179	3.179	3.137
10	4.965	4.103	3.708	3.478	3.326	3.217	3.135	3.020	3.020	2.978

In Excel, you can compute the value of this function at (n, d) by the formula

`= FINV(0.05, n, d)` The 0.05 is the value of alpha (α).

Use Excel to re-create this table.

24. tech Ex The formula for the body mass index $M(w, h)$, if w is given in kilograms and h is given in meters, is

$$M(w, h) = \frac{w}{h^2}$$ See Example 3.

Use this formula to complete the following table in Excel:

$w \rightarrow$, $h \downarrow$

	70	80	90	100	110	120	130
1.8							
1.85							
1.9							
1.95							
2							
2.05							
2.1							
2.15							
2.2							
2.25							
2.3							

tech Ex *In Exercises 25–28, use either a graphing calculator or a spreadsheet to complete each table. Express all your answers as decimals rounded to four decimal places.*

25. ●

x	y	$f(x, y) = x^2\sqrt{1 + xy}$
3	1	
1	15	
0.3	0.5	
56	4	

26. ●

x	y	$f(x, y) = x^2 e^y$
0	2	
−1	5	
1.4	2.5	
11	9	

27. ●

x	y	$f(x, y) = x \ln(x^2 + y^2)$
3	1	
1.4	−1	
e	0	
0	e	

28. ●

x	y	$f(x, y) = \frac{x}{x^2 - y^2}$
−1	2	
0	0.2	
0.4	2.5	
10	0	

29. Brand Z's annual sales are affected by the sales of related products X and Y as follows: Each \$1 million increase in sales of brand X causes a \$2.1 million decline in sales of brand Z, whereas each \$1 million increase in sales of brand Y results in an increase of \$0.4 million in sales of brand Z. Currently, brands X, Y, and Z are each selling \$6 million per year. Model the sales of brand Z using a linear function.

30. Let $f(x, y, z) = 43.2 - 2.3x + 11.3y - 4.5z$. Complete the following: An increase of 1 in the value of y causes the value of f to ___ by ___, whereas increasing the value of x by 1 and ___ the value of z by ___ causes a decrease of 11.3 in the value of f.

In Exercises 31–34, find the distance between the given pairs of points.

31. ● $(1, -1)$ and $(2, -2)$ **32.** ● $(1, 0)$ and $(6, 1)$

33. ● $(a, 0)$ and $(0, b)$ **34.** ● (a, a) and (b, b)

35. Find the value of k such that $(1, k)$ is equidistant from $(0, 0)$ and $(2, 1)$.

36. Find the value of k such that (k, k) is equidistant from $(-1, 0)$ and $(0, 2)$.

37. Describe the set of points (x, y) such that $(x-2)^2+(y+1)^2=9$.

38. Describe the set of points (x, y) such that $(x+3)^2+(y-1)^2=4$.

Applications

39. ● ***Marginal Cost*** Your weekly cost (in dollars) to manufacture x cars and y trucks is

$$C(x, y) = 240{,}000 + 6000x + 4000y$$

What is the marginal cost of a car? Of a truck?

40. ● ***Marginal Cost*** Your weekly cost (in dollars) to manufacture x bicycles and y tricycles is

$$C(x, y) = 24{,}000 + 60x + 20y$$

What is the marginal cost of a bicycle? Of a tricycle?

41. ● ***Marginal Cost*** Your sales of online video and audio clips are booming. Your Internet provider, Moneydrain.com, wants to get in on the action and has offered you unlimited technical assistance and consulting if you agree to pay Moneydrain 3¢ for every video clip and 4¢ for every audio clip you sell on the site. Further, Moneydrain agrees to charge you only $10 per month to host your site. Set up a (monthly) cost function for the scenario, and describe each variable.

42. ● ***Marginal Cost*** Your Cabaret nightspot "Jazz on Jupiter" has become an expensive proposition: You are paying monthly costs of $50,000 just to keep the place running. On top of that, your regular cabaret artist is charging you $3000 per performance, and your jazz ensemble is charging $1000 per hour. Set up a (monthly) cost function for the scenario, and describe each variable.

Scientific Research *In 2004, physics research in the U.S appeared to be losing ground to Europe and other countries as evidenced in the following graph. The graph shows the number of articles published in the prominent physics research journal Physical Review:*[4]

Articles in *Physical Review* (Thousands)

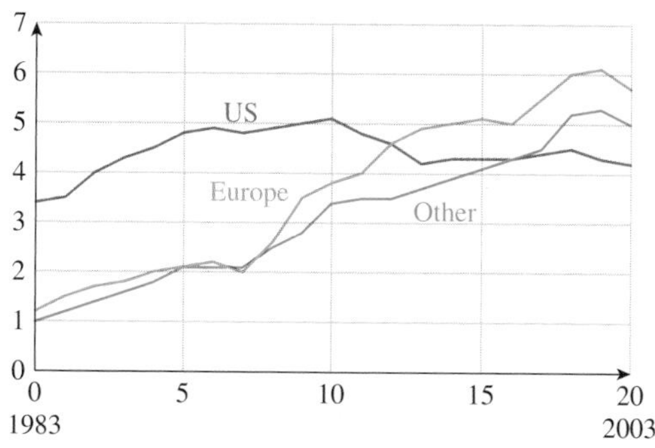

Exercises 43 and 44 are based on mathematical models derived from the graphical data shown above.

43. ● In each year from 1983 to 2003, the percentage y of research articles in *Physical Review* written by researchers in the U.S. can be approximated by

$$y = 82 - 0.78t - 1.02x \text{ percentage points} \quad (0 \le t \le 20)$$

where t is the year since 1983 and x is the percentage of articles written by researchers in Europe.

a. In 2003, researchers in Europe wrote 38% of the articles published by the journal that year. What percentage was written by researchers in the U.S.?

b. In 1983, researchers in the U.S. wrote 61% of the articles published that year. What percentage was written by researchers in Europe?

c. What are the units of measurement of the coefficient of t?

44. ● The number z of research articles in *Physical Review* that were written by researchers in the U.S. from 1993 through 2003 can be approximated by

$$z = 5960 - 0.71x + 0.50y \quad (3000 \le x, y \le 6000)$$

articles each year, where x is the number of articles written by researchers in Europe and y is the number written by researchers in other countries (excluding Europe and the U.S.).

a. In the year 2000, approximately 5500 articles were written by researchers in Europe, and 4500 by researchers in other countries. How many articles (to the nearest 100) were written by researchers in the U.S.?

b. According to the model, if 5000 articles were written in Europe and an equal number by researchers in the U.S. and other countries, what would that number be?

c. What is the significance of the fact that the coefficient of x is negative?

45. ● ***Career Choices*** Graduating MBAs who do not become consultants often join investment banking, venture capital, or high-technology companies. The following linear model is based on data on Harvard Business School MBAs:[5]

$$c(x, y, z) = 48.4 + 0.06x - 0.40y - 1.3z$$

Here, c is the percentage of MBAs who become consultants, x is the percentage who join high technology companies, y is the percentage who join investment banking companies, and z is the percentage who join venture capital companies.

a. In 1999, approximately 18% of Harvard MBAs joined high technology companies, 12% joined investment banking companies, and 12% joined venture capital companies. Use the model to estimate the percentage who became consultants. (Round to the nearest one percent.)

[4] SOURCE: The American Physical Society/*New York Times,* May 3, 2003, p. A1.

[5] The model is based on a regression of the data from 1995 to 1999. SOURCE: Harvard Business School/*The New York Times,* January 19, 2000, p. C1.

b. In 1997, approximately 32% of Harvard MBAs became consultants, 16% joined investment banking companies, and 8% joined venture capital companies. Use the model to estimate the percentage who joined high technology companies. (Round to the nearest one percent.)

c. Complete the following: For every 1-point rise in the percentage of Harvard MBAs who join investment banking companies, there is a ___-point ___ in the percentage who become consultants, assuming the number joining high technology companies and venture capital companies are unchanged.

46. ● ***Career Choices*** Refer to the preceding exercise. An alternative, interaction model based on Harvard Business School MBAs is

$$c(y, z) = 44.3 - 0.28y + 0.04yz - 1.6z$$

Here, c is the percentage of MBAs who become consultants, y is the percentage who join investment banking companies, and z is the percentage who join venture capital companies.[6]

a. In 1999, approximately 12% joined investment banking companies and 12% joined venture capital companies. Use the model to estimate the percentage who became consultants. (Round to the nearest one percent.)

b. In 1997, approximately 32% of Harvard MBAs became consultants and 8% joined venture capital companies. Use the model to estimate the percentage who joined investment banking companies. (Round to the nearest one percent.)

47. ***Online Revenue*** Let us look once again at the example we used to introduce the chapter. Your major online bookstore is in direct competition with Amazon.com, BN.com, and Borders.com. Your company's daily revenue in dollars is given by

$$R(x, y, z) = 10{,}000 - 0.01x - 0.02y - 0.01z + 0.00001yz$$

where x, y, and z are the online daily revenues of Amazon.com, BN.com, and Borders.com, respectively.

a. If, on a certain day, Amazon.com shows revenue of \$12,000, while BN.com and Borders.com each show \$5000, what does the model predict for your company's revenue that day?

b. If Amazon.com and BN.com each show daily revenue of \$5000, give an equation showing how your daily revenue depends on that of Borders.com.

48. ***Online Revenue*** Repeat the preceding exercise, using the revised revenue function

$$R(x, y, z) = \$20{,}000 - 0.02x - 0.04y - 0.01z + 0.00001yz$$

49. ***Modeling the Growth of Wireless with a Linear Function*** The following table shows the approximate number of wireless phone subscribers and the number of cell sites in the U.S. in 1997, 2002, and 2005.[7]

	1997	2002	2005
Subscribers (millions)	60	110	200
Cell sites (thousands)	50	100	180

Model the number of subscribers as a function of the number of cell sites and time, using a linear function of the form

$$s(c, t) = Ac + Bt + C \quad (A, B, C \text{ constants})$$

where s represents the number of subscribers (in millions), c represents the number of cell sites (in thousands), and t is time in years since 1997.

50. ***Modeling Sales with a Linear Function*** The following table shows Toyota's sales, in millions of vehicles, in the U.S. and Japan in 1991, 1996, and 2001.[8]

	1991	1996	2001
U.S.	1.0	1.2	1.7
Japan	2.3	2.0	1.7

Model Toyota sales in Japan as a function of sales in the U.S. and time, using a linear function of the form

$$j(u, t) = Au + Bt + C \quad (A, B, C \text{ constants})$$

where j represents annual Toyota sales (in millions of vehicles) in Japan, u represents sales in the U.S., and t is time in years since 1991.

51. ***Utility*** Suppose your newspaper is trying to decide between two competing desktop publishing software packages, Macro Publish and Turbo Publish. You estimate that if you purchase x copies of Macro Publish and y copies of Turbo Publish, your company's daily productivity will be

$$U(x, y) = 6x^{0.8}y^{0.2} + x$$

where $U(x, y)$ is measured in pages per day (U is called a *utility function*). If $x = y = 10$, calculate the effect of increasing x by one unit, and interpret the result.

52. ***Housing Costs***[9] The cost C (in dollars) of building a house is related to the number k of carpenters used and the number e of electricians used by

$$C(k, e) = 15{,}000 + 50k^2 + 60e^2$$

If $k = e = 10$, compare the effects of increasing k by one unit and of increasing e by one unit. Interpret the result.

[6] Ibid.

[7] 2002 figures are estimates. SOURCES: Cellular Telecommunications and Internet association/*New York Times,* February 14, 2002, p. G1, *Wired.com,* 2005.

[8] SOURCE: Toyota Motor North America/*New York Times,* February 17, 2002, p. BU1.

[9] Based on an Exercise in *Introduction to Mathematical Economics* by A. L. Ostrosky Jr. and J. V. Koch (Waveland Press, Illinois, 1979).

53. *Volume* The volume of an ellipsoid with cross-sectional radii a, b, and c is $V(a,b,c) = \frac{4}{3}\pi abc$.

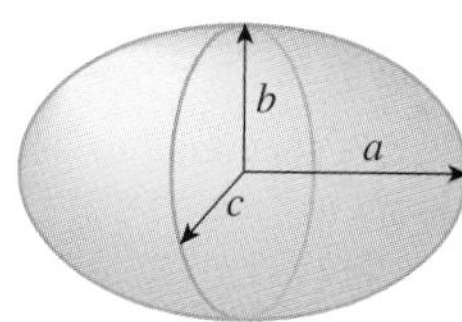

a. Find at least two sets of values for a, b and c such that $V(a,b,c) = 1$.

b. Find the value of a such that $V(a,a,a) = 1$, and describe the resulting ellipsoid.

54. *Volume* The volume of a right elliptical cone with height h and radii a and b of its base is $V(a,b,h) = \frac{1}{3}\pi abh$.

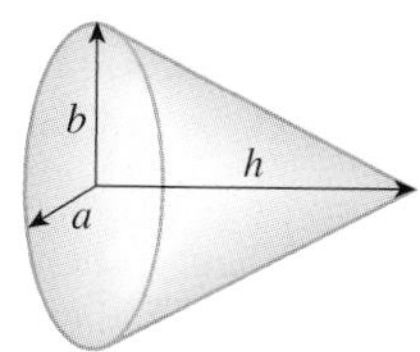

a. Find at least two sets of values for a, b and h such that $V(a,b,h) = 1$.

b. Find the value of a such that $V(a,a,a) = 1$, and describe the resulting cone.

Exercises 55–58 involve "Cobb-Douglas" productivity functions. These functions have the form

$$P(x,y) = Kx^a y^{1-a}$$

where P stands for the number of items produced per year, x is the number of employees, and y is the annual operating budget. (The numbers K and a are constants that depend on the situation we are looking at, with $0 \le a \le 1$.*)*

55. ● ***Productivity*** How many items will be produced per year by a company with 100 employees and an annual operating budget of \$500,000 if $K = 1000$ and $a = 0.5$? (Round your answer to one significant digit.)

56. ● ***Productivity*** How many items will be produced per year by a company with 50 employees and an annual operating budget of \$1,000,000 if $K = 1000$ and $a = 0.5$? (Round your answer to one significant digit.)

57. *Modeling Production with Cobb-Douglas* Two years ago my piano manufacturing plant employed 1000 workers, had an operating budget of \$1 million, and turned out 100 pianos. Last year I slashed the operating budget to \$10,000, and production dropped to 10 pianos.

a. Use the data for each of the two years and the Cobb-Douglas formula to obtain two equations in K and a.

b. Take logs of both sides in each equation and obtain two linear equations in a and $\log K$.

c. Solve these equations to obtain values for a and K.

d. Use these values in the Cobb-Douglas formula to predict production if I increase the operating budget back to \$1 million but lay off half the work force.

58. *Modeling Production with Cobb-Douglas* Repeat the preceding exercise using the following data: Two years ago—1000 employees, \$1 million operating budget, 100 pianos; Last year—1000 employees, \$100,000 operating budget, 10 pianos.

59. *Pollution* The burden of man-made aerosol sulfate in the earth's atmosphere, in grams per square meter, is

$$B(x,n) = \frac{xn}{A}$$

where x is the total weight of aerosol sulfate emitted into the atmosphere per year and n is the number of years it remains in the atmosphere. A is the surface area of the earth, approximately 5.1×10^{14} square meters.[10]

a. Calculate the burden, given the 1995 estimated values of $x = 1.5 \times 10^{14}$ grams per year, and $n = 5$ days.

b. What does the function $W(x,n) = xn$ measure?

60. *Pollution* The amount of aerosol sulfate (in grams) was approximately 45×10^{12} grams in 1940 and has been increasing exponentially ever since, with a doubling time of approximately 20 years.[11] Use the model from the preceding exercise to give a formula for the atmospheric burden of aerosol sulfate as a function of the time t in years since 1940 and the number of years n it remains in the atmosphere.

61. *Alien Intelligence* Frank Drake, an astronomer at the University of California at Santa Cruz, devised the following equation to estimate the number of planet-based civilizations in our Milky Way galaxy willing and able to communicate with Earth:[12]

$$N(R, f_p, n_e, f_l, f_i, f_c, L) = Rf_p n_e f_l f_i f_c L$$

R = the number of new stars formed in our galaxy each year

f_p = the fraction of those stars that have planetary systems

n_e = the average number of planets in each such system that can support life

f_l = the fraction of such planets on which life actually evolves

f_i = the fraction of life-sustaining planets on which intelligent life evolves

f_c = the fraction of intelligent-life-bearing planets on which the intelligent beings develop the means and the will to communicate over interstellar distances

L = the average lifetime of such technological civilizations (in years)

[10] SOURCE: Robert J. Charlson and Tom M. L. Wigley, "Sulfate Aerosol and Climatic Change," *Scientific American,* February, 1994, pp. 48–57.

[11] Ibid.

[12] SOURCE: "First Contact" (Plume Books/Penguin Group)/*The New York Times,* October 6, 1992, p. C1.

a. What would be the effect on N if any one of the variables were doubled?
b. How would you modify the formula if you were interested only in the number of intelligent-life-bearing planets in the galaxy?
c. How could one convert this function into a linear function?
d. (For discussion) Try to come up with an estimate of N.

62. ***More Alien Intelligence*** The formula given in the preceding exercise restricts attention to planet-based civilizations in our galaxy. Give a formula that includes intelligent planet-based aliens from the galaxy Andromeda. (Assume that all the variables used in the formula for the Milky Way have the same values for Andromeda.)

63. tech Ex ***Level Curves*** The height of each point in a hilly region is given as a function of its coordinates by the formula

$$f(x, y) = y^2 - x^2$$

a. Use technology to plot the curves on which the height is 0, 1, and 2 on the same set of axes. These are called **level curves of *f*.**
b. Sketch the curve $f(x, y) = 3$ *without* using technology.
c. Sketch the curves $f(y, x) = 1$ and $f(y, x) = 2$ without using technology.

64. tech Ex ***Isotherms*** The temperature (in degrees Fahrenheit) at each point in a region is given as a function of the coordinates by the formula

$$T(x, y) = 60.5(x - y^2)$$

a. Use technology to sketch the curves on which the temperature is 0°, 30°, and 90°. These curves are called **isotherms.**
b. Sketch the isotherms corresponding to 20°, 50°, and 100° *without* using technology.
c. What do the isotherms corresponding to negative temperatures look like?

Communication and Reasoning Exercises

65. ● Let $f(x, y) = \frac{x}{y}$. How are $f(x, y)$ and $f(y, x)$ related?

66. ● Let $f(x, y) = x^2y^3$. How are $f(x, y)$ and $f(-x, -y)$ related?

67. ● Give an example of a function of the two variables x and y with the property that interchanging x and y has no effect.

68. ● Give an example of a function f of the two variables x and y with the property that $f(x, y) = -f(y, x)$.

69. ● Give an example of a function f of the three variables x, y, and z with the property that $f(x, y, z) = f(y, x, z)$ and $f(-x, -y, -z) = -f(x, y, z)$.

70. ● Give an example of a function f of the three variables x, y, and z with the property that $f(x, y, z) = f(y, x, z)$ and $f(-x, -y, -z) = f(x, y, z)$.

71. ● Illustrate by means of an example how a real-valued function of the two variables x and y gives different real-valued functions of one variable when we restrict y to be different constants.

72. ● Illustrate by means of an example how a real-valued function of one variable x gives different real-valued functions of the two variables y and z when we substitute for x suitable functions of y and z.

73. If f is a linear function of x and y, show that if we restrict y to be a fixed constant, then the resulting function of x is linear. Does the slope of this linear function depend on the choice of y?

74. If f is an interaction function of x and y, show that if we restrict y to be a fixed constant, then the resulting function of x is linear. Does the slope of this linear function depend on the choice of y?

75. Suppose that $C(x, y)$ represents the cost of x CDs and y cassettes. If $C(x, y + 1) < C(x + 1, y)$ for every $x \geq 0$ and $y \geq 0$, what does this tell you about the cost of CDs and cassettes?

76. Suppose that $C(x, y)$ represents the cost of renting x DVDs and y video games. If $C(x + 2, y) < C(x, y + 1)$ for every $x \geq 0$ and $y \geq 0$, what does this tell you about the cost of renting DVDs and video games?

● basic skills tech Ex technology exercise

8.2 Three-Dimensional Space and the Graph of a Function of Two Variables

Just as functions of a single variable have graphs, so do functions of two or more variables. Recall that the graph of $f(x)$ consists of all points $(x, f(x))$ in the xy-plane. By analogy, we would like to say that the graph of a function of *two* variables, $f(x, y)$, consists of all points of the form $(x, y, f(x, y))$. Thus, we need three axes: the x-, y-, and z-axes. In other words, our graph will live in **three-dimensional space,** or **3-space.**[13]

Just as we had two mutually perpendicular axes in two-dimensional space (the xy-plane; see Figure 4a), so we have three mutually perpendicular axes in three-dimensional space (Figure 4b).

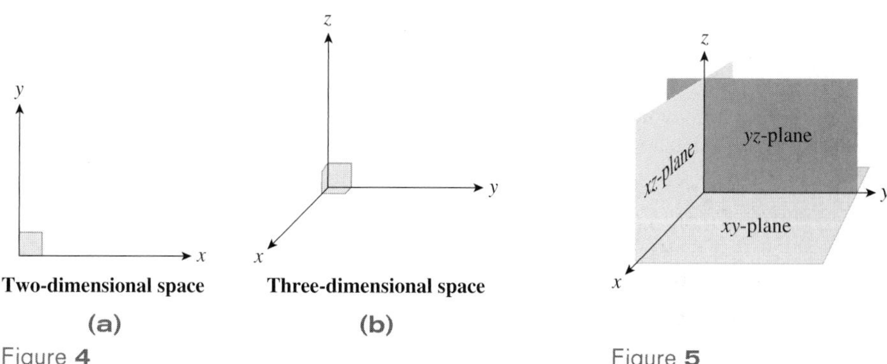

Figure **4**

Figure **5**

In both 2-space and 3-space, the axis labeled with the last letter goes up. Thus, the z-direction is the "up" direction in 3-space, rather than the y-direction.

Three important planes are associated with these axes: the xy-plane, the yz-plane, and the xz-plane. These planes are shown in Figure 5. Any two of these planes intersect in one of the axes (for example, the xy- and xz-planes intersect in the x-axis) and all three meet at the origin. Notice that the xy-plane consists of all points with z-coordinate zero, the xz-plane consists of all points with $y = 0$, and the yz-plane consists of all points with $x = 0$.

In 3-space, each point has *three* coordinates, as you might expect: the x-coordinate, the y-coordinate, and the z-coordinate. To see how this works, look at the following examples.

Example 1 Plotting Points in Three Dimensions

Locate the points $P(1, 2, 3)$, $Q(-1, 2, 3)$, $R(1, -1, 0)$, and $S(1, 2, -2)$ in 3-space.

Solution To locate P, the procedure is similar to the one we used in 2-space: Start at the origin, proceed 1 unit in the x direction, then proceed 2 units in the y direction, and finally, proceed three units in the z direction. We wind up at the point P shown in Figures 6a and 6b.

Here is another, extremely useful way of thinking about the location of P. First, look at the x- and y-coordinates, obtaining the point $(1, 2)$ in the xy-plane. The point we want is then three units vertically above the point $(1, 2)$ because the z-coordinate of a point is just its height above the xy-plane. This strategy is shown in Figure 6c.

---

[13] If we were dealing instead with a function of *three* variables, then we would need to go to *four-dimensional* space. Here we run into visualization problems (to say the least!) so we won't discuss the graphs of functions of three or more variables in this text.

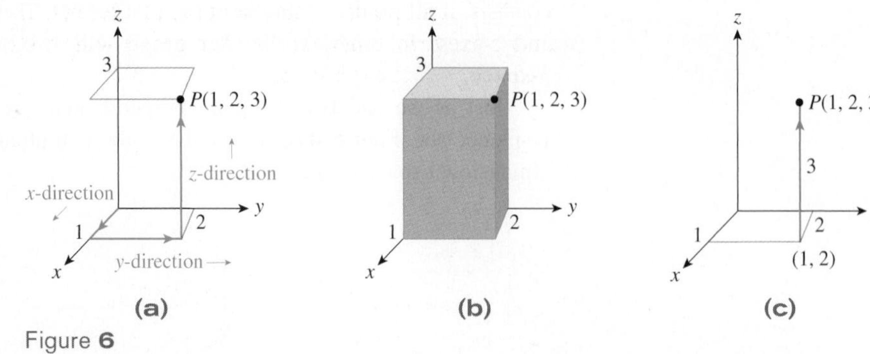

Figure 6

Plotting the points Q, R and S is similar, using the convention that negative coordinates correspond to moves back, left, or down (see Figure 7).

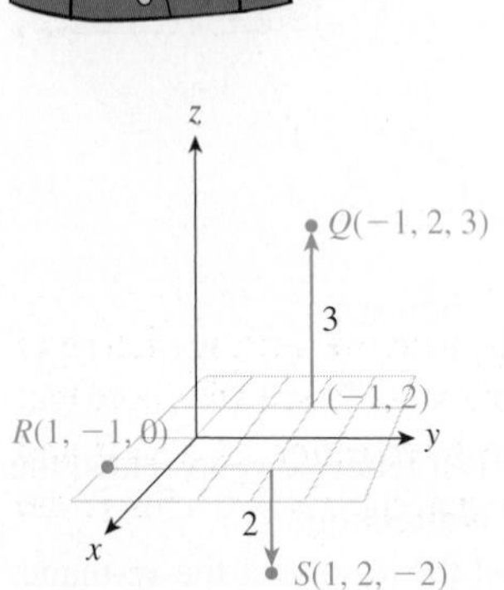
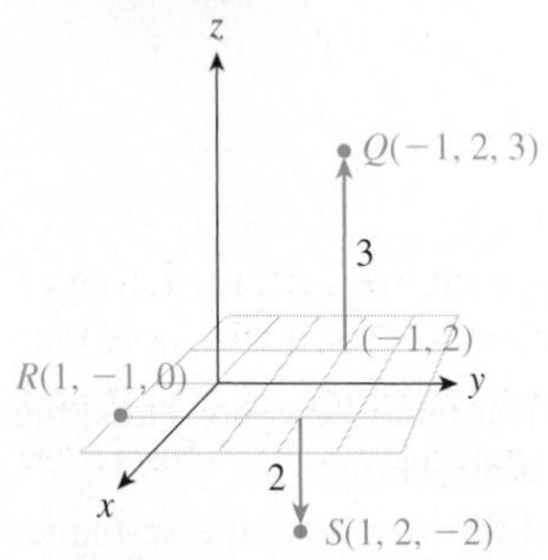

Figure 7

Our next task is to describe the graph of a function $f(x, y)$ of two variables.

Graph of a Function of Two Variables

The **graph of the function *f* of two variables** is the set of all points $(x, y, f(x, y))$ in three-dimensional space, where we restrict the values of (x, y) to lie in the domain of f. In other words, the graph is the set of all the points (x, y, z) with $z = f(x, y)$.

For *every* point (x, y) in the domain of f, the z-coordinate of the corresponding point on the graph is given by evaluating the function at (x, y). Thus, there will be a point on the graph above *every* point in the domain of f, so that the graph is usually a *surface* of some sort.

Example 2 Graph of a Function of Two Variables

Describe the graph of $f(x, y) = x^2 + y^2$.

Solution Your first thought might be to make a table of values. You could choose some values for x and y and then, for each such pair, calculate $z = x^2 + y^2$. For example, you might get the following table:

$x \rightarrow$

$y \downarrow$	**−1**	**0**	**1**
−1	2	1	2
0	1	0	1
1	2	1	2

$f(x, y) = x^2 + y^2$

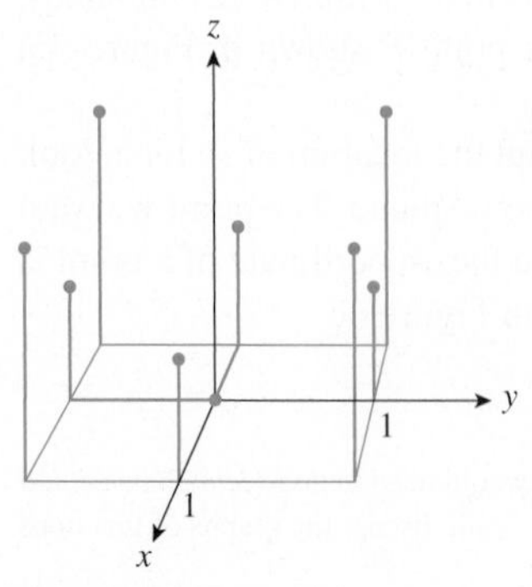

Figure 8

This gives the following nine points on the graph of f: $(-1, -1, 2)$, $(-1, 0, 1)$,\ $(-1, 1, 2)$, $(0, -1, 1)$, $(0, 0, 0)$, $(0, 1, 1)$, $(1, -1, 2)$, $(1, 0, 1)$, and $(1, 1, 2)$. These points are shown in Figure 8.

The points on the xy-plane we chose for our table are the grid points in the xy-plane, and the corresponding points on the graph are marked with solid dots. The problem is that this small number of points hardly tells us what the surface looks like, and even if we plotted more points, it is not clear that we would get anything more than a mass of dots on the page.

What can we do? There are several alternatives. One place to start is to use technology to draw the graph.* We then obtain something like Figure 9. This particular surface is called a **paraboloid.**

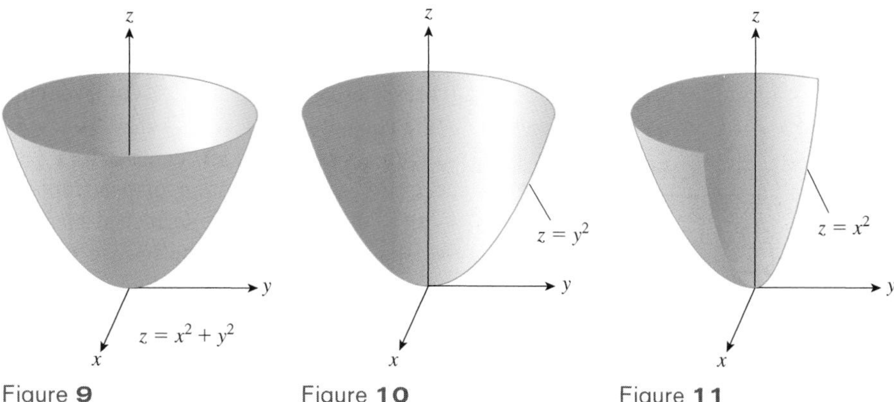

Figure **9** Figure **10** Figure **11**

If we slice vertically through this surface along the yz-plane, we get the picture in Figure 10. The shape of the front edge, where we cut, is a parabola. To see why, note that the yz-plane is the set of points where $x = 0$. To get the intersection of $x = 0$ and $z = x^2 + y^2$, we substitute $x = 0$ in the second equation, getting $z = y^2$. This is the equation of a parabola in the yz-plane.

Similarly, we can slice through the surface with the xz-plane by setting $y = 0$. This gives the parabola $z = x^2$ in the xz-plane (Figure 11).

We can also look at horizontal slices through the surface, that is, slices by planes parallel to the xy-plane. These are given by setting $z = c$ for various numbers c. For example, if we set $z = 1$, we will see only the points with height 1. Substituting in the equation $z = x^2 + y^2$ gives the equation

$$1 = x^2 + y^2$$

which is the equation of a circle of radius 1. If we set $z = 4$, we get the equation of a circle of radius 2:

$$4 = x^2 + y^2$$

In general, if we slice through the surface at height $z = c$, we get a circle (of radius $\sqrt{c}$). Figure 12 shows several of these circles.

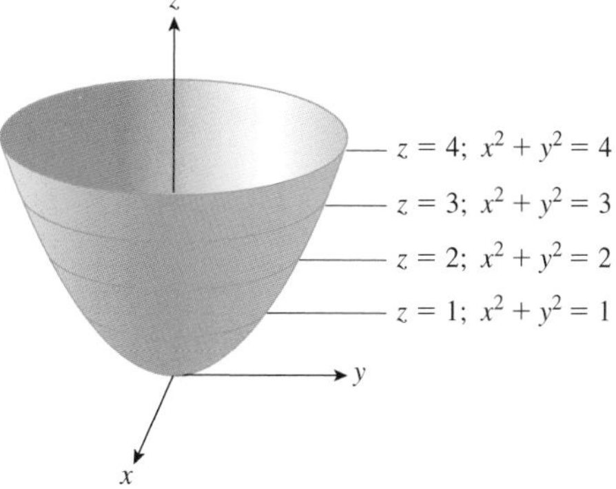

Figure **12**

* See Example 3 for a discussion of the use of a spreadsheet to draw a surface.

Looking at these circular slices, we see that this surface is the one we get by taking the parabola $z = x^2$ and spinning it around the z-axis. This is an example of what is known as a **surface of revolution.**

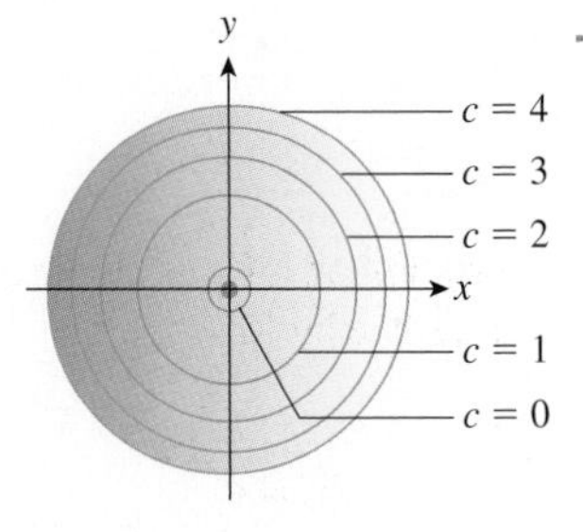

Level curves of the paraboloid $z = x^2 + y^2$

Figure **13**

+ *Before we go on...* Notice that each horizontal slice through the surface in Example 2 was obtained by putting $z = constant$. This gave us an equation in x and y that described a curve. These curves are called the **level curves** of the surface $z = f(x, y)$. In Example 2, the equations are of the form $x^2 + y^2 = constant$, and so the level curves are circles. Figure 13 shows the level curves for $c = 0, 1, 2, 3$, and 4.

The level curves give a contour map or topographical map of the surface. Each curve shows all of the points on the surface at a particular height c. You can use this contour map to visualize the shape of the surface. Imagine moving the contour at $c = 1$ to a height of 1 unit above the xy-plane, the contour at $c = 2$ to a height of 2 units above the xy-plane, and so on. You will end up with something like Figure 12. ■

The following summary includes the techniques we have just used plus some additional ones:

Analyzing the Graph of a Function of Two Variables

If possible, use technology to render the graph of a given function $z = f(x, y)$. Given the function $z = f(x, y)$, you can analyze its graph as follows:

Step 1 Obtain the ***x*-, *y*-, and *z*-intercepts** (the places where the surface crosses the coordinate axes).

***x*-Intercept(s):** Set $y = 0$ and $z = 0$ and solve for x.

***y*-Intercept(s):** Set $x = 0$ and $z = 0$ and solve for y.

***z*-Intercept:** Set $x = 0$ and $y = 0$ and compute z.

z-intercept

x-intercept

y-intercept

Step 2 Slice the surface along planes parallel to the xy-, yz-, and xz-planes.

***z = constant* (level curves)** Set $z = constant$ and analyze the resulting curves. These are the curves resulting from horizontal slices.

x = constant Set $x = constant$ and analyze the resulting curves. These are the curves resulting from slices parallel to the yz-plane.

y = constant Set $y = constant$ and analyze the resulting curves. These are the curves resulting from slices parallel to the xz-plane.

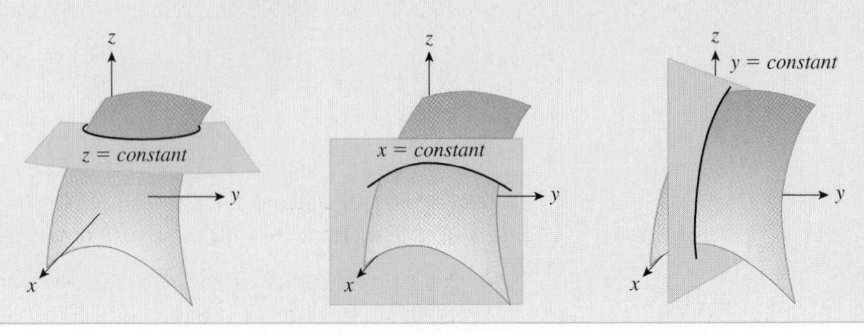

Spreadsheets often have built-in features to render surfaces such as the paraboloid in Example 2. In the following example, we use Excel to graph another surface and then analyze it as above.

Example 3 Analyzing a Surface

Describe the graph of $f(x, y) = x^2 - y^2$.

Solution First we obtain a picture of the graph using technology. Figure 14 was obtained using the three-dimensional Excel graphing utility you can find online by following:

Chapter 8 → Tools → Excel Surface Graphing Utility

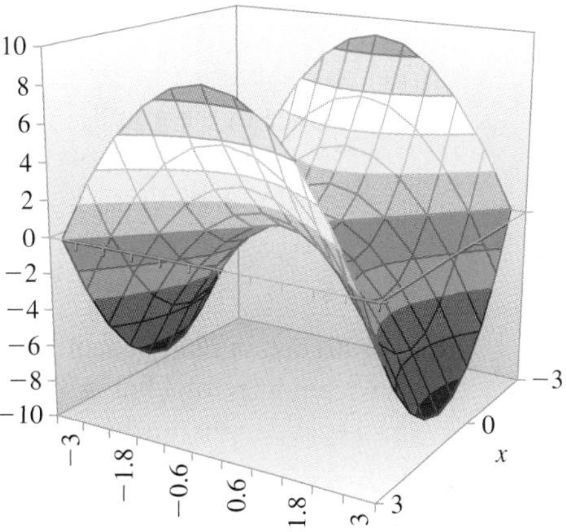

Figure 14

See the Technology Guides at the end of the chapter to find out how to obtain a similar graph from scratch on an ordinary Excel sheet.

The graph shows an example of a "saddle point" at the origin (we return to this idea in a Section 8.4). To analyze the graph for the features shown in the box above, replace $f(x, y)$ by z to obtain

$$z = x^2 - y^2$$

Step 1 ***Intercepts*** Setting any two of the variables x, y, and z equal to zero results in the third also being zero, so the x-, y-, and z-intercepts are all 0. In other words, the surface touches all three axes in exactly one point, the origin.

Step 1 ***Slices*** Slices in various directions show more interesting features.

Slice by $x = c$ This gives $z = c^2 - y^2$, which is the equation of a parabola that opens downward. You can see two of these slices ($c = -3, c = 3$) as the front and back edges of the surface in Figure 14. [More are shown in Figure 15a.]

Slice by $y = c$ This gives $z = x^2 - c^2$, which is the equation of a parabola once again—this time, opening upward. You can see two of these slices ($c = -3, c = 3$) as the left and right edges of the surface in Figure 14. [More are shown in Figure 15b.]

Slice by $z = c$ This gives $x^2 - y^2 = c$, which is a hyperbola. The level curves for various values of c are visible in Figure 14 as the boundaries between the different

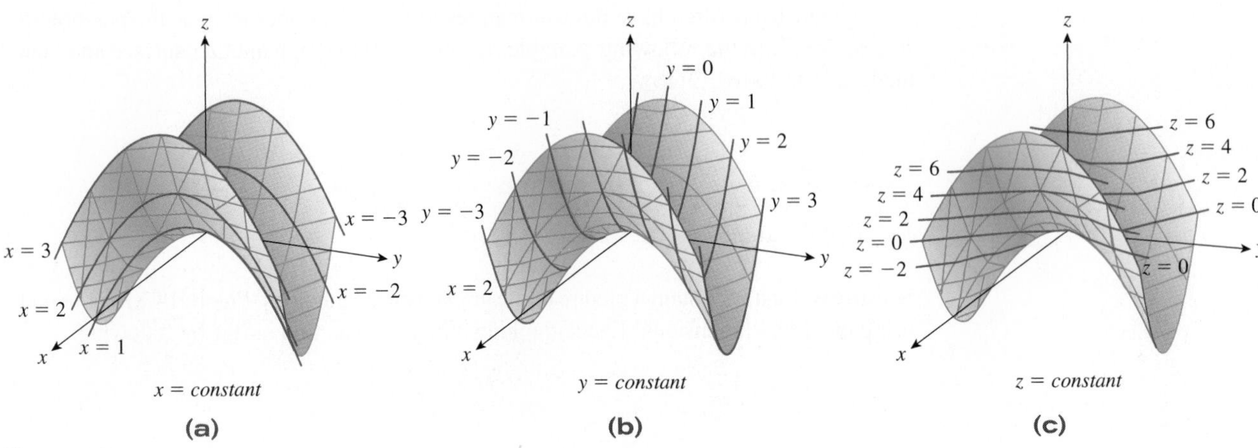

Figure 15

shadings in the graph. [See Figure 15c.] The case $c = 0$ is interesting: The equation $x^2 - y^2 = 0$ can be rewritten as $x = \pm y$ (why?), which represents two lines at right-angles to each other.

To obtain really beautiful renderings of surfaces, you could use one of the commercial computer algebra software packages, such as Mathematica® or Maple®. These packages can do much more than render surfaces and can be used, for example, to compute derivatives and antiderivatives, to solve equations algebraically, and to perform a variety of algebraic computations.

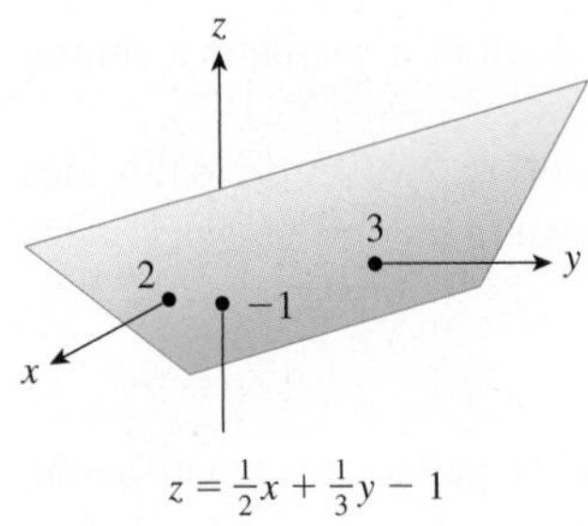

Figure 16

Example 4 Graph of a Linear Function

Describe the graph of $g(x, y) = \frac{1}{2}x + \frac{1}{3}y - 1$.

Solution Notice first that g is a linear function of x and y. Figure 16 shows a portion of the graph, which is a plane.

We can get a good idea of what plane this is by looking at the x-, y-, and z-intercepts.

x-intercept Set $y = z = 0$, which gives $x = 2$.

y-intercept Set $x = z = 0$, which gives $y = 3$.

z-intercept Set $x = y = 0$, which gives $z = -1$.

Three points are enough to define a plane, so we can say that the plane is the one passing through the three points $(2, 0, 0)$, $(0, 3, 0)$, and $(0, 0, -1)$.

Note It can be shown that the graph of every linear function of two variables is a plane. What do the level curves look like? ■

8.2 EXERCISES

● denotes basic skills exercises

tech Ex indicates exercises that should be solved using technology

1. ● Sketch the cube with vertices (0, 0, 0), (1, 0, 0), (0, 1, 0), (0, 0, 1), (1, 1, 0), (1, 0, 1), (0, 1, 1), and (1, 1, 1). hint [see Example 1]
2. ● Sketch the cube with vertices $(-1,-1,-1)$, $(1,-1,-1)$, $(-1,1,-1)$, $(-1,-1,1)$, $(1,1,-1)$, $(1,-1,1)$, $(-1,1,1)$, and $(1,1,1)$.
3. ● Sketch the pyramid with vertices $(1,1,0)$, $(1,-1,0)$, $(-1,1,0)$, $(-1,-1,0)$, and $(0,0,2)$.
4. ● Sketch the solid with vertices $(1,1,0)$, $(1,-1,0)$, $(-1,1,0)$, $(-1,-1,0)$, $(0,0,-1)$, and $(0,0,1)$.

Sketch the planes in Exercises 5–10.

5. ● $z=-2$
6. ● $z=4$
7. ● $y=2$
8. ● $y=-3$
9. ● $x=-3$
10. ● $x=2$

Match each equation in Exercises 11–18 with one of the graphs below. (If necessary, use technology to render the surfaces.) hint [see Examples 2, 3, 4]

11. ● $f(x,y)=1-3x+2y$
12. ● $f(x,y)=1-\sqrt{x^2+y^2}$
13. ● $f(x,y)=1-(x^2+y^2)$
14. ● $f(x,y)=y^2-x^2$
15. ● $f(x,y)=-\sqrt{1-(x^2+y^2)}$
16. ● $f(x,y)=1+(x^2+y^2)$
17. ● $f(x,y)=\dfrac{1}{x^2+y^2}$
18. ● $f(x,y)=3x-2y+1$

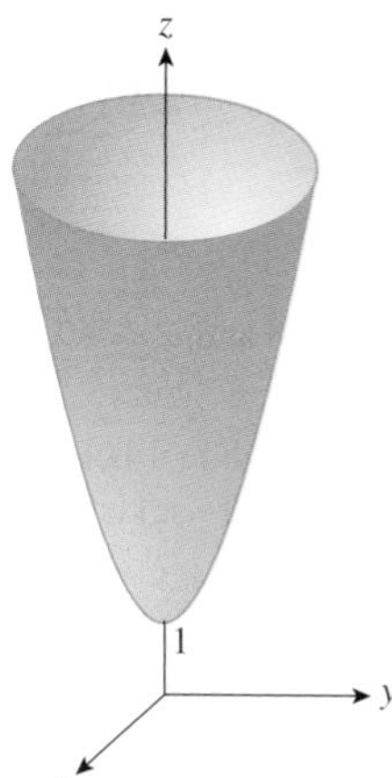

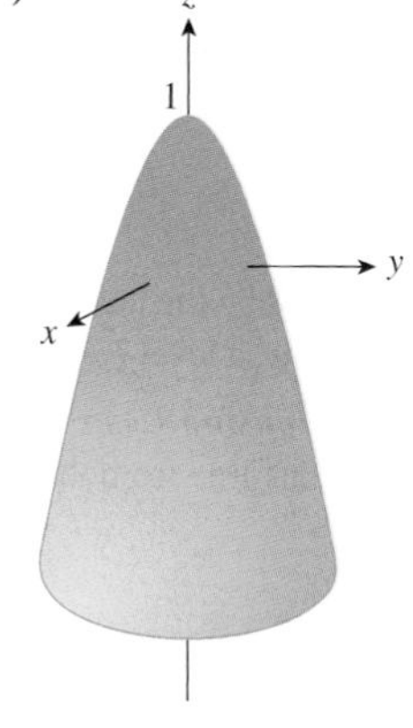

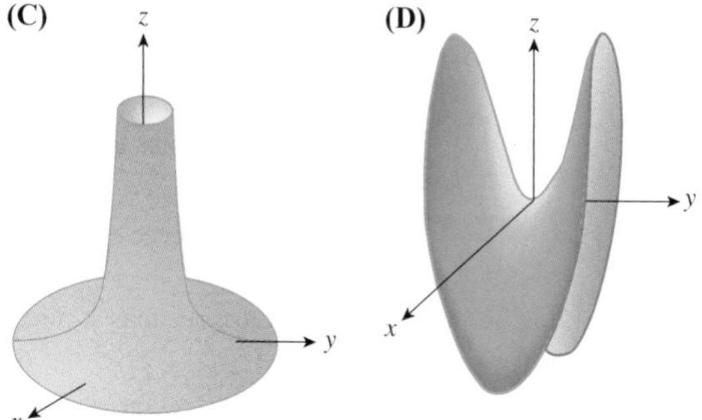

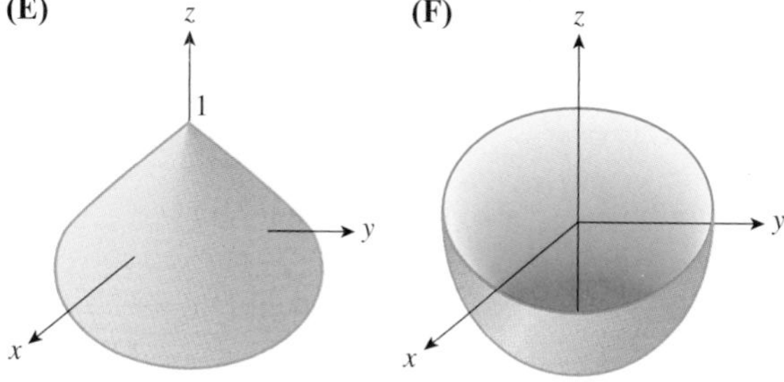

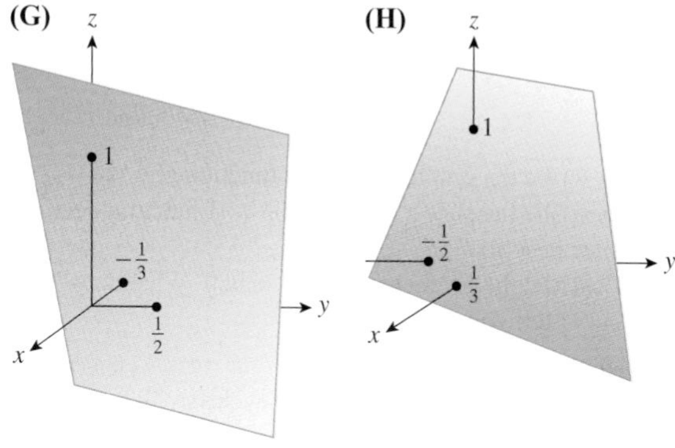

Sketch the graphs of the functions in Exercises 19–40. hint [see Example 4]

19. ● $f(x,y)=1-x-y$
20. ● $f(x,y)=x+y-2$
21. ● $g(x,y)=2x+y-2$
22. ● $g(x,y)=3-x+2y$
23. ● $h(x,y)=x+2$
24. ● $h(x,y)=3-y$
25. ● $r(x,y)=x+y$
26. ● $r(x,y)=x-y$

tech Ex *Use of technology is suggested in Exercises 27–40.*
hint [see Example 3]

27. ● $s(x, y) = 2x^2 + 2y^2$. Show cross sections at $z = 1$ and $z = 2$.

28. ● $s(x, y) = -(x^2 + y^2)$. Show cross sections at $z = -1$ and $z = -2$.

29. ● $t(x, y) = x^2 + 2y^2$. Show cross sections at $x = 0$ and $z = 1$.

30. ● $t(x, y) = \frac{1}{2}x^2 + y^2$. Show cross sections at $x = 0$ and $z = 1$.

31. ● $f(x, y) = 2 + \sqrt{x^2 + y^2}$. Show cross sections at $z = 3$ and $y = 0$.

32. ● $f(x, y) = 2 - \sqrt{x^2 + y^2}$. Show cross sections at $z = 0$ and $y = 0$.

33. ● $f(x, y) = -2\sqrt{x^2 + y^2}$. Show cross sections at $z = -4$ and $y = 1$.

34. ● $f(x, y) = 2 + 2\sqrt{x^2 + y^2}$. Show cross sections at $z = 4$ and $y = 1$.

35. ● $f(x, y) = y^2$

36. ● $g(x, y) = x^2$

37. ● $h(x, y) = \frac{1}{y}$

38. ● $k(x, y) = e^y$

39. ● $f(x, y) = e^{-(x^2+y^2)}$

40. ● $g(x, y) = \frac{1}{\sqrt{x^2 + y^2}}$

Applications

41. ● ***Marginal Cost (Linear Model)*** Your weekly cost (in dollars) to manufacture x cars and y trucks is

$$C(x, y) = 240{,}000 + 6000x + 4000y$$

a. Describe the graph of the cost function C.
b. Describe the slice $x = 10$. What cost function does this slice describe?
c. Describe the level curve $z = 480{,}000$. What does this curve tell you about costs?

42. ● ***Marginal Cost (Linear Model)*** Your weekly cost (in dollars) to manufacture x bicycles and y tricycles is

$$C(x, y) = 24{,}000 + 60x + 20y$$

a. Describe the graph of the cost function C.
b. Describe the slice by $y = 100$. What cost function does this slice describe?
c. Describe the level curve $z = 72{,}000$. What does this curve tell you about costs?

43. ● ***Market Share (Cars and Light Trucks)*** Based on data in the 1980s and 1990s, the relationship between the domestic market shares of three major U.S. manufacturers of cars and light trucks could be modeled by

$$x_3 = 0.66 - 2.2x_1 - 0.02x_2$$

where x_1, x_2, and x_3 are, respectively, the fractions of the market held by Chrysler, Ford, and General Motors.[14] Thinking of General Motors' market share as a function of the shares of the other two manufacturers, describe the graph of the resulting function. How are the different slices by $x_1 = constant$ related to one another? What does this say about market share?

44. ● ***Market Share (Cereals)*** Based on data in the 1980s and 1990s, the relationship among the domestic market shares of three major manufacturers of breakfast cereal is

$$x_1 = -0.4 + 1.2x_2 + 2x_3$$

where x_1, x_2, and x_3 are, respectively, the fractions of the market held by Kellogg, General Mills, and General Foods.[15] Thinking of Kellogg's market share as a function of shares of the other two manufacturers, describe the graph of the resulting function. How are the different slices by $x_2 = constant$ related to one another? What does this say about market share?

45. ● ***Marginal Cost (Interaction Model)*** Your weekly cost (in dollars) to manufacture x cars and y trucks is

$$C(x, y) = 240{,}000 + 6000x + 4000y - 20xy$$

(Compare with Exercise 41.)

a. Describe the slices x = constant and y = constant.
b. Is the graph of the cost function a plane? How does your answer relate to part (a)?
c. What are the slopes of the slices $x = 10$ and $x = 20$? What does this say about cost?

46. ● ***Marginal Cost (Interaction Model)*** Repeat the preceding exercise using the weekly cost to manufacture x bicycles and y tricycles given by

$$C(x, y) = 24{,}000 + 60x + 20y + 0.3xy$$

(Compare with Exercise 42.)

47. ● ***Housing Costs***[16] The cost C of building a house is related to the number k of carpenters used and the number e of electricians used by

$$C(k, e) = 15{,}000 + 50k^2 + 50e^2$$

Describe the level curves $C = 30{,}000$ and $C = 40{,}000$. What do these level curves represent?

48. ● ***Housing Costs***[17] The cost C of building a house (in a different area from that in the previous exercise) is related to the

[14] The model is based on a linear regression. Source of data: Ward's AutoInfoBank/*The New York Times*, July 29, 1998, p. D6.

[15] The models are based on a linear regression. Source of data: Bloomberg Financial Markets/*The New York Times*, November 28, 1998, p. C1.

[16] Based on an exercise in *Introduction to Mathematical Economics* by A. L. Ostrosky Jr. and J. V. Koch (Waveland Press, Illinois, 1979).

[17] Ibid.

number k of carpenters used and the number e of electricians used by

$$C(k, e) = 15{,}000 + 70k^2 + 40e^2$$

Describe the slices by the planes $k = 2$ and $e = 2$. What do these slices represent?

49. ***Area*** The area of a rectangle of height h and width w is $A(h, w) = hw$. Sketch a few level curves of A. If the perimeter $h + w$ of the rectangle is constant, which h and w give the largest area? (We suggest you draw in the line $h + w = c$ for several values of c.)

50. ***Area*** The area of an ellipse with semiminor axis a and semimajor axis b is $A(a, b) = \pi ab$. Sketch the graph of A. If $a^2 + b^2$ is constant, what a and b give the largest area?

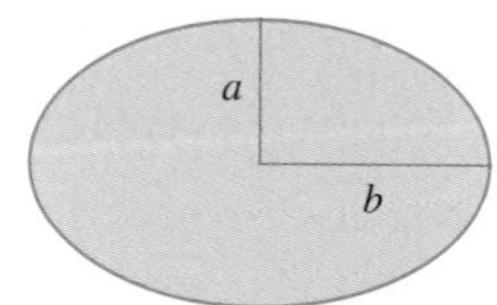

Graphing technology is suggested for Exercises 51–54.

51. techEx ***Production (Cobb-Douglas Model)*** Graph the level curves at $z = 0, 1, 2$ and 3 of $P(x, y) = Kx^a y^{1-a}$ if $K = 1$ and $a = 0.5$. Here, x is the number of workers, y is the operating budget, and $P(x, y)$ is the productivity. Interpret the level curve at $z = 3$.

52. techEx ***Production (Cobb-Douglas Model)*** Graph the level curves at $z = 0, 1, 2$ and 3 of $P(x, y) = Kx^a y^{1-a}$ if $K = 1$ and $a = 0.25$. Here, x is the number of workers, y is the operating budget, and $P(x, y)$ is the productivity. Interpret the level curve at $z = 0$.

53. techEx ***Utility*** Suppose that your newspaper is trying to decide between two competing desktop publishing software packages, Macro Publish and Turbo Publish. You estimate that if you purchase x copies of Macro Publish and y copies of Turbo Publish, your company's daily productivity will be

$$U(x, y) = 6x^{0.8}y^{0.2} + x$$

where $U(x, y)$ is measured in pages per day (U is called a *utility function*). Graph the level curves at $z = 0, 10, 20$, and 30. What does the level curve at $z = 0$ tell you?

54. techEx ***Utility*** Suppose that your small publishing company is trying to decide between two competing desktop publishing software packages, Macro Publish and Turbo Publish. You estimate that if you purchase x copies of Macro Publish and y copies of Turbo Publish, your company's daily productivity will be given by

$$U(x, y) = 5x^{0.2}y^{0.8} + x$$

where $U(x, y)$ is measured in pages per day. Graph the level curves at $z = 0, 10, 20$ and 30. Give a formula for the level curve at $z = 30$ specifying y as a function of x. What does this curve tell you?

Communication and Reasoning Exercises

55. ● Complete the following: The graph of a linear function of two variables is a _____ .

56. ● Complete the following: The level curves of a linear function of two variables are ____ .

57. ● Your study partner Slim claims that because the surface $z = f(x, y)$ you have been studying is a plane, it follows that all the slices $x =$ *constant* and $y =$ *constant* are straight lines. Do you agree or disagree? Explain.

58. ● Your other study partner Shady just told you that the surface $z = xy$ you have been trying to graph must be a plane because you've already found that the slices $x =$ *constant* and $y =$ *constant* are all straight lines. Do you agree or disagree? Explain.

59. Why do we not sketch the graphs of functions of three or more variables?

60. The surface of a mountain can be thought of as the graph of what function?

61. Show that the distance between the points (x, y, z) and (a, b, c) is given by the following **three-dimensional distance formula:**

$$d = \sqrt{(x-a)^2 + (y-b)^2 + (z-c)^2}$$

or

$$d = \sqrt{(\Delta x)^2 + (\Delta y)^2 + (\Delta z)^2}$$

The following diagram should be of assistance:

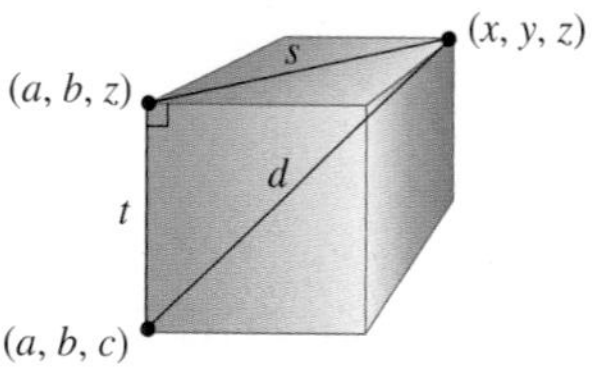

62. Use the result of the preceding exercise to show that the sphere of radius r centered at the origin has equation

$$x^2 + y^2 + z^2 = r^2$$

63. Why is three-dimensional space used to represent the graph of a function of two variables?

64. Why is it that we can sketch the graphs of functions of two variables on the two-dimensional flat surfaces of these pages?

8.3 Partial Derivatives

Recall that if f is a function of x, then the derivative df/dx measures how fast f changes as x increases. If f is a function of two or more variables, we can ask how fast f changes as each variable increases while the others remain fixed. These rates of change are called the "partial derivatives of f," and they measure how each variable contributes to the change in f. Here is a more precise definition.

Partial Derivatives

The **partial derivative of f with respect to x** is the derivative of f with respect to x, when all other variables are treated as constant. Similarly, the **partial derivative of f with respect to y** is the derivative of f with respect to y, with all other variables treated as constant, and so on for other variables. The partial derivatives are written as $\frac{\partial f}{\partial x}, \frac{\partial f}{\partial y}$, and so on. The symbol ∂ is used (instead of d) to remind us that there is more than one variable and that we are holding the other variables fixed.

quick **Examples**

1. Let $f(x, y) = x^2 + y^2$.

$$\frac{\partial f}{\partial x} = 2x + 0 = 2x$$ Because y^2 is treated as a constant

$$\frac{\partial f}{\partial y} = 0 + 2y = 2y$$ Because x^2 is treated as a constant

2. Let $z = x^2 + xy$.

$$\frac{\partial z}{\partial x} = 2x + y$$ $\frac{\partial}{\partial x}(xy) = \frac{\partial}{\partial x}(x \cdot \text{constant}) = \text{constant} = y$

$$\frac{\partial z}{\partial y} = 0 + x = x$$ $\frac{\partial}{\partial y}(xy) = \frac{\partial}{\partial x}(\text{constant} \cdot y) = \text{constant} = x$

3. Let $f(x, y) = x^2y + y^2x - xy + y$.

$$\frac{\partial f}{\partial x} = 2xy + y^2 - y$$ y is treated as a constant

$$\frac{\partial f}{\partial y} = x^2 + 2xy - x + 1$$ x is treated as a constant

Interpretation

$\frac{\partial f}{\partial x}$ is the rate at which f changes as x changes, for a fixed (constant) y.

$\frac{\partial f}{\partial y}$ is the rate at which f changes as y changes, for a fixed (constant) x.

Example 1 Marginal Cost: Linear Model

We return to Example 1 from Section 8.1. Suppose that you own a company that makes two models of speakers, the Ultra Mini and the Big Stack. Your total monthly cost (in dollars) to make x Ultra Minis and y Big Stacks is given by

$$C(x, y) = 10{,}000 + 20x + 40y$$

What is the significance of $\frac{\partial C}{\partial x}$ and of $\frac{\partial C}{\partial y}$?

Solution First we compute these partial derivatives:

$$\frac{\partial C}{\partial x} = 20$$

$$\frac{\partial C}{\partial y} = 40$$

We interpret the results as follows: $\frac{\partial C}{\partial x} = 20$ means that the cost is increasing at a rate of \$20 per additional Ultra Mini (if production of Big Stacks is held constant); $\frac{\partial C}{\partial y} = 40$ means that the cost is increasing at a rate of \$40 per additional Big Stack (if production of Ultra Minis is held constant). In other words, these are the **marginal costs** of each model of speaker.

+ *Before we go on...* How much does the cost rise if you increase x by Δx and y by Δy? In Example 1, the change in cost is given by

$$\Delta C = 20\Delta x + 40\Delta y = \frac{\partial C}{\partial x}\Delta x + \frac{\partial C}{\partial y}\Delta y$$

This suggests the **chain rule for several variables.** Part of this rule says that if x and y are both functions of t, then C is a function of t through them, and the rate of change of C with respect to t can be calculated as

$$\frac{dC}{dt} = \frac{\partial C}{\partial x} \cdot \frac{dx}{dt} + \frac{\partial C}{\partial y} \cdot \frac{dy}{dt}$$

We shall not have a chance to use this interesting result in this book. ■

Example 2 Marginal Cost: Interaction Model

Another possibility for the cost function in the preceding example is the interaction model

$$C(x, y) = 10{,}000 + 20x + 40y + 0.1xy$$

a. Now what are the marginal costs of the two models of speakers?

b. What is the marginal cost of manufacturing Big Stacks at a production level of 100 Ultra Minis and 50 Big Stacks per month?

Solution

a. We compute the partial derivatives:

$$\frac{\partial C}{\partial x} = 20 + 0.1y$$

$$\frac{\partial C}{\partial y} = 40 + 0.1x$$

Thus, the marginal cost of manufacturing Ultra Minis increases by \$0.1 or 10¢ for each Big Stack that is manufactured. Similarly, the marginal cost of manufacturing Big Stacks increases by 10¢ for each Ultra Mini that is manufactured.

b. From part (a), the marginal cost of manufacturing Big Stacks is

$$\frac{\partial C}{\partial y} = 40 + 0.1x$$

At a production level of 100 Ultra Minis and 50 Big Stacks per month, we have $x = 100$ and $y = 50$. Thus, the marginal cost of manufacturing Big Stacks at these production levels is

$$\left.\frac{\partial C}{\partial y}\right|_{(100,50)} = 40 + 0.1(100) = \$50 \text{ per Big Stack}$$

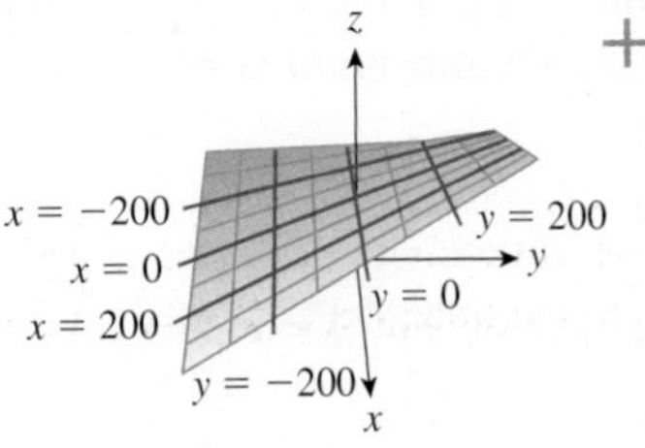

Figure **17**

+*Before we go on...* A portion of the surface $z = 10{,}000 + 20x + 40y + 0.1xy$ from Example 2 is shown in Figure 17, together with some of the slices through $x = constant$ and $y = constant$.

These slices are straight lines whose slopes are given by the partial derivatives (which represent the marginal costs when x and y are nonnegative):

$$y = -200: \quad \text{Slope} = \left.\frac{\partial z}{\partial x}\right|_{(x,-200)} = 20 + 0.1(-200) = 0$$

$$y = 0: \quad \text{Slope} = \left.\frac{\partial z}{\partial x}\right|_{(x,0)} = 20 + 0.1(0) = 20$$

$$y = 200: \quad \text{Slope} = \left.\frac{\partial z}{\partial x}\right|_{(x,200)} = 20 + 0.1(200) = 40$$

Notice that these slopes increase as y increases, as we can confirm in Figure 17.

$$x = -200 \quad \text{Slope} = \left.\frac{\partial z}{\partial y}\right|_{(-200,y)} = 40 + 0.1(-200) = 20$$

$$x = 0 \quad \text{Slope} = \left.\frac{\partial z}{\partial y}\right|_{(0,y)} = 40 + 0.1(0) = 40$$

$$x = 200 \quad \text{Slope} = \left.\frac{\partial z}{\partial y}\right|_{(200,y)} = 40 + 0.1(200) = 60$$

Notice that these slopes increase as x increases, as we can confirm in Figure 17. ■

Partial derivatives of functions of three variables are obtained in the same way as those for functions of two variables, as the following example shows:

Example 3 Function of Three Variables

Calculate $\frac{\partial f}{\partial x}, \frac{\partial f}{\partial y}$ and $\frac{\partial f}{\partial z}$ if $f(x, y, z) = xy^2z^3 - xy$.

Solution Although we now have three variables, the calculation remains the same: $\partial f/\partial x$ is the derivative of f with respect to x, with *both* other variables, y and z, held constant:

$$\frac{\partial f}{\partial x} = y^2z^3 - y$$

Similarly, $\partial f/\partial y$ is the derivative of f with respect to y, with both x and z held constant:

$$\frac{\partial f}{\partial y} = 2xyz^3 - x$$

Finally, to find $\partial f/\partial z$, we hold both x and y constant and take the derivative with respect to z.

$$\frac{\partial f}{\partial z} = 3xy^2z^2$$

Note The procedure for finding a partial derivative is the same for any number of variables: To get the partial derivative with respect to any one variable, we treat all the others as constants. ■

Geometric Interpretation of Partial Derivatives

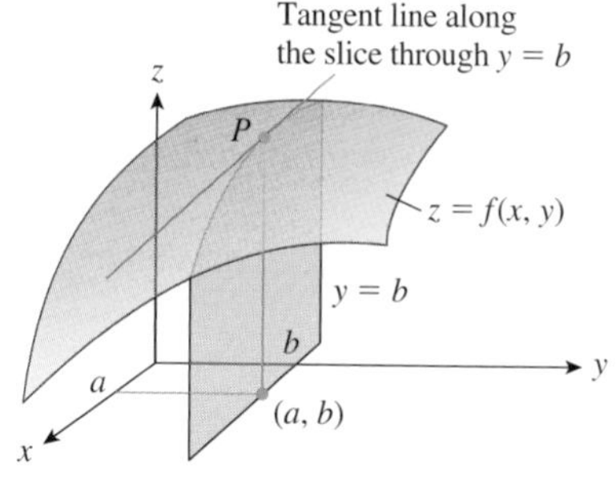

$\left.\frac{\partial f}{\partial x}\right|_{(a,b)}$ is the slope of the tangent line at the point $P(a, b, f(a, b))$ along the slice through $y = b$.

Figure **18**

Recall that if f is a function of one variable x, then the derivative df/dx gives the slopes of the tangent lines to its graph. Now, suppose that f is a function of x and y. By definition, $\partial f/\partial x$ is the derivative of the function of x we get by holding y fixed. If we evaluate this derivative at the point (a, b), we are holding y fixed at the value b, taking the ordinary derivative of the resulting function of x, and evaluating this at $x = a$. Now, holding y fixed at b amounts to slicing through the graph of f along the plane $y = b$, resulting in a curve. Thus, the partial derivative is the slope of the tangent line to this curve at the point where $x = a$ and $y = b$, along the plane $y = b$ (Figure 18).

This fits with our interpretation of $\partial f/\partial x$ as the rate of increase of f with increasing x when y is held fixed at b.

The other partial derivative, $\partial f/\partial y|_{(a,\,b)}$ is, similarly, the slope of the tangent line at the same point $P(a, b, f(a, b))$ but along the slice by the plane $x = a$. You should draw the corresponding picture for this on your own.

Second-Order Partial Derivatives

Just as for functions of a single variable, we can calculate second derivatives. Suppose, for example, that we have a function of x and y, say, $f(x, y) = x^2 - x^2y^2$. We know that

$$\frac{\partial f}{\partial x} = 2x - 2xy^2$$

If we take the partial derivative with respect to x once again, we obtain

$$\frac{\partial}{\partial x}\left(\frac{\partial f}{\partial x}\right) = 2 - 2y^2 \qquad \text{Take } \frac{\partial}{\partial x} \text{ of } \frac{\partial f}{\partial x}$$

(The symbol $\partial/\partial x$ means "the partial derivative with respect to x," just as d/dx stands for "the derivative with respect to x.") This is called the **second-order partial derivative** and is written $\frac{\partial^2 f}{\partial x^2}$. We get the following derivatives similarly:

$$\frac{\partial f}{\partial y} = -2x^2 y$$

$$\frac{\partial^2 f}{\partial y^2} = -2x^2 \qquad \text{Take } \frac{\partial}{\partial y} \text{ of } \frac{\partial f}{\partial y}$$

Now what if we instead take the partial derivative with respect to y of $\partial f/\partial x$?

$$\frac{\partial^2 f}{\partial y \partial x} = \frac{\partial}{\partial y}\left(\frac{\partial f}{\partial x}\right) \qquad \text{Take } \frac{\partial}{\partial y} \text{ of } \frac{\partial f}{\partial x}$$

$$= \frac{\partial}{\partial y}[2x - 2xy^2] = -4xy$$

Here, $\frac{\partial^2 f}{\partial y \partial x}$ means "first take the partial derivative with respect to x and then with respect to y," and is called a **mixed partial derivative.** If we differentiate in the opposite order, we get

$$\frac{\partial^2 f}{\partial x \partial y} = \frac{\partial}{\partial x}\left(\frac{\partial f}{\partial y}\right) = \frac{\partial}{\partial x}[-2x^2 y] = -4xy$$

the same expression as $\frac{\partial^2 f}{\partial y \partial x}$. This is no coincidence: The mixed partial derivatives $\frac{\partial^2 f}{\partial x \partial y}$ and $\frac{\partial^2 f}{\partial y \partial x}$ are always the same as long as the first partial derivatives are both differentiable functions of x and y and the mixed partial derivatives are continuous. Because all the functions we shall use are of this type, we can take the derivatives in any order we like when calculating mixed derivatives.

Here is another notation for partial derivatives that is especially convenient for second-order partial derivatives:

f_x means $\frac{\partial f}{\partial x}$

f_y means $\frac{\partial f}{\partial y}$

f_{xy} means $(f_x)_y = \frac{\partial^2 f}{\partial y \partial x}$ (Note the order in which the derivatives are taken.)

f_{yx} means $(f_y)_x = \frac{\partial^2 f}{\partial x \partial y}$

8.3 EXERCISES

● denotes basic skills exercises

In Exercises 1–18, calculate $\frac{\partial f}{\partial x}, \frac{\partial f}{\partial y}, \left.\frac{\partial f}{\partial x}\right|_{(1,-1)}$, *and* $\left.\frac{\partial f}{\partial y}\right|_{(1,-1)}$ *when defined.* *hint* [see Quick Examples p. 562]

1. ● $f(x, y) = 10{,}000 - 40x + 20y$

2. ● $f(x, y) = 1000 + 5x - 4y$

3. ● $f(x, y) = 3x^2 - y^3 + x - 1$

4. ● $f(x, y) = x^{1/2} - 2y^4 + y + 6$

5. ● $f(x, y) = 10{,}000 - 40x + 20y + 10xy$

6. ● $f(x, y) = 1000 + 5x - 4y - 3xy$

7. ● $f(x, y) = 3x^2 y$

8. ● $f(x, y) = x^4 y^2 - x$

9. ● $f(x, y) = x^2y^3 - x^3y^2 - xy$

10. ● $f(x, y) = x^{-1}y^2 + xy^2 + xy$

11. ● $f(x, y) = (2xy + 1)^3$

12. ● $f(x, y) = \dfrac{1}{(xy + 1)^2}$

13. $f(x, y) = e^{x+y}$

14. $f(x, y) = e^{2x+y}$

15. $f(x, y) = 5x^{0.6}y^{0.4}$

16. $f(x, y) = -2x^{0.1}y^{0.9}$

17. $f(x, y) = e^{0.2xy}$

18. $f(x, y) = xe^{xy}$

In Exercises 19–28, find $\dfrac{\partial^2 f}{\partial x^2}, \dfrac{\partial^2 f}{\partial y^2}, \dfrac{\partial^2 f}{\partial x \partial y}$, *and* $\dfrac{\partial^2 f}{\partial y \partial x}$, *and evaluate them all at (1, −1) if possible.* hint [see Discussion on pp. 565–566]

19. ● $f(x, y) = 10{,}000 - 40x + 20y$

20. ● $f(x, y) = 1000 + 5x - 4y$

21. ● $f(x, y) = 10{,}000 - 40x + 20y + 10xy$

22. ● $f(x, y) = 1000 + 5x - 4y - 3xy$

23. ● $f(x, y) = 3x^2y$

24. $f(x, y) = x^4y^2 - x$

25. $f(x, y) = e^{x+y}$

26. $f(x, y) = e^{2x+y}$

27. $f(x, y) = 5x^{0.6}y^{0.4}$

28. $f(x, y) = -2x^{0.1}y^{0.9}$

In Exercises 29–40, find $\dfrac{\partial f}{\partial x}, \dfrac{\partial f}{\partial y}, \dfrac{\partial f}{\partial z}$, *and their values at (0, −1, 1) if possible.* hint [see Example 3]

29. ● $f(x, y, z) = xyz$

30. ● $f(x, y, z) = xy + xz - yz$

31. $f(x, y, z) = -\dfrac{4}{x + y + z^2}$

32. $f(x, y, z) = \dfrac{6}{x^2 + y^2 + z^2}$

33. $f(x, y, z) = xe^{yz} + ye^{xz}$

34. $f(x, y, z) = xye^z + xe^{yz} + e^{xyz}$

35. $f(x, y, z) = x^{0.1}y^{0.4}z^{0.5}$

36. $f(x, y, z) = 2x^{0.2}y^{0.8} + z^2$

37. $f(x, y, z) = e^{xyz}$

38. $f(x, y, z) = \ln(x + y + z)$

39. $f(x, y, z) = \dfrac{2000z}{1 + y^{0.3}}$

40. $f(x, y, z) = \dfrac{e^{0.2x}}{1 + e^{-0.1y}}$

Applications

41. ● ***Marginal Cost (Linear Model)*** Your weekly cost (in dollars) to manufacture x cars and y trucks is

$$C(x, y) = 240{,}000 + 6000x + 4000y$$

Calculate and interpret $\dfrac{\partial C}{\partial x}$ and $\dfrac{\partial C}{\partial y}$. hint [see Example 1]

42. ● ***Marginal Cost (Linear Model)*** Your weekly cost (in dollars) to manufacture x bicycles and y tricycles is

$$C(x, y) = 24{,}000 + 60x + 20y$$

Calculate and interpret $\dfrac{\partial C}{\partial x}$ and $\dfrac{\partial C}{\partial y}$.

43. ● ***Scientific Research*** In each year from 1983 to 2003, the percentage y of research articles in *Physical Review* written by researchers in the U.S. can be approximated by

$$y = 82 - 0.78t - 1.02x \text{ percentage points} \quad (0 \le t \le 20)$$

where t is the year since 1983 and x is the percentage of articles written by researchers in Europe.[18] Calculate and interpret $\dfrac{\partial y}{\partial t}$ and $\dfrac{\partial y}{\partial x}$.

44. ● ***Scientific Research*** The number z of research articles in *Physical Review* that were written by researchers in the U.S. from 1993 through 2003 can be approximated by

$$z = 5960 - 0.71x + 0.50y \qquad (3000 \le x, y \le 6000)$$

articles each year, where x is the number of articles written by researchers in Europe and y is the number written by researchers in other countries (excluding Europe and the U.S.).[19] Calculate and interpret $\dfrac{\partial z}{\partial x}$ and $\dfrac{\partial z}{\partial y}$.

45. ● ***Marginal Cost (Interaction Model)*** Your weekly cost (in dollars) to manufacture x cars and y trucks is

$$C(x, y) = 240{,}000 + 6000x + 4000y - 20xy$$

(Compare with Exercise 41.) Compute the marginal cost of manufacturing cars at a production level of 10 cars and 20 trucks. hint [see Example 2]

46. ● ***Marginal Cost (Interaction Model)*** Your weekly cost (in dollars) to manufacture x bicycles and y tricycles is

$$C(x, y) = 24{,}000 + 60x + 20y + 0.3xy$$

(Compare with Exercise 42.) Compute the marginal cost of manufacturing tricycles at a production level of 10 bicycles and 20 tricycles.

47. ● ***Brand Loyalty*** The fraction of Mazda car owners who chose another new Mazda can be modeled by the following function:[20]

$$M(c, f, g, h, t) = 1.1 - 3.8c + 2.2f + 1.9g - 1.7h - 1.3t$$

Here, c is the fraction of Chrysler car owners who remained loyal to Chrysler, f is the fraction of Ford car owners remaining loyal to Ford, g the corresponding figure for General Motors, h the corresponding figure for Honda, and t for Toyota.

a. Calculate $\dfrac{\partial M}{\partial c}$ and $\dfrac{\partial M}{\partial f}$ and interpret the answers.

[18] SOURCE: The American Physical Society/*New York Times,* May 3, 2003, p. A1.

[19] Ibid.

[20] The model is an approximation of a linear regression based on data from the period 1988–1995. Source for data: Chrysler, Maritz Market Research, Consumer Attitude Research, and Strategic Vision/*The New York Times,* November 3, 1995, p. D2.

b. In 1995 it was observed that $c = 0.56$, $f = 0.56$, $g = 0.72$, $h = 0.50$, and $t = 0.43$. According to the model, what percentage of Mazda owners remained loyal to Mazda? (Round your answer to the nearest percentage point.)

48. ● ***Brand Loyalty*** The fraction of Mazda car owners who chose another new Mazda can be modeled by the following function:[21]

$$M(c, f) = 9.4 + 7.8c + 3.6c^2 - 38f - 22cf + 43f^2$$

where c is the fraction of Chrysler car owners who remained loyal to Chrysler and f is the fraction of Ford car owners remaining loyal to Ford.

a. Calculate $\frac{\partial M}{\partial c}$ and $\frac{\partial M}{\partial f}$ evaluated at the point (0.7, 0.7), and interpret the answers.

b. In 1995, it was observed that $c = 0.56$, and $f = 0.56$. According to the model, what percentage of Mazda owners remained loyal to Mazda? (Round your answer to the nearest percentage point.)

49. ***Family Income*** The following model is based on statistical data on the median family incomes of black and white families in the U.S. for the period 1950–2000:[22]

$$z = 13{,}000 + 350t + 9900x + 220xt$$

where

z = median family income

t = year ($t = 0$ represents 1950)

$$x = \begin{cases} 0 & \text{if the income was for a black family} \\ 1 & \text{if the income was for a white family} \end{cases}$$

a. Use the model to estimate the median income of a black family in 1960.

b. Use the model to estimate the median income of a white family in 1960.

c. According to the model, how fast was the median income for a black family increasing in 1960?

d. According to the model, how fast was the median income for a white family increasing in 1960?

e. Do the answers to parts (c) and (d) suggest that the income gap between white and black families was widening or narrowing in the second half of the twentieth century?

50. ***Life Expectancy*** The following model is based on life expectancy for men and women in the U.S. for the period 1900–2000:[23]

$$z = 50.9 + 0.325t - 1.95x - 0.055xt$$

where:

z = life expectancy of a person born in the U.S.

t = year of birth ($t = 0$ represents 1900)

$$x = \begin{cases} 0 & \text{if the person was a female} \\ 1 & \text{if the person was a male} \end{cases}$$

a. Use the model to estimate, to the nearest year, the life expectancy of a female born in 1950.

b. Use the model to estimate, to the nearest year, the life expectancy of a male born in 1950.

c. According to the model, how fast was the life expectancy for a female increasing in 1950?

d. According to the model, how fast was the life expectancy for a male increasing in 1950?

e. Do the answers you have given suggest that the gap between male and female life expectancy was widening or narrowing in the twentieth century?

51. ***Marginal Cost*** Your weekly cost (in dollars) to manufacture x cars and y trucks is

$$C(x, y) = 200{,}000 + 6000x + 4000y - 100{,}000e^{-0.01(x+y)}$$

What is the marginal cost of a car? Of a truck? How do these marginal costs behave as total production increases?

52. ***Marginal Cost*** Your weekly cost (in dollars) to manufacture x bicycles and y tricycles is

$$C(x, y) = 20{,}000 + 60x + 20y + 50\sqrt{xy}$$

What is the marginal cost of a bicycle? Of a tricycle? How do these marginal costs behave as x and y increase?

53. ***Average Cost*** If you average your costs over your total production, you get the **average cost,** written $\bar{C}$:

$$\bar{C}(x, y) = \frac{C(x, y)}{x + y}$$

Find the average cost for the cost function in Exercise 51. Then find the marginal average cost of a car and the marginal average cost of a truck at a production level of 50 cars and 50 trucks. Interpret your answers.

54. ***Average Cost*** Find the average cost for the cost function in Exercise 52 (see the preceding exercise). Then find the marginal average cost of a bicycle and the marginal average cost of a tricycle at a production level of 5 bicycles and 5 tricycles. Interpret your answers.

---

[21] The model is an approximation of a second-order regression based on data from the period 1988–1995. Source for data: Ibid.

[22] Incomes are in constant 1997 dollars. The model is a multiple regression model and coefficients are rounded to two significant digits. Source for data: Statistical Abstract of the United States, 1999, U.S. Census Bureau/ *The New York Times,* December 19, 1999, p. WK5.

[23] The model is a multiple regression model and coefficients are rounded to 3 significant digits. Source for data: Ibid.

● basic skills

55. ***Marginal Revenue*** As manager of an auto dealership, you offer a car rental company the following deal: You will charge \$15,000 per car and \$10,000 per truck, but you will then give the company a discount of \$5000 times the square root of the total number of vehicles it buys from you. Looking at your marginal revenue, is this a good deal for the rental company?

56. ***Marginal Revenue*** As marketing director for a bicycle manufacturer, you come up with the following scheme: You will offer to sell a dealer x bicycles and y tricycles for

$$R(x, y) = 3500 - 3500e^{-0.02x-0.01y} \text{ dollars}$$

Find your marginal revenue for bicycles and for tricycles. Are you likely to be fired for your suggestion?

57. ***Research Productivity*** Here we apply a variant of the Cobb-Douglas function to the modeling of research productivity. A mathematical model of research productivity at a particular physics laboratory is

$$P = 0.04x^{0.4}y^{0.2}z^{0.4}$$

where P is the annual number of groundbreaking research papers produced by the staff, x is the number of physicists on the research team, y is the laboratory's annual research budget, and z is the annual National Science Foundation subsidy to the laboratory. Find the rate of increase of research papers per government-subsidy dollar at a subsidy level of \$1,000,000 per year and a staff level of 10 physicists if the annual budget is \$100,000.

58. ***Research Productivity*** A major drug company estimates that the annual number P of patents for new drugs developed by its research team is best modeled by the formula

$$P = 0.3x^{0.3}y^{0.4}z^{0.3}$$

where x is the number of research biochemists on the payroll, y is the annual research budget, and z is the size of the bonus awarded to discoverers of new drugs. Assuming that the company has 12 biochemists on the staff, has an annual research budget of \$500,000 and pays \$40,000 bonuses to developers of new drugs, calculate the rate of growth in the annual number of patents per new research staff member.

59. ***Utility*** Your newspaper is trying to decide between two competing desktop publishing software packages, Macro Publish and Turbo Publish. You estimate that if you purchase x copies of Macro Publish and y copies of Turbo Publish, your company's daily productivity will be

$$U(x, y) = 6x^{0.8}y^{0.2} + x$$

$U(x, y)$ is measured in pages per day.

a. Calculate $\left.\frac{\partial U}{\partial x}\right|_{(10,5)}$ and $\left.\frac{\partial U}{\partial y}\right|_{(10,5)}$ to two decimal places, and interpret the results.

b. What does the ratio $\left.\frac{\partial U}{\partial x}\right|_{(10,5)} \Big/ \left.\frac{\partial U}{\partial y}\right|_{(10,5)}$ tell about the usefulness of these products?

60. ***Grades***[24] A production formula for a student's performance on a difficult English examination is given by

$$g(t, x) = 4tx - 0.2t^2 - x^2$$

where g is the grade the student can expect to get, t is the number of hours of study for the examination, and x is the student's grade point average.

a. Calculate $\left.\frac{\partial g}{\partial t}\right|_{(10,3)}$ and $\left.\frac{\partial g}{\partial x}\right|_{(10,3)}$ and interpret the results.

b. What does the ratio $\left.\frac{\partial g}{\partial t}\right|_{(10,3)} \Big/ \left.\frac{\partial g}{\partial x}\right|_{(10,3)}$ tell about the relative merits of study and grade point average?

61. ***Electrostatic Repulsion*** If positive electric charges of Q and q coulombs are situated at positions (a, b, c) and (x, y, z) respectively, then the force of repulsion they experience is given by

$$F = K\frac{Qq}{(x-a)^2 + (y-b)^2 + (z-c)^2}$$

where $K \approx 9 \times 10^9$, F is given in newtons, and all positions are measured in meters. Assume that a charge of 10 coulombs is situated at the origin, and that a second charge of 5 coulombs is situated at $(2, 3, 3)$ and moving in the y-direction at one meter per second. How fast is the electrostatic force it experiences decreasing? (Round the answer to one significant digit.)

62. ***Electrostatic Repulsion*** Repeat the preceding exercise, assuming that a charge of 10 coulombs is situated at the origin and that a second charge of 5 coulombs is situated at $(2, 3, 3)$ and moving in the negative z direction at one meter per second. (Round the answer to one significant digit.)

63. ***Investments*** Recall that the compound interest formula for annual compounding is

$$A(P, r, t) = P(1 + r)^t$$

where A is the future value of an investment of P dollars after t years at an interest rate of r.

a. Calculate $\frac{\partial A}{\partial P}$, $\frac{\partial A}{\partial r}$, and $\frac{\partial A}{\partial t}$, all evaluated at $(100, 0.10, 10)$. (Round your answers to two decimal places.) Interpret your answers.

[24] Based on an exercise in *Introduction to Mathematical Economics* by A. L. Ostrosky Jr. and J. V. Koch (Waveland Press, Illinois, 1979).

b. What does the function $\left.\frac{\partial A}{\partial P}\right|_{(100,\,0.10,\,t)}$ of t tell about your investment?

64. ***Investments*** Repeat the preceding exercise, using the formula for continuous compounding:

$$A(P, r, t) = Pe^{rt}$$

65. ***Modeling with the Cobb-Douglas Production Formula*** Assume you are given a production formula of the form

$$P(x, y) = Kx^a y^b \quad (a + b = 1)$$

a. Obtain formulas for $\frac{\partial P}{\partial x}$ and $\frac{\partial P}{\partial y}$, and show that $\frac{\partial P}{\partial x} = \frac{\partial P}{\partial y}$ precisely when $x/y = a/b$.

b. Let x be the number of workers a firm employs and let y be its monthly operating budget in thousands of dollars. Assume that the firm currently employs 100 workers and has a monthly operating budget of $200,000. If each additional worker contributes as much to productivity as each additional $1000 per month, find values of a and b that model the firm's productivity.

66. ***Housing Costs***[25] The cost C of building a house is related to the number k of carpenters used and the number e of electricians used by

$$C(k, e) = 15{,}000 + 50k^2 + 60e^2$$

If three electricians are currently employed in building your new house and the marginal cost per additional electrician is the same as the marginal cost per additional carpenter, how many carpenters are being used? (Round your answer to the nearest carpenter.)

67. ***Nutrient Diffusion*** Suppose that one cubic centimeter of nutrient is placed at the center of a circular petri dish filled with water. We might wonder how the nutrient is distributed after a time of t seconds. According to the classical theory of diffusion, the concentration of nutrient (in parts of nutrient per part of water) after a time t is given by

$$u(r, t) = \frac{1}{4\pi Dt} e^{-\frac{r^2}{4Dt}}$$

Here D is the *diffusivity,* which we will take to be 1, and r is the distance from the center in centimeters. How fast is the concentration increasing at a distance of 1 cm from the center 3 seconds after the nutrient is introduced?

68. ***Nutrient Diffusion*** Refer back to the preceding exercise. How fast is the concentration increasing at a distance of 4 cm from the center 4 seconds after the nutrient is introduced?

[25] Based on an Exercise in *Introduction to Mathematical Economics* by A.L. Ostrosky Jr. and J.V. Koch (Waveland Press, Illinois, 1979).

Communication and Reasoning Exercises

69. ● Given that $f(a, b) = r$, $f_x(a, b) = s$, and $f_y(a, b) = t$, complete the following: ___ is increasing at a rate of ___ units per unit of x, ___ is increasing at a rate of ___ units per unit of y, and the value of ___ is ___ when $x =$ ___ and $y =$ ___.

70. ● A firm's productivity depends on two variables, x and y. Currently, $x = a$ and $y = b$, and the firm's productivity is 4000 units. Productivity is increasing at a rate of 400 units per unit *decrease* in x, and is decreasing at a rate of 300 units per unit increase in y. What does all of this information tell you about the firm's productivity function $g(x, y)$?

71. ● Complete the following: Let $f(x, y, z)$ be the cost to build a development of x cypods (one-bedroom units) in the city-state of Utarek, Mars, y argaats (two-bedroom units), and z orbici (singular: orbicus; three-bedroom units) in $\overline{\overline{Z}}$ (zonars, the designated currency in Utarek).[26] Then $\frac{\partial f}{\partial z}$ measures _____ and has units _____.

72. ● Complete the following: Let $f(t, x, y)$ be the projected number of citizens of the Principality State of Voodice, Luna[27] in year t since its founding, assuming the presence of x lunar vehicle factories and y domed settlements. Then $\frac{\partial f}{\partial x}$ measures _____ and has units _____.

73. ● Give an example of a function $f(x, y)$ with $f_x(1, 1) = -2$ and $f_y(1, 1) = 3$.

74. ● Give an example of a function $f(x, y, z)$ that has all of its partial derivatives nonzero constants.

75. The graph of $z = b + mx + ny$ (b, m, and n constants) is a plane.

a. Explain the geometric significance of the numbers b, m, and n.

b. Show that the equation of the plane passing through (h, k, l) with slope m in the x direction (in the sense of $\partial/\partial x$) and slope n in the y direction is

$$z = l + m(x - h) + n(y - k)$$

76. The **tangent plane** to the graph of $f(x, y)$ at $P(a, b, f(a, b))$ is the plane containing the lines tangent to the slice through the graph by $y = b$ (as in Figure 18) and the slice through the graph by $x = a$. Use the result of the preceding exercise to show that the equation of the tangent plane is

$$z = f(a, b) + f_x(a, b)(x - a) + f_y(a, b)(y - b)$$

[26] SOURCE: www.marsnext.com/comm/zonars.html.

[27] SOURCE: www.voodice.info.

● basic skills

8.4 Maxima and Minima

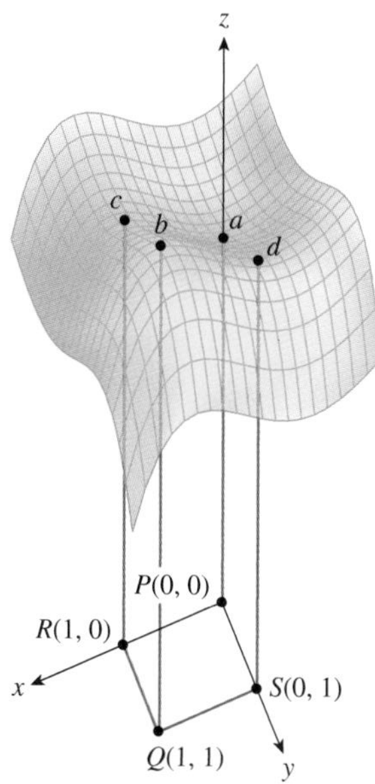

Figure **19**

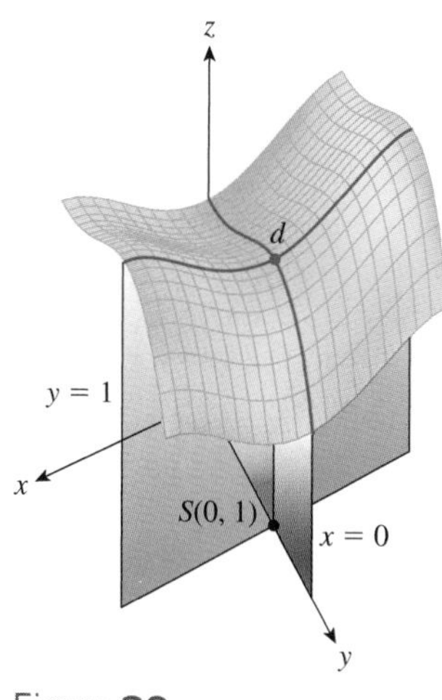

Figure **20**

In Chapter 5 on applications of the derivative, we saw how to locate relative extrema of a function of a single variable. In this section we extend our methods to functions of two variables. Similar techniques work for functions of three or more variables.

Figure 19 shows a portion of the graph of the function $f(x, y) = 2(x^2 + y^2) - (x^4 + y^4) + 3$. The graph resembles a "flying carpet," and several interesting points, marked a, b, c, and d are shown.

1. The point a has coordinates $(0, 0, f(0, 0))$, is directly above the origin $(0, 0)$, and is the lowest point in its vicinity; water would puddle there. We say that f has a **relative minimum** at $(0, 0)$ because $f(0, 0)$ is smaller than $f(x, y)$ for any (x, y) near $(0, 0)$.
2. Similarly, the point b is higher than any point in its vicinity. Thus, we say that f has a **relative maximum** at $(1, 1)$.
3. The points c and d represent a new phenomenon and are called **saddle points.** They are neither relative maxima nor relative minima but seem to be a little of both.

To see more clearly what features a saddle point has, look at Figure 20, which shows a portion of the graph near the point d.

If we slice through the graph along $y = 1$, we get a curve on which d is the *lowest* point. Thus, d looks like a relative minimum along this slice. On the other hand, if we slice through the graph along $x = 0$, we get another curve, on which d is the *highest* point, so d looks like a relative maximum along this slice. This kind of behavior characterizes a saddle point: f has a **saddle point** at (r, s) if f has a relative minimum at (r, s) along some slice through that point and a relative maximum along another slice through that point. If you look at the other saddle point, c, in Figure 19, you see the same characteristics.

While numerical information can help us locate the approximate position of relative extrema and saddle points, calculus permits us to locate these points accurately as we did for functions of a single variable. Look once again at Figure 19, and notice the following:

- The points P, Q, R and S are all in the **interior** of the domain of f; that is, none of them lies on the boundary of the domain. Said another way, we can move some distance in any direction from any of these points without leaving the domain of f.
- The tangent lines along the slices through these points parallel to the x- and y-axes are *horizontal*. Thus, the partial derivatives $\partial f/\partial x$ and $\partial f/\partial y$ are zero when evaluated at any of the points P, Q, R and S. This gives us a way of locating candidates for relative extrema and saddle points.

The following summary generalizes and also expands on some of what we have just said:

Relative and Absolute Maxima and Minima

The function $f(x, y, \ldots)$ has a **relative maximum** at $(r, s, \ldots)$ if $f(r, s, \ldots) \geq f(x, y, \ldots)$ for every point $(x, y, \ldots)$ near $(r, s, \ldots)$. in the domain of f. We say that $f(x, y, \ldots)$ has an **absolute maximum** at $(r, s, \ldots)$ if $f(r, s, \ldots) \geq f(x, y, \ldots)$ for every point $(x, y, \ldots)$ in the domain of f. The terms **relative minimum** and **absolute minimum** are defined in a similar way.

Locating Candidates for Relative Extrema and Saddle Points in the Interior of the Domain of *f*:

- Set $\dfrac{\partial f}{\partial x} = 0$, $\dfrac{\partial f}{\partial y} = 0, \ldots$ simultaneously, and solve for $x, y, \ldots$.
- Check that the resulting points $(x, y, \ldots)$ are in the interior of the domain of *f*.

Points at which all the partial derivatives of *f* are zero are called **critical points.** Thus, the critical points are the only candidates for relative extrema and saddle points in the interior of the domain of *f*.*

quick Examples

1. Let $f(x, y) = x^3 + (y-1)^2$. Then $\dfrac{\partial f}{\partial x} = 3x^2$ and $\dfrac{\partial f}{\partial y} = 2(y-1)$. Thus, we solve the system

$$3x^2 = 0 \quad \text{and} \quad 2(y-1) = 0$$

The first equation gives $x = 0$, and the second gives $y = 1$. Thus, the only critical point is $(0, 1)$. Because the domain of *f* is the whole Cartesian plane, the point $(0, 1)$ is interior, and hence a candidate for a relative extremum or saddle point.†

2. Let $f(x, y) = e^{-(x^2+y^2)}$. Taking partial derivatives and setting them equal to zero gives

$$-2xe^{-(x^2+y^2)} = 0 \qquad \text{We set } \frac{\partial f}{\partial x} = 0.$$

$$-2ye^{-(x^2+y^2)} = 0 \qquad \text{We set } \frac{\partial f}{\partial y} = 0.$$

The first equation implies that $x = 0$,‡ and the second implies that $y = 0$. Thus, the only critical point is $(0, 0)$. This point is interior, and hence a candidate for a relative extremum or saddle point.

* We'll be looking at extrema on the *boundary* of the domain of a function in the next section. What we are calling critical points correspond to the *stationary* points of a function of one variable. We shall not consider the analogs of the singular points.

† In fact, it is a saddle point. (Can you see why?).

‡ Recall that if a product of two numbers is zero, then one or the other must be zero. In this case the number $e^{-(x^2+y^2)}$ can't be zero (since e^u is never zero), which gives the result claimed.

In the next example we first locate all critical points, and then classify each one as a relative maximum, minimum, saddle point, or none of these.

Example 1 Locating and Classifying Critical Points

Locate all critical points of $f(x, y) = x^2y - x^2 - 2y^2$. Graph the function to classify the critical points as relative maxima, minima, saddle points, or none of these.

Solution The partial derivatives are

$$f_x = 2xy - 2x = 2x(y-1)$$
$$f_y = x^2 - 4y$$

Setting these equal to zero gives

$$x = 0 \quad \text{or} \quad y = 1$$
$$x^2 = 4y$$

We get a solution by choosing either $x = 0$ or $y = 1$ and substituting into $x^2 = 4y$.

Case 1: $x = 0$ Substituting into $x^2 = 4y$ gives $0 = 4y$ and hence $y = 0$. Thus, the critical point for this case is $(x, y) = (0, 0)$.

Case 2: $y = 1$ Substituting into $x^2 = 4y$ gives $x^2 = 4$ and hence $x = \pm 2$. Thus, we get two critical points for this case: (2, 1) and (−2, 1).

We now have three critical points altogether: (0, 0), (2, 1), and (−2, 1). We get the corresponding points on the graph by substituting for x and y in the equation for f to get the z-coordinates. The points are (0, 0, 0), (2, 1, −2), and (−2, 1, −2).

Classifying the Critical Points Graphically To classify the critical points graphically, we look at the graph of f shown in Figure 21.

Examining the graph carefully, we see that the point (0, 0, 0) is a relative maximum. As for the other two critical points, are they saddle points or are they relative maxima? They *seem* to be relative maxima along the y-direction, but the slice in the x-direction (through $x = 1$) seems to be horizontal. However, a diagonal slice (along $x = \pm y$) shows these two points as minima and so they are saddle points. (If you don't believe this, we will get more evidence below and in a later example.)

Classifying the Critical Points Numerically We can use a tabular representation of the function to classify the critical points numerically. The following tabular representation of the function can be obtained using Excel. (See the Excel Technology Guide discussion of Section 8.1 Example 3 at the end of the chapter for information on using Excel to generate such a table.)

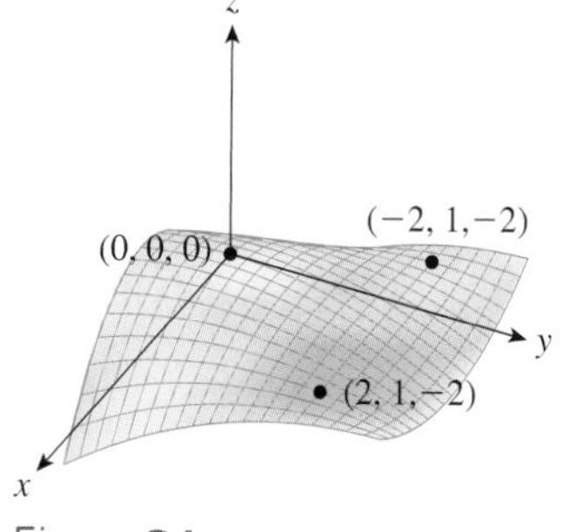

Figure **21**

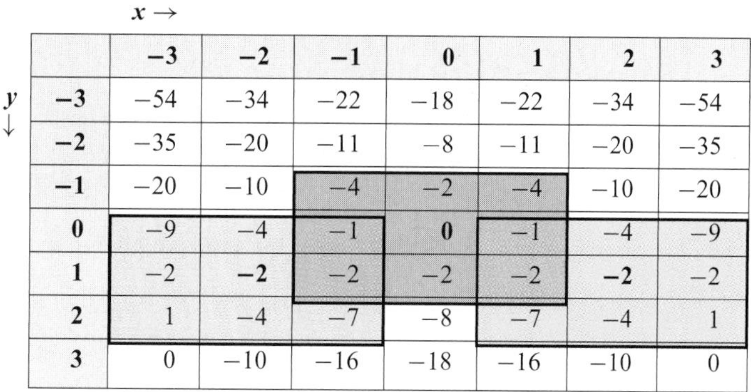

$y \downarrow$ \ $x \rightarrow$	**−3**	**−2**	**−1**	**0**	**1**	**2**	**3**
−3	−54	−34	−22	−18	−22	−34	−54
−2	−35	−20	−11	−8	−11	−20	−35
−1	−20	−10	−4	−2	−4	−10	−20
0	−9	−4	−1	0	−1	−4	−9
1	−2	**−2**	−2	−2	−2	**−2**	−2
2	1	−4	−7	−8	−7	−4	1
3	0	−10	−16	−18	−16	−10	0

The shaded and colored cells show rectangular neighborhoods of the three critical points (0, 0), (2, 1), and (−2, 1). (Notice that they overlap.) The values of f at the points are at the centers of these rectangles. Looking at the gray neighborhood of $(x, y) = (0, 0)$, we see that $f(0, 0) = 0$ is the largest value of f in the shaded cells, suggesting that f has a maximum at (0, 0). The shaded neighborhood of (2, 1) on the right shows $f(2, 1) = -2$ as the maximum along some slices (e.g., the vertical slice), and a minimum along the diagonal slice from top left to bottom right. This is what results in a saddle point on the graph. The point (−2, 1) is similar, and thus f also has a saddle point at (−2, 1).

Q: Is there an algebraic way of deciding whether a given point is a relative maximum, relative minimum, or saddle point?

A: There is a "second derivative test" for functions of two variables, stated as follows. ■

Second Derivative Test for Functions of Two Variables

Suppose (a, b) is a critical point in the interior of the domain of the function f of two variables. Let H be the quantity

$$H = f_{xx}(a, b)f_{yy}(a, b) - [f_{xy}(a, b)]^2$$

H is called the *Hessian.*

Then, if H is *positive,*

- f has a relative minimum at (a, b) if $f_{xx}(a, b) > 0$.
- f has a relative maximum at (a, b) if $f_{xx}(a, b) < 0$.

If H is *negative,*

- f has a saddle point at (a, b).

If $H = 0$, the test tells us nothing, so we need to look at the graph or a numerical table to see what is going on.

quick **Examples**

1. Let $f(x, y) = x^2 - y^2$. Then

$$f_x = 2x \quad \text{and} \quad f_y = -2y$$

which gives (0, 0) as the only critical point. Also,

$$f_{xx} = 2,\ f_{xy} = 0, \quad \text{and} \quad f_{yy} = -2$$

Note that these are constant

which gives $H = (2)(-2) - 0^2 = -4$. Because H is negative, we have a saddle point at (0, 0).

2. Let $f(x, y) = x^2 + 2y^2 + 2xy + 4x$. Then

$$f_x = 2x + 2y + 4 \quad \text{and} \quad f_y = 2x + 4y$$

Setting these equal to zero gives a system of two linear equations in two unknowns:

$$x + y = -2$$
$$x + 2y = 0$$

This system has solution $(-4, 2)$, so this is our only critical point. The second partial derivatives are $f_{xx} = 2$, $f_{xy} = 2$, and $f_{yy} = 4$, so $H = (2)(4) - 2^2 = 4$. Since $H > 0$ and $f_{xx} > 0$, we have a relative minimum at $(-4, 2)$.

Note There is a second derivative test for functions of three or more variables, but it is considerably more complicated. We stick with functions of two variables for the most part in this book. The justification of the second derivative test is beyond the scope of this book. ■

Example 2 Using the Second Derivative Test

Use the second derivative test to analyze the function $f(x, y) = x^2y - x^2 - 2y^2$ discussed in Example 1, and confirm the results we got there.

Solution We saw in Example 1 that the first-order derivatives are

$$f_x = 2xy - 2x = 2x(y - 1)$$
$$f_y = x^2 - 4y$$

and the critical points are (0, 0), (2, 1), and (−2, 1). We also need the second derivatives:

$$f_{xx} = 2y - 2$$
$$f_{xy} = 2x$$
$$f_{yy} = -4$$

The point (0, 0): $f_{xx}(0, 0) = -2$, $f_{xy}(0, 0) = 0$, $f_{yy}(0, 0) = -4$, so $H = 8$. Because $H > 0$ and $f_{xx}(0, 0) < 0$, the second derivative test tells us that f has a relative maximum at (0, 0).

The point (2, 1): $f_{xx}(2, 1) = 0$, $f_{xy}(2, 1) = 4$ and $f_{yy}(2, 1) = -4$, so $H = -16$. Since $H < 0$, we know that f has a saddle point at (2, 1).

The point (−2, 1): $f_{xx}(-2, 1) = 0$, $f_{xy}(-2, 1) = -4$ and $f_{yy}(-2, 1) = -4$, so once again $H = -16$, and f has a saddle point at (−2, 1).

Deriving the Regression Formulas

Back in Section 1.5, we presented the following set of formulas for the **regression** or **best-fit** line associated with a given set of data points $(x_1, y_1), (x_2, y_2), \dots, (x_n, y_n)$.

Regression Line

The line that best fits the n data points $(x_1, y_1), (x_2, y_2), \dots, (x_n, y_n)$ has the form

$$y = mx + b$$

where

$$m = \frac{n\left(\sum xy\right) - \left(\sum x\right)\left(\sum y\right)}{n\left(\sum x^2\right) - \left(\sum x\right)^2}$$

$$b = \frac{\sum y - m\left(\sum x\right)}{n}$$

n = number of data points

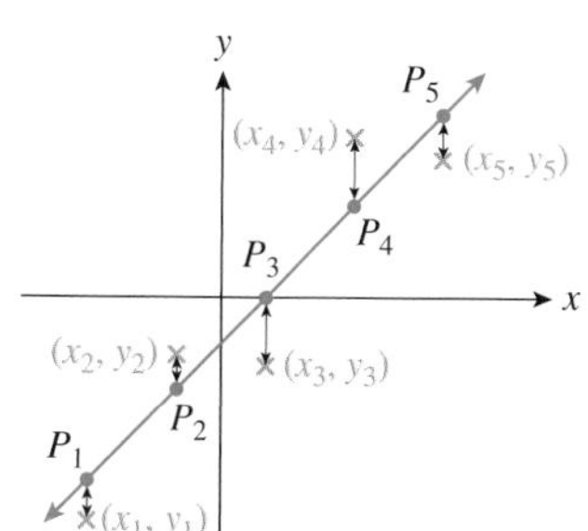

Figure 22

We now show how to derive these formulas. Recall that the regression line is defined to be the line that minimizes the sum of the squares of the **residuals,** measured by the vertical distances shown in Figure 22, which shows a regression line associated with $n = 5$ data points. In the figure, the points $P_1, \dots, P_n$ on the regression line have coordinates

$(x_1, mx_1 + b)$, $(x_2, mx_2 + b)$, ..., $(x_n, mx_n + b)$. The residuals are the quantities $y_{\text{Observed}} - y_{\text{Predicted}}$:

$$y_1 - (mx_1 + b), y_2 - (mx_2 + b), \ldots, y_n - (mx_n + b)$$

The sum of the squares of the residuals is therefore

$$S(m, b) = [y_1 - (mx_1 + b)]^2 + [y_2 - (mx_2 + b)]^2 + \cdots + [y_n - (mx_n + b)]^2$$

and this is the quantity we must minimize by choosing m and b. Because we reason that there is a line that minimizes this quantity, there must be a relative minimum at that point. We shall see in a moment that the function S has at most one critical point, which must therefore be the desired absolute minimum. To obtain the critical points of S, we set the partial derivatives equal to zero and solve:

$$S_m = 0: \quad -2x_1[y_1 - (mx_1 + b)] - \cdots - 2x_n[y_n - (mx_n + b)] = 0$$
$$S_b = 0: \quad -2[y_1 - (mx_1 + b)] - \cdots - 2[y_n - (mx_n + b)] = 0$$

Dividing by -2 and gathering terms allows us to rewrite the equations as

$$m(x_1^2 + \cdots + x_n^2) + b(x_1 + \cdots + x_n) = x_1y_1 + \cdots + x_ny_n$$
$$m(x_1 + \cdots + x_n) + nb = y_1 + \cdots + y_n$$

We can rewrite these equations more neatly using $\sum$-notation:

$$m\left(\sum x^2\right) + b\left(\sum x\right) = \sum xy$$
$$m\left(\sum x\right) + nb = \sum y$$

This is a system of two linear equations in the two unknowns m and b. It may or may not have a unique solution. When there is a unique solution, we can conclude that the best fit line is given by solving these two equations for m and b. Alternatively, there is a general formula for the solution of any system of two equations in two unknowns, and if we apply this formula to our two equations, we get the regression formulas above.

8.4 EXERCISES

● denotes basic skills exercises

◆ denotes challenging exercises

tech Ex indicates exercises that should be solved using technology

In Exercises 1–4, classify each labeled point on the graph as one of the following:

(A) a relative maximum

(B) a relative minimum

(C) a saddle point

(D) a critical point but neither a relative extremum nor a saddle point

(E) none of the above

1. ● *hint* [see Example 1]

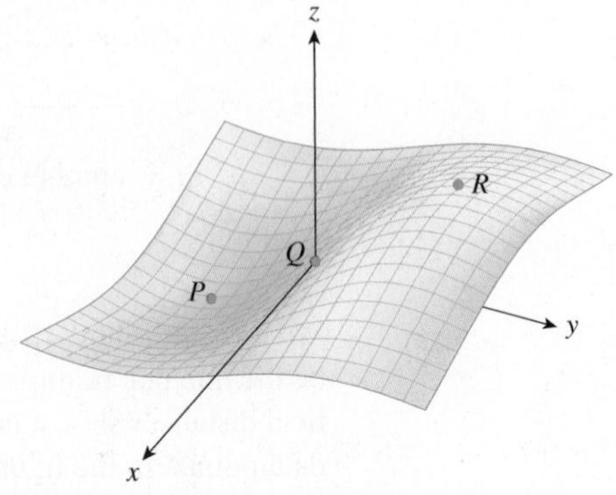

2. ●

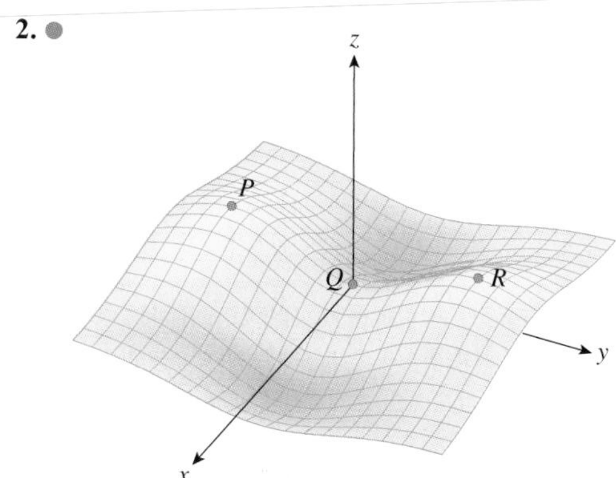

3. ●

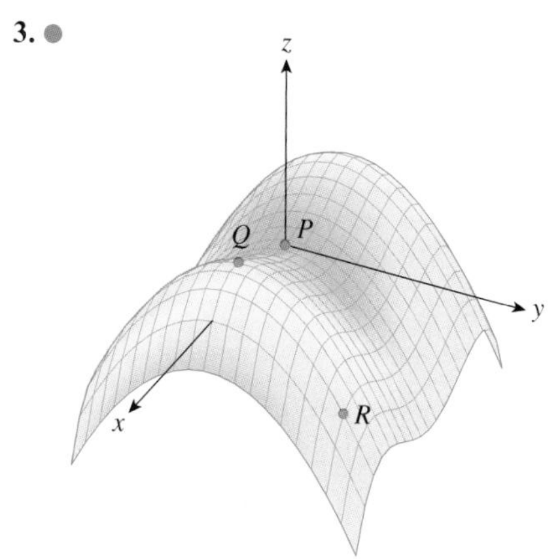

4. ●

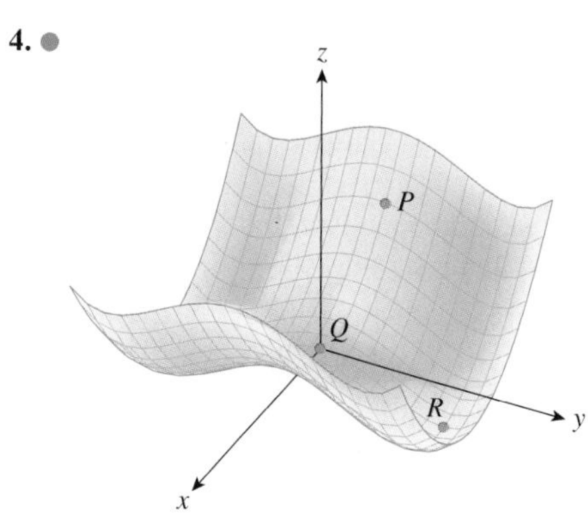

In Exercises 5–10, classify the shaded value in each table as one of the following:

(A) a relative maximum
(B) a relative minimum
(C) a saddle point
(D) neither a relative extremum nor a saddle point

5. ●

y ↓ \ x →	−3	−2	−1	0	1	2
−3	10	5	2	1	2	5
−2	9	4	1	0	1	4
−1	10	5	2	1	2	5
0	13	8	5	4	5	8
1	18	13	10	9	10	13
2	25	20	17	16	17	20
3	34	29	26	25	26	29

6. ●

y ↓ \ x →	−3	−2	−1	0	1	2
−3	5	0	−3	−4	−3	0
−2	8	3	0	−1	0	3
−1	9	4	1	0	1	4
0	8	3	0	−1	0	3
1	5	0	−3	−4	−3	0
2	0	−5	−8	−9	−8	−5
3	−7	−12	−15	−16	−15	−12

7. ●

y ↓ \ x →	−3	−2	−1	0	1	2
−3	5	0	−3	−4	−3	0
−2	8	3	0	−1	0	3
−1	9	4	1	0	1	4
0	8	3	0	−1	0	3
1	5	0	−3	−4	−3	0
2	0	−5	−8	−9	−8	−5
3	−7	−12	−15	−16	−15	−12

8. ●

y ↓ \ x →	−3	−2	−1	0	1	2
−3	2	3	2	−1	−6	−13
−2	3	4	3	0	−5	−12
−1	2	3	2	−1	−6	−13
0	−1	0	−1	−4	−9	−16
1	−6	−5	−6	−9	−14	−21
2	−13	−12	−13	−16	−21	−28
3	−22	−21	−22	−25	−30	−37

9. ● $x \rightarrow$; $y \downarrow$

	−3	−2	−1	0	1	2
−3	4	5	4	1	−4	−11
−2	3	4	3	0	−5	−12
−1	4	5	4	1	−4	−11
0	7	8	7	4	−1	−8
1	12	13	12	9	4	−3
2	19	20	19	16	11	4
3	28	29	28	25	20	13

10. ● $x \rightarrow$; $y \downarrow$

	−3	−2	−1	0	1	2
−3	100	101	100	97	92	85
−2	99	100	99	96	91	84
−1	98	99	98	95	90	83
0	91	92	91	88	83	76
1	72	73	72	69	64	57
2	35	36	35	32	27	20
3	−26	−25	−26	−29	−34	−41

Locate and classify all the critical points of the functions in Exercises 11–28. hint [see Example 2]

11. ● $f(x, y) = x^2 + y^2 + 1$

12. ● $f(x, y) = 4 - (x^2 + y^2)$

13. ● $g(x, y) = 1 - x^2 - x - y^2 + y$

14. ● $g(x, y) = x^2 + x + y^2 - y - 1$

15. ● $h(x, y) = x^2y - 2x^2 - 4y^2$

16. ● $h(x, y) = x^2 + y^2 - y^2x - 4$

17. ● $s(x, y) = e^{x^2+y^2}$

18. ● $s(x, y) = e^{-(x^2+y^2)}$

19. ● $t(x, y) = x^4 + 8xy^2 + 2y^4$

20. ● $t(x, y) = x^3 - 3xy + y^3$

21. ● $f(x, y) = x^2 + y - e^y$

22. ● $f(x, y) = xe^y$

23. ● $f(x, y) = e^{-(x^2+y^2+2x)}$

24. ● $f(x, y) = e^{-(x^2+y^2-2x)}$

25. $f(x, y) = xy + \frac{2}{x} + \frac{2}{y}$

26. $f(x, y) = xy + \frac{4}{x} + \frac{2}{y}$

27. $g(x, y) = x^2 + y^2 + \frac{2}{xy}$

28. $g(x, y) = x^3 + y^3 + \frac{3}{xy}$

29. Refer back to Exercise 11. Which (if any) of the critical points of $f(x, y) = x^2 + y^2 + 1$ are absolute extrema?

30. Refer back to Exercise 12. Which (if any) of the critical points of $f(x, y) = 4 - (x^2 + y^2)$ are absolute extrema?

31. tech Ex Refer back to Exercise 15. Which (if any) of the critical points of $h(x, y) = x^2y - 2x^2 - 4y^2$ are absolute extrema?

32. tech Ex Refer back to Exercise 16. Which (if any) of the critical points of $h(x, y) = x^2 + y^2 - y^2x - 4$ are absolute extrema?

Applications

33. ● ***Brand Loyalty*** Suppose the fraction of Mazda car owners who chose another new Mazda can be modeled by the following function:[28]

$$M(c, f) = 11 + 8c + 4c^2 - 40f - 20cf + 40f^2$$

where c is the fraction of Chrysler car owners who remained loyal to Chrysler and f is the fraction of Ford car owners remaining loyal to Ford. Locate and classify all the critical points and interpret your answer. hint [see Example 2]

34. ● ***Brand Loyalty*** Repeat the preceding exercise using the function:

$$M(c, f) = -10 - 8f - 4f^2 + 40c + 20fc - 40c^2$$

35. ***Pollution Control*** The cost of controlling emissions at a firm goes up rapidly as the amount of emissions reduced goes up. Here is a possible model:

$$C(x, y) = 4000 + 100x^2 + 50y^2$$

where x is the reduction in sulfur emissions, y is the reduction in lead emissions (in pounds of pollutant per day), and C is the daily cost to the firm (in dollars) of this reduction. Government clean-air subsidies amount to \$500 per pound of sulfur and \$100 per pound of lead removed. How many pounds of pollutant should the firm remove each day in order to minimize *net* cost (cost minus subsidy)?

36. ***Pollution Control*** Repeat the preceding exercise using the following information:

$$C(x, y) = 2000 + 200x^2 + 100y^2$$

with government subsidies amounting to \$100 per pound of sulfur and \$500 per pound of lead removed per day.

37. ***Revenue*** Your company manufactures two models of speakers, the Ultra Mini and the Big Stack. Demand for each depends partly on the price of the other. If one is expensive, then more people will buy the other. If p_1 is the price of the

[28] This model is not accurate, although it was inspired by an approximation of a second-order regression based on data from the period 1988–1995. Source for original data: Chrysler, Maritz Market Research, Consumer Attitude Research, and Strategic Vision/*The New York Times*, November 3, 1995, p. D2.

Ultra Mini, and p_2 is the price of the Big Stack, demand for the Ultra Mini is given by

$$q_1(p_1, p_2) = 100{,}000 - 100p_1 + 10p_2$$

where q_1 represents the number of Ultra Minis that will be sold in a year. The demand for the Big Stack is given by

$$q_2(p_1, p_2) = 150{,}000 + 10p_1 - 100p_2$$

Find the prices for the Ultra Mini and the Big Stack that will maximize your total revenue.

38. ***Revenue*** Repeat the preceding exercise, using the following demand functions:

$$q_1(p_1, p_2) = 100{,}000 - 100p_1 + p_2$$
$$q_2(p_1, p_2) = 150{,}000 + p_1 - 100p_2$$

39. ***Luggage Dimensions*** American Airlines requires that the total outside dimensions (length + width + height) of a checked bag not exceed 62 inches.[29] What are the dimensions of the largest volume bag that you can check on an American flight?

40. ***Luggage Dimensions*** American Airlines requires that the total outside dimensions (length + width + height) of a carry-on bag not exceed 45 inches.[30] What are the dimensions of the largest volume bag that you can carry on an American flight?

41. ***Package Dimensions*** The U.S. Postal Service (USPS) will accept only packages with length plus girth of no more than 108 inches.[31] (See the figure.)

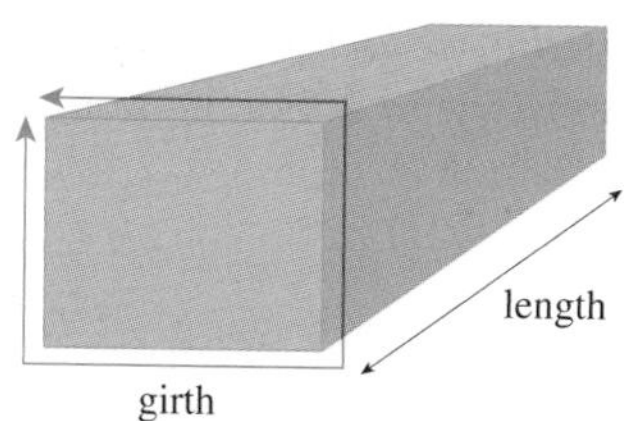

What are the dimensions of the largest volume package that the USPS will accept? What is its volume?

42. ***Package Dimensions*** United Parcel Service (UPS) will accept only packages with length no more than 108 inches and length plus girth no more than 130 inches.[32] (See figure for the preceding exercise.) What are the dimensions of the largest volume package that UPS will accept? What is its volume?

[29] According to information on its website (www.aa.com) as of August, 2002.

[30] Ibid.

[31] The requirement for priority Mail as of July, 2002.

[32] The requirement as of July, 2002.

Communication and Reasoning Exercises

43. ● Sketch the graph of a function that has one extremum and no saddle points.

44. ● Sketch the graph of a function that has one saddle point and one extremum.

45. Sketch the graph of a function that has one relative extremum, no absolute extrema, and no saddle points.

46. Sketch the graph of a function that has infinitely many absolute maxima.

47. ● Let $H = f_{xx}(a, b)f_{yy}(a, b) - [f_{xy}(a, b)]^2$. What condition on H guarantees that f has a relative extremum at the point (a, b)?

48. ● Let H be as in the preceding exercise. Give an example to show that it is possible to have $H = 0$ and a relative minimum at (a, b).

49. Suppose that when the graph of $f(x, y)$ is sliced by a vertical plane through (a, b) parallel to either the xz-plane or the yz-plane, the resulting curve has a relative maximum at (a, b). Does this mean that f has a relative maximum at (a, b)? Explain your answer.

50. Suppose that f has a relative maximum at (a, b). Does it follow that, if the graph of f is sliced by a vertical plane parallel to either the xz-plane or the yz-plane, the resulting curve has a relative maximum at (a, b)? Explain your answer.

51. ***Average Cost*** Let $C(x, y)$ be any cost function. Show that when the average cost is minimized, the marginal costs C_x and C_y both equal the average cost. Explain why this is reasonable.

52. ***Average Profit*** Let $P(x, y)$ be any profit function. Show that when the average profit is maximized, the marginal profits P_x and P_y both equal the average profit. Explain why this is reasonable.

53. ◆ The tangent plane to a graph was introduced in Exercise 76 in the preceding section. Use the equation of the tangent plane given there to explain why the tangent plane is parallel to the xy-plane at a relative maximum or minimum of $f(x, y)$.

54. ◆ Use the equation of the tangent plane given in Exercise 76 in the preceding section to explain why the tangent plane is parallel to the xy-plane at a saddle point of $f(x, y)$.

8.5 Constrained Maxima and Minima and Applications

So far we have looked only at the relative extrema of functions with no constraints. However, in Section 5.2 we saw examples in which we needed to find the maximum or minimum of an objective function subject to one or more constraints on the independent variables. For instance, consider the following problem:

$$\text{Minimize } S = xy + 2xz + 2yz \qquad \text{subject to } xyz = 4 \text{ with } x > 0,\ y > 0, z > 0$$

Our strategy for solving such problems is essentially the same as the strategy we used earlier. First, we use the constraint equations to eliminate variables. In the examples in this section, we are able to reduce our objective function to a function of only two variables. Next, we locate any critical points, and then determine whether they are maxima, minima, or neither.

An alternative method, called the *method of Lagrange Multipliers,* can be used even when it is impossible to eliminate variables using the constraint equations.

First, we see how to solve the above constrained minimization problem using the first method.

Example 1 Constrained Minimization Problem

Minimize $S = xy + 2xz + 2yz$ subject to $xyz = 4$ with $x > 0$, $y > 0$, $z > 0$.

Solution As suggested in the above discussion, we proceed as follows:

Solve the constraint equation for one of the variables and then substitute in the objective function. The constraint equation is $xyz = 4$. Solving for z gives

$$z = \frac{4}{xy}$$

The objective function is $S = xy + 2xz + 2yz$, so substituting $z = 4/xy$ gives

$$S = xy + 2x\frac{4}{xy} + 2y\frac{4}{xy}$$
$$= xy + \frac{8}{y} + \frac{8}{x}$$

Minimize the resulting function of two variables. We use the method in Section 8.4 to find the minimum of $S = xy + \frac{8}{y} + \frac{8}{x}$ for $x > 0$ and $y > 0$: We look for critical points:

$$S_x = y - \frac{8}{x^2} \qquad S_y = x - \frac{8}{y^2}$$

$$S_{xx} = \frac{16}{x^3} \qquad S_{xy} = 1 \qquad S_{yy} = \frac{16}{y^3}$$

We now equate the first partial derivatives to zero:

$$y = \frac{8}{x^2} \qquad \text{and} \qquad x = \frac{8}{y^2}$$

To solve for x and y, we substitute the first of these equations in the second, getting

$$x = \frac{x^4}{8}$$
$$x^4 - 8x = 0$$
$$x(x^3 - 8) = 0$$

The two solutions are $x = 0$, which we reject because x cannot be zero, and $x = 2$. Substituting $x = 2$ in $y = 8/x^2$ gives $y = 2$ also. Thus, the only critical point is (2, 2). To apply the second derivative test, we compute

$$S_{xx}(2, 2) = 2 \qquad S_{xy}(2, 2) = 1 \qquad S_{yy}(2, 2) = 2$$

and find that $H = 3 > 0$, so we have a relative minimum at (2, 2).

The corresponding value of z is given by the constraint equation:

$$z = \frac{4}{xy} = \frac{4}{4} = 1$$

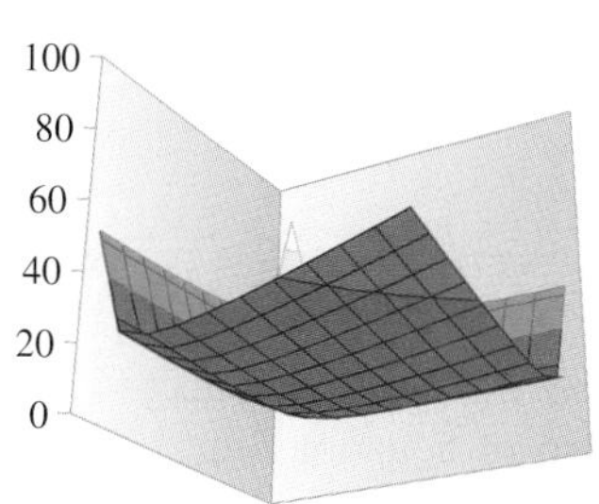

Graph of $S = xy + \frac{8}{y} + \frac{8}{x}$ $(0.2 \le x \le 5,\ 0.2 \le y \le 5)$

Figure **23**

The corresponding value of the objective function is

$$S = xy + \frac{8}{y} + \frac{8}{x} = 4 + \frac{8}{2} + \frac{8}{2} = 12$$

Figure 23 shows a portion of the graph of $S = xy + \dfrac{8}{y} + \dfrac{8}{x}$ for positive x and y (drawn using the Excel 3-D Grapher in the Chapter 8 utilities available online), and suggests that there is a single absolute minimum, which must be at our only candidate point (2, 2).

We conclude that the minimum of S is 12 and occurs at (2, 2, 1).

Example **2** Minimizing Area

Find the dimensions of an open-top rectangular box that has a volume of 4 cubic feet and the smallest possible surface area.

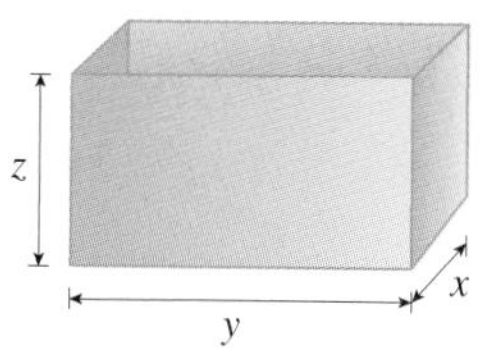

Figure **24**

Solution Our first task is to rephrase this request as a mathematical optimization problem. Figure 24 shows a picture of the box with dimensions x, y, and z.

We want to minimize the total surface area, which is given by

$$A = xy + 2xz + 2yz \qquad \text{Base + Sides + Front and Back}$$

This is our objective function. We can't simply choose x, y, and z to all be zero; however, because the enclosed volume must be 4 cubic feet. So,

$$xyz = 4 \qquad \text{Constraint}$$

This is our constraint equation. Other unstated constraints are $x > 0$, $y > 0$, and $z > 0$, because the dimensions of the box must be positive. We now restate the problem as follows:

$$\text{Minimize } A = xy + 2xz + 2yz \quad \text{subject to } xyz = 4,\ x > 0, y > 0, z > 0$$

But this is exactly the problem in Example 1, which has a solution $x = 2$, $y = 2$, $z = 1$, $A = 12$. Thus, the required dimensions of the box are

$$x = 2 \text{ ft}, y = 2 \text{ ft}, z = 1 \text{ ft}$$

requiring a total surface area of 12 ft^2.

Q: *In Example 1 we checked that we had a relative minimum at $(x, y) = (2, 2)$ and we were persuaded graphically that this was probably an absolute minimum. Can we be sure that this relative minimum is an absolute minimum?*

A: Yes. There must be a least surface area among all boxes that hold 4 cubic feet. (Why?) Because this would give a relative minimum of *A* and because the only possible relative minimum of *A* occurs at (2, 2), this is the absolute minimum. ■

The Method of Lagrange Multipliers

Suppose we have a constrained optimization problem in which it is difficult or impossible to solve a constraint equation for one of the variables. Then we can use the method of **Lagrange multipliers** to avoid this difficulty. We restrict attention to the case of a single constraint equation, although the method generalizes to any number of constraint equations.

Locating Relative Extrema Using the Method of Lagrange Multipliers

To locate the candidates for relative extrema of a function $f(x, y, \ldots)$ subject to the constraint $g(x, y, \ldots) = 0$, we solve the following system of equations for $x, y, \ldots$ and λ:

$$f_x = \lambda g_x$$
$$f_y = \lambda g_y$$
$$\ldots$$
$$g = 0$$

The unknown λ is called a **Lagrange multiplier.** The points $(x, y, \ldots)$ that occur in solutions are then the candidates for the relative extrema of f subject to $g = 0$.

Although the justification for the method of Lagrange multipliers is beyond the scope of this text, we will demonstrate by example how it is used.

Example 3 Using Lagrange Multipliers

Use the method of Lagrange multipliers to find the maximum value of $f(x, y) = 2xy$ subject to $x^2 + 4y^2 = 32$.

Solution We start by rewriting the problem in standard form:

$$\text{Maximize } f(x, y) = 2xy \quad \text{subject to } x^2 + 4y^2 - 32 = 0$$

Here, $g(x, y) = x^2 + 4y^2 - 32$, and the system of equations we need to solve is thus

$$f_x = \lambda g_x \quad \text{or} \quad 2y = 2\lambda x$$
$$f_y = \lambda g_y \quad \text{or} \quad 2x = 8\lambda y$$
$$g = 0 \quad \text{or} \quad x^2 + 4y^2 - 32 = 0$$

A convenient way to solve such a system is to solve one of the equations for λ and then substitute in the remaining equations. Thus, we start by solving the first equation to obtain

$$\lambda = \frac{y}{x}$$

(A word of caution: Because we divided by x, we made the implicit assumption that $x \neq 0$, so before continuing we should check what happens if $x = 0$. But if $x = 0$, then the first equation, $2y = 2\lambda x$, tells us that $y = 0$ as well, and this contradicts the third equation: $x^2 + 4y^2 - 32 = 0$. Thus, we can rule out the possibility that $x = 0$.) Substituting in the remaining equations gives

$$x = 4\lambda y = \frac{4y^2}{x} \quad \text{or} \quad x^2 = 4y^2$$
$$x^2 + 4y^2 - 32 = 0$$

Notice how we have reduced the number of unknowns and also the number of equations by one. We can now substitute $x^2 = 4y^2$ in the last equation, obtaining

$$4y^2 + 4y^2 - 32 = 0$$
$$8y^2 = 32$$
$$y = \pm 2$$

We now substitute back to obtain

$$x^2 = 4y^2 = 16$$

or $\quad x = \pm 4$

We don't need the value of λ, so we won't solve for it. Thus, the candidates for relative extrema are given by $x = \pm 4$ and $y = \pm 2$, that is, the four points $(-4, -2)$, $(-4, 2)$, $(4, -2)$, and $(4, 2)$. Recall that we are seeking the values of x and y that give the maximum value for $f(x, y) = 2xy$. Because we now have only four points to choose from, we compare the values of f at these four points and conclude that the maximum value of f occurs when $(x, y) = (-4, -2)$ or $(4, 2)$.

Something is suspicious in Example 3. We didn't check to see whether these candidates were relative extrema to begin with, let alone absolute extrema! How do we justify this omission? One of the difficulties with using the method of Lagrange Multipliers is that it does not provide us with a test analogous to the second derivative test for functions of several variables. However, if you grant that the function in question does have an absolute maximum, then we require no test, because one of the candidates must give this maximum.

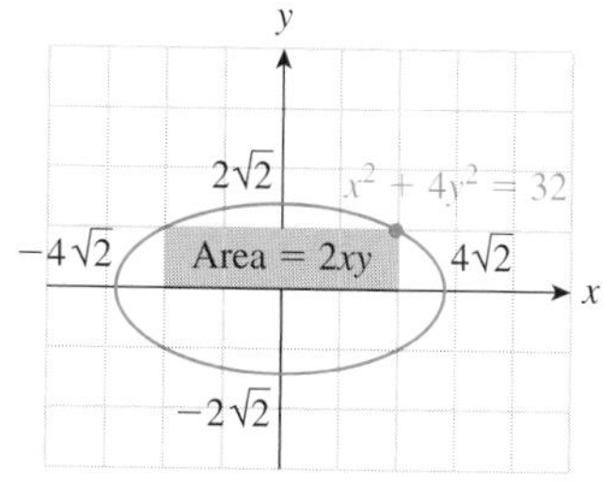

Figure 25

Q: *But how do we know that the given function has an absolute maximum?*

A: The best way to see this is by giving a geometric interpretation. The constraint $x^2 + 4y^2 = 32$ tells us that the point (x, y) must lie on the ellipse shown in Figure 25. The function $f(x, y) = 2xy$ gives the area of the rectangle shaded in Figure 25.

Because there must be a largest such rectangle, the function f must have an absolute maximum for at least one pair of coordinates (x, y). ■

As a last example, we show how to use Lagrange Multipliers to solve the minimization problem in Example 1:

Example 4 Using Lagrange Multipliers: Function of Three Variables

Use the method of Lagrange multipliers to find the minimum value of $S = xy + 2xz + 2yz$ subject to $xyz = 4$ with $x > 0, y > 0, z > 0$.

Solution We start by rewriting the problem in standard form:

Maximize $f(x, y, z) = xy + 2xz + 2yz$
subject to $xyz - 4 = 0$ (with $x > 0, y > 0, z > 0$)

Here, $g(x, y, z) = xyz - 4$, and the system of equations we need to solve is thus

$$f_x = \lambda g_x \quad \text{or} \quad y + 2z = \lambda yz$$
$$f_y = \lambda g_y \quad \text{or} \quad x + 2z = \lambda xz$$
$$f_z = \lambda g_z \quad \text{or} \quad 2x + 2y = \lambda xy$$
$$g = 0 \quad \text{or} \quad xyz - 4 = 0$$

As in the last example, we solve one of the equations for λ and substitute in the others. The first equation gives

$$\lambda = \frac{1}{z} + \frac{2}{y}$$

Substituting this into the second and third equations gives

$$x + 2z = x + \frac{2xz}{y}$$

or $\quad 2 = \dfrac{2x}{y}$ $\quad$ Subtract x from both sides and then divide by z.

giving $\quad y = x$

Substituting the expression for λ into the third equation gives

$$2x + 2y = \frac{xy}{z} + 2x$$

or $\quad 2 = \dfrac{x}{z}$ $\quad$ Subtract $2x$ from both sides and then divide by y.

giving $\quad z = \dfrac{x}{2}$

Now we have both y and z in terms of x. We substitute these values in the last (constraint) equation:

$$x(x)\left(\frac{x}{2}\right) - 4 = 0$$
$$x^3 = 8$$
$$x = 2$$

Thus, $y = x = 2$, and $z = \dfrac{x}{2} = 1$. Therefore, the only critical point occurs at (2, 2, 1) as we found in Example 1, and the corresponding value of S is

$$S = xy + 2xz + 2yz = (2)(2) + 2(2)(1) + 2(2)(1) = 12$$

+ *Before we go on...* Again, the method of Lagrange Multipliers does not tell us whether the critical point in Example 4 is a maximum, minimum, or neither. However, if you grant that the function in question does have an absolute minimum, then the values we found must give this minimum value. ■

FAQs When to Use Lagrange Multipliers

Q: *When can I use the method of Lagrange multipliers? When should I use it?*

A: We have discussed the method only when there is a single equality constraint. There is a generalization, which we do not discuss, that works when there are more equality constraints (we need to introduce one multiplier for each constraint). So, if you have a problem with more than one equality constraint, or with any inequality constraints, you must use the method we discussed earlier in this section. On the other hand, if you have one equality constraint, and it would be difficult to solve it for one of the variables, then you should use Lagrange multipliers. We have noted in the exercises where you might use Lagrange multipliers. ■

8.5 EXERCISES

● denotes basic skills exercises

◆ denotes challenging exercises

In Exercises 1–6, use substitution to solve the given optimization problem. hint [see Example 1]

1. ● Find the maximum value of $f(x, y, z) = 1 - x^2 - y^2 - z^2$ subject to $z = 2y$. Also find the corresponding point(s) (x, y, z).

2. ● Find the minimum value of $f(x, y, z) = x^2 + y^2 + z^2 - 2$ subject to $x = y$. Also find the corresponding point(s) (x, y, z).

3. ● Find the maximum value of $f(x, y, z) = 1 - x^2 - x - y^2 + y - z^2 + z$ subject to $3x = y$. Also find the corresponding point(s) (x, y, z).

4. ● Find the minimum value of $f(x, y, z) = 2x^2 + 2x + y^2 - y + z^2 - z - 1$ subject to $z = 2y$. Also find the corresponding point(s) (x, y, z).

5. ● Minimize $S = xy + 4xz + 2yz$ subject to $xyz = 1$ with $x > 0, y > 0, z > 0$.

6. ● Minimize $S = xy + xz + yz$ subject to $xyz = 2$ with $x > 0$, $y > 0, z > 0$.

In Exercises 7–18, use Lagrange Multipliers to solve the given optimization problem. hint [see Example 3]

7. ● Find the maximum value of $f(x, y) = xy$ subject to $x + 2y = 40$. Also find the corresponding point(s) (x, y).

8. ● Find the maximum value of $f(x, y) = xy$ subject to $3x + y = 60$. Also find the corresponding point(s) (x, y).

9. ● Find the maximum value of $f(x, y) = 4xy$ subject to $x^2 + y^2 = 8$. Also find the corresponding point(s) (x, y).

10. ● Find the maximum value of $f(x, y) = xy$ subject to $y = 3 - x^2$. Also find the corresponding point(s) (x, y).

11. ● Find the minimum value of $f(x, y) = x^2 + y^2$ subject to $x + 2y = 10$. Also find the corresponding point(s) (x, y).

12. ● Find the minimum value of $f(x, y) = x^2 + y^2$ subject to $xy^2 = 16$. Also find the corresponding point(s) (x, y).

13. ● The problem in Exercise 1. hint [see Example 4]

14. ● The problem in Exercise 2.

15. ● The problem in Exercise 3.

16. ● The problem in Exercise 4.

17. ● The problem in Exercise 5.

18. ● The problem in Exercise 6.

Applications

Exercises 19–22 were solved in Section 5.2. This time, use the method of Lagrange Multipliers to solve them.

19. ● ***Fences*** I want to fence in a rectangular vegetable patch. The fencing for the east and west sides costs \$4 per foot, and the fencing for the north and south sides costs only \$2 per foot. I have a budget of \$80 for the project. What is the largest area I can enclose?

20. ● ***Fences*** My orchid garden abuts my house so that the house itself forms the northern boundary. The fencing for the southern boundary costs \$4 per foot, and the fencing for the east and west sides costs \$2 per foot. If I have a budget of \$80 for the project, what is the largest area I can enclose this time?

21. ● ***Revenue*** Hercules Films is deciding on the price of the video release of its film *Son of Frankenstein*. Its marketing people estimate that at a price of p dollars, it can sell a total of $q = 200{,}000 - 10{,}000p$ copies. What price will bring in the greatest revenue?

22. ● ***Profit*** Hercules Films is also deciding on the price of the video release of its film *Bride of the Son of Frankenstein*. Again, marketing estimates that at a price of p dollars it can sell $q = 200{,}000 - 10{,}000p$ copies, but each copy costs \$4 to make. What price will give the greatest *profit?*

23. ● ***Geometry*** At what points on the sphere $x^2 + y^2 + z^2 = 1$ is the product xyz a maximum? (The method of Lagrange multipliers can be used.)

24. ● ***Geometry*** At what point on the surface $z = (x^2 + x + y^2 + 4)^{1/2}$ is the quantity $x^2 + y^2 + z^2$ a minimum? (The method of Lagrange multipliers can be used.)

25. ***Geometry*** What point on the surface $z = x^2 + y - 1$ is closest to the origin? [*Hint:* Minimize the square of the distance from (x, y, z) to the origin.]

26. ***Geometry*** What point on the surface $z = x + y^2 - 3$ is closest to the origin? [*Hint:* Minimize the square of the distance from (x, y, z) to the origin.]

27. ***Geometry*** Find the point on the plane $-2x + 2y + z - 5 = 0$ closest to $(-1, 1, 3)$. [*Hint:* Minimize the square of the distance from the given point to a general point on the plane.]

28. ***Geometry*** Find the point on the plane $2x - 2y - z + 1 = 0$ closest to $(1, 1, 0)$.

29. ● ***Construction Cost*** A closed rectangular box is made with two kinds of materials. The top and bottom are made with heavy-duty cardboard costing 20¢ per square foot, and the sides are made with lightweight cardboard costing 10¢ per square foot. Given that the box is to have a capacity of 2 cubic feet, what should its dimensions be if the cost is to be minimized? hint [see Example 2]

30. ● ***Construction Cost*** Repeat the preceding exercise assuming that the heavy-duty cardboard costs 30¢ per square foot, the lightweight cardboard costs 5¢ per square foot, and the box is to have a capacity of 6 cubic feet.

31. ● ***Package Dimensions*** The U.S. Postal Service (USPS) will accept only packages with length plus girth no more than 108 inches.[33] (See the figure.)

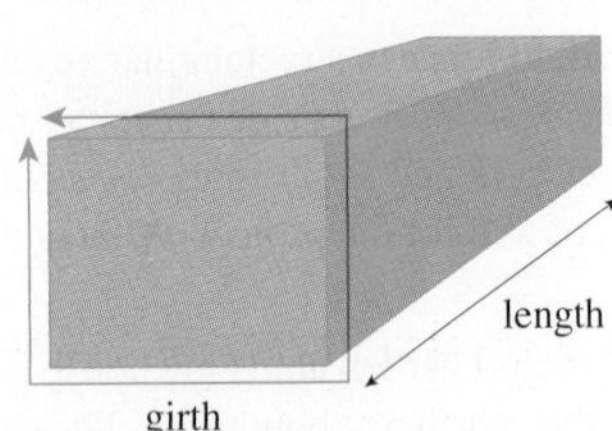

What are the dimensions of the largest volume package the USPS will accept? What is its volume? (This exercise is the same as Exercise 41 in the preceding section. This time, solve it using Lagrange Multipliers.)

32. ● ***Package Dimensions*** United Parcel Service (UPS) will accept only packages with length no more than 108 inches and length plus girth no more than 130 inches.[34] (See the figure for the preceding exercise.) What are the dimensions of the largest volume package UPS will accept? What is its volume? (This exercise is the same as Exercise 42 in the preceding section. This time, solve it using Lagrange Multipliers.)

33. ***Construction Cost*** My company wishes to manufacture boxes similar to those described in Exercise 29 as cheaply as possible, but unfortunately the company that manufactures the cardboard is unable to give me price quotes for the heavy-duty and lightweight cardboard. Find formulas for the dimensions of the box in terms of the price per square foot of heavy-duty and lightweight cardboard.

34. ***Construction Cost*** Repeat the preceding exercise, assuming that only the bottoms of the boxes are to be made using heavy-duty cardboard.

35. ***Geometry*** Find the dimensions of the rectangular box with largest volume that can be inscribed above the xy-plane and under the paraboloid $z = 1 - (x^2 + y^2)$.

36. ***Geometry*** Find the dimensions of the rectangular box with largest volume that can be inscribed above the xy-plane and under the paraboloid $z = 2 - (2x^2 + y^2)$.

Communication and Reasoning Exercises

37. ● Outline two methods of solution of the problem "*Maximize $f(x, y, z)$ subject to $g(x, y, z) = 0$*" and give an advantage and disadvantage of each.

38. ● Suppose we know that $f(x, y)$ has both partial derivatives in its domain $D\colon x > 0, y > 0$, and that (a, b) is the only point in D such that $f_x(a, b) = f_y(a, b) = 0$. Must it be the case that f has an absolute maximum at (a, b)? Explain.

39. ● Under what circumstances would it be necessary to use the method of Lagrange multipliers?

40. ● Under what circumstances would the method of Lagrange multipliers not apply?

41. ● Restate the following problem as a maximization problem of the form "*Maximize $f(x, y)$ subject to $g(x, y) = 0$*":

Find the maximum value of $h(x) = 1 - 2x^2$

42. ● Restate the following problem as a maximization problem of the form "*Maximize $f(x, y, z)$ subject to $g(x, y, z) = 0$*":

Find the maximum value of $h(x, y) = 1 - 2(x^2 + y^2)$

43. If the partial derivatives of a function of several variables are never 0, is it possible for the function to have relative extrema on some domain? Explain your answer.

44. ◆ A **linear programming problem in two variables** is a problem of the form: "*Maximize (or minimize) $f(x, y)$ subject to constraints of the form $C(x, y) \geq 0$ or $C(x, y) \leq 0$.*" Here, the objective function f and the constraints C are linear functions. There may be several linear constraints in one problem. Explain why the solution cannot occur in the interior of the domain of f.

45. ◆ Refer back to Exercise 44. Explain why the solution will actually be at a corner of the domain of f (where two or more of the line segments that make up the boundary meet). This result—or rather a slight generalization of it—is known as the Fundamental Theorem of Linear Programming.

[33] The requirement for priority Mail as of July, 2002.

[34] The requirement as of July, 2002.

8.6 Double Integrals and Applications

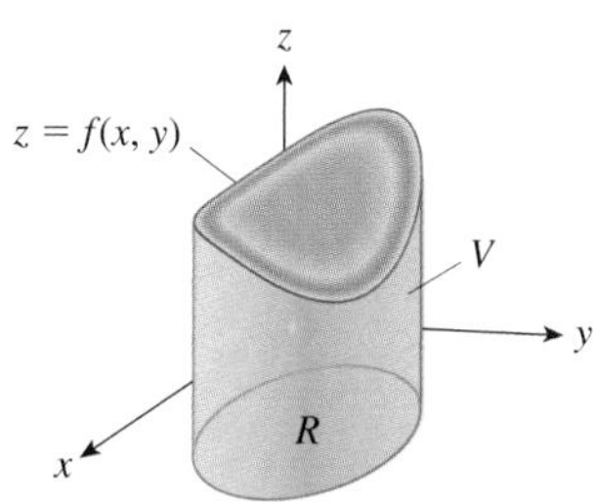

Figure **26**

When discussing functions of one variable, we computed the area under a graph by integration. The analog for the graph of a function of two variables is the *volume V* under the graph, as in Figure 26.

Think of the region R in the xy-plane as the "shadow" under the portion of the surface $z = f(x, y)$ shown.

By analogy with the definite integral of a function of one variable, we make the following definition:

Geometric Definition of the Double Integral

The **double integral of $f(x, y)$ over the region R in the xy-plane** is defined as

(Volume *above* the region R and under the graph of f)
− (Volume *below* the region R and above the graph of f)

We denote the double integral of $f(x, y)$ over the region R by $\iint_R f(x, y)\,dx\,dy$.

quick Example

Take $f(x, y) = 2$ and take R to be the rectangle $0 \le x \le 1,\ 0 \le y \le 1$. Then the graph of f is a flat horizontal surface $z = 2$, and

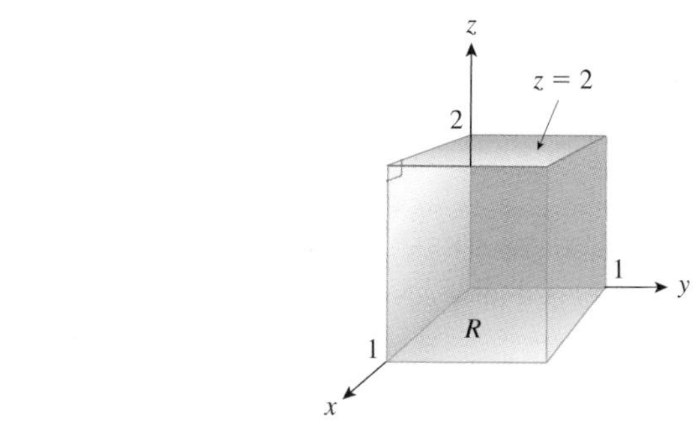

$$\iint_R f(x, y)\,dx\,dy = \text{Volume of box}$$
$$= \text{Width} \times \text{Length} \times \text{Height} = 1 \times 1 \times 2 = 2$$

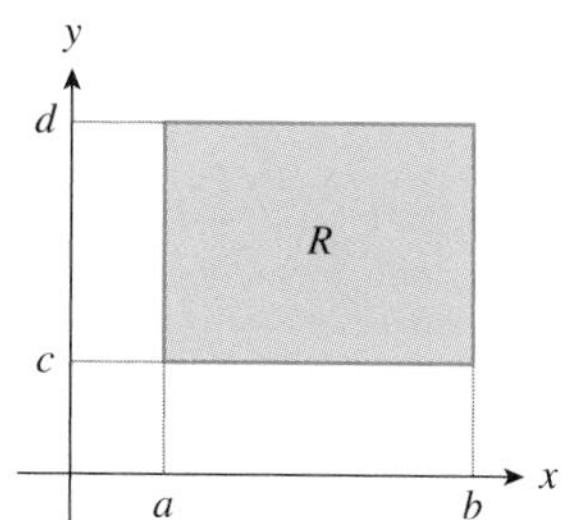

Figure **27**

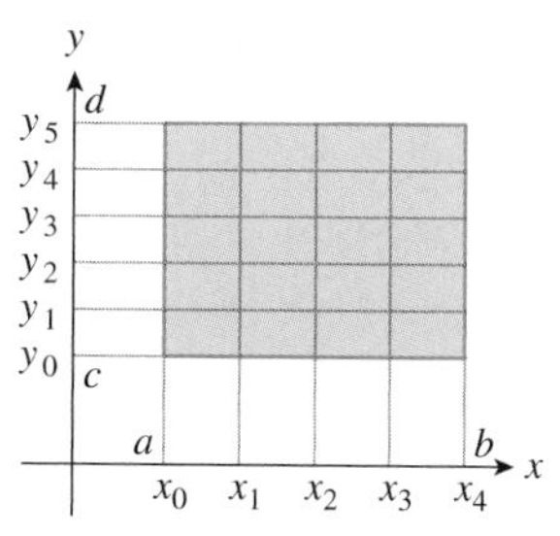

Figure **28**

As we saw in the case of the definite integral of a function of one variable, we also desire *numerical* and *algebraic* definitions for two reasons: (1) to make the mathematical definition more precise, so as not to rely on the notion of "volume," and (2) for direct computation of the integral using technology or analytical tools.

We start with the simplest case, when the region R is a rectangle $a \le x \le b$ and $c \le y \le d$ (see Figure 27). To compute the volume over R, we mimic what we did to find the area under the graph of a function of one variable. We break up the interval $[a, b]$ into m intervals all of width $\Delta x = (b - a)/m$, and we break up $[c, d]$ into n intervals all of width $\Delta y = (d - c)/n$. Figure 28 shows an example with $m = 4$ and $n = 5$.

This gives us mn rectangles defined by $x_{i-1} \le x \le x_i$ and $y_{j-1} \le y \le y_j$. Over one of these rectangles, f is approximately equal to its value at one corner—say $f(x_i, y_j)$.

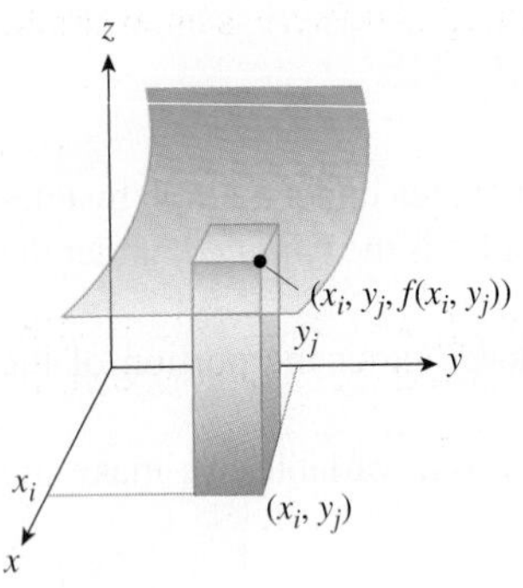

Figure **29**

The volume under f over this small rectangle is then approximately the volume of the rectangular brick (size exaggerated) shown in Figure 29. This brick has height $f(x_i, y_j)$, and its base is Δx by Δy. Its volume is therefore $f(x_i, y_j)\Delta x\,\Delta y$. Adding together the volumes of all of the bricks over the small rectangles in R, we get

$$\iint_R f(x, y)\,dx\,dy \approx \sum_{j=1}^{n}\sum_{i=1}^{m} f(x_i, y_j)\Delta x\,\Delta y$$

This double sum is called a **double Riemann sum.** We define the double integral to be the limit of the Riemann sums as m and n go to infinity.

Algebraic Definition of the Double Integral

$$\iint_R f(x, y)\,dx\,dy = \lim_{n\to\infty}\lim_{m\to\infty}\sum_{j=1}^{n}\sum_{i=1}^{m} f(x_i, y_j)\Delta x\,\Delta y$$

Note This definition is adequate (the limit exists) when f is continuous. More elaborate definitions are needed for general functions. ■

This definition also gives us a clue about how to compute a double integral. The innermost sum is $\sum_{i=1}^{m} f(x_i, y_j)\Delta x$, which is a Riemann sum for $\int_a^b f(x, y_j)\,dx$. The innermost limit is therefore

$$\lim_{m\to\infty}\sum_{i=1}^{m} f(x_i, y_j)\Delta x = \int_a^b f(x, y_j)\,dx$$

The outermost limit is then also a Riemann sum, and we get the following way of calculating double integrals:

Computing the Double Integral over a Rectangle

If R is the rectangle $a \le x \le b$ and $c \le y \le d$, then

$$\iint_R f(x, y)\,dx\,dy = \int_c^d \left(\int_a^b f(x, y)\,dx\right) dy = \int_a^b \left(\int_c^d f(x, y)\,dy\right) dx$$

The second formula comes from switching the order of summation in the double sum.

quick **Example**

If R is the rectangle $1 \le x \le 2$ and $1 \le y \le 3$, then

$$\iint_R 1\,dx\,dy = \int_1^3 \left(\int_1^2 1\,dx\right) dy$$

$$= \int_1^3 [x]_{x=1}^2\,dy \qquad \text{Evaluate the inner integral}$$

$$= \int_1^3 1\,dy \qquad [x]_{x=1}^2 = 2 - 1 = 1$$

$$= [y]_{y=1}^3 = 3 - 1 = 2$$

The Quick Example used a constant function for the integrand. Here is an example in which the integrand is not constant.

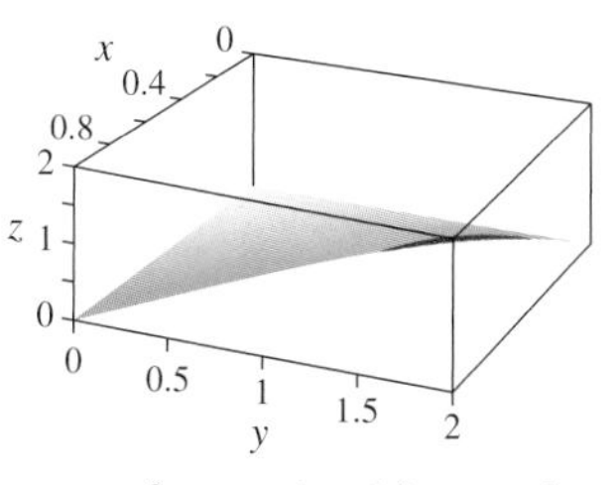

$z = xy$, $0 \le x \le 1$ and $0 \le y \le 2$

Figure **30**

Example 1 Double Integral over a Rectangle

Let R be the rectangle $0 \le x \le 1$ and $0 \le y \le 2$. Compute $\iint_R xy\,dx\,dy$. This integral gives the volume of the part of the boxed region under the surface $z = xy$ shown in Figure 30.

Solution

$$\iint_R xy\,dx\,dy = \int_0^2 \int_0^1 xy\,dx\,dy$$

(We usually drop the parentheses around the inner integral like this.) As in the Quick Example, we compute this **iterated integral** from the inside out. First we compute

$$\int_0^1 xy\,dx$$

To do this computation, we do as we did when finding partial derivatives: We treat y as a constant. This gives

$$\int_0^1 xy\,dx = \left[\frac{x^2}{2} \cdot y\right]_{x=0}^1 = \frac{1}{2}y - 0 = \frac{y}{2}$$

We can now calculate the outer integral.

$$\int_0^2 \int_0^1 xy\,dx\,dy = \int_0^2 \frac{y}{2}\,dy = \left[\frac{y^2}{4}\right]_0^2 = 1$$

+ *Before we go on...* We could also reverse the order of integration in Example 1.

$$\int_0^1 \int_0^2 xy\,dy\,dx = \int_0^1 \left(\left[x \cdot \frac{y^2}{2}\right]_{y=0}^2\right) dx = \int_0^1 2x\,dx = \left[x^2\right]_0^1 = 1 \quad \blacksquare$$

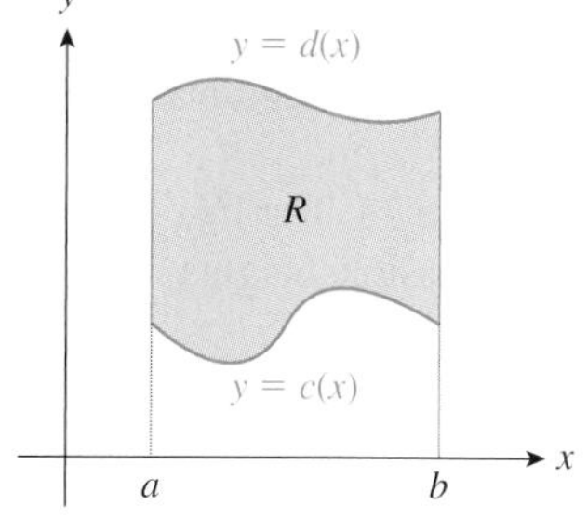

Figure **31**

Often we need to integrate over regions R that are not rectangular. There are two cases that come up. The first is a region like the one shown in Figure 31.

In this region, the bottom and top sides are defined by functions $y = c(x)$ and $y = d(x)$, respectively, so that the whole region can be described by the inequalities $a \le x \le b$ and $c(x) \le y \le d(x)$. To evaluate a double integral over such a region, we have the following formula:

Computing the Double Integral over a Nonrectangular Region

If R is the region $a \le x \le b$ and $c(x) \le y \le d(x)$ (Figure 31), then we integrate over R according to the following equation:

$$\iint_R f(x, y)\,dx\,dy = \int_a^b \int_{c(x)}^{d(x)} f(x, y)\,dy\,dx$$

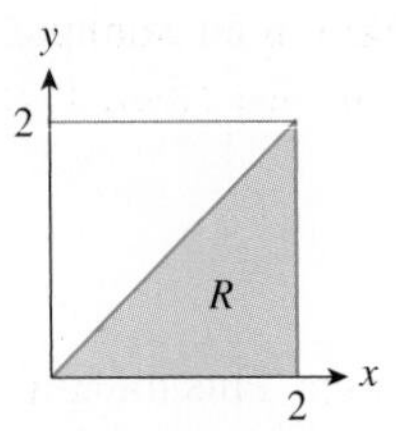

Figure **32**

Example **2** Double Integral over a Nonrectangular Region

R is the triangle shown in Figure 32. Compute $\iint_R x\,dx\,dy$.

Solution R is the region described by $0 \le x \le 2$, $0 \le y \le x$. We have

$$\iint_R x\,dx\,dy = \int_0^2 \int_0^x x\,dy\,dx$$

$$= \int_0^2 [xy]_{y=0}^{x}\,dx$$

$$= \int_0^2 x^2\,dx$$

$$= \left[\frac{x^3}{3}\right]_0^2 = \frac{8}{3}$$

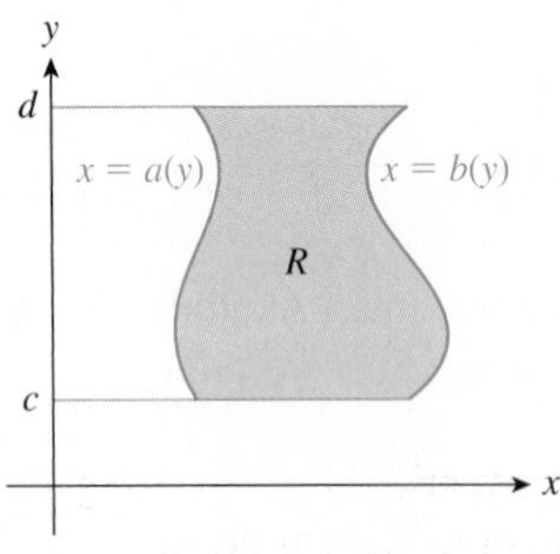

Figure **33**

The second type of region is shown in Figure 33.
This is the region described by $c \le y \le d$ and $a(y) \le x \le b(y)$. To evaluate a double integral over such a region, we have the following formula:

Double Integral over a Nonrectangular Region (continued)

If R is the region $c \le y \le d$ and $a(y) \le x \le b(y)$ (Figure 33), then we integrate over R according to the following equation:

$$\iint_R f(x, y)\,dx\,dy = \int_c^d \int_{a(y)}^{b(y)} f(x, y)\,dx\,dy$$

Example **3** Double Integral over a Nonrectangular Region

Redo Example 2, integrating in the opposite order.

Solution We can integrate in the opposite order if we can describe the region in Figure 32 in the way shown in Figure 33. In fact, it is the region $0 \le y \le 2$ and $y \le x \le 2$. To see this, we draw a horizontal line through the region, as in Figure 34. The line extends from $x = y$ on the left to $x = 2$ on the right, so $y \le x \le 2$. The possible heights for such a line are $0 \le y \le 2$. We can now compute the integral:

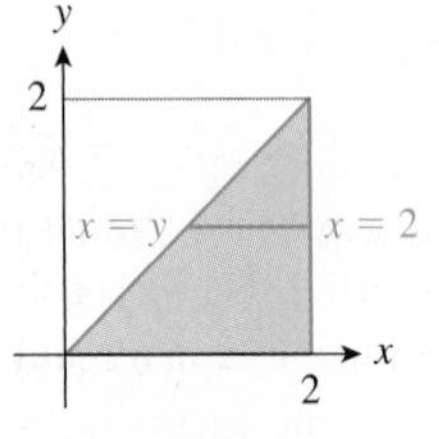

Figure **34**

$$\iint_R x\,dx\,dy = \int_0^2 \int_y^2 x\,dx\,dy$$

$$= \int_0^2 \left[\frac{x^2}{2}\right]_{x=y}^{2} dy$$

$$= \int_0^2 \left(2 - \frac{y^2}{2}\right) dy$$

$$= \left[2y - \frac{y^3}{6}\right]_0^2 = \frac{8}{3}$$

Note Many regions can be described in two different ways, as we saw in Examples 2 and 3. Sometimes one description will be much easier to work with than the other, so it pays to consider both. ■

Applications

There are many applications of double integrals besides finding volumes. For example, we can use them to find *averages*. Remember that the average of $f(x)$ on $[a, b]$ is given by $\int_a^b f(x)\,dx$ divided by $(b - a)$, the length of the interval.

Average of a Function of Two Variables

The average of $f(x, y)$ on the region R is

$$\bar{f} = \frac{1}{A}\iint_R f(x, y)\,dx\,dy$$

Here, A is the area of R. We can compute the area A geometrically, or by using the techniques from the chapter on applications of the integral, or by computing

$$A = \iint_R 1\,dx\,dy$$

quick **Example**

The average value of $f(x, y) = xy$ on the rectangle given by $0 \le x \le 1$ and $0 \le y \le 2$ is

$$\bar{f} = \frac{1}{2}\iint_R xy\,dx\,dy \qquad \text{The area of the rectangle is 2.}$$

$$= \frac{1}{2}\int_0^2\int_0^1 xy\,dx\,dy$$

$$= \frac{1}{2}\cdot 1 = \frac{1}{2} \qquad \text{We calculated the integral in Example 1.}$$

GoodShoot/SuperStock

Figure **35**

Example 4 Average Revenue

Your company is planning to price its new line of subcompact cars at between \$10,000 and \$15,000. The marketing department reports that if the company prices the cars at p dollars per car, the demand will be between $q = 20{,}000 - p$ and $q = 25{,}000 - p$ cars sold in the first year. What is the average of all the possible revenues your company could expect in the first year?

Solution Revenue is given by $R = pq$ as usual, and we are told that

$$10{,}000 \le p \le 15{,}000$$

and $$20{,}000 - p \le q \le 25{,}000 - p$$

This domain D of prices and demands is shown in Figure 35.

To average the revenue R over the domain D, we need to compute the area A of D. Using either calculus or geometry, we get $A = 25{,}000{,}000$. We then need to integrate R over D:

$$\iint_D pq\,dp\,dq = \int_{10,000}^{15,000} \int_{20,000-p}^{25,000-p} pq\,dq\,dp$$

$$= \int_{10,000}^{15,000} \left[\frac{pq^2}{2}\right]_{q=20,000-p}^{25,000-p} dp$$

$$= \frac{1}{2}\int_{10,000}^{15,000} [p(25,000-p)^2 - p(20,000-p)^2]\,dp$$

$$= \frac{1}{2}\int_{10,000}^{15,000} [225,000,000p - 10,000p^2]\,dp$$

$$\approx 3,072,900,000,000,000$$

The average of all the possible revenues your company could expect in the first year is therefore

$$\bar{R} = \frac{3,072,900,000,000,000}{25,000,000} \approx \$122,900,000$$

+ *Before we go on...* To check that the answer obtained in Example 4 is reasonable, notice that the revenues at the corners of the domain are \$100,000,000 per year, \$150,000,000 per year (at two corners), and \$75,000,000 per year. Some of these are smaller than the average and some larger, as we would expect. ■

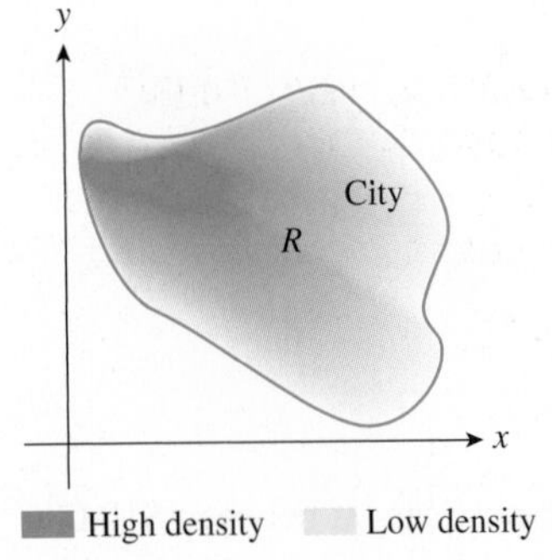

Figure **36**

Another useful application of the double integral comes about when we consider density. For example, suppose that $P(x, y)$ represents the population density (in people per square mile, say) in the city shown in Figure 36.

If we break the city up into small rectangles (for example, city blocks), then the population in the small rectangle $x_{i-1} \le x \le x_i$ and $y_{j-1} \le y \le y_j$ is approximately $P(x_i, y_j)\Delta x \Delta y$. Adding up all of these population estimates, we get

$$\text{Total population} \approx \sum_{j=1}^{n}\sum_{i=1}^{m} P(x_i, y_j)\,\Delta x\,\Delta y$$

Since this is a double Riemann sum, when we take the limit as m and n go to infinity, we get the following calculation of the population of the city:

$$\text{Total population} = \iint_{\text{City}} P(x, y)\,dx\,dy$$

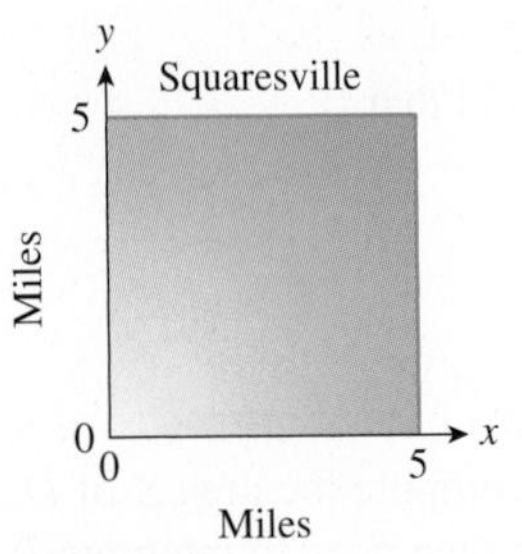

Figure **37**

Example **5** Population

Squaresville is a city in the shape of a square 5 miles on a side. The population density at a distance of x miles east and y miles north of the southwest corner is $P(x, y) = x^2 + y^2$ thousand people per square mile. Find the total population of Squaresville.

Solution Squaresville is pictured in Figure 37, in which we put the origin in the southwest corner of the city.

To compute the total population, we integrate the population density over the city S.

$$\begin{aligned}\text{Total population} &= \iint_{\text{Squaresville}} P(x, y)\,dx\,dy \\ &= \int_0^5 \int_0^5 (x^2 + y^2)\,dx\,dy \\ &= \int_0^5 \left[\frac{x^3}{3} + xy^2\right]_{x=0}^{5} dy \\ &= \int_0^5 \left[\frac{125}{3} + 5y^2\right] dy \\ &= \frac{1250}{3} \approx 417 \text{ thousand people}\end{aligned}$$

+ *Before we go on...* Note that the average population density is the total population divided by the area of the city, which is about 17,000 people per square mile. Compare this calculation with the calculations of averages in the previous two examples. ■

8.6 EXERCISES

● denotes basic skills exercises

Compute the integrals in Exercises 1–16.

1. ● $\int_0^1 \int_0^1 (x - 2y)\,dx\,dy$ hint [see Example 1]

2. ● $\int_{-1}^1 \int_0^2 (2x + 3y)\,dx\,dy$

3. ● $\int_0^1 \int_0^2 (ye^x - x - y)\,dx\,dy$

4. ● $\int_1^2 \int_2^3 \left(\frac{1}{x} + \frac{1}{y}\right) dx\,dy$

5. ● $\int_0^2 \int_0^3 e^{x+y}\,dx\,dy$

6. ● $\int_0^1 \int_0^1 e^{x-y}\,dx\,dy$

7. ● $\int_0^1 \int_0^{2-y} x\,dx\,dy$

8. ● $\int_0^1 \int_0^{2-y} y\,dx\,dy$

9. ● $\int_{-1}^1 \int_{y-1}^{y+1} e^{x+y}\,dx\,dy$

10. ● $\int_0^1 \int_y^{y+2} \frac{1}{\sqrt{x+y}}\,dx\,dy$

11. ● $\int_0^1 \int_{-x^2}^{x^2} x\,dy\,dx$

12. ● $\int_1^4 \int_{-\sqrt{x}}^{\sqrt{x}} \frac{1}{x}\,dy\,dx$

13. ● $\int_0^1 \int_0^x e^{x^2}\,dy\,dx$

14. ● $\int_0^1 \int_0^{x^2} e^{x^3+1}\,dy\,dx$

15. ● $\int_0^2 \int_{1-x}^{8-x} (x + y)^{1/3}\,dy\,dx$

16. ● $\int_1^2 \int_{1-2x}^{x^2} \frac{x+1}{(2x+y)^3}\,dy\,dx$

In Exercises 17–24, find $\iint_R f(x, y)\,dx\,dy$, where R is the indicated domain. (Remember that you often have a choice as to the order of integration.)

17. ● $f(x, y) = 2$
hint [see Example 2]

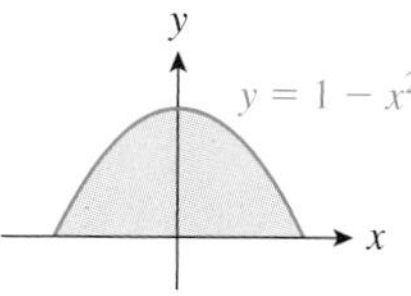

18. ● $f(x, y) = x$

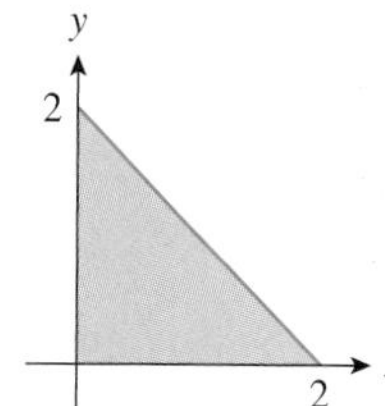

19. ● $f(x, y) = 1 + y$
hint [see Example 3]

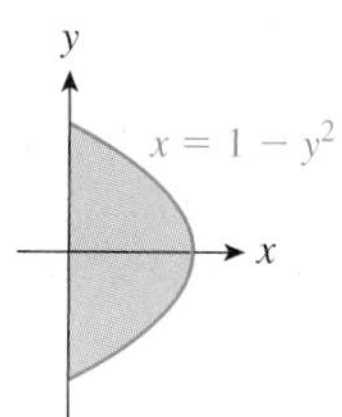

20. ● $f(x, y) = e^{x+y}$

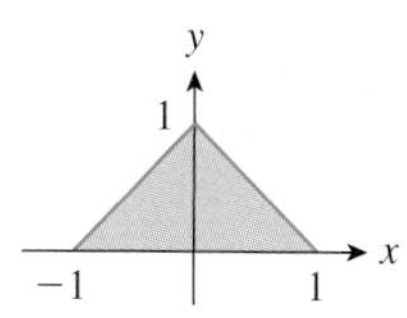

21. ● $f(x, y) = xy^2$

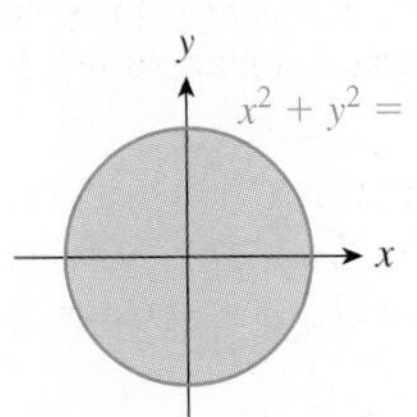

22. ● $f(x, y) = xy^2$

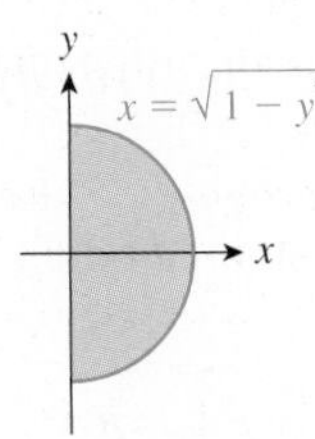

23. ● $f(x, y) = x^2 + y^2$

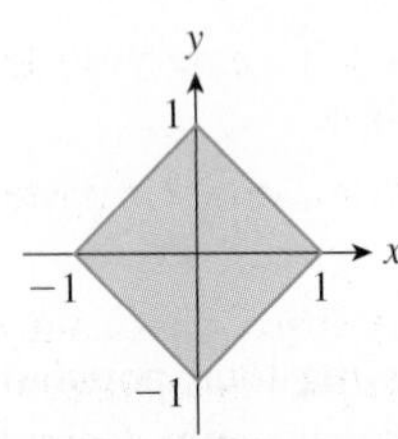

24. ● $f(x, y) = x^2$

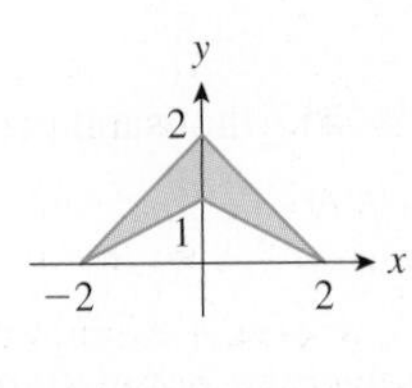

In Exercises 25–30, find the average value of the given function over the indicated domain. hint [see Quick Examples p. 591]

25. ● $f(x, y) = y$

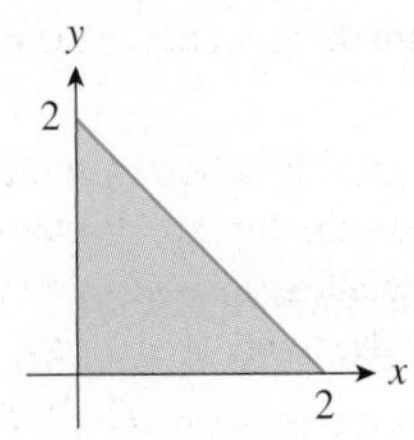

26. ● $f(x, y) = 2 + x$

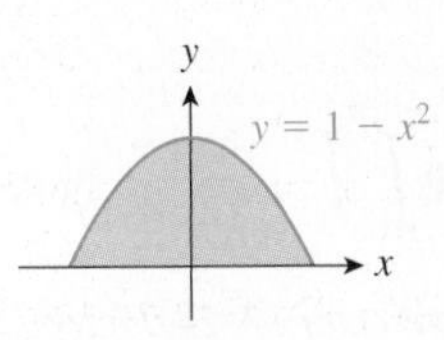

27. ● $f(x, y) = e^y$

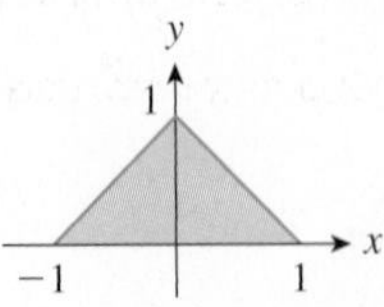

28. ● $f(x, y) = y$

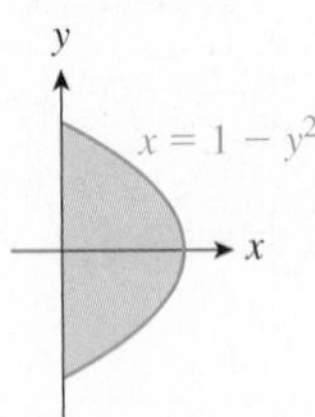

29. ● $f(x, y) = x^2$

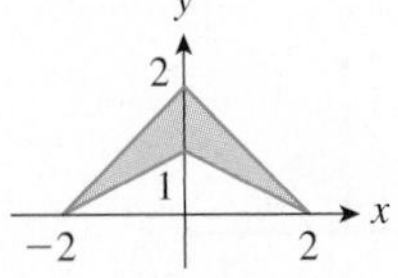

30. ● $f(x, y) = x^2 + y^2$

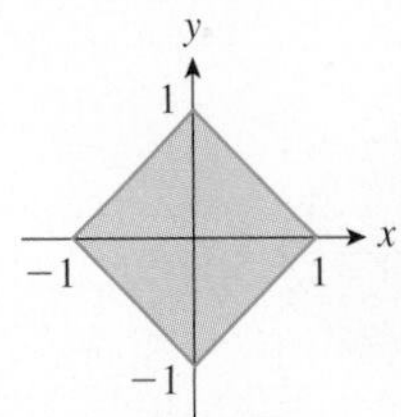

In Exercises 31–36, sketch the region over which you are integrating, then write down the integral with the order of integration reversed (changing the limits of integration as necessary).

31. $\int_0^1 \int_0^{1-y} f(x, y)\,dx\,dy$

32. $\int_{-1}^1 \int_0^{1+y} f(x, y)\,dx\,dy$

33. $\int_{-1}^1 \int_0^{\sqrt{1+y}} f(x, y)\,dx\,dy$

34. $\int_{-1}^1 \int_0^{\sqrt{1-y}} f(x, y)\,dx\,dy$

35. $\int_1^2 \int_1^{4/x^2} f(x, y)\,dy\,dx$

36. $\int_1^{e^2} \int_0^{\ln x} f(x, y)\,dy\,dx$

37. ● Find the volume under the graph of $z = 1 - x^2$ over the region $0 \le x \le 1$ and $0 \le y \le 2$.

38. ● Find the volume under the graph of $z = 1 - x^2$ over the triangle $0 \le x \le 1$ and $0 \le y \le 1 - x$.

39. ● Find the volume of the tetrahedron shown in the figure. Its corners are (0, 0, 0), (1, 0, 0), (0, 1, 0), and (0, 0, 1).

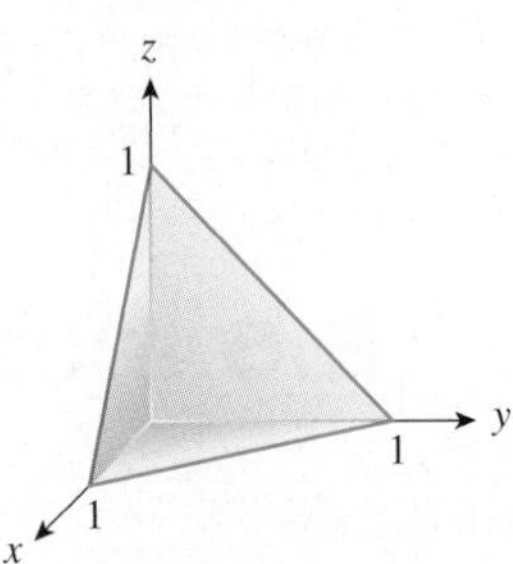

40. Find the volume of the tetrahedron with corners at (0, 0, 0), $(a, 0, 0)$, $(0, b, 0)$, and $(0, 0, c)$.

Applications

41. ● ***Productivity*** A productivity model at the Handy Gadget Company is

$$P = 10{,}000x^{0.3}y^{0.7}$$

where P is the number of gadgets the company turns out per month, x is the number of employees at the company, and y is the monthly operating budget in thousands of dollars. Because the company hires part-time workers, it uses anywhere between 45 and 55 workers each month, and its operating budget varies from \$8000 to \$12,000 per month. What is the average of the possible numbers of gadgets it can turn out per month? (Round the answer to the nearest 1000 gadgets.) hint [see Quick Examples p. 591]

42. ● ***Productivity*** Repeat the preceding exercise using the productivity model

$$P = 10{,}000x^{0.7}y^{0.3}$$

43. ● ***Revenue*** Your latest CD-ROM of clip art is expected to sell between $q = 8000 - p^2$ and $q = 10{,}000 - p^2$ copies if priced at p dollars. You plan to set the price between \$40 and

\$50. What is the average of all the possible revenues you can make? *hint* [see Example 4]

44. ● ***Revenue*** Your latest DVD drive is expected to sell between $q = 180{,}000 - p^2$ and $q = 200{,}000 - p^2$ units if priced at p dollars. You plan to set the price between \$300 and \$400. What is the average of all the possible revenues you can make?

45. ● ***Revenue*** Your self-published novel has demand curves between $p = 15{,}000/q$ and $p = 20{,}000/q$. You expect to sell between 500 and 1000 copies. What is the average of all the possible revenues you can make?

46. ● ***Revenue*** Your self-published book of poetry has demand curves between $p = 80{,}000/q^2$ and $p = 100{,}000/q^2$. You expect to sell between 50 and 100 copies. What is the average of all the possible revenues you can make?

47. ● ***Population Density*** The town of West Podunk is shaped like a rectangle 20 miles from west to east and 30 miles from north to south (see the figure). It has a population density of $P(x, y) = e^{-0.1(x+y)}$ hundred people per square mile x miles east and y miles north of the southwest corner of town. What is the total population of the town? *hint* [see Example 5]

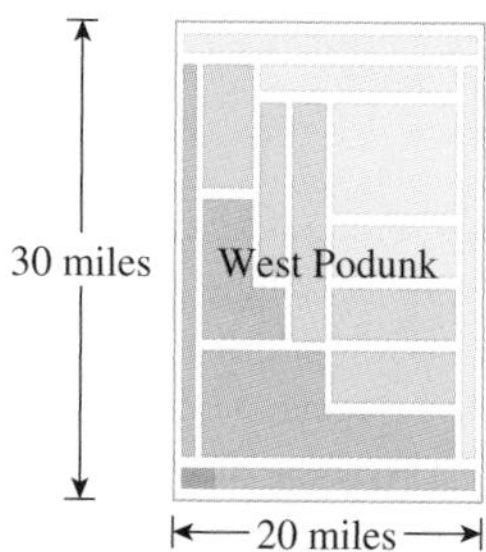

48. ● ***Population Density*** The town of East Podunk is shaped like a triangle with an east-west base of 20 miles and a north-south height of 30 miles (see the figure). It has a population density of $P(x, y) = e^{-0.1(x+y)}$ hundred people per square mile x miles east and y miles north of the southwest corner of town. What is the total population of the town?

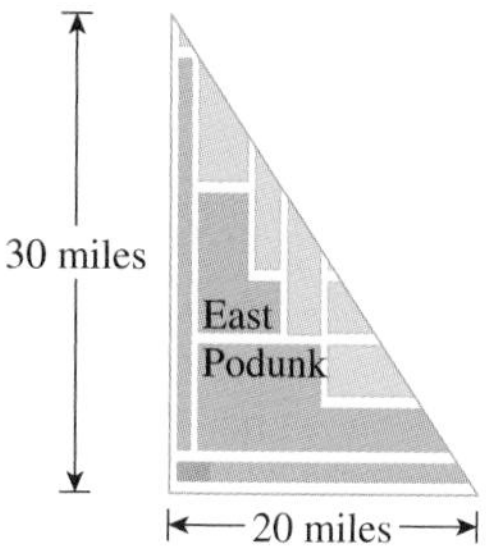

49. ● ***Temperature*** The temperature at the point (x, y) on the square with vertices $(0, 0)$, $(0, 1)$, $(1, 0)$ and $(1, 1)$ is given by $T(x, y) = x^2 + 2y^2$. Find the average temperature on the square.

50. ● ***Temperature*** The temperature at the point (x, y) on the square with vertices $(0, 0)$, $(0, 1)$, $(1, 0)$ and $(1, 1)$ is given by $T(x, y) = x^2 + 2y^2 - x$. Find the average temperature on the square.

Communication and Reasoning Exercises

51. ● Explain how double integrals can be used to compute the area between two curves in the xy plane.

52. ● Explain how double integrals can be used to compute the volume of solids in 3-space.

53. ● Complete the following: The first step in calculating an integral of the form $\int_a^b \int_{r(x)}^{s(x)} f(x, y)\,dy\,dx$ is to evaluate the integral _____, obtained by holding ___ constant and integrating with respect to ___ .

54. ● If the units of $f(x, y)$ are zonars per square meter, and x and y are given in meters, what are the units of $\int_a^b \int_{r(x)}^{s(x)} f(x, y)\,dy\,dx$?

55. ● If the units of $\int_a^b \int_{r(x)}^{s(x)} f(x, y)\,dy\,dx$ are paintings, the units of x are picassos, and the units of y are dalis, what are the units of $f(x, y)$?

56. ● Complete the following: If the region R is bounded on the left and right by vertical lines and on the top and bottom by the graphs of functions of x, then we integrate over R by first integrating with respect to ____ and then with respect to ___,

57. Show that if a, b, c and d are constant, then $\int_a^b \int_c^d f(x) g(y)\,dx\,dy = \int_c^d f(x)\,dx \int_a^b g(y)\,dy$. Test this result on the integral $\int_0^1 \int_1^2 ye^x\,dx\,dy$.

58. Refer to Exercise 57. If $a, b, c,$ and d are constants, can $\displaystyle\int_a^b \int_c^d \frac{f(x)}{g(y)}\,dx\,dy$ be expressed as a product of two integrals? Explain.

Chapter 8 Review

KEY CONCEPTS

8.1 Functions of Several Variables from the Numerical and Algebraic Viewpoints

A real-valued function, f, of $x, y, z, \ldots$ *p. 540*

Cost functions *p. 541*

A linear function of the variables $x_1, x_2, \ldots, x_n$ is a function of the form $f(x_1, x_2, \ldots, x_n) = a_0 + a_1x_1 + \cdots + a_nx_n$ ($a_0, a_1, \ldots, a_n$ constants) *p. 542*

Representing functions of two variables numerically *p. 543*

Using Excel to represent a function of two variables *p. 544*

Equation of the circle of radius r centered at the origin: $x^2 + y^2 = r^2$ *p. 545*

Newton's Law of Gravity:

$$F(x, y) = G\frac{Mm}{(x-a)^2 + (y-b)^2} \quad p.\ 546$$

8.2 Three-Dimensional Space and the Graph of a Function of Two Variables

Plotting points in three dimensions *p. 553*

Graph of a function f of two variables *p. 554*

Analyzing the graph of a function of two variables: *p. 556*

Graph of a linear function *p. 558*

8.3 Partial Derivatives

Definition of partial derivatives *p. 562*

Application to marginal cost: linear cost function *p. 562*

Application to marginal cost: interactive cost function *p. 563*

Geometric interpretation of partial derivatives *p. 565*

Second order partial derivatives *p. 565*

8.4 Maxima and Minima

Definition of relative maximum and minimum *p. 571*

Locating candidates for relative maxima and minima *p. 572*

Second derivative test for a function of two variables *p. 574*

Using the second derivative test *p. 575*

Derivation of regression line:

$$m = \frac{n\left(\sum xy\right) - \left(\sum x\right)\left(\sum y\right)}{n\left(\sum x^2\right) - \left(\sum x\right)^2}$$

$$b = \frac{\sum y - m\left(\sum x\right)}{n} \quad n = \text{number}$$

of data points *p. 575*

8.5 Constrained Maxima and Minima and Applications

Constrained maximum and minimum problem *p. 580*

Solving constrained maxima and minima problems by eliminating variables (one constraint) *p. 581*

The method of Lagrange Multipliers *p. 582*

Using Lagrange Multipliers *p. 582, 583*

8.6 Double Integrals and Applications

Geometric definition of the double integral *p. 587*

Algebraic definition of the double integral

$$\iint_R f(x, y)\,dx\,dy = \lim_{n\to\infty}\lim_{m\to\infty}\sum_{j=1}^{n}\sum_{i=1}^{m} f(x_i, y_j)\Delta x\Delta y$$

p. 588

Computing the double integral over a rectangle *p. 588*

Computing the double integral over nonrectangular regions *p. 589, 590*

Average of $f(x, y)$ on the region R:

$$\bar{f} = \frac{1}{A}\iint_R f(x, y)\,dx\,dy \quad p.\ 591$$

REVIEW EXERCISES

1. Let $g(x, y, z) = xy(x + y - z) + x^2$. Evaluate $g(0, 0, 0)$, $g(1, 0, 0)$, $g(0, 1, 0)$, $g(x, x, x)$ and $g(x, y + k, z)$.

2. Let $f(x, y, z) = 2.72 - 0.32x - 3.21y + 12.5z$. Complete the following: f___ by ___ units for every 1 unit of increase in x, and___ by___ units for every unit of increase in z.

3. Let $h(x, y) = 2x^2 + xy - x$. Complete the following table of values.

$y \downarrow$ \ $x \rightarrow$	−1	0	1
−1			
0			
1			

4. Give a formula for a (single) function f with the property that $f(x, y) = -f(y, x)$ and $f(1, -1) = 3$.

In Exercises 5–10, compute the partial derivatives shown for the given function.

5. $f(x, y) = x^2 + xy$; find f_x, f_y, and f_{yy}.

6. $f(x, y) = \dfrac{6}{xy} + \dfrac{xy}{6}$; find f_x, f_y, and f_{yy}.

7. $f(x, y) = 4x + 5y - 6xy$; find $f_{xx}(1, 0) - f_{xx}(3, 2)$

8. $f(x, y) = e^{xy} + e^{3x^2-y^2}$; find $\dfrac{\partial f}{\partial x}$ and $\dfrac{\partial^2 f}{\partial x \partial y}$.

9. $f(x, y, z) = \dfrac{x}{x^2 + y^2 + z^2}$; find $\dfrac{\partial f}{\partial x}, \dfrac{\partial f}{\partial y}, \dfrac{\partial f}{\partial z}$ and $\left.\dfrac{\partial f}{\partial x}\right|_{(0,1,0)}$.

10. $f(x, y, z) = x^2 + y^2 + z^2 + xyz$; find $f_{xx} + f_{yy} + f_{zz}$.

In Exercises 11–15, locate and classify all critical points.

11. $f(x, y) = (x - 1)^2 + (2y - 3)^2$

12. $g(x, y) = (x - 1)^2 - 3y^2 + 9$

13. $h(x, y) = e^{xy}$

14. $j(x, y) = xy + x^2$

15. $f(x, y) = \ln(x^2 + y^2) - (x^2 + y^2)$

In Exercises 16–19, solve the following constrained optimization problems by using substitution to eliminate a variable. (Do not use Lagrange Multipliers.)

16. Find the minimum value of $f(x, y, z) = x^2 + y^2 + z^2 - 1$ subject to $x = y + z$. Also find the corresponding point(s) (x, y, z).

17. Find the largest value of xyz subject to $x + y + z = 1$ with $x > 0, y > 0, z > 0$. Also find the corresponding point(s) (x, y, z).

18. Minimize $S = xy + x^2z^2 + 4yz$ subject to $xyz = 1$ with $x > 0, y > 0, z > 0$.

19. Find the point on the surface $z = \sqrt{x^2 + 2(y - 3)^2}$ closest to the origin.

In Exercises 20–24, use Lagrange Multipliers to solve the given optimization problem.

20. Find the maximum value of $f(x, y) = xy$ subject to $y = e^{-x}$. Also find the corresponding point(s) (x, y).

21. Find the minimum value of $f(x, y) = x^2 + y^2$ subject to $xy = 2$. Also find the corresponding point(s) (x, y).

22. The problem in Exercise 16.

23. The problem in Exercise 18.

24. The problem in Exercise 19.

In Exercises 25–30, compute the given quantities.

25. $\int_0^1 \int_0^2 (2xy)\, dx\, dy$

26. $\int_1^2 \int_0^1 xye^{x+y}\, dx\, dy$

27. $\int_0^2 \int_0^{2x} \frac{1}{x^2 + 1}\, dy\, dx$

28. The average value of xye^{x+y} over the rectangle $0 \le x \le 1$, $1 \le y \le 2$.

29. $\iint_R (x^2 - y^2)\, dx\, dy$, where R is the region shown in the figure

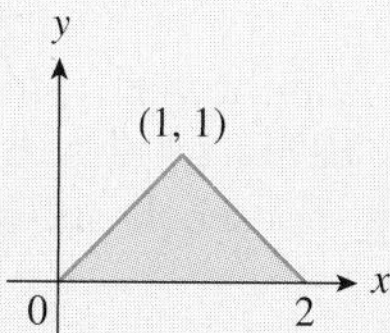

30. The volume under the graph of $z = 1 - y$ over the region in the xy plane between the parabola $y = 1 - x^2$ and the x-axis.

Applications

31. ***Website Traffic*** OHaganBooks.com has two principal competitors: JungleBooks.com and FarmerBooks.com. Current website traffic at OHaganBooks.com is estimated at 5000 hits per day. This number is predicted to decrease by 0.8 for every new customer of JungleBooks.com and by 0.6 for every new customer of FarmerBooks.com.

    a. Use this information to model the daily website traffic at OHaganBooks.com as a linear function of the new customers of its two competitors.

    b. According to the model, if Junglebooks.com gets 100 new customers and OHaganBooks.com traffic drops to 4770 hits per day, how many new customers has FarmerBooks.com obtained?

32. ***Website Traffic*** Refer to the model in Exercise 31.

    a. The model in Exercise 31 did not take into account the growth of the total online consumer base. OHaganBooks.com expects to get approximately one additional hit per day for every 10,000 new Internet shoppers. Modify your model in part (a) so as to include this information using a new independent variable.

    b. How many new Internet shoppers would it take to offset the effects on traffic at OHaganBooks.com of 100 new customers at each of its competitor sites?

33. ***Internet Advertising*** To increase business at OHaganBooks.com, you have purchased banner ads at well-known Internet portals and have advertised on television. The following interaction model shows the average number h of hits per day as a function of monthly expenditures x on banner ads and y on television advertising (x and y are in dollars).

$$h(x, y) = 1800 + 0.05x + 0.08y + 0.00003xy$$

    a. Based on your model, how much traffic can you anticipate if you spend \$2000 per month for banner ads and \$3000 per month on television advertising?

    b. Evaluate $\frac{\partial h}{\partial y}$, specify its units of measurement, and indicate whether it increases or decreases with increasing x.

    c. How much should the company spend on banner ads to obtain 1 hit per day for each \$5 spent per month on television advertising?

34. ***Internet Advertising*** Refer to the model in Exercise 33. One or more of the following five statements is correct. Identify which one(s).

    (A) If nothing is spent on television advertising, one more dollar spent per month in banner ads will buy approximately 0.05 hits per day at OHaganBooks.com

    (B) If nothing is spent on television advertising, one more hit per day at OHaganBooks.com will cost the company about 5¢ per month in banner ads.

    (C) If nothing is spent on banner ads, one more hit per day at OHaganBooks.com will cost the company about 5¢ per month in banner ads.

(D) If nothing is spent on banner ads, one more dollar spent per month in banner ads will buy approximately 0.05 hits per day at OHaganBooks.com

(E) Hits at OHaganBooks.com cost approximately 5¢ per month spent on banner ads, and this cost increases at a rate of 0.003¢ per month, per hit.

35. ***Productivity*** The holiday season is now at its peak and OHaganBooks.com has been understaffed and swamped with orders. The current backlog (orders unshipped for two or more days) has grown to a staggering 50,000, and new orders are coming in at a rate of 5000 per day. Research based on productivity data at OHaganBooks.com results in the following model:

$$P(x, y) = 1000x^{0.9}y^{0.1} \text{ additional orders filled per day}$$

where x is the number of additional personnel hired and y is the daily budget (excluding salaries) allocated to eliminating the backlog. How many additional orders will be filled per day if the company hires 10 additional employees and budgets an additional $1000 per day? (Round the answer to the nearest 100.)

36. ***Productivity*** Refer to the model in Exercise 35. In addition to the daily budget, extra staffing costs the company $150 per day for every new staff member hired. In order to fill at least 15,000 orders per day at a minimum total daily cost, how many new staff members should the company hire? (Use the method of Lagrange Multipliers).

37. ***Profit*** If OHaganBooks.com sells x paperback books and y hardcover books per week, it will make an average weekly profit of

$$P(x, y) = 3x + 10y \text{ dollars}$$

If it sells between 1200 and 1500 paperback books and between 1800 and 2000 hardcover books per week, what is the average of all its possible weekly profits?

CASE STUDY: Modeling Household Income

Bill Varie/Corbis

The Millennium Real Estate Development Corporation is interested in developing housing projects for medium-sized families that have high household incomes. To decide which income bracket to target, the company has asked you, a paid consultant, for an analysis of household income and household size in the United States up to the year 2000. In particular, Millennium is interested in three issues:

- The relationship between household size and household income and the effect of increasing household size on household income.
- The household size that corresponds to the highest household income.
- The change in the relationship between household size and household income over time.
- Some near-term projections of household income vs. household size following the year 2000 (to, say, 2005).

You decide that a good place to start would be with a visit to the Census Bureau's website at http://www.census.gov. After some time battling with search engines, you discover detailed information on household size vs. household income[35] for the period

[35] Household income is adjusted for inflation and given in 2000 dollars. SOURCE: Bureau of the Census, 2002; www.census.gov/hhes/income/histinc.

1967–2000. The following table summarizes the information on median household income:

Median Household Income by Household Size and Year

Household Size →

Year ↓	1	2	3	4	5	6	7
1967	10,321	27,507	36,680	39,520	40,241	39,630	36,658
1968	11,364	29,055	37,756	41,598	41,889	41,032	39,400
1969	11,947	30,507	38,959	43,345	44,300	43,903	41,364
1970	11,993	30,346	38,826	43,181	44,661	44,572	41,241
1971	12,104	30,058	38,330	43,209	44,378	44,060	40,738
1972	12,816	31,489	40,562	46,308	47,280	46,634	42,622
1973	13,730	32,465	41,111	46,674	48,569	48,653	45,718
1974	13,930	32,317	40,067	46,041	48,008	47,181	45,064
1975	13,640	31,704	39,968	44,980	46,796	45,811	41,500
1976	14,400	32,761	40,634	45,986	47,569	47,368	44,093
1977	14,898	32,981	41,294	47,072	48,098	48,131	43,562
1978	16,132	34,962	43,963	49,497	50,803	50,334	48,902
1979	16,259	35,607	44,773	49,708	51,718	50,427	49,969
1980	16,240	34,833	43,249	48,570	49,457	48,580	46,423
1981	16,719	34,394	42,929	47,882	47,531	49,012	44,672
1982	17,159	34,717	42,013	47,464	46,706	46,732	40,762
1983	17,734	34,758	42,419	48,161	46,251	44,368	38,650
1984	18,266	35,884	44,316	49,243	48,911	44,924	41,714
1985	18,238	36,628	45,514	50,188	48,737	47,714	43,370
1986	18,329	38,144	46,755	52,267	51,523	49,508	41,979
1987	18,584	38,679	47,300	54,039	52,109	48,824	45,452
1988	19,675	39,429	47,767	54,442	50,689	51,939	44,573
1989	19,997	40,268	48,919	54,942	52,970	47,607	44,020
1990	19,701	40,263	47,205	53,250	50,428	48,995	46,362
1991	19,125	38,670	47,368	53,326	50,524	45,696	42,280
1992	18,606	38,389	46,580	53,111	50,853	44,760	40,010
1993	18,896	38,150	46,360	53,032	49,685	48,336	38,957
1994	18,672	39,082	47,241	53,817	50,800	49,128	42,152
1995	19,159	40,085	47,433	55,615	51,325	49,700	43,805
1996	19,564	40,756	48,988	56,194	52,298	46,391	44,095
1997	20,075	42,096	50,412	56,885	53,934	49,716	45,306
1998	21,267	43,804	51,778	58,971	56,671	51,790	49,221
1999	21,791	44,798	52,910	61,776	56,269	53,630	53,898
2000	21,468	44,530	54,196	61,847	60,295	54,841	54,663

You notice that the table is actually a numerical representation of the median household income I as a function of two variables, the household size n and the year t.

The numbers are a bit overwhelming, so you decide to use Excel to graph the data as a surface (Figure 38).

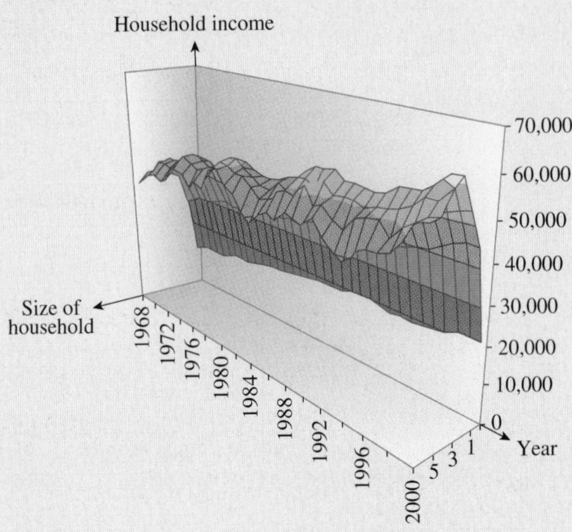

Figure **38**

Now you definitely see two trends. First, the household income peaks at around 5 or 6 people per household, and then drops off at both ends. In fact, the slices through $t = constant$ look parabolic. Second, the household income for all household sizes seems to increase more or less linearly with time (the slices through $n = constant$ are approximately linear).

At this point you realize that a mathematical model of these data would be useful; not only would it "smooth out the bumps" but it would give you a way to complete the project for Millennium. Although technology can give you a regression model for data such as this, it is up to you to decide on the form of the model. It is in choosing an appropriate model that your analysis of the graph comes in handy. Because I appears to vary quadratically with the household size, you would like a general quadratic of the form

$$I = a + bn + cn^2$$

for each value of time t. Also, because I should vary linearly with time t, you would like

$$I = mt + k$$

for each value of n. Putting these together, you get the following candidate model

$$I(n, t) = a_1 + a_2 n + a_3 n^2 + a_4 t$$

where a_1, a_2, a_3, and a_4 are constants you need to determine.

You decide to use Excel to generate your model. The specific software tool you need is called the "Analysis Toolpack" which comes with Excel. (It is found in the Tools menu as "Data Analysis." If it is missing, select Add-Ins from the Tools menu and check "Analysis Toolpack.")

Now you are set to do regression analysis. However, the data as shown in the table are not in a form Excel can use for regression; the data need to be organized into columns, as shown below.

Microsoft Excel - CS 8 Modeling Household Income.xls

File Edit View Insert Format Tools Data Window Help

	A	B	C	D	E
1	n	n^2	t	I	
2	1	1	0	10,321	
3	1	1	1	11,364	
4	1	1	2	11,947	
5			3	11,993	
	1	1			
35	1	1	33	21,468	
36	2	4	0	27,507	
37	2	4	1	29,055	
38			1	30,507	
	2	4			
69	2	4	33	44,530	
70	3	9	0	36,680	
71	3	9	1	37,756	
72			2	38,959	
	7	49			
237	7	49	31	49,221	
238	7	49	32	53,898	
239	7	49	33	54,663	
240					
241					

The headings of each column show the variables n and t, with the income i in column D. (Instead of using the calendar year for t, we have represented 1967 by $t = 0$.) Notice that the columns of the original table are in column D, one beneath the other. Thus, Columns A–C show the independent variables (and n^2, which we will treat as an independent variable for the regression), and column D contains the dependent variable.

You now select Data Analysis from the Tools menu. Under "Type of Analysis" you select "Regression," identify where the dependent and independent variables are (D1–D239 for the Y range, and A1–C239 for the X range), check "Labels," and hit "OK."

Regression

Input

Input Y Range: $D$1:$D$239

Input X Range: $A$1:$C$239

☑ Labels ☐ Constant is Zero

☐ Confidence Level: 95 %

OK Cancel Help

Output options

○ Output Range:

◉ New Worksheet Ply:

○ New Workbook

Residuals

☐ Residuals ☐ Residual Plots

☐ Standardized Residuals ☐ Line Fit Plots

Normal Probability

☐ Normal Probability Plots

A portion of the output is shown below, with some of the important statistics highlighted.

Microsoft Excel - CS 8 Modeling Household Income.xls

File Edit View Insert Format Tools Data Window Help Adobe PDF

	A	B	C	D	E	F	G
1	SUMMARY OUTPUT						
2							
3	*Regression Statistics*						
4	Multple R	0.96837683					
5	R Square	0.93775369					
6	Adjusted R Sq	0.93695566					
7	Standard Erro	2934.33151					
8	Observations	238					
9							
10	ANOVA						
11		*df*	*SS*	*MS*	*F*	*Significance F*	
12	Regression	3	3.0354E+10	1.0118E+10	1175.08632	9.669E–141	
13	Residual	234	2014810524	8610301.38			
14	Total	237	3.2368E+10				
15							
16		*Coefficients*	*Standard Erro*	*t Stat*	*P-value*	*Lower 95%*	
17	Intercept	-5777.9625	846.966847	-6.8219465	7.61E-11	-7446.6159	
18	n	21007.9513	449.435606	46.7429617	1.13E-120	20122.4949	
19	n^2	-2139.0571	54.9072983	-38.957609	2.89E-104	-2247.2328	
20	t	352.056554	19.3874338	18.1590073	1.42E-46	313.860363	
21							
22							

The desired constants a_1, a_2, a_3, and a_4 appear in the coefficients column at the bottom left, in the correct order: a_1 is the "intercept,", a_2 is the coefficient of n, and so on. Thus, if we round to 5 significant digits, we have

$$a_1 = -5778.0 \quad a_2 = 21{,}008 \quad a_3 = -2139.1 \quad a_4 = 352.06$$

which gives our regression model:

$$I(n, t) = -5778.0 + 21{,}008n - 2139.1n^2 + 352.06t$$

Fine, you say to yourself, now you have the model, but how good a fit is it to the data? That is where the "Multiple R" at the top of the data analysis comes in. R is called the **multiple coefficient of correlation,** and generalizes the coefficient of correlation discussed in the section on regression in Chapter 1: The closer R is to 1, the better the fit. We can interpret its square, given in the table as "R Square" with value 0.938, as indicating that approximately 94% of the variation in median income is explained by the regression model, indicating an excellent fit. The "P-values" at bottom right are also indicators of the appropriateness of the model; a P-value close to zero indicates a high degree of confidence that the corresponding coefficient is really nonzero, whereas a P-value close to 1 indicates low confidence (there is a P-value for each coefficient). Because all the values are extremely tiny, you are confident indeed that the model is an appropriate one. Another statistical indicator is the value of "F" on the right—an indicator of confidence in the model as a whole. The fact that it too is large and its "Significance F" is tiny is yet another good sign.[36]

[36] We are being deliberately vague about the exact meaning of these statistics, which are discussed fully in many applied statistics texts.

As comforting as these statistics are, nothing can be quite as persuasive as a graph. You turn to the graphing software of your choice and notice that the graph of the model appears to be a faithful representation of the data. (See Figure 2.)

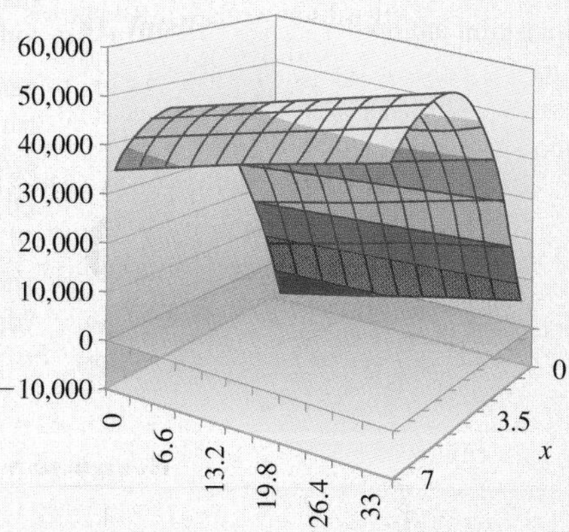

Figure **2**

Now you get to work, using the model to address the questions posed by Millennium.

1. *The relationship between household size and household income and the effect of increasing household size on household income*. You already have a quantitative relationship in the form of the regression model. As for the second part of the question, the rate of change of median household income with respect to household size is given by the partial derivative:

$$\frac{\partial I}{\partial n} = 21{,}008 - 4278.2n \text{ dollars per additional family member}$$

Thus, for example, in a household of 4 people,

$$\frac{\partial I}{\partial n} = 21{,}008 - 4278.2(4) \approx \$3895 \text{ per additional family member}$$

On the other hand, when $n = 5$, one has

$$\frac{\partial I}{\partial n} = 21{,}008 - 4278.2(5) = -\$383 \text{ per additional family member}$$

Notice that the derivative is independent of time: the rate of change of average family income with respect to household size is independent of the date (according to your model).

2, 3. *The household size corresponding to the highest household income and the change in the relationship over time*. Although a glance at the graph shows you that there are no relative maxima, holding t constant (that is, on any given year) gives a relative maximum along the corresponding slice when

$$\frac{\partial I}{\partial n} = 0$$

or $$21{,}008 - 4278.2n = 0,$$

which gives $$n = \frac{21{,}008}{4278.2} \approx 4.91$$

In other words, households of 5 tend to have the highest household incomes. Again, $\partial I/\partial n$ does not depend on t, so that this optimal household size seems independent of time t.

4. *Some near-term projections of household income vs. household size.* As we have seen throughout the book, extrapolation can be a risky venture; however, *near-term* extrapolation from a good model can be reasonable. You enter the model in an Excel spreadsheet to obtain the following predicted median household incomes for the years 2001–2005:

		Household Size →						
		1	**2**	**3**	**4**	**5**	**6**	**7**
Year ↓	**2001**	25,061	39,652	49,964	55,998	57,755	55,232	48,432
	2002	25,413	40,004	50,316	56,351	58,107	55,585	48,784
	2003	25,765	40,356	50,668	56,703	58,459	55,937	49,136
	2004	26,117	40,708	51,020	57,055	58,811	56,289	49,488
	2005	26,469	41,060	51,372	57,407	59,163	56,641	49,840

Exercises

1. Use Excel to obtain an interaction model of the form

$$I(n, t) = a_1 + a_2 n + a_3 t + a_4 nt$$

Compare the fit of this model with that of the quadratic model above. Comment on the result.

2. How much is there to be gained by including a term of the form $a_5 t^2$ in the original model? (Perform the regression and analyze the result by referring to the P-value for the resulting coefficient of t^2.)

3. The following table shows some data on U.S. population (in thousands) vs. age and year. (This table can be found as an Excel file online by following Chapter 8 → Case Study Excel Data)

Year (0 = 1990) →

Age ↓	**0**	**2**	**4**	**6**	**8**	**8.5**
2.5	18,851	19,489	19,694	19,324	19,020	18,974
7.5	18,058	18,285	18,742	19,425	19,912	19,931
12.5	17,191	18,065	18,666	18,949	19,184	19,291
17.5	17,763	17,170	17,707	18,644	19,460	19,554
22.5	19,137	19,085	18,451	17,562	17,685	17,796
27.5	21,233	20,152	19,142	18,993	18,621	18,513
32.5	21,909	22,237	22,141	21,328	20,163	19,965
37.5	19,980	21,092	21,973	22,550	22,600	22,589
42.5	17,793	18,806	19,714	20,809	21,875	22,014
47.5	13,823	15,362	16,685	18,438	18,850	19,007
52.5	11,370	12,059	13,199	13,931	15,727	15,973
57.5	10,474	10,487	10,937	11,362	12,408	12,631
62.5	10,619	10,440	10,079	9,997	10,256	10,358
67.5	10,076	9,973	9,963	9,895	9,575	9,515
72.5	8,022	8,467	8,733	8,778	8,781	8,780
77.5	6,146	6,392	6,575	6,873	7,195	7,238
82.5	3,934	4,135	4,350	4,559	4,712	4,748
87.5	2,050	2,170	2,287	2,395	2,533	2,560
92.5	765	860	956	1,024	1,094	1,108
97.5	206	231	249	287	317	324
102.5	37	44	50	57	63	62

Use multiple regression to construct **(a)** a linear model and **(b)** an interaction model for the data (round all coefficients to four significant digits). Does the interaction model give a significantly better fit in terms of the multiple regression coefficient? Referring to the linear model, does the *P*-value for the coefficient of y provide strong evidence that the population profile has been changing with time? (A *P*-value of α indicates that we can be certain with a confidence level of $1 - \alpha$ that the associated coefficient is nonzero.)

4. Graph the data from the preceding exercise and decide whether the linear model gives a faithful representation of the actual data. If not, propose and construct an alternative model. How is the confidence level in the coefficient of y changed?
5. According to your model in the preceding question, why does the age-group with maximum population not change over time? Propose a model in which it does. Construct such a model, and test the additional coefficient(s).

TI-83/84 Technology Guide

Section 8.1

Example 1 You own a company that makes two models of speakers: the Ultra Mini and the Big Stack. Your total monthly cost (in dollars) to make x Ultra Minis and y Big Stacks is given by

$$C(x, y) = 10{,}000 + 20x + 40y$$

Compute several values of this function.

Solution with Technology You can have a TI-83/84 compute $C(x, y)$ numerically as follows:

1. In the "Y=" screen, enter

```
Y1 = 10000+20X+40Y
```

2. To evaluate, say, $C(10, 30)$ (the cost to make 10 Ultra Minis and 30 Big Stacks), enter

```
10→X
30→Y
Y1
```

```
10→X
                10
30→Y
                30
Y1
             11400
```

and the calculator will evaluate the function and give the answer, $C(10, 30) = 11{,}400$.

This procedure is too laborious if you want to calculate $f(x, y)$ for a large number of different values of x and y.

EXCEL Technology Guide

Section 8.1

Example 1 You own a company that makes two models of speakers: the Ultra Mini and the Big Stack. Your total monthly cost (in dollars) to make x Ultra Minis and y Big Stacks is given by

$$C(x, y) = 10{,}000 + 20x + 40y$$

Compute several values of this function.

Solution with Technology Spreadsheets like Excel handle functions of several variables easily. The following setup shows how a table of values of C can be created, using values of x and y you enter:

Microsoft Excel - ETG 8-1 Two Models of Speakers.xls

	A	B	C	D
1	x	y	C(x, y)	
2	10	30	=10000+20*A2+40*B2	
3	20	30		
4	15	0		
5	0	30		
6	30	30		
7				
8				

→

Microsoft Excel - ETG 8-1 Two Models of Speakers.xls

	A	B	C	D
1	x	y	C(x, y)	
2	10	30	11400	
3	20	30	11600	
4	15	0	10300	
5	0	30	11200	
6	30	30	11800	
7				
8				

A disadvantage of this layout is that it's not easy to enter values of x and y systematically in two columns. Can you find a way to remedy this? (See Example 3 for one method.)

Example **3** Use technology to create a table of values of the body mass index

$$M(w, h) = \frac{0.45w}{(0.0254h)^2}$$

Solution with Technology We can use this formula to recreate a table in Excel, as follows:

Microsoft Excel - ETG 8-1 Body Mass Index.xls

File Edit View Insert Format Tools Data Window Help Adobe

	A	B	C	D
1		130	140	150
2	60	=0.45*B$1/(0.0254*$A2)^2		
3	61			
4	62			
5	63			
6	64			
7	65			
8	66			
9	67			
10				

In the formula in cell B2 we have used B$1 instead of B1 for the w-coordinate because we want all references to w to use the same row (1). Similarly, we want all references to h to refer to the same column (A), so we used $A2 instead of A2.

We copy the formula in cell B2 to all of the red shaded area to obtain the desired table:

Microsoft Excel - ETG 8-1 Body Mass Index.xls

File Edit View Insert Format Tools Data Window Help Adobe PD

	A	B	C	D	E
1		130	140	150	160
2	60	25.18755038	27.12505425	29.06255813	31.00006
3	61	24.36849808	26.24299793	28.11749778	29.991997
4	62	23.58875685	25.40327661	27.21779637	29.03231
5	63	22.84585068	24.60322381	26.36059694	28.11797
6	64	22.13749545	23.84037971	25.54326398	27.24614
7	65	21.46158138	23.11247226	24.76336314	26.414254
8	66	20.81615733	22.41740021	24.01864308	25.619885
9	67	20.19941665	21.75321793	23.30701921	24.8608204
10	[illegible]	[illegible]	21.11812182	[illegible]	

Section **8.2**

Example **3** Describe the graph of $f(x, y) = x^2 - y^2$.

Solution with Technology

1. Set up a table showing a range of values of x and y and the corresponding values of the function (see Example 3 in Section 8.1):

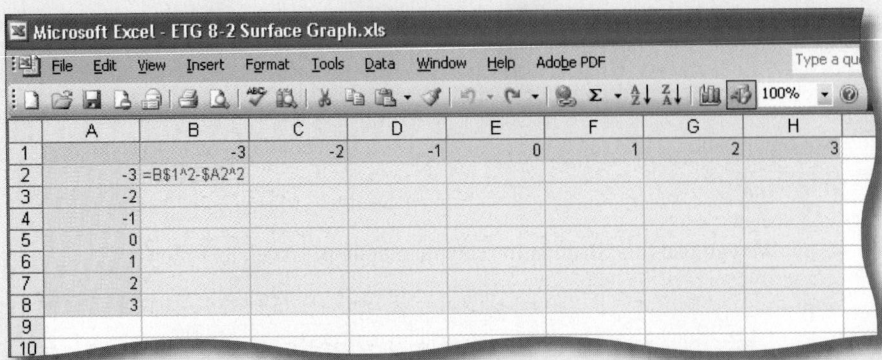

Microsoft Excel - ETG 8-2 Surface Graph.xls

	A	B	C	D	E	F	G	H
1		-3	-2	-1	0	1	2	3
2	-3	=B1^2-A2^2						
3	-2							
4	-1							
5	0							
6	1							
7	2							
8	3							
9								
10								

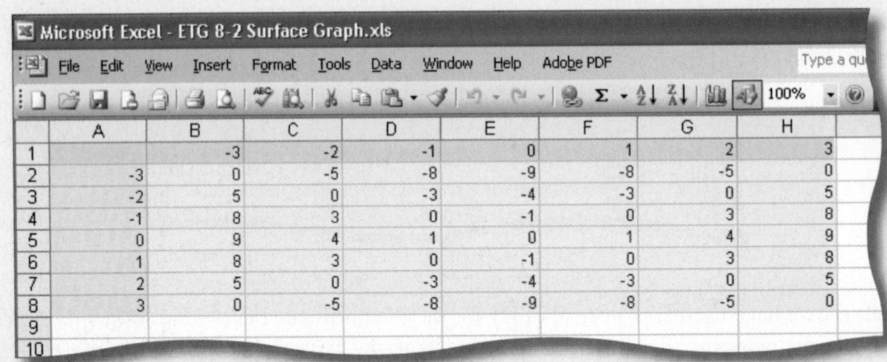

Microsoft Excel - ETG 8-2 Surface Graph.xls

	A	B	C	D	E	F	G	H
1		-3	-2	-1	0	1	2	3
2	-3	0	-5	-8	-9	-8	-5	0
3	-2	5	0	-3	-4	-3	0	5
4	-1	8	3	0	-1	0	3	8
5	0	9	4	1	0	1	4	9
6	1	8	3	0	-1	0	3	8
7	2	5	0	-3	-4	-3	0	5
8	3	0	-5	-8	-9	-8	-5	0
9								
10								

2. Select the cells with the values (B2: H8) and insert a chart, with the "Surface" option selected and "Series in Columns" selected as the data option, to obtain a graph like the following:

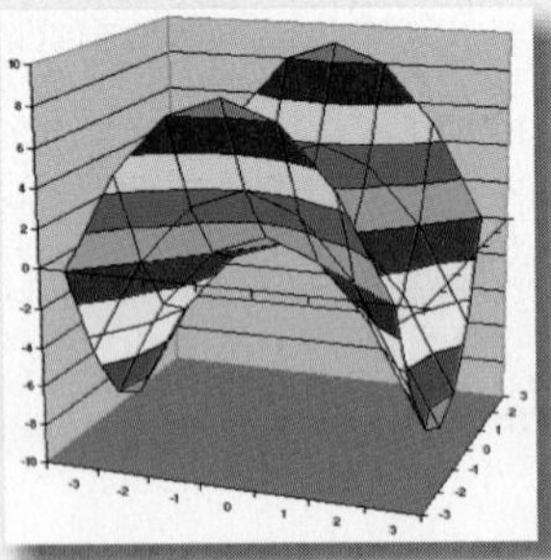

S Calculus Applied to Probability and Statistics

CASE STUDY Creating a Family Trust

You are a financial planning consultant at a neighborhood bank. A 22-year-old client asks you the following question: "I would like to set up my own insurance policy by opening a trust account into which I can make monthly payments starting now, so that upon my death or my ninety-fifth birthday—whichever comes sooner—the trust can be expected to be worth $500,000. How much should I invest each month?" Assuming a 5% rate of return on investments, how should you respond**?**

White Packert/Getty Images

Online you will find:

- A Web-based version of this chapter
- Numerical integration utilities
- A normal distribution utility

Introduction

To answer the question on the previous page, we must know something about the probability of the client's dying at various ages. There are so many possible ages to consider (particularly because we should consider the possibilities month by month) that it would be easier to treat his age at death as a *continuous* variable, one that can take on any real value (between 22 and 95 in this case). The mathematics needed to do probability and statistics with continuous variables is calculus.

The material on statistics in this chapter is accessible to any reader with a "common-sense" knowledge of probability, but it also supplements any previous study you may have made of probability and statistics without using calculus.

S.1 Continuous Random Variables and Histograms

Suppose that you have purchased stock in Colossal Conglomerate, Inc., and each day you note the closing price of the stock. The result each day is a real number X (the closing price of the stock) in the unbounded interval $[0, +\infty)$. Or, suppose that you time several people running a 50-meter dash. The result for each runner is a real number X, the race time in seconds. In both cases, the value of X is somewhat random. Moreover, X can take on essentially any real value in some interval, rather than, say, just integer values. For this reason, we refer to X as a **continuous random variable.** Here is the formal definition.

Continuous Random Variable

A **random variable** is a function X that assigns to each possible outcome in an experiment a real number. If X may assume any value in some given interval I (the interval may be bounded or unbounded), it is called a **continuous** random variable. If it can assume only a number of separated values, it is called a **discrete** random variable.

quick Examples

1. Roll a die and take X to be the number on the uppermost face. Then X is a discrete random variable with possible values 1, 2, 3, 4, 5, and 6.
2. Locate a star in the cosmos and take X to be its distance from the solar system in light years. Then X is a continuous random variable whose values are real numbers in the interval $(0, +\infty)$.
3. Open the business section of your newspaper and take X to be the closing price of Colossal Conglomerate stock. Then X can take on essentially any positive real value, so we can think of X as a continuous random variable.

If X is a random variable, we are usually interested in the **probability** that X takes on a value in a certain range. For instance, if X is the closing price of Colossal Conglomerate stock and we find that 60% of the time the price is between \$10 and \$20, we would say

The probability that X is between \$10 and \$20 is .6.

We can write this statement mathematically as follows:

$$P(10 \le X \le 20) = .6 \qquad \text{The probability that } 10 \le X \le 20 \text{ is } .6$$

We can use a bar chart, called a **probability distribution histogram,** to display the probabilities that X lies in selected ranges. This is shown in the following example:

Example 1 College Population by Age

The following table shows the distribution according to age of U.S. residents (16 years old and over) attending college in 1980.*

Age (years)	15–19	20–24	25–29	30–34	35–?
Number in 1980 (millions)	2.7	4.8	1.9	1.2	1.8

Draw the probability distribution histogram for X = the age of a randomly chosen college student.

Solution Summing the entries in the bottom row, we see that the total number of students in 1980 was 12.4 million. We can therefore convert all the data in the table to probabilities by dividing by this total.

X = Age (years)	15–19	20–24	25–29	30–34	35–?
Probability	.22	.39	.15	.10	.15

The probabilities in the above table have been rounded, with the consequence that they add to 1.01 instead of the expected 1. In the category 15–19, we have actually included anyone at least 15 years old and less than 20 years old. For example, someone 19 and a half years old would be in this range. We would like to write 15–20 instead, but this would be ambiguous, because we would not know where to count someone who was exactly 20 years old. However, the probability that a college student is *exactly* 20 years old (and not, say, 20 years and 1 second) is essentially 0, so it doesn't matter.† We can therefore rewrite the table with the following ranges.

X = Age (years)	15–20	20–25	25–30	30–35	≥ 35
Probability	.22	.39	.15	.10	.15

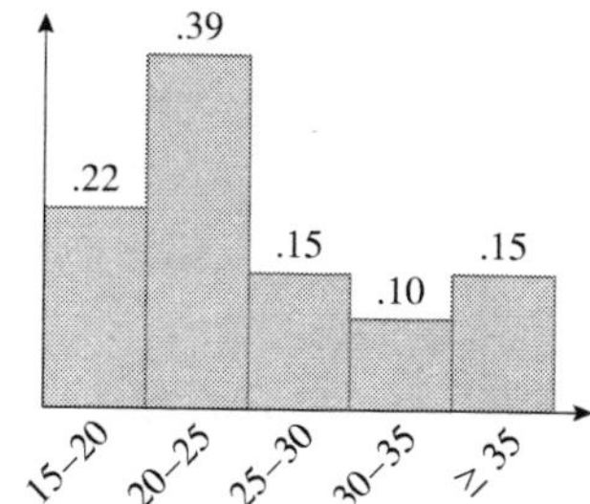

Figure 1

The table tells us that, for instance,

$$P(15 \le X \le 20) = .22$$

and

$$P(X \ge 35) = .15$$

The probability distribution histogram is the bar graph we get from these data (Figure 1).

---

* SOURCE: 1980 Census of Population, U.S. Department of Commerce/Bureau of the Census.

† Also see the discussion after Example 2 on next page.

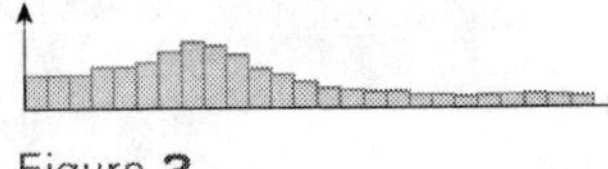
Figure 2

Before we go on... Had the grouping into ranges been finer—for instance into divisions of one year instead of five, then the histogram would appear smoother, and with lower bars, as in Figure 2 (why?).

This smoother looking distribution suggests a smooth curve. It is this kind of curve that we shall be studying in the next section.

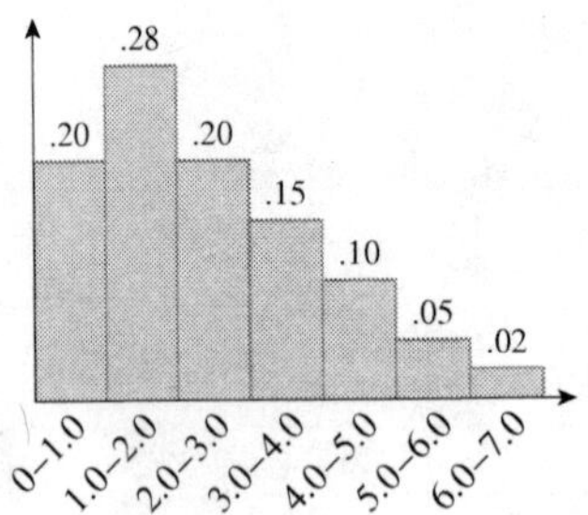

Figure 3

Example 2 Age of a Rented Car

A survey finds the following probability distribution for the age of a rented car.*

Age (years)	0–1	1–2	2–3	3–4	4–5	5–6	6–7
Probability	.20	.28	.20	.15	.10	.05	.02

Plot the associated probability distribution histogram, and use it to evaluate (or estimate) the following:

a. $P(0 \le X \le 4)$ **b.** $P(X \ge 4)$

c. $P(2 \le X \le 3.5)$ **d.** $P(X = 4)$

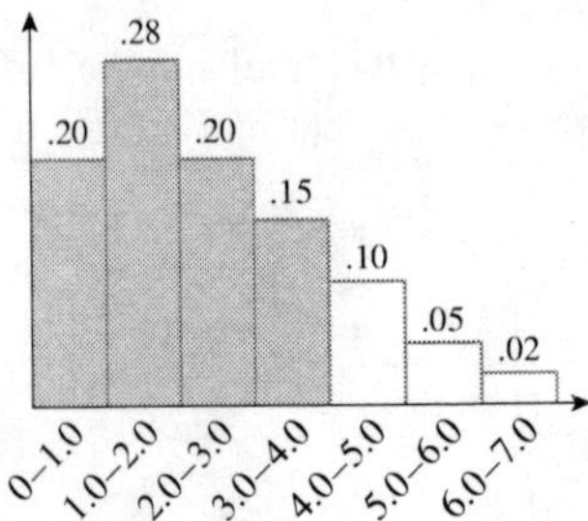

Figure 4

Solution The histogram is shown in Figure 3.

a. We can calculate $P(0 \le X \le 4)$ from the table by adding the corresponding probabilities:

$$P(0 \le X \le 4) = .20 + .28 + .20 + .15 = .83$$

This corresponds to the shaded region of the histogram shown in Figure 4.

Notice that because each rectangle has width equal to 1 unit and height equal to the associated probability, its *area* is equal to the probability that X is in the associated range. Thus $P(0 \le X \le 4)$ is also equal to the area of the shaded region.

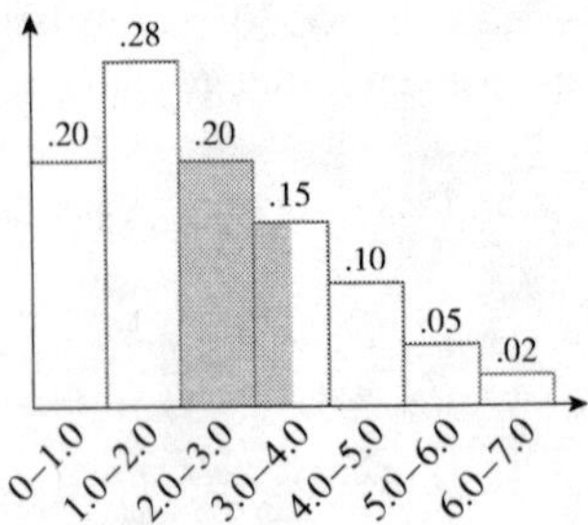

Figure 5

b. Similarly, $P(X \ge 4)$ is given by the area of the *unshaded* portion of Figure 4, so

$$P(X \ge 4) = .10 + .05 + .02 = .17$$

(Notice that $P(0 \le X \le 4) + P(X \ge 4) = 1$. Why?)

c. To calculate $P(2 \le X \le 3.5)$, we need to make an educated guess, because neither the table nor the histogram has subdivisions of width .5. Referring to the graph, we can approximate the probability by the shaded area shown in Figure 5.

Thus,

$$P(2 \le X \le 3.5) \approx .20 + \frac{1}{2}(.15) = .275$$

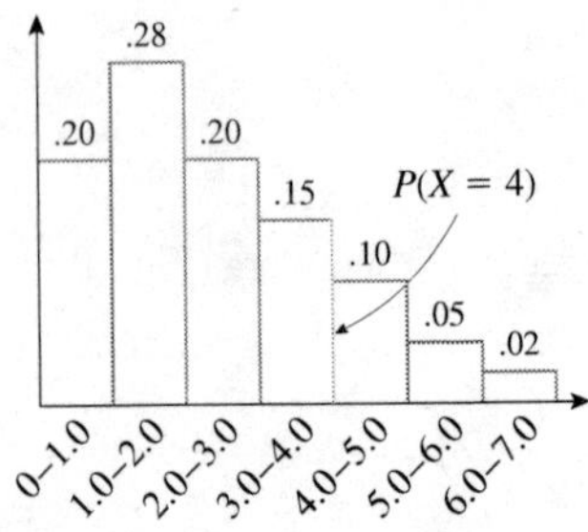

Figure 6

d. To calculate $P(X = 4)$, we would need to calculate $P(4 \le X \le 4)$. But this would correspond to a region of the histogram with zero area (Figure 6), so we conclude that $P(X = 4) = 0$.

*As in the preceeding example, we allow the brackets to intersect. However, because the probability that a car is *exactly* 1 or 2 or 3 or . . . years old (to a fraction of a second) is essentially zero, we can ignore the apparent overlap. The discussion at the end of this example further clarifies this point.

Q: *In the above example, $P(X = 4)$ was zero. Is it true that $P(X = a)$ is zero for every number a in the interval associated with X?*

A: As a general rule, yes. If X is a *continuous* random variable, then X can assume infinitely many values, and so it is reasonable that the probability of its assuming any specific value we choose beforehand is zero. ■

Caution

If you wish to use a histogram to calculate probability as *area*, make sure that the subdivisions for X have width 1—for instance, $1 \le X \le 2$, $2 \le X \le 3$, and so on.

The histogram in Example 1 (Figure 1) had bars corresponding to larger ranges for X. The first bar has a width of 5 units, so its area is 5×0.22, which is 5 times the probability that $15 \le X \le 20$. If you wish to use a histogram to give probability as area, divide the area by the width of the intervals.

There is another way around this problem that we shall not use, but which is used by working statisticians: Draw your histograms so that the heights are not necessarily the probabilities but are chosen so that the *area* of each bar gives the corresponding probability. This is necessary if, for example, the bars do not all have the same width.

S.1 EXERCISES

● denotes basic skills exercises

In Exercises 1–10, identify the random variable (for example, "X is the price of rutabagas"), say whether it is continuous or discrete, and if continuous, give its interval of possible values.

1. ● A die is cast and the number that appears facing up is recorded.

2. ● A die is cast and the time (in seconds) it takes for the die to become still is recorded.

3. ● A dial is spun, and the angle the pointer makes with the vertical is noted. (See the figure.)

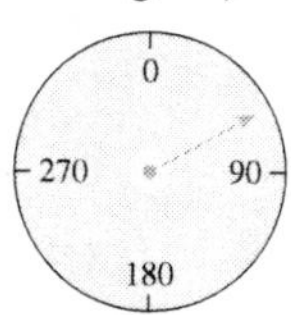

4. ● A dial is spun, and the quadrant in which the pointer comes to rest is noted.

5. ● The temperature is recorded at midday.

6. ● The U.S. Balance of Payments is recorded (fractions of a dollar permitted).

7. ● The U.S. Balance of Payments is recorded, rounded to the nearest billion dollars.

8. ● The time it takes a new company to become profitable is recorded.

9. ● In each batch of 100 computer chips manufactured, the number that fail to work is recorded.

10. ● The time it takes a TV set to break down after sale is recorded.

In Exercises 11–14, sketch the probability distribution histogram of the given continuous random variable.

11. ●

X = height of a jet fighter (ft.)	0–20,000	20,000–30,000	30,000–40,000	40,000–50,000	50,000–60,000
Probability	.1	.2	.3	.3	.1

12. ●

X = time to next eruption of a volcano (yrs.)	0–2000	2000–3000	3000–4000	4000–5000	5000–6000
Probability	.1	.3	.3	.2	.1

13.

X = average temperature (°F)	0–50	50–60	60–70	70–80	80–90
Number of cities	4	7	2	5	2

14.

X = Cost of a used car ($)	0–2000	2000–4000	4000–6000	6000–8000	8000–10,000
Number of cars	200	500	800	500	500

Applications

15. ***U.S. Population, Female*** The following table shows the number of females in the U.S. in 2000, broken down by age.[1] Numbers are in millions.

Age	0–18	18–25	25–35	35–45	45–55	55–65	65–75	75 and over
Number	35.2	13.3	19.8	22.7	19.2	12.6	10.1	10.5

Construct the associated probability distribution (with probabilities rounded to four decimal places) and use the distribution to compute the following.

a. $P(18 \le X \le 55)$ **b.** $P(X \le 45)$ **c.** $P(X \ge 45)$

16. ***U.S. Population, Male*** The following table shows the number of males in the U.S. in 2000, broken down by age.[2] Numbers are in thousands.

Age	0–18	18–25	25–35	35–45	45–55	55–65	65–75	75 and over
Number	37.1	13.9	20.1	22.4	18.5	11.6	8.3	6.1

Construct the associated probability distribution (with probabilities rounded to four decimal places) and use the distribution to compute the following.

a. $P(25 \le X \le 65)$ **b.** $P(X \le 18)$ **c.** $P(X \ge 15)$

17. ***Meteors*** The following histogram shows part of the probability distribution of the size (in megatons of released energy) of large meteors that hit the Earth's atmosphere. (A large meteor is one that releases at least one megaton of energy, equivalent to the energy released by a small nuclear bomb.)[3]

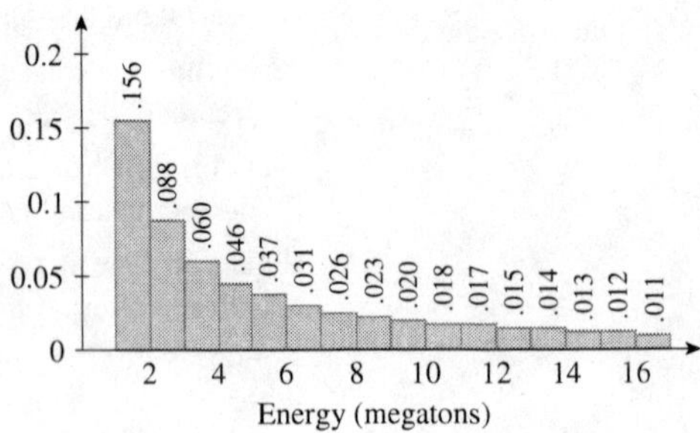

Calculate or estimate the following probabilities.

a. That a large meteor hitting the Earth's atmosphere will release between 1 and 4 megatons of energy.

b. That a large meteor hitting the Earth's atmosphere will release between 3 and 4.5 megatons of energy.

c. That a large meteor will release at least 5 megatons of energy.

---

[1] SOURCE: U.S. Census Bureau, Census 2000 Summary File 1, obtained from http://factfinder.census.gov/.

[2] Ibid.

[3] The authors' model, based on data released by NASA International Near-Earth-Object Detection Workshop/*The New York Times*, January 25, 1994, p. C1.

18. ***Meteors*** Repeat the preceding exercise using the following histogram for meteor impacts on the planet Zor in the Cygnus III system in Andromeda.

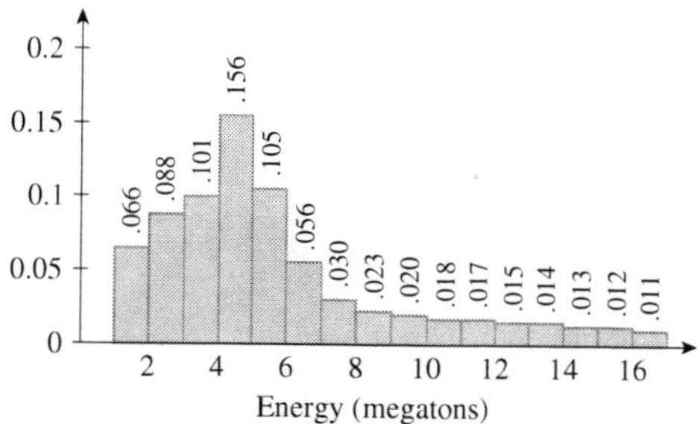

19. ***Quality Control*** An automobile parts manufacturer makes heavy-duty axles with a cross-section radius of 2.3 cm. In order for one of its axles to meet the accuracy standard demanded by the customer, the radius of the cross section cannot be off by more than 0.02 cm. Construct a histogram with $X =$ the measured radius of an axle, using categories of width 0.01 cm, so that all of the following conditions are met.

a. X lies in the interval [2.26, 2.34].

b. 80% of the axles have a cross-sectional radius between 2.29 and 2.31.

c. 10% of the axles are rejected.

20. ***Damage Control*** As a campaign manager for a presidential candidate who always seems to be getting himself into embarrassing situations, you have decided to conduct a statistical analysis of the number of times per week he makes a blunder. Construct a histogram with $X =$ the number of times he blunders in a week, using categories of width 1 unit, so that all of the following conditions are met.

a. X lies in the interval [0, 10].

b. During a given week, there is an 80% chance that he will make 3 to 5 blunders.

c. Never a week goes by that he doesn't make at least one blunder.

d. On occasion, he has made 10 blunders in one week.

Communication and Reasoning Exercises

21. How is a random variable related to the outcomes in an experiment?

22. Give an example of an experiment and two associated continuous random variables.

23. You are given a probability distribution histogram with the bars having a width of 2 units. How is the probability $P(a \leq X \leq b)$ related to the area of the corresponding portion of the histogram?

24. You are given a probability distribution histogram with the bars having a width of 1 unit, and you wish to convert it into one with bars of width 2 units. How would you go about this?

● basic skills

S.2 Probability Density Functions: Uniform, Exponential, Normal, and Beta

We have seen that a histogram is a convenient way to picture the probability distribution associated with a continuous random variable X and that if we use subdivisions of 1 unit, the probability $P(c \leq X \leq d)$ is given by the area under the histogram between $X = c$ and $X = d$. But we have also seen that it is difficult to calculate probabilities for ranges of X that are not a whole number of units. To motivate the solution to this problem, let us look once again at Example 2 in Section S.1:

Example 1 Car Rentals

A survey finds the following probability distribution for the age of a rented car.

Age (years)	0–1	1–2	2–3	3–4	4–5	5–6	6–7
Probability	.20	.28	.20	.15	.10	.05	.02

The histogram of this distribution is shown in Figure 7a, and it suggests a curve something like the one given in Figure 7b.*

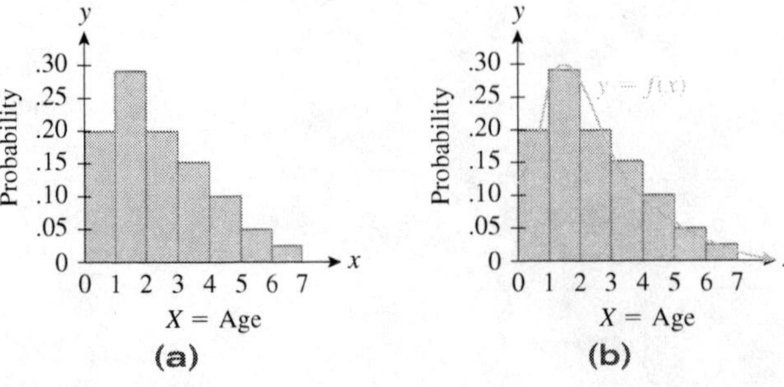

Figure **7**

This curve is the graph of some function *f*, which we call a **probability density function.** We take the domain of *f* to be $[0, +\infty)$, because this is the possible range of values X can take (in principle). In general, a probability density function will have some (possibly unbounded) interval as its domain. Also, we use x to refer to specific values of X, so it is no coincidence that we are calling the horizontal axis the x-axis.

Suppose now that as in Section S.1, we wanted to calculate the probability that a rented car is between 0 and 4 years old. Referring to the table, we find

$$P(0 \le X \le 4) = .20 + .28 + .20 + .15 = .83$$

Referring to Figure 8, we can obtain the same result by adding the areas of the corresponding bars, because each bar has a width of 1 unit. Ideally, our probability density curve should have the property that the area under it for $0 \le X \le 4$ is the same, that is,

$$P(0 \le X \le 4) = \int_0^4 f(x)\, dx = .83$$

(This area is shown in Figure 8.)

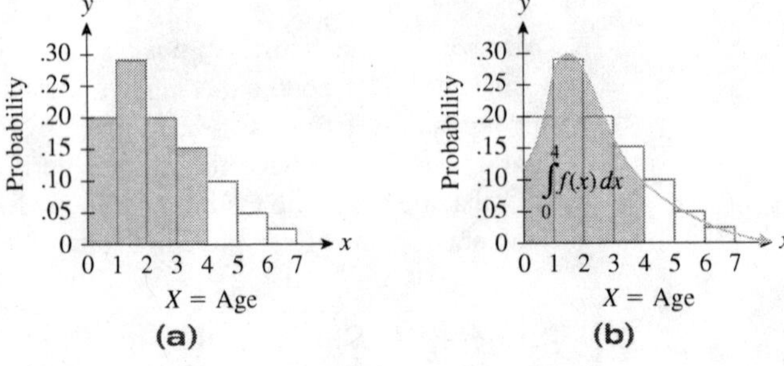

Figure **8**

*There are many similarly shaped curves suggested by the bar graph. The question of finding the most appropriate curve is one we shall be considering below.

Now, what happens if we want to find $P(2 \le X \le 3.5)$? In the previous section we estimated this by taking half of the rectangle between 3 and 4 (see Figure 9).

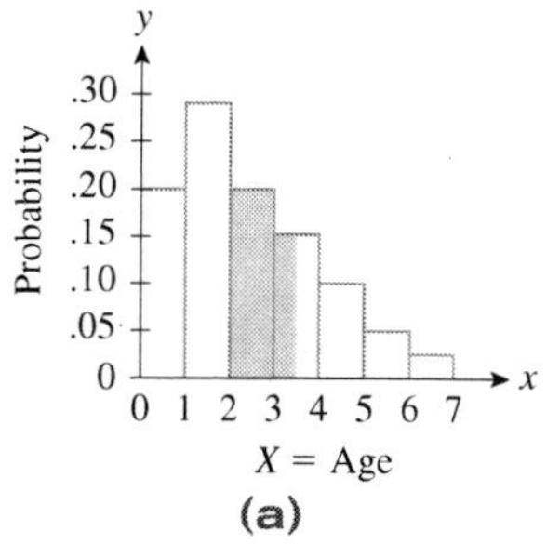

(a)

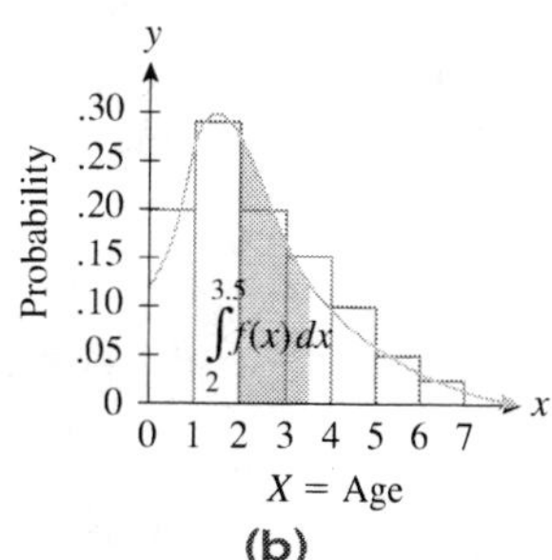

(b)

Figure 9

Instead, we could use the definite integral

$$P(2 \le X \le 3.5) = \int_{2}^{3.5} f(x)\,dx$$

Before we go on... Although we haven't given you a formula for $f(x)$, we would *like* $f(x)$ to behave as described above. Here is something else we would like: Because a car has probability 1 of having an age between 0 and $+\infty$, we want

$$P(0 \le X < +\infty) = \int_{0}^{+\infty} f(x)\,dx = 1$$

The discussion in Example 1 motivates the following.

Probability Density Function

A **probability density function** is a function f defined on an interval (a, b) and having the following properties.

a. $f(x) \ge 0$ for every x

b. $\displaystyle\int_{a}^{b} f(x)\,dx = 1$

We allow a, b, or both to be infinite, as in the above example. This would make the integral in (b) an improper one.

Probability Associated with a Continuous Random Variable

A continuous random variable X is specified by a probability density function f. The probability $P(c \le X \le d)$ is specified by

$$P(c \le X \le d) = \int_{c}^{d} f(x)\,dx$$

quick **Example**

Let $f(x) = \frac{2}{x^2}$ on the interval $[a, b] = [1, 2]$. Then property (a) holds, because $\frac{2}{x^2}$ is positive on the interval $[1, 2]$. For property (b),

$$\int_a^b f(x)\,dx = \int_1^2 \frac{2}{x^2}\,dx = \left[-\frac{2}{x}\right]_1^2 = -1 + 2 = 1$$

If X is specified by this probability density function, then

$$P(1.5 \le X \le 2) = \int_{1.5}^2 \frac{2}{x^2}\,dx = \frac{1}{3}$$

Note If X is specified by a probability density function f, then

$$P(X = c) = P(c \le X \le c) = \int_c^c f(x)\,dx = 0$$

showing once again that there is a zero probability that X will assume any specified value. ■

Uniform Density Function

A **uniform density function** f is a density function that is constant, making it the simplest kind of density function. Because we require $f(x) = k$ for some constant k, requirement (b) in the definition of a probability density function tells us that

$$1 = \int_a^b f(x)\,dx = \int_a^b k\,dx = k(b - a)$$

Thus, we must have

$$k = \frac{1}{b - a}$$

In other words, a uniform density function must have the following form.

Uniform Density Function

The **uniform density function on the interval [*a*, *b*]** is given by

$$f(x) = \frac{1}{b - a}$$

Its graph is a horizontal line.

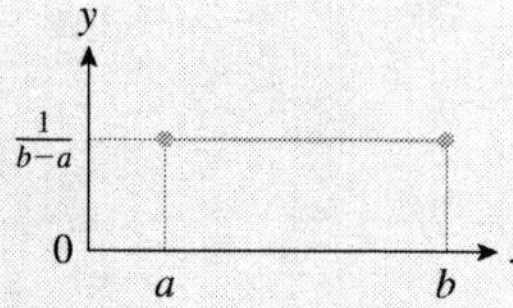

Calculating Probability with a Uniform Density Function

Because probability is given by area, it is not hard to compute probabilities based on a uniform density function.

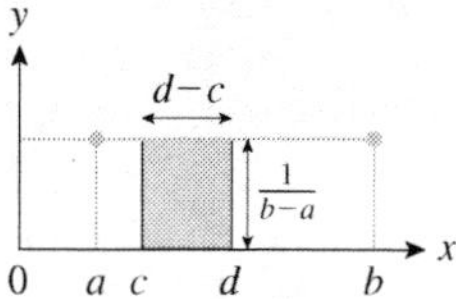

$$P(c \le X \le d) = \text{Area of shaded rectangle} = \frac{d-c}{b-a}$$

If X is specified by a uniform density function, we say that X is **uniformly distributed** or that X has a **uniform distribution**.

quick Example

Let X be a random real number between 0 and 5. Then X has a uniform distribution given by

$$f(x) = \frac{1}{5-0} = \frac{1}{5}$$

and $P(2 \le X \le 4.5) = \dfrac{4.5-2}{5-0} = .5.$

Example 2 Spinning a Dial

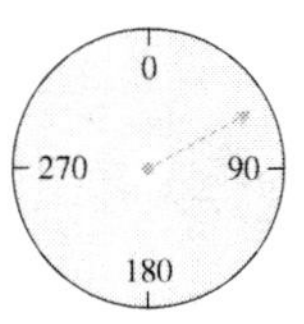

Figure **10**

Suppose that you spin the dial shown in Figure 10 so that it comes to rest at a random position. Model this with a suitable distribution, and use it to find the probability that the dial will land somewhere between 5° and 300°.

Solution We take X to be the angle at which the pointer comes to rest, so we use the interval [0, 360]. Because all angles are equally likely, the probability density function should not depend on x and therefore should be constant. That is, we take f to be uniform.

$$f(x) = \frac{1}{b-a} = \frac{1}{360-0} = \frac{1}{360}$$

Thus,

$$P(5 \le X \le 300) = \frac{300-5}{360-0} = \frac{295}{360} \approx .8194$$

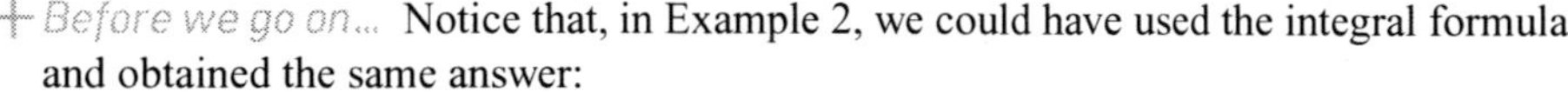

Before we go on... Notice that, in Example 2, we could have used the integral formula and obtained the same answer:

$$\int_5^{300} \frac{1}{360}\,dx = \frac{1}{360}(300-5) = \frac{295}{360}$$

You can also check the following probabilities. Why are these the answers you expect?

$$P(0 \le X \le 90) = 1/4$$
$$P(90 \le X \le 180) = 1/4$$
$$P(0 \le X \le 180) = 1/2$$
$$P(0 \le X \le 270) = 3/4$$
$$P(0 \le X \le 120) = 1/3$$

Exponential Density Functions

Suppose that troubled saving and loan (S&L) institutions are failing continuously at a fractional rate of 5% per year. What is the probability that a troubled S&L will fail sometime within the next T years?

To answer the question, suppose that you started with 100 troubled S&Ls. Because they are failing continuously at a fractional rate of 5% per year, the number left after T years is given by the decay equation

$$\text{Number left} = 100e^{-0.05T}$$

so

$$\begin{aligned}\text{Number that fail} &= \text{Total number} - \text{Number left}\\ &= 100 - 100e^{-0.05T}\\ &= 100(1 - e^{-0.05T})\end{aligned}$$

Thus, the percentage that will have failed by that time—and hence the probability that we are asking for—is given by

$$P = \frac{100(1 - e^{-0.05T})}{100} = 1 - e^{-0.05T}$$

Now let X be the number of years a randomly chosen troubled S&L will take to fail. We have just calculated the probability that X is between 0 and T. In other words,

$$P(0 \le X \le T) = 1 - e^{-0.05T}$$

Notice that this result can also be obtained by calculating a certain integral:

$$\int_0^T 0.05e^{-0.05x}\,dx = \left[e^{-0.05x}\right]_0^T = 1 - e^{-0.05T}$$

Thus,

$$P(0 \le X \le T) = \int_0^T 0.05e^{-0.05x}\,dx$$

and so we use $f(x) = 0.05e^{-0.05x}$ as a probability density function to model this situation.

Q: Does this function satisfy the mathematical conditions necessary for it to be a probability density function?

A: First, the domain of f is $[0, +\infty)$, because x refers to the number of years from now. Checking requirements (a) and (b) for a probability density function,

a. $0.05e^{-0.05x} \ge 0$,

b. $$\begin{aligned}\int_0^{+\infty} 0.05e^{-0.05x}\,dx &= \lim_{M\to+\infty}\int_0^M 0.05e^{-0.05x}\,dx\\ &= \lim_{M\to+\infty}\left[-e^{-0.05x}\right]_0^M\\ &= \lim_{M\to+\infty}(e^0 - e^{-0.05M}) = 1 - 0 = 1.\end{aligned}$$

■

There is nothing special about the number 0.05. Any function of the form

$$f(x) = ae^{-ax}$$

with a a positive constant is a probability density function. A density function of this form is referred to as an **exponential density function.**

Exponential Density Function

An **exponential density function** is a function of the form

$$f(x) = ae^{-ax} \text{ (a a positive constant)}$$

with domain $[0, +\infty)$. Its graph is shown in Figure 11. If X is specified by an exponential density function, we say that X is **exponentially distributed** or that X has an **exponential distribution.**

quick Example

Continuing the example in the text, we find that the probability that a given troubled S&L will fail between 2 and 4 years from now is

$$P(2 \le X \le 4) = \int_2^4 0.05e^{-0.05x}\,dx = \left[-e^{-0.05x}\right]_2^4 = -e^{-0.2} + e^{-0.1} \approx .086$$

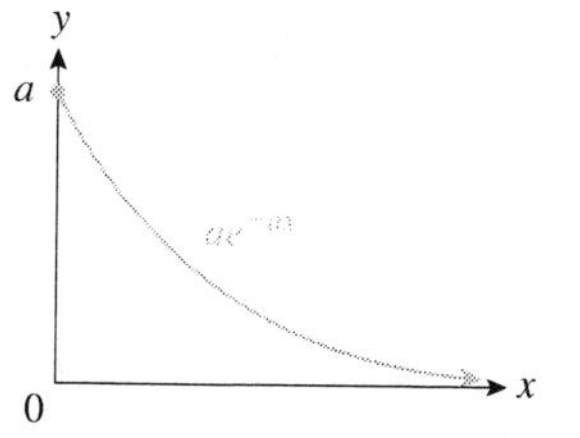

Figure 11

The probability that it will last 5 or more years is

$$P(X \ge 5) = \int_5^{+\infty} 0.05e^{-0.05x}\,dx$$

$$= \lim_{M\to+\infty} \int_5^{M} 0.05e^{-0.05x}\,dx$$

$$= \lim_{M\to+\infty} \left[-e^{-0.05x}\right]_5^M = \lim_{M\to+\infty} (e^{-0.25} - e^{-0.05M}) = e^{-0.25} \approx .779$$

So there is an 8.6% chance that a given S&L will fail between 2 and 4 years from now, and a 77.9% chance that it will last 5 or more years.

Example 3 Radioactive Decay

Plutonium 239 decays continuously at a rate of 0.00284% per year. If X is the time a randomly chosen plutonium atom will decay, write down the associated probability density function, and use it to compute the probability that a plutonium atom will decay between 100 and 500 years from now.

Solution Using the discussion on failing S&Ls as our guide, we see that $a = 0.0000284$, so the probability density function is

$$f(x) = 0.0000284e^{-0.0000284x}$$

For the second part of the question,

$$P(100 \le X \le 500) = \int_{100}^{500} (0.0000284e^{-0.0000284x})\,dx$$

$$\approx .011$$

Thus, there is a 1.1% chance that a plutonium atom will decay sometime during the given 400 year period.

Normal Density Functions

Perhaps the most interesting class of probability density functions are the **normal density functions,** defined as follows.[4]

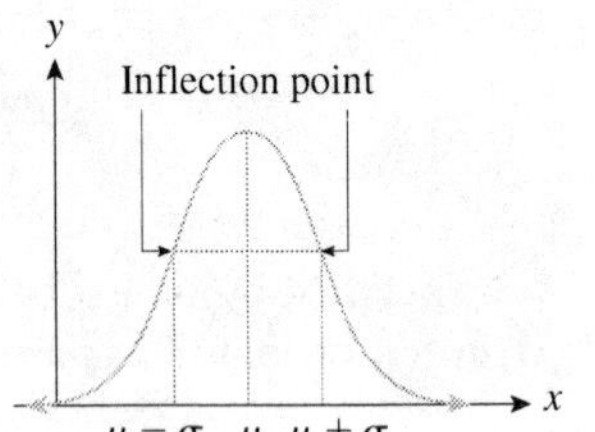

Figure **12**

Normal Density Function

A **normal density function** is a function of the form

$$f(x) = \frac{1}{\sigma\sqrt{2\pi}} e^{-\frac{(x-\mu)^2}{2\sigma^2}}$$

with domain $(-\infty, +\infty)$. The quantity μ is called the **mean** and can be any real number, while σ is called the **standard deviation** and can be any positive real number. The graph of a normal density function is shown in Figure 12. If X is specified by a normal density function, we say that X is **normally distributed** or that X has a **normal distribution.**

The following properties can be checked using calculus and a little algebra.

Properties of a Normal Density Curve

a. It is "bell-shaped" with the peak occurring at $x = \mu$.
b. It is symmetric about the vertical line $x = \mu$.
c. It is concave down in the range $\mu - \sigma \le x \le \mu + \sigma$.
d. It is concave up outside that range, with inflection points at $x = \mu - \sigma$ and $x = \mu + \sigma$.

The normal density function applies in many situations that involve measurement and testing. For instance, repeated imprecise measurements of the length of a single object, a measurement made on many items from an assembly line, and collections of SAT scores tend to be distributed normally. It is partly for this reason that the normal density curve is so important in quality control and in assessing the results of standardized tests.

In order to use the normal density function to compute probabilities, we need to calculate integrals of the form $\int_a^b f(x)\,dx$. However, the antiderivative of the normal density function cannot be expressed in terms of any commonly used functions. Traditionally, statisticians and others have used tables coupled with transformation techniques to evaluate such integrals. This approach is rapidly becoming obsolete as the technology of spreadsheets, handheld computers and programmable calculators puts the ability to do numerical integration quickly and accurately in everybody's hands (literally). In keeping with this trend, in the Technology Guides at the end of this chapter we show how to use technology to do the calculations in the following example.

[4] You may recall encountering exercises using the normal density function in the chapter on integration.

Example 4 Quality Control

Pressure gauges manufactured by Precision Corp. must be checked for accuracy before being placed on the market. To test a pressure gauge, a worker uses it to measure the pressure of a sample of compressed air known to be at a pressure of exactly 50 pounds per square inch. If the gauge reading is off by more than 1% (0.5 pounds), the gauge is rejected. Assuming that the reading of a pressure gauge under these circumstances is a normal random variable with mean 50 and standard deviation 0.5, find the percentage of gauges rejected.

using Technology

See the Technology Guides at the end of the chapter to find how to compute the definite integral of a normal density function using a TI-83/84 or Excel.

Solution For a gauge to be accepted, its reading X must be 50 to within 1%, in other words, $49.5 \le X \le 50.5$. Thus, the probability that a gauge will be accepted is $P(49.5 \le X \le 50.5)$. X is a normal random variable with $\mu = 50$ and $\sigma = 0.5$. The formula tells us that

$$P(49.5 \le X \le 50.5) = \int_{49.5}^{50.5} f(x)\,dx$$

where f is the normal density function with mean $\mu = 50$ and standard deviation $\sigma = 0.5$:

$$f(x) = \frac{1}{\sigma\sqrt{2\pi}} e^{-\frac{(x-\mu)^2}{2\sigma^2}}$$
$$= \frac{1}{0.5\sqrt{2\pi}} e^{-\frac{(x-50)^2}{0.5}}$$

Using technology, we can calculate that

$$P(49.5 \le X \le 50.5) = \int_{49.5}^{50.5} f(x)\,dx \approx .6827$$

In other words, 68.27% of the gauges will be accepted. Thus, the remaining 31.73% of the gauges will be rejected.

+ Before we go on... As we mentioned above, the traditional and still common way of calculating normal probabilities is to use tables. The tables most commonly published are for the **standard normal distribution,** the one with mean 0 and standard deviation 1. If X is a normal variable with mean μ and standard deviation σ, the variable $Z = (X - \mu)/\sigma$ is a standard normal variable (see the exercises). Thus, to use a table we first write

$$P(a \le X \le b) = P\left(\frac{a-\mu}{\sigma} \le Z \le \frac{b-\mu}{\sigma}\right)$$

and then use the table to calculate the latter probability. ■

Q: *Why can we assume in Example 4 that the reading of a pressure gauge is given by a normal distribution? Why is the normal distribution so common in this kind of situation?*

A: The reason for this is rather deep. There is a theorem in probability theory called the Central Limit Theorem, which says that a large class of probability density functions, given, for example, by repeated measurement of the same random variable, may be approximated by normal density functions. ■

Beta Density Functions

There are many random variables whose values are percentages or fractions. These variables have density functions defined on [0, 1]. A large class of random variables, such as the percentage of new businesses that turn a profit in their first year, the percentage of banks that default in a given year, and the percentage of time a plant's machinery is inactive, can be modeled by a **beta density function.**

Beta Density Function

A **beta density function** is a function of the form

$$f(x) = (\beta + 1)(\beta + 2)x^{\beta}(1 - x)$$

with domain [0, 1]. The number β can be any constant ≥ 0. Figure 13 shows the graph of $f(x)$ for several values of β.

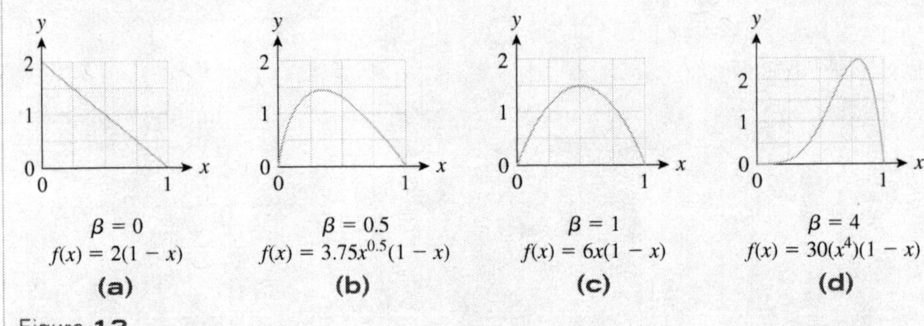

Figure **13**

If X is specified by a beta density function, we say that X has a **beta distribution.**

Example **5** Downsizing in the Utilities Industry

A utilities industry consultant predicts a cutback in the Canadian utilities industry during 2000–2005 by a percentage specified by a beta distribution with $\beta = 0.25$. Calculate the probability that Ontario Hydro will downsize by between 10% and 30% during the given five-year period.*

Solution The beta density function with $\beta = 0.25$ is

$$\begin{aligned} f(x) &= (\beta + 1)(\beta + 2)x^{\beta}(1 - x) \\ &= 2.8125x^{0.25}(1 - x) \\ &= 2.8125(x^{0.25} - x^{1.25}) \end{aligned}$$

Thus,

$$\begin{aligned} P(0.10 \leq X \leq 0.30) &= \int_{0.10}^{0.30} 2.8125(x^{0.25} - x^{1.25})\, dx \\ &= 2.8125 \int_{0.10}^{0.30} (x^{0.25} - x^{1.25})\, dx \\ &= 2.8125 \left[\frac{x^{1.25}}{1.25} - \frac{x^{2.25}}{2.25} \right]_{0.10}^{0.30} \\ &\approx .2968 \end{aligned}$$

* This model is fictitious. Ontario Hydro did announce plans to downsize by 8.4% in 1995, however (*Report on Business* (Canada), February 15, 1994, p. B1).

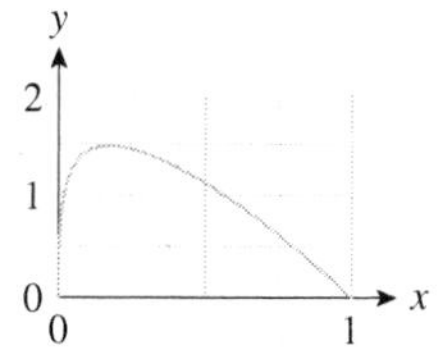

Figure 14

So there is approximately a 30% chance that Ontario Hydro will downsize by between 10% and 30%.

Before we go on... Figure 14 shows the density function. Notice that its shape is "in between" those for $\beta = 0$ and $\beta = 0.5$ in Figure 13. ■

S.2 EXERCISES

● denotes basic skills exercises

◆ denotes challenging exercises

tech Ex indicates exercises that should be solved using technology

In Exercises 1–12, check whether the given function is a probability density function. If a function fails to be a probability density function, say why.

1. ● $f(x) = 1$ on $[0, 1]$

2. ● $f(x) = x$ on $[0, 2]$

3. ● $f(x) = \frac{x}{2}$ on $[0, 1]$

4. ● $f(x) = 2$ on $\left[0, \frac{1}{2}\right]$

5. $f(x) = \frac{3}{2}(x^2 - 1)$ on $[0, 2]$

6. $f(x) = \frac{1}{3}(1 - x^2)$ on $[0, 1]$

7. $f(x) = \frac{1}{x}$ on $[1, e]$

8. $f(x) = e^x$ on $[0, \ln 2]$

9. $f(x) = 2xe^{-x^2}$ on $[0, +\infty)$

10. $f(x) = -2xe^{-x^2}$ on $(-\infty, 0]$

11. $f(x) = xe^{-x^2}$ on $(-\infty, +\infty)$

12. $f(x) = |x|\, e^{-x^2}$ on $(-\infty, +\infty)$

In Exercises 13–16, find the values of k for which the given functions are probability density functions.

13. $f(x) = 2k$ on $[-1, 1]$

14. $f(x) = k$ on $[-2, 0]$

15. $f(x) = ke^{kx}$ on $[0, 1]$

16. $f(x) = kxe^{x^2}$ on $[0, 1]$

In Exercises 17–26, say which kind of probability density function is most appropriate for the given random variable: uniform, exponential, normal, beta, or none of these.

17. The time it takes a Carbon-14 atom to decay.

18. The time it takes you to drive home.

19. The SAT score of a randomly selected student.

20. The value of a random number between 0 and 1.

21. The time of day at a randomly chosen moment.

22. The time it takes a careless driver to be involved in an accident.

23. The fraction of fast-food restaurants that are profitable in their first year.

24. The time it will take for the sun to die.

25. The time it takes before a gambler loses on a bet.

26. The length of a 2006 Ford Mustang® tailpipe.

Applications

Unless otherwise stated, round answers to all applications to four decimal places.

27. ● ***Salaries*** Assuming that workers' salaries in your company are uniformly distributed between \$10,000 and \$40,000 per year, find the probability that a randomly chosen worker earns an annual salary between \$14,000 and \$20,000.

28. ● ***Grades*** The grade point averages of members of the Gourmet Society are uniformly distributed between 2.5 and 3.5. Find the probability that a randomly chosen member of the society has a grade point average between 3 and 3.2.

29. ***Boring Television Series*** Your company's new series "Avocado Comedy Hour" has been a complete flop, with viewership continuously declining at a rate of 30% per month. Use a suitable density function to calculate the probability that a randomly chosen viewer will be lost sometime in the next three months.

30. ***Bad Investments*** Investments in junk bonds are declining continuously at a rate of 5% per year. Use a suitable density function to calculate the probability that a dollar invested in junk bonds will be pulled out of the junk bond market within the next two years.

31. ***Radioactive Decay*** The half-life of Carbon-14 is 5730 years. What is the probability that a randomly selected Carbon-14 atom will not yet have decayed in 4000 years' time?

32. ***Radioactive Decay*** The half-life of Plutonium-239 is 24,400 years. What is the probability that a randomly selected Plutonium-239 atom will not yet have decayed in 40,000 years' time?

33. ***The Doomsday Meteor*** The probability[5] that a "doomsday meteor" will hit the Earth in any given year and release a billion megatons or more of energy is on the order of .000 000 01.

a. What is the probability that the Earth will be hit by a doomsday meteor at least once during the next 100 years? (Use an exponential distribution with $a = 0.000\ 000\ 01$. Give the answer correct to 2 significant digits.)

b. What is the probability that the Earth has been hit by a doomsday meteor at least once since the appearance of life (about 4 billion years ago)?

34. ***Galactic Cataclysm*** The probability that the galaxy MX-47 will explode within the next million years is estimated to be .0003.

a. What is the probability that MX-47 will explode within the next 5 million years? (Use an exponential distribution with $a = 0.0003$.)

b. What is the probability that MX-47 will still be around 10 million years hence?

Exercises 35–42 use the normal probability density function and require the use of either technology or a table of values of the standard normal distribution.

35. tech Ex ***Physical Measurements*** Repeated measurements of a metal rod yield a mean of 5.3 inches, with a standard deviation of 0.1. What is the probability that the rod is between 5.25 and 5.35 inches long?

36. tech Ex ***IQ Testing*** Repeated measurements of a student's IQ yield a mean of 135, with a standard deviation of 5. What is the probability that the student has an IQ between 132 and 138?

37. tech Ex ***Psychology Tests*** It is known that subjects score an average of 100 points on a new personality test. If the standard deviation is 10 points, what percentage of all subjects will score between 75 and 80?

38. tech Ex ***Examination Scores*** Professor Easy's students earned an average grade of 3.5, with a standard deviation of 0.2. What percentage of his students earned between 3.5 and 3.9?

39. tech Ex ***Operating Expenses*** The cash operating expenses of the regional *Bell* companies during the first half of 1994 were distributed about a mean of \$29.87 per access line per month, with a standard deviation of \$2.65. *Ameritech Corporation*'s operating expenses were \$28.00 per access line per month.[6] Assuming a normal distribution of operating expenses, estimate the percentage of regional Bell companies whose operating expenses were closer to the mean than those of Ameritech.

40. tech Ex ***Operating Expenses*** *Nynex Corporation*'s operating expenses were \$35.80 per access line per month in the first half of 1994.[7] Referring to the distribution in the previous exercise, estimate the percentage of regional Bell companies whose operating expenses were higher than those of Nynex.

41. tech Ex ***Operating Expenses*** *SBC Corporation* (formerly Southwestern Bell) had operating expenses of \$27.70 per access line per month in the first half of 1994.[8] Could SBC justifiably claim that its operating expenses were among the lowest 25% of all the regional Bell companies? Explain. (Use the normal distribution of the above exercises.)

42. tech Ex ***Operating Expenses*** *U.S. West Corporation* had operating expenses of \$29.10 per access line per month in the first half of 1994.[9] Were U.S. West's operating expenses closer to the mean than those of most other regional Bells? Explain. (Use the normal distribution of the above exercises.)

Cumulative Distribution *If f is a probability density function defined on the interval (a, b), then the* ***cumulative distribution function*** *F is given by*

$$F(x) = \int_a^x f(t)\,dt$$

Exercises 43–52 deal with the cumulative distribution function.

43. ◆ Why is $F'(x) = f(x)$?

44. ◆ Use the result of the previous exercise to show that

$$P(c \le X \le d) = F(d) - F(c)$$

for $a \le c \le d \le b$.

45. ◆ Show that $F(a) = 0$ and $F(b) = 1$.

46. ◆ Can $F(x)$ can have any local extrema? (Give a reason for your answer.)

47. Find the cumulative distribution functions for the situation described in Exercise 27.

48. Find the cumulative distribution functions for the situation described in Exercise 28.

49. Find the cumulative distribution functions for the situation described in Exercise 29.

50. Find the cumulative distribution functions for the situation described in Exercise 30.

51. Find the cumulative distribution functions for the situation described in Exercise 31.

52. Find the cumulative distribution functions for the situation described in Exercise 32.

[5] SOURCE: NASA International Near-Earth-Object Detection Workshop/*The New York Times*, January 25, 1994, p. C1.

[6] SOURCE: NatWest Securities/Company Reports/*The New York Times*, November 22, 1994, p. D1.

[7] Ibid.

[8] Ibid.

[9] Ibid.

Communication and Reasoning Exercises

53. Why is a probability density function often more convenient than a histogram?

54. Give an example of a probability density function that is increasing everywhere on its domain.

55. Give an example of a probability density function that is concave up everywhere on its domain.

56. ◆ Suppose that X is a normal random variable with mean μ and standard deviation σ, and that Z is a standard normal variable. Using the substitution $z = (x - \mu)/\sigma$ in the integral, show that

$$P(a \le X \le b) = P\left(\frac{a-\mu}{\sigma} \le Z \le \frac{b-\mu}{\sigma}\right)$$

57. Your friend thinks that if f is a probability density function for the continuous random variable X, then $f(a)$ is the probability that $X = a$. Explain to your friend why this is wrong.

58. ◆ Not satisfied with your explanation in the previous exercise, your friend then challenges you by asking, "If $f(a)$ is not the probability that $X = a$, then just what does $f(a)$ signify?" How would you respond?

59. ◆ Your friend now thinks that if F is a *cumulative* probability density function for the continuous random variable X, then $F(a)$ is the probability that $X = a$. Explain why your friend is *still* wrong.

60. ◆ Once again not satisfied with your explanation in the previous exercise, your friend challenges you by asking, "If $F(a)$ is not the probability that $X = a$, then just what does $F(a)$ signify?" How would you respond?

● basic skills ◆ challenging tech Ex technology exercise

S.3 Mean, Median, Variance, and Standard Deviation

Mean

In the last section we saw that if savings and loan institutions are continuously failing at a rate of 5% per year, then the associated probability density function is

$$f(x) = 0.05e^{-0.05x}$$

with domain $[0, +\infty)$. An interesting and important question to ask is: What is the average length of time such an institution will last before failing? To answer this question, we use the following:

Mean or Expected Value

If X is a continuous random variable with probability density function f defined on an interval with (possibly infinite) endpoints a and b, then the **mean** or **expected value** of X is

$$E(X) = \int_a^b x f(x)\, dx$$

$E(X)$ is also called the **average value** of X. It is what we expect to get if we take the average of many values of X obtained in experiments.

quick Example

Let X have probability density function given by $f(x) = 3x^2$, with domain $[0, 1]$. Then

$$E(X) = \int_a^b x f(x)\, dx = \int_0^1 (x \cdot 3x^2)\, dx = \int_0^1 3x^3\, dx = \left[\frac{3x^4}{4}\right]_0^1 = \frac{3}{4}$$

We shall explain shortly why $E(X)$ is given by the integral formula.

Example 1 Failing S&Ls

Given that troubled S&Ls are failing continuously at a rate of 5% per year, how long will the average troubled S&L last?

Solution If X is the number of years that a given S&L will last, we know that its probability density function is $f(x) = 0.05e^{-0.05x}$. To answer the question we compute $E(X)$.

$$\begin{aligned} E(X) &= \int_a^b xf(x)\,dx \\ &= \int_0^{+\infty} (0.05xe^{-0.05x})\,dx \\ &= \lim_{M\to+\infty} \int_0^M (0.05xe^{-0.05x})\,dx \end{aligned}$$

Using integration by parts, we get

$$E(X) = \lim_{M\to+\infty} -0.05\left[e^{-0.05x}(20x + 400)\right]_0^M = (0.05)(400) = 20$$

Thus, the expected lifespan of a troubled S&L is 20 years.

+Before we go on... Notice that in Example 1, the answer, 20, is the reciprocal of the failure rate 0.05. This is true in general: if $f(x) = ae^{-ax}$, then $E(X) = 1/a$. ■

Q: *Why is $E(X)$ given by the integral formula on p. 19?*

A: Suppose for simplicity that the domain of f is a finite interval $[a, b]$. Break up the interval into n subintervals $[x_{k-1}, x_k]$, each of length Δx, as we did for Riemann sums. Now, the probability of seeing a value of X in $[x_{k-1}, x_k]$ is approximately $f(x_k)\Delta x$ (the approximate area under the graph of f over $[x_{k-1}, x_k]$). Think of this as the fraction of times we expect to see values of X in this range. These values, all close to x_k, then contribute approximately $x_k f(x_k)\Delta x$ to the average, if we average together many observations of X. Adding together all of these contributions, we get

$$E(X) \approx \sum_{k=1}^{n} x_k f(x_k)\Delta x$$

Now, these approximations get better as $n \to \infty$, and the sum above is a Riemann sum converging to

$$E(X) = \int_a^b xf(x)\,dx$$

which is the formula we have been using. ■

We can compute, one by one, the expected values of the distributions we discussed in the preceding section.

Mean of a Uniform Distribution

If X is uniformly distributed on $[a, b]$, then

$$E(X) = \frac{a+b}{2}$$

quick **Example**

Suppose that you spin the dial shown so that it comes to rest at a random position X.

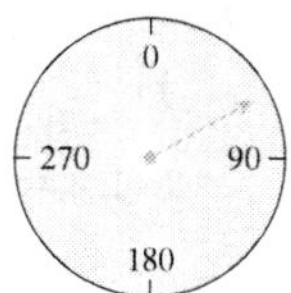

Then $E(X) = \dfrac{0+360}{2} = 180°$.

This formula is not surprising, if you think about it for a minute. We'll leave the actual computation as one of the exercises.

Mean of an Exponential Distribution

If X is exponentially distributed with density function $f(x) = ae^{-ax}$, then

$$E(X) = \frac{1}{a}$$

quick **Example**

If Internet startup companies are failing at a rate of 10% per year, then the expected lifetime of an Internet startup company is

$$E(X) = \frac{1}{0.1} = 10 \text{ years}$$

We saw why this formula works in Example 1.

Mean of a Normal Distribution

If X is normally distributed with parameters μ and σ, then

$$E(X) = \mu$$

quick **Example**

If the final exam scores in your class are normally distributed with mean 72.6 and standard deviation 8.3, then the expected value for a test score is

$$E(X) = \mu = 72.6$$

That is why we called μ the mean, but we ought to do the calculation. Here we go.

$$E(X) = \int_{-\infty}^{+\infty} x \cdot \frac{1}{\sigma\sqrt{2\pi}} e^{-(x-\mu)^2/(2\sigma^2)}\, dx$$

$$= \int_{-\infty}^{+\infty} (\sigma w + \mu) \frac{1}{\sqrt{2\pi}} e^{-w^2/2}\, dw \qquad \text{After substituting } w = (x-\mu)/\sigma$$

$$= \frac{\sigma}{\sqrt{2\pi}} \int_{-\infty}^{+\infty} w e^{-w^2/2}\, dw + \mu \int_{-\infty}^{+\infty} \frac{1}{\sqrt{2\pi}} e^{-w^2/2}\, dw$$

Now, the first integral can be done easily (substitute $v = -w^2/2$) and converges to 0. The second integral we recognize as the area under another normal curve (the one with $\mu = 0$ and $\sigma = 1$), so it is equal to 1. Therefore, the whole thing simplifies to

$$E(X) = \mu$$

as claimed.

Mean of a Beta Distribution

If X has a beta distribution with density function $f(x) = (\beta + 1)(\beta + 2)x^\beta(1 - x)$, then

$$E(X) = \frac{\beta + 1}{\beta + 3}$$

Again, we shall leave this as an exercise.

Example 2 Downsizing in the Utilities Industry

A utilities industry consultant predicts a cutback in the Canadian Utilities industry during 2008–2012 by a percentage specified by a beta distribution with $\beta = 0.25$. What is the expected size of the cutback by Ontario Hydro?*

Solution Because $\beta = 0.25$,

$$E(X) = \frac{\beta + 1}{\beta + 3} = \frac{1.25}{3.25} \approx 0.38$$

Therefore, we can expect about a 38% cutback by Ontario Hydro.

* This model is fictitious. Ontario Hydro did announce plans to downsize by 8.4% in 1995, however (*Report on Business* (Canada), February 15, 1994, p. B1).

+ *Before we go on...* What $E(X)$ really tells us is that the *average* downsizing of many utilities will be 38%. Some will cut back more, and some will cut back less. ■

There is a generalization of the mean that we shall use below. If X is a random variable on the interval (a, b) with probability density function f, and if g is any function defined on that interval, then we can define the **expected value of g** to be

$$E(g(X)) = \int_a^b g(x) f(x)\, dx$$

Thus, in particular, the mean is just the expected value of the function $g(x) = x$. We can interpret this as the average we expect if we compute $g(x)$ for many experimental values x of X.

Variance and Standard Deviation

Statisticians use the variance and standard deviation of a continuous random variable X as a way of measuring its dispersion, or the degree to which is it "scattered." The definitions are as follows:

Variance and Standard Deviation

Let X be a continuous random variable with density function f defined on the interval (a, b), and let $\mu = E(X)$ be the mean of X. Then the **variance** of X is given by

$$Var(X) = E((X - \mu)^2) = \int_a^b (x - \mu)^2 f(x)\,dx$$

The **standard deviation** of X is the square root of the variance,

$$\sigma(X) = \sqrt{Var(X)}$$

Notes

1. In order to calculate the variance and standard deviation, we first need to calculate the mean.
2. $Var(X)$ is the expected value of the function $(x - \mu)^2$, which measures the square of the distance of X from its mean. It is for this reason that $Var(X)$ is sometimes called the *mean square deviation*, and $\sigma(X)$ is called the *root mean square deviation*. $Var(X)$ will be larger if X tends to wander far away from its mean, and smaller if the values of X tend to cluster near its mean.
3. The reason we take the square root in the definition of $\sigma(X)$ is that $Var(X)$ is the expected value of the *square* of the deviation from the mean, and thus is measured in square units. Its square root $\sigma(X)$, therefore, gives us a measure in ordinary units.

Once again, let us compute the variances and standard deviations of the distributions we discussed in the previous section. We'll leave the actual computations (or special cases) for the exercises.

Variance and Standard Deviation of Some Distributions

Uniform Distribution

If X is uniformly distributed on $[a, b]$, then

$$Var(X) = \frac{(b - a)^2}{12}$$

and

$$\sigma(X) = \frac{b - a}{\sqrt{12}}$$

Exponential Distribution
If X has the exponential distribution function $f(x) = ae^{-ax}$, then

$$Var(X) = \frac{1}{a^2}$$

and

$$\sigma(X) = \frac{1}{a}$$

Normal Distribution
If X is normally distributed with parameters μ and σ, then

$$Var(X) = \sigma^2$$

and

$$\sigma(X) = \sigma$$ This is what you might have expected.

Beta Distribution
If X has a beta distribution with density function $f(x) = (\beta+1)(\beta+2)x^\beta(1-x)$, then

$$Var(X) = \frac{2(\beta+1)}{(\beta+4)(\beta+3)^2}$$

and

$$\sigma(X) = \sqrt{\frac{2(\beta+1)}{(\beta+4)(\beta+3)^2}}$$

You can see the significance of the standard deviation quite clearly in the normal distribution. As we mentioned in the previous section, σ is the distance from the maximum at μ to the points of inflection at $\mu - \sigma$ and $\mu + \sigma$. The larger σ is, the wider the bell. Figure 15 shows three normal distributions with three different standard deviations (all with $\mu = 0.5$).

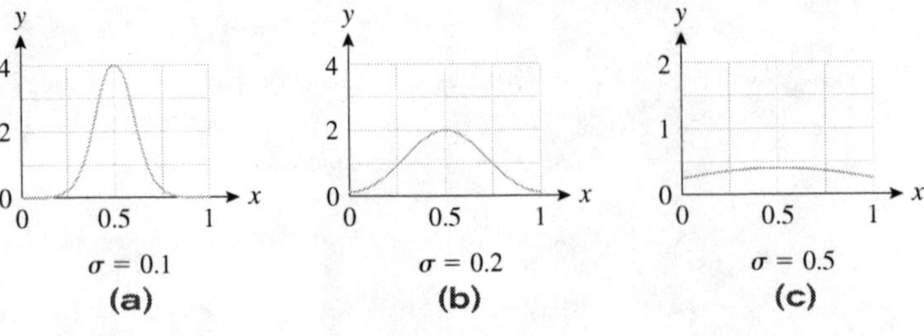

Figure 15

Again, a small standard deviation means that the values of X will be close to the mean with high probability, while a large standard deviation means that the values may wander far away with high probability.

Median

The *median income* in the U.S. is the income M such that half the population earns incomes $\leq M$ (so the other half earns incomes $\geq M$). In terms of probability, we can think of income as a random variable X. Then the probability that $X \leq M$ is $1/2$, and the probability that $X \geq M$ is also $1/2$.

Median

Let X be a continuous random variable. The **median** of X is the number M such that

$$P(X \leq M) = \frac{1}{2}$$

Then, $P(M \leq X) = \frac{1}{2}$ also.

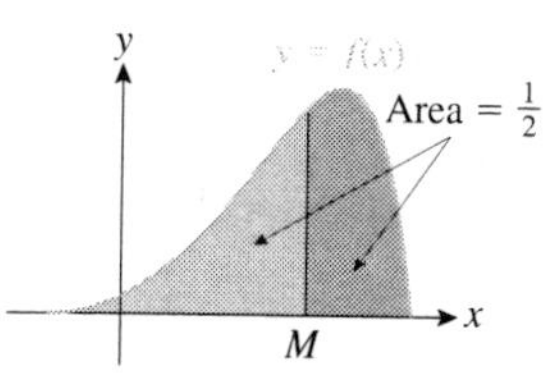

Figure **16**

If f is the probability density function for X with domain $[a, b]$, then we can calculate M by solving the equation

$$P(a \leq X \leq M) = \int_a^M f(x)\, dx = \frac{1}{2}$$

for M. Graphically, the vertical line $x = M$ divides the total area under the graph of f into two equal parts (Figure 16).

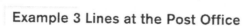

Q: *What is the difference between the median and the mean?*

A: Roughly speaking, the median divides the area under the distribution curve into two equal parts, while the mean is the value of X at which the graph would *balance*. If a probability curve has as much area to the left of the mean as to the right, then the mean is equal to the median. This is true of uniform and normal distributions, which are *symmetric* about their means. On the other hand, the medians and means are different for the exponential distributions and most of the beta distributions, because their areas are not distributed symmetrically. ■

Example 3 Lines at the Post Office

The time in minutes between individuals joining the line at an Ottawa Post Office is a random variable with the exponential distribution

$$f(x) = 2e^{-2x} \quad (x \geq 0)$$

Find the mean and median time between individuals joining the line and interpret the answers.

Solution The expected value for an exponential distribution $f(x) = ae^{-ax}$ is $1/a$. Here, $a = 2$, so $E(X) = 1/2$. We interpret this to mean that, on average, a new person will join the line every half a minute, or 30 seconds. For the median, we must solve

$$\int_a^M f(x)\, dx = \frac{1}{2}$$

That is,

$$\int_0^M (2e^{-2x})\, dx = \frac{1}{2}$$

Evaluating the integral gives

$$-[e^{-2x}]_0^M = \frac{1}{2}$$

or

$$1 - e^{-2M} = \frac{1}{2}$$

$$e^{-2M} = \frac{1}{2}$$

$$-2M = \ln\left(\frac{1}{2}\right) = -\ln 2$$

Thus,

$$M = \frac{\ln 2}{2} \approx 0.3466 \text{ minutes}$$

This means that half the people get in line less than 0.3466 minutes (about 21 seconds) after the previous person, while half arrive more than 0.3466 minutes later. The mean time for a new person to arrive in line is larger than this because there are some occasional long waits between people, and these pull the average up.

Sometimes we cannot solve the equation $\int_a^M f(x)\,dx = 1/2$ for M analytically, as the next example shows.

Example 4 Median

Find the median of the random variable with beta density function for $\beta = 4$.

Solution Here,

$$\begin{aligned} f(x) &= (\beta+1)(\beta+2)x^{\beta}(1-x) \\ &= 30x^4(1-x) \end{aligned}$$

Thus we must solve

$$\int_0^M (30x^4(1-x))\,dx = \frac{1}{2}$$

That is,

$$30\int_0^M (x^4 - x^5)\,dx = \frac{1}{2}$$

So

$$30\left[\frac{M^5}{5} - \frac{M^6}{6}\right] = \frac{1}{2}$$

or, multiplying through and clearing denominators,

$$12M^5 - 10M^6 - 1 = 0$$

This is a degree six polynomial equation that has no easy factorization. Because there is no general analytical method for obtaining the solution, the only method we can use is numerical. Figure 17 shows three successive views of a TI-83/84 plot of `Y=12X^5 - 10X^6 - 1`, obtained by zooming in toward one of the zeros.

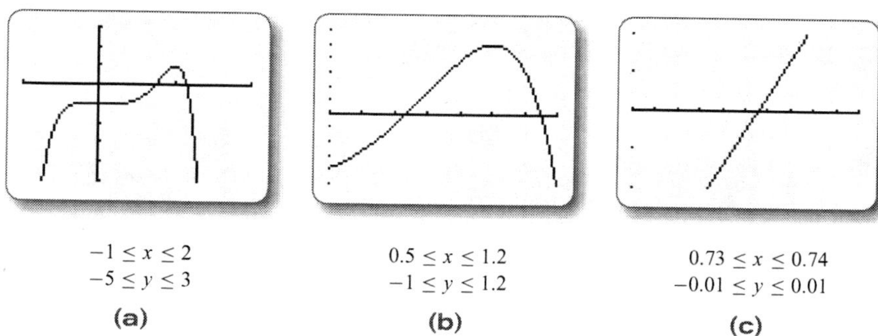

$-1 \le x \le 2$
$-5 \le y \le 3$
(a)

$0.5 \le x \le 1.2$
$-1 \le y \le 1.2$
(b)

$0.73 \le x \le 0.74$
$-0.01 \le y \le 0.01$
(c)

Figure **17**

In the first two plots we can see two zeros, one between 0.7 and 0.8 and the other between 1.1 and 1.2. We are interested only in the zero that occurs between 0 and 1 (why?). In the third plot, each tick on the horizontal axis represents 0.001, and we see that $M \approx 0.736$ to three decimal places.

+ *Before we go on...* This method required us first to calculate $\int_a^M f(x)\,dx$ analytically. What if even this is impossible to do? We could solve the equation $\int_a^M f(x)\,dx = 1/2$ graphically by having the calculator compute and graph this function of M by numerical integration. For example, to redo the above example on the TI-83/84, enter

```
Y1=fnInt(30T^4(1-T),T,0,X)-0.5
```

which corresponds to

$$y = \int_0^x 30t^4(1-t)\,dt - \frac{1}{2}$$

a function of x. Because the median of M is the solution obtained by setting $y = 0$, we can obtain the answer by plotting Y_1 and finding its x-intercept. The plot should be identical to the one we obtained above, except half as high (why?). ■

S.3 EXERCISES

● denotes basic skills exercises
◆ denotes challenging exercises
tech Ex indicates exercises that should be solved using technology

Find the expected value $E(X)$, the variance $Var(X)$ and the standard deviation $\sigma(X)$ for each of the density functions in Exercises 1–20.

1. ● $f(x) = \frac{1}{3}$ on $[0, 3]$
2. ● $f(x) = 3$ on $\left[0, \frac{1}{3}\right]$
3. $f(x) = \frac{x}{50}$ on $[0, 10]$
4. $f(x) = 5x$ on $[0, \sqrt{2/5}]$
5. $f(x) = \frac{3}{2}(1 - x^2)$ on $[0, 1]$
6. $f(x) = \frac{3}{4}(1 - x^2)$ on $[-1, 1]$
7. $f(x) = e^x$ on $[0, \ln 2]$
8. $f(x) = \frac{1}{x}$ on $[1, e]$
9. $f(x) = 0.1e^{-0.1x}$ on $[0, +\infty)$
10. $f(x) = 4e^{4x}$ on $(-\infty, 0]$

11. $f(x) = 0.03e^{0.03x}$ on $(-\infty, 0]$

12. $f(x) = 0.02e^{-0.02x}$ on $[0, +\infty)$

13. $f(x) = \frac{2}{x^3}$ on $[1, +\infty)$ 14. $f(x) = \frac{1}{2\sqrt{x}}$ on $(0, 1]$

15. ● Normal density function with $\mu = 1$ and $\sigma = 1$ on $(-\infty, +\infty)$

16. ● Normal density function with $\mu = -1$ and $\sigma = 1$ on $(-\infty, +\infty)$

17. ● Beta density function with $\beta = 0.5$

18. ● Beta density function with $\beta = 1.5$

19. ● Beta density function with $\beta = 3.2$

20. ● Beta density function with $\beta = 4.6$

tech Ex *Use a graphing calculator or computer to find E(X), Var(X) and σ(X) for each of the density functions in Exercises 21–24. (Round all answers to four significant digits.)*

21. tech Ex $f(x) = \frac{4}{\pi(1+x^2)}$ on $[0, 1]$

22. tech Ex $f(x) = \frac{3}{\pi\sqrt{1-x^2}}$ on $\left[\frac{1}{2}, 1\right]$

23. tech Ex $f(x) = 2xe^{-x^2}$ on $[0, +\infty)$

24. tech Ex $f(x) = -2xe^{-x^2}$ on $(-\infty, 0]$

Find the medians of the random variables with the probability density functions given in Exercises 25–34.

25. ● $f(x) = 0.25$ on $[0, 4]$ 26. ● $f(x) = 4$ on $[0, 0.25]$

27. $f(x) = 3e^{-3x}$ on $[0, +\infty)$

28. $f(x) = 0.5e^{-0.5x}$ on $[0, +\infty)$

29. $f(x) = 0.03e^{0.03x}$ on $(-\infty, 0]$

30. $f(x) = 0.02e^{-0.02x}$ on $[0, +\infty)$

31. $f(x) = 2(1-x)$ on $[0, 1]$ 32. $f(x) = \frac{1}{x^2}$ on $[1, +\infty)$

33. $f(x) = \frac{1}{2\sqrt{x}}$ on $(0, 1]$ 34. $f(x) = \frac{1}{x}$ on $[1, e]$

35. ***Mean of a Uniform Distribution*** Verify the formula for the mean of a uniform distribution by computing the integral.

36. ***Mean of a Beta Distribution*** Verify the formula for the mean of a beta distribution by computing the integral.

37. ***Variance of a Uniform Distribution*** Verify the formula for the variance of a uniform distribution by computing the integral.

38. ***Variance of an Exponential Distribution*** Verify the formula for the variance of an exponential distribution by computing the integral.

39. ***Median of an Exponential Random Variable*** Show that if X is a random variable with density function $f(x) = ae^{-ax}$ on $[0, +\infty)$, then X has median $\ln 2/a$.

40. ***Median of a Uniform Random Variable*** Show that if X is a uniform random variable taking values in the interval $[a, b]$, then X has median $(a+b)/2$.

tech Ex *Use technology to find the medians of the random variables with the probability density functions given in Exercises 41–50. (Round all answers to two decimal places.)*

41. $f(x) = \frac{3}{2}\left(1-x^2\right)$ on $[0, 1]$

42. $f(x) = \frac{3}{4}\left(1-x^2\right)$ on $[-1, 1]$

43. Beta density function with $\beta = 2$

44. Beta density function with $\beta = 3$

45. Beta density function with $\beta = 2.5$

46. Beta density function with $\beta = 0.5$

47. $f(x) = \frac{4}{\pi(1+x^2)}$ on $[0, 1]$

48. $f(x) = \frac{3}{\pi\sqrt{1-x^2}}$ on $\left[\frac{1}{2}, 1\right]$

49. $f(x) = 2xe^{-x^2}$ on $[0, +\infty)$

50. $f(x) = -2xe^{-x^2}$ on $(-\infty, 0]$

The **mean square** of a random variable X with density function f is given by the formula

$$E(X^2) = \int_a^b x^2 f(x)\, dx$$

51–60. In Exercises 1–10, compute $E(X^2)$. In each case, compute also $E(X^2) - E(X)^2$.

61. Compare the answers in 51–60 to those in 1–10, and hence suggest a formula expressing $E(X^2)$ in terms of $E(X)$ and $Var(X)$.

62. ◆ Calculate $E(e^{tX}) = \int_a^b e^{tx} f(x)dx$ with $f(x) = 0.1e^{-0.1x}$ on $[0, +\infty)$. Then evaluate $\left.\frac{d}{dt}E\left(e^{tX}\right)\right|_{t=0}$ and $\left.\frac{d^2}{dt^2}E\left(e^{tX}\right)\right|_{t=0}$ comparing these answers with the answer to Exercise 59. What do you notice?

Applications

63. ● ***Salaries*** Assuming that workers' salaries in your company are uniformly distributed between \$10,000 and \$40,000 per year, calculate the average salary in your company.

64. ● ***Grades*** The grade point averages (GPAs) of members of the Gourmet Society are uniformly distributed between 2.5 and 3.5. Find the average GPA in the Gourmet Society.

65. ***Boring Television Series*** Your company's new series "Avocado Comedy Hour" has been a complete flop, with viewership continuously declining at a rate of 30% per month. How long will the average viewer continue to watch the show?

66. ***Bad Investments*** Investments in junk bonds are declining continuously at a rate of 5% per year. How long will an average dollar remain invested in junk bonds?

● basic skills ◆ challenging tech Ex technology exercise

67. ***Radioactive Decay*** The half-life of carbon-14 is 5730 years. How long, to the nearest year, do you expect it to take for a randomly selected carbon-14 atom to decay?

68. ***Radioactive Decay*** The half-life of plutonium-239 is 24,400 years. How long, to the nearest year, do you expect it to take for a randomly selected plutonium-239 atom to decay?

69. ***The Doomsday Meteor*** The probability[10] that a "doomsday meteor" will hit the Earth in any given year and release a billion megatons or more of energy is on the order of 0.000 000 01. When do you expect the Earth to be hit by a doomsday meteor? (Use an exponential distribution with $a = 0.000\ 000\ 01$.)

70. ***Galactic Cataclysm*** The probability that the galaxy MX-47 will explode within the next million years is estimated to be 0.0003. When do you expect MX-47 to explode? (Use an exponential distribution with $a = 0.0003$.)

Exercises 71–74 use the normal probability density function and require the use of technology for numerical integration. (Alternatively, see Exercise 61.) Find the root mean square value for X (i.e., $\sqrt{E(X^2)}$) in each exercise.

71. tech Ex ***Physical Measurements*** Repeated measurements of a metal rod yield a mean of 5.3 inches, with a standard deviation of 0.1.

72. tech Ex ***IQ Testing*** Repeated measurements of a student's IQ yield a mean of 135, with a standard deviation of 5.

73. tech Ex ***Psychology Tests*** It is known that subjects score an average of 100 points on a new personality test, with a standard deviation of 10 points.

74. tech Ex ***Examination Scores*** Professor May's students earned an average grade of 3.5 with a standard deviation of 0.2.

75. ◆ ***Learning*** A graduate psychology student finds that 64% of all first semester calculus students in Prof. Mean's class have a working knowledge of the derivative by the end of the semester.

    a. Take X = percentage of students who have a working knowledge of calculus after 1 semester, and find a beta density function that models X, assuming that the performance of students in Prof. Mean's is average.

    b. Find the median of X (rounded to two decimal places) and comment on any difference between the median and the mean.

76. ◆ ***Plant Shutdowns*** An automobile plant is open an average of 78% of the year.

    a. Take X = fraction of the year for which the plant is open, and find a beta density function that models X.

    b. Find the median of X (rounded to two decimal places) and comment on any difference between the median and the mean.

Communication and Reasoning Exercises

77. Sketch the graph of a probability distribution function with the property that its median is larger than its mean.

78. Sketch the graph of a probability distribution function with a large standard deviation and a small mean.

79. ● Complete the following sentence. The ___ measures the degree to which the values of X are distributed, while the ___ is the value of X such that half the measurements of X are below and half are above (for a large number of measurements).

80. ● Complete the following sentence. (See Exercise 61.) Given two of the quantities ___, ___ and ___, we can calculate the third using the formula ___.

81. A value of X for which the probability distribution function f has a local maximum is called a **mode** of the distribution. (If there is more than one mode, the distribution is called bimodal (2 modes), trimodal (3 modes), etc. as the case may be.) If a distribution has a single mode, what does it tell you?

82. Referring to Exercise 81, sketch a bimodal distribution whose mean coincides with neither of the modes.

[10] Source: NASA International Near-Earth-Object Detection Workshop, *New York Times,* January 25, 1994, p. C1.

Chapter S Review

KEY CONCEPTS

S.1 Continuous Random Variables and Histograms

Random variables, continuous and discrete *p. 2*

Probability *p. 2*

Probability distribution histogram *p. 3*

S.2 Probability Density Functions: Uniform, Exponential, Normal, and Beta

Probability density function *p. 9*

Calculation of probability from a probability density function *p. 9*

Uniform density function on $[a, b]$: $f(x) = 1/(b-a)$ *p. 10*

Exponential density function on $[0, +\infty)$: $f(x) = ae^{-ax}$ *p. 13*

Normal density function on $(-\infty, +\infty)$:

$$f(x) = \frac{1}{\sigma\sqrt{2\pi}}e^{-\frac{(x-\mu)^2}{2\sigma^2}} \quad p.\ 14$$

Beta density function on [0, 1]: $f(x) = (\beta+1)(\beta+2)x^{\beta}(1-x)$ *p. 16*

S.3 Mean, Median, Variance, and Standard Deviation

Mean, expected, or average value of a random variable *p. 19*

Mean of a uniform distribution: $(a+b)/2$ *p. 21*

Mean of an exponential distribution: $1/a$ *p. 21*

Mean of a normal distribution: μ *p. 21*

Mean of a beta distribution: $(\beta+1)/(\beta+3)$ *p. 22*

Expected value of a function of a random variable *p. 22*

Variance and standard deviation of a random variable *p. 23*

Variance and standard deviation of a uniform distribution: $Var(X) = (b-a)^2/12$, $\sigma(X) = (b-a)/\sqrt{12}$ *p. 23*

Variance and standard deviation of an exponential distribution: $Var(X) = 1/a^2$, $\sigma(X) = 1/a$ *p. 24*

Variance and standard deviation of a normal distribution: $Var\ (X) = \sigma^2$, $\sigma(X) = \sigma$ *p. 24*

Variance and standard deviation of a beta distribution: $Var(X) = 2(\beta+1)/[(\beta+4)(\beta+3)^2]$, $\sigma(X) = \sqrt{2(\beta+1)/[(\beta+4)(\beta+3)^2]}$ *p. 24*

Median of a random variable *p. 25*

REVIEW EXERCISES

In each of Exercises 1–10, **a.** *determine the value of k that makes the function a probability density function,* **b.** *find the expected value of the corresponding random variable, and* **c.** *find the variance and standard deviation of the random variable.*

1. $f(x) = k$ on $[-2, 2]$

2. $f(x) = k$ on $[1, 10]$

3. $f(x) = kx$ on $[0, 4]$

4. $f(x) = kx$ on $[0, 10]$

5. $f(x) = kx^2$ on $[-1, 1]$

6. $f(x) = kx^2$ on $[0, 1]$

7. $f(x) = k(1-x^2)$ on $[-1, 1]$

8. $f(x) = k(1-x^2)$ on $[0, 1]$

9. $f(x) = ke^x$ on $(-\infty, 0]$

10. $f(x) = ke^{-x}$ on $[0, +\infty)$

11. If X is the random variable with the distribution from Exercise 1, find $P(-1 \le X \le 1)$.

12. If X is the random variable with the distribution from Exercise 2, find $P(1 \le X \le 4)$.

13. If X is the random variable with the distribution from Exercise 3, find $P(0 \le X \le 2)$.

14. If X is the random variable with the distribution from Exercise 4, find $P(4 \le X \le 6)$.

15. If X is the random variable with the distribution from Exercise 5, find $P(1/2 \le X \le 1)$.

16. If X is the random variable with the distribution from Exercise 6, find $P(1/2 \le X \le 1)$.

17. If X is the random variable with the distribution from Exercise 7, find $P(0 \le X \le 1/2)$.

18. If X is the random variable with the distribution from Exercise 8, find $P(0 \le X \le 1/2)$.

19. If X is the random variable with the distribution from Exercise 9, find $P(X \le -1)$.

20. If X is the random variable with the distribution from Exercise 10, find $P(2 \le X)$.

21–30. Find the medians of the distributions given in Exercises 1–10.

Applications

31. ***Farm Population, Female*** OHagansBooks.com is considering a new advertising campaign aimed at women living on farms. The following table shows the number of females residing on U.S. farms in 1990, broken down by age.[11] Numbers are in thousands.

Age	0–15	15–25	25–35	35–45	45–55	55–65	65–75	75–95
Number	459	265	247	319	291	291	212	126

[11] SOURCE: Economic Research Service, U.S. Department of Agriculture and Bureau of the Census, U.S. Department of Commerce, 1990.

OHaganBooks.com is interested in the probability of reaching various age groups with random mailings to farms. Construct the associated probability distribution for the ages of women living on farms (with probabilities rounded to four decimal places) and use the distribution to compute the following:

a. $P(15 \le X \le 55)$ **b.** $P(X \le 45)$ **c.** $P(X \ge 45)$

32. ***Farm Population, Male*** OHagansBooks.com is considering a new advertising campaign aimed at men living on farms. The following table shows the number of males residing on U.S. farms in 1990, broken down by age.[12] Numbers are in thousands.

Age	0–15	15–25	25–35	35–45	45–55	55–65	65–75	75–95
Number	480	324	285	314	302	314	247	118

OHaganBooks.com is interested in the probability of reaching various age groups with random mailings to farms. Construct the associated probability distribution for the ages of men living on farms (with probabilities rounded to four decimal places) and use the distribution to compute the following:

a. $P(25 \le X \le 65)$ **b.** $P(X \le 15)$ **c.** $P(X \ge 15)$

33. ***Quality Control*** OHaganBooks.com is worried about quality control of the boxes they use to ship their books. The widths of the boxes are normally distributed with a mean of 6 inches and a standard deviation of 0.1 inches. Any box with a width smaller than 5.8 inches must be rejected. Find the probability that a randomly chosen box will be rejected. (Give your answer to three significant digits.)

34. ***Book Weight*** OHaganBooks.com stocks books of many sizes. The weights of the books are normally distributed with a mean of 10 ounces and a standard deviation of 2 ounces. If a customer chooses a book at random, what is the probability that it will weight at least 11 ounces? (Give your answer to three significant digits.)

35. ***Book Sales*** Few books sell well. For each new book published, OHaganBooks.com orders a certain number of copies and tracks how many they can sell in the first year. It has found that the fraction, X, of copies they sell of the number they ordered, is a random variable with a beta distribution with parameter $\beta = 0.6$. Find the probability that a given book will sell, in its first year, between 0.5 and 0.7 of the number of copies ordered. (Give your answer to three significant digits.)

36. ***Book Sales*** Given the information in Exercise 35, what is the expected fraction of new books sold in the first year, and what is the standard deviation?

[12] Ibid.

CASE STUDY: Creating a Family Trust

White Packert/Getty Images

Your position as financial consultant to the clients of Family Bank, Inc., often entails your having to give financial advice to clients with complex questions about savings. One of your newer clients, Malcolm Adams, recently graduated from college and 22 years old, presents you with a perplexing question. "I would like to set up my own insurance policy by opening a trust account into which I can make monthly payments starting now, so that upon my death or my ninety-fifth birthday—whichever comes sooner—the trust can be expected to be worth $500,000. How much should I invest each month?"

This is not one of those questions that you can answer by consulting a table, so you promise Malcolm an answer by the next day and begin to work on the problem. After a little thought, you realize that the question is one about *expected value*—the expected future value of an annuity into which monthly payments are made. Because the annuity would terminate upon his death (or his ninety-fifth birthday), you decide that you need a model for the probability distribution of the life span of a male in the United States. To obtain this information, you consult mortality tables and come up with the histogram in

Figure 18 (you work with the actual numbers, but they are not important for the discussion to follow).[13]

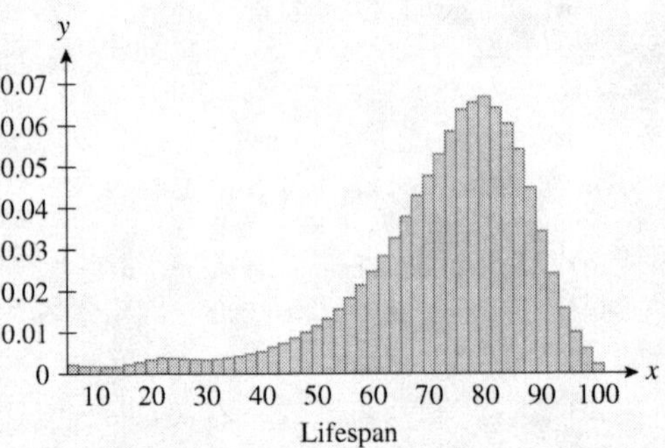

Figure **18**

From the data, you calculate that the mean is $\mu = 70.778$ and the standard deviation is $\sigma = 16.5119$.

Next, you decide to model these data with a suitable probability density function. You rule out the uniform and exponential density functions, because they have the wrong shape, and you first try the normal distribution. The normal distribution is

$$f(x) = \frac{1}{\sigma\sqrt{2\pi}}e^{-\frac{(x-\mu)^2}{2\sigma^2}}$$

$$= \frac{1}{16.5119\sqrt{2\pi}}e^{-\frac{(x-70.778)^2}{2(16.5119)^2}}$$

Figure 19 shows the graph of the normal density function superimposed on the actual data.

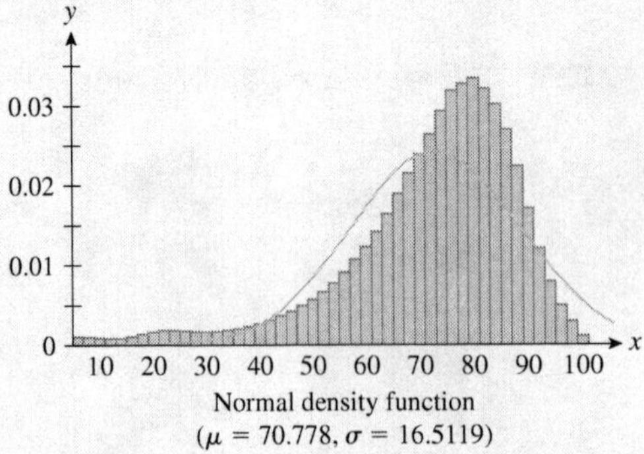

Figure **19**

This does not seem like a very good fit at all! Because the actual histogram looks as though it is "pushed over" to the right, you think of the beta distribution, which has that general shape. The beta distribution is given by

$$f(x) = (\beta + 1)(\beta + 2)x^{\beta}(1 - x)$$

[13] Probabilities are normalized (scaled) so that the total area of the histogram is one square unit. Thus the area (not the height) of each bar is the probability of mortality in a two-year period. The data on which the histogram is based were obtained from the 1980 Standard Ordinary Mortality Table, Male Lives (SOURCE: Black/Skipper, *Life Insurance,* Eleventh Edition (Englewood Cliffs, NJ: Prentice-Hill, Inc., 1987), p. 314).

where β can be obtained from the mean μ using the equation

$$\mu = \frac{\beta + 1}{\beta + 3}$$

There is one catch: the beta distribution assumes that X is between 0 and 1, whereas your distribution is between 0 and 100. This doesn't deter you: all you need to do is scale the X-values to $\frac{1}{100}$ of their original value. Thus you substitute $\mu = \frac{1}{100}(70.778) = 0.70778$ in the above equation and solve for β, you obtain $\beta = 3.8442$. You then plot the associated beta function (after scaling it to fit the range $0 \le X \le 100$) and again discover that, although better, the fit still leaves something to be desired (Figure 20).

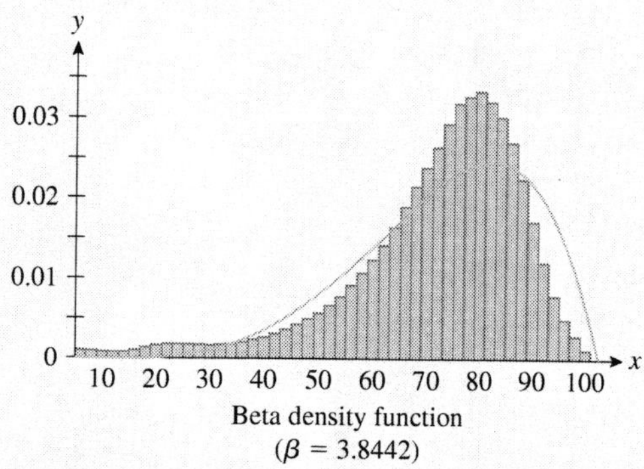

Figure **20**

Now you just want some function that fits the data. You turn to your statistical software and ask it to find the cubic equation that best fits the data using the least squares method. It promptly tells you that the cubic function that best fits the data is

$$f(x) = ax^3 + bx^2 + cx + d$$

where

$$a = -3.815484 \times 10^{-7}$$
$$b = 5.7399145 \times 10^{-5}$$
$$c = -0.0020856085$$
$$d = 0.0190315095$$

Its graph is shown in Figure 21. Note that the curve, although erratic for small values of X, fits the large peak on the right more closely than the others.

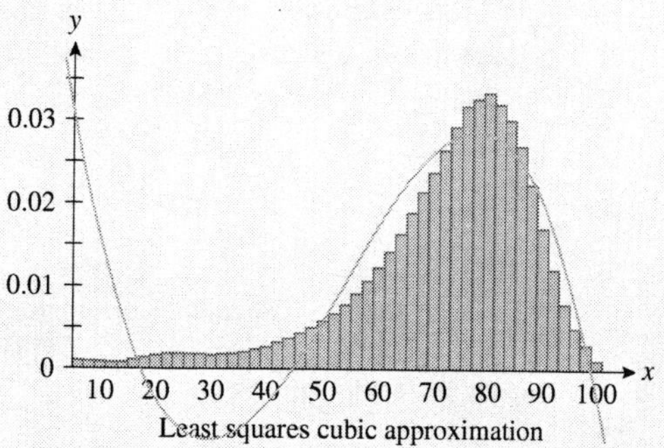

Figure **21**

Encouraged, you use the same software to obtain a quartic (degree 4) approximation and you find:

$$f(x) = ax^4 + bx^3 + cx^2 + dx + e$$

where

$$a = -9.583507 \times 10^{-9}$$
$$b = 1.650155 \times 10^{-6}$$
$$c = -8.523081 \times 10^{-5}$$
$$d = 0.0016190575$$
$$e = -0.007865381$$

Figure 22 shows the result.

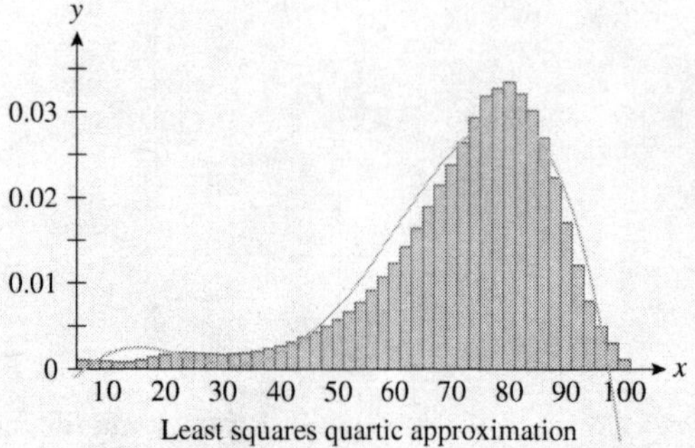

Figure **22**

This seems like the best fit of them all—especially for the range of X you are interested in: $22 \leq X \leq 95$. (Malcolm is 22 years old and the trust will mature at 95.)

Now that you have the density function you wish to use, you use it to find the expected future value of an annuity into which monthly payments are made. The simplest formula for the future value V of an annuity is

$$V = 12P\left[\frac{\left(1+\frac{i}{12}\right)^{12n} - 1}{i}\right]$$

(This is a standard formula from finance. This formula assumes that interest is paid at the end of each month.) Here, P is the monthly payment—the quantity that Malcolm wants to know—i is the interest rate, and n is the number of years for which payments are made. Because Malcolm will be making investments starting at age 22, this means that $n = x - 22$, so the future value of his annuity at age x is

$$V(x) = 12P\left[\frac{\left(1+\frac{i}{12}\right)^{12(x-22)} - 1}{i}\right]$$

As for the interest rate i, you decide to use a conservative estimate of 5%.

Now the expected value of $V(X)$ is given by

$$E(V) = \int_{22}^{95} V(x)f(x)\,dx$$

where $f(x)$ is the quartic approximation to the distribution function. Because Malcolm wants this to be \$500,000, you set

$$
\begin{aligned}
500{,}000 &= \int_{22}^{95} V(x) f(x)\, dx \\
&= \int_{22}^{95} 12P\left(\frac{\left(1+\frac{i}{12}\right)^{12(x-22)}-1}{i}\right) f(x)\, dx \\
&= P\int_{22}^{95} 12\left(\frac{\left(1+\frac{0.05}{12}\right)^{12(x-22)}-1}{0.05}\right) f(x)\, dx
\end{aligned}
$$

Solving for P,

$$
P = \frac{500{,}000}{\displaystyle\int_{22}^{95} 12\left(\frac{\left(1+\frac{0.05}{12}\right)^{12(x-22)}-1}{0.05}\right) f(x)\, dx}
$$

You now calculate the integral numerically (using the quartic approximation to $f(x)$), obtaining

$$
P \approx \frac{500{,}000}{3{,}409.8019} \approx \$146.64 \text{ per month}
$$

The next day, you can tell Malcolm that at a 5% interest rate, his family can expect the trust to be worth \$500,000 upon maturity if he deposits \$146.64 each month.

Exercises

1. How much smaller will the payments be if the interest rate is 6%?

2. How much larger would the payments be if Malcolm began payments at the age of 30?

3. Repeat the original calculation using the normal distribution described above. Give reasons for the discrepancy between the answers, explaining why your answer is smaller or larger than the one calculated above.

4. Repeat Exercise 3 using the cubic distribution.

5. If Malcolm wanted to terminate the trust at age 65, which model would you use for the probability density? Give reasons for your choice.

6. Suppose you were told by your superior that, because the expected male life span is 71, you could have saved yourself a lot of trouble by using the formula for the future value of an annuity maturing at age 71. Based on that, the payment comes out to about \$198 per month. Why is it higher? Why is it the wrong amount?

7. Explain how an insurance company might use the above calculations to compute life insurance premiums.

Section S.2

Example **4** Pressure gauges manufactured by Precision Corp. must be checked for accuracy before being placed on the market. To test a pressure gauge, a worker uses it to measure the pressure of a sample of compressed air known to be at a pressure of exactly 50 pounds per square inch. If the gauge reading is off by more than 1% (0.5 pounds), the gauge is rejected. Assuming that the reading of a pressure gauge under these circumstances is a normal random variable with mean 50 and standard deviation 0.5, find the percentage of gauges rejected.

Solution with Technology As in the text, the solution of this example comes down to the calculation

$$P(49.5 \le X \le 50.5) = \int_{49.5}^{50.5} f(x)\,dx$$

where f is the normal distribution with mean $\mu = 50$ and standard deviation $\sigma = 0.5$;

$$\begin{aligned} f(x) &= \frac{1}{\sigma\sqrt{2\pi}} e^{-\frac{(x-\mu)^2}{2\sigma^2}} \\ &= \frac{1}{0.5\sqrt{2\pi}} e^{-\frac{(x-50)^2}{0.5}} \end{aligned}$$

There are two methods to calculate this integral on a TI-83/84.

***Method 1:** Calculate the integral directly.*

1. Enter

```
Y1=(1/(0.5(2π)^0.5))e^(-(X-50)^2/0.5)
```

in the Y= screen.

```
Plot1 Plot2 Plot3
\Y1=(1/(0.5(2π)^
0.5))e^(-(X-50)^
2/0.5)
\Y2=
\Y3=
\Y4=
\Y5=
```

2. Enter

```
fnInt(Y1,X,49.5,50.5)
```

in the home screen.

```
fnInt(Y1,X,49.5,
50.5)
        .6826894921
```

***Method 2:** Use the built-in normal distribution function.*

The TI-83/84 has a built-in normal distribution function.

1. Press 2nd VARS to obtain the selection of distribution functions. The second function, `normalcdf`, gives $P(a \le X \le b)$ directly.

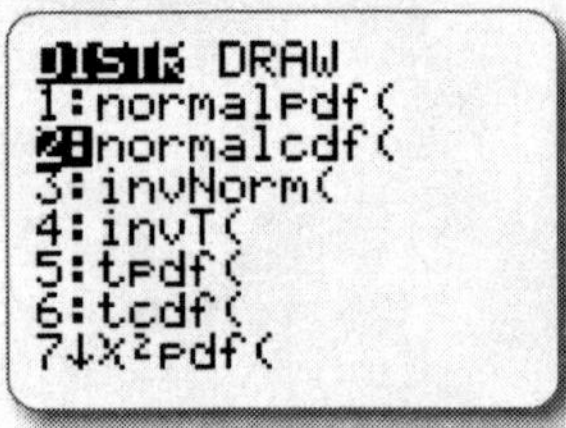

2. To compute $P(49.5 \le X \le 50.5)$, enter

```
normalcdf(49.5,50.5,50,.5)
```

Format: normalcdf(Lower bound, Upper bound, μ, σ)

in the home screen.

```
normalcdf(49.5,5
0.5,50,.5)
        .6826894809
```

Both methods yield an answer of approximately 0.6827. In other words, 68.27% of the gauges will be accepted. Thus, the remaining 31.73% of the gauges will be rejected.

Section S.2

Example 4 Pressure gauges manufactured by Precision Corp. must be checked for accuracy before being placed on the market. To test a pressure gauge, a worker uses it to measure the pressure of a sample of compressed air known to be at a pressure of exactly 50 pounds per square inch. If the gauge reading is off by more than 1% (0.5 pounds), the gauge is rejected. Assuming that the reading of a pressure gauge under these circumstances is a normal random variable with mean 50 and standard deviation 0.5, find the percentage of gauges rejected.

Solution with Technology As in the text, the solution of this example comes down to the calculation

$$P(49.5 \leq X \leq 50.5) = \int_{49.5}^{50.5} f(x)\, dx$$

where f is the normal distribution with mean $\mu = 50$ and standard deviation $\sigma = 0.5$;

$$f(x) = \frac{1}{\sigma\sqrt{2\pi}} e^{-\frac{(x-\mu)^2}{2\sigma^2}}$$

$$= \frac{1}{0.5\sqrt{2\pi}} e^{-\frac{(x-50)^2}{0.5}}$$

Excel has built-in statistical software that allows you to compute $P(a \leq X \leq b)$. The function `NORMDIST(a,μ,σ,1)` computes $P(X \leq a)$ for the normal distribution with mean μ and standard deviation σ. (The last argument, 1, tells Excel that we want the cumulative distribution, i.e., the integral, rather than the value of the density function at a.) To compute $P(49.5 \leq X \leq 50.5)$ in Excel, enter

```
=NORMDIST(50.5,50,0.5,1)
  -NORMDIST(49.5,50,0.5,1)
```

in any vacant cell.

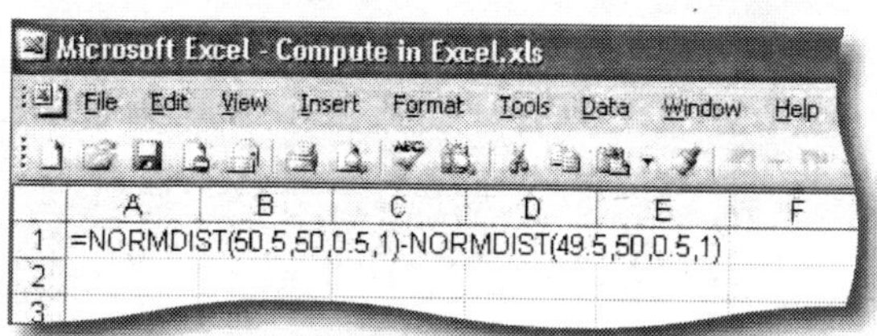

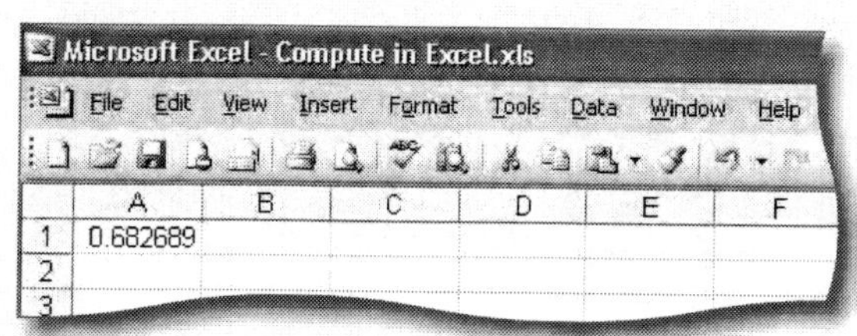

Excel yields an answer of approximately 0.6827. In other words, 68.27% of the gauges will be accepted. Thus, the remaining 31.73% of the gauges will be rejected.

Answers to Odd-Numbered Exercises

S.1

1. X is the number of the uppermost face; discrete. **3.** X is the angle the pointer makes with the vertical; continuous with interval of values [0, 360). **5.** X is the temperature at midday; continuous. There are many possible intervals of values, such as (-Ï, +Ï), [-1,000, 1000], or [–150, 150] (degrees Fahrenheit) which would be reasonable on earth. **7.** X is the U.S. Balance of Payments, rounded to the nearest billion dollars; discrete. **9.** X is the number of computer chips that fail to work in a batch of 100; discrete.

11. **13.**

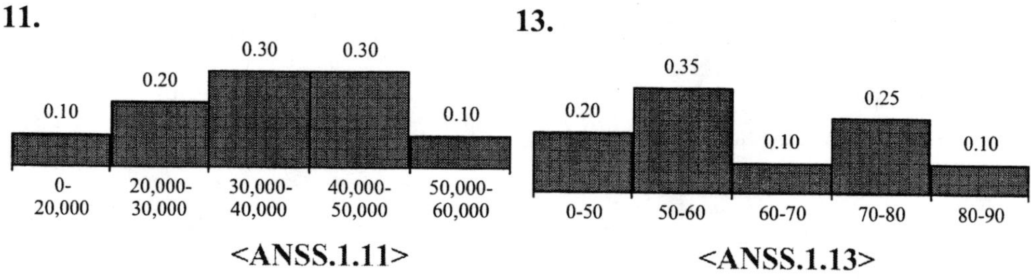

<ANSS.1.11> <ANSS.1.13>

15.

Age	0-18	18–25	25–35	35-45	45–55	55-65	65-75	75 and over
Probability	.2455	.0927	.1381	.1583	.1339	.0879	.0704	.0732

(a) .5230 **(b)** .6346 **(c)** .3654

17. (a) .304 **(b)** .083 **(c)** .65

19.

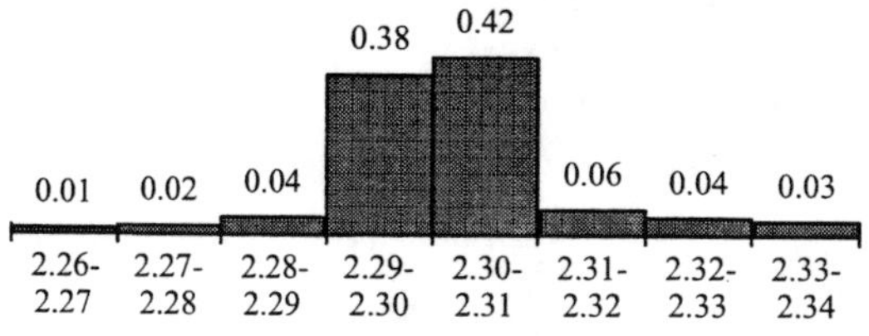

<ANSS.1.19>

21. A random variable assigns a number to each outcome in an experiment. **23.** It is half the corresponding area.

S.2

1. Yes **3.** No; the integral $\neq 1$ **5.** No; the function is not ≥ 0 **7.** Yes **9.** Yes **11.** No; both conditions fail **13.** 1/4 **15.** ln 2 **17.** Exponential **19.** Normal **21.** Uniform **23.** Beta **25.** Exponential **27.** .2 **29.** .5934 **31.** .6164 **33. (a)** .000 0010 **(b)** 1 **35.** .3829 **37.** .01654 **39.** 51.96% **41.** Yes. The probability that a regional Bell had lower operating expenses than SBC was .2064. In other words, approximately 21% of the companies should have had lower operating costs than SBC (according to the normal distribution). **43.** By the Fundamental Theorem of Calculus, F(x) as given is an antiderivative of f(x). In other words, $F'(x) = f(x)$, as required. **45.** By definition of F(x), F(a) = $\int_a^a f(t)\,dt$, which is zero because the lower and upper limits agree, and F(b) = $\int_a^b f(t)\,dt$ = 1. **47.** $F(x) = \frac{x-10,000}{30,000}$ **49.** $1-e^{-0.3x}$ **51.** $1-e^{-0.000121x}$ **53.** A probability density function allows us to compute probabilities algebraically using a single function (often specified by a formula) rather than numerically by adding the values of the bars in a histogram. **55.** An example is $f(x) = 3x^2$ on [0, 1]. **57.** The probability associated with a continuous random variable is given by the area under the probability density function curve; P(a ≤ X ≤ b) = È$_a^b$f(x) dx. Thus the probability that X = a is È$_a^a$ f(x) dx = 0. **59.** If F is the cumulative probability density, then F(a) is the probability that X ≤ a, and not the probability that X = a.

S.3

1. E(X) = 3/2, Var(X) = 3/4, ß(X) = $\sqrt{3}/2$ **3.** E(X) =20/3, Var(X) = 50/9, ß(X) = $\sqrt{50}/3$ **5.** E(X) = 3/8, Var(X) = 0.059375, ß(X) = 0.2437 **7.** E(X) = 0.3863, Var(X) = 0.03909, ß(X) = 0.1977 **9.** E(X) = 10, Var(X) = 100, ß(X) = 10 **11.** E(X) = -33.3333, Var(X) = 1111.1111, ß(X) = 33.3333 **13.** E(X) = 2, Var(X) = +Ï, ß(X) = +Ï **15.** E(X) = 1, Var(X) = 1, ß(X) = 1 **17.** E(X) = 0.4286, Var(X) = 0.05442, ß(X) = 0.2333 **19.** E(X) = 0.6774, Var(X) = 0.0304, ß(X) = 0.1742 **21.** E(X) = 0.4413, Var(X) = 0.07852, ß(X) = 0.2802 **23.** E(X) = 0.8862, Var(X) = 0.2146, ß(X) = 0.4633 **25.** 2 **27.** 0.2310 **29.** -23.1049 **31.** 0.2929 **33.** 0.25 **35-40.** Proofs **41.** 0.35 **43.** 0.61 **45.** 0.65 **47.** 0.41 **49.** 0.83 **51.** $E(X^2) = 3$, $E(X^2)-E(X)^2 = 3/4$ **52.** $E(X^2) = 1/27$, $E(X^2)-E(X)^2 = 1/108$ **55.** $E(X^2) = 1/5$, $E(X^2)-E(X)^2 = 0.059375$ **57.** $E(X^2) = 0.1883$, $E(X^2)-E(X)^2 = 0.0391$ **59.** $E(X^2) = 200$, $E(X^2) - E(X)^2 = 100$ **61.** Comparing answers suggests that $E(X^2) - E(X)^2 = Var(X)$. Thus, $E(X^2) = E(X)^2 + Var(X)$. **63.** \$25,000 **65.** $3\frac{1}{3}$ months **67.** 8,267 years **69.** In 100,000,000 years **71.** 5.3009 **73.** 100.4988 **75. (a)** ∫ = 2.5556, $f(x) = 16.1975x^{2.5556}(1-x)$ **(b)** M(X) = 0.66, a little larger than the mean. This indicates that more students scored above the mean than below it.

77.

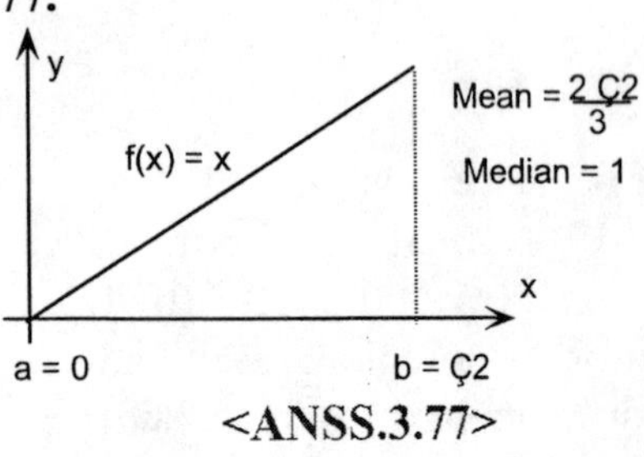

<ANSS.3.77>

79. Missing words: variance (or standard deviation), median. **81.** Values of X are more likely to be close to the mode than to any other value. In particular, an interval about the mode determines the most popular values of X.

Chapter S Review

1. $k = \frac{1}{4}$, E(X) = 0, Var(X) $= \frac{4}{3}$, ß(X) $= \frac{2}{\sqrt{3}}$ **3.** $k = \frac{1}{8}$, E(X) $= \frac{8}{3}$, Var(X) $= \frac{8}{9}$, ß(X) $= \frac{2\sqrt{2}}{3}$ **5.** $k = \frac{3}{2}$, E(X) = 0, Var(X) $= \frac{3}{5}$, ß(X) $= \sqrt{\frac{3}{5}}$ **7.** $k = \frac{3}{4}$, E(X) = 0, Var(X) $= \frac{1}{5}$, ß(X) $= \frac{1}{\sqrt{5}}$ **9.** k = 1, E(X) = -1, Var(X) = 1, ß(X) = 1 **11.** 1/2 **13.** 1/4 **15.** 7/16 **17.** 11/32 **19.** 1/e ‡ .3679 **21.** 0 **23.** $2\sqrt{2}$ **25.** 0 **27.** 0 **29.** -ln 2 ‡ -0.693

31.

Age	0-15	15-25	25-35	35-45	45-55	55-65	65-75	75-95
Probability	.2077	.1199	.1118	.1443	.1317	.1317	.0959	.0570

(a) .5077 **(b)** .5837 **(c)** .4163

33. .0228 **35.** .243

Answers to Selected Exercises

Chapter 0

Section 0.1

1. -48 **3.** $2/3$ **5.** -1 **7.** 9 **9.** 1 **11.** 33 **13.** 14 **15.** $5/18$ **17.** 13.31 **19.** 6 **21.** $43/16$ **23.** 0 **25.** `3*(2-5)` **27.** `3/(2-5)` **29.** `(3-1)/(8+6)` **31.** `3-(4+7)/8` **33.** `2/(3+x)-x*y^2` **35.** `3.1x^3-4x^(-2)-60/(x^2-1)` **37.** `(2/3)/5` **39.** `3^(4-5)*6` **41.** `3*(1+4/100)^(-3)` **43.** `3^(2*x-1)+4^x-1` **45.** `2^(2x^2-x+1)` **47.** `4*e^(-2*x)/(2-3e^(-2*x))` or `4*(e^(-2*x))/(2-3e^(-2*x))` **49.** `3(1-(-1/2)^2)^2+1`

Section 0.2

1. 27 **3.** -36 **5.** $4/9$ **7.** $-1/8$ **9.** 16 **11.** 2 **13.** 32 **15.** 2 **17.** x^5 **19.** $-\dfrac{y}{x}$ **21.** $\dfrac{1}{x}$ **23.** x^3y **25.** $\dfrac{z^4}{y^3}$ **27.** $\dfrac{x^6}{y^6}$ **29.** $\dfrac{x^4y^6}{z^4}$ **31.** $\dfrac{3}{x^4}$ **33.** $\dfrac{3}{4x^{2/3}}$ **35.** $1-0.3x^2-\dfrac{6}{5x}$ **37.** 2 **39.** $1/2$ **41.** $4/3$ **43.** $2/5$ **45.** 7 **47.** 5 **49.** -2.668 **51.** $3/2$ **53.** 2 **55.** 2 **57.** ab **59.** $x+9$ **61.** $x\sqrt[3]{a^3+b^3}$ **63.** $\dfrac{2y}{\sqrt{x}}$ **65.** $3^{1/2}$ **67.** $x^{3/2}$ **69.** $(xy^2)^{1/3}$ **71.** $x^{3/2}$ **73.** $\dfrac{3}{5}x^{-2}$ **75.** $\dfrac{3}{2}x^{-1.2}-\dfrac{1}{3}x^{-2.1}$ **77.** $\dfrac{2}{3}x-\dfrac{1}{2}x^{0.1}+\dfrac{4}{3}x^{-1.1}$ **79.** $(x^2+1)^{-3}-\dfrac{3}{4}(x^2+1)^{-1/3}$ **81.** $\sqrt[3]{2^2}$ **83.** $\sqrt[3]{x^4}$ **85.** $\sqrt[5]{\sqrt{x}\sqrt[3]{y}}$ **87.** $-\dfrac{3}{2\sqrt[4]{x}}$ **89.** $\dfrac{0.2}{\sqrt[3]{x^2}}+\dfrac{3\sqrt{x}}{7}$ **91.** $\dfrac{3}{4\sqrt{(1-x)^5}}$ **93.** 64 **95.** $\sqrt{3}$ **97.** $1/x$ **99.** xy **101.** $\left(\dfrac{y}{x}\right)^{1/3}$ **103.** ± 4 **105.** $\pm 2/3$ **107.** $-1, -1/3$ **109.** -2 **111.** 16 **113.** ± 1 **115.** $33/8$

Section 0.3

1. $4x^2+6x$ **3.** $2xy-y^2$ **5.** x^2-2x-3 **7.** $2y^2+13y+15$ **9.** $4x^2-12x+9$ **11.** x^2+2+1/x^2 **13.** $4x^2-9$ **15.** y^2-1/y^2 **17.** $2x^3+6x^2+2x-4$ **19.** $x^4-4x^3+6x^2-4x+1$ **21.** $y^5+4y^4+4y^3-y$ **23.** $(x+1)(2x+5)$ **25.** $(x^2+1)^5(x+3)^3(x^2+x+4)$ **27.** $-x^3(x^3+1)\sqrt{x+1}$ **29.** $(x+2)\sqrt{(x+1)^3}$ **31. a.** $x(2+3x)$ **b.** $x=0, -2/3$ **33. a.** $2x^2(3x-1)$ **b.** $x=0, 1/3$ **35. a.** $(x-1)(x-7)$ **b.** $x=1, 7$ **37. a.** $(x-3)(x+4)$ **b.** $x=3, -4$ **39. a.** $(2x+1)(x-2)$ **b.** $x=-1/2, 2$ **41. a.** $(2x+3)(3x+2)$ **b.** $x=-3/2, -2/3$ **43. a.** $(3x-2)(4x+3)$ **b.** $x=2/3, -3/4$ **45. a.** $(x+2y)^2$ **b.** $x=-2y$ **47. a.** $(x^2-1)(x^2-4)$ **b.** $x=\pm 1, \pm 2$

Section 0.4

1. $\dfrac{2x^2-7x-4}{x^2-1}$ **3.** $\dfrac{3x^2-2x+5}{x^2-1}$ **5.** $\dfrac{x^2-x+1}{x+1}$ **7.** $\dfrac{x^2-1}{x}$ **9.** $\dfrac{2x-3}{x^2y}$ **11.** $\dfrac{(x+1)^2}{(x+2)^4}$ **13.** $\dfrac{-1}{\sqrt{(x^2+1)^3}}$ **15.** $\dfrac{-(2x+y)}{x^2(x+y)^2}$

Section 0.5

1. -1 **3.** 5 **5.** $13/4$ **7.** $43/7$ **9.** -1 **11.** $(c-b)/a$ **13.** $x=-4, 1/2$ **15.** No solutions **17.** $\pm\sqrt{\dfrac{5}{2}}$ **19.** -1 **21.** $-1, 3$ **23.** $\dfrac{1\pm\sqrt{5}}{2}$ **25.** 1 **27.** $\pm 1, \pm 3$ **29.** $\pm\sqrt{\dfrac{-1\pm\sqrt{5}}{2}}$ **31.** $-1, -2, -3$ **33.** -3 **35.** 1 **37.** -2 **39.** $1, \pm\sqrt{5}$ **41.** $\pm 1, \pm\dfrac{1}{\sqrt{2}}$ **43.** $-2, -1, 2, 3$

Section 0.6

1. $0, 3$ **3.** $\pm\sqrt{2}$ **5.** $-1, -5/2$ **7.** -3 **9.** $0, -1, 1$ **11.** $x=-1$ ($x=-2$ is not a solution.) **13.** $-2, -3/2, -1$ **15.** -1 **17.** $\pm\sqrt[4]{2}$ **19.** ± 1 **21.** ± 3 **23.** $2/3$ **25.** $-4, -1/4$

Chapter 1

Section 1.1

1. a. 2 **b.** 0.5 **3. a.** -1.5 **b.** 8 **c.** -8 **5. a.** -7 **b.** -3 **c.** 1 **d.** $4y-3$ **e.** $4(a+b)-3$ **7. a.** 3 **b.** 6 **c.** 2 **d.** 6 **e.** a^2+2a+3 **f.** $(x+h)^2+2(x+h)+3$ **9. a.** 2 **b.** 0 **c.** $65/4$ **d.** x^2+1/x **e.** $(s+h)^2+1/(s+h)$ **f.** $(s+h)^2+1/(s+h)-(s^2+1/s)$ **11. a.** 1 **b.** 1 **c.** 0 **d.** 27 **13. a.** Yes; $f(4)=63/16$ **b.** Not defined **c.** Not defined **15. a.** Not defined **b.** Not defined **c.** Yes, $f(-10)=0$ **17. a.** $h(2x+h)$ **b.** $2x+h$ **19. a.** $-h(2x+h)$ **b.** $-(2x+h)$ **21.** `0.1*x^2-4*x+5`

x	0	1	2	3	4	5	6	7	8	9	10
$f(x)$	5	1.1	-2.6	-6.1	-9.4	-12.5	-15.4	-18.1	-20.6	-22.9	-25

23. `(x^2-1)/(x^2+1)`

x	0.5	1.5	2.5	3.5	4.5	5.5	6.5	7.5	8.5	9.5	10.5
$h(x)$	-0.6000	0.3846	0.7241	0.8491	0.9059	0.9360	0.9538	0.9651	0.9727	0.9781	0.9820

25. a. $P(5) = 117$, $P(10) = 132$, and $P(9.5) \approx 131$. Approximately 117 million people were employed in the U.S. on July 1, 1995, 132 million people on July 1, 2000, and 131 million people on January 1, 2000. **b.** [5, 11]. **27. a.** [0, 10]. $t \geq 0$ is not an appropriate domain because it would predict U.S. trade with China into the indefinite future with no basis. **b.** \$280 billion; U.S. trade with China in 2004 was valued at approximately \$280 billion. **29. a.** (2) **b.** \$36.8 billion **31. a.** 358,600 **b.** 361,200 **c.** \$6.00 **33. a.** $P(0) = 200$: At the start of 1995, the processor speed was 200 megahertz. $P(4) = 500$: At the start of 1999, the processor speed was 500 megahertz. $P(5) = 1100$: At the start of 2000, the processor speed was 1100 megahertz. **b.** Midway through 2001 **c:**

t	0	1	2	3	4	5	6	7	8	9
$P(t)$	200	275	350	425	500	1100	1700	2300	2900	3500

35. a. `(0.08*t+0.6)*(t<8)+(0.355*t-1.6)*(t>=8)`
b:

t	0	1	2	3	4	5	6	7	8	9	10	11
$C(t)$	0.6	0.68	0.76	0.84	0.92	1	1.08	1.16	1.24	1.595	1.95	2.305

37. $T(26{,}000) = \$730 + 0.15(26{,}000 - 7300) = \$3535$; $T(65{,}000) = \$4090 + 0.25(65{,}000 - 29{,}700) = \$12{,}915$
39. a. \$12,000 **b.** $N(q) = 2000 + 100q^2 - 500q$; $N(20) = \$32{,}000$ **41. a.** `100*(1-12200/t^4.48)` **b:**

t	9	10	11	12	13	14	15	16	17	18	19	20
$p(t)$	35.2	59.6	73.6	82.2	87.5	91.1	93.4	95.1	96.3	97.1	97.7	98.2

c. 82.2% **d.** 14 months **43.** t; m **45.** $y(x) = 4x^2 - 2$ (or $f(x) = 4x^2 - 2$) **47.** $N(t) = 200 + 10t$ ($N =$ number of sound files, $t =$ time in days) **49.** As the text reminds us: to evaluate f of a quantity (such as $x + h$) replace x everywhere by the *whole quantity* $x + h$, getting $f(x + h) = (x + h)^2 - 1$. **51.** False: Functions with infinitely many points in their domain (such as $f(x) = x^2$) cannot be specified numerically.

Section 1.2

1. a. 20 **b.** 30 **c.** 30 **d.** 20 **e.** 0 **3. a.** −1 **b.** 1.25 **c.** 0 **d.** 1 **e.** 0 **5. a.** (I) **b.** (IV) **c.** (V) **d.** (VI) **e.** (III) **f.** (II)

7.

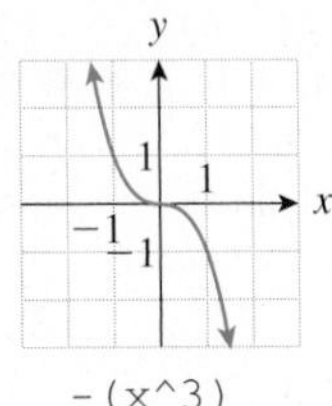

`-(x^3)`

9.

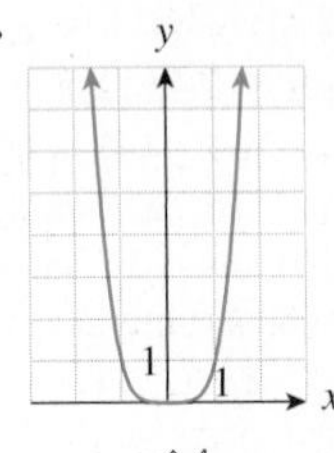

`x^4`

11.

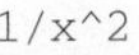

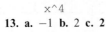

`1/x^2`

13. a. −1 **b.** 2 **c.** 2

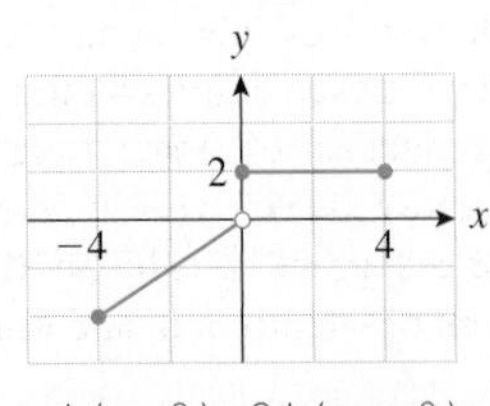

`x*(x<0)+2*(x>=0)`

15. a. 1 **b.** 0 **c.** 1

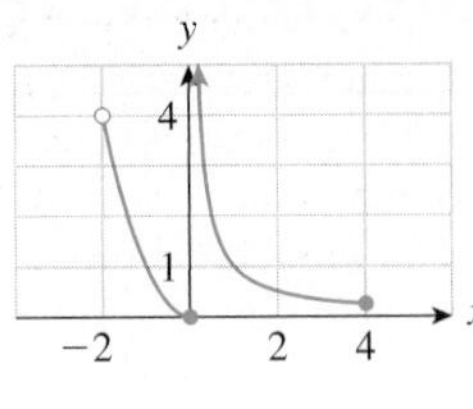

`(x^2)*(x<=0)+(1/x)*(0<x)`

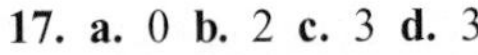

17. a. 0 **b.** 2 **c.** 3 **d.** 3

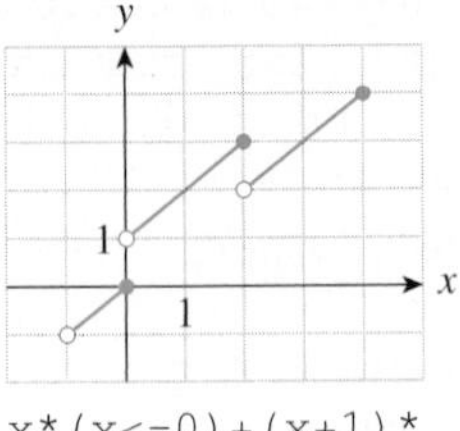

`x*(x<=0)+(x+1)*(0<x)*(x<=2)+x*(2<x)`

19. $f(6) \approx 2000$, $f(9) \approx 2800$, $f(7.5) \approx 2500$. In 1996, 2,000,000 SUVs were sold. In 1999, 2,800,000 were sold, and in the year beginning July, 1997, 2,500,000 were sold.
21. $f(6) - f(5)$; SUV sales increased more from 1995 to 1996 than from 1999 to 2000. **23. a.** [−1.5, 1.5]
b. $N(-0.5) \approx 131$, $N(0) \approx 132$, $N(1) \approx 132$. In July 1999, approximately 131 million people were employed. In January 2000 and January 2001, approximately 132 million people were employed. **c.** [0.5, 1.5]; Employment was falling during the period July 2000–July 2001. **25. a.** (C) **b.** \$20.80 per shirt if the team buys 70 shirts. Graph:

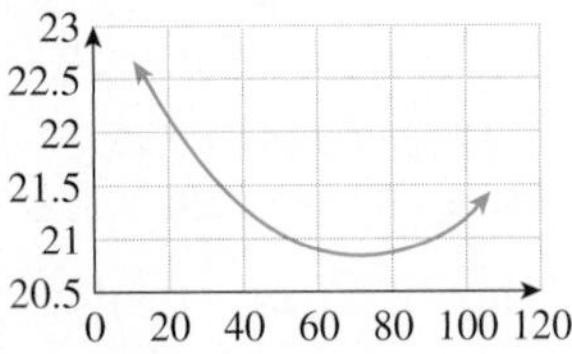

27. A quadratic model (B) is the best choice; the other models either predict perpetually increasing value of the euro or perpetually decreasing value of the euro.
29. a. `100*(1-12200/t^4.48)` **b.** Graph:

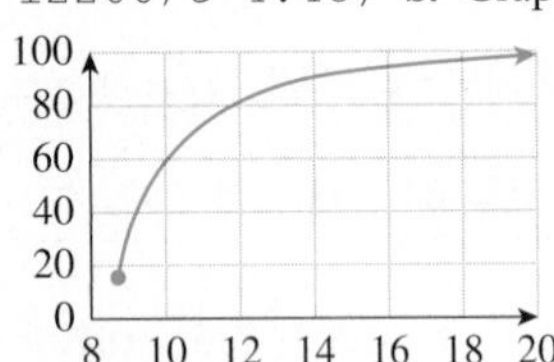

c. 82% **d.** 14 months
31. Midway through 2001

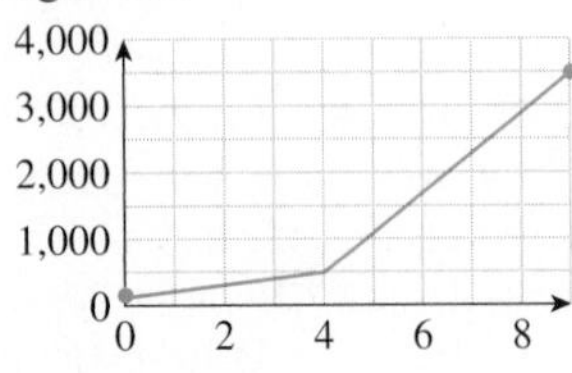

33. a. `(0.08*t+0.6)*(t<8)+(0.355*t-1.6)*(t>=8)`
Graph:

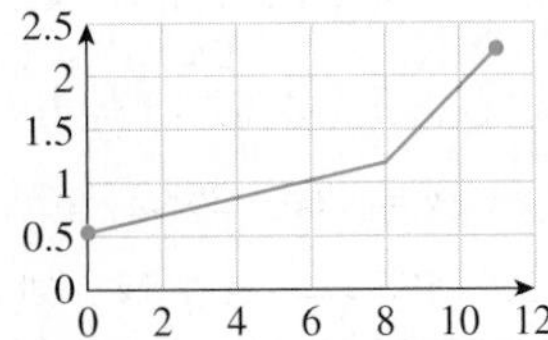

b. 2001

35. True. We can construct a table of values from any graph by reading off a set of values. **37.** False. In a numerically specified function, only certain values of the function are specified, giving only certain points on the graph. **39.** They are different portions of the graph of the associated equation $y = f(x)$. **41.** The graph of $g(x)$ is the same as the graph of $f(x)$, but shifted 5 units to the right.

Section 1.3

1. Missing value: 11; $m = 3$ **3.** Missing value: -4; $m = -1$ **5.** Missing value: 7; $m = 3/2$ **7.** $f(x) = -x/2 - 2$ **9.** $f(0) = -5$, $f(x) = -x - 5$ **11.** f is linear: $f(x) = 4x + 6$ **13.** g is linear: $g(x) = 2x - 1$ **15.** $-3/2$ **17.** $1/6$ **19.** Undefined **21.** 0 **23.** $-4/3$

25.

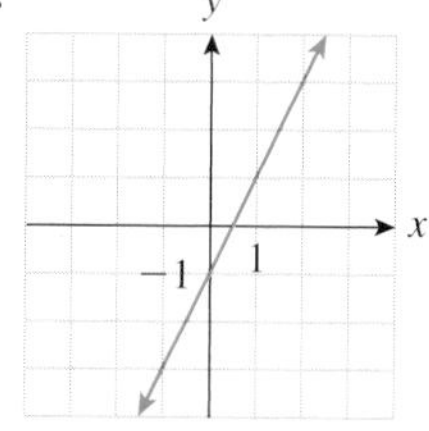

27.

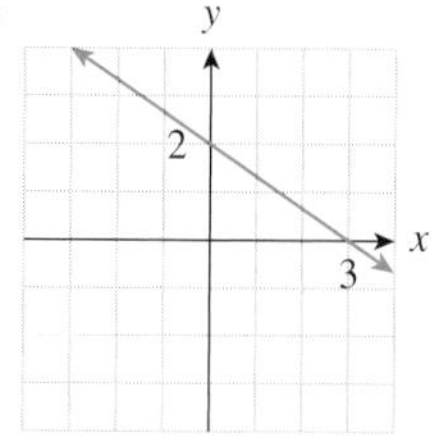

29.

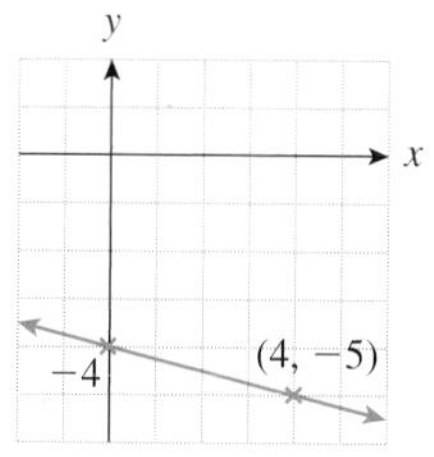

31.

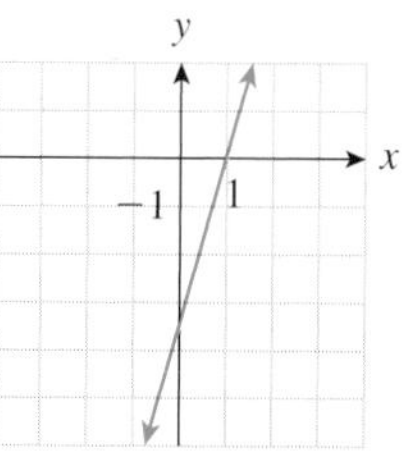

33.

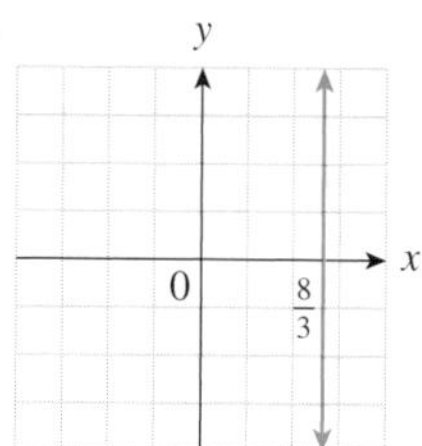

35.

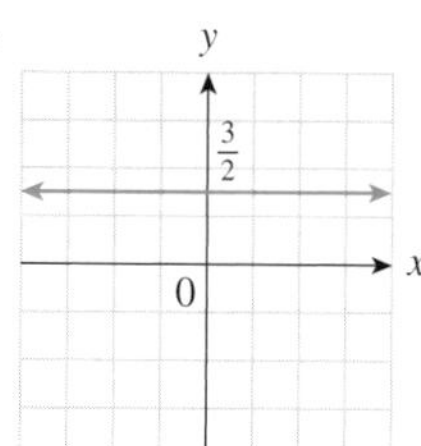

37.

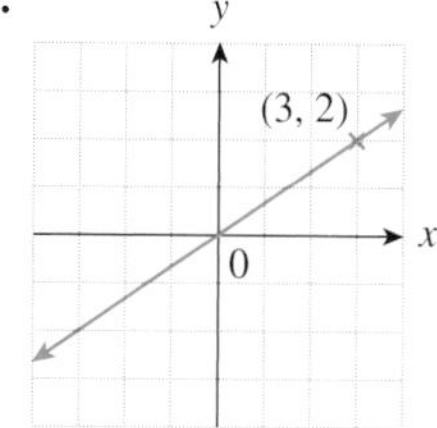

39. 2 **41.** 2 **43.** -2 **45.** Undefined **47.** 1.5 **49.** -0.09 **51.** $1/2$ **53.** $(d - b)/(c - a)$ **55. a.** 1 **b.** $1/2$ **c.** 0 **d.** 3 **e.** $-1/3$ **f.** -1 **g.** Undefined **h.** $-1/4$ **i.** -2 **57.** $y = 3x$ **59.** $y = \frac{1}{4}x - 1$ **61.** $y = 10x - 203.5$ **63.** $y = -5x + 6$ **65.** $y = -3x + 2.25$ **67.** $y = -x + 12$ **69.** $y = 2x + 4$ **71.** Compute the corresponding successive changes Δx in x and Δy in y, and compute the ratios $\Delta y/\Delta x$. If the answer is always the same number, then the values in the table come from a linear function. **73.** $f(x) = -\frac{a}{b}x + \frac{c}{b}$. If $b = 0$, then $\frac{a}{b}$ is undefined, and y cannot be specified as a function of x. (The graph of the resulting equation would be a vertical line.) **75.** slope, 3 **77.** If m is positive then y will increase as x increases; if m is negative then y will decrease as x increases; if m is zero then y will not change as x changes. **79.** The slope increases, since an increase in the y-coordinate of the second point increases Δy while leaving Δx fixed.

Section 1.4

1. $C(x) = 1500x + 1200$ per day **a.** \$5700 **b.** \$1500 **c.** \$1500 **3.** Fixed cost $= \$8000$, marginal cost $= \$25$ per bicycle **5. a.** $C(x) = 0.4x + 70$, $R(x) = 0.5x$, $P(x) = 0.1x - 70$ **b.** $P(500) = -20$; a loss of \$20 **c.** 700 copies **7.** $q = -40p + 2000$ **9. a.** $q = -p + 156.4$; 53.4 million phones **b.** \$1, 1 million **11. a.** Demand: $q = -60p + 150$; supply: $q = 80p - 60$ **b.** \$1.50 each **13. a.** (1996, 125) and (1997, 135) or (1998, 140) and (1999, 150). **b.** The number of new in-ground pools increased most rapidly during the periods 1996–1997 and 1998–1999, when it rose by 10,000 new pools in a year. **15.** $N = 400 + 50t$ million transactions. The slope gives the additional number of online shopping transactions per year, and is measured in (millions of) transactions per year. **17. a.** $s = 14.4t + 240$; Medicare spending is predicted to rise at a rate of \$14.4 billion per year **b.** \$816 billion **19. a.** 2.5 ft/sec **b.** 20 feet along the track **c.** after 6 seconds **21. a.** 130 miles per hour **b.** $s = 130t - 1300$ **c.** After 5 seconds **23.** $F = 1.8C + 32$; 86°F; 72°F; 14°F; 7°F **25.** $I(N) = 0.05N + 50{,}000$; $N = \$1{,}000{,}000$; marginal income is $m = 5¢$ per dollar of net profit. **27.** $w = 2n - 58$; 42 billion pounds **29.** $c = 0.075m - 1.5$; 0.75 pounds **31.** $T(r) = (1/4)r + 45$; $T(100) = 70°F$ **33.** $P(x) = 100x - 5132$, with domain [0, 405]. For profit, $x \geq 52$ **35.** 5000 units **37.** $FC/(SP - VC)$ **39.** $P(x) = 579.7x - 20{,}000$, with domain $x \geq 0$; $x = 34.50$ g per day for break even **41.** Increasing by \$355,000 per year **43. a.** $y = -30t + 200$ **b.** $y = 50t - 200$

c. $y = \begin{cases} -30t + 200 & \text{if } 0 \leq t \leq 5 \\ 50t - 200 & \text{if } 5 < t \leq 9 \end{cases}$ **d.** 150

45. $C(t) = \begin{cases} -1{,}400t + 30{,}000 & \text{if } 0 \leq t \leq 5 \\ 7{,}400t - 14{,}000 & \text{if } 5 < t \leq 10 \end{cases}$

$C(3) = 25{,}800$ students

47. $d(r) = \begin{cases} -40r + 74 & \text{if } 1.1 \leq r \leq 1.3 \\ \frac{130r}{3} - \frac{103}{3} & \text{if } 1.3 < r \leq 1.6 \end{cases}$; $d(1) = 34\%$

49. Bootlags per zonar; bootlags **51.** It must increase by 10 units each day, including the third. **53.** (B) **55.** Increasing the number of items from the breakeven results in a profit: Because the slope of the revenue graph is larger than the slope of the cost graph, it is higher than the cost graph to the right of the point of intersection, and hence corresponds to a profit.

Section 1.5

1. 6 **3.** 86 **5. a.** 0.5 (better fit) **b.** 0.75 **7. a.** 27.42 **b.** 27.16 (better fit)

9. $y = 1.5x - 0.6667$

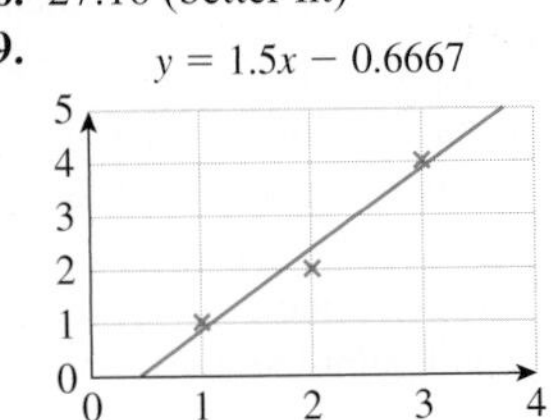

11. $y = 0.4118x + 0.9706$

13. a. $r = 0.9959$ (best, not perfect) **b.** $r = 0.9538$ **c.** $r = 0.3273$ (worst)

15.

	x	y	xy	x^2
	3	500	1500	9
	5	600	3000	25
	7	800	5600	49
Totals	15	1900	10100	83

$y = 75x + 258.33$; 858.33 million

17. $y = 2.5t + 5.67$; \$13.17 billion **19.** $y = 0.135x + 0.15$; 6.9 million jobs **21. a.** $y = 1.62x - 23.87$. Graph:

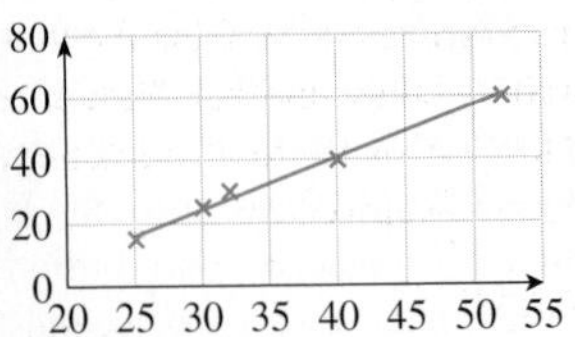

b. Each acre of cultivated land produces about 1.62 tons of soybeans **23. a.** Regression line: $y = -0.40x + 29$. Graph:

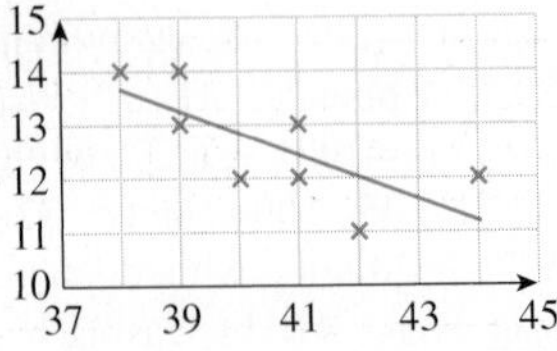

The graph suggests a relationship between x and y. **b.** The poverty rate declines by 0.40% for each \$1000 increase in the median household income. **c.** $r \approx -0.7338$; not a strong correlation **25. a.** $p = 0.13t + 0.22$. Graph:

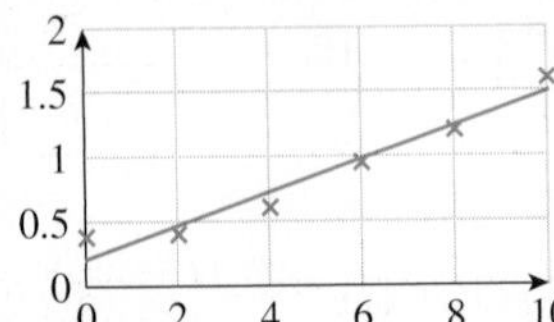

b. Yes; the first and last points lie above the regression line, while the central points lie below it, suggesting a curve.

c.

Microsoft Excel - Ch 1-5 Answer.xls

	A	B	C	D	E
1	t	p (Observed)	p (predicted)	Residual	
2	0	0.38	0.22	0.16	
3	2	0.4	0.48	-0.08	
4	4	0.6	0.74	-0.14	
5	6	0.95	1	-0.05	
6	8	1.2	1.26	-0.06	
7	10	1.6	1.52	0.08	
8					
9					

Notice that the residuals are positive at first, then become negative, and then become positive, confirming the impression from the graph. **27.** The line that passes through (a, b) and (c, d) gives a sum-of-squares error SSE = 0, which is the smallest value possible. **29.** The regression line is the line passing through the given points. **31.** 0 **33.** No. The regression line through $(-1, 1)$, $(0, 0)$, and $(1, 1)$ passes through none of these points.

Chapter 1 Review

1. a. 1 **b.** −2 **c.** 0 **d.** −1 **3. a.** 1 **b.** 0 **c.** 0 **d.** −1

5.

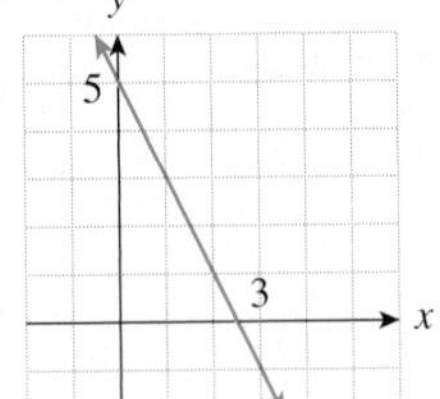

7.

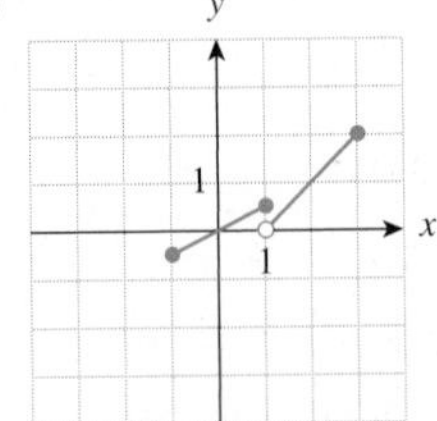

9. Absolute value **11.** Linear **13.** Quadratic **15.** $y = -x + 1$ **17.** $y = (1/2)x - 1$ **19.** The first line, $y = x + 1$, is the better fit. **21.** $y \approx 0.857x + 1.24$, $r \approx 0.92$ **23. a.** (A) **b.** (A) Leveling off (B) Rising (C) Rising; they begin to fall after 7 months (D) Rising **25. a.** 2080 hits per day **b.** Probably not. This model predicts that Web site traffic will start to decrease as advertising increases beyond \$8500 per month, and then drop toward zero. **27. a.** $q = -60p + 950$ **b.** 50 novels per month **c.** \$10, for a profit of \$1200.

Chapter 2

Section 2.1

1. Vertex: $(-3/2, -1/4)$; y-intercept: 2; x-intercepts: −2, −1

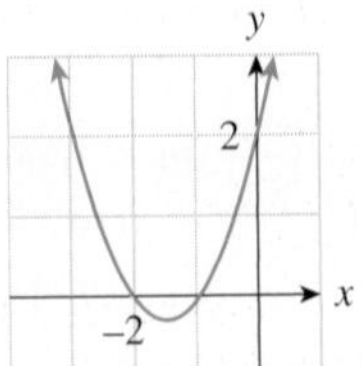

3. Vertex: (2,0); y-intercept: −4; x-intercept: 2

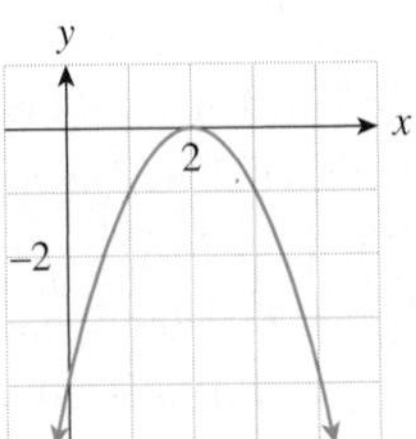

5. Vertex: (−20, 900); y-intercept: 500; x-intercepts: −50, 10

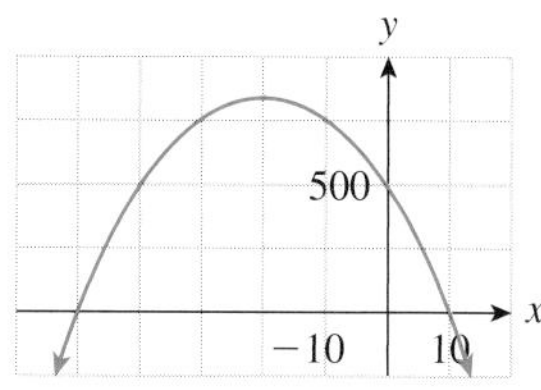

7. Vertex: (−1/2, −5/4); y-intercept: −1; x-intercepts: $-1/2 \pm \sqrt{5}/2$

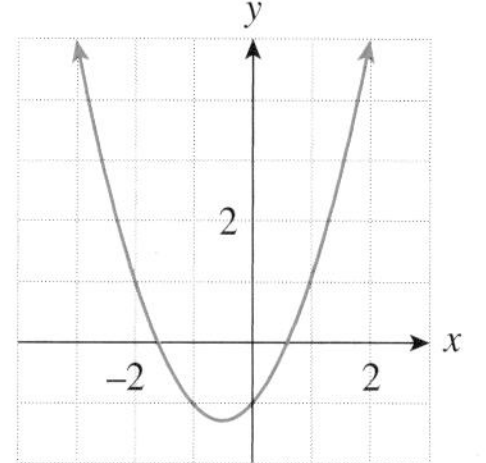

9. Vertex: (0, 1); y-intercept: 1; No x-intercepts

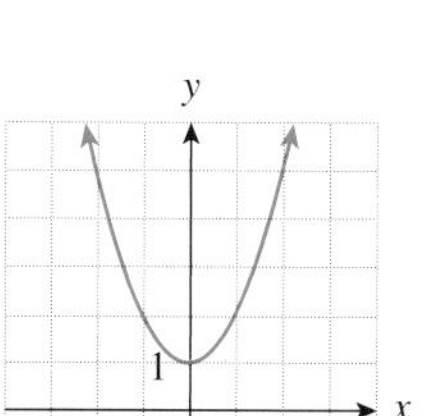

11. $R = -4p^2 + 100p$; Maximum revenue when $p = \$12.50$

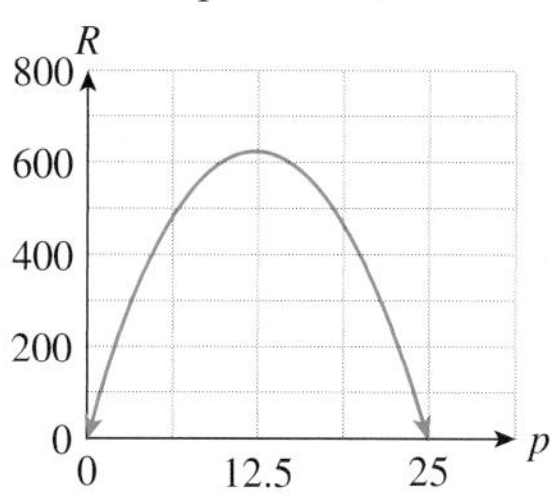

13. $R = -2p^2 + 400p$; Maximum revenue when $p = \$100$

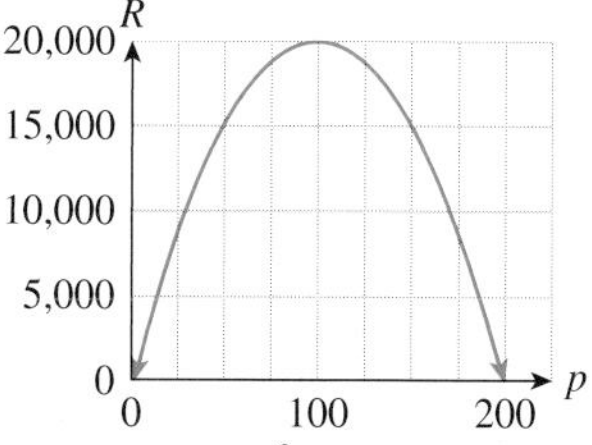

15. $y = -0.7955x^2 + 4.4591x - 1.6000$

17. $y = -1.1667x^2 - 6.1667x - 3.0000$

19. a. Positive because the data suggest a curve that is concave up. **b.** (C) **c.** 1995. The parabola rises to the left of the vertex and thus predicts increasing trade as we go back in time, contradicting history. **21.** 1985 ($t = 15$); 3525 pounds

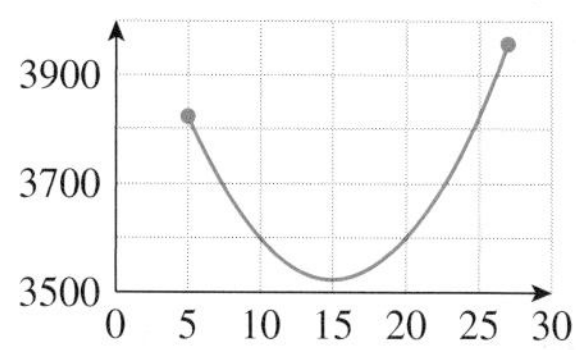

23. 5000 pounds. The model is not trustworthy for vehicle weights larger than 5000 pounds, because it predicts increasing fuel economy with increasing weight, and 5000 is close to the upper limit of the domain of the function.

25. Maximum revenue when $p = \$140$, $R = \$9800$

27. Maximum revenue with 70 houses, $R = \$9,800,000$

29. a. $q = -560x + 1400$; $R = -560x^2 + 1400x$
b. $P = -560x^2 + 1400x - 30$; $x = \$1.25$; $P = \$845$ per month

31. $C = -200x + 620$; $P = -400x^2 + 1400x - 620$
$x = \$1.75$ per log-on; $P = \$605$ per month

33. a. $q = -10p + 400$ **b.** $R = -10p^2 + 400p$
c. $C = -30p + 4200$
d. $P = -10p^2 + 430p - 4200$; $p = \$21.50$

35. $C(t) = 2.7t^2 - 4.5t + 50$; \$120.2 billion, which agrees with the actual value to the nearest \$1 billion.

37. a. $S(t) = -12.27t^2 + 227.23t + 64.39$

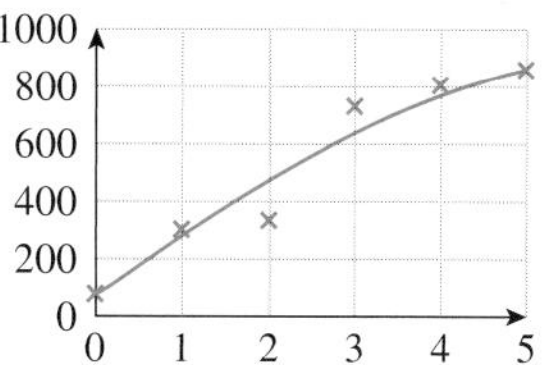

b. 986,000 units **c.** Mathematical regression cannot reliably be used to make predictions about sales. (Answers will vary.)

39. The x-coordinate of the vertex represents the unit price that leads to the maximum revenue, the y-coordinate of the vertex gives the maximum possible revenue, the x-intercepts give the unit prices that result in zero revenue, and the y-intercept gives the revenue resulting from zero unit price (which is obviously zero).

41. Graph the data to see whether the points suggest a curve rather than a straight line. If the curve suggested by the graph is concave up or concave down, then a quadratic model would be a likely candidate. **43.** If $q = mp + b$ (with $m < 0$), then the revenue is given by $R = pq = mp^2 + bp$. This is the equation of a parabola with $a = m < 0$, and so is concave down. Thus the vertex is the highest point on the parabola, showing that there is a single highest value for R, namely, the y-coordinate of the vertex.

45. Because $R = pq$, the demand must be given by
$$q = \frac{R}{p} = \frac{-50p^2 + 60p}{p} = -50p + 60.$$

Section 2.2

1. `4^x`

x	−3	−2	−1	0	1	2	3
$f(x)$	$\frac{1}{64}$	$\frac{1}{16}$	$\frac{1}{4}$	1	4	16	64

3. `3^(-x)`

x	−3	−2	−1	0	1	2	3
$f(x)$	27	9	3	1	$\frac{1}{3}$	$\frac{1}{9}$	$\frac{1}{27}$

5. `2*2^x` or `2*(2^x)`

x	−3	−2	−1	0	1	2	3
$g(x)$	$\frac{1}{4}$	$\frac{1}{2}$	1	2	4	8	16

7. `-3*2^(-x)`

x	−3	−2	−1	0	1	2	3
$h(x)$	−24	−12	−6	−3	$-\frac{3}{2}$	$-\frac{3}{4}$	$-\frac{3}{8}$

9. `2^x-1`

x	−3	−2	−1	0	1	2	3
$r(x)$	$-\frac{7}{8}$	$-\frac{3}{4}$	$-\frac{1}{2}$	0	1	3	7

11. `2^(x-1)`

x	-3	-2	-1	0	1	2	3
$s(x)$	$\frac{1}{16}$	$\frac{1}{8}$	$\frac{1}{4}$	$\frac{1}{2}$	1	2	4

13. **15.** **17.**

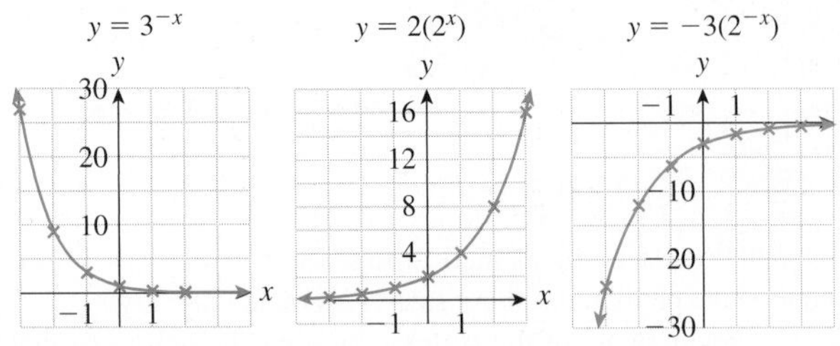

19. Both; $f(x) = 4.5(3^x)$, $g(x) = 2(1/2)^x$, or $2(2^{-x})$ **21.** Neither **23.** g; $g(x) = 4(0.2)^x$
25. `e^(-2*x)` or `EXP(-2*x)`

x	-3	-2	-1	0	1	2	3
$f(x)$	403.4	54.60	7.389	1	0.1353	0.01832	0.002479

27. `1.01*2.02^(-4*x)`

x	-3	-2	-1	0	1	2	3
$h(x)$	4662	280.0	16.82	1.01	0.06066	0.003643	0.0002188

29. `50*(1+1/3.2)^(2*x)`

x	-3	-2	-1	0	1	2	3
$r(x)$	9.781	16.85	29.02	50	86.13	148.4	255.6

31. `2^(x-1)`; **not** `2^x-1` **33.** `2/(1-2^(-4*x))`; **not** `2/1-2^-4*x`; **not** `2/1-2^(-4*x)` **35.** `(3+x)^(3*x)/(x+1)` or `((3+x)^(3*x))/(x+1)`; **not** `(3+x)^(3*x)/x+1`; **not** `(3+x^(3*x))/(x+1)` **37.** `2*e^((1+x)/x)` or `2*EXP((1+x)/x)`; **not** `2*e^1+x/x`; **not** `2*e^(1+x)/x`; **not** `2*EXP(1+x)/x`

39.

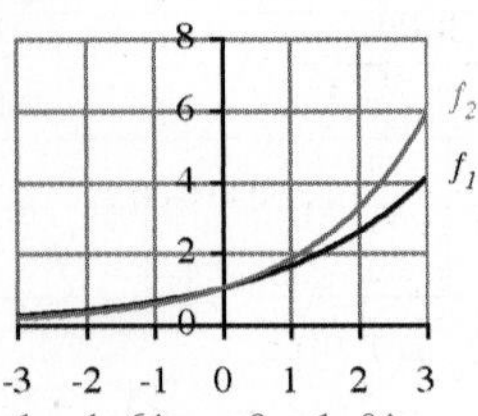

`y1=1.6^x` `y2=1.8^x`

41.

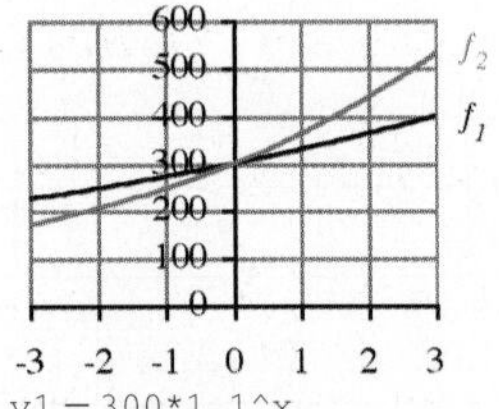

`y1=300*1.1^x`
`y2=300*1.1^(2*x)`

43.

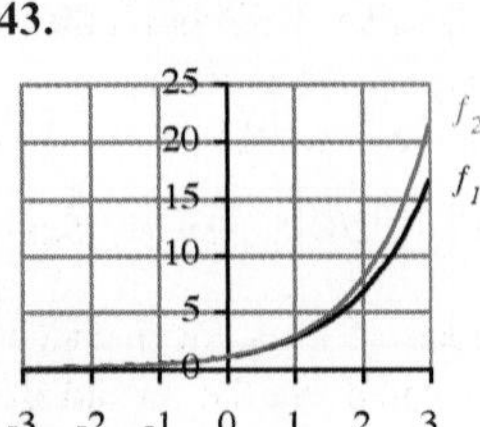

`Y1=2.5^(1.02*x)`
`y2=e^(1.02*x)` or `exp(1.02*x)`

45.

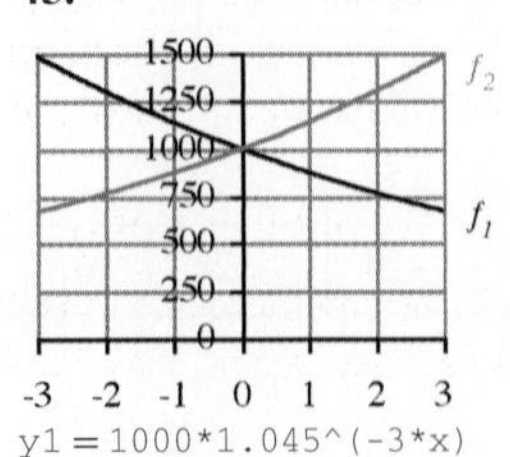

`y1=1000*1.045^(-3*x)`
`y2 = 1000*1.045^(3*x)`

47. $f(x) = 500(0.5)^x$ **49.** $f(x) = 10(3)^x$ **51.** $f(x) = 500(0.45)^x$ **53.** $f(x) = -100(1.1)^x$ **55.** $y = 4(3^x)$ **57.** $y = -1(0.2^x)$ **59.** $y = 2.1213(1.4142^x)$ **61.** $y = 3.6742(0.9036^x)$ **63.** $f(t) = 5000e^{0.10t}$ **65.** $f(t) = 1000e^{-0.063t}$ **67.** $y = 1.0442(1.7564)^x$ **69.** $y = 15.1735(1.4822)^x$ **71.** $y = 1000(2^{t/3})$; 65,536,000 bacteria after 2 days **73.** $A(t) = 5000(1.0439)^t$; £6198 **75.** At the beginning of 2014 **77.** 31.0 grams, 9.25 grams, 2.76 grams **79.** 20,000 years **81.** 53 mg **83. a.** $P = 40t + 360$ **b.** $P = 360(1.1006)^t$. Neither model is applicable. **85. a.** $P = 180(1.01121)^t$ million **b.** 4 decimal places **c.** 351 million **87. a.** $y = 50{,}000(1.5^{t/2})$, t = time in years since two years ago **b.** 91,856 tags **89.** $491.82
91. a.

Year	1950	2000	2050	2100
$C(t)$ parts per million	561	669	799	953

b. 2010 ($t = 260$)
93. a. $P(t) = 0.339(1.169)^t$. Graph:

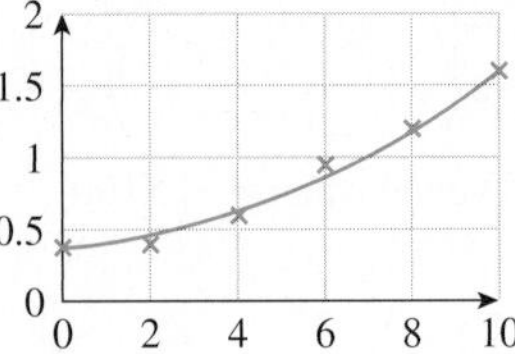

b. $1.9 million
95. a. $y = 5.4433(1.0609)^t$. Graph:

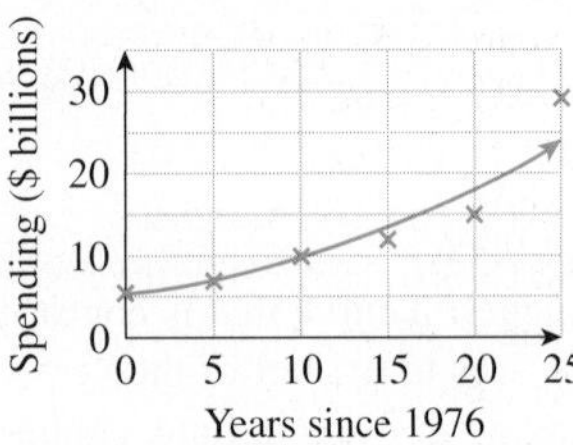

b. 609% **c.** $16 billion
97. (B) **99.** Exponential functions of the form $f(x) = A(b^x)$ $(b > 0)$ increase rapidly for large values of x. In real-life situations, such as population growth, this model is reliable only for relatively short periods of growth. Eventually, population growth tapers off because of pressures such as limited resources and overcrowding. **101.** Linear functions better: cost models where there is a fixed cost and a variable cost; simple interest, where interest is paid on the original amount invested. Exponential models better: compound interest, population growth. (In both of these, the rate of growth depends on the present number of items, rather than on some fixed quantity.) **103.** Take the ratios y_2/y_1 and y_3/y_2. If they are the same, the points fit on an exponential curve. **105.** This reasoning is suspect—the bank need not use its computer resources to update all the accounts every minute, but can instead use the continuous compounding formula to calculate the balance in any account at any time.

Section 2.3

1.

Logarithmic Form	$\log_{10} 10{,}000 = 4$	$\log_4 16 = 2$	$\log_3 27 = 3$	$\log_5 5 = 1$	$\log_7 1 = 0$	$\log_4 \frac{1}{16} = -2$

3.

Exponential Form	$(0.5)^2 = 0.25$	$5^0 = 1$	$10^{-1} = 0.1$	$4^3 = 64$	$2^8 = 256$	$2^{-2} = \frac{1}{4}$

5. 1.4650 **7.** −1.1460 **9.** −0.7324 **11.** 6.2657

13.

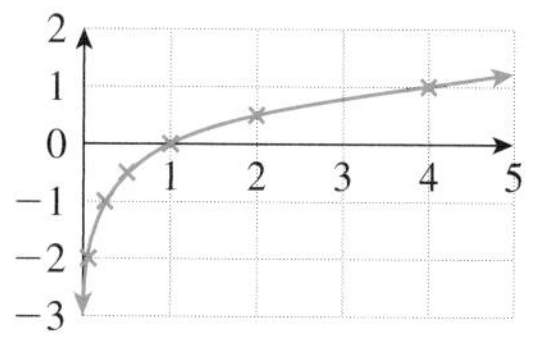

15.

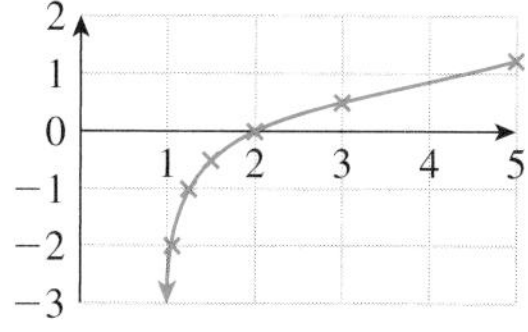

17.

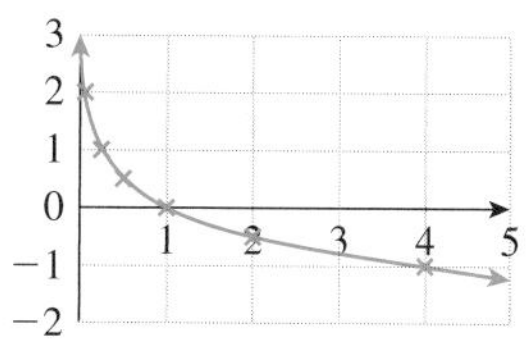

19. $Q = 1000e^{-t \ln 2}$ **21.** $Q = 1000e^{t(\ln 2)/2}$ **23.** Doubling time = $2 \ln 2$ **25.** Half-life = $(\ln 2)/4$ **27.** $f(x) = 4(7.389)^x$ **29.** $f(t) = 2.1e^{0.0009995t}$ **31.** $f(t) = 10e^{-0.01309}$ **33.** 3.36 years **35.** 11 years **37.** 23.1% **39.** 63,000 years old **41.** 8 years **43.** 151 months **45.** 12 years **47.** 13.08 years **49.** 1600 years **51. a.** $b = 3^{1/6} \approx 1.20$ **b.** 3.8 months **53. a.** $Q(t) = Q_0 e^{-0.139t}$ **b.** 3 years **55.** 2360 million years **57.** 3.2 hours **59.** 3.89 days **61. a.** $P(t) = 6.591 \ln t - 17.69$ **b.** 1 digit **c.** (A) **63.** $M(t) = 11.622 \ln t - 7.1358$. The model is unsuitable for large values of t since, for sufficiently large values of t, $M(t)$ will eventually become larger than 100%. **65. a.** About 1.259×10^{24} ergs **b.** about 2.24% **d.** 1000 **67. a.** 75 dB, 69 dB, 61 dB **b.** $D = 95 - 20 \log r$ **c.** 57,000 feet **69.** The logarithm of a negative number, were it defined, would be the power to which a base must be raised to give that negative number. But raising a base to a power never results in a negative number, so there can be no such number as the logarithm of a negative number. **71.** $\log_4 y$ **73.** 8 **75.** x **77.** Any logarithmic curve $y = \log_b t + C$ will eventually surpass 100%, and hence not be suitable as a long-term predictor of market share. **79.** Time is increasing logarithmically with population; Solving $P = Ab^t$ for t gives $t = \log_b(P/A) = \log_b P - \log_b A$, which is of the form $t = \log_b P + C$.

Section 2.4

1. $N = 7, A = 6, b = 2$; `7/(1+6*2^-x)`

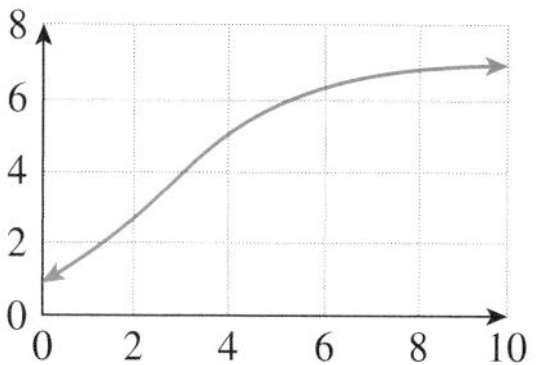

3. $N = 10, A = 4, b = 0.3$; `10/(1+4*0.3^-x)`

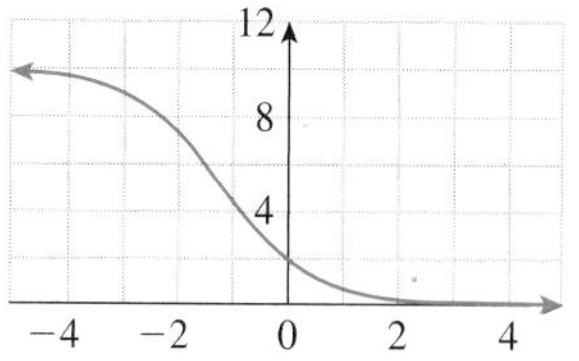

5. $N = 4, A = 7, b = 1.5$; `4/(1+7*1.5^-x)`

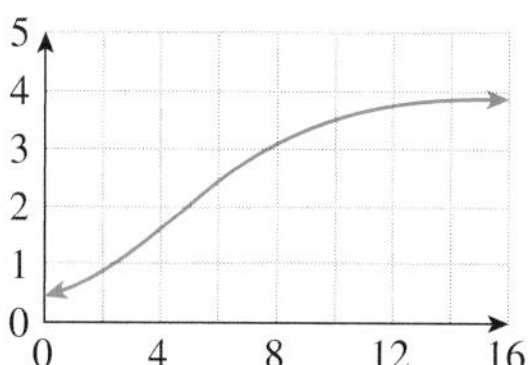

7. $f(x) = \dfrac{200}{1 + 19(2^{-x})}$ **9.** $f(x) = \dfrac{6}{1 + 2^{-x}}$

11. (B) **13.** (B) **15.** (C)

17. $y = \dfrac{7.2}{1 + 2.4(1.05)^{-x}}$

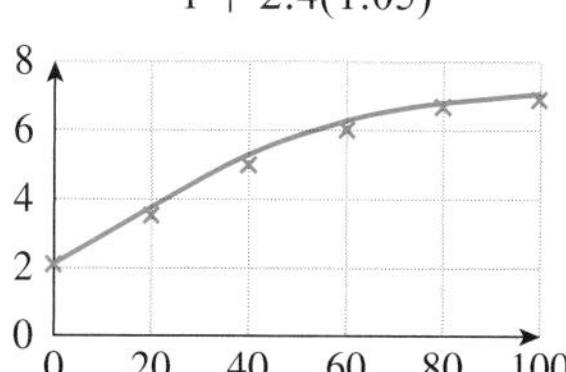

19. $y = \dfrac{97}{1 + 2.2(0.942)^{-x}}$

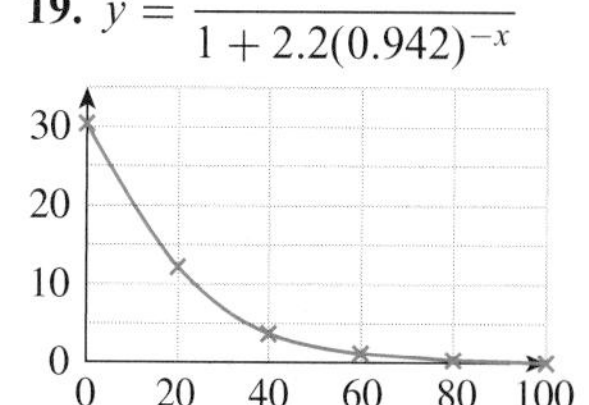

21. a. (A) **b.** 20% per year **23. a.** 91% **b.** $P(x) \approx 14.33(1.05)^x$ **c.** \$38,000 **25.** $N(t) = \dfrac{10{,}000}{1 + 9(1.25)^{-t}}$; $N(7) \approx 3463$ cases **27.** $N(t) = \dfrac{3000}{1 + 29(2^{1/5})^{-t}}$; $t = 16$ days **29. a.** $A(t) = \dfrac{6.3}{1 + 4.8(1.2)^{-t}}$; 6300 articles **b.** 5200 articles **31. a.** $N(t) = \dfrac{82.8}{1 + 21.8(7.14)^{-t}}$. The model predicts that book sales will level off at around 82.8 million books per year. **b.** Not consistent; 15% of the market is represented by more than double the predicted value. This shows the difficulty in making long-term predictions from regression models obtained from a small amount of data. **c.** 2001

33. $N(t) = \dfrac{5}{1 + 1.080(1.056)^{-t}}$; $t = 17$, or 2010. **35.** Just as diseases are communicated via the spread of a pathogen (such as a virus), new technology is communicated via the spread of information (such as advertising and publicity). Further, just as the spread of a disease is ultimately limited by the number of susceptible individuals, so the spread of a new technology is ultimately limited by the size of the potential market. **37.** It can be used to predict where the sales of a new commodity might level off.

Chapter 2 Review

1.

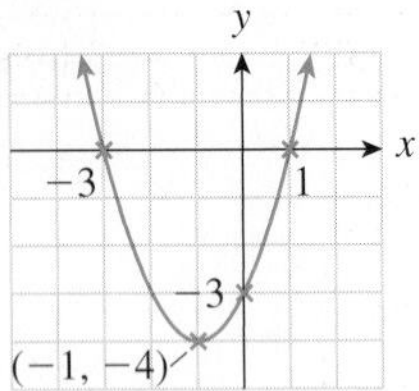

3. f: $f(x) = 5(1/2)^x$, or $5(2^{-x})$

5.

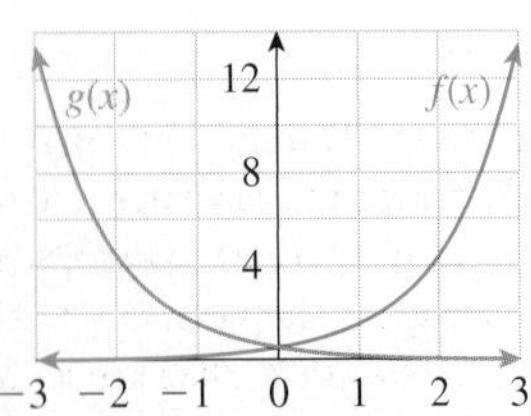

7.

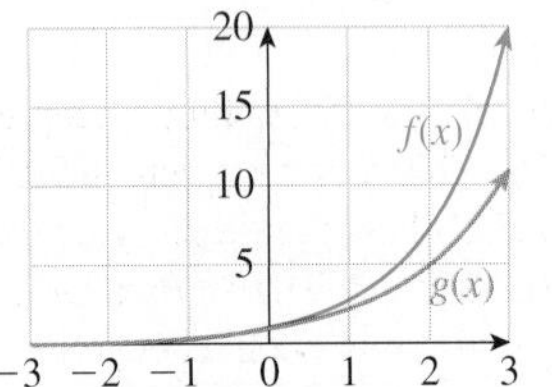

9. \$3484.85 **11.** \$3705.48 **13.** \$3485.50 **15.** $f(x) = 4.5(9^x)$ **17.** $f(x) = \frac{2}{3}3^x$ **19.** $-\frac{1}{2}\log_3 4$ **21.** $\frac{1}{3}\log 1.05$

23.

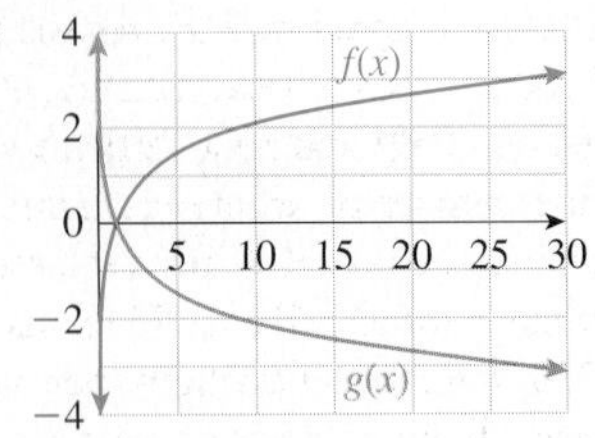

25. $Q = 5e^{-0.00693t}$ **27.** $Q = 2.5e^{0.347t}$ **29.** 10.2 years **31.** 10.8 years **33.** $f(x) = \frac{900}{1 + 8(1.5)^{-x}}$ **35.** $f(x) = \frac{20}{1 + 3(0.8)^{-x}}$ **37. a.** \$8500 per month; an average of approximately 2100 hits per day **b.** \$29,049 per month **c.** The fact that −0.000005, the coefficient of c^2, is negative. **39.** $R = -60p^2 + 950p$; $p = \$7.92$ per novel, Monthly revenue = \$3760.42 **41. a.** 10, 34 **b.** About 360,000 pounds **43.** 2008 **45.** 32.8 hours **47.** (C)

Chapter 3

Section 3.1

1. 0 **3.** 4 **5.** Does not exist **7.** 1.5 **9.** 0.5 **11.** Diverges to $+\infty$ **13.** 0 **15.** 1 **17.** 0 **19. a.** −2 **b.** −1 **21. a.** 2 **b.** 1 **c.** 0 **d.** $+\infty$ **23. a.** 0 **b.** 2 **c.** −1 **d.** Does not exist **e.** 2 **f.** $+\infty$ **25. a.** 1 **b.** 1 **c.** 2 **d.** Does not exist **e.** 1 **f.** 2 **27. a.** 1 **b.** $+\infty$ **c.** $+\infty$ **d.** $+\infty$ **e.** not defined **f.** −1 **29. a.** −1 **b.** $+\infty$ **c.** $-\infty$ **d.** Does not exist **e.** 2 **f.** 1 **31.** 7.0; In the long term, the number of research articles in *Physics Review* written by researchers in Europe approaches 7000 per year. **33.** 470. This suggests that students whose parents earn an exceptionally large income score an average of 470 on the SAT verbal test. **35.** $\lim_{t\to 1^-} C(t) = 0.06$, $\lim_{t\to 1^+} C(t) = 0.08$, so $\lim_{t\to 1} C(t)$ does not exist. **37.** $\lim_{t\to+\infty} I(t) = +\infty$, $\lim_{t\to+\infty}(I(t)/E(t)) \approx 2.5$. In the long term, U.S. imports from China will rise without bound and be 2.5 times U.S. exports to China. In the real world, imports and exports cannot rise without bound. Thus, the given models should not be extrapolated far into the future. **39.** $\lim_{t\to+\infty} n(t) \approx 80$. Online book sales can be expected to level off at 80 million per year in the long term. **41.** To approximate $\lim_{x\to a} f(x)$ numerically, choose values of x closer and closer to, and on either side of $x = a$, and evaluate $f(x)$ for each of them. The limit (if it exists) is then the number that these values of $f(x)$ approach. A disadvantage of this method is that it may never give the exact value of the limit, but only an approximation. (However, we can make this as accurate as we like.) **43.** It is possible for $\lim_{x\to a} f(x)$ to exist even though $f(a)$ is not defined. An example is $\lim_{x\to 1} \frac{x^2 - 3x + 2}{x - 1}$.
45. Any situation in which there is a sudden change can be modeled by a function in which $\lim_{t\to a^+} f(t)$ is not the same as $\lim_{t\to a^-} f(t)$ One example is the value of a stock market index before and after a crash: $\lim_{t\to a^-} f(t)$ is the value immediately before the crash at time $t = a$, while $\lim_{t\to a^+} f(t)$ is the value immediately after the crash. Another example might be the price of a commodity that is suddenly increased from one level to another. **47.** An example is $f(x) = (x - 1)(x - 2)$.

Section 3.2

1. Continuous on its domain **3.** Continuous on its domain **5.** Discontinuous at $x = 0$ **7.** Discontinuous at $x = -1$ **9.** Continuous on its domain **11.** Discontinuous at $x = -1$ and 0 **13.** (A), (B), (D), (E) **15.** 0 **17.** −1 **19.** No value possible **21.** −1 **23.** Continuous on its domain **25.** Continuous on its domain **27.** Discontinuity at $x = 0$ **29.** Discontinuity at $x = 0$ **31.** Continuous on its domain **33.** Not unless the domain of the function consists of all real numbers. (It is impossible for a function to be continuous at points not in its domain.) For example, $f(x) = 1/x$ is continuous on its domain—the set of nonzero real numbers—but not at $x = 0$. **35.** True. If the graph of a function has a break in its graph at any point a, then it cannot be continuous at the point a.
37. Answers may vary.

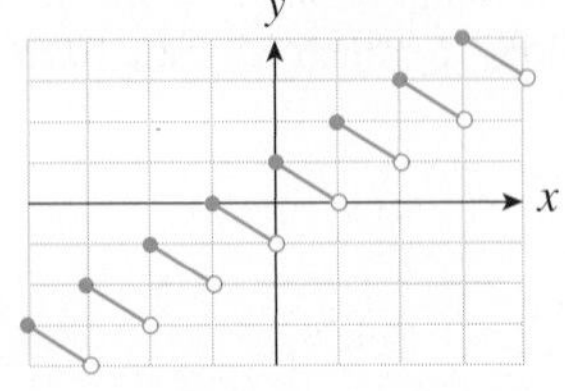

39. Answers may vary. The price of OHaganBooks.com stock suddenly drops by \$10 as news spreads of a government investigation. Let $f(x)$ = Price of OHaganBooks.com stock.

Section 3.3

1. $x = 1$ **3.** 2 **5.** 1 **7.** 2 **9.** 0 **11.** 6 **13.** 4 **15.** 2 **17.** 0 **19.** 0 **21.** 12 **23.** Diverges to $+\infty$ **25.** Does not exist; left and right (infinite) limits differ **27.** 3/2 **29.** 1/2 **31.** Diverges to $+\infty$ **33.** 0 **35.** 3/2 **37.** 1/2 **39.** Diverges to $-\infty$ **41.** 0 **43.** Discontinuity at $x = 0$ **45.** Continuous everywhere **47.** Discontinuity at $x = 0$ **49.** Discontinuity at $x = 0$ **51. a.** 0.49, 1.16. Shortly before 1999, annual advertising expenditures were close to \$0.49 billion. Shortly after 1999, annual advertising expenditures were close to \$1.16 billion. **b.** Not continuous; Movie advertising expenditures jumped suddenly in 1999. **53.** 1.59; If the trend continues indefinitely, the annual spending on police will be 1.59 times the annual spending on courts in the long run. **55.** $\lim_{t\to+\infty} I(t) = +\infty$, $\lim_{t\to+\infty} (I(t)/E(t)) = 2.5$. In the long term, U.S. imports from China will rise without bound and be 2.5 times U.S. exports to China. In the real world, imports and exports cannot rise without bound. Thus, the given models should not be extrapolated far into the future. **57.** $\lim_{t\to+\infty} p(t) = 100$. The percentage of children who learn to speak approaches 100% as their age increases. **59.** Yes; $\lim_{t\to 8^-} C(t) = \lim_{t\to 8^+} C(t) = 1.24$. **61.** To evaluate $\lim_{x\to a} f(x)$ algebraically, first check whether $f(x)$ is a closed-form function. Then check whether $x = a$ is in its domain. If so, the limit is just $f(a)$; that is, it is obtained by substituting $x = a$. If not, then try to first simplify $f(x)$ in such a way as to transform it into a new function such that $x = a$ is in its domain, and then substitute. A disadvantage of this method is that it is sometimes extremely difficult to evaluate limits algebraically, and rather sophisticated methods are often needed. **63.** She is wrong. Closed-form functions are continuous only at points in their domains, and $x = 2$ is not in the domain of the closed-form function $f(x) = 1/(x-2)^2$. **65.** The statement may not be true, for instance, if $f(x) = \begin{cases} x+2 & \text{if } x < 0 \\ 2x-1 & \text{if } x \geq 0 \end{cases}$, then $f(0)$ is defined and equals -1, and yet $\lim_{x\to 0} f(x)$ does not exist. The statement can be corrected by requiring that f be a closed-form function: "If f is a closed form function, and $f(a)$ is defined, then $\lim_{x\to a} f(x)$ exists and equals $f(a)$." **67.** Answers may vary, for example

$$f(x) = \begin{cases} 0 & \text{if } x \text{ is any number other than 1 or 2} \\ 1 & \text{if } x = 1 \text{ or } 2 \end{cases}$$

Section 3.4

1. -3 **3.** 0.3 **5.** $-\$25{,}000$ per month **7.** -200 items per dollar **9.** \$1.33 per month **11.** 0.75 percentage point increase in unemployment per 1 percentage point increase in the deficit **13.** 4 **15.** 2 **17.** 7/3

19.

h	Ave. Rate of Change
1	2
0.1	0.2
0.01	0.02
0.001	0.002
0.0001	0.0002

21.

h	Ave. Rate of Change
1	−0.1667
0.1	−0.2381
0.01	−0.2488
0.001	−0.2499
0.0001	−0.24999

23.

h	Ave. Rate of Change
1	9
0.1	8.1
0.01	8.01
0.001	8.001
0.0001	8.0001

25. a. -0.25 million people per year. During the period 2000–2004, employment in the U.S. decreased at an average rate of 0.25 million people per year. **b.** Zero people per year. During the period 1999–2002 the average rate of change of employment in the U.S. was zero people per year. **27. a.** 1998–2000. The number of companies that invested in venture capital each year was increasing most rapidly during the period 1998–2000, when it grew at an average rate of 650 companies per year. **b.** 1999–2001. The number of companies that invested in venture capital each year was decreasing most rapidly during the period 1999–2001, when it decreased at an average rate of 50 companies per year. **29. a.** [3, 5]; -0.25 thousand articles per year. During the period 1993–1995, the number of articles authored by U.S. researchers decreased at an average rate of 250 articles per year. **b.** Percentage rate ≈ -0.1765, Average rate $= -0.09$ thousand articles/year. Over the period 1993–2003, the number of articles authored by U.S. researchers decreased at an average rate of 90 per year, representing a 17.65% decrease over that period. **31. a.** 75 teams per year **b.** Decreased **33. a.** 250 million transactions per year, −150 million transactions per year, 50 million transactions per year. Over the period January 2000–January 2001, the (annual) number of online shopping transactions in the U.S. increased at an average rate of 250 million per year. From January 2001 to January 2002, this number decreased at an average rate of 150 million per year. From January 2000 to January 2002, this number increased at an average rate of 50 million per year. **b.** The average rate of change of $N(t)$ over [0, 2] is the average of the rates of change over [0, 1] and [1, 2]. **35. a.** (C) **b.** (A) **c.** (B) **d.** Approximately -0.0063 (to two significant digits) billion dollars per year, ($-\$6{,}300{,}000$ per year). This is much less than the (positive) slope of the regression line, $0.0125 \approx 0.013$ billion dollars per year, (\$13,000,000 per year).

37. Answers may vary

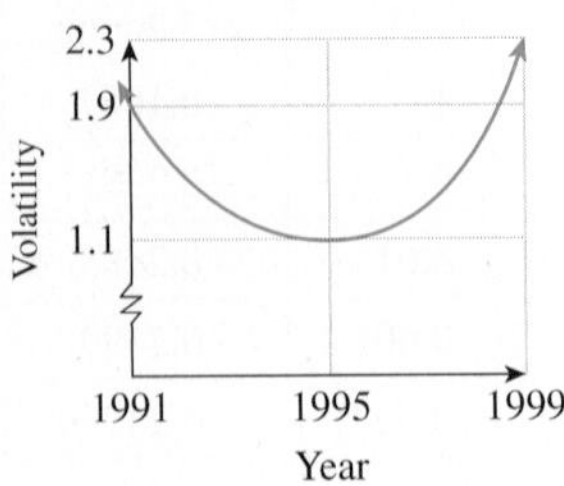

39. The index was increasing at an average rate of 300 points per day. **41.** \$0.08 per year. The value of the euro in U.S. dollars was growing at an average rate of about \$0.08 per year over the period June 2000–June 2004. **43. a.** 8.85 manatee deaths per 100,000 boats; 23.05 manatee deaths per 100,000 boats **b.** More boats result in more manatee deaths per additional boat. **45. a.** \$305 million per year; Over the period 1997–1999, annual advertising revenues increased at an average rate of \$305 million per year. **b.** (A) **c.** \$590 million per year; The model projects annual advertising revenues to increase by \$590 million per year in 2000. **47. a.** −0.88, −0.79, −0.69, −0.60, −0.51, −0.42 **b.** For household incomes between \$40,000 and \$40,500, the poverty rate decreases at an average rate of 0.69 percentage points per \$1000 increase in the median household income. **c.** (B) **d.** (B). **49.** The average rate of change of f over an interval $[a, b]$ can be determined numerically, using a table of values; graphically, by measuring the slope of the corresponding line segment through two points on the graph; or algebraically, using an algebraic formula for the function. Of these, the least precise is the graphical method, because it relies on reading coordinates of points on a graph. **51.** Answers will vary.

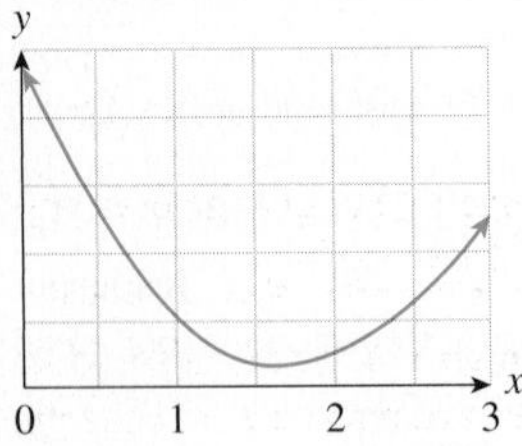

53. 6 units of quantity A per unit of quantity C **55.** (A)
57. Yes. Here is an example:

Year	2000	2001	2002	2003
Revenue (\$ billion)	10	20	30	5

59. (A)

Section 3.5

1. 6 **3.** −5.5

5.

h	1	0.1	0.01
Ave. rate	39	39.9	39.99

Instantaneous Rate = 40 rupees per day

7.

h	1	0.1	0.01
Ave. rate	140	66.2	60.602

Instantaneous Rate = 60 rupees per day

9.

h	10	1
C_{ave}	4.799	4.7999

$C'(1{,}000) = \$4.8$ per item

11.

h	10	1
C_{ave}	99.91	99.90

$C'(100) = \$99.90$ per item

13. a. R **b.** P **15. a.** P **b.** R **17. a.** Q **b.** P **19.** 1/2 **21.** 0 **23. a.** Q **b.** R **c.** P **25. a.** R **b.** Q **c.** P **27. a.** (1, 0) **b.** None **c.** (−2, 1) **29. a.** (−2, 0.3), (0, 0), (2, −0.3) **b.** None **c.** None **31.** $(a, f(a))$; $f'(a)$ **33.** (B) **35. a.** (A) **b.** (C) **c.** (B) **d.** (B) **e.** (C) **37.** −2 **39.** −1.5 **41.** −5 **43.** 16 **45.** 0 **47.** −0.0025

49. a. 3 **b.** $y = 3x + 2$

51. a. $\frac{3}{4}$ **b.** $y = \frac{3}{4}x + 1$

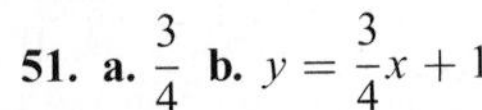

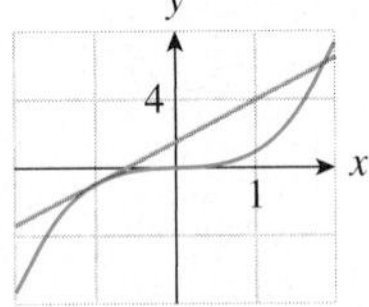

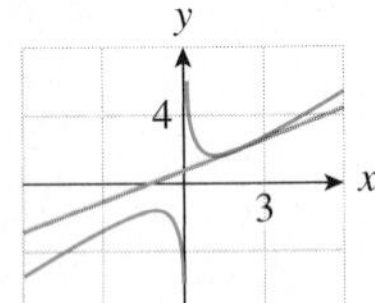

53. a. $\frac{1}{4}$ **b.** $y = \frac{1}{4}x + 1$

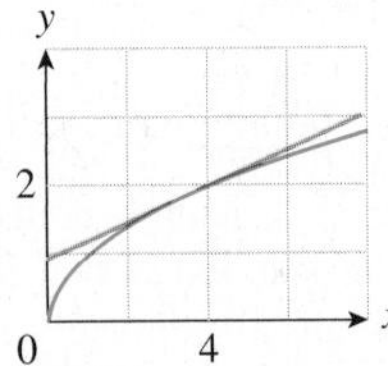

55. 1.000 **57.** 1.000 **59.** (C) **61.** (A) **63.** (F)

65.

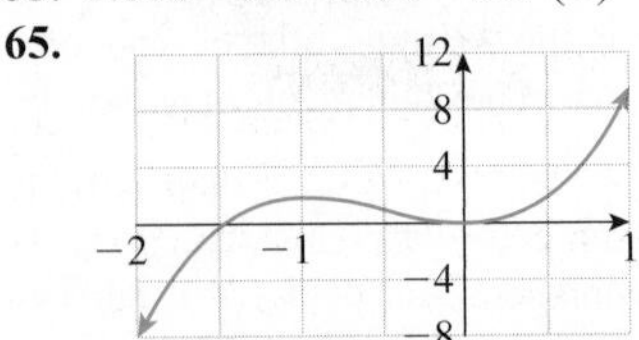

$x = -1.5, x = 0$

67. Note: Answers depend on the form of technology used.
Excel ($h = 0.1$):

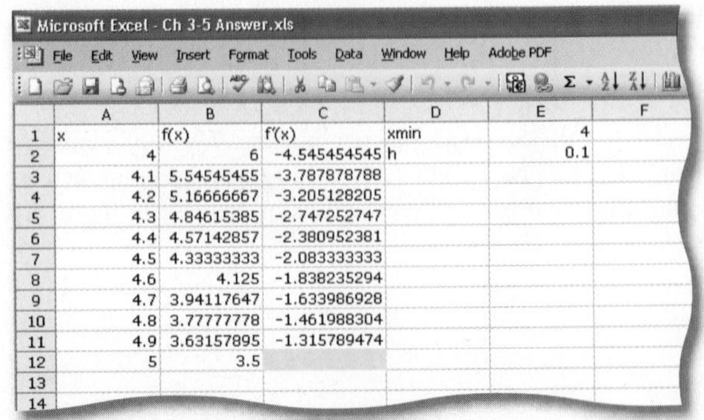

Microsoft Excel - Ch 3-5 Answer.xls

File Edit View Insert Format Tools Data Window Help Adobe PDF

	A	B	C	D	E	F
1	x	f(x)	f'(x)	xmin	4	
2	4	6	-4.545454545	h	0.1	
3	4.1	5.54545455	-3.787878788			
4	4.2	5.16666667	-3.205128205			
5	4.3	4.84615385	-2.747252747			
6	4.4	4.57142857	-2.380952381			
7	4.5	4.33333333	-2.083333333			
8	4.6	4.125	-1.838235294			
9	4.7	3.94117647	-1.633986928			
10	4.8	3.77777778	-1.461988304			
11	4.9	3.63157895	-1.315789474			
12	5	3.5				
13						
14						

Graphs:

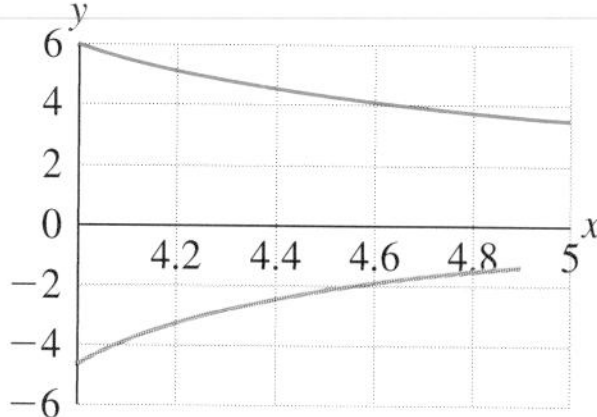

The top curve is $y = f(x)$; the bottom curve is $y = f'(x)$.
69. $q(100) = 50{,}000$, $q'(100) = -500$. A total of 50,000 pairs of sneakers can be sold at a price of \$100, but the demand is decreasing at a rate of 500 pairs per \$1 increase in the price.
71. a. Sales in 2000 were approximately 160,000 pools per year, and increasing at a rate of 6000 per year. **b.** Decreasing because the slope is decreasing. **73. a.** (B) **b.** (B) **c.** (A) **d.** 1992 **e.** 0.05. In 1996, the total number of state prisoners was increasing at a rate of approximately 50,000 prisoners per year.
75. a. −96 ft/sec **b.** −128 ft/sec **77. a.** \$0.044 per year. The value of the euro was increasing at an average rate of about \$0.044 per year over the period January 2000–January 2004. **b.** −\$0.10 per year. In January, 2000, the value of the euro was decreasing at a rate of about \$0.10 per year. **c.** The value of the euro was decreasing in January 2000, and then began to increase.
79. a. \$305 million per year **b.** (A) **c.** \$685 million/year. In December 2000, AOL's advertising revenue was projected to be increasing at a rate of \$685 million per year. **81.** $A(0) = 4.5$ million; $A'(0) = 60{,}000$ **83. a.** 60% of children can speak at the age of 10 months. At the age of 10 months, this percentage is increasing by 18.2 percentage points per month. **b.** As t increases, p approaches 100 percentage points (all children eventually learn to speak), and dp/dt approaches zero because the percentage stops increasing. **85.** $S(5) \approx 109$, $\left.\frac{dS}{dt}\right|_{t=5} \approx 9.1$.
After 5 weeks, sales are 109 pairs of sneakers per week, and sales are increasing at a rate of 9.1 pairs per week each week.
87. a. $P(50) \approx 62$, $P'(50) \approx 0.96$; 62% of U.S. households with an income of \$50,000 have a computer. This percentage is increasing at a rate of 0.96 percentage points per \$1000 increase in household income. **b.** P' decreases toward zero.
Graphs:

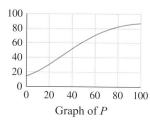

Graph of P

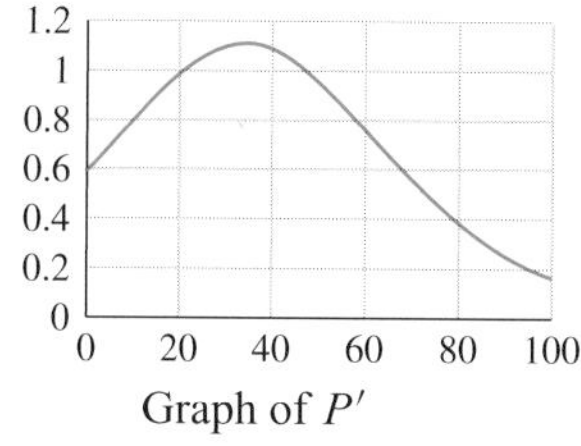

Graph of P'

89. a. (D) **b.** 33 days after the egg was laid **c.** 50 days after the egg was laid. Graph:

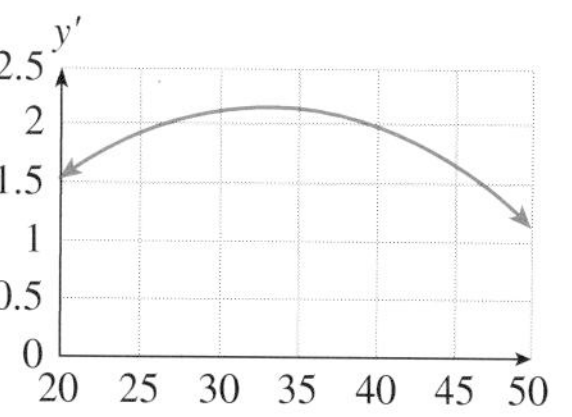

91. $L(0.95) = 31.2$ meters and $L'(0.95) = -304.2$ meters/warp. Thus, at a speed of warp 0.95, the spaceship has an observed length of 31.2 meters and its length is decreasing at a rate of 304.2 meters per unit warp, or 3.042 meters per increase in speed of 0.01 warp. **93.** The difference quotient is not defined when $h = 0$ because there is no such number as $0/0$. **95.** The derivative is positive and decreasing toward zero. **97.** Company B. Although the company is currently losing money, the derivative is positive, showing that the profit is increasing. Company A, on the other hand, has profits that are declining. **99.** (C) is the only graph in which the instantaneous rate of change on January 1 is greater than the one-month average rate of change. **101.** The tangent to the graph is horizontal at that point, and so the graph is almost horizontal near that point.
103. Answers may vary.

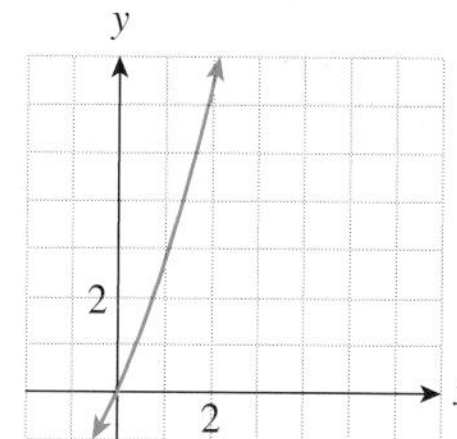

105. If $f(x) = mx + b$, then its average rate of change over any interval $[x, x + h]$ is $\frac{m(x+h) + b - (mx + b)}{h} = m$. Because this does not depend on h, the instantaneous rate is also equal to m. **107.** Increasing because the average rate of change appears to be rising as we get closer to 5 from the left (see the bottom row).
109. Answers may vary

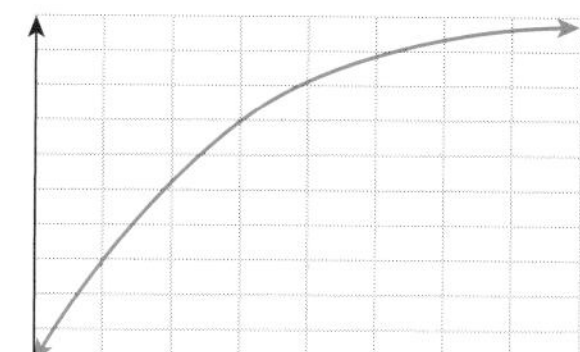

111. Answers may vary

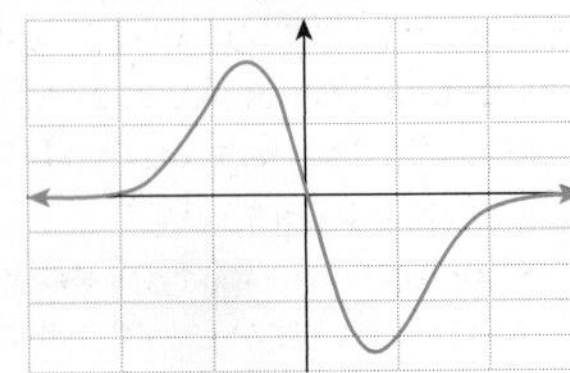

113. (B)
115. Answers may vary.

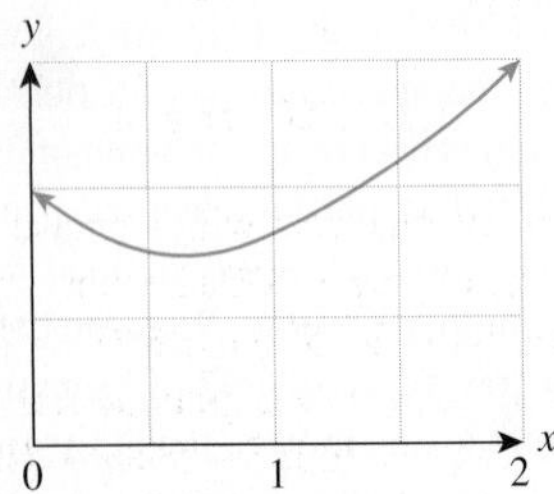

Section 3.6

1. 4 **3.** 3 **5.** 7 **7.** 4 **9.** 14 **11.** 1 **13.** m **15.** $2x$ **17.** 3 **19.** $6x+1$ **21.** $2-2x$ **23.** $3x^2+2$ **25.** $1/x^2$ **27.** m **29.** −1.2 **31.** 30.6 **33.** −7.1 **35.** 4.25 **37.** −0.6 **39.** $y=4x-7$ **41.** $y=-2x-4$ **43.** $y=-3x-1$ **45.** $s'(t)=-32t$; $s'(4)=-128$ ft/sec **47.** Annual U.S. imports from China were increasing by \$13.5 billion per year in 2000. **49.** $R'(t)=34t+100$. Annual U.S. sales of bottled water were increasing by 440 million gallons per year in 2000. **51.** $f'(8)=26.6$ manatee deaths per 100,000 boats. At a level of 800,000 boats, the number of manatee deaths is increasing at a rate of 26.6 manatees per 100,000 additional boats. **53.** The algebraic method because it gives the exact value of the derivative. The other two approaches give only approximate values (except in some special cases). **55.** Because the algebraic computation of $f'(a)$ is exact and not an approximation, it makes no difference whether one uses the balanced difference quotient or the ordinary difference quotient in the algebraic computation. **57.** The computation results in a limit that cannot be evaluated.

Section 3.7

1. $5x^4$ **3.** $-4x^{-3}$ **5.** $-0.25x^{-0.75}$ **7.** $8x^3+9x^2$ **9.** $-1-1/x^2$

11. $\frac{dy}{dx}=10(0)=0$ (constant multiple and power rule)

13. $\frac{dy}{dx}=\frac{d}{dx}(x^2)+\frac{d}{dx}(x)$ (sum rule) $=2x+1$ (power rule)

15. $\frac{dy}{dx}=\frac{d}{dx}(4x^3)+\frac{d}{dx}(2x)-\frac{d}{dx}(1)$ (sum and difference)
$=4\frac{d}{dx}(x^3)+2\frac{d}{dx}(x)-\frac{d}{dx}(1)$ (constant multiples)
$=12x^2+2$ (power rule)

17. $f'(x)=2x-3$ **19.** $f'(x)=1+0.5x^{-0.5}$ **21.** $g'(x)=-2x^{-3}+3x^{-2}$ **23.** $g'(x)=-\frac{1}{x^2}+\frac{2}{x^3}$ **25.** $h'(x)=-\frac{0.8}{x^{1.4}}$ **27.** $h'(x)=-\frac{2}{x^3}-\frac{6}{x^4}$ **29.** $r'(x)=-\frac{2}{3x^2}+\frac{0.1}{2x^{1.1}}$ **31.** $r'(x)=\frac{2}{3}-\frac{0.1}{2x^{0.9}}-\frac{4.4}{3x^{2.1}}$ **33.** $t'(x)=|x|/x-1/x^2$ **35.** $s'(x)=\frac{1}{2\sqrt{x}}-\frac{1}{2x\sqrt{x}}$ **37.** $s'(x)=3x^2$ **39.** $t'(x)=1-4x$ **41.** $2.6x^{0.3}+1.2x^{-2.2}$ **43.** $1.2(1-|x|/x)$ **45.** $3at^2-4a$ **47.** $5.15x^{9.3}-99x^{-2}$ **49.** $-\frac{2.31}{t^{2.1}}-\frac{0.3}{t^{0.4}}$ **51.** $4\pi r^2$ **53.** 3 **55.** −2 **57.** −5

59. $y=3x+2$

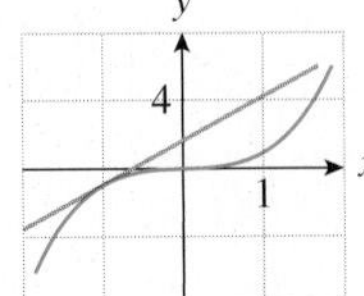

61. $y=\frac{3}{4}x+1$

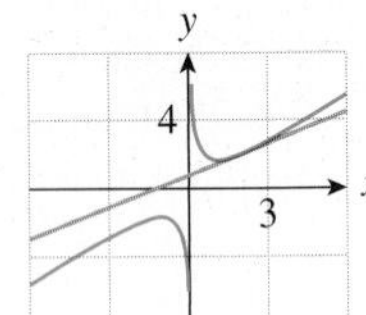

63. $y=\frac{1}{4}x+1$

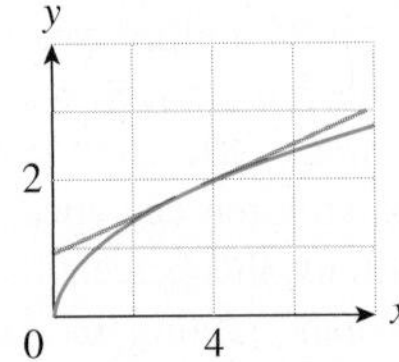

65. $x=-3/4$ **67.** No such values **69.** $x=1,-1$

73. **75.**

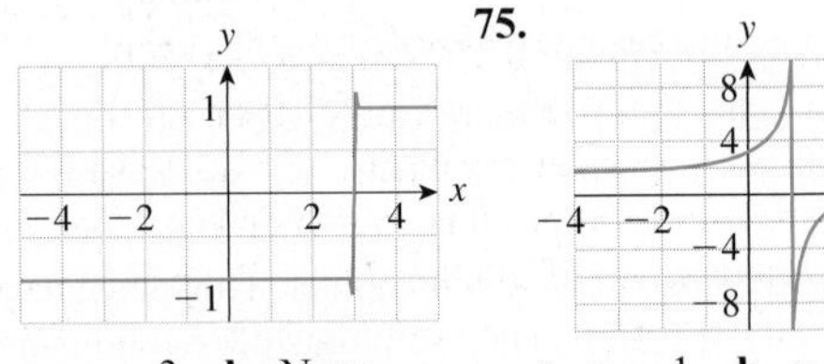

(73) **a.** $x=3$ **b.** None (75) **a.** $x=1$ **b.** $x=4.2$

77. a. $f'(1)=1/3$ **b.** Not differentiable at 0 **79. a.** Not differentiable at 1 **b.** Not differentiable at 0 **81.** Yes; 0 **83.** Yes; 12 **85.** No; 3 **87.** Yes; 3/2 **89.** Yes; Diverges to $-\infty$ **91.** Yes; Diverges to $-\infty$ **93. a.** $s'(t)=3.04t+9.45$ **b.** 52 teams/year **95.** $P'(t)=-5.2t+13$; increasing at a rate of 2.6 percentage points per year **97.** 0.55 **99. a.** $s'(t)=-32t$; 0, −32, −64, −96, −128 ft/sec **b.** 5 seconds; downward at 160 ft/sec **101. a.** $E'(t)=0.072t-0.10$. In January 2004 the value of the euro was increasing at a rate of \$0.188 per year. **b.** (D) **103. a.** $f'(x)=7.1x-30.2$ manatees per 100,000 boats. **b.** Increasing; the number of manatees killed per additional 100,000 boats increases as the number of boats increases. **c.** $f'(8)=26.6$ manatees per 100,000 additional boats. At a level of 800,000 boats, the number of manatee deaths is increasing at a rate of 26.6 manatees per 100,000 additional

boats. **105. a.** $c(t) - m(t)$ measures the combined market share of the other three providers (Comcast, Earthlink, and AOL); $c'(t) - m'(t)$ measures the rate of change of the combined market share of the other three providers. **b.** (A) **c.** (A) **d.** 3.72% per year. In 1992, the combined market share of the other three providers was increasing at a rate of about 3.72 percentage points per year. **107.** After graphing the curve $y = 3x^2$, draw the line passing through $(-1, 3)$ with slope -6. **109.** The slope of the tangent line of g is twice the slope of the tangent line of f. **111.** $g'(x) = -f'(x)$ **113.** The left-hand side is not equal to the right-hand side. The *derivative* of the left-hand side is equal to the right-hand side, so your friend should have written $\frac{d}{dx}(3x^4 + 11x^5) = 12x^3 + 55x^4$ **115.** The derivative of a constant times a function is the constant times the derivative of the function, so that $f'(x) = (2)(2x) = 4x$. Your enemy mistakenly computed the *derivative* of the constant times the derivative of the function. (The derivative of a product of two functions is not the product of the derivative of the two functions. The rule for taking the derivative of a product is discussed in the next chapter.).
117. Answers may vary.

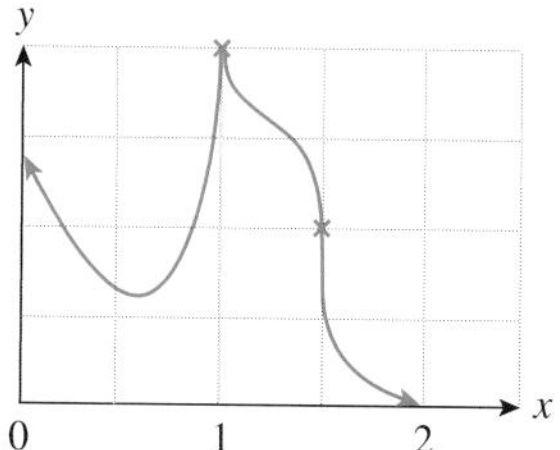

Section 3.8

1. $C'(1000) = \$4.80$ per item **3.** $C'(100) = \$99.90$ per item **5.** $C'(x) = 4$; $R'(x) = 8 - x/500$; $P'(x) = 4 - x/500$; $P'(x) = 0$ when $x = 2000$. Thus, at a production level of 2000, the profit is stationary (neither increasing nor decreasing) with respect to the production level. This may indicate a maximum profit at a production level of 2000. **7. a.** (B) **b.** (C) **c.** (C) **9. a.** $C'(x) = 2250 - 0.04x$. The cost is going up at a rate of \$2,249,840 per television commercial. The exact cost of airing the fifth television commercial is $C(5) - C(4) = \$2,249,820$. **b.** $\bar{C}(x) = 150/x + 2250 - 0.02x$; $\bar{C}(4) = \$2,287,420$ per television commercial. The average cost of airing the first four television commercials is \$2,287,420. **11. a.** $R'(x) = 0.90$, $P'(x) = 0.80 - 0.002x$ **b.** Revenue: \$450, Profit: \$80, Marginal revenue: \$0.90, Marginal profit: −\$0.20. The total revenue from the sale of 500 copies is \$450. The profit from the production and sale of 500 copies is \$80. Approximate revenue from the sale of the 501st copy is 90¢. Approximate loss from the sale of the 501st copy is 20¢. **c.** $x = 400$. The profit is a maximum when you produce and sell 400 copies. **13.** The profit on the sale of 1000 DVDs is \$3000, and is decreasing at a rate of \$3 per additional DVD sold. **15.** $P \approx \$257.07$ and $dP/dx \approx 5.07$. Your current profit is \$257.07 per month, and this would increase at a rate of \$5.07 per additional magazine in sales. **17. a.** \$2.50 per pound **b.** $R(q) = 20{,}000/q^{0.5}$ **c.** $R(400) = \$1000$. This is the monthly revenue that will result from setting the price at \$2.50 per pound. $R'(400) = -\$1.25$ per pound of tuna. Thus, at a demand level of 400 pounds per month, the revenue is decreasing at a rate of \$1.25 per pound. **d.** The fishery should raise the price (to reduce the demand). **19.** $P'(50) = \$350$. This means that, at an employment level of 50 workers, the firm's daily profit will increase at a rate of \$350 per additional worker it hires. **21. a.** (B) **b.** (B) **c.** (C) **23. a.** $C(x) = 500{,}000 + 1{,}600{,}000x - 100{,}000\sqrt{x}$; $C'(x) = 1{,}600{,}000 - \frac{50{,}000}{\sqrt{x}}$; $\bar{C}(x) = \frac{500{,}000}{x} + 1{,}600{,}000 - \frac{100{,}000}{\sqrt{x}}$ **b.** $C'(3) \approx \$1{,}570{,}000$ per spot, $\bar{C}(3) \approx \$1{,}710{,}000$ per spot. The average cost will decrease as x increases. **25. a.** $C'(q) = 200q$; $C'(10) = \$2000$ per one-pound reduction in emissions. **b.** $S'(q) = 500$. Thus $S'(q) = C'(q)$ when $500 = 200q$, or $q = 2.5$ pounds per day reduction. **c.** $N(q) = C(q) - S(q) = 100q^2 - 500q + 4000$. This is a parabola with lowest point (vertex) given by $q = 2.5$. The net cost at this production level is $N(2.5) = \$3375$ per day. The value of q is the same as that for part (b). The net cost to the firm is minimized at the reduction level for which the cost of controlling emissions begins to increase faster than the subsidy. This is why we get the answer by setting these two rates of increase equal to each other. **27.** $M'(10) \approx 0.0002557$ mpg/mph. This means that, at a speed of 10 mph, the fuel economy is increasing at a rate of 0.0002557 miles per gallon per 1-mph increase in speed. $M'(60) = 0$ mpg/mph. This means that, at a speed of 60 mph, the fuel economy is neither increasing nor decreasing with increasing speed. $M'(70) \approx -0.00001799$. This means that, at 70 mph, the fuel economy is decreasing at a rate of 0.00001799 miles per gallon per 1-mph increase in speed. Thus 60 mph is the most fuel-efficient speed for the car. **29.** (C) **31.** (D) **33.** (B)
35. Cost is often measured as a function of the number of items x. Thus, $C(x)$ is the cost of producing (or purchasing, as the case may be) x items. **a.** The average cost function $\bar{C}(x)$ is given by $\bar{C}(x) = C(x)/x$. The marginal cost function is the derivative, $C'(x)$, of the cost function. **b.** The average cost $\bar{C}(r)$ is the slope of the line through the origin and the point on the graph where $x = r$. The marginal cost of the rth unit is the slope of the tangent to the graph of the cost function at the point where $x = r$. **c.** The average cost function $\bar{C}(x)$ gives the average cost of producing the first x items. The marginal cost function $C'(x)$ is the rate at which cost is changing with respect to the number of items x, or the incremental cost per item, and approximates the cost of producing the $(x + 1)$st item. **37.** The marginal cost **39.** Not necessarily. For example, it may be the case that the marginal cost of the 101st item is larger than the average cost of the first 100 items (even though the marginal cost is decreasing). Thus, adding this additional item will *raise* the average cost. **41.** The circumstances described suggest that the average cost function is at a relatively low point at the current production level, and so it would be appropriate to advise the company to maintain current production levels; raising or lowering the production level will result in increasing average costs.

Chapter 3 Review

1. 5 **3.** Does not exist **5. a.** -1 **b.** 3 **c.** Does not exist **7.** $-4/5$ **9.** -1 **11.** Diverges to $-\infty$

13.

h	1	0.01	0.001
Ave. Rate of Change	-0.5	-0.9901	-0.9990

Slope ≈ -1

15.

h	1	0.01	0.001
Avg. Rate of Change	6.3891	2.0201	2.0020

Slope ≈ 2

17. a. (i) P (ii) Q (iii) R (iv) S **19.** (i) Q (ii) None (iii) None (iv) None **21. a.** (B) **b.** (B) **c.** (B) **d.** (A) **e.** (C) **23.** $2x+1$ **25.** $2/x^2$ **27.** $50x^4+2x^3-1$ **29.** $9x^2+x^{-2/3}$ **31.** $1-2/x^3$ **33.** $-4/(3x^2)+0.2/x^{1.1}+1.1x^{0.1}/3.2$ **35.** `50*x^4+2*x^3-1` **37.** `9*x^2+1/(x^2)^(1/3)`

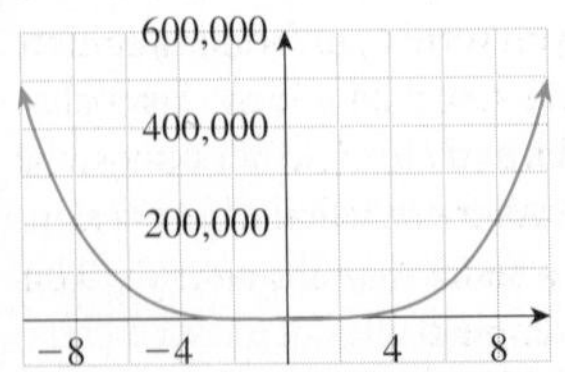

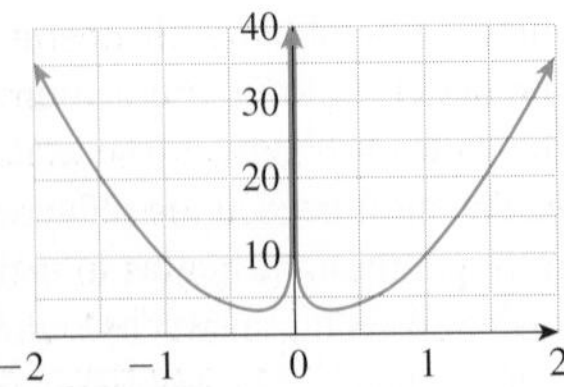

39. a. $P(3) = 25$: O'Hagan purchased the stock at \$25. $\lim_{t\to 3^-} P(t) = 25$: The value of the stock had been approaching \$25 up to the time he bought it. $\lim_{t\to 3^+} P(t) = 10$: The value of the stock dropped to \$10 immediately after he bought it. **b.** Continuous but not differentiable. Interpretation: the stock price changed continuously but suddenly reversed direction (and started to go up) the instant O'Hagan sold it. **41. a.** 500 books per week **b.** [3, 4], [4, 5] **c.**[3, 5]; 650 books per week **43. a.** 274 books per week **b.** 636 books per week **c.** No; the function w begins to decrease after $t = 14$. Graph:

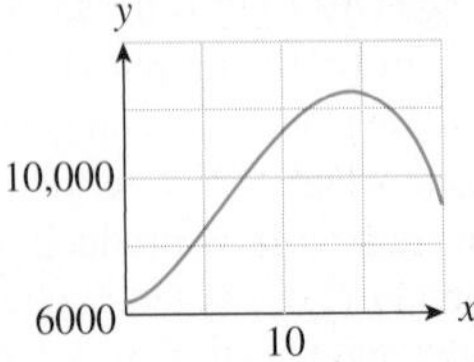

45. a. \$2.88 per book **b.** \$3.715 per book **c.** Approximately −\$0.000104 per book, per additional book sold. **d.** At a sales level of 8000 books per week, the cost is increasing at a rate of \$2.88 per book (so that the 8001st book costs approximately \$2.88 to sell), and it costs an average of \$3.715 per book to sell the first 8000 books. Moreover, the average cost is decreasing at a rate of \$0.000104 per book, per additional book sold.

Chapter 4

Section 4.1

1. 3 **3.** $3x^2$ **5.** $2x+3$ **7.** $210x^{1.1}$ **9.** $-2/x^2$ **11.** $2x/3$ **13.** $3(4x^2-1)+3x(8x)=36x^2-3$ **15.** $3x^2(1-x^2)+x^3(-2x)=3x^2-5x^4$ **17.** $2(2x+3)+(2x+3)(2)=8x+12$ **19.** $3\sqrt{x}/2$ **21.** $(x^2-1)+2x(x+1)=(x+1)(3x-1)$ **23.** $(x^{-0.5}+4)(x-x^{-1})+(2x^{0.5}+4x-5)(1+x^{-2})$ **25.** $8(2x^2-4x+1)(x-1)$ **27.** $(1/3.2-3.2/x^2)(x^2+1)+2x(x/3.2+3.2/x)$ **29.** $2x(2x+3)(7x+2)+2x^2(7x+2)+7x^2(2x+3)$ **31.** $5.3(1-x^{2.1})(x^{-2.3}-3.4)-2.1x^{1.1}(5.3x-1)\cdot(x^{-2.3}-3.4)-2.3x^{-3.3}(5.3x-1)(1-x^{2.1})$

33. $\dfrac{1}{2\sqrt{x}}\left(\sqrt{x}+\dfrac{1}{x^2}\right)+(\sqrt{x}+1)\left(\dfrac{1}{2\sqrt{x}}-\dfrac{2}{x^3}\right)$

35. $\dfrac{2(3x-1)-3(2x+4)}{(3x-1)^2}=-14/(3x-1)^2$

37.
$$\frac{(4x+4)(3x-1)-3(2x^2+4x+1)}{(3x-1)^2}=(6x^2-4x-7)/(3x-1)^2$$

39. $\dfrac{(2x-4)(x^2+x+1)-(x^2-4x+1)(2x+1)}{(x^2+x+1)^2}=(5x^2-5)/(x^2+x+1)^2$

41. $\dfrac{(0.23x^{-0.77}-5.7)(1-x^{-2.9})-2.9x^{-3.9}(x^{0.23}-5.7x)}{(1-x^{-2.9})^2}$

43. $\dfrac{\frac{1}{2}x^{-1/2}(x^{1/2}-1)-\frac{1}{2}x^{-1/2}(x^{1/2}+1)}{(x^{1/2}-1)^2}=\dfrac{-1}{\sqrt{x}(\sqrt{x}-1)^2}$

45. $-3/x^4$

47. $\dfrac{[(x+1)+(x+3)](3x-1)-3(x+3)(x+1)}{(3x-1)^2}=(3x^2-2x-13)/(3x-1)^2$

49. $\dfrac{[(x+1)(x+2)+(x+3)(x+2)+(x+3)(x+1)](3x-1)-3(x+3)(x+1)(x+2)}{(3x-1)^2}$

51. $4x^3-12x^2+2x-480$ **53.** $1+2/(x+1)^2$ **55.** $2x-1-2/(x+1)^2$ **57.** $4x^3-2x$ **59.** 64 **61.** 3 **63.** $y=12x-8$ **65.** $y=x/4+1/2$ **67.** $y=-2$ **69.** $q'(5)=1000$ units/month (sales are increasing at a rate of 1000 units per month); $p'(5)=-\$10$/month (the price of a sound system is dropping at a rate of \$10 per month); $R'(5)=900{,}000$ (revenue is increasing at a rate of \$900,000 per month) **71.** \$242 million; increasing at a rate of \$39 million per year **73.** Decreasing at a rate of \$1 per day **75.** Decreasing at a rate of approximately \$0.10 per month

77. $M'(x)=\dfrac{3000(3600x^{-2}-1)}{(x+3600x^{-1})^2}$; $M'(10)\approx 0.7670$ mpg/mph. This means that, at a speed of 10 mph, the fuel economy is increasing at a rate of 0.7670 miles per gallon per one mph increase in speed. $M'(60)=0$ mpg/mph. This means that, at a speed of 60 mph, the fuel economy is neither increasing nor decreasing with increasing speed. $M'(70)\approx -0.0540$. This means that, at 70 mph, the fuel economy is decreasing at a rate of

0.0540 miles per gallon per one mph increase in speed. 60 mph is the most fuel-efficient speed for the car. (In the next chapter we shall discuss how to locate largest values in general.) **79.** Increasing at a rate of about \$3420 million per year.

81. $R'(p) = -\dfrac{5.625}{(1+0.125p)^2}$; $R'(4) = -2.5$ thousand organisms per hour, per 1000 organisms. This means that the reproduction rate of organisms in a culture containing 4000 organisms is declining at a rate of 2500 organisms per hour, per 1000 additional organisms. **83.** Oxygen consumption is decreasing at a rate of 1600 milliliters per day. This is due to the fact that the number of eggs is decreasing, because $C'(25)$ is positive. **85. a.** $c(t) - m(t)$ represents the combined market share of the other three providers (Comcast, Earthlink, and AOL). $m(t)/c(t)$ represents MSN's market share as a fraction of the four providers considered. **b.** $\dfrac{d}{dt}\left(\dfrac{m(t)}{c(t)}\right)\Big|_{t=3} \approx -0.043$ (or -4.3 percentage points) per year. In June, 2003, MSN's market share as a fraction of the four providers considered was decreasing at a rate of about 0.043 (or 4.3 percentage points) per year. **87.** The analysis is suspect, because it seems to be asserting that the annual increase in revenue, which we can think of as dR/dt, is the product of the annual increases, dp/dt in price, and dq/dt in sales. However, because $R = pq$, the product rule implies that dR/dt is not the product of dp/dt and dq/dt, but is instead $\dfrac{dR}{dt} = \dfrac{dp}{dt}\cdot q + p\cdot\dfrac{dq}{dt}$. **89.** Answers will vary; $q = -p + 1000$ is one example. **91.** Mine; it is increasing twice as fast as yours. The rate of change of revenue is given by $R'(t) = p'(t)q(t)$ because $q'(t) = 0$ Thus, $R'(t)$ does not depend on the selling price $p(t)$. **93.** (A)

Section 4.2

1. $4(2x+1)$ **3.** $-(x-1)^{-2}$ **5.** $2(2-x)^{-3}$ **7.** $(2x+1)^{-0.5}$ **9.** $-4(4x-1)^{-2}$ **11.** $-3/(3x-1)^2$ **13.** $4(x^2+2x)^3(2x+2)$ **15.** $-4x(2x^2-2)^{-2}$ **17.** $-5(2x-3)(x^2-3x-1)^{-6}$ **19.** $-6x/(x^2+1)^4$ **21.** $1.5(0.2x-4.2)(0.1x^2-4.2x+9.5)^{0.5}$ **23.** $4(2s-0.5s^{-0.5})(s^2-s^{0.5})^3$ **25.** $-x/\sqrt{1-x^2}$ **27.** $-[(x+1)(x^2-1)]^{-3/2}(3x-1)(x+1)$ **29.** $6.2(3.1x-2)+6.2/(3.1x-2)^3$ **31.** $2[(6.4x-1)^2+(5.4x-2)^3][12.8(6.4x-1)+16.2(5.4x-2)^2]$ **33.** $-2(x^2-3x)^{-3}(2x-3)(1-x^2)^{0.5}-x(x^2-3x)^{-2}(1-x^2)^{-0.5}$ **35.** $-56(x+2)/(3x-1)^3$ **37.** $3z^2(1-z^2)/(1+z^2)^4$ **39.** $3[(1+2x)^4-(1-x)^2]^2[8(1+2x)^3+2(1-x)]$ **41.** $-0.43(x+1)^{-1.1}[2+(x+1)^{-0.1}]^{3.3}$ **43.** $-\dfrac{\left(\frac{1}{\sqrt{2x+1}}-2x\right)}{\left(\sqrt{2x+1}-x^2\right)^2}$ **45.** $54(1+2x)^2\left(1+(1+2x)^3\right)^2\left(1+\left(1+(1+2x)^3\right)^3\right)^2$ **47.** $(100x^{99}-99x^{-2})dx/dt$ **49.** $(-3r^{-4}+0.5r^{-0.5})dr/dt$ **51.** $4\pi r^2 dr/dt$ **53.** $-47/4$ **55.** $1/3$ **57.** $-5/3$ **59.** $1/4$ **61.** $y = 35(7+0.2t)^{-0.25}$; -0.11 percentage points per month. **63.** $\dfrac{dP}{dn}\Big|_{n=10} = 146{,}454.9$. At an employment level of 10 engineers, Paramount will increase its profit at a rate of \$146,454.90 per additional engineer hired. **65.** $-\$30$ per additional ruby sold. The revenue is decreasing at a rate of \$30 per additional ruby sold. **67.** $\dfrac{dy}{dt} = \dfrac{dy}{dx}\dfrac{dx}{dt} = (1.5)(-2) = -3$ murders per 100,000 residents/yr each year. **69.** 0.000158 manatees per boat, or 15.8 manatees per 100,000 boats. Approximately 15.8 more manatees are killed each year for each additional 100,000 registered boats. **71.** 12π mi²/h **73.** $\$200{,}000\pi$/week $\approx$ \$628,000/week **75. a.** $q'(4) \approx 333$ units per month **b.** $dR/dq = \$800$/unit **c.** $dR/dt \approx \$267{,}000$ per month **77.** 3% per year **79.** 8% per year **81.** The glob squared, times the derivative of the glob. **83.** The derivative of a quantity cubed is three times the (original) quantity squared, times the derivative of the quantity. Thus, the correct answer is $3(3x^3-x)^2(9x^2-1)$. **85.** Following the calculation thought experiment, pretend that you are evaluating the function at a specific value of x. If the last operation you would perform is addition or subtraction, look at each summand separately. If the last operation is multiplication, use the product rule first; if it is division, use the quotient rule first; if it is any other operation (such as raising a quantity to a power or taking a radical of a quantity), then use the chain rule first. **87.** An example is

$$f(x) = \sqrt{x+\sqrt{x+\sqrt{x+\sqrt{x+\sqrt{x+1}}}}}.$$

Section 4.3

1. $1/(x-1)$ **3.** $1/(x\ln 2)$ **5.** $2x/(x^2+3)$ **7.** e^{x+3} **9.** $-e^{-x}$ **11.** $4^x\ln 4$ **13.** $2^{x^2-1}\,2x\ln 2$ **15.** $1+\ln x$ **17.** $2x\ln x+(x^2+1)/x$ **19.** $10x(x^2+1)^4\ln x+(x^2+1)^5/x$ **21.** $3/(3x-1)$ **23.** $4x/(2x^2+1)$ **25.** $(2x-0.63x^{-0.7})/(x^2-2.1x^{0.3})$ **27.** $-2/(-2x+1)+1/(x+1)$ **29.** $3/(3x+1)-4/(4x-2)$ **31.** $1/(x+1)+1/(x-3)-2/(2x+9)$ **33.** $5.2/(4x-2)$ **35.** $2/(x+1)-9/(3x-4)-1/(x-9)$ **37.** $\dfrac{1}{(x+1)\ln 2}$ **39.** $\dfrac{1-1/t^2}{(t+1/t)\ln 3}$ **41.** $\dfrac{2\ln|x|}{x}$ **43.** $\dfrac{2}{x}-\dfrac{2\ln(x-1)}{x-1}$ **45.** $e^x(1+x)$ **47.** $1/(x+1)+3e^x(x^3+3x^2)$ **49.** $e^x(\ln|x|+1/x)$ **51.** $2e^{2x+1}$ **53.** $(2x-1)e^{x^2-x+1}$ **55.** $2xe^{2x-1}(1+x)$ **57.** $4(e^{2x-1})^2$ **59.** $2\cdot 3^{2x-4}\ln 3$ **61.** $2\cdot 3^{2x+1}\ln 3+3e^{3x+1}$ **63.** $\dfrac{2x3^{x^2}[(x^2+1)\ln 3-1]}{(x^2+1)^2}$ **65.** $-4/(e^x-e^{-x})^2$ **67.** $5e^{5x-3}$ **69.** $-\dfrac{\ln x+1}{(x\ln x)^2}$ **71.** $2(x-1)$ **73.** $\dfrac{1}{x\ln x}$ **75.** $\dfrac{1}{2x\ln x}$ **77.** $y = (e/\ln 2)(x-1) \approx 3.92(x-1)$ **79.** $y = x$ **81.** $y = -[1/(2e)](x-1)+e$ **83.** Average price: \$1.4 million; increasing at a rate of about \$220,000 per year. **85.** \$451.00 per year **87.** \$446.02 per year **89.** 300 articles per year **91.** 3,300,000 cases/week; 11,000,000 cases/week; 640,000 cases/week **93.** 310 articles per year **95.** 277,000 people/yr **97.** 0.000283 g/yr **99. a.** (A) **b.** The verbal SAT increases by

approximately 1 point. **c.** $S'(x)$ decreases with increasing x, so that as parental income increases, the effect on SAT scores decreases. **101. a.** -6.25 years/child; When the fertility rate is 2 children per woman, the average age of a population is dropping at a rate of 6.25 years per one-child increase in the fertility rate. **b.** 0.160
103. a. $W'(t) = -\dfrac{1500(0.77)(1.16)^{-t}(-1)\ln(1.16)}{(1+0.77(1.16)^{-t})^2}$

$\approx \dfrac{171.425(1.16)^{-t}}{(1+0.77(1.16)^{-t})^2}$; $W'(6) \approx 40.624 \approx 41$

to two significant digits. The constants in the model are specified to two and three significant digits, so we cannot expect the answer to be accurate to more than two digits. In other words, all digits from the third on are probably meaningless. The answer tells one that in 1996, the number of authorized wiretaps was increasing at a rate of approximately 41 wiretaps per year.
b. (A) Graph: **105. a.**

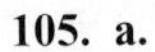

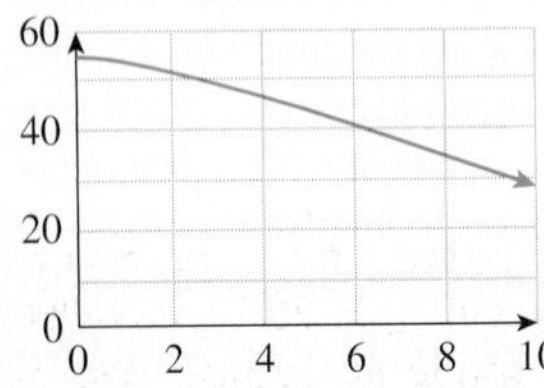

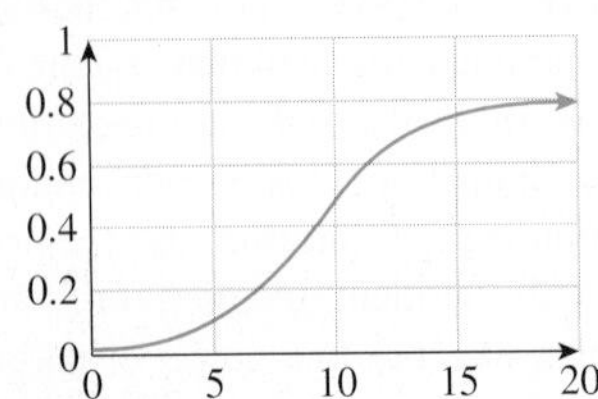

$p'(10) \approx 0.09$, so the percentage of firms using numeric control is increasing at a rate of 9 percentage points per year after 10 years. **b.** 0.80. Thus, in the long run, 80% of all firms will be using numeric control.
c. $p'(t) = 0.3816e^{4.46-0.477t}/(1+e^{4.46-0.477t})^2$.
$p'(10) = 0.0931$. Graph:

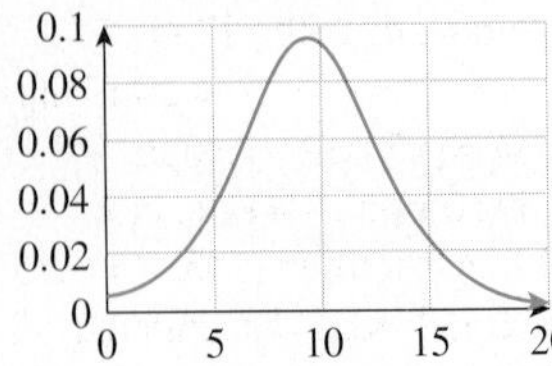

d. 0. Thus, in the long run, the percentage of firms using numeric control will stop increasing.
107. $R(t) = 350e^{-0.1t}(39t+68)$ million dollars; $R(2) \approx \$42$ billion; $R'(2) \approx \$7$ billion per year **109.** e raised to the glob, times the derivative of the glob. **111.** 2 raised to the glob, times the derivative of the glob, times the natural logarithm of 2.
113. The power rule does not apply when the exponent is not constant. The derivative of 3 raised to a quantity is 3 raised to the quantity, times the derivative of the quantity, times ln 3. Thus, the correct answer is $3^{2x}2\ln 3$. **115.** No. If $N(t)$ is exponential, so is its derivative. **117.** If $f(x) = e^{kx}$, then the fractional rate of change is $\dfrac{f'(x)}{f(x)} = \dfrac{ke^{kx}}{e^{kx}} = k$, the fractional growth rate. **119.** If $A(t)$ is growing exponentially, then $A(t) = A_0e^{kt}$ for constants A_0 and k. Its percentage rate of change is then

$\dfrac{A'(t)}{A(t)} = \dfrac{kA_0e^{kt}}{A_0e^{kt}} = k$, a constant.

Section 4.4

1. $-2/3$ **3.** x **5.** $(y-2)/(3-x)$ **7.** $-y$
9. $-\dfrac{y}{x(1+\ln x)}$ **11.** $-x/y$ **13.** $-2xy/(x^2-2y)$
15. $-(6+9x^2y)/(9x^3-x^2)$ **17.** $3y/x$
19. $(p+10p^2q)/(2p-q-10pq^2)$
21. $(ye^x-e^y)/(xe^y-e^x)$ **23.** $se^{st}/(2s-te^{st})$
25. $ye^x/(2e^x+y^3e^y)$ **27.** $(y-y^2)/(-1+3y-y^2)$
29. $-y/(x+2y-xye^y-y^2e^y)$ **31. a.** 1 **b.** $y=x-3$
33. a. -2 **b.** $y=-2x$ **35. a.** -1 **b.** $y=-x+1$
37. a. -2000 **b.** $y=-2000x+6000$ **39. a.** 0 **b.** $y=1$
41. a. -0.1898 **b.** $y=-0.1898x+1.4721$

43. $\dfrac{2x+1}{4x-2}\left[\dfrac{2}{2x+1}-\dfrac{4}{4x-2}\right]$

45. $\dfrac{(3x+1)^2}{4x(2x-1)^3}\left[\dfrac{6}{3x+1}-\dfrac{1}{x}-\dfrac{6}{2x-1}\right]$

47. $(8x-1)^{1/3}(x-1)\left[\dfrac{8}{3(8x-1)}+\dfrac{1}{x-1}\right]$

49. $(x^3+x)\sqrt{x^3+2}\left[\dfrac{3x^2+1}{x^3+x}+\dfrac{1}{2}\dfrac{3x^2}{x^3+2}\right]$

51. $x^x(1+\ln x)$ **53.** $-\$3000$ per worker. The monthly budget to maintain production at the fixed level P is decreasing by approximately \$3000 per additional worker at an employment level of 100 workers and a monthly operating budget of \$200,000.
55. -125 T-shirts per dollar; when the price is set at \$5, the demand is dropping by 125 T-shirts per \$1 increase in price.
57. $\left.\dfrac{dk}{de}\right|_{e=15} = -0.307$ carpenters per electrician. This means that, for a \$200,000 house whose construction employs 15 electricians, adding one more electrician would cost as much as approximately 0.307 additional carpenters. In other words, one electrician is worth approximately 0.307 carpenters.
59. a. 22.93 hours. (The other root is rejected because it is larger than 30.) **b.** $\dfrac{dt}{dx} = \dfrac{4t-20x}{0.4t-4x}$; $\left.\dfrac{dt}{dx}\right|_{x=3.0} \approx -11.2$ hours per grade point. This means that, for a 3.0 student who scores 80 on the examination, 1 grade point is worth approximately 11.2 hours.
61. $\dfrac{dr}{dy} = 2\dfrac{r}{y}$, so $\dfrac{dr}{dt} = 2\dfrac{r}{y}\dfrac{dy}{dt}$ by the chain rule.
63. x, y, y, x
65. Then $\ln y = \ln f(x) + \ln g(x)$, and $\dfrac{1}{y}\dfrac{dy}{dx} = \dfrac{f'(x)}{f(x)} + \dfrac{g'(x)}{g(x)}$, so $\dfrac{dy}{dx} = y\left(\dfrac{f'(x)}{f(x)}+\dfrac{g'(x)}{g(x)}\right) = f(x)g(x)\left(\dfrac{f'(x)}{f(x)}+\dfrac{g'(x)}{g(x)}\right) = f'(x)g(x)+f(x)g'(x)$.
67. Writing $y=f(x)$ specifies y as an explicit function of x. This can be regarded as an equation giving y as an *implicit* function of x. The procedure of finding dy/dx by implicit differentiation is then the same as finding the derivative of y as an explicit function of x: we take d/dx of both sides. **69.** Differentiate both sides of the equation $y=f(x)$ with respect to y to get $1 = f'(x)\cdot\dfrac{dx}{dy}$, giving $\dfrac{dx}{dy} = \dfrac{1}{f'(x)} = \dfrac{1}{dy/dx}$.

Chapter 4 Review

1. $e^x(x^2+2x-1)$ **3.** $20x(x^2-1)^9$
5. $e^x(x^2+1)^9(x^2+20x+1)$
7. $3^x[(x-1)\ln 3-1]/(x-1)^2$ **9.** $2xe^{x^2-1}$
11. $2x/(x^2-1)$ **13.** $x=(1-\ln 2)/2$
15. None **17.** $\dfrac{2x-1}{2y}$ **19.** $-y/x$
21.
$$\frac{(2x-1)^4(3x+4)}{(x+1)(3x-1)^3}\left[\frac{8}{2x-1}+\frac{3}{3x+4}-\frac{1}{x+1}-\frac{9}{3x-1}\right]$$
23. $y=x+2$

25. $R'(0)=p'(0)q(0)+p(0)q'(0)$
$=(-1)(1000)+20(200)=\$3000$ per week (rising)

27. $R=pq$ gives $R'=p'q+pq'$. Thus, $R'/R=R'/(pq)=(p'q+pq')/pq=p'/p+q'/q$

29. \$110 per year **31.** $s'(t)=\dfrac{2460.7e^{-0.55(t-4.8)}}{(1+e^{-0.55(t-4.8)})^2}$; 553 books per week **33.** 616.8 hits per day per week

57. Answers will vary.

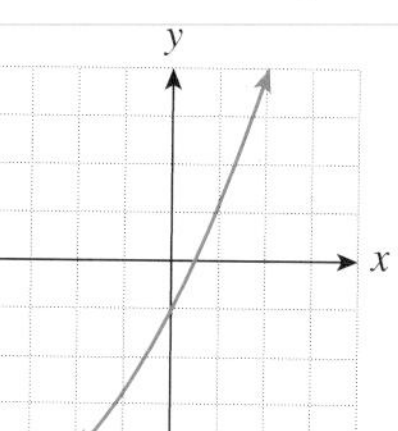

59. Answers will vary.

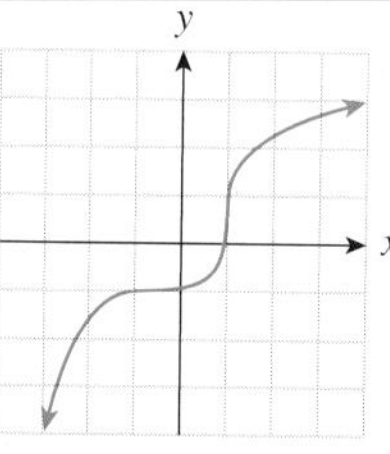

61. Not necessarily; it could be neither a relative maximum nor a relative minimum, as in the graph of $y=x^3$ at the origin.
63. Answers will vary.

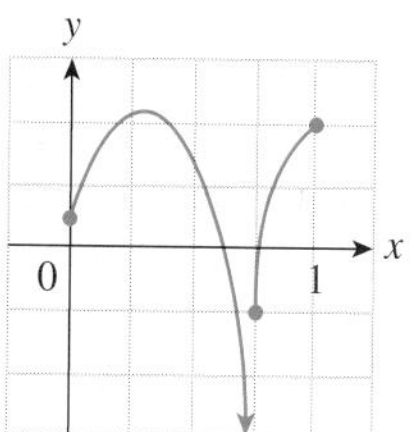

Chapter 5

Section 5.1

1. Absolute min.: $(-3,-1)$, relative max: $(-1,1)$, relative min: $(1,0)$, absolute max: $(3,2)$ **3.** Absolute min: $(3,-1)$ and $(-3,-1)$, absolute max: $(1,2)$ **5.** Absolute min: $(-3,0)$ and $(1,0)$, absolute max: $(-1,2)$ and $(3,2)$ **7.** Relative min: $(-1,1)$ **9.** Absolute min: $(-3,-1)$, relative max: $(-2,2)$, relative min: $(1,0)$, absolute max: $(3,3)$ **11.** Relative max: $(-3,0)$, absolute min: $(-2,-1)$, stationary non-extreme point: $(1,1)$ **13.** Absolute max: $(0,1)$, absolute min: $(2,-3)$, relative max: $(3,-2)$ **15.** Absolute min: $(-4,-16)$, absolute max: $(-2,16)$, absolute min: $(2,-16)$, absolute max: $(4,16)$
17. Absolute min: $(-2,-10)$, absolute max: $(2,10)$
19. Absolute min: $(-2,-4)$, relative max: $(-1,1)$, relative min: $(0,0)$ **21.** Relative max: $(-1,5)$, absolute min: $(3,-27)$ **23.** Absolute min: $(0,0)$ **25.** Absolute maxima at $(0,1)$ and $(2,1)$, absolute min at $(1,0)$ **27.** Relative maximum at $(-2,-1/3)$, relative minimum at $(-1,-2/3)$, absolute maximum at $(0,1)$ **29.** Relative min: $(-2,5/3)$, relative max: $(0,-1)$, relative min: $(2,5/3)$ **31.** Relative max: $(0,0)$; absolute min: $(1/3,-2\sqrt{3}/9)$ **33.** Relative max: $(0,0)$, absolute min: $(1,-3)$ **35.** No relative extrema **37.** Absolute min: $(1,1)$ **39.** Relative max: $(-1,1+1/e)$, absolute min: $(0,1)$, absolute max: $(1,e-1)$ **41.** Relative max: $(-6,-24)$, relative min: $(-2,-8)$ **43.** Absolute max $(1/\sqrt{2},\sqrt{e/2})$, absolute min: $(-1/\sqrt{2},-\sqrt{e/2})$ **45.** Relative min at $(0.15,-0.52)$ and $(2.45,8.22)$, relative max at $(1.40,0.29)$ **47.** Absolute max at $(-5,700)$, relative max at $(3.10,28.19)$ and $(6,40)$, absolute min at $(-2.10,-392.69)$ and relative min at $(5,0)$. **49.** Stationary minimum at $x=-1$ **51.** Stationary minima at $x=-2$ and $x=2$, stationary maximum at $x=0$ **53.** Singular minimum at $x=0$, stationary non-extreme point at $x=1$ **55.** Stationary minimum at $x=-2$, singular non-extreme points at $x=-1$ and $x=1$, stationary maximum at $x=2$

Section 5.2

1. $x=y=5$; $P=25$ **3.** $x=y=3$; $S=6$ **5.** $x=2$, $y=4$; $F=20$ **7.** $x=20$, $y=10$, $z=20$; $P=4000$
9. 5×5 **11.** 5000 MP3 players, giving an average cost of \$30 per MP3 player **13.** $\sqrt{40}\approx 6.32$ pounds of pollutant per day, for an average cost of about \$1265 per pound **15.** 2.5 lb
17. $5\times 10=50$ square feet **19.** \$10 **21.** \$30
23. a. \$1.41 per pound **b.** 5000 pounds **c.** \$7071.07 per month
25. 34.5¢ per pound, for an annual (per capita) revenue of \$5.95
27. \$42.50 per ruby, for a weekly profit of \$408.33 **29. a.** 656 headsets, for a profit of \$28,120 **b.** \$143 per headset
31. $13\frac{1}{3}$ in $\times\ 3\frac{1}{3}$ in $\times\ 1\frac{1}{3}$ in for a volume of $1600/27\approx$ 59 cubic inches **33.** $5\times 5\times 5$ cm **35.** $l=w=h\approx 20.67$ in, volume ≈ 8827 in^3 **37.** $l=30$ in, $w=15$ in, $h=30$ in
39. $l=36$ in, $w=h=18$ in, $V=11{,}664$ in^3 **41. a.** 1.6 years, or year 2001.6; **b.** $R_{max}=\$28{,}241$ million **43.** $t=2.5$ or midway through 1972.; $D(2.5)/S(2.5)\approx 4.09$ The number of new (approved) drugs per \$1 billion of spending on research and development reached a high of around 4 approved drugs per \$1 billion midway through 1972. **45.** 30 years from now
47. 55 days **49.** 1600 copies. At this value of x, average profit equals marginal profit; beyond this the marginal profit is smaller than the average. **51.** Increasing most rapidly in 1992; increasing least rapidly in 1980 **53.** Maximum when $t=17$ days. This means that the embryo's oxygen consumption is increasing most rapidly 17 days after the egg is laid. **55.** $h=r\approx 11.7$ cm
57. 25 additional trees **59.** 71 employees **61.** Fourth quarter of 2003 ($t\approx 3.7$); 160 thousand iPods per quarter
63. Graph of derivative:

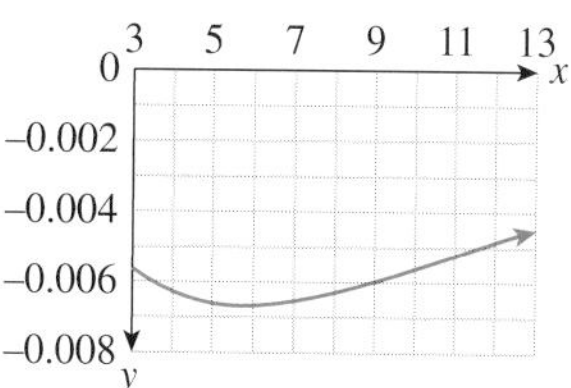

Absolute minimum occurs at approximately $t = 6$, with value approximately -0.0067. The fraction of bottled water sales due to sparkling water was decreasing most rapidly in 1996. At that time it was decreasing at a rate of 0.67 percentage points per year. **65.** You should sell them in 17 years' time, when they will be worth approximately \$3960. **67.** (D) **69.** The problem is uninteresting because the company can accomplish the objective by cutting away the entire sheet of cardboard, resulting in a box with surface area zero. **71.** Not all absolute extrema occur at stationary points; some may occur at an endpoint or singular point of the domain, as in Exercises 23, 24, 51 and 52. **73.** The minimum of dq/dp is the fastest that the demand is dropping in response to increasing price.

Section 5.3

1. 6 **3.** $4/x^3$ **5.** $-0.96x^{-1.6}$ **7.** $e^{-(x-1)}$ **9.** $2/x^3 + 1/x^2$
11. a. $a = -32$ ft/sec^2 **b.** $a = -32$ ft/sec^2
13. a. $a = 2/t^3 + 6/t^4$ ft/sec^2 **b.** $a = 8$ ft/sec^2
15. a. $a = -1/(4t^{3/2}) + 2$ ft/sec^2
b. $a = 63/32$ ft/sec^2 **17.** $(1, 0)$ **19.** $(1, 0)$ **21.** None
23. $(-1, 0)$, $(1, 1)$ **25.** Points of inflection at $x = -1$ and $x = 1$ **27.** One point of inflection, at $x = -2$ **29.** Points of inflection at $x = -2$, $x = 0$, $x = 2$ **31.** Points of inflection at $x = -2$ and $x = 2$

33. Absolute min at $(-1, 0)$; no points of inflection

35. Relative max at $(-2, 21)$; relative min at $(1, -6)$; point of inflection at $(-1/2, 15/2)$

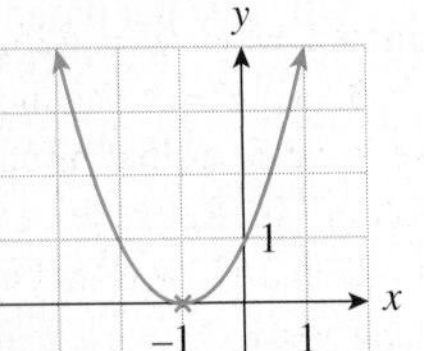

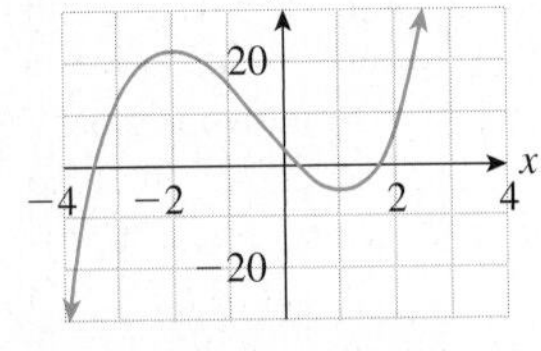

37. Absolute min at $(-4, -16)$ and $(2, -16)$; absolute max at $(-2, 16)$ and $(4, 16)$; point of inflection at $(0, 0)$

39. Absolute min at $(0, 0)$; points of inflection at $(1/3, 11/324)$ and $(1, 1/12)$

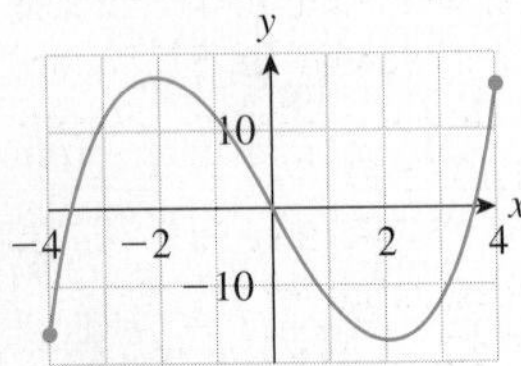

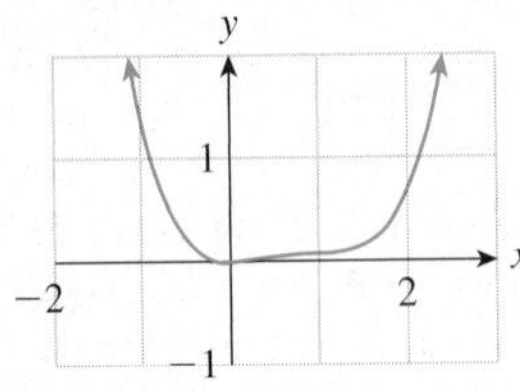

41. Relative min at $(-2, 5/3)$ and $(2, 5/3)$; relative max at $(0, -1)$; vertical asymptotes: $x = \pm 1$

43. Relative min at $(1, 2)$; relative max at $(-1, -2)$; vertical asymptote: $y = 0$

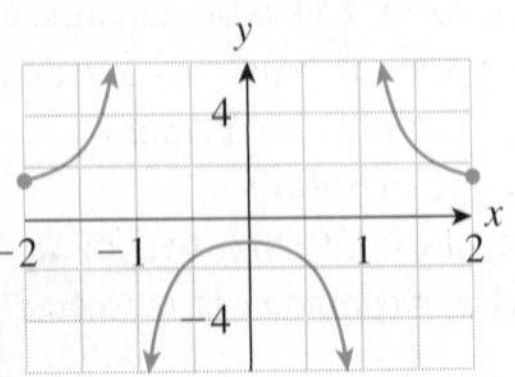

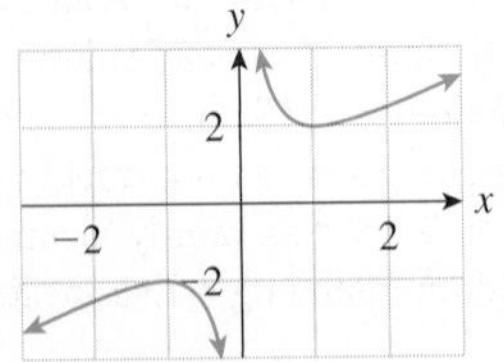

45. Relative maximum at $(-2, -1/3)$; relative minimum at $(-1, -2/3)$; no points of inflection

47. No extrema; points of inflection at $(0, 0)$, $(-3, -9/4)$, and $(3, 9/4)$

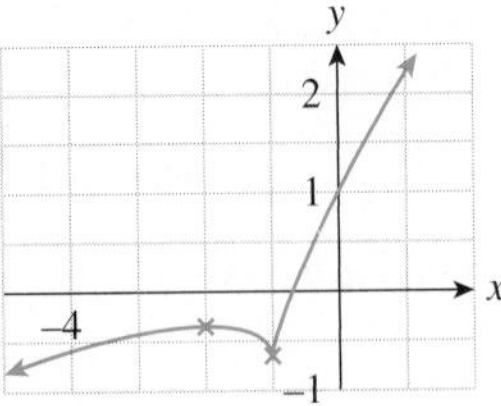

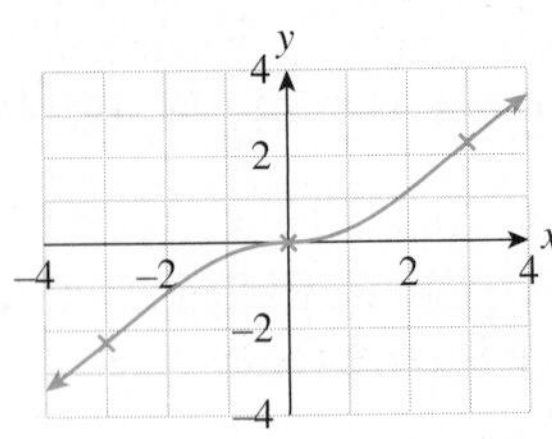

49. Absolute min at $(1, 1)$; vertical asymptote at $x = 0$

51. No relative extrema; point of inflection at $(1, 1)$ and $(-1, 1)$; vertical asymptote at $x = 0$

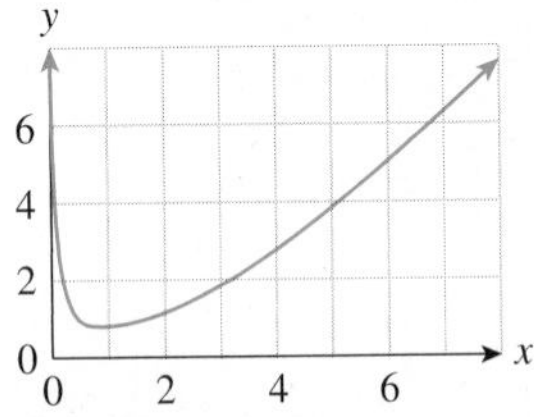

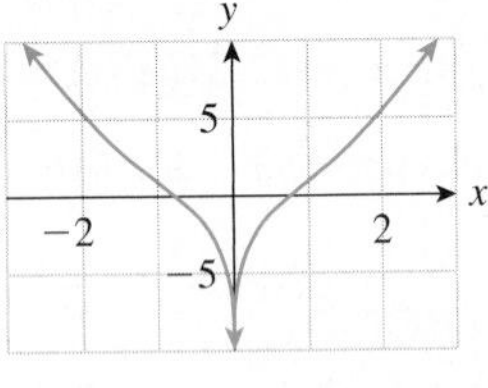

53. Absolute min at $(0, 1)$, absolute max at $(1, e - 1)$, relative max at $(-1, 1 + e^{-1})$

55. Absolute min at $(1.40, -1.49)$; points of inflection: $(0.21, 0.61)$, $(0.79, -0.55)$

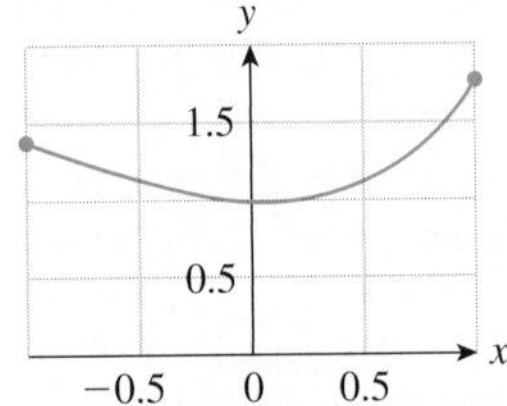

57. Relative min at $(-0.46, 0.73)$; relative max at $(0.91, 1.73)$; absolute min at $(3.73, -10.22)$; points of inflection at $(0.20, 1.22)$ and $(2.83, -5.74)$

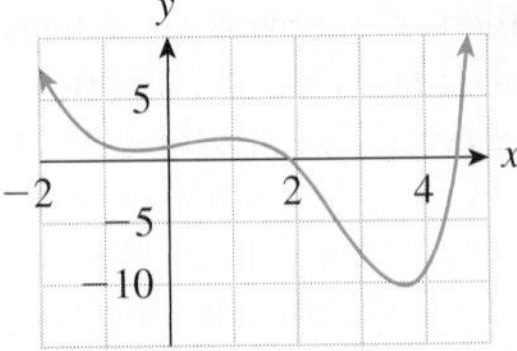

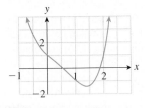

59. -3.8 m/s^2 **61.** $6t - 2$ ft/s^2; increasing **63.** Accelerating by 34 million gals/yr^2 **65. a.** 400 ml **b.** 36 ml/day **c.** -1 ml/day^2 **67. a.** Two years into the epidemic **b.** Two years into the epidemic **69. a.** 2000 **b.** 2002 **c.** 1998 **71.** Concave up for $8 < t < 20$, concave down for $0 < t < 8$, point of inflection around $t = 8$. The percentage of articles written by researchers in the U.S. was decreasing most rapidly at around $t = 8$ (1991). **73. a.** (B) **b.** (B) **c.** (A) **75. a.** There are no points of inflection in the graph of S. **b.** Because the graph is concave up, the derivative of S is increasing, and so the rate of *decrease* of SAT scores with increasing numbers of prisoners is diminishing. In other words, the apparent effect of more prisoners is diminishing.

77. a. $\left.\dfrac{d^2n}{ds^2}\right|_{s=3} = -21.494$. Thus, for a firm with annual sales of \$3 million, the rate at which new patents are produced decreases with increasing firm size. This means that the returns (as measured in the number of new patents per increase of \$1 million in sales) are diminishing as the firm size increases.

b. $\left.\dfrac{d^2n}{ds^2}\right|_{s=7} = 13.474$. Thus, for a firm with annual sales of \$7 million, the rate at which new patents are produced increases with increasing firm size by 13.474 new patents per \$1 million increase in annual sales. **c.** There is a point of inflection when $s \approx 5.4587$, so that in a firm with sales of \$5,458,700 per year, the number of new patents produced per additional \$1 million in sales is a minimum. **79.** Concave down; (C). Graph:

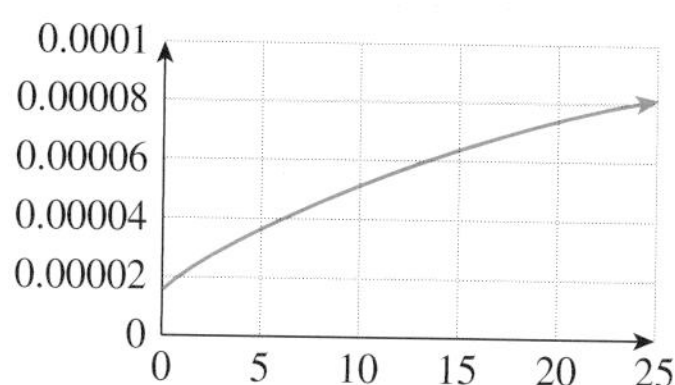

81. About \$570 per year, after about 12 years **83.** Increasing most rapidly in 17.64 years, decreasing most rapidly now (at $t = 0$) **85.** Nonnegative **87.** Daily sales were decreasing most rapidly in June, 2002.

89.

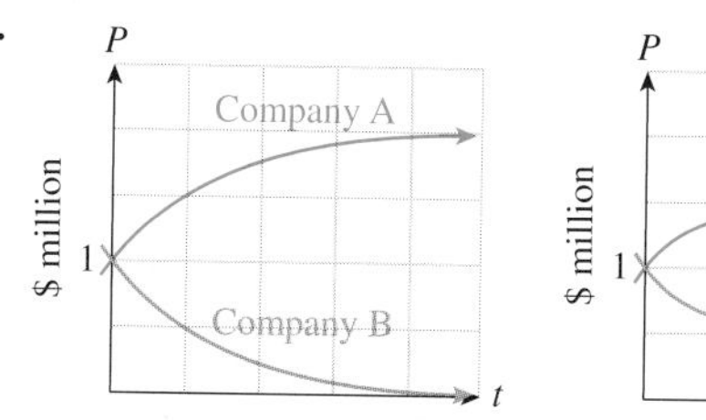

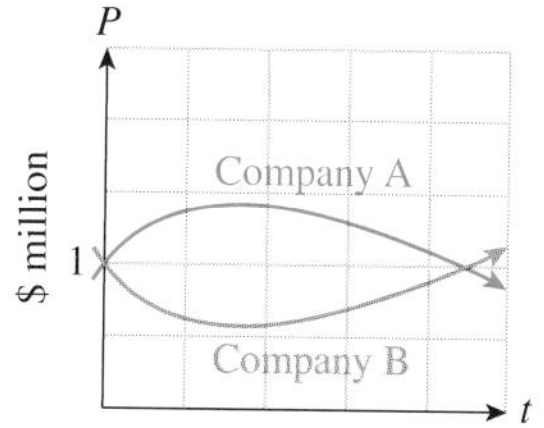

91. At a point of inflection, the graph of a function changes either from concave up to concave down, or vice versa. If it changes from concave up to concave down, then the derivative changes from increasing to decreasing, and hence has a relative maximum. Similarly, if it changes from concave down to concave up, the derivative has a relative minimum.

Section 5.4

1. $P = 10{,}000$; $\dfrac{dP}{dt} = 1000$ **3.** Let R be the annual revenue of my company, and let q be annual sales. $R = 7000$ and $\dfrac{dR}{dt} = -700$. Find $\dfrac{dq}{dt}$. **5.** Let p be the price of a pair of shoes, and let q be the demand for shoes. $\dfrac{dp}{dt} = 5$. Find $\dfrac{dq}{dt}$. **7.** Let T be the average global temperature, and let q be the number of Bermuda shorts sold per year. $T = 60$ and $\dfrac{dT}{dt} = 0.1$. Find $\dfrac{dq}{dt}$. **9. a.** $6/(100\pi) \approx 0.019$ km/sec **b.** $6/(8\sqrt{\pi}) \approx 0.4231$ km/sec **11.** $3/(4\pi) \approx 0.24$ ft/min **13.** 7.5 ft/sec **15.** Decreasing at a rate of \$1.66 per player per week **17.** Monthly sales will drop at a rate of 26 T-shirts per month. **19.** Raise the price by 3¢ per week. **21.** The daily operating budget is dropping at a rate of \$2.40 per year. **23.** The price is decreasing at a rate of approximately 31¢ per pound per month. **25.** $2300/\sqrt{4100} \approx 36$ miles/hour. **27.** 10.7 ft/sec **29.** The y-coordinate is decreasing at a rate of 16 units per second. **31.** \$1814 per year **33.** Their prior experience must increase at a rate of approximately 0.97 years every year. **35.** $\dfrac{2500}{9\pi}\left(\dfrac{3}{5000}\right)^{2/3} \approx 0.63$ m/sec **37.** $\sqrt{\dfrac{1+128\pi}{4\pi}} \approx 1.6$ cm/sec **39.** 0.5137 computers per household, and increasing at a rate of 0.0230 computers per household per year. **41.** The average SAT score was 904.71 and decreasing at a rate of 0.11 per year. **43.** Decreasing by 2 percentage points per year **45.** The section is called "related rates" because the goal is to compute the rate of change of a quantity based on a knowledge of the rate of change of a related quantity. **47.** Answers may vary: A rectangular solid has dimensions 2 cm × 5 cm × 10 cm, and each side is expanding at a rate of 3 cm/second. How fast is the volume increasing? **51.** Linear **53.** Let x = my grades and y = your grades. If $dx/dt = 2\,dy/dt$, then $dy/dt = (1/2)\,dx/dt$.

Section 5.5

1. $E = 1.5$; the demand is going down 1.5% per 1% increase in price at that price level; revenue is maximized when $p = \$25$; weekly revenue at that price is \$12,500. **3. a.** $E = 6/7$; the demand is going down 6% per 7% increase in price at that price level; thus a price increase is in order. **b.** Revenue is maximized when $p = 100/3 \approx \$33.33$ **c.** Demand would be $(100 - 100/3)^2 = (200/3)^2 \approx 4444$ cases per week.
5. a. $E = (4p - 33)/(-2p + 33)$ **b.** 0.54; The demand for $E = mc^2$ T-shirts is going down by about 0.54% per 1% increase in the price. **c.** \$11 per shirt for a daily revenue of \$1331
7. a. $E = 1.81$. Thus, the demand is elastic at the given tuition level, showing that a decrease in tuition will result in an increase in revenue. **b.** They should charge an average of \$2250 per student, and this will result in an enrollment of about 4950 students, giving a revenue of about \$11,137,500. **9. a.** $E = 51$; the demand is going down 51% per 1% increase in price at that price level; thus a large price decrease is advised.
b. Revenue is maximized when $p = ¥0.50$. **c.** Demand would be $100e^{-3/4+1/2} \approx 78$ paint-by-number sets per month.
11. a. $E = -\dfrac{mp}{mp+b}$ **b.** $p = -\dfrac{b}{2m}$ **13. a.** $E = r$
b. E is independent of p. **c.** If $r = 1$, then the revenue is not affected by the price. If $r > 1$, then the revenue is always elastic, while if $r < 1$, the revenue is always inelastic. This is an unrealistic model because there should always be a price at which the revenue is a maximum. **15. a.** $q = -1500p + 6000$. **b.** \$2 per hamburger, giving a total weekly revenue of \$6000.
17. $E \approx 0.77$. At a family income level of \$20,000, the fraction of children attending a live theatrical performance is increasing

by 0.77% per 1% increase in household income. **19. a.** $E \approx 0.46$. The demand for computers is increasing by 0.46% per one percent increase in household income. **b.** E decreases as income increases. **c.** Unreliable; it predicts a likelihood greater than 1 at incomes of \$123,000 and above. In a more appropriate model, one would expect the curve to level off at or below 1. **d.** $E \approx 0$ **21.** $\frac{Y}{Q} \cdot \frac{dQ}{dY} = \beta$. An increase in income of x% will result in an increase in demand of βx%. (Note that we do *not* take the negative here, because we expect an increase in income to produce an *increase* in demand.) **23. a.** $q = 1000e^{-0.30p}$ **b.** At $p = \$3$, $E = 0.9$; at $p = \$4$, $E = 1.2$; at $p = \$5$, $E = 1.5$ **c.** $p = \$3.33$ **d.** $p = \$5.36$. Selling at a lower price would increase demand, but you cannot sell more than 200 pounds anyway. You should charge as much as you can and still be able to sell all 200 pounds. **25.** The price is lowered. **27.** Start with $R = pq$, and differentiate with respect to p to obtain $\frac{dR}{dp} = q + p\frac{dq}{dp}$. For a stationary point, $dR/dp = 0$, and so $q + p\frac{dq}{dp} = 0$. Rearranging this result gives $p\frac{dq}{dp} = -q$, and hence $-\frac{dq}{dp} \cdot \frac{p}{q} = 1$, or $E = 1$, showing that stationary points of R correspond to points of unit elasticity. **29.** The distinction is best illustrated by an example. Suppose that q is measured in weekly sales and p is the unit price in dollars. Then the quantity $-dq/dp$ measures the drop in weekly sales per \$1 increase in price. The elasticity of demand E, on the other hand, measures the *percentage* drop in sales per *one percent* increase in price. Thus, $-dq/dp$ measures absolute change, while E measures fractional, or percentage, change.

Chapter 5 Review

1. Relative max: $(-1, 5)$, Absolute min: $(-2, -3)$ and $(1, -3)$ **3.** Absolute max: $(-1, 5)$, Absolute min: $(1, -3)$ **5.** Absolute min: $(1, 0)$ **7.** Absolute min: $(-2, -1/4)$ **9.** Relative max at $x = 1$, point of inflection at $x = -1$ **11.** Relative max at $x = -2$, relative min at $x = 1$, point of inflection at $x = -1$ **13.** One point of inflection, at $x = 0$ **15. a.** $a = 4/t^4 - 2/t^3$ m/sec² **b.** 2 m/sec² **17.** Relative max: $(-2, 16)$; absolute min: $(2, -16)$; point of inflection: $(0, 0)$; no horizontal or vertical asymptotes

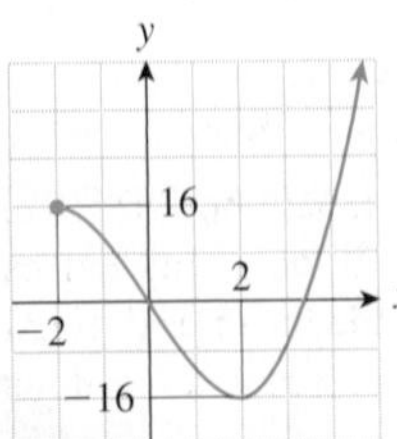

19. Relative min: $(-3, -2/9)$; relative max: $(3, 2/9)$; inflection: $(-3\sqrt{2}, -5\sqrt{2}/36)$, $(3\sqrt{2}, 5\sqrt{2}/36)$; vertical asymptote: $x = 0$; horizontal asymptote: $y = 0$

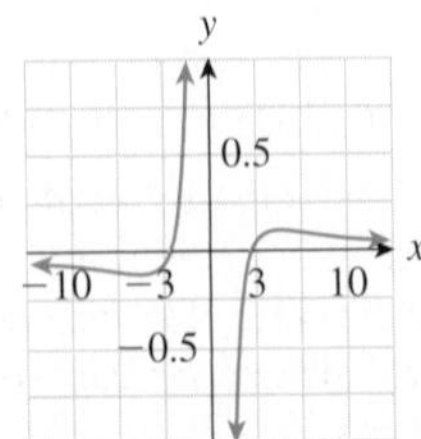

21. Relative max at (0,0), absolute min at $(1, -2)$, no asymptotes

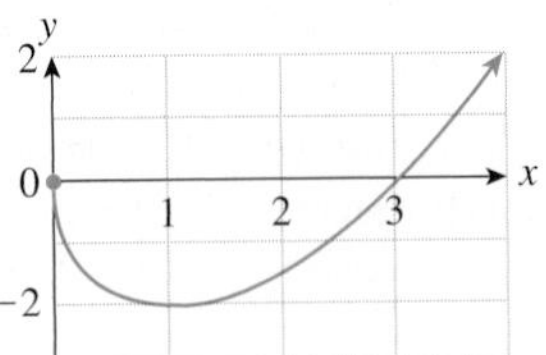

23. \$22.14 per book **25.** \$24 per copy **27.** For maximum revenue, the company should charge \$22.14 per copy. At this price, the cost is decreasing at a linear rate with increasing price, while the revenue is not decreasing (its derivative is zero). Thus, the profit is increasing with increasing price, suggesting that the maximum profit will occur at a higher price. **29.** $E = \frac{2p^2 - 33p}{-p^2 + 33p + 9}$ **31.** \$22.14 per book **33.** $E = 6$; The demand is dropping at a rate of 6% per 1% increase in the price. **35.** Week 5 **37.** 10,500; If weekly sales continue as predicted by the model, they will level off at around 10,500 books per week in the long-term. **39. a–d.** $10/\sqrt{2}$ ft/sec

Chapter 6

Section 6.1

1. $x^6/6 + C$ **3.** $6x + C$ **5.** $x^2/2 + C$ **7.** $x^3/3 - x^2/2 + C$ **9.** $x + x^2/2 + C$ **11.** $-x^{-4}/4 + C$ **13.** $x^{3.3}/3.3 - x^{-0.3}/0.3 + C$ **15.** $u^3/3 - \ln|u| + C$ **17.** $\frac{2x^{3/2}}{3} + C$ **19.** $3x^5/5 + 2x^{-1} - x^{-4}/4 + 4x + C$ **21.** $2\ln|u| + u^2/8 + C$ **23.** $\ln|x| - \frac{2}{x} + \frac{1}{2x^2} + C$ **25.** $3x^{1.1}/1.1 - x^{5.3}/5.3 - 4.1x + C$ **27.** $\frac{x^{0.9}}{0.3} + \frac{40}{x^{0.1}} + C$ **29.** $2.55t^2 - 1.2\ln|t| - \frac{15}{t^{0.2}} + C$ **31.** $2e^x + 5\ln|x| + x/4 + C$ **33.** $12.2x^{0.5} + x^{1.5}/9 - e^x + C$ **35.** $\frac{2^x}{\ln 2} - \frac{3^x}{\ln 3} + C$ **37.** $\frac{100(1.1^x)}{\ln(1.1)} + C$ **39.** $-1/x - 1/x^2 + C$ **41.** $f(x) = x^2/2 + 1$ **43.** $f(x) = e^x - x - 1$ **45.** $C(x) = 5x - x^2/20{,}000 + 20{,}000$ **47.** $C(x) = 5x + x^2 + \ln x + 994$ **49. a.** $s = t^3/3 + t + C$ **b.** $C = 1$; $s = t^3/3 + t + 1$ **51.** 320 ft/s downwards **53. a.** $v(t) = -32t + 16$ **b.** $s(t) = -16t^2 + 16t + 185$; zenith at $t = 0.5$ sec $s = 189$ feet, 4 feet above the top of the tower. **57.** $(1280)^{1/2} \approx 35.78$ ft/sec **59. a.** 80 ft/sec **b.** 60 ft/sec **c.** 1.25 seconds **61.** $\sqrt{2} \approx 1.414$ times as fast **63.** $I(t) = 30{,}000 + 1000t$; $I(13) = \$43{,}000$ **65. a.** $H'(t) = 3.5t + 65$ billion dollars per year **b.** $H(t) = 1.75t^2 + 65t + 700$ billion dollars **67.** $S(t) \approx \frac{17}{3}t^3 + 50t^2 + 2300t - 7503$ million gallons. Approximately 43,000 million gallons. **69.** They differ by a constant, $G(x) - F(x) =$ Constant **71.** Antiderivative, marginal **73.** $\int f(x)\,dx$ represents the total cost of manufacturing

x items. The units of $\int f(x)\,dx$ are the product of the units of $f(x)$ and the units of x. **75.** $\int(f(x)+g(x))\,dx$ is, by definition, an antiderivative of $f(x)+g(x)$. Let $F(x)$ be an antiderivative of $f(x)$ and let $G(x)$ be an antiderivative of $g(x)$. Then, because the derivative of $F(x)+G(x)$ is $f(x)+g(x)$ (by the rule for sums of derivatives), this means that $F(x)+G(x)$ is an antiderivative of $f(x)+g(x)$. In symbols, $\int(f(x)+g(x))\,dx =$ $F(x)+G(x)+C = \int f(x)\,dx + \int g(x)\,dx$, the sum of the indefinite integrals. **77.** $\int x\cdot 1\,dx = \int x\,dx = x^2/2+C$, whereas $\int x\,dx \cdot \int 1\,dx = (x^2/2+D)\cdot(x+E)$, which is not the same as $x^2/2+C$, no matter what values we choose for the constants C, D and E. **79.** If you take the *derivative* of the *indefinite integral* of $f(x)$, you obtain $f(x)$ back. On the other hand, if you take the *indefinite integral* of the *derivative* of $f(x)$, you obtain $f(x)+C$.

Section 6.2

1. $(3x-5)^4/12+C$ **3.** $(3x-5)^4/12+C$ **5.** $-e^{-x}+C$ **7.** $-e^{-x}+C$ **9.** $\frac{1}{2}e^{(x+1)^2}+C$ **11.** $(3x+1)^6/18+C$ **13.** $(-2x+2)^{-1}/2+C$ **15.** $1.6(3x-4)^{3/2}+C$ **17.** $2e^{(0.6x+2)}+C$ **19.** $(3x^2+3)^4/24+C$ **21.** $(x^2+1)^{2.3}/4.6+C$ **23.** $x+3e^{3.1x-2}+C$ **25.** $2(3x^2-1)^{3/2}/9+C$ **27.** $-(1/2)e^{-x^2+1}+C$ **29.** $-(1/2)e^{-(x^2+2x)}+C$ **31.** $(x^2+x+1)^{-2}/2+C$ **33.** $(2x^3+x^6-5)^{1/2}/3+C$ **35.** $(x-2)^7/7+(x-2)^6/3+C$ **37.** $4[(x+1)^{5/2}/5-(x+1)^{3/2}/3]+C$ **39.** $20\ln\left|1-e^{-0.05x}\right|+C$ **41.** $3e^{-1/x}+C$ **43.** $(e^x-e^{-x})/2+C$ **45.** $\ln(e^x+e^{-x})+C$ **47.** $(e^{2x^2-2x}+e^{x^2})/2+C$ **53.** $-e^{-x}+C$ **55.** $(1/2)e^{2x-1}+C$ **57.** $(2x+4)^3/6+C$ **59.** $(1/5)\ln|5x-1|+C$ **61.** $(1.5x)^4/6+C$ **63.** $\frac{1.5^{3x}}{3\ln(1.5)}+C$ **65.** $\frac{2^{3x+4}-2^{-3x+4}}{3\ln 2}+C$ **67.** $f(x)=(x^2+1)^4/8-1/8$ **69.** $f(x)=(1/2)e^{x^2-1}$ **71.** $C(x)=5x-1/(x+1)+995.5$ **73. a.** $N(t)=35\ln(5+e^{0.2t})-63$ **b.** 80,000 articles **75. a.** $s=(t^2+1)^5/10+t^2/2+C$ **b.** $C=9/10$; $s=(t^2+1)^5/10+t^2/2+9/10$ **77.** $S(t)=\frac{17}{3}(t-1990)^3+50(t-1990)^2+$ $2300(t-1900)-7503$ million gallons. $S(2003)\approx 43{,}000$ million gallons. **79.** None; the substitution $u=x$ simply replaces the letter x throughout by the letter u, and thus does not change the integral at all. For instance, the integral $\int x(3x^2+1)\,dx$ becomes $\int u(3u^2+1)\,du$ if we substitute $u=x$. **81.** The purpose of substitution is to introduce a new variable that is defined in terms of the variable of integration. One cannot say $u=u^2+1$, because u is not a new variable. Instead, define $w=u^2+1$ (or any other letter different from u). **83.** The integral $\int x(x^2+1)\,dx$ can be solved by the substitution $u=x^2+1$, because it leads to $\frac{1}{2}\int u\,du = \frac{1}{4}u^2+C = \frac{(x^2+1)^2}{4}+C$.

Section 6.3

1. 30 **3.** 22 **5.** −2 **7.** 0 **9.** 4 **11.** 6 **13.** 0.7456 **15.** 2.3129 **17.** 2.5048 **19.** 1 **21.** 1/2 **23.** 1/4 **25.** 2 **27.** 0 **29.** 6 **31.** 0 **33.** 0.5 **35.** 3.3045, 3.1604, 3.1436 **37.** 0.0275, 0.0258, 0.0256 **39.** \$99.95 **41.** 19 billion gallons **43.** \$22.5 billion **45. a.** Left sum: about 46,000 articles, Right sum: about 55,000 articles **b.** 50.5; A total of about 50,500 articles in *Physics Review* were written by researchers in Europe in the 16-year period beginning 1983. **47.** 54,000 students **49.** −\$1 billion. **51.** 8160; This represents the total number of wiretaps authorized by U.S. courts from 1998 through 2003. **53.** 91.2 ft **55.** $\int_{-10}^{10} R(t)\,dt \approx \$23{,}000$. The median household income rose a total of approximately \$23,000 from 1980 to 2000. **57.** Yes. The Riemann sum gives an estimated area of 420 square feet. **59. a.** The area represents the total amount earned by households in the period 2000 through 2003, in millions of dollars. **b.** $\int_{10}^{14} A(t)\,dt \approx 26{,}000{,}000$. The total amount earned by households from 2000 through 2003 was approximately \$26 trillion.

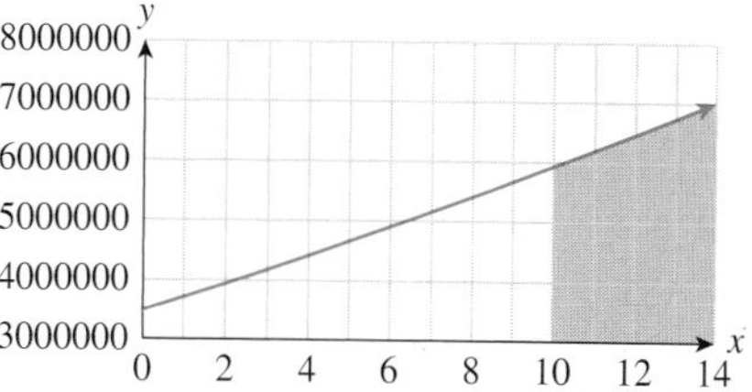

61. a. 99.4% **b.** 0 (to at least 15 decimal places) **63.** Stays the same. **65.** Increases. **67.** The area under the curve and above the x-axis equals the area above the curve and below the x-axis. **69.** Answers will vary. One example: Let $r(t)$ be the rate of change of net income at time t. If $r(t)$ is negative, then the net income is decreasing, so the change in net income, represented by the definite integral of $r(t)$, is negative. **71.** Answers may vary:

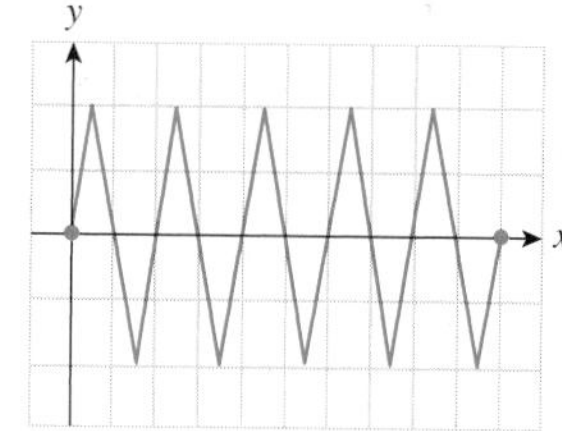

73. The total cost is $c(1)+c(2)+\cdots+c(60)$, which is represented by the Riemann sum approximation of $\int_1^{61} c(t)\,dt$ with $n=60$.

75. $[f(x_1)+f(x_2)+\cdots+f(x_n)]\Delta x = \sum_{k=1}^{n} f(x_k)\Delta x$

77. There is no simple way of knowing for certain how accurate your answer is, but here is a rule of thumb: If increasing n does not change the value of the answer when rounded to three decimal places, then the answer can be taken to be accurate to three decimal places.

Section 6.4

1. 14/3 **3.** 5 **5.** 0 **7.** 40/3 **9.** −0.9045 **11.** $2(e-1)$ **13.** 2/3 **15.** $1/\ln 2$ **17.** $4^6 - 1 = 4095$ **19.** $(e^1 - e^{-3})/2$ **21.** $3/(2\ln 2)$ **23.** $50(e^{-1} - e^{-2})$ **25.** $e^{2.1} - e^{-0.1}$ **27.** 0 **29.** $(5/2)(e^3 - e^2)$ **31.** $(1/3)[\ln 26 - \ln 7]$ **33.** $\dfrac{0.1}{2.2\ln(1.1)}$ **35.** $e - e^{1/2}$ **37.** $2 - \ln 3$ **39.** −4/21 **41.** $3^{5/2}/10 - 3^{3/2}/6 + 1/15$ **43.** 1/2 **45.** 16/3 **47.** 56/3 **49.** 1/2 **51.** \$783 **53.** 296 miles **55.** 20 billion gallons **57.** \$23,000 **59.** 68 milliliters **61.** 907 T-shirts **63.** 9 gallons **67. c.** 2,100,000 iPods **69. a.** 8200 wiretaps **b.** The actual number of wiretaps is 8160, which agrees with the answer in part (a) to two significant digits. Therefore, the integral in part (a) does give an accurate estimate. **73.** They are related by the Fundamental Theorem of Calculus, which states (summarized briefly) that the definite integral of a suitable function can be calculated by evaluating the indefinite integral at the two endpoints and subtracting. **75.** The total sales from time a to time b are obtained from the marginal sales by taking its *definite integral* from a to b. **77.** An example is $v(t) = t - 5$. **79.** An example is $f(x) = e^{-x}$. **81.** By the FTC, $\int_a^x f(t)\,dt = G(x) - G(a)$ where G is an antiderivative of f. Hence, $F(x) = G(x) - G(a)$. Taking derivatives of both sides, $F'(x) = G'(x) + 0 = f(x)$, as required. The result gives us a formula, in terms of area, for an antiderivative of any continuous function.

Chapter 6 Review

1. $\dfrac{x^3}{3} - 5x^2 + 2x + C$ **3.** $4x^3/15 + 4/(5x) + C$ **5.** $-e^{-2x+11}/2 + C$ **7.** $\dfrac{1}{22}(x^2+4)^{11} + C$ **9.** $-\dfrac{5}{2}e^{-2x} + C$ **11.** $(x+2) + \ln|x+2| + C$ or $x + \ln|x+2| + C$ **13.** 1 **15.** −4 **17.** $5/12 \approx 0.4167$ **19.** 0.7778, 0.7500, 0.7471 **21.** 0 **23.** 1/4 **25.** $2 + e - e^{-1}$ **27.** 52/9 **29.** $[\ln 5 - \ln 2]/8 = \ln(2.5)/8$ **31.** 32/3 **33.** $(1 - e^{-25})/2$ **35. a.** $100{,}000 - 10p^2$; **b.** \$100 **37.** 25,000 copies **39.** 39,200 hits **41.** About 86,000 books

Chapter 7

Section 7.1

1. $2e^x(x-1) + C$ **3.** $-e^{-x}(2+3x) + C$ **5.** $e^{2x}(2x^2 - 2x - 1)/4 + C$ **7.** $-e^{-2x+4}(2x^2 + 2x + 3)/4 + C$ **9.** $2^x[(2-x)/\ln 2 + 1/(\ln 2)^2] + C$ **11.** $-3^{-x}[(x^2-1)/\ln 3 + 2x/(\ln 3)^2 + 2/(\ln 3)^3] + C$ **13.** $-e^{-x}(x^2 + x + 1) + C$ **15.** $\dfrac{1}{7x}(x+2)^7 - \dfrac{1}{56}(x+2)^8 + C$ **17.** $-\dfrac{x}{2(x-2)^2} - \dfrac{1}{2(x-2)} + C$ **19.** $(x^4 \ln x)/4 - x^4/16 + C$ **21.** $(t^3/3 + t)\ln(2t) - t^3/9 - t + C$ **23.** $(3/4)t^{4/3}(\ln t - 3/4) + C$ **25.** $x\log_3 x - x/\ln 3 + C$ **27.** $e^{2x}(x/2 - 1/4) - 4e^{3x}/3 + C$ **29.** $e^x(x^2 - 2x + 2) - e^{x^2}/2 + C$ **31.** e **33.** 38229/286 **35.** $(7/2)\ln 2 - 3/4$ **37.** 1/4 **39.** $1 - 11e^{-10}$ **41.** $4\ln 2 - 7/4$ **43.** $28{,}800{,}000(1 - 2e^{-1})$ ft. **45.** $5001 + 10x - 1/(x+1) - [\ln(x+1)]/(x+1)$ **47.** \$33,598 **49.** \$170,000 million **51.** Answers will vary. Examples are xe^{x^2} and $e^{x^2} = 1 \cdot e^{x^2}$ **53.** $n + 1$ times

Section 7.2

1. 8/3 **3.** 4 **5.** 1 **7.** $e - 3/2$ **9.** 2/3 **11.** 3/10 **13.** 1/20 **15.** 4/15 **17.** $2\ln 2 - 1$ **19.** $8\ln 4 + 2e - 16$ **21.** 0.9138 **23.** 0.3222 **25.** 112.5. This represents your total profit for the week, \$112.50. **27. a.** The area represents the accumulated U.S. trade deficit with China (total excess value of imports over exports) for the 8-year period 1996–2004. **b.** 640. The U.S. accumulated a \$640 billion trade deficit with China over the period 1996–2004. **29. a.** \$3600 billion. **b.** This is the area of the region between the graphs of $P(t)$ and $I(t)$ for $10 \le t \le 20$. **31.** The area between the export and import curves represents Canada's accumulated trade surplus (that is, the total excess of exports over imports) from January, 1997 to January, 2001. **33.** (A) **35.** The claim is wrong because the area under a curve can only represent income if the curve is a graph of income *per unit time*. The value of a stock price is not income per unit time—the income can only be realized when the stock is sold, and it amounts to the current market price. The total net income (per share) from the given investment would be the stock price on the date of sale minus the purchase price of \$40.

Section 7.3

1. Average = 2

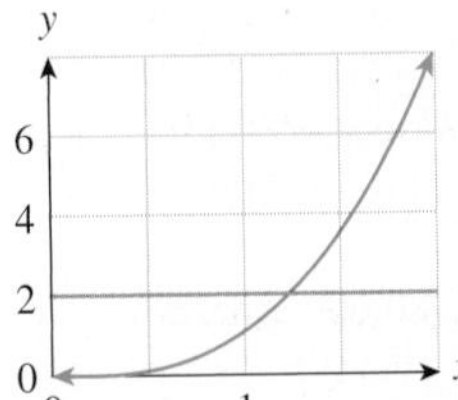

3. Average = 1

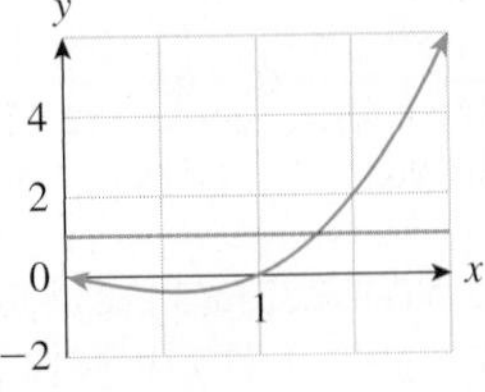

5. Average $= (1 - e^{-2})/2$

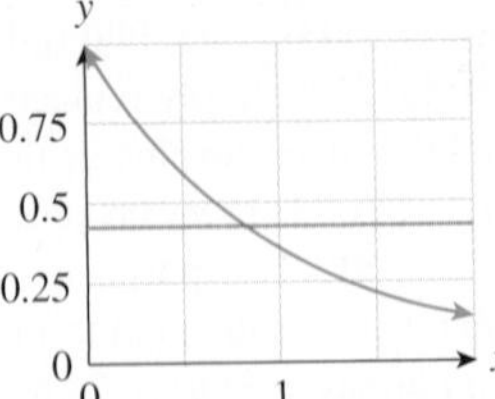

7.

x	0	1	2	3	4	5	6	7
$r(x)$	3	5	10	3	2	5	6	7
$\bar{r}(x)$			6	6	5	10/3	13/3	6

9.

x	0	1	2	3	4	5	6	7
$r(x)$	1	2	6	7	11	15	10	2
$\bar{r}(x)$			3	5	8	11	12	9

11. Moving average: $\bar{f}(x)=x^3-(15/2)x^2+25x-125/4$

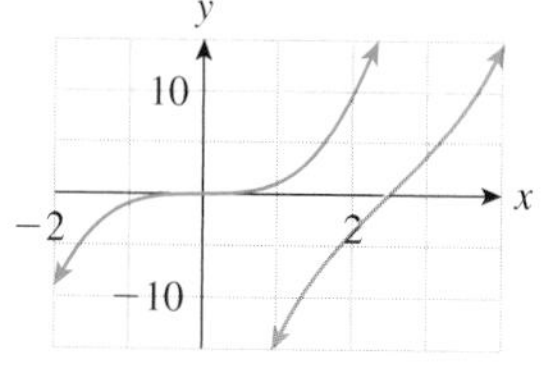

13. Moving average: $\bar{f}(x)=(3/25)[x^{5/3}-(x-5)^{5/3}]$

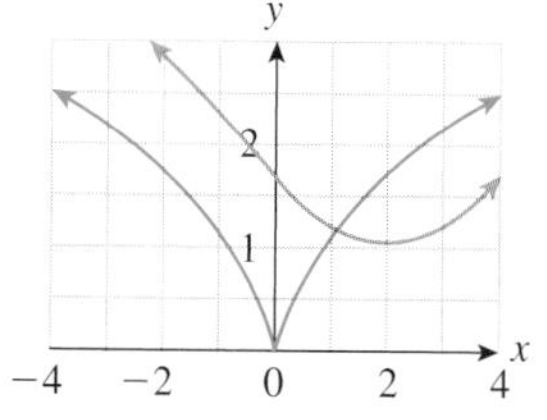

15. $\bar{f}(x)=\frac{2}{5}(e^{0.5x}-e^{0.5(x-5)})$

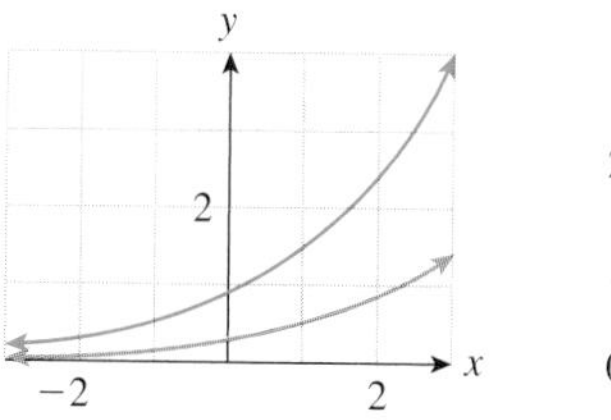

17. $\bar{f}(x)=\frac{2}{15}(x^{3/2}-(x-5)^{3/2})$

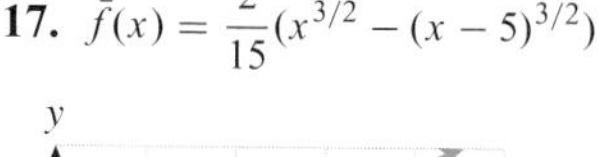

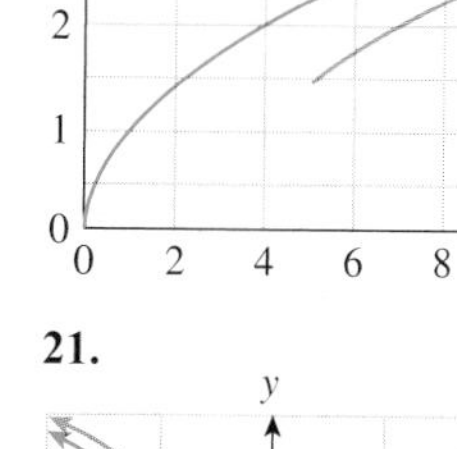

19.

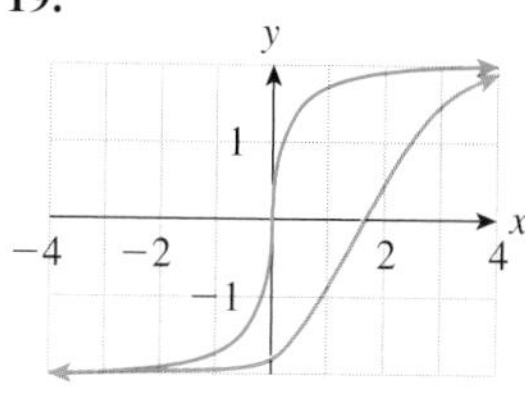

21.

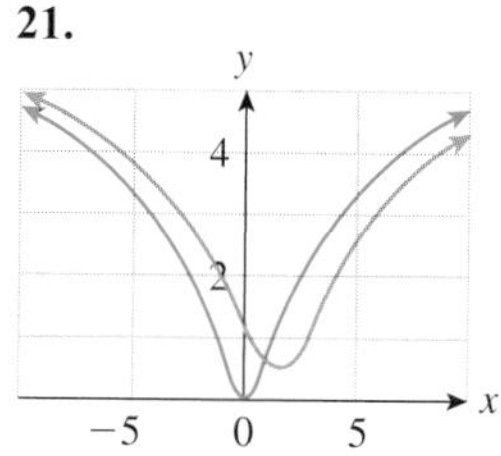

23. 127 million people **25.** \$1.7345 million **27.** \$10,410.88 **29.** \$1500

31.

Year t	1995	1996	1997	1998	1999	2000	2001	2002	2003	2004
Employment (millions)	117	120	123	126	129	132	132	130	130	131
Moving average (millions)				122	125	128	130	131	131	131

Some changes are larger, and others are smaller.

33. a.

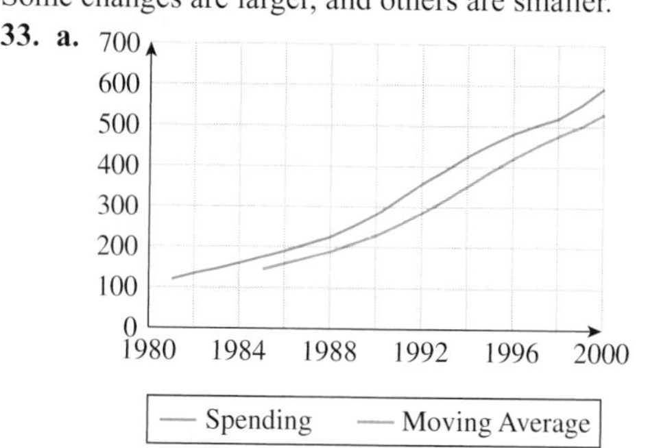

b. \$31 billion per year; Public spending on health care in the U.S. was increasing at a rate of approximately \$31 billion per year during the given period.

35. a. 4300 million gallons per year

b. $\frac{1}{2}\left[\frac{17}{3}[t^3-(t-2)^3]+50[t^2-(t-2)^2]+4600\right]$

c. Quadratic **37. a.** $s=14.4t+240$ **b.** $\bar{s}(t)=14.4t+211.2$ **c.** The slope of the moving average is the same as the slope of the original function.

39. $\bar{f}(x)=mx+b-\frac{ma}{2}$

41. a.

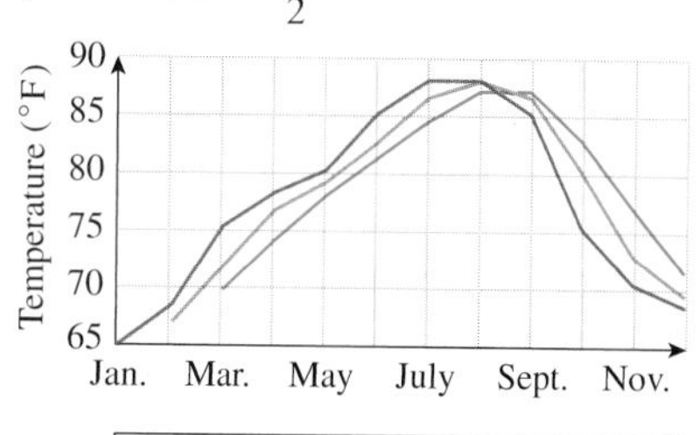

b. The 24-month moving average is constant and equal to the year-long average of approximately 77°. **c.** A quadratic model could not be used to predict temperatures beyond the given 12-month period, since temperature patterns are periodic, whereas parabolas are not. **43.** The moving average "blurs" the effects of short-term oscillations in the price, and shows the longer-term trend of the stock price. **45.** The area above the x-axis equals the area below the x-axis. Example: $y=x$ on $[-1, 1]$ **47.** This need not be the case; for instance, the function $f(x)=x^2$ on $[0, 1]$ has average value $1/3$, whereas the value midway between the maximum and minimum is $1/2$. **49.** (C). A shorter term moving average most closely approximates the original function, since it averages the function over a shorter period, and continuous functions change by only a small amount over a small period.

Section 7.4

1. \$6.25 **3.** \$512 **5.** \$119.53 **7.** \$900 **9.** \$416.67 **11.** \$326.27 **13.** \$25 **15.** \$0.50 **17.** \$386.29 **19.** \$225 **21.** \$25.50 **23.** \$12,684.63 **25.** $TV=\$300{,}000$, $FV=\$434{,}465.45$ **27.** $TV=\$350{,}000$, $FV=\$498{,}496.61$ **29.** $TV=\$389{,}232.76$, $FV=\$547{,}547.16$ **31.** $TV=\$100{,}000$, $PV=\$82{,}419.99$ **33.** $TV=\$112{,}500$, $PV=\$92{,}037.48$ **35.** $TV=\$107{,}889.50$, $PV=\$88{,}479.69$ **37.** $\bar{p}=\$5000$, $\bar{q}=10{,}000$, $CS=\$25$ million, $PS=\$100$ million. The total social gain is \$125 million. **39.** $CS=\frac{1}{2m}(b-m\bar{p})^2$ **41.** €140 billion **43.** \$940 billion **45.** €160 billion **47.** \$850 billion **49.** \$1,943,162.44 **51.** \$3,086,245.73 **53.** \$58,961.74 **55.** \$1,792,723.35 **57.** Total **59.** She is correct, provided there is a positive rate of return, in which case the future value (which includes interest) is greater than the total value (which does not). **61.** $PV<TV<FV$

Section 7.5

1. Diverges **3.** Converges to $2e$ **5.** Converges to e^2 **7.** Converges to $1/2$ **9.** Converges to $1/108$ **11.** Converges to $3 \times 5^{2/3}$ **13.** Diverges **15.** Diverges **17.** Converges to $\frac{5}{4}(3^{4/5}-1)$. **19.** Diverges **21.** Converges to 0

23. Diverges **25.** Diverges **27.** \$870 million **29.** 7100 billion cigarettes **31.** No; You will not sell more than 2000 of them. **33.** The integral diverges, and so the number of graduates each year will rise without bound. **35. a.** $R(t) = 350e^{-0.1t}(39t + 68)$ million dollars/yr; **b.** \$1,603,000 million **37.** \$27,000 billion **39.** $\int_0^{+\infty} N(t)\,dt$ diverges, indicating that there is no bound to the expected future total online sales of books. $\int_{-\infty}^0 N(t)\,dt$ converges to approximately 1.889, indicating that total online sales of books prior to 1997 amounted to approximately 1.889 million books **41.** 1 **43.** 0.1587 **45.** \$70,833 **47. a.** 2.468 meteors on average **b.** The integral diverges. We can interpret this as saying that the number of impacts by meteors smaller than 1 megaton is very large. (This makes sense because, for example, this number includes meteors no larger than a grain of dust.) **49. a.** $\Gamma(1) = 1$; $\Gamma(2) = 1$ **51.** The integral does not converge, so the number given by the FTC is meaningless. **53.** Yes; the integrals converge to 0, and the FTC also gives 0. **55.** In all cases, you need to rewrite the improper integral as a limit and use technology to evaluate the integral of which you are taking the limit. Evaluate for several values of the endpoint approaching the limit. In the case of an integral in which one of the limits of integration is infinite, you may have to instruct the calculator or computer to use more subdivisions as you approach $+\infty$.

Section 7.6

1. $y = \frac{x^3}{3} + \frac{2x^{3/2}}{3} + C$ **3.** $\frac{y^2}{2} = \frac{x^2}{2} + C$ **5.** $y = Ae^{x^2/2}$ **7.** $y = -\frac{2}{(x+1)^2 + C}$ **9.** $y = \pm\sqrt{(\ln x)^2 + C}$ **11.** $y = \frac{x^4}{4} - x^2 + 1$ **13.** $y = (x^3 + 8)^{1/3}$ **15.** $y = 2x$ **17.** $y = e^{x^2/2} - 1$ **19.** $y = -\frac{2}{\ln(x^2+1) + 2}$ **21.** With $s(t)$ = monthly sales after t months, $\frac{ds}{dt} = -0.05s$; $s = 1000$ when $t = 0$. Solution: $s = 1000e^{-0.05t}$ quarts per month. **23.** $H(t) = 75 + 115e^{-0.04274t}$ degrees Fahrenheit after t minutes. **25.** With $S(t)$ = total sales after t months, $\frac{dS}{dt} = 0.1(100{,}000 - S)$; $S(0) = 0$. Solution: $S = 100{,}000(1 - e^{-0.1t})$ monitors after t months. **27. a.** $\frac{dp}{dt} = k(D(p) - S(p)) = k(20{,}000 - 1{,}000p)$ **b.** $p = 20 - Ae^{-kt}$ **c.** $p = 20 - 10e^{-0.2231t}$ dollars after t months. **29.** $q = 0.6078e^{-0.05p}p^{1.5}$

33. $S = \dfrac{2/1999}{e^{-0.5t} + 1/1999}$ It will take about 27 months to saturate the market. Graph:

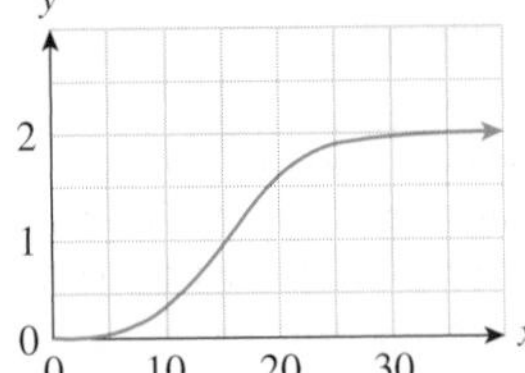

35. a. $y = be^{Ae^{-at}}$, A = constant **b.** $y = 10e^{-0.69315e^{-t}}$ Graph:

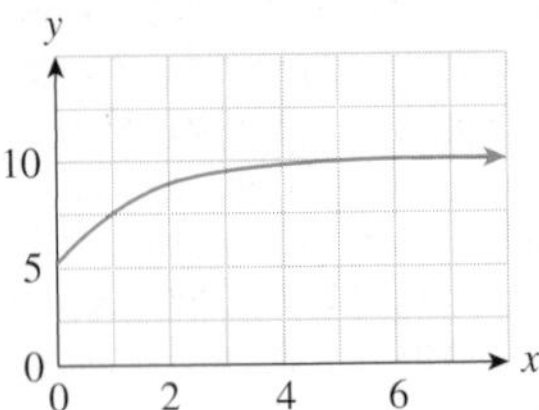

37. A general solution gives all possible solutions to the equation, using at least one arbitrary constant. A particular solution is one specific function that satisfies the equation. We obtain a particular solution by substituting specific values for any arbitrary constants in the general solution. **39.** Example: $y'' = x$ has general solution $y = \frac{1}{6}x^3 + Cx + D$ (integrate twice).

41. $y' = -4e^{-x} + 3$

Chapter 7 Review

1. $(x^2 - 2x + 4)e^x + C$ **3.** $(1/3)x^3 \ln 2x - x^3/9 + C$ **5.** $-e^2 - 39/e^2$ **7.** $1/4$ **9.** $3(3^{2/3} - 1)/2$ **11.** $\frac{3}{2 \cdot 2^{1/3}} - \frac{1}{2}$ **13.** $\frac{2\sqrt{2}}{3}$ **15.** -1 **17.** $e - 2$ **19.** $3x - 2$ **21.** $\frac{3}{14}[x^{7/3} - (x-2)^{7/3}]$ **23.** \$1600 **25.** \$2500 **27.** $y = -\frac{3}{x^3 + C}$ **29.** $y = \sqrt{2\ln|x| + 1}$ **31. a.** \$1,062,500; **b.** $997{,}500e^{0.06t}$ **33.** Approximately \$910,000 **35.** \$51 million

Chapter 8

Section 8.1

1. a. 1 **b.** 1 **c.** 2 **d.** $a^2 - a + 5$ **e.** $y^2 + x^2 - y + 1$ **f.** $(x+h)^2 + (y+k)^2 - (x+h) + 1$ **3. a.** 0 **b.** 0.2 **c.** -0.1 **d.** $0.18a + 0.2$ **e.** $0.1x + 0.2y - 0.01xy$ **f.** $0.2(x+h) + 0.1(y+k) - 0.01(x+h)(y+k)$ **5. a.** 1 **b.** e **c.** e **d.** e^{x+y+z} **e.** $e^{x+h+y+k+z+l}$ **7. a.** Does not exist **b.** 0 **c.** 0 **d.** $xyz/(x^2 + y^2 + z^2)$ **e.** $(x+h)(y+k)(z+l)/[(x+h)^2 + (y+k)^2 + (z+l)^2]$ **9. a.** Increases; 2.3 **b.** Decreases; 1.4 **c.** Decreases; 1 unit increase in z **11.** Neither **13.** Linear **15.** Linear **17.** Interaction **19. a.** 107 **b.** -14 **c.** -113

21.

$y \downarrow$ \ $x \rightarrow$	10	20	30	40
10	52	107	162	217
20	94	194	294	394
30	136	281	426	571
40	178	368	558	748

25. 18, 4, 0.0965, 47,040 **27.** 6.9078, 1.5193, 5.4366, 0 **29.** Let z = annual sales of Z (in millions of dollars), x = annual sales of X, and y = annual sales of Y. The model is $z = -2.1x + 0.4y + 16.2$ **31.** $\sqrt{2}$ **33.** $\sqrt{a^2 + b^2}$ **35.** 1/2 **37.** Circle with center (2, −1) and radius 3 **39.** The marginal cost of cars is \$6000 per car. The marginal cost of trucks is \$4000 per truck. **41.** $C(x, y) = 10 + 0.03x + 0.04y$ where C is the cost in dollars, x = # video clips sold per month, y = # audio clips sold per month **43. a.** 28% **b.** 21% **c.** Percentage points per year **45. a.** 29% **b.** 7% **c.** 0.4-point drop **47. a.** \$9980 **b.** $R(z) = 9850 + 0.04z$ **49.** $s(c, t) = 1.2c - 2t$ **51.** $U(11, 10) - U(10, 10) \approx 5.75$. This means that, if your company now has 10 copies of Macro Publish and 10 copies of Turbo Publish, then the purchase of one additional copy of Macro Publish will result in a productivity increase of approximately 5.75 pages per day. **53. a.** Answers will vary. $(a, b, c) = (3, 1/4, 1/\pi)$; $(a, b, c) = (1/\pi, 3, 1/4)$.
b. $a = \left(\frac{3}{4\pi}\right)^{1/3}$. The resulting ellipsoid is a sphere with radius a.

55. 7,000,000 **57. a.** $100 = K(1{,}000)^a(1{,}000{,}000)^{1-a}$; $10 = K(1{,}000)^a(10{,}000)^{1-a}$ **b.** $\log K - 3a = -4$; $\log K - a = -3$ **c.** $a = 0.5$, $K \approx 0.003162$ **d.** $P = 71$ pianos (to the nearest piano) **59. a.** 4×10^{-3} gram per square meter **b.** The total weight of sulfates in the Earth's atmosphere **61. a.** The value of N would be doubled. **b.** $N(R, f_p, n_e, f_l, f_i, L) = Rf_pn_ef_lf_iL$, where here L is the average lifetime of an intelligent civilization **c.** Take the logarithm of both sides, since this would yield the linear function $\ln(N) = \ln(R) + \ln(f_p) + \ln(n_e) + \ln(f_l) + \ln(f_i) + \ln(f_c) + \ln(L)$.

63. a. **b.** **c.**

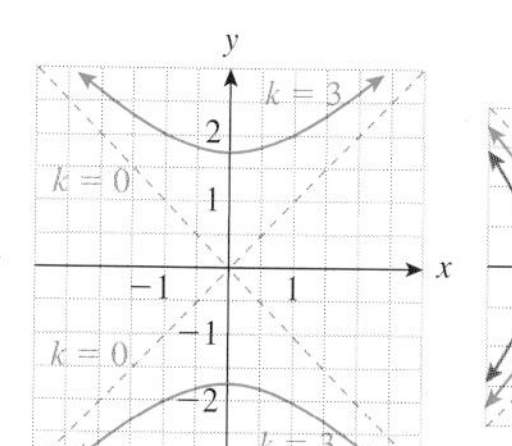

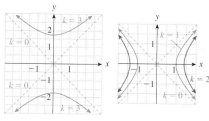

65. They are reciprocals of each other. **67.** For example, $f(x, y) = x^2 + y^2$. **69.** For example, $f(x, y, z) = xyz$ **71.** For example, take $f(x, y) = x + y$. Then setting $y = 3$ gives $f(x, 3) = x + 3$. This can be viewed as a function of the single variable x. Choosing other values for y gives other functions of x. **73.** If $f = ax + by + c$, then fixing $y = k$ gives $f = ax + (bk + c)$, a linear function with slope a and intercept $bk + c$. The slope is independent of the choice of $y = k$. **75.** CDs cost more than cassettes.

Section 8.2

1.

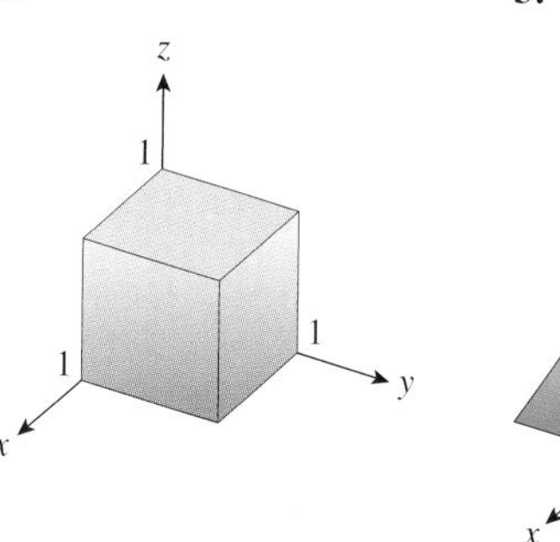

3.

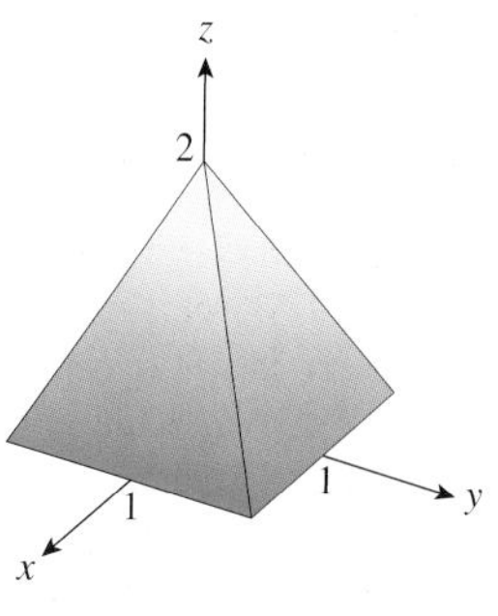

5.

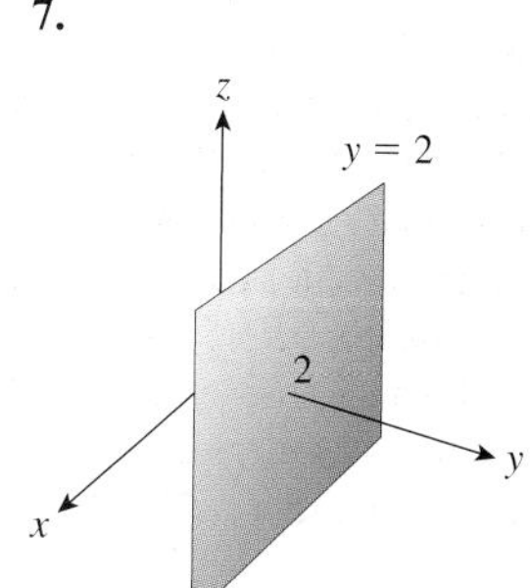

7.

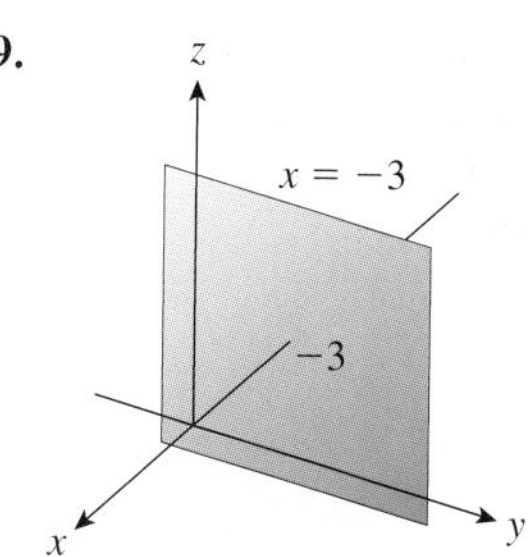

9.

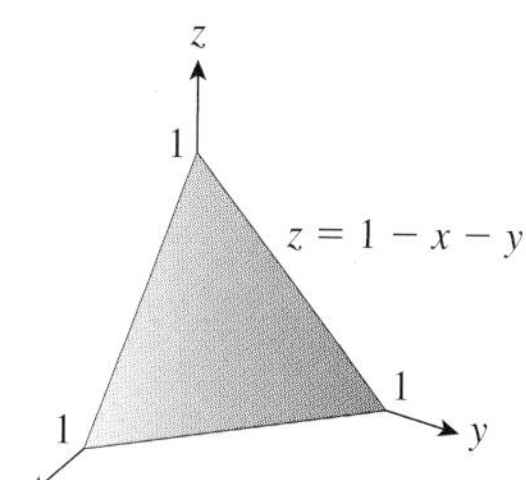

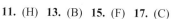

11. (H) **13.** (B) **15.** (F) **17.** (C)

19.

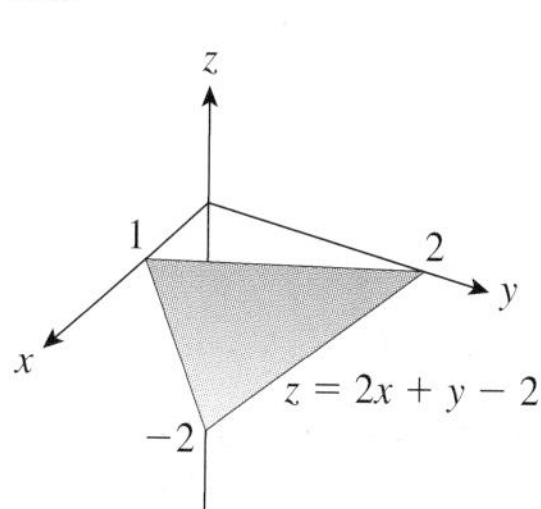

21.

23. **25.**

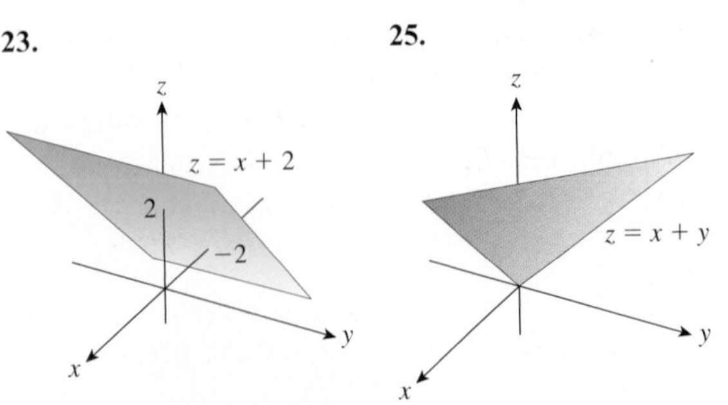

27. **29.**

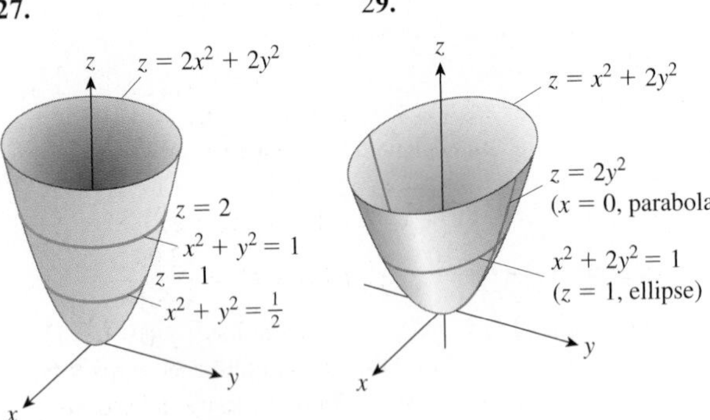

31. **33.**

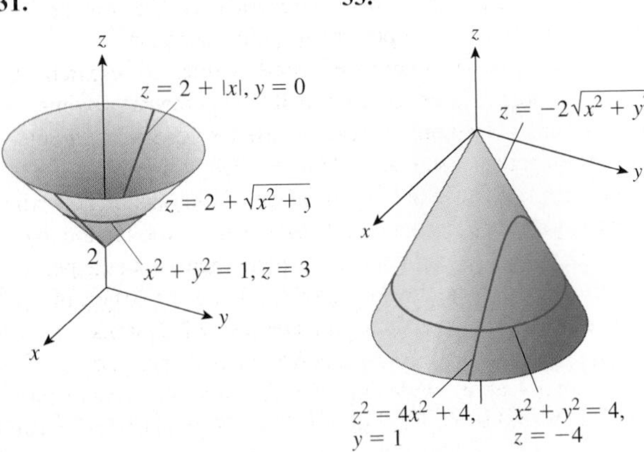

35. **37.**

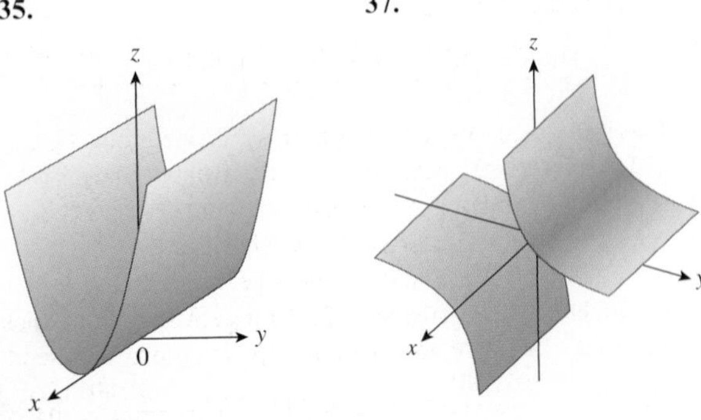

39.

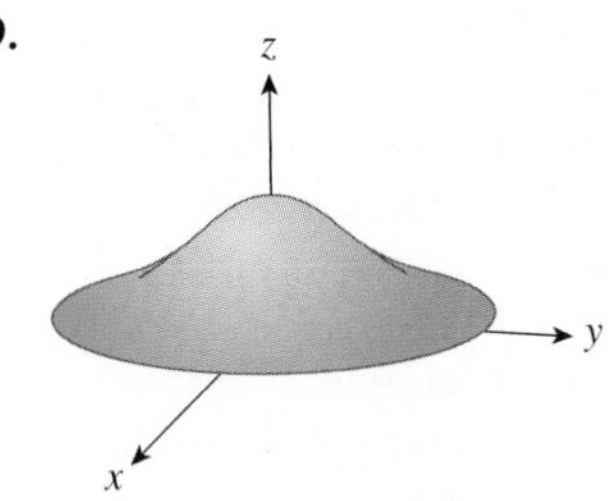

41. a. The graph is a plane with x-intercept -40, y-intercept -60, and z-intercept 240,000. **b.** The slice $x = 10$ is the straight line with equation $z = 300{,}000 + 4000y$. It describes the cost function for the manufacture of trucks if car production is held fixed at 10 cars per week. **c.** The level curve $z = 480{,}000$ is the straight line $6000x + 4000y = 240{,}000$. It describes the number of cars and trucks you can manufacture to maintain weekly costs at \$480,000. **43.** The graph is a plane with x_1-intercept 0.3, x_2-intercept 33, and x_3-intercept 0.66. The slices by $x_1 =$ constant are straight lines that are parallel to each other. Thus, the rate of change of General Motors' share as a function of Ford's share does not depend on Chrysler's share. Specifically, GM's share decreases by 0.02 percentage points per 1 percentage-point increase in Ford's market share, regardless of Chrysler's share. **45. a.** The slices $x =$ constant and $y =$ constant are straight lines. **b.** No. Even though the slices $x =$ constant and $y =$ constant are straight lines, the level curves are not, and so the surface is not a plane. **c.** The slice $x = 10$ has a slope of 3800. The slice $x = 20$ has a slope of 3600. Manufacturing more cars lowers the marginal cost of manufacturing trucks. **47.** Both level curves are quarter-circles. (We see only the portion in the first quadrant because $e \geq 0$ and $k \geq 0$.) The level curve $C = 30{,}000$ represents the relationship between the number of electricians and the number of carpenters used in building a home that costs \$30,000. Similarly for the level curve $C = 40{,}000$. **49.** The following figure shows several level curves together with several lines of the form $h + w = c$.

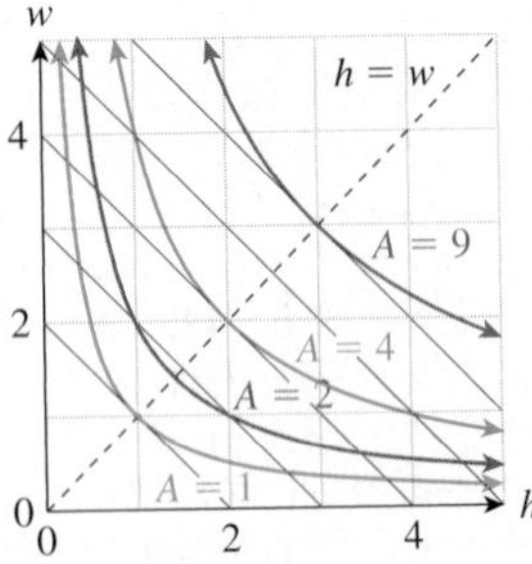

From the figure, thinking of the curves as contours on a map, we see that the largest value of A anywhere along any of the lines $h + w = c$ occurs midway along the line, when $h = w$. Thus, the largest area rectangle with a fixed perimeter occurs when $h = w$ (that is, when the rectangle is a square).

51. The level curve at $z = 3$ has the form $3 = x^{0.5}y^{0.5}$, or $y = 9/x$, and shows the relationship between the number of workers and the operating budget at a production level of 3 units.

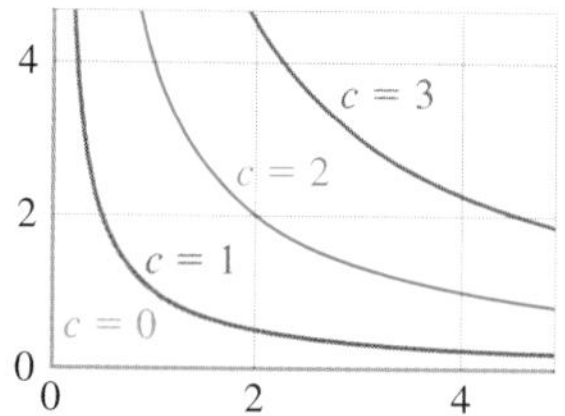

53. The level curve at $z = 0$ consists of the nonnegative y-axis $(x = 0)$ and tells us that zero utility corresponds to zero copies of Macro Publish, regardless of the number of copies of Turbo Publish. (Zero copies of Turbo Publish does not necessarily result in zero utility, according to the formula.)

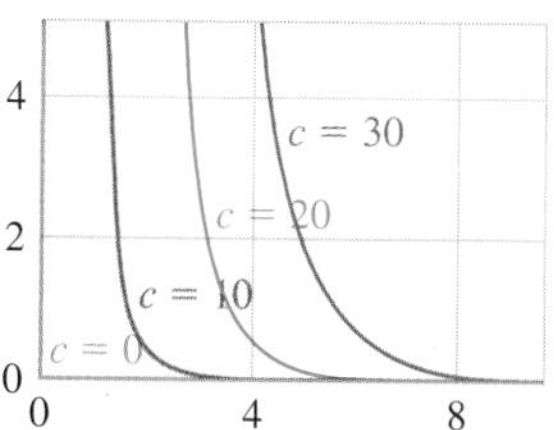

55. Plane **57.** Agree: any slice through a plane is a straight line. **59.** The graph of a function of three or more variables lives in four-dimensional (or higher) space, which makes it difficult to draw and visualize. **63.** We need one dimension for each of the variables plus one dimension for the value of the function.

Section 8.3

1. $f_x(x, y) = -40$; $f_y(x, y) = 20$; $f_x(1, -1) = -40$; $f_y(1, -1) = 20$ **3.** $f_x(x, y) = 6x + 1$; $f_y(x, y) = -3y^2$; $f_x(1, -1) = 7$; $f_y(1, -1) = -3$ **5.** $f_x(x, y) = -40 + 10y$; $f_y(x, y) = 20 + 10x$; $f_x(1, -1) = -50$; $f_y(1, -1) = 30$ **7.** $f_x(x, y) = 6xy$; $f_y(x, y) = 3x^2$; $f_x(1, -1) = -6$; $f_y(1, -1) = 3$ **9.** $f_x(x, y) = 2xy^3 - 3x^2y^2 - y$; $f_y(x, y) = 3x^2y^2 - 2x^3y - x$; $f_x(1, -1) = -4$; $f_y(1, -1) = 4$ **11.** $f_x(x, y) = 6y(2xy + 1)^2$; $f_y(x, y) = 6x(2xy + 1)^2$; $f_x(1, -1) = -6$; $f_y(1, -1) = 6$ **13.** $f_x(x, y) = e^{x+y}$; $f_y(x, y) = e^{x+y}$; $f_x(1, -1) = 1$; $f_y(1, -1) = 1$ **15.** $f_x(x, y) = 3x^{-0.4}y^{0.4}$; $f_y(x, y) = 2x^{0.6}y^{-0.6}$; $f_x(1, -1)$ undefined; $f_y(1, -1)$ undefined **17.** $f_x(x, y) = 0.2ye^{0.2xy}$; $f_y(x, y) = 0.2xe^{0.2xy}$; $f_x(1, -1) = -0.2e^{-0.2}$; $f_y(1, -1) = 0.2e^{-0.2}$ **19.** $f_{xx}(x, y) = 0$; $f_{yy}(x, y) = 0$; $f_{xy}(x, y) = f_{yx}(x, y) = 0$; $f_{xx}(1, -1) = 0$; $f_{yy}(1, -1) = 0$; $f_{xy}(1, -1) = f_{yx}(1, -1) = 0$ **21.** $f_{xx}(x, y) = 0$; $f_{yy}(x, y) = 0$; $f_{xy}(x, y) = f_{yx}(x, y) = 10$; $f_{xx}(1, -1) = 0$; $f_{yy}(1, -1) = 0$; $f_{xy}(1, -1) = f_{yx}(1, -1) = 10$ **23.** $f_{xx}(x, y) = 6y$; $f_{yy}(x, y) = 0$; $f_{xy}(x, y) = f_{yx}(x, y) = 6x$; $f_{xx}(1, -1) = -6$; $f_{yy}(1, -1) = 0$; $f_{xy}(1, -1) = f_{yx}(1, -1) = 6$ **25.** $f_{xx}(x, y) = e^{x+y}$; $f_{yy}(x, y) = e^{x+y}$; $f_{xy}(x, y) = f_{yx}(x, y) = e^{x+y}$; $f_{xx}(1, -1) = 1$; $f_{yy}(1, -1) = 1$; $f_{xy}(1, -1) = f_{yx}(1, -1) = 1$ **27.** $f_{xx}(x, y) = -1.2x^{-1.4}y^{0.4}$; $f_{yy}(x, y) = -1.2x^{0.6}y^{-1.6}$; $f_{xy}(x, y) = f_{yx}(x, y) = 1.2x^{-0.4}y^{-0.6}$; $f_{xx}(1, -1)$ undefined; $f_{yy}(1, -1)$ undefined; $f_{xy}(1, -1)$ & $f_{yx}(1, -1)$ undefined **29.** $f_x(x, y, z) = yz$; $f_y(x, y, z) = xz$; $f_z(x, y, z) = xy$; $f_x(0, -1, 1) = -1$; $f_y(0, -1, 1) = 0$; $f_z(0, -1, 1) = 0$ **31.** $f_x(x, y, z) = 4/(x + y + z^2)^2$; $f_y(x, y, z) = 4/(x + y + z^2)^2$; $f_z(x, y, z) = 8z/(x + y + z^2)^2$; $f_x(0, -1, 1)$ undefined; $f_y(0, -1, 1)$ undefined; $f_z(0, -1, 1)$ undefined **33.** $f_x(x, y, z) = e^{yz} + yze^{xz}$; $f_y(x, y, z) = xze^{yz} + e^{xz}$; $f_z(x, y, z) = xy(e^{yz} + e^{xz})$; $f_x(0, -1, 1) = e^{-1} - 1$; $f_y(0, -1, 1) = 1$; $f_z(0, -1, 1) = 0$ **35.** $f_x(x, y, z) = 0.1x^{-0.9}y^{0.4}z^{0.5}$; $f_y(x, y, z) = 0.4x^{0.1}y^{-0.6}z^{0.5}$; $f_z(x, y, z) = 0.5x^{0.1}y^{0.4}z^{-0.5}$; $f_x(0, -1, 1)$ undefined; $f_y(0, -1, 1)$ undefined, $f_z(0, -1, 1)$ undefined **37.** $f_x(x, y, z) = yze^{xyz}$, $f_y(x, y, z) = xze^{xyz}$, $f_z(x, y, z) = xye^{xyz}$; $f_x(0, -1, 1) = -1$; $f_y(0, -1, 1) = f_z(0, -1, 1) = 0$ **39.** $f_x(x, y, z) = 0$; $f_y(x, y, z) = -\dfrac{600z}{y^{0.7}(1 + y^{0.3})^2}$; $f_z(x, y, z) = \dfrac{2{,}000}{1 + y^{0.3}}$; $f_x(0, -1, 1)$ undefined; $f_y(0, -1, 1)$ undefined; $f_z(0, -1, 1)$ undefined **41.** $\partial C/\partial x = 6000$, the marginal cost to manufacture each car is \$6000. $\partial C/\partial y = 4000$, the marginal cost to manufacture each truck is \$4000. **43.** $\partial y/\partial t = -0.78$. The number of articles written by researchers in the U.S. was decreasing at a rate of 0.78 percentage points per year. $\partial y/\partial x = -1.02$. The number of articles written by researchers in the U.S. was decreasing at a rate of 1.02 percentage points per one percentage point increase in articles written in Europe. **45.** \$5600 per car **47. a.** $\partial M/\partial c = -3.8$, $\partial M/\partial f = 2.2$. For every 1 point increase in the percentage of Chrysler owners who remain loyal, the percentage of Mazda owners who remain loyal decreases by 3.8 points. For every 1 point increase in the percentage of Ford owners who remain loyal, the percentage of Mazda owners who remain loyal increases by 2.2 points. **b.** 16% **49. a.** \$16,500 **b.** \$28,600 **c.** \$350 per year **d.** \$570 per year **e.** Widening **51.** The marginal cost of cars is $\$6000 + 1{,}000e^{-0.01(x+y)}$ per car. The marginal cost of trucks is $\$4000 + 1{,}000e^{-0.01(x+y)}$ per truck. Both marginal costs decrease as production rises.

53. $\bar{C}(x, y) = \dfrac{200{,}000 + 6{,}000x + 4{,}000y - 100{,}000e^{-0.01(x+y)}}{x + y}$; $\bar{C}_x(50, 50) = -\$2.64$ per car. This means that at a production level of 50 cars and 50 trucks per week, the average cost per vehicle is decreasing by \$2.64 for each additional car manufactured. $\bar{C}_y(50, 50) = -\$22.64$ per truck. This means that at a production level of 50 cars and 50 trucks per week, the average cost per vehicle is decreasing by \$22.64 for each additional truck manufactured. **55.** No; your marginal revenue from the sale of cars is $\$15{,}000 - \dfrac{2{,}500}{\sqrt{x + y}}$ per car and $\$10{,}000 - \dfrac{2{,}500}{\sqrt{x + y}}$ per truck from the sale of trucks. These increase with increasing x and y. In other words, you will earn more revenue per vehicle with increasing sales, and so the rental company will pay more for each additional vehicle it buys.

57. $P_z(10{,}100{,}000,\ 1{,}000{,}000) \approx 0.0001010$ papers/\$ **59.** $U_x(10, 5) = 5.18$, $U_y(10, 5) = 2.09$. This means that, if 10 copies of Macro Publish and 5 copies of Turbo Publish are purchased, the company's daily productivity is increasing at a rate of 5.18 pages per day for each additional copy of Macro purchased and by 2.09 pages per day for each additional copy of Turbo purchased. **b.** $\dfrac{U_x(10, 5)}{U_y(10, 5)} \approx 2.48$ is the ratio of the usefulness of one additional copy of Macro to one of Turbo. Thus, with 10 copies of Macro and 5 copies of Turbo, the company can expect approximately 2.48 times the productivity per additional copy of Macro compared to Turbo. **61.** 6×10^9 N/sec **63. a.** $A_P(100, 0.1, 10) = 2.59$; $A_r(100, 0.1, 10) = 2{,}357.95$; $A_t(100, 0.1, 10) = 24.72$. Thus, for a \$100 investment at 10% interest, after 10 years the accumulated amount is increasing at a rate of \$2.59 per \$1 of principal, at a rate of \$2,357.95 per increase of 1 in r (note that this would correspond to an increase in the interest rate of 100%), and at a rate of \$24.72 per year. **b.** $A_P(100, 0.1, t)$ tells you the rate at which the accumulated amount in an account bearing 10% interest with a principal of \$100 is growing per \$1 increase in the principal, t years after the investment. **65. a.** $P_x = Ka\left(\dfrac{y}{x}\right)^b$ and $P_y = Kb\left(\dfrac{x}{y}\right)^a$. They are equal precisely when $\dfrac{a}{b} = \left(\dfrac{x}{y}\right)^b\left(\dfrac{x}{y}\right)^a$. Substituting $b = 1 - a$ now gives $\dfrac{a}{b} = \dfrac{x}{y}$. **b.** The given information implies that $P_x(100, 200) = P_y(100, 200)$. By part (a), this occurs precisely when $a/b = x/y = 100/200 = 1/2$. But $b = 1 - a$, so $a/(1 - a) = 1/2$, giving $a = 1/3$ and $b = 2/3$. **67.** Decreasing at 0.0075 parts of nutrient per part of water/sec **69.** f is increasing at a rate of s units per unit of x, f is increasing at a rate of t units per unit of y, and the value of f is r when $x = a$ and $y = b$ **71.** The marginal cost of building an additional orbicus; zonars per unit. **73.** Answers will vary. One example is $f(x, y) = -2x + 3y$. Others are $f(x, y) = -2x + 3y + 9$ and $f(x, y) = xy - 3x + 2y + 10$. **75. a.** b is the z-intercept of the plane. m is the slope of the intersection of the plane with the xz-plane. n is the slope of the intersection of the plane with the yz-plane. **b.** Write $z = b + rx + sy$. We are told that $\partial z/\partial x = m$, so $r = m$. Similarly, $s = n$. Thus, $z = b + mx + ny$. We are also told that the plane passes through (h, k, l). Substituting gives $l = b + mh + nk$. This gives b as $l - mh - nk$. Substituting in the equation for z therefore gives $z = l - mh - nk + mx + ny = l + m(x - h) + n(y - k)$, as required.

Section 8.4

1. P: relative minimum; Q: none of the above; R: relative maximum **3.** P: saddle point; Q: relative maximum; R: none of the above **5.** Relative minimum **7.** Neither **9.** Saddle point **11.** Relative minimum at (0, 0, 1) **13.** Relative maximum at (−1/2, 1/2, 3/2) **15.** Relative maximum at (0, 0, 0), saddle points at (±4, 2, −16) **17.** Relative minimum at (0, 0, 1) **19.** Relative minimum at (−2, ±2, −16), (0, 0) a critical point that is not a relative extremum **21.** Saddle point at (0, 0, −1) **23.** Relative maximum at $(-1, 0, e)$ **25.** Relative minimum at $(2^{1/3}, 2^{1/3}, 3(2^{2/3}))$ **27.** Relative minimum at (1, 1, 4) and (−1, −1, 4) **29.** Absolute minimum at (0, 0, 1) **31.** None; the relative maximum at (0, 0, 0) is not absolute. (look at, say, (10, 10)). **33.** Minimum of 1/3 at $(c, f) = (2/3, 2/3)$. Thus, at least 1/3 of all Mazda owners would choose another new Mazda, and this lowest loyalty occurs when 2/3 of Chrysler and Ford owners remain loyal to their brands. **35.** It should remove 2.5 pounds of sulfur and 1 pound of lead per day. **37.** You should charge \$580.81 for the Ultra Mini and \$808.08 for the Big Stack. **39.** $l = w = h \approx 20.67$ in, volume ≈ 8827 cubic inches. **41.** 18 in × 18 in × 36 in, volume = 11,664 cubic inches

43.

45.

47. H must be positive. **49.** No. In order for there to be a relative maximum at (a, b), *all* vertical planes through (a, b) should yield a curve with a relative maximum at (a, b). It could happen that a slice by another vertical plane through (a, b) (such as $x - a = y - b$) does not yield a curve with a relative maximum at (a, b). [An example is $f(x, y) = x^2 + y^2 - \sqrt{xy}$, at the point (0, 0). Look at the slices through $x = 0$, $y = 0$ and $y = x$.] **51.** $\bar{C}_x = \dfrac{\partial}{\partial x}\left(\dfrac{C}{x + y}\right) = \dfrac{(x + y)C_x - C}{(x + y)^2}$. If this is zero, then $(x + y)C_x = C$, or $C_x = \dfrac{C}{x + y} = \bar{C}$. Similarly, if $\bar{C}_y = 0$ then $C_y = \bar{C}$. This is reasonable because if the average cost is decreasing with increasing x, then the average cost is greater than the marginal cost C_x. Similarly, if the average cost is increasing with increasing x, then the average cost is less than the marginal cost C_x. Thus, if the average cost is stationary with increasing x, then the average cost equals the marginal cost C_x. (The situation is similar for the case of increasing y.) **53.** The equation of the tangent plane at the point (a, b) is $z = f(a, b) + f_x(a, b)(x - a) + f_y(a, b)(y - b)$. If f has a relative extremum at (a, b), then $f_x(a, b) = 0 = f_y(a, b)$. Substituting these into the equation of the tangent plane gives $z = f(a, b)$, a constant. But the graph of $z = constant$ is a plane parallel to the xy-plane.

Section 8.5

1. 1; (0, 0, 0) **3.** 1.35; (1/10, 3/10, 1/2) **5.** Minimum value = 6 at (1, 2, 1/2) **7.** 200; (20, 10) **9.** 16; (2, 2) and (−2, −2) **11.** 20; (2, 4) **13.** 1; (0, 0, 0)

15. 1.35; (1/10, 3/10, 1/2) **17.** Minimum value = 6 at (1, 2, 1/2) **19.** 5 × 10 = 50 sq. ft. **21.** $10 **23.** $(1/\sqrt{3}, 1/\sqrt{3}, 1/\sqrt{3})$, $(-1/\sqrt{3}, -1/\sqrt{3}, 1/\sqrt{3})$, $(1/\sqrt{3}, -1/\sqrt{3}, -1/\sqrt{3})$, $(-1/\sqrt{3}, 1/\sqrt{3}, -1/\sqrt{3})$ **25.** (0, 1/2, −1/2) **27.** (−5/9, 5/9, 25/9) **29.** $l \times w \times h = 1 \times 1 \times 2$ **31.** 18 in × 18 in × 36 in, volume = 11,664 cubic inches **33.** $(2l/h)^{1/3} \times (2l/h)^{1/3} \times 2^{1/3}(h/l)^{2/3}$, where l = cost of lightweight cardboard and h = cost of heavy-duty cardboard per square foot **35.** 1 × 1 × 1/2 **37.** Method 1: Solve $g(x, y, z) = 0$ for one of the variables and substitute in $f(x, y, z)$. Then find the maximum value of the resulting function of 2 variables. Advantage (Answers may vary): We can use the second derivative test to check whether the resulting critical points are maxima, minima, saddle points, or none of these. Disadvantage (Answers may vary): We may not be able to solve $g(x, y, z) = 0$ for one of the variables. Method 2: Use the method of Lagrange Multipliers. Advantage (Answers may vary): We do not need to solve the constraint equation for one of the variables. Disadvantage (Answers may vary): The method does not tell us whether the critical points obtained are maxima, minima, saddle points, or none of these. **39.** If the only constraint is an equality constraint, and if it is impossible to eliminate one of the variables in the objective function by substitution (solving the constraint equation for a variable or some other method). **41.** Answers may vary: Maximize $f(x, y) = 1 - x^2 - y^2$ subject to $x = y$. **43.** Yes. There may be relative extrema at points on the boundary of the domain of the function. The partial derivatives of the function need not be 0 at such points. **45.** If the solution were located in the interior of one of the line segments making up the boundary of the domain of *f*, then the derivative of a certain function would be 0. This function is obtained by substituting the linear equation $C(x, y) = 0$ in the linear objective function. But because the result would again be a linear function, it is either constant, or its derivative is a nonzero constant. In either event, extrema lie on the boundary of that line segment; that is, at one of the corners of the domain.

Section 8.6

1. −1/2 **3.** $e^2/2 - 7/2$ **5.** $(e^3 - 1)(e^2 - 1)$ **7.** 7/6 **9.** $(e^3 - e - e^{-1} + e^{-3})/2$ **11.** 1/2 **13.** $(e - 1)/2$ **15.** 45/2 **17.** 8/3 **19.** 4/3 **21.** 0 **23.** 2/3 **25.** 2/3 **27.** $2(e - 2)$ **29.** 2/3

31. $\int_0^1 \int_0^{1-x} f(x, y)\,dy\,dx$

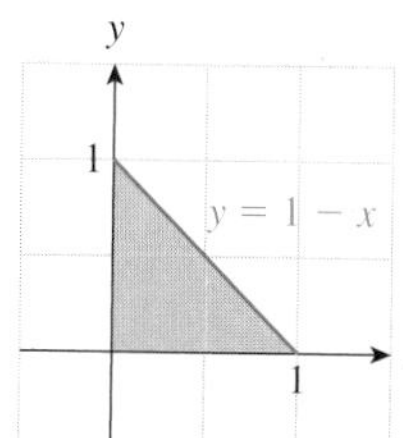

33. $\int_0^{\sqrt{2}} \int_{x^2-1}^{1} f(x, y)\,dy\,dx$

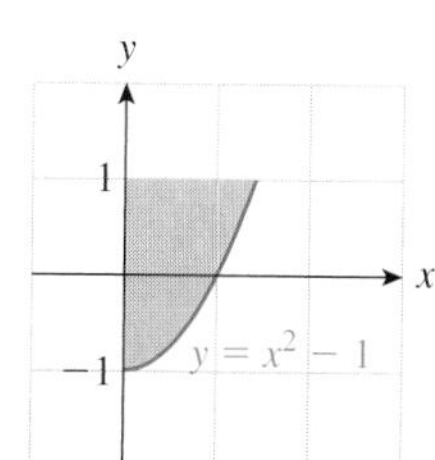

35. $\int_1^4 \int_1^{2/\sqrt{y}} f(x, y)\,dx\,dy$

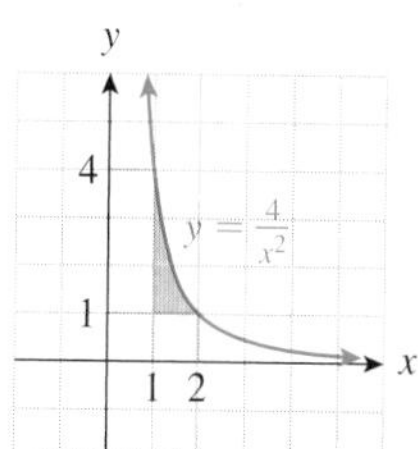

37. 4/3 **39.** 1/6 **41.** 162,000 gadgets **43.** Average revenue is $312,750. **45.** Average revenue is $17,500. **47.** 8216 **49.** 1 degree **51.** The area between the curves $y = r(x)$ and $y = s(x)$ and the vertical lines $x = a$ and $x = b$ is given by $\int_a^b \int_{r(x)}^{s(x)} dy\,dx$ assuming that $r(x) \le s(x)$ for $a \le x \le b$. **53.** The first step in calculating an integral of the form $\int_a^b \int_{r(x)}^{s(x)} f(x, y)\,dy\,dx$ is to evaluate the integral $\int_{r(x)}^{s(x)} f(x, y)\,dy$, obtained by holding x constant and integrating with respect to y. **55.** Paintings per picasso per dali **57.** Left-hand side is $\int_a^b \int_c^d f(x)g(y)\,dx\,dy = \int_a^b \left(g(y) \int_c^d f(x)\,dx\right)dy$ (since $g(y)$ is treated as a constant in the inner integral) = $\left(\int_c^d f(x)\,dx\right) \int_a^b g(y)\,dy$ (since $\int_c^d f(x)\,dx$ is a constant and can therefore be taken outside the integral). $\int_0^1 \int_1^2 ye^x\,dx\,dy = \frac{1}{2}(e^2 - e)$ no matter how we compute it.

Chapter 8 Review

1. 0; 1; 0; $x^3 + x^2$; $x(y + k)(x + y + k - z) + x^2$ **3.** Reading left to right, starting at the top: 4, 0, 0, 3, 0, 1, 2, 0, 2 **5.** $f_x = 2x + y$, $f_y = x$, $f_{yy} = 0$ **7.** 0 **9.** $\frac{\partial f}{\partial x} = \frac{-x^2 + y^2 + z^2}{(x^2 + y^2 + z^2)^2}$, $\frac{\partial f}{\partial y} = -\frac{2xy}{(x^2 + y^2 + z^2)^2}$, $\frac{\partial f}{\partial z} = -\frac{2xz}{(x^2 + y^2 + z^2)^2}$, $\left.\frac{\partial f}{\partial x}\right|_{(0,1,0)} = 1$ **11.** Absolute minimum at (1, 3/2) **13.** Saddle point at (0, 0) **15.** Absolute maximum at each point on the circle $x^2 + y^2 = 1$ **17.** 1/27 at (1/3, 1/3, 1/3) **19.** $(0, 2, \sqrt{2})$ **21.** 4; $(\sqrt{2}, \sqrt{2})$ and $(-\sqrt{2}, -\sqrt{2})$ **23.** Minimum value = 5 at (2, 1, 1/2) **25.** 2 **27.** ln 5 **29.** 4/5 **31. a.** $h(x, y) = 5000 - 0.8x - 0.6y$ hits per day (x = number of new customers at JungleBooks.com, y = number of new customers at FarmerBooks.com) **b.** 250 **33. a.** 2320 hits per day **b.** $0.08 + 0.00003x$ hits (daily) per dollar spent on television advertising per month; increases with increasing x **c.** $4000 per month **35.** About 15,800 orders per day **37.** $23,050

ANSWERS TO SELECTED EXERCISES

Chapter 9

Section 9.1

1.

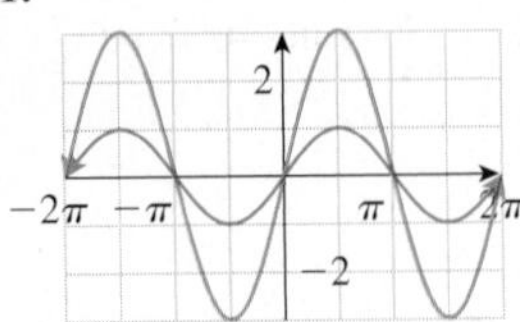

3.

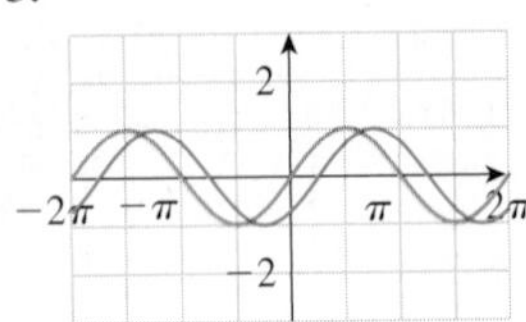

5.

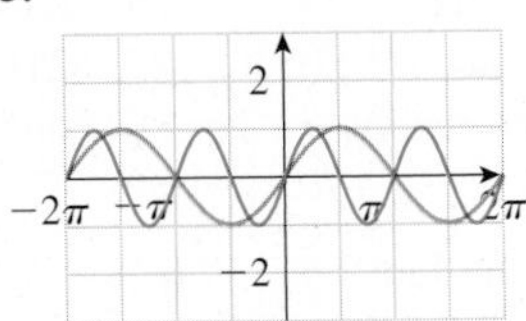

7.

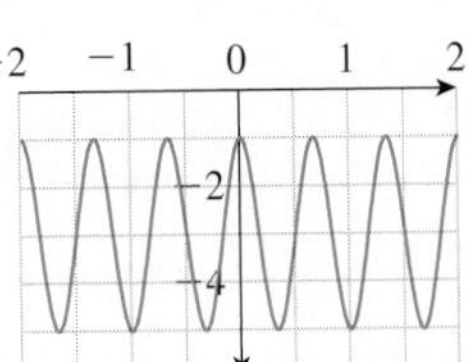

9.

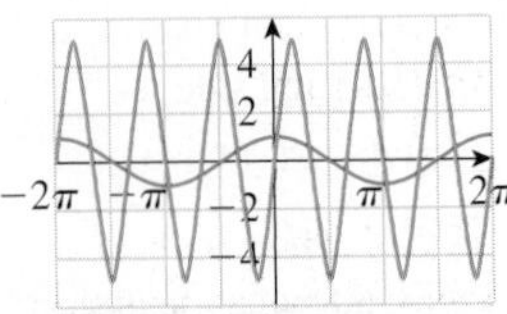

11.

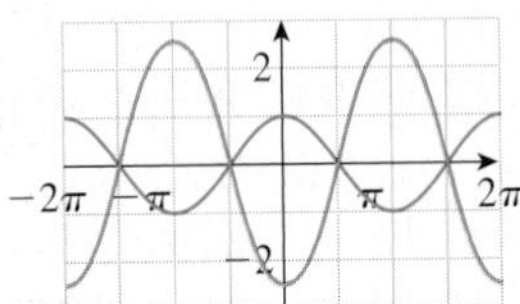

13. $f(x) = \sin(2\pi x) + 1$ **15.** $f(x) = 1.5 \sin(4\pi(x - 0.25))$
17. $f(x) = 50 \sin(\pi(x - 5)/10) - 50$ **19.** $f(x) = \cos(2\pi x)$
21. $f(x) = 1.5 \cos(4\pi(x - 0.375))$
23. $f(x) = 40 \cos(\pi(x - 10)/10) + 40$
25. $f(t) = 4.2 \sin(\pi/2 - 2\pi t) + 3$
27. $g(x) = 4 - 1.3 \sin[\pi/2 - 2.3(x - 4)]$ **31.** $\sqrt{3}/2$
37. $\tan(x + \pi) = \tan(x)$ **39. a.** $2\pi/0.602 \approx 10.4$ years.
b. Maximum: $58.8 + 57.7 = 116.5 \approx 117$; minimum: $58.8 - 57.7 = 1.1 \approx 1$
c. $1.43 + P/4 + P = 1.43 + 13.05 \approx 14.5$ years, or midway through 2011 **41. a.** Maximum sales occurred when $t \approx 4.5$ (during the first quarter of 1996). Minimum sales occurred when $t \approx 2.2$ (during the third quarter of 1995) and $t \approx 6.8$ (during the third quarter of 1996). **b.** Maximum quarterly revenues were \$0.561 billion; minimum quarterly revenues were \$0.349 billion. **c.** maximum: $0.455 + 0.106 = 0.561$; minimum: $0.455 - 0.106 = 0.349$ **43.** Amplitude $= 0.106$, vertical offset $= 0.455$, phase shift $= -1.61/1.39 \approx -1.16$ angular frequency $= 1.39$, period $= 4.52$. In 1995 and 1996, quarterly revenue from the sale of computers at Computer City fluctuated in cycles of 4.52 quarters about a baseline of \$0.455 billion. Every cycle, quarterly revenue peaked at \$0.561 billion (\$0.106 billion above the baseline) and dipped to a low of \$0.349 billion. Revenue peaked early in the middle of the first quarter of 1996 (at $t = -1.16 + (5/4) \times 4.52 = 4.49$).
45. $P(t) = 7.5 \sin[\pi(t - 13)/26] + 12.5$
47. $s(t) = 7.5 \sin(\pi(t - 9)/6) + 87.5$
49. $s(t) = 7.5 \cos(\pi t/6) + 87.5$
51. $d(t) = 5 \sin(2\pi(t - 1.625)/13.5) + 10$
53. a. $u(t) = 2.5 \sin(2\pi(t - 0.75)) + 7.5$
b. $c(t) = 1.04^t[2.5 \sin(2\pi(t - 0.75)) + 7.5]$
55. a. $P \approx 8,\ C \approx 6,\ A \approx 2,\ \alpha \approx 8$ (Answers may vary)

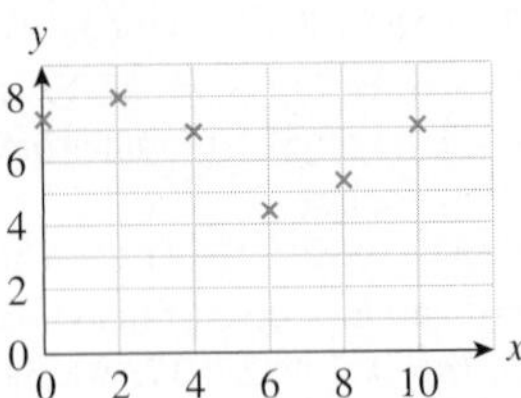

b. $C(t) = 1.755 \sin[0.636(t - 9.161)] + 6.437$

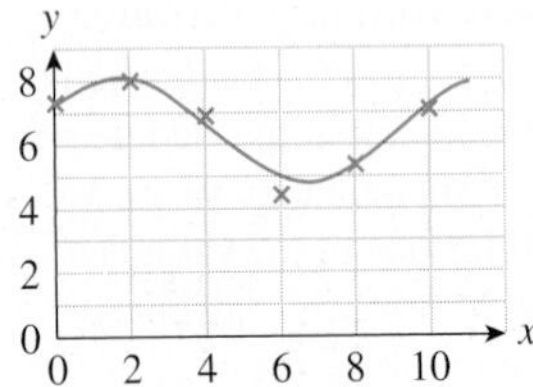

c. 9.9, 4.7%, 8.2%

57. a.

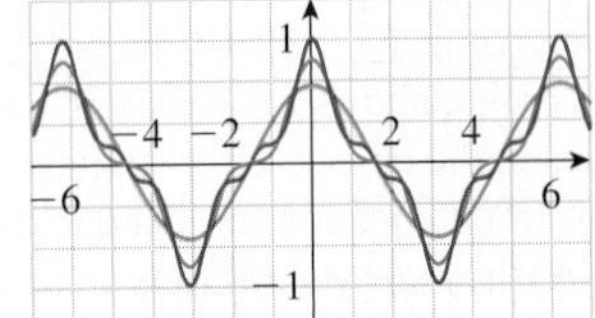

b. $y_{11} = \frac{2}{\pi}\cos x + \frac{2}{3\pi}\cos 3x + \frac{2}{5\pi}\cos 5x + \frac{2}{7\pi}\cos 7x + \frac{2}{9\pi}\cos 9x + \frac{2}{11\pi}\cos 11x$

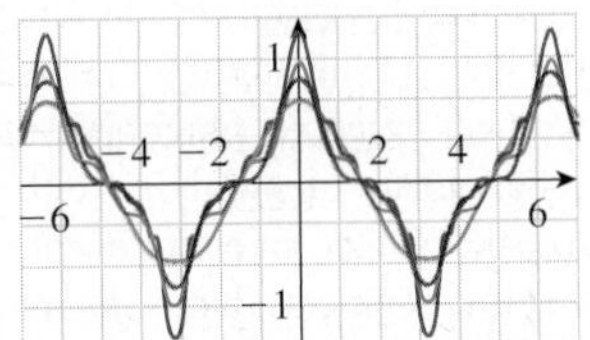

c. $y_{11} = \frac{6}{\pi}\cos\frac{x}{2} + \frac{6}{3\pi}\cos\frac{3x}{2} + \frac{6}{5\pi}\cos\frac{5x}{2} + \frac{6}{7\pi}\cos\frac{7x}{2} + \frac{6}{9\pi}\cos\frac{9x}{2} + \frac{6}{11\pi}\cos\frac{11x}{2}$

59. The period is approximately 12.6 units

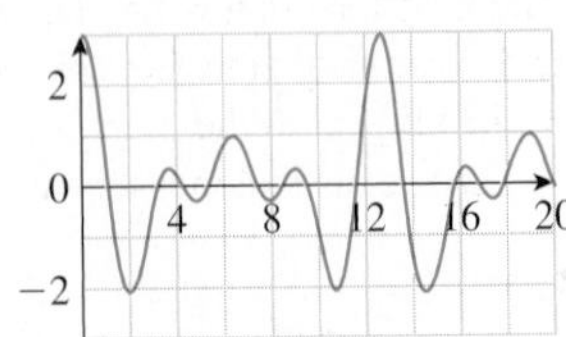

61. Lows: $B - A$; Highs: $B + A$ **63.** He is correct. The other trig functions can be obtained from the sine function by first using the formula $\cos x = \sin(x + \pi/2)$ to obtain cosine, and then using the formulas

$$\tan x = \frac{\sin x}{\cos x},\quad \cot x = \frac{\cos x}{\sin x},\quad \sec x = \frac{1}{\cos x},\quad \csc x = \frac{1}{\sin x}$$

to obtain the rest. **65.** The largest B can be is A. Otherwise, if B is larger than A, the low figure for sales would have the negative value of $A - B$.

Section 9.2

1. $\cos x + \sin x$ **3.** $(\cos x)(\tan x) + (\sin x)(\sec^2 x)$
5. $-2\csc x \cot x - \sec x \tan x + 3$ **7.** $\cos x - x\sin x + 2x$
9. $(2x - 1)\tan x + (x^2 - x + 1)\sec^2 x$
11. $-[\csc^2 x(1 + \sec x) + \cot x \sec x \tan x]/(1 + \sec x)^2$
13. $-2\cos x \sin x$ **15.** $2\sec^2 x \tan x$ **17.** $\pi \cos\left[\frac{\pi}{5}(x - 4)\right]$
19. $-(2x - 1)\sin(x^2 - x)$
21. $(2.2x^{1.2} + 1.2)\sec(x^{2.2} + 1.2x - 1)\tan(x^{2.2} + 1.2x - 1)$
23. $\sec x \tan x \tan(x^2 - 1) + 2x \sec x \sec^2(x^2 - 1)$
25. $e^x[-\sin(e^x) + \cos x - \sin x]$ **27.** $\sec x$
33. $e^{-2x}[-2\sin(3\pi x) + 3\pi\cos(3\pi x)]$
35. $1.5[\sin(3x)]^{-0.5}\cos(3x)$
37. $\frac{x^4 - 3x^2}{(x^2 - 1)^2}\sec\left(\frac{x^3}{x^2 - 1}\right)\tan\left(\frac{x^3}{x^2 - 1}\right)$
39. $\frac{\cot(2x - 1)}{x} - 2\ln|x|\csc^2(2x - 1)$
41. a. Not differentiable at 0 **b.** $f'(1) \approx 0.5403$
43. 0 **45.** 2 **47.** Does not exist **49.** $1/\sec^2 y$
51. $-[1 + y\cos(xy)]/[1 + x\cos(xy)]$
53. $c'(t) = 7\pi\cos[2\pi(t - 0.75)]$; $c'(0.75) \approx$ \$21.99 per *year* $\approx$ \$0.42 per week **55.** $N'(6) \approx -32.12$ On January 1, 2003, the number of sunspots was decreasing at a rate of 32.12 sunspots per year.
57. $c'(t) = 1.035^t[\ln(1.035)(0.8\sin(2\pi t) + 10.2) + 1.6\pi\cos(2\pi t)]$; $c'(1) = 1.035[10.2\ln|1.035| + 1.6\pi] \approx$ \$5.57 per year, or \$0.11 per week.
59. a. $d(t) = 5\cos(2\pi t/13.5) + 10$
b. $d'(t) = -(10\pi/13.5)\sin(2\pi t/13.5)$; $d'(7) \approx 0.270$. At noon, the tide was rising at a rate of 0.270 feet per hour.
61. a. (III) **b.** Increasing at a rate of 0.157 degrees per thousand years **63.** -6; 6 **65.** Answers will vary. Examples: $f(x) = \sin x$; $f(x) = \cos x$ **67.** Answers will vary. Examples: $f(x) = e^{-x}$; $f(x) = -2e^{-x}$ **69.** The graph of $\cos x$ slopes down over the interval $(0, \pi)$, so that its derivative is negative over that interval. The function $-\sin x$, and not $\sin x$, has this property. **71.** The derivative of $\sin x$ is $\cos x$. When $x = 0$, this is $\cos(0) = 1$. Thus, the tangent to the graph of $\sin x$ at the point $(0, 0)$ has slope 1, which means it slopes upward at 45°.

Section 9.3

1. $-\cos x - 2\sin x + C$ **3.** $2\sin x + 4.3\cos x - 9.33x + C$
5. $3.4\tan x + (\sin x)/1.3 - 3.2e^x + C$
7. $(7.6/3)\sin(3x - 4) + C$ **9.** $-(1/6)\cos(3x^2 - 4) + C$
11. $-2\cos(x^2 + x) + C$ **13.** $(1/6)\tan(3x^2 + 2x^3) + C$
15. $-(1/6)\ln|\cos(2x^3)| + C$
17. $3\ln|\sec(2x - 4) + \tan(2x - 4)| + C$
19. $(1/2)\sin(e^{2x} + 1) + C$ **21.** -2 **23.** $\ln(2)$ **25.** 0
27. 1 **33.** $-\frac{1}{4}\cos(4x) + C$ **35.** $-\sin(-x + 1) + C$
37. $[\cos(-1.1x - 1)]/1.1 + C$ **39.** $-\frac{1}{4}\ln|\sin(-4x)| + C$
41. 0 **43.** 2π **45.** $-x\cos x + \sin x + C$
47. $\left[\frac{x^2}{2} - \frac{1}{4}\right]\sin(2x) + \frac{x}{2}\cos(2x) + C$
49. $-\frac{1}{2}e^{-x}\cos x - \frac{1}{2}e^{-x}\sin x + C$ **51.** $\pi^2 - 4$
53. Average $= 2/\pi$

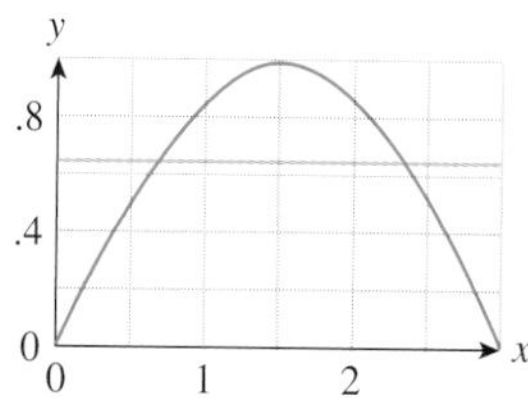

55. Diverges **57.** Converges to 1/2
59. $C(t) = 0.04t + \frac{2.6}{\pi}\cos\left[\frac{\pi}{26}(t - 25)\right] + 1.02$
61. 12 feet **63.** 79 sunspots
65. $P(t) = 7.5\sin[(\pi/26(t - 13)] + 12.5$; 7.7%
67. a. Average voltage over [0, 1/6] is zero; 60 cycles per second.
b.

y
25,000
20,000
15,000
10,000
5,000
0
0 0.04 0.08 0.12 x

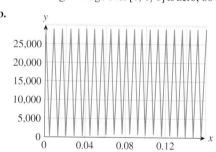

c. 116.673 volts. **69.** \$50,000 **71.** It is always zero.
73. 1 **75.** $s = -\frac{K}{\omega^2}\sin(\omega t - \alpha) + Lt + M$ for constants L and M

Chapter 9 Review

1. $f(x) = 1 + 2\sin x$
3. $f(x) = 2 + 2\sin[\pi(x - 1)] = 2 + 2\sin[\pi(x + 1)]$
5. $f(x) = 1 + 2\cos(x - \pi/2)$
7. $f(x) = 2 + 2\cos[\pi(x + 1/2)] = 2 + 2\cos[\pi(x - 3/2)]$
9. $-2x\sin(x^2 - 1)$ **11.** $2e^x\sec^2(2e^x - 1)$
13. $4x\sin(x^2)\cos(x^2)$ **15.** $2\sin(2x - 1) + C$
17. $\tan(2x^2 - 1) + C$ **19.** $-\frac{1}{2}\ln|\cos(x^2 + 1)| + C$ **21.** 1
23. $-x^2\cos x + 2x\sin x + 2\cos x + C$
25. $s(t) = 10{,}500 + 1500\sin[(2\pi/52)t - \pi] \approx 10{,}500 + 1500\sin(0.12083t - 3.14159)$ **27.** \$222,300

ANSWERS TO SELECTED EXERCISES